Complete Solutions Manual

for

Stewart, Redlin, and Watson's

Precalculus
Mathematics for Calculus

Fifth Edition

Andrew Bulman-Fleming

THOMSON

BROOKS/COLE

Australia • Brazil • Canada • Mexico • Singapore • Spain • United Kingdom • United States

Printer: Thomson/West

ISBN-13: 978-0-534-49316-5
ISBN-10: 0-534-49316-5

Thomson Higher Education
10 Davis Drive
Belmont, CA 94002-3098
USA

For more information about our products, contact us at:
Thomson Learning Academic Resource Center
1-800-423-0563

For permission to use material from this text or product, submit a request online at
http://www.thomsonrights.com.
Any additional questions about permissions can be submitted by email to **thomsonrights@thomson.com.**

Contents

1 Fundamentals 1

2 Functions 125

9 Systems of Equations and Inequalities   497

10 Analytic Geometry   599

11 Sequences and Series 661

12 Limits: A Preview of Calculus 703

1 Fundamentals

1.1 Real Numbers

1. **(a)** Natural number: 50
   (b) Integers: $0, -10, 50$
   (c) Rational numbers: $0, -10, 50, \frac{22}{7}, 0.538, 1.2\overline{3}, -\frac{1}{3}$
   (d) Irrational numbers: $\sqrt{7}, \sqrt[3]{2}$

2. **(a)** Natural numbers: $11, \sqrt{16}$
   (b) Integers: $-11, 11, \sqrt{16}$
   (c) Rational numbers: $1.001, 0.333\ldots, -11, 11, \frac{13}{15}, \sqrt{16}, 3.14, \frac{15}{3}$
   (d) Irrational number: $-\pi$

3. Commutative Property for addition

4. Commutative Property for multiplication

5. Associative Property for addition

6. Distributive Property

7. Distributive Property

8. Distributive Property

9. Commutative Property for multiplication

10. Distributive Property

11. $x + 3 = 3 + x$

12. $7(3x) = (7 \cdot 3)x$

13. $4(A + B) = 4A + 4B$

14. $5x + 5y = 5(x + y)$

15. $3(x + y) = 3x + 3y$

16. $(a - b)8 = 8a - 8b$

17. $4(2m) = (4 \cdot 2)m = 8m$

18. $\frac{4}{3}(-6y) = \left[\frac{4}{3}(-6)\right]y = -8y$

19. $-\frac{5}{2}(2x - 4y) = -\frac{5}{2}(2x) + \frac{5}{2}(4y) = -5x + 10y$

20. $(3a)(b + c - 2d) = 3ab + 3ac - 6ad$

21. **(a)** $\frac{3}{10} + \frac{4}{15} = \frac{9}{30} + \frac{8}{30} = \frac{17}{30}$
    (b) $\frac{1}{4} + \frac{1}{5} = \frac{5}{20} + \frac{4}{20} = \frac{9}{20}$

22. **(a)** $\frac{2}{3} - \frac{3}{5} = \frac{10}{15} - \frac{9}{15} = \frac{1}{15}$
    (b) $1 + \frac{5}{8} - \frac{1}{6} = \frac{24}{24} + \frac{15}{24} - \frac{4}{24} = \frac{35}{24}$

23. **(a)** $\frac{2}{3}\left(6 - \frac{3}{2}\right) = \frac{2}{3} \cdot 6 - \frac{2}{3} \cdot \frac{3}{2} = 4 - 1 = 3$
    (b) $0.25\left(\frac{8}{9} + \frac{1}{2}\right) = \frac{1}{4}\left(\frac{16}{18} + \frac{9}{18}\right) = \frac{1}{4} \cdot \frac{25}{18} = \frac{25}{72}$

24. **(a)** $\left(3 + \frac{1}{4}\right)\left(1 - \frac{4}{5}\right) = \left(\frac{12}{4} + \frac{1}{4}\right)\left(\frac{5}{5} - \frac{4}{5}\right) = \frac{13}{4} \cdot \frac{1}{5} = \frac{13}{20}$
    (b) $\left(\frac{1}{2} - \frac{1}{3}\right)\left(\frac{1}{2} + \frac{1}{3}\right) = \left(\frac{3}{6} - \frac{2}{6}\right)\left(\frac{3}{6} + \frac{2}{6}\right) = \frac{1}{6} \cdot \frac{5}{6} = \frac{5}{36}$

25. **(a)** $\frac{2 - \frac{2}{3}}{\frac{2}{3}} = 2 \cdot \frac{3}{2} - \frac{2}{3} \cdot \frac{1}{2} = 3 - \frac{1}{3} = \frac{9}{3} - \frac{1}{3} = \frac{8}{3}$
    (b) $\frac{\frac{1}{12}}{\frac{1}{8} - \frac{1}{9}} = \frac{\frac{1}{12}}{\frac{1}{8} - \frac{1}{9}} \cdot \frac{72}{72} = \frac{6}{9 - 8} = \frac{6}{1} = 6$

26. **(a)** $\frac{2 - \frac{3}{4}}{\frac{1}{2} - \frac{1}{3}} = \frac{2 - \frac{3}{4}}{\frac{1}{2} - \frac{1}{3}} \cdot \frac{12}{12} = \frac{24 - 9}{6 - 4} = \frac{15}{2}$
    (b) $\frac{\frac{2}{5} + \frac{1}{2}}{\frac{1}{10} + \frac{3}{15}} = \frac{\frac{2}{5} + \frac{1}{2}}{\frac{1}{10} + \frac{1}{5}} = \frac{\frac{2}{5} + \frac{1}{2}}{\frac{1}{10} + \frac{1}{5}} \cdot \frac{10}{10} = \frac{4 + 5}{1 + 2} = \frac{9}{3} = 3$

27. **(a)** $2 \cdot 3 = 6$ and $2 \cdot \frac{7}{2} = 7$, so $3 < \frac{7}{2}$
    (b) $-6 > -7$
    (c) $3.5 = \frac{7}{2}$

28. **(a)** $3 \cdot \frac{2}{3} = 2$ and $3 \cdot 0.67 = 2.01$, so $\frac{2}{3} < 0.67$
    (b) $\frac{2}{3} > -0.67$
    (c) $|0.67| = |-0.67|$

29. **(a)** False
    (b) True

30. **(a)** True. $\frac{10}{11} = \frac{10}{11} \cdot \frac{13}{13} = \frac{130}{143}$ and $\frac{12}{13} = \frac{12}{13} \cdot \frac{11}{11} = \frac{132}{143}$. Therefore $\frac{10}{11} < \frac{12}{13}$, because $\frac{130}{143} < \frac{132}{143}$.
    (b) False

31. **(a)** False
    (b) True

32. **(a)** False
    (b) True

33. (a) $x > 0$

    (b) $t < 4$

    (c) $a \geq \pi$

    (d) $-5 < x < \frac{1}{3}$

    (e) $|p - 3| \leq 5$

34. (a) $y < 0$

    (b) $z > 1$

    (c) $b \leq 8$

    (d) $0 < w \leq 17$

    (e) $|y - \pi| \geq 2$

35. (a) $A \cup B = \{1, 2, 3, 4, 5, 6, 7, 8\}$

    (b) $A \cap B = \{2, 4, 6\}$

36. (a) $B \cup C = \{2, 4, 6, 7, 8, 9, 10\}$

    (b) $B \cap C = \{8\}$

37. (a) $A \cup C = \{1, 2, 3, 4, 5, 6, 7, 8, 9, 10\}$

    (b) $A \cap C = \{7\}$

38. (a) $A \cup B \cup C = \{1, 2, 3, 4, 5, 6, 7, 8, 9, 10\}$

    (b) $A \cap B \cap C = \varnothing$

39. (a) $B \cup C = \{x \mid x \leq 5\}$

    (b) $B \cap C = \{x \mid -1 < x < 4\}$

40. (a) $A \cap C = \{x \mid -1 < x \leq 5\}$

    (b) $A \cap B = \{x \mid -2 \leq x < 4\}$

41. $(-3, 0) = \{x \mid -3 < x < 0\}$

42. $(2, 8] = \{x \mid 2 < x \leq 8\}$

43. $[2, 8) = \{x \mid 2 \leq x < 8\}$

44. $\left[-6, -\frac{1}{2}\right] = \left\{x \mid -6 \leq x \leq -\frac{1}{2}\right\}$

45. $[2, \infty) = \{x \mid x \geq 2\}$

46. $(-\infty, 1) = \{x \mid x < 1\}$

47. $x \leq 1 \quad \Leftrightarrow \quad x \in (-\infty, 1]$

48. $1 \leq x \leq 2 \quad \Leftrightarrow \quad x \in [1, 2]$

49. $-2 < x \leq 1 \quad \Leftrightarrow \quad x \in (-2, 1]$

50. $x \geq -5 \quad \Leftrightarrow \quad x \in [-5, \infty)$

51. $x > -1 \quad \Leftrightarrow \quad x \in (-1, \infty)$

52. $-5 < x < 2 \quad \Leftrightarrow \quad x \in (-5, 2)$

53. (a) $[-3, 5]$

    (b) $(-3, 5]$

54. (a) $[0, 2)$

    (b) $(-2, 0]$

55. $(-2, 0) \cup (-1, 1) = (-2, 1)$

56. $(-2, 0) \cap (-1,) = (-1, 0)$

57. $[-4, 6] \cap [0, 8) = [0, 6]$

58. $[-4, 6] \cup [0, 8) = [-4, 8)$

59. $(-\infty, -4) \cup (4, \infty)$

60. $(-\infty, 6] \cap (2, 10) = (2, 6]$

61. (a) $|100| = 100$

 (b) $|-73| = 73$

62. (a) $\left|\sqrt{5} - 5\right| = -\left(\sqrt{5} - 5\right) = 5 - \sqrt{5}$, since $5 > \sqrt{5}$.

 (b) $|10 - \pi| = 10 - \pi$, since $10 > \pi$.

63. (a) $\left||-6| - |-4|\right| = |6 - 4| = |2| = 2$

 (b) $\frac{-1}{|-1|} = \frac{-1}{1} = -1$

64. (a) $\left|2 - |-12|\right| = |2 - 12| = |-10| = 10$

 (b) $-1 - \left|1 - |-1|\right| = -1 - |1 - 1| = -1 - |0| = -1$

65. (a) $|(-2) \cdot 6| = |-12| = 12$

 (b) $\left|\left(-\frac{1}{3}\right)(-15)\right| = |5| = 5$

66. (a) $\left|\frac{-6}{24}\right| = \left|-\frac{1}{4}\right| = \frac{1}{4}$

 (b) $\left|\frac{7-12}{12-7}\right| = \left|-\frac{5}{5}\right| = |-1| = 1$

67. $|(-2) - 3| = |-5| = 5$

68. $|-2.5 - 1.5| = |-4| = 4$

69. (a) $|17 - 2| = 15$

 (b) $|21 - (-3)| = |21 + 3| = |24| = 24$

 (c) $\left|-\frac{3}{10} - \frac{11}{8}\right| = \left|-\frac{12}{40} - \frac{55}{40}\right| = \left|-\frac{67}{40}\right| = \frac{67}{40}$

70. (a) $\left|\frac{7}{15} - \left(-\frac{1}{21}\right)\right| = \left|\frac{49}{105} + \frac{5}{105}\right| = \left|\frac{54}{105}\right| = \left|\frac{18}{35}\right| = \frac{18}{35}$

 (b) $|-38 - (-57)| = |-38 + 57| = |19| = 19.$

 (c) $|-2.6 - (-1.8)| = |-2.6 + 1.8| = |-0.8| = 0.8.$

71. (a) Let $x = 0.777\ldots$. So $10x = 7.7777\ldots$ $\Leftrightarrow$ $x = 0.7777\ldots$ $\Leftrightarrow$ $9x = 7$. Thus, $x = \frac{7}{9}$.

 (b) Let $x = 0.2888\ldots$. So $100x = 28.8888\ldots$ $\Leftrightarrow$ $10x = 2.8888\ldots$ $\Leftrightarrow$ $90x = 26$. Thus, $x = \dfrac{26}{90} = \dfrac{13}{45}$.

 (c) Let $x = 0.575757\ldots$. So $100x = 57.5757\ldots$ $\Leftrightarrow$ $x = 0.5757\ldots$ $\Leftrightarrow$ $99x = 57$. Thus, $x = \dfrac{57}{99} = \dfrac{19}{33}$.

72. (a) Let $x = 5.2323\ldots$. So $100x = 523.2323\ldots$ $\Leftrightarrow$ $1x = 5.2323\ldots$ $\Leftrightarrow$ $99x = 518$. Thus, $x = \dfrac{518}{99}$.

 (b) Let $x = 1.3777\ldots$. So $100x = 137.7777\ldots$ $\Leftrightarrow$ $10x = 13.7777\ldots$ $\Leftrightarrow$ $90x = 124$. Thus, $x = \dfrac{124}{90} = \dfrac{62}{45}$.

 (c) Let $x = 2.13535\ldots$. So $1000x = 2135.3535\ldots$ $\Leftrightarrow$ $10x = 21.3535\ldots$ $\Leftrightarrow$ $990x = 2114$. Thus, $x = \dfrac{2114}{990} = \dfrac{1057}{495}$.

73. Distributive Property

74.

Day	T_O	T_G	$T_O - T_G$	$|T_O - T_G|$
Sunday	68	77	-9	9
Monday	72	75	-3	3
Tuesday	74	74	0	0
Wednesday	80	75	5	5
Thursday	77	69	8	8
Friday	71	70	1	1
Saturday	70	71	-1	1

$T_O - T_G$ gives more information because it tells us which city had the higher temperature.

75. (a) When $L = 60$, $x = 8$, and $y = 6$, we have $L + 2(x + y) = 60 + 2(8 + 6) = 60 + 28 = 88$. Because $88 \leq 108$ the post office will accept this package.

When $L = 48$, $x = 24$, and $y = 24$, we have $L + 2(x + y) = 48 + 2(24 + 24) = 48 + 96 = 144$, and since $144 \not\leq 108$, the post office will *not* accept this package.

(b) If $x = y = 9$, then $L + 2(9 + 9) \leq 108 \quad \Leftrightarrow \quad L + 36 \leq 108 \quad \Leftrightarrow \quad L \leq 72$. So the length can be as long as 72 in. $= 6$ ft.

76. (a) Negative since $a > 0 \quad \Leftrightarrow \quad -a < 0$.

(b) Positive since $b < 0 \quad \Leftrightarrow \quad -b > 0$.

(c) Positive since the product of two negative numbers is positive.

(d) Positive since $a - b = a + (-b)$ is the sum of two positive numbers.

(e) Negative $c - a = c + (-a)$ is the sum of two negative numbers.

(f) Positive since a is positive and bc is positive by part (c).

(g) Negative. ab is negative (the product of a positive and a negative) and ac is negative for the same reason. Finally, the sum of two negative numbers is negative.

(h) Negative, since bc is positive by Part (c) and $a(bc)$ is the product of two positive number, therefore positive, hence and $-abc$ is negative.

(i) Positive since a is known to be positive and b^2 is also positive, being a square. The product of two positive numbers is positive.

77. Let $x = \dfrac{m_1}{n_1}$ and $y = \dfrac{m_2}{n_2}$ be rational numbers. Then $x + y = \dfrac{m_1}{n_1} + \dfrac{m_2}{n_2} = \dfrac{m_1 n_2 + m_2 n_1}{n_1 n_2}$,

$x - y = \dfrac{m_1}{n_1} - \dfrac{m_2}{n_2} = \dfrac{m_1 n_2 - m_2 n_1}{n_1 n_2}$, and $x \cdot y = \dfrac{m_1}{n_1} \cdot \dfrac{m_2}{n_2} = \dfrac{m_1 m_2}{n_1 n_2}$. This shows that the sum, difference, and product of two rational numbers are again rational numbers. However the product of two irrational numbers is not necessarily irrational; for example, $\sqrt{2} \cdot \sqrt{2} = 2$, which is rational. Also, the sum of two irrational numbers is not necessarily irrational; for example, $\sqrt{2} + (-\sqrt{2}) = 0$ which is rational.

78. $\frac{1}{2} + \sqrt{2}$ is irrational. Since the sum of two rational numbers is rational (see Exercise 77), if $\frac{1}{2} + \sqrt{2}$ were rational, then sum $\left(\frac{1}{2} + \sqrt{2}\right) + \left(-\frac{1}{2}\right) = \sqrt{2}$ is rational. But this is a contradiction. In general the sum of a rational number and an irrational number is irrational. Zero is rational and the product of zero and any real number is zero. If the rational number is not zero, $\dfrac{a}{b} \neq 0$, then the product of it and any irrational number w is irrational. Again, if we assume the product is rational, say $\dfrac{a}{b} \cdot w = \dfrac{c}{d}$, then since $\dfrac{a}{b} \neq 0$, we have $\dfrac{b}{a} \neq 0$ so $\dfrac{b}{a}\left(\dfrac{a}{b} \cdot w\right) = \dfrac{b}{a} \cdot \dfrac{c}{d} \quad \Leftrightarrow \quad w = \dfrac{bc}{ad}$ which is rational. But w is irrational.

79.

x	1	2	10	100	1000
$\frac{1}{x}$	1	$\frac{1}{2}$	$\frac{1}{10}$	$\frac{1}{100}$	$\frac{1}{1000}$

As x gets large, the fraction $\dfrac{1}{x}$ gets small. Mathematically, we say that $\dfrac{1}{x}$ goes to zero.

x	1	0.5	0.1	0.01	0.001
$\frac{1}{x}$	1	$\frac{1}{0.5} = 2$	$\frac{1}{0.1} = 10$	$\frac{1}{0.01} = 100$	$\frac{1}{0.001} = 1000$

As x gets small, the fraction $\dfrac{1}{x}$ gets large. Mathematically, we say that $\dfrac{1}{x}$ goes to infinity.

80. (a) Construct the number $\sqrt{2}$ on the number line by transferring the length of the hypotenuse of a right triangle with legs of length 1 and 1.

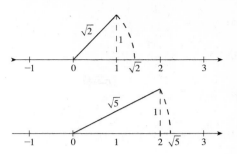

(b) Construct a right triangle with legs of length 1 and 2. By the Pythagorean Theorem, the length of the hypotenuse is $\sqrt{1^2 + 2^2} = \sqrt{5}$. Then transfer the length of the hypotenuse to the number line.

(c) Construct a right triangle with legs of length $\sqrt{2}$ and 2 [construct $\sqrt{2}$ as in part (a)]. By the Pythagorean Theorem, the length of the hypotenuse is $\sqrt{\left(\sqrt{2}\right)^2 + 2^2} = \sqrt{6}$. Then transfer the length of the hypotenuse to the number line.

81. (a) Subtraction is not commutative. For example, $5 - 1 \neq 1 - 5$.

(b) Division is not commutative. For example, $5 \div 1 \neq 1 \div 5$.

1.2   Exponents and Radicals

1. $\dfrac{1}{\sqrt{5}} = 5^{-1/2}$

2. $\sqrt[3]{7^2} = 7^{2/3}$

3. $4^{2/3} = \sqrt[3]{4^2} = \sqrt[3]{16}$

4. $11^{-3/2} = \left(11^{3/2}\right)^{-1} = \left(\sqrt{11^3}\right)^{-1} = \dfrac{1}{\sqrt{11^3}}$

5. $\sqrt[5]{5^3} = 5^{3/5}$

6. $2^{-1.5} = 2^{-3/2} = \dfrac{1}{\sqrt{2^3}} = \dfrac{1}{\sqrt{8}}$

7. $a^{2/5} = \sqrt[5]{a^2}$

8. $\dfrac{1}{\sqrt{x^5}} = \dfrac{1}{x^{5/2}} = x^{-5/2}$

9. (a) $-3^2 = -9$

(b) $(-3)^2 = 9$

(c) $(-3)^0 = 1$

10. (a) $5^2 \cdot \left(\frac{1}{5}\right)^3 = 5^2 \cdot 5^{-3} = 5^{2-3} = 5^{-1} = \frac{1}{5}$

(b) $\dfrac{10^7}{10^4} = 10^{7-4} = 10^3 = 1{,}000$

(c) $\dfrac{3}{3^{-2}} = 3^{1-(-2)} = 3^3 = 27$

11. (a) $\dfrac{4^{-3}}{2^{-8}} = \dfrac{\left(2^2\right)^{-3}}{2^{-8}} = \dfrac{2^{-6}}{2^{-8}} = 2^{-6-(-8)} = 2^{-6+8}$
$= 2^2 = 4$

(b) $\dfrac{3^{-2}}{9} = \dfrac{3^{-2}}{3^2} = \dfrac{1}{3^{2-(-2)}} = \dfrac{1}{3^4} = \dfrac{1}{81}$

(c) $\left(\dfrac{1}{4}\right)^{-2} = (4)^2 = 16$

12. (a) $\left(\dfrac{2}{3}\right)^{-3} = \left(\dfrac{3}{2}\right)^3 = \dfrac{3^3}{2^3} = \dfrac{27}{8}$

(b) $\left(\dfrac{3}{2}\right)^{-2} \cdot \dfrac{9}{16} = \left(\dfrac{2}{3}\right)^2 \cdot \dfrac{9}{16} = \dfrac{2^2}{3^2} \cdot \dfrac{9}{16} = \dfrac{4}{9} \cdot \dfrac{9}{16} = \dfrac{1}{4}$

(c) $\left(\dfrac{1}{2}\right)^4 \cdot \left(\dfrac{5}{2}\right)^{-2} = \left(\dfrac{1}{2}\right)^4 \cdot \left(\dfrac{2}{5}\right)^2 = \dfrac{1}{2^4} \cdot \dfrac{2^2}{5^2}$
$= \dfrac{1}{2^{4-2}} \cdot \dfrac{1}{5^2} = \dfrac{1}{2^2 \cdot 5^2} = \dfrac{1}{100}$

13. (a) $\sqrt{16} = \sqrt{4^2} = 4$

(b) $\sqrt[4]{16} = \sqrt[4]{2^4} = 2$

(c) $\sqrt[4]{\dfrac{1}{16}} = \sqrt[4]{\left(\dfrac{1}{2}\right)^4} = \dfrac{1}{2}$

14. (a) $\sqrt{64} = \sqrt{8^2} = 8$

(b) $\sqrt[3]{-64} = \sqrt[3]{(-4)^3} = -4$

(c) $\sqrt[5]{-32} = \sqrt[5]{(-2)^5} = -2$

15. (a) $\sqrt[3]{\dfrac{8}{27}} = \dfrac{\sqrt[3]{8}}{\sqrt[3]{27}} = \dfrac{2}{3}$

   (b) $\sqrt[3]{\dfrac{-1}{64}} = \dfrac{\sqrt[3]{-1}}{\sqrt[3]{64}} = -\dfrac{1}{4}$

   (c) $\dfrac{\sqrt[5]{-3}}{\sqrt[5]{96}} = \sqrt[5]{\dfrac{-3}{96}} = \sqrt[5]{\dfrac{-1}{32}} = \dfrac{\sqrt[5]{-1}}{\sqrt[5]{32}} = -\dfrac{1}{2}$

16. (a) $\sqrt{7}\sqrt{28} = \sqrt{7}\sqrt{4 \cdot 7} = \sqrt{7} \cdot 2 \cdot \sqrt{7} = 2 \cdot 7 = 14$

   (b) $\dfrac{\sqrt{48}}{\sqrt{3}} = \sqrt{\dfrac{48}{3}} = \sqrt{16} = 4$

   (c) $\sqrt[4]{24}\sqrt[4]{54} = \sqrt[4]{8 \cdot 3}\sqrt[4]{2 \cdot 27} = \sqrt[4]{2^3 \cdot 3 \cdot 2 \cdot 3^3}$
$$= \sqrt[4]{2^4 \cdot 3^4} = 2 \cdot 3 = 6$$

17. (a) $\left(\dfrac{4}{9}\right)^{-1/2} = \left(\dfrac{2^2}{3^2}\right)^{-1/2} = \dfrac{2^{-1}}{3^{-1}} = \dfrac{3}{2}$

   (b) $(-32)^{2/5} = \left[(-2)^5\right]^{2/5} = (-2)^2 = 4$

   (c) $-32^{2/5} = -\left((2^5)^{2/5}\right) = -2^2 = -4$

18. (a) $1024^{-0.1} = \left(2^{10}\right)^{-0.1} = 2^{-1} = \tfrac{1}{2}$

   (b) $\left(-\dfrac{27}{8}\right)^{2/3} = \left(\sqrt[3]{-\dfrac{27}{8}}\right)^2 = \left(-\dfrac{3}{2}\right)^2 = \dfrac{9}{4}$

   (c) $\left(\dfrac{25}{64}\right)^{-3/2} = \left(\sqrt{\dfrac{64}{25}}\right)^3 = \left(\dfrac{8}{5}\right)^3 = \dfrac{512}{125}$

19. When $x = 3$, $y = 4$, $z = -1$ we have $\sqrt{x^2 + y^2} = \sqrt{3^2 + 4^2} = \sqrt{9 + 16} = \sqrt{25} = 5$.

20. When $x = 3$, $y = 4$, $z = -1$ we have
$$\sqrt[4]{x^3 + 14y + 2z} = \sqrt[4]{3^3 + 14\,(4) + 2\,(-1)} = \sqrt[4]{27 + 56 - 2} = \sqrt[4]{81} = \sqrt[4]{3^4} = 3.$$

21. When $x = 3$, $y = 4$, $z = -1$ we have
$$(9x)^{2/3} + (2y)^{2/3} + z^{2/3} = (9 \cdot 3)^{2/3} + (2 \cdot 4)^{2/3} + (-1)^{2/3} = \left(3^3\right)^{2/3} + \left(2^3\right)^{2/3} + (1)^{1/3} = 3^2 + 2^2 + 1 = 9 + 4 + 1 = 14$$

22. When $x = 3$, $y = 4$, $z = -1$ we have $(xy)^{2z} = (3 \cdot 4)^{2 \cdot (-1)} = 12^{-2} = \tfrac{1}{144}$.

23. $\sqrt{32} + \sqrt{18} = \sqrt{16 \cdot 2} + \sqrt{9 \cdot 2} = \sqrt{4^2 \cdot 2} + \sqrt{3^2 \cdot 2} = 4\sqrt{2} + 3\sqrt{2} = 7\sqrt{2}$

24. $\sqrt{75} + \sqrt{48} = \sqrt{25 \cdot 3} + \sqrt{16 \cdot 3} = \sqrt{5^2 \cdot 3} + \sqrt{4^2 \cdot 3} = 5\sqrt{3} + 4\sqrt{3} = 9\sqrt{3}$

25. $\sqrt[5]{96} + \sqrt[5]{3} = \sqrt[5]{32 \cdot 3} + \sqrt[5]{3} = \sqrt[5]{2^5 \cdot 3} + \sqrt[5]{3} = 2\sqrt[5]{3} + \sqrt[5]{3} = 3\sqrt[5]{3}$

26. $\sqrt[4]{48} - \sqrt[4]{3} = \sqrt[4]{16 \cdot 3} - \sqrt[4]{2^3 \cdot 2} = \sqrt[4]{2^4 \cdot 3} - \sqrt[4]{3} = 2\sqrt[4]{3} - \sqrt[4]{3} = \sqrt[4]{3}$

27. $a^9 a^{-5} = a^{9-5} = a^4$

28. $(3y^2)(4y^5) = 3 \cdot 4y^{2+5} = 12y^7$

29. $(12x^2 y^4)(\tfrac{1}{2}x^5 y) = (12 \cdot \tfrac{1}{2})x^{2+5}y^{4+1} = 6x^7 y^5$

30. $(6y)^3 = 6^3 y^3 = 216y^3$

31. $\dfrac{x^9 (2x)^4}{x^3} = 2^4 \cdot x^{9+4-3} = 16x^{10}$

32. $\dfrac{a^{-3}b^4}{a^{-5}b^5} = a^{-3-(-5)}b^{4-5} = a^2 b^{-1} = \dfrac{a^2}{b}$

33. $b^4 (\tfrac{1}{3}b^2)(12b^{-8}) = \tfrac{12}{3}b^{4+2-8} = 4b^{-2} = \dfrac{4}{b^2}$

34. $(2s^3 t^{-1})(\tfrac{1}{4}s^6)(16t^4) = \dfrac{2 \cdot 16}{4}s^{3+6}t^{-1+4} = 8s^9 t^3$

35. $(rs)^3 (2s)^{-2} (4r)^4 = r^3 s^3 2^{-2} s^{-2} 4^4 r^4 = r^3 s^3 2^{-2} s^{-2} 2^{2\cdot4} r^4 = 2^{-2+8}r^{3+4}s^{3-2} = 2^6 r^7 s = 64r^7 s$

36. $(2u^2 v^3)^3 (3u^3 v)^{-2} = 2^3 u^6 v^9 \cdot 3^{-2}u^{-6}v^{-2} = \dfrac{2^3}{3^2}u^{6-6}v^{9-2} = \tfrac{8}{9}v^7$

37. $\dfrac{(6y^3)^4}{2y^5} = \dfrac{6^4 y^{3\cdot4}}{2y^5} = \dfrac{6^4}{2}y^{12-5} = 648y^7$

38. $\dfrac{(2x^3)^2 (3x^4)}{(x^3)^4} = \dfrac{2^2 x^6 \cdot 3x^4}{x^{12}} = 12x^{6+4-12} = 12x^{-2} = \dfrac{12}{x^2}$

39. $\dfrac{(x^2 y^3)^4 (xy^4)^{-3}}{x^2 y} = \dfrac{x^8 y^{12} x^{-3} y^{-12}}{x^2 y} = x^{8-3-2}y^{12-12-1} = x^3 y^{-1} = \dfrac{x^3}{y}$

40. $\left(\dfrac{c^4 d^3}{cd^2}\right)\left(\dfrac{d^2}{c^3}\right)^3 = \dfrac{c^4 d^3}{cd^2} \cdot \dfrac{d^6}{c^9} = c^{4-1-9}d^{3+6-2} = c^{-6}d^7 = \dfrac{d^7}{c^6}$

41. $\dfrac{(xy^2 z^3)^4}{(x^3 y^2 z)^3} = \dfrac{x^4 y^8 z^{12}}{x^9 y^6 z^3} = x^{4-9}y^{8-6}z^{12-3} = x^{-5}y^2 z^9 = \dfrac{y^2 z^9}{x^5}$

42. $\left(\dfrac{xy^{-2}z^{-3}}{x^2 y^3 z^{-4}}\right)^{-3} = \dfrac{x^{-3}y^6 z^9}{x^{-6}y^{-9}z^{12}} = x^{-3-(-6)}y^{6-(-9)}z^{9-12} = x^3 y^{15}z^{-3} = \dfrac{x^3 y^{15}}{z^3}$

43. $\left(\dfrac{q^{-1}rs^{-2}}{r^{-5}sq^{-8}}\right)^{-1} = \dfrac{qr^{-1}s^2}{r^5 s^{-1}q^8} = q^{1-8}r^{-1-5}s^{2-(-1)} = q^{-7}r^{-6}s^3 = \dfrac{s^3}{q^7 r^6}$

44. $(3ab^2 c)\left(\dfrac{2a^2 b}{c^3}\right)^{-2} = 3ab^2 c \cdot \dfrac{2^{-2}a^{-4}b^{-2}}{c^{-6}} = \tfrac{3}{4}a^{1-4}b^{2-2}c^{1-(-6)} = \tfrac{3}{4}a^{-3}b^0 c^7 = \dfrac{3c^7}{4a^3}$

45. $\sqrt[4]{x^4} = |x|$

46. $\sqrt[5]{x^{10}} = \left(x^{10}\right)^{1/5} = x^2$

47. $\sqrt[4]{16x} = \sqrt[4]{2^4 x^8} = 2x^2$

48. $\sqrt[3]{x^3 y^6} = \left(x^3 y^6\right)^{1/3} = xy^2$

49. $\sqrt{a^2 b^6} = a^{2/2}b^{6/2} = ab^3$

50. $\sqrt[3]{a^2 b}\,\sqrt[3]{a^4 b} = \sqrt[3]{a^6 b^2} = \left(a^6 b^2\right)^{1/3} = a^2 b^{2/3} = a^2\sqrt[3]{b^2}$

51. $\sqrt[3]{\sqrt{64x^6}} = \left(8\,|x^3|\right)^{1/3} = 2\,|x|$

52. $\sqrt[4]{x^4 y^2 z^2} = \sqrt[4]{x^4}\,\sqrt[4]{y^2 z^2} = |x|\,\sqrt[4]{y^2 z^2} = |x|\,\sqrt{|yz|}$

53. $x^{2/3}x^{1/5} = x^{(10/15+3/15)} = x^{13/15}$

54. $\left(2x^{3/2}\right)(4x)^{-1/2} = \left(2x^{3/2}\right)\left(2^2 x\right)^{-1/2} = \left(2x^{3/2}\right)\left(2^{-1}x^{-1/2}\right) = 2^{1-1}\cdot x^{3/2-1/2} = 2^0 \cdot x = x$

55. $\left(-3a^{1/4}\right)(9a)^{-3/2} = \left(-1\cdot 3a^{1/4}\right)\left(3^2 a\right)^{-3/2} = \left(-1\cdot 3a^{1/4}\right)\left(3^{-3}a^{-3/2}\right) = -1\cdot 3^{1-3}\cdot a^{1/4-3/2}$
$\qquad = -1\cdot 3^{-3}a^{-5/4} = \dfrac{-1}{3^3 \cdot a^{5/4}} = \dfrac{-1}{9a^{5/4}}$

56. $\left(-2a^{3/4}\right)\left(5a^{3/2}\right) = -10a^{3/4}a^{3/2} = -10a^{(3/4+6/4)} = -10a^{9/4}$

57. $(4b)^{1/2}\left(8b^{2/5}\right) = \sqrt{4}\cdot 8b^{1/2}b^{2/5} = 16b^{(5/10+4/10)} = 16b^{9/10}$

58. $(8x^6)^{-2/3} = \left(2^3\right)^{-2/3}\left(x^6\right)^{-2/3} = 2^{-6/3}x^{-12/3} = 2^{-2}x^{-4} = \dfrac{1}{4x^4}$

59. $\left(c^2 d^3\right)^{-1/3} = c^{-2/3}d^{-1} = \dfrac{1}{c^{2/3}d}$

60. $\left(4x^6 y^8\right)^{3/2} = \left(2^2\right)^{3/2}\left(x^6\right)^{3/2}\left(y^8\right)^{3/2} = 2^{6/2}x^{18/2}y^{24/2} = 2^3 x^9 y^{12} = 8x^9 y^{12}$

61. $\left(y^{3/4}\right)^{2/3} = y^{(3/4)\cdot(2/3)} = y^{1/2}$

62. $\left(a^{2/5}\right)^{-3/4} = a^{(2/5)\cdot(-3/4)} = a^{-6/20} = a^{-3/10} = \dfrac{1}{a^{3/10}}$

63. $\left(2x^4 y^{-4/5}\right)^3\left(8y^2\right)^{2/3} = 2^3 x^{12}y^{-12/5}8^{2/3}y^{4/3} = 2^{3+2}x^{12}y^{(-12/5+4/3)} = \dfrac{32x^{12}}{y^{16/15}}\cdot$ [Note that $8^{2/3} = \left(8^{1/3}\right)^2 = 2^2$.]

64. $\left(x^{-5}y^3 z^{10}\right)^{-3/5} = x^{15/5}y^{-9/5}z^{-30/5} = x^3 y^{-9/5}z^{-6} = \dfrac{x^3}{y^{9/5}z^6}$

65. $\left(\dfrac{x^6 y}{y^4}\right)^{5/2} = \dfrac{x^{15}y^{5/2}}{y^{10}} = x^{15}y^{5/2-10} = x^{15}y^{-15/2} = \dfrac{x^{15}}{y^{15/2}}$

66. $\left(\dfrac{-2x^{1/3}}{y^{1/2}z^{1/6}}\right)^4 = \dfrac{(-2)^4 x^{4/3}}{y^{4/2}z^{4/6}} = \dfrac{16x^{4/3}}{y^2 z^{2/3}}$

67. $\left(\dfrac{3a^{-2}}{4b^{-1/3}}\right)^{-1} = \dfrac{3^{-1}a^2}{4^{-1}b^{1/3}} = \dfrac{4a^2}{3b^{1/3}}$

68. $\dfrac{\left(y^{10}z^{-5}\right)^{1/5}}{\left(y^{-2}z^3\right)^{1/3}} = \dfrac{y^2 z^{-1}}{y^{-2/3}z} = y^{2-(-2/3)}z^{-1-1} = y^{8/3}z^{-2} = \dfrac{y^{8/3}}{z^2}$

69. $\dfrac{(9st)^{3/2}}{(27s^3t^{-4})^{2/3}} = \dfrac{27s^{3/2}t^{3/2}}{9s^2t^{-8/3}} = 3s^{3/2-2}t^{3/2+8/3} = 3s^{-1/2}t^{25/6} = \dfrac{3t^{25/6}}{s^{1/2}}$

70. $\left(\dfrac{a^2b^{-3}}{x^{-1}y^2}\right)^3 \left(\dfrac{x^{-2}b^{-1}}{a^{3/2}y^{1/3}}\right) = \dfrac{a^6b^{-9}}{x^{-3}y^6} \cdot \dfrac{x^{-2}b^{-1}}{a^{3/2}y^{1/3}} = a^{6-(3/2)}b^{-9-1}x^{-2-(-3)}y^{-6-1/3} = a^{9/2}b^{-10}x^1y^{-19/3} = \dfrac{a^{9/2}x}{b^{10}y^{19/3}}$

71. (a) $69{,}300{,}000 = 6.93 \times 10^7$

   (b) $7{,}200{,}000{,}000{,}000 = 7.2 \times 10^{12}$

   (c) $0.000028536 = 2.8536 \times 10^{-5}$

   (d) $0.0001213 = 1.213 \times 10^{-4}$

72. (a) $129{,}540{,}000 = 1.2954 \times 10^8$

   (b) $7{,}259{,}000{,}000 = 7.259 \times 10^9$

   (c) $0.0000000014 = 1.4 \times 10^{-9}$

   (d) $0.0007029 = 7.029 \times 10^{-4}$

73. (a) $3.19 \times 10^5 = 319{,}000$

   (b) $2.721 \times 10^8 = 272{,}100{,}000$

   (c) $2.670 \times 10^{-8} = 0.00000002670$

   (d) $9.999 \times 10^{-9} = 0.000000009999$

74. (a) $7.1 \times 10^{14} = 710{,}000{,}000{,}000{,}000$

   (b) $6 \times 10^{12} = 6{,}000{,}000{,}000{,}000$

   (c) $8.55 \times 10^{-3} = 0.00855$

   (d) $6.257 \times 10^{-10} = 0.0000000006257$

75. (a) $5{,}900{,}000{,}000{,}000$ mi$= 5.9 \times 10^{12}$ mi

   (b) 0.0000000000004 cm $= 4 \times 10^{-13}$ cm

   (c) 33 billion billion molecules $= 33 \times 10^9 \times 10^9 = 3.3 \times 10^{19}$ molecules

76. (a) $93{,}000{,}000$ mi $= 9.3 \times 10^7$ mi

   (b) $0.00000000000000000000000053$ g $= 5.3 \times 10^{-23}$ g

   (c) $5{,}970{,}000{,}000{,}000{,}000{,}000{,}000{,}000$ kg $= 5.97 \times 10^{24}$ kg

77. $\left(7.2 \times 10^{-9}\right)\left(1.806 \times 10^{-12}\right) = 7.2 \times 1.806 \times 10^{-9} \times 10^{-12} \approx 13.0 \times 10^{-21} = 1.3 \times 10^{-20}$

78. $\left(1.062 \times 10^{24}\right)\left(8.61 \times 10^{19}\right) = 1.062 \times 8.61 \times 10^{24} \times 10^{19} \approx 9.14 \times 10^{43}$

79. $\dfrac{1.295643 \times 10^9}{(3.610 \times 10^{-17})(2.511 \times 10^6)} = \dfrac{1.295643}{3.610 \times 2.511} \times 10^{9+17-6} \approx 0.1429 \times 10^{19} = 1.429 \times 10^{19}$

80. $\dfrac{(73.1)\left(1.6341 \times 10^{28}\right)}{0.0000000019} = \dfrac{(7.31 \times 10)\left(1.6341 \times 10^{28}\right)}{1.9 \times 10^{-9}} = \dfrac{7.31 \times 1.6341}{1.9} \times 10^{1+28-(-9)} \approx 6.3 \times 10^{38}$

81. $\dfrac{(0.0000162)(0.01582)}{(594621000)(0.0058)} = \dfrac{\left(1.62 \times 10^{-5}\right)\left(1.582 \times 10^{-2}\right)}{\left(5.94621 \times 10^8\right)\left(5.8 \times 10^{-3}\right)} = \dfrac{1.62 \times 1.582}{5.94621 \times 5.8} \times 10^{-5-2-8+3} 0.074 \times 10^{-12}$

   $= 7.4 \times 10^{-14}$

82. $\dfrac{\left(3.542 \times 10^{-6}\right)^9}{(5.05 \times 10^4)^{12}} = \dfrac{(3.542)^9 \times 10^{-54}}{(5.05)^{12} \times 10^{48}} = \dfrac{87747.96}{275103767.10} \times 10^{-54-48} \approx 3.19 \times 10^{-4} \times 10^{-102} \approx 3.19 \times 10^{-106}$

83. (a) $\dfrac{1}{\sqrt{10}} = \dfrac{1}{\sqrt{10}} \cdot \dfrac{\sqrt{10}}{\sqrt{10}} = \dfrac{\sqrt{10}}{10}$

   (b) $\sqrt{\dfrac{2}{x}} = \sqrt{\dfrac{2}{x}} \cdot \sqrt{\dfrac{x}{x}} = \dfrac{\sqrt{2x}}{x}$

   (c) $\sqrt{\dfrac{x}{3}} = \sqrt{\dfrac{x}{3}} \cdot \sqrt{\dfrac{3}{3}} = \dfrac{\sqrt{3x}}{3}$

84. (a) $\sqrt{\dfrac{5}{12}} = \sqrt{\dfrac{5}{12}} \cdot \sqrt{\dfrac{12}{12}} = \dfrac{\sqrt{60}}{12} = \dfrac{\sqrt{4 \cdot 15}}{12} = \dfrac{\sqrt{4} \cdot \sqrt{15}}{12} = \dfrac{2\sqrt{15}}{12} = \dfrac{\sqrt{15}}{6}$

   (b) $\sqrt{\dfrac{x}{6}} = \sqrt{\dfrac{x}{6}} \cdot \sqrt{\dfrac{6}{6}} = \dfrac{\sqrt{6x}}{6}$

   (c) $\sqrt{\dfrac{y}{2z}} = \sqrt{\dfrac{y}{2z}} \cdot \sqrt{\dfrac{2z}{2z}} = \dfrac{\sqrt{2yz}}{2z}$

85. (a) $\dfrac{2}{\sqrt[3]{x}} = \dfrac{2}{\sqrt[3]{x}} \cdot \dfrac{\sqrt[3]{x^2}}{\sqrt[3]{x^2}} = \dfrac{2\sqrt[3]{x^2}}{x}$

(b) $\dfrac{1}{\sqrt[4]{y^3}} = \dfrac{1}{\sqrt[4]{y^3}} \cdot \dfrac{\sqrt[4]{y}}{\sqrt[4]{y}} = \dfrac{\sqrt[4]{y}}{y}$

(c) $\dfrac{x}{y^{2/5}} = \dfrac{x}{\sqrt[5]{y^2}} \cdot \dfrac{\sqrt[5]{y^3}}{\sqrt[5]{y^3}} = \dfrac{x\sqrt[5]{y^3}}{y}$

86. (a) $\dfrac{1}{\sqrt[4]{a}} = \dfrac{1}{\sqrt[4]{a}} \cdot \dfrac{\sqrt[4]{a^3}}{\sqrt[4]{a^3}} = \dfrac{\sqrt[4]{a^3}}{a}$

(b) $\dfrac{a}{\sqrt[3]{b^2}} = \dfrac{a}{\sqrt[3]{b^2}} \cdot \dfrac{\sqrt[3]{b}}{\sqrt[3]{b}} = \dfrac{a\sqrt[3]{b}}{b}$

(c) $\dfrac{1}{c^{3/7}} = \dfrac{1}{\sqrt[7]{c^3}} \cdot \dfrac{\sqrt[7]{c^4}}{\sqrt[7]{c^4}} = \dfrac{\sqrt[7]{c^4}}{c}$

87. (a) b^5 is negative since a negative number raised to an odd power is negative.

(b) b^{10} is positive since a negative number raised to an even power is positive.

(c) ab^2c^3 we have (positive)(negative)^2(negative)^3 = (positive)(positive)(negative) which is negative.

(d) Since $b - a$ is negative, $(b-a)^3 = $ (negative)^3 which is negative.

(e) Since $b - a$ is negative, $(b-a)^4 = $ (negative)^4 which is positive.

(f) $\dfrac{a^3c^3}{b^6c^6} = \dfrac{\text{(positive)}^3\,\text{(negative)}^3}{\text{(negative)}^6\,\text{(negative)}^6} = \dfrac{\text{(positive)}\,\text{(negative)}}{\text{(positive)}\,\text{(positive)}} = \dfrac{\text{negative}}{\text{positive}}$ which is negative.

88. (a) $\dfrac{a^m}{a^n} = \dfrac{a\cdot a\cdot a\cdot\cdots\cdot a\ (m\text{ factors})}{a\cdot a\cdot a\cdot\cdots\cdot a\ (n\text{ factors})} = a\cdot a\cdot a\cdot\cdots\cdot a\ (m-n\text{ factors}) = a^{m-n},\ a \neq 0$

(b) $\left(\dfrac{a}{b}\right)^n = \dfrac{a}{b}\cdot\dfrac{a}{b}\cdot\cdots\cdot\dfrac{a}{b}\ (n\text{ factors}) = \dfrac{a\cdot a\cdot a\cdot\cdots\cdot a\ (n\text{ factors})}{b\cdot b\cdot b\cdot\cdots\cdot b\ (n\text{ factors})} = \dfrac{a^n}{b^n},\ b \neq 0$

(c) $\left(\dfrac{a}{b}\right)^{-n} = \left[\left(\dfrac{a}{b}\right)^{-1}\right]^n = \left[\dfrac{1}{\left(\dfrac{a}{b}\right)}\right]^n = \left(\dfrac{b}{a}\right)^n = \dfrac{b^n}{a^n},\ a \neq 0, b \neq 0$. The first equality follows from Law 3. The second equality is given by the Negative Exponents Law. The third equality is simplification, and the fourth equality follows from Law 5.

89. Since one light year is 5.9×10^{12} miles, Centauri is about $4.3 \times 5.9 \times 10^{12} \approx 2.54 \times 10^{13}$ miles away or $25{,}400{,}000{,}000{,}000$ miles away.

90. 9.3×10^7 mi $= 186{,}000\,\dfrac{\text{mi}}{\text{s}} \times t$ s $\Leftrightarrow$ $t = \dfrac{9.3 \times 10^7}{186{,}000}$ s $= 500$ s $= 8\frac{1}{3}$ min.

91. Volume $= $ (average depth)(area) $= \left(3.7 \times 10^3 \text{ m}\right)\left(3.6 \times 10^{14} \text{ m}^2\right)\left(\dfrac{10^3 \text{ liters}}{\text{m}^3}\right) \approx 1.33 \times 10^{21}$ liters

92. Each person's share is equal to $\dfrac{\text{national debt}}{\text{population}} = \dfrac{7.529 \times 10^{12}}{2.949 \times 10^8} \approx 2.55 \times 10^4 = \$25{,}500.$

93. The number of molecules is equal to

$$(\text{volume})\cdot\left(\dfrac{\text{liters}}{\text{m}^3}\right)\cdot\left(\dfrac{\text{molecules}}{22.4 \text{ liters}}\right) = (5\cdot 10\cdot 3)\cdot(10^3)\cdot\left(\dfrac{6.02 \times 10^{23}}{22.4}\right) \approx 4.03 \times 10^{27}$$

94. First convert 1135 feet to miles. This gives 1135 ft $= 1135 \cdot \dfrac{1 \text{ mile}}{5280 \text{ feet}} = 0.215$ mi. Thus the distance you can see is given by $D = \sqrt{2rh + h^2} = \sqrt{2(3960)(0.215) + (0.215)^2} \approx \sqrt{1702.8} \approx 41.3$ miles.

95. (a) Using $f = 0.4$ and substituting $d = 65$, we obtain $s = \sqrt{30fd} = \sqrt{30 \times 0.4 \times 65} \approx 28$ mi/h.

(b) Using $f = 0.5$ and substituting $s = 50$, we find d. This gives $s = \sqrt{30fd}$ $\Leftrightarrow$ $50 = \sqrt{30\cdot(0.5)\,d}$ $\Leftrightarrow$ $50 = \sqrt{15d}$ $\Leftrightarrow$ $2500 = 15d$ $\Leftrightarrow$ $d = \frac{500}{3} \approx 167$ feet.

96. Since 1 day $= 86{,}400$ s, 365.25 days $= 31{,}557{,}600$ s. Substituting, we obtain $d = \left(\dfrac{6.67 \times 10^{-11} \times 1.99 \times 10^{30}}{4\pi^2}\right)^{1/3} \cdot$ $\left(3.15576 \times 10^7\right)^{2/3} \approx 1.5 \times 10^{11}$ m $= 1.5 \times 10^8$ km.

97. (a) Substituting the given values we get $V = 1.486 \dfrac{75^{2/3} \cdot 0.050^{1/2}}{24.1^{2/3} \cdot 0.040} \approx 17.707$ ft/s.

(b) Since the volume of the flow is $V \cdot A$, the canal discharge is $17.707 \cdot 75 \approx 1328.0$ ft^3/s.

98. Since $10^6 = 10^3 \cdot 10^3$ it would take 1000 days ≈ 2.74 years to spend the million dollars.

Since $10^9 = 10^3 \cdot 10^6$ it would take $10^6 = 1{,}000{,}000$ days ≈ 2739.72 years to spend the billion dollars.

99. (a) $\dfrac{18^5}{9^5} = \left(\dfrac{18}{9}\right)^5 = 2^5 = 32$

(b) $20^6 \cdot (0.5)^6 = (20 \cdot 0.5)^6 = 10^6 = 1{,}000{,}000$

100. (a)

n	1	2	5	10	100
$2^{1/n}$	$2^{1/1} = 2$	$2^{1/2} = 1.414$	$2^{1/5} = 1.149$	$2^{1/10} = 1.072$	$2^{1/100} = 1.007$

So when n gets large, $2^{1/n}$ decreases to 1.

(b)

n	1	2	5	10	100
$\left(\frac{1}{2}\right)^{1/n}$	$\left(\frac{1}{2}\right)^{1/1} = 0.5$	$\left(\frac{1}{2}\right)^{1/2} = 0.707$	$\left(\frac{1}{2}\right)^{1/5} = 0.871$	$\left(\frac{1}{2}\right)^{1/10} = 0.933$	$\left(\frac{1}{2}\right)^{1/100} = 0.993$

So when n gets large, $\left(\frac{1}{2}\right)^{1/n}$ increases to 1.

101. (a) Since $\frac{1}{2} > \frac{1}{3}$, $2^{1/2} > 2^{1/3}$.

(b) $\left(\frac{1}{2}\right)^{1/2} = 2^{-1/2}$ and $\left(\frac{1}{2}\right)^{1/3} = 2^{-1/3}$. Since $-\frac{1}{2} < -\frac{1}{3}$, we have $\left(\frac{1}{2}\right)^{1/2} < \left(\frac{1}{2}\right)^{1/3}$.

(c) We find a common root: $7^{1/4} = 7^{3/12} = \left(7^3\right)^{1/12} = 343^{1/12}$; $4^{1/3} = 4^{4/12} = \left(4^4\right)^{1/12} = 256^{1/12}$. So $7^{1/4} > 4^{1/3}$.

(d) We find a common root: $\sqrt[3]{5} = 5^{1/3} = 5^{2/6} = \left(5^2\right)^{1/6} = 25^{1/6}$; $\sqrt{3} = 3^{1/2} = 3^{3/6} = \left(3^3\right)^{1/6} = 27^{1/6}$. So $\sqrt[3]{5} < \sqrt{3}$.

1.3 Algebraic Expressions

1. Type: trinomial. Terms: x^2, $-3x$, and 7. Degree: 2.

2. Type: binomial. Terms: $2x^5$ and $4x^2$. Degree: 5.

3. Type: monomial. Terms: -8. Degree: 0.

4. Type: monomial. Terms: $\frac{1}{2}x^7$. Degree: 7.

5. Type: four-term polynomial. Terms: x, $-x^2$, x^3, and $-x^4$. Degree: 4.

6. Type: binomial. Terms: $\sqrt{2}x$ and $-\sqrt{3}$. Degree: 1.

7. $(12x - 7) - (5x - 12) = 12x - 7 - 5x + 12 = 7x + 5$

8. $(5 - 3x) + (2x - 8) = -x - 3$

9. $(3x^2 + x + 1) + (2x^2 - 3x - 5) = 5x^2 - 2x - 4$

10. $(3x^2 + x + 1) - (2x^2 - 3x - 5) = 3x^2 + x + 1 - 2x^2 + 3x + 5 = x^2 + 4x + 6$

11. $(x^3 + 6x^2 - 4x + 7) - (3x^2 + 2x - 4) = x^3 + 6x^2 - 4x + 7 - 3x^2 - 2x + 4 = x^3 + 3x^2 - 6x + 11$

12. $3(x - 1) + 4(x + 2) = 3x - 3 + 4x + 8 = 7x + 5$

13. $8(2x + 5) - 7(x - 9) = 16x + 40 - 7x + 63 = 9x + 103$

14. $4(x^2 - 3x + 5) - 3(x^2 - 2x + 1) = 4x^2 - 12x + 20 - 3x^2 + 6x - 3 = x^2 - 6x + 17$

15. $2(2 - 5t) + t^2(t - 1) - (t^4 - 1) = 4 - 10t + t^3 - t^2 - t^4 + 1 = -t^4 + t^3 - t^2 - 10t + 5$

16. $5(3t - 4) - (t^2 + 2) - 2t(t - 3) = 15t - 20 - t^2 - 2 - 2t^2 + 6t = -3t^2 + 21t - 22$

17. $\sqrt{x}\left(x - \sqrt{x}\right) = x^{1/2}\left(x - x^{1/2}\right) = x^{1/2}x - x^{1/2}x^{1/2} = x^{3/2} - x$

18. $x^{3/2}\left(\sqrt{x} - 1/\sqrt{x}\right) = x^{3/2}\left(x^{1/2} - x^{-1/2}\right) = x^{3/2}x^{1/2} - x^{3/2}x^{-1/2} = x^2 - x$

19. $(3t - 2)(7t - 5) = 21t^2 - 15t - 14t + 10 = 21t^2 - 29t + 10$

20. $(4x - 1)(3x + 7) = 12x^2 + 28x - 3x - 7 = 12x^2 + 25x - 7$

21. $(x + 2y)(3x - y) = 3x^2 - xy + 6xy - 2y^2 = 3x^2 + 5xy - 2y^2$

22. $(4x - 3y)(2x + 5y) = 8x^2 + 20xy - 6xy - 15y^2 = 8x^2 + 14xy - 15y^2$

23. $(1 - 2y)^2 = 1 - 4y + 4y^2$

24. $(3x + 4)^2 = (3x)^2 + 2(3x)(4) + (4)^2 = 9x^2 + 24x + 16$

25. $\left(2x^2 + 3y^2\right)^2 = \left(2x^2\right)^2 + 2\left(2x^2\right)\left(3y^2\right) + \left(3y^2\right)^2 = 4x^4 + 12x^2y^2 + 9y^4$

26. $\left(c + \dfrac{1}{c}\right)^2 = (c)^2 + 2\,(c)\left(\dfrac{1}{c}\right) + \left(\dfrac{1}{c}\right)^2 = c^2 + 2 + \dfrac{1}{c^2}$

27. $(2x - 5)\left(x^2 - x + 1\right) = 2x^3 - 2x^2 + 2x - 5x^2 + 5x - 5 = 2x^3 - 7x^2 + 7x - 5$

28. $(1 + 2x)\left(x^2 - 3x + 1\right) = x^2 - 3x + 1 + 2x^3 - 6x^2 + 2x = 2x^3 - 5x^2 - x + 1$

29. $\left(x^2 - a^2\right)\left(x^2 + a^2\right) = \left(x^2\right)^2 - \left(a^2\right)^2 = x^4 - a^4$ (difference of squares)

30. $\left(x^{1/2} + y^{1/2}\right)\left(x^{1/2} - y^{1/2}\right) = \left(x^{1/2}\right)^2 - \left(y^{1/2}\right)^2 = x - y$

31. $\left(\sqrt{a} - \dfrac{1}{b}\right)\left(\sqrt{a} + \dfrac{1}{b}\right) = (\sqrt{a})^2 - \left(\dfrac{1}{b}\right)^2 = a - \dfrac{1}{b^2}$ (difference of squares)

32. $\left(\sqrt{h^2 + 1} + 1\right)\left(\sqrt{h^2 + 1} - 1\right) = \left(\sqrt{h^2 + 1}\right)^2 - (1)^2 = h^2 + 1 - 1 = h^2$

33. $\left(1 + a^3\right)^3 = 1 + 3\left(a^3\right) + 3\left(a^3\right)^2 + \left(a^3\right)^3 = 1 + 3a^3 + 3a^6 + a^9$ (perfect cube)

34. $(1 - 2y)^3 = (1)^3 - 3\,(1)^2\,(2y) + 3\,(1)\,(2y)^2 - (2y)^3 = 1 - 6y + 12y^2 - 8y^3$

35. $\left(x^2 + x - 1\right)\left(2x^2 - x + 2\right) = x^2\left(2x^2 - x + 2\right) + x\left(2x^2 - x + 2\right) - \left(2x^2 - x + 2\right)$
$$= 2x^4 - x^3 + 2x^2 + 2x^3 - x^2 + 2x - 2x^2 + x - 2 = 2x^4 + x^3 - x^2 + 3x - 2$$

36. $\left(3x^3 + x^2 - 2\right)\left(x^2 + 2x - 1\right) = 3x^3\left(x^2 + 2x - 1\right) + x^2\left(x^2 + 2x - 1\right) - 2\left(x^2 + 2x - 1\right)$
$$= 3x^5 + 6x^4 - 3x^3 + x^4 + 2x^3 - x^2 - 2x^2 - 4x + 2 = 3x^5 + 7x^4 - x^3 - 3x^2 - 4x + 2$$

37. $\left(1 + x^{4/3}\right)\left(1 - x^{2/3}\right) = 1 - x^{2/3} + x^{4/3} - x^{6/3} = 1 - x^{2/3} + x^{4/3} - x^2$

38. $(1 - b)^2\,(1 + b)^2 = [(1 - b)(1 + b)]^2 = \left(1 - b^2\right)^2 = 1 - 2b^2 + b^4$

39. $\left(3x^2y + 7xy^2\right)\left(x^2y^3 - 2y^2\right) = 3x^4y^4 - 6x^2y^3 + 7x^3y^5 - 14xy^4 = 3x^4y^4 + 7x^3y^5 - 6x^2y^3 - 14xy^4$ (arranging in decreasing powers of x)

40. $\left(x^4y - y^5\right)\left(x^2 + xy + y^2\right) = x^6y + x^5y^2 + x^4y^3 - x^2y^5 - xy^6 - y^7$

41. $(x + y + z)(x - y - z) = [x + (y + z)][x - (y + z)] = x^2 - (y + z)^2 = x^2 - \left(y^2 + 2yz + z^2\right) = x^2 - y^2 - 2yz - z^2$

42. $\left(x^2 - y + z\right)\left(x^2 + y - z\right) = \left[x^2 - (y - z)\right]\left[x^2 + (y - z)\right] = \left(x^2\right)^2 - (y - z)^2$
$$= x^4 - \left(y^2 - 2yz + z^2\right) = x^4 - y^2 + 2yz - z^2$$

43. $-2x^3 + 16x = -2x\left(x^2 - 8\right)$

44. $2x^4 + 4x^3 - 14x^2 = 2x^2\left(x^2 + 2x - 7\right)$

45. $y\,(y - 6) + 9\,(y - 6) = (y - 6)(y + 9)$

46. $(z + 2)^2 - 5\,(z + 2) = (z + 2)[(z + 2) - 5] = (z + 2)(z - 3)$

47. $2x^2y - 6xy^2 + 3xy = xy\,(2x - 6y + 3)$

48. $-7x^4y^2 + 14xy^3 + 21xy^4 = 7xy^2\left(-x^3 + 2y + 3y^2\right)$

49. $x^2 + 2x - 3 = (x - 1)(x + 3)$

50. $x^2 - 6x + 5 = (x - 5)(x - 1)$

51. $8x^2 - 14x - 15 = (2x - 5)(4x + 3)$

52. $6y^2 + 11y - 21 = (y + 3)(6y - 7)$

53. $(3x + 2)^2 + 8(3x + 2) + 12 = [(3x + 2) + 2][(3x + 2) + 6] = (3x + 4)(3x + 8)$

54. $2(a + b)^2 + 5(a + b) - 3 = [(a + b) + 3][2(a + b) - 1] = (a + b + 3)(2a + 2b - 1)$

55. $9a^2 - 16 = (3a)^2 - 4^2 = (3a - 4)(3a + 4)$

56. $(x + 3)^2 - 4 = (x + 3)^2 - 2^2 = [(x + 3) - 2][(x + 3) + 2] = (x + 1)(x + 5)$

57. $27x^3 + y^3 = (3x)^3 + y^3 = (3x + y)[(3x)^2 + 3xy + y^2] = (3x + y)(9x^2 - 3xy + y^2)$

58. $8s^3 - 125t^6 = (2s)^3 - (5t^2)^3 = (2s - 5t^2)[(2s)^2 + (2s)(5t) + (5t)^2] = (2s - 5t^2)(4s^2 + 10st + 25t^2)$

59. $x^2 + 12x + 36 = x^2 + 2(6x) + 6^2 = (x + 6)^2$

60. $16z^2 - 24z + 9 = (4z)^2 - 2(4z)(3) + 3^2 = (4z - 3)^2$

61. $x^3 + 4x^2 + x + 4 = x^2(x + 4) + 1(x + 4) = (x + 4)(x^2 + 1)$

62. $3x^3 - x^2 + 6x - 2 = x^2(3x - 1) + 2(3x - 1) = (3x - 1)(x^2 + 2)$

63. $2x^3 + x^2 - 6x - 3 = x^2(2x + 1) - 3(2x + 1) = (2x + 1)(x^2 - 3)$. This can be further factored as $(2x + 1)(x - \sqrt{3})(x - \sqrt{3})$.

64. $-9x^3 - 3x^2 + 3x + 1 = -3x^2(3x + 1) + 1(3x + 1) = (3x + 1)(-3x^2 + 1) = (3x + 1)(1 - 3x^2)$. This can be further factored as $(3x + 1)(1 - \sqrt{3}x)(1 + \sqrt{3}x)$.

65. $x^3 + x^2 + x + 1 = x^2(x + 1) + 1(x + 1) = (x + 1)(x^2 + 1)$

66. $x^5 + x^4 + x + 1 = x^4(x + 1) + 1(x + 1) = (x + 1)(x^4 + 1)$

67. $x^{5/2} - x^{1/2} = x^{1/2}(x^2 - 1) = \sqrt{x}(x - 1)(x + 1)$

68. Start by factoring out the power of x with the smallest exponent, that is, $x^{-3/2}$. So
$$x^{-3/2} + 2x^{-1/2} + x^{1/2} = x^{-3/2}(1 + 2x + x^2) = \frac{(1 + x)^2}{x^{3/2}}.$$

69. Start by factoring out the power of $(x^2 + 1)$ with the smallest exponent, that is, $(x^2 + 1)^{-1/2}$. So
$$(x^2 + 1)^{1/2} + 2(x^2 + 1)^{-1/2} = (x^2 + 1)^{-1/2}[(x^2 + 1) + 2] = \frac{x^2 + 3}{\sqrt{x^2 + 1}}.$$

70. $2x^{1/3}(x - 2)^{2/3} - 5x^{4/3}(x - 2)^{-1/3} = x^{1/3}(x - 2)^{-1/3}[2(x - 2) - 5x] = x^{1/3}(x - 2)^{-1/3}(2x - 4 - 5x)$
$$= x^{1/3}(x - 2)^{-1/3}(-3x - 4) = \frac{(-3x - 4)\sqrt[3]{x}}{\sqrt[3]{x - 2}}$$

71. $12x^3 + 18x = 6x(2x^2 + 3)$

72. $5ab - 8abc = ab(5 - 8c)$

73. $x^2 - 2x - 8 = (x - 4)(x + 2)$

74. $y^2 - 8y + 15 = (y - 3)(y - 5)$

75. $2x^2 + 5x + 3 = (2x + 3)(x + 1)$

76. $9x^2 - 36x - 45 = 9(x^2 - 4x - 5) = 9(x - 5)(x + 1)$

77. $6x^2 - 5x - 6 = (3x + 2)(2x - 3)$

78. $r^2 - 6rs + 9s^2 = (r - 3s)^2$

79. $25s^2 - 10st + t^2 = (5s - t)^2$

80. $x^2 - 36 = (x - 6)(x + 6)$

81. $4x^2 - 25 = (2x - 5)(2x + 5)$

82. $49 - 4y^2 = (7 - 2y)(7 + 2y)$

83. $(a + b)^2 - (a - b)^2 = [(a + b) - (a - b)][(a + b) + (a - b)] = (2b)(2a) = 4ab$

84. $\left(1+\dfrac{1}{x}\right)^2 - \left(1-\dfrac{1}{x}\right)^2 = \left[\left(1+\dfrac{1}{x}\right)-\left(1-\dfrac{1}{x}\right)\right]\left[\left(1+\dfrac{1}{x}\right)+\left(1-\dfrac{1}{x}\right)\right]$

$$= \left(1+\dfrac{1}{x}-1+\dfrac{1}{x}\right)\left(1+\dfrac{1}{x}+1-\dfrac{1}{x}\right) = \left(\dfrac{2}{x}\right)(2) = \dfrac{4}{x}$$

85. $x^2\left(x^2-1\right) - 9\left(x^2-1\right) = \left(x^2-1\right)\left(x^2-9\right) = (x-1)(x+1)(x-3)(x+3)$

86. $\left(a^2-1\right)b^2 - 4\left(a^2-1\right) = \left(a^2-1\right)\left(b^2-4\right) = (a-1)(a+1)(b-2)(b+2)$

87. $8x^3 + 125 = (2x)^3 + 5^3 = (2x+5)\left[(2x)^2 - (2x)(5) + 5^2\right] = (2x+5)\left(4x^2 - 10x + 25\right)$

88. $x^6 + 64 = x^6 + 2^6 = \left(x^2\right)^3 + (4)^3 = \left(x^2+4\right)\left[\left(x^2\right)^2 - 4\left(x^2\right) + (4)^2\right] = \left(x^2+4\right)\left(x^4 - 4x^2 + 16\right)$

89. $x^6 - 8y^3 = \left(x^2\right)^3 - (2y)^3 = \left(x^2-2y\right)\left[\left(x^2\right)^2 + \left(x^2\right)(2y) + (2y)^2\right] = \left(x^2-2y\right)\left(x^4 + 2x^2y + 4y^2\right)$

90. $27a^3 - b^6 = (3a)^3 - \left(b^2\right)^3 = \left(3a-b^2\right)\left[(3a)^2 + (3a)\left(b^2\right) + \left(b^2\right)^2\right] = \left(3a-b^2\right)\left(9a^2 + 3ab^2 + b^4\right)$

91. $x^3 + 2x^2 + x = x\left(x^2 + 2x + 1\right) = x(x+1)^2$

92. $3x^3 - 27x = 3x\left(x^2 - 9\right) = 3x(x-3)(x+3)$

93. $x^3 + 3x^2 - x - 3 = \left(x^3 + 3x^2\right) + (-x-3) = x^2(x+3) - (x+3) = (x+3)\left(x^2-1\right) = (x+3)(x-1)(x+1)$

94. $y^3 - 3y^2 - 4y + 12 = \left(y^3 - 3y^2\right) + (-4y+12) = y^2(y-3) + (-4)(y-3)$

$$= (y-3)\left(y^2-4\right) = (y-3)(y-2)(y+2) \text{ (factor by grouping)}$$

95. $2x^3 + 4x^2 + x + 2 = \left(2x^3 + 4x^2\right) + (x+2) = 2x^2(x+2) + (1)(x+2) = (x+2)\left(2x^2+1\right)$ (factor by grouping)

96. $3x^3 + 5x^2 - 6x - 10 = x^2(3x+5) - 2(3x+5) = \left(x^2-2\right)(3x+5)$

97. $(x-1)(x+2)^2 - (x-1)^2(x+2) = (x-1)(x+2)\left[(x+2)-(x-1)\right] = 3(x-1)(x+2)$

98. $y^4(y+2)^3 + y^5(y+2)^4 = y^4(y+2)^3\left[(1) + y(y+2)\right] = y^4(y+2)^3\left(y^2+2y+1\right) = y^4(y+2)^3(y+1)^2$

99. Start by factoring $y^2 - 7y + 10$, and then substitute $a^2 + 1$ for y. This gives

$$\left(a^2+1\right)^2 - 7\left(a^2+1\right) + 10 = \left[\left(a^2+1\right)-2\right]\left[\left(a^2+1\right)-5\right] = \left(a^2-1\right)\left(a^2-4\right) = (a-1)(a+1)(a-2)(a+2).$$

100. $\left(a^2+2a\right)^2 - 2\left(a^2+2a\right) - 3 = \left[\left(a^2+2a\right)-3\right]\left[\left(a^2+2a\right)+1\right] = \left(a^2+2a-3\right)\left(a^2+2a+1\right)$

$$= (a-1)(a+3)(a+1)^2$$

101. $5\left(x^2+4\right)^4(2x)(x-2)^4 + \left(x^2+4\right)^5(4)(x-2)^3$

$$= 2\left(x^2+4\right)^4(x-2)^3\left[(5)(x)(x-2) + \left(x^2+4\right)(2)\right] = 2\left(x^2+4\right)^4(x-2)^3\left(5x^2 - 10x + 2x^2 + 8\right)$$

$$= 2\left(x^2+4\right)^4(x-2)^3\left(7x^2 - 10x + 8\right)$$

102. $3(2x-1)^2(2)(x+3)^{1/2} + (2x-1)^3\left(\tfrac{1}{2}\right)(x+3)^{-1/2}$

$$= (2x-1)^2(x+3)^{-1/2}\left[6(x+3) + (2x-1)\left(\tfrac{1}{2}\right)\right] = (2x-1)^2(x+3)^{-1/2}\left(6x + 18 + x - \tfrac{1}{2}\right)$$

$$= (2x-1)^2(x+3)^{-1/2}\left(7x + \tfrac{35}{2}\right)$$

103. $\left(x^2+3\right)^{-1/3} - \tfrac{2}{3}x^2\left(x^2+3\right)^{-4/3} = \left(x^2+3\right)^{-4/3}\left[\left(x^2+3\right) - \tfrac{2}{3}x^2\right] = \left(x^2+3\right)^{-4/3}\left(\tfrac{1}{3}x^2 + 3\right) = \dfrac{\tfrac{1}{3}x^2 + 3}{\left(x^2+3\right)^{4/3}}$

104. $\tfrac{1}{2}x^{-1/2}(3x+4)^{1/2} - \tfrac{3}{2}x^{1/2}(3x+4)^{-1/2} = \tfrac{1}{2}x^{-1/2}(3x+4)^{-1/2}\left[(3x+4) - 3x\right] = \tfrac{1}{2}x^{-1/2}(3x+4)^{-1/2}(4)$

$$= 2x^{-1/2}(3x+4)^{-1/2}$$

105. (a) $\frac{1}{2}\left[(a+b)^2 - \left(a^2 + b^2\right)\right] = \frac{1}{2}\left[a^2 + 2ab + b^2 - a^2 - b^2\right] = \frac{1}{2}\left(2ab\right) = ab$.

(b) $\left(a^2 + b^2\right)^2 - \left(a^2 - b^2\right)^2 = \left[\left(a^2 + b^2\right) - \left(a^2 - b^2\right)\right]\left[\left(a^2 + b^2\right) + \left(a^2 - b^2\right)\right]$
$$= \left(a^2 + b^2 - a^2 + b^2\right)\left(a^2 + b^2 + a^2 - b^2\right) = \left(2b^2\right)\left(2a^2\right) = 4a^2b^2$$

(c) LHS $= \left(a^2 + b^2\right)\left(c^2 + d^2\right) = a^2c^2 + a^2d^2 + b^2c^2 + b^2d^2$.

RHS $= \left(ac + bd\right)^2 + \left(ad - bc\right)^2 = a^2c^2 + 2abcd + b^2d^2 + a^2d^2 - 2abcd + b^2c^2 = a^2c^2 + a^2d^2 + b^2c^2 + b^2d^2$.

So LHS $=$ RHS, that is, $\left(a^2 + b^2\right)\left(c^2 + d^2\right) = \left(ac + bd\right)^2 + \left(ad - bc\right)^2$.

(d) $4a^2c^2 - \left(c^2 - b^2 + a^2\right)^2 = (2ac)^2 - \left(c^2 - b^2 + a^2\right)$
$$= \left[(2ac) - \left(c^2 - b^2 + a^2\right)\right]\left[(2ac) + \left(c^2 - b^2 + a^2\right)\right] \text{ (difference of squares)}$$
$$= \left(2ac - c^2 + b^2 - a^2\right)\left(2ac + c^2 - b^2 + a^2\right)$$
$$= \left[b^2 - \left(c^2 - 2ac + a^2\right)\right]\left[\left(c^2 + 2ac + a^2\right) - b^2\right] \text{ (regrouping)}$$
$$= \left[b^2 - (c - a)^2\right]\left[(c + a)^2 - b^2\right] \text{ (perfect squares)}$$
$$= [b - (c - a)]\,[b + (c - a)]\,[(c + a) - b]\,[(c + a) + b] \text{ (each factor is a difference of squares)}$$
$$= (b - c + a)(b + c - a)(c + a - b)(c + a + b)$$
$$= (a + b - c)(-a + b + c)(a - b + c)(a + b + c)$$

(e) $x^4 + 3x^2 + 4 = \left(x^4 + 4x^2 + 4\right) - x^2 = \left(x^2 + 2\right)^2 - x^2 = \left[\left(x^2 + 2\right) - x\right]\left[\left(x^2 + 2\right) + x\right]$
$$= \left(x^2 - x + 2\right)\left(x^2 + x + 2\right)$$

106. Difference of Cubes: $(A - B)\left(A^2 + AB + B^2\right) = A^3 + A^2B + AB^2 - A^2B - AB^2 - B^3 = A^3 - B^3$

Sum of Cubes: $(A + B)\left(A^2 - AB + B^2\right) = A^3 - A^2B + AB^2 + A^2B - AB^2 + B^3 = A^3 + B^3$

107. The volume of the shell is the difference between the volumes of the outside cylinder (with radius R) and the inside cylinder

(with radius r). Thus $V = \pi R^2 h - \pi r^2 h = \pi \left(R^2 - r^2\right) h = \pi (R - r)(R + r) h = 2\pi \cdot \dfrac{R + r}{2} \cdot h \cdot (R - r)$. The

average radius is $\dfrac{R + r}{2}$ and $2\pi \cdot \dfrac{R + r}{2}$ is the average circumference (length of the rectangular box), h is the height, and

$R - r$ is the thickness of the rectangular box. Thus $V = \pi R^2 h - \pi r^2 h = 2\pi \cdot \dfrac{R + r}{2} \cdot h \cdot (R - r) = 2\pi \cdot (\text{average radius}) \cdot$

(height) $\cdot$ (thickness)

108. (a) Moved portion $=$ field $-$ habitat

(b) Using the difference of squares, we get $b^2 - (b - 2x)^2 = [b - (b - 2x)]\,[b + (b - x)] = 2x\,(2b - 2x) = 4x\,(b - x)$.

109. (a) The degree of the product is the sum of the degrees.

(b) The degree of a sum is at most the largest of the degrees — it could be smaller than either. For example, the degree of
$\left(x^3\right) + \left(-x^3 + x\right) = x$ is 1.

110. (a) $528^2 - 527^2 = (528 - 527)(528 + 527) = 1\,(1055) = 1055$

(b) $122^2 - 120^2 = (122 - 120)(122 + 120) = 2\,(242) = 484$

(c) $1020^2 - 1010^2 = (1020 - 1010)(1020 + 1010) = 10\,(2030) = 20{,}300$

(d) $49 \cdot 51 = (50 - 1)(50 + 1) = 50^2 - 1 = 2500 - 1 = 2499$

(e) $998 \cdot 1002 = (1000 - 2)(1000 + 2) = 1000^2 - 2^2 = 1{,}000{,}000 - 4 = 999{,}996$

111. (a) $A^4 - B^4 = \left(A^2 - B^2\right)\left(A^2 + B^2\right) = (A - B)(A + B)\left(A^2 + B^2\right)$

$A^6 - B^6 = \left(A^3 - B^3\right)\left(A^3 + B^3\right)$ (difference of squares)

$= (A - B)\left(A^2 + AB + B^2\right)(A + B)\left(A^2 - AB + B^2\right)$ (difference and sum of cubes)

(b) $12^4 - 7^4 = 20{,}736 - 2{,}401 = 18{,}335$; $12^6 - 7^6 = 2{,}985{,}984 - 117{,}649 = 2{,}868{,}335$

(c) $18{,}335 = 12^4 - 7^4 = (12 - 7)(12 + 7)\left(12^2 + 7^2\right) = 5\,(19)\,(144 + 49) = 5\,(19)\,(193)$

$2{,}868{,}335 = 12^6 - 7^6 = (12 - 7)(12 + 7)\left[12^2 + 12\,(7) + 7^2\right]\left[12^2 - 12\,(7) + 7^2\right]$

$= 5\,(19)\,(144 + 84 + 49)\,(144 - 84 + 49) = 5\,(19)\,(277)\,(109)$

112.

$$
\begin{array}{r}
A + 1 \\
\times \quad A - 1 \\
\hline
-A - 1 \\
A^2 + A \\
\hline
A^2 \qquad - 1
\end{array}
\qquad
\begin{array}{r}
A^2 + A + 1 \\
\times \quad A - 1 \\
\hline
-A^2 - A - 1 \\
A^3 + A^2 + A \\
\hline
A^3 \qquad\qquad - 1
\end{array}
\qquad
\begin{array}{r}
A^3 + A^2 + A + 1 \\
\times \quad A - 1 \\
\hline
-A^3 - A^2 - A - 1 \\
A^4 + A^3 + A^2 + A \\
\hline
A^4 \qquad\qquad\qquad - 1
\end{array}
$$

Based on the pattern, we suspect that $A^5 - 1 = (A - 1)\left(A^4 + A^3 + A^2 + A + 1\right)$. Check:

$$
\begin{array}{r}
A^4 + A^3 + A^2 + A + 1 \\
\times \qquad\qquad\qquad A - 1 \\
\hline
-A^4 - A^3 - A^2 - A - 1 \\
A^5 + A^4 + A^3 + A^2 + A \\
\hline
A^5 \qquad\qquad\qquad\qquad - 1
\end{array}
$$

The general pattern is $A^n - 1 = (A - 1)\left(A^{n-1} + A^{n-2} + \cdots + A^2 + A + 1\right)$, where n is a positive integer.

113. (a) $x^4 + x^2 - 2 = \left(x^2 - 1\right)\left(x^2 + 2\right) = (x - 1)(x + 1)\left(x^2 + 2\right)$

(b) $x^4 + 2x^2 + 9 = \left(x^4 + 6x^2 + 9\right) - 4x^2 = \left(x^2 + 3\right)^2 - (2x)^2 = \left[\left(x^2 + 3\right) - 2x\right]\left[\left(x^2 + 3\right) + 2x\right]$

$= \left(x^2 - 2x + 3\right)\left(x^2 + 2x + 3\right)$

(c) $x^4 + 4x^2 + 16 = \left(x^4 + 8x^2 + 16\right) - 4x^2 = \left(x^2 + 4\right)^2 - (2x)^2$

$= \left[\left(x^2 + 4\right) - 2x\right]\left[\left(x^2 + 4\right) + 2x\right] = \left(x^2 - 2x + 4\right)\left(x^2 + 2x + 4\right)$

(d) $x^4 + 2x^2 + 1 = \left(x^2 + 1\right)^2$

1.4   Rational Expressions

1. The domain of $4x^2 - 10x + 3$ is all real numbers.

2. The domain of $-x^4 + x^3 + 9x$ is all real numbers.

3. Since $x - 4 \neq 0$ we have $x \neq 4$. Domain: $\{x \mid x \neq 4\}$

4. Since $3x + 6 \neq 0$ we have $x \neq -2$. Domain: $\{x \mid x \neq -2\}$

5. Since $x + 3 \geq 0 \quad \Leftrightarrow \quad x \geq -3$. Domain; $\{x \mid x \geq -3\}$

6. Since $x - 1 > 0 \quad \Leftrightarrow \quad x > 1$. Domain; $\{x \mid x > 1\}$

7. $\dfrac{3\,(x + 2)\,(x - 1)}{6\,(x - 1)^2} = \dfrac{3\,(x - 1) \cdot (x + 2)}{3\,(x - 1) \cdot 2\,(x - 1)} = \dfrac{x + 2}{2\,(x - 1)}$

8. $\dfrac{4\left(x^2 - 1\right)}{12\,(x + 2)\,(x - 1)} = \dfrac{4\,(x + 1)\,(x - 1)}{12\,(x + 2)\,(x - 1)} = \dfrac{x + 1}{3\,(x + 2)}$

9. $\dfrac{x - 2}{x^2 - 4} = \dfrac{x - 2}{(x - 2)\,(x + 2)} = \dfrac{1}{x + 2}$

10. $\dfrac{x^2 - x - 2}{x^2 - 1} = \dfrac{(x - 2)\,(x + 1)}{(x - 1)\,(x + 1)} = \dfrac{x - 2}{x - 1}$

11. $\dfrac{x^2 + 6x + 8}{x^2 + 5x + 4} = \dfrac{(x + 2)\,(x + 4)}{(x + 1)\,(x + 4)} = \dfrac{x + 2}{x + 1}$

12. $\dfrac{x^2 - x - 12}{x^2 + 5x + 6} = \dfrac{(x - 4)\,(x + 3)}{(x + 2)\,(x + 3)} = \dfrac{x - 4}{x + 2}$

13. $\dfrac{y^2+y}{y^2-1} = \dfrac{y\,(y+1)}{(y-1)\,(y+1)} = \dfrac{y}{y-1}$

14. $\dfrac{y^2-3y-18}{2y^2+5y+3} = \dfrac{(y-6)\,(y+3)}{(2y+3)\,(y+1)}$

15. $\dfrac{2x^3-x^2-6x}{2x^2-7x+6} = \dfrac{x\left(2x^2-x-6\right)}{(2x-3)\,(x-2)} = \dfrac{x\,(2x+3)\,(x-2)}{(2x-3)\,(x-2)} = \dfrac{x\,(2x+3)}{2x-3}$

16. $\dfrac{1-x^2}{x^3-1} = \dfrac{(1-x)\,(1+x)}{(x-1)\,(x^2+x+1)} = \dfrac{-(x-1)\,(1+x)}{(x-1)\,(x^2+x+1)} = \dfrac{-(x+1)}{x^2+x+1}$

17. $\dfrac{4x}{x^2-4} \cdot \dfrac{x+2}{16x} = \dfrac{4x}{(x-2)\,(x+2)} \cdot \dfrac{x+2}{16x} = \dfrac{1}{4\,(x-2)}$

18. $\dfrac{x^2-25}{x^2-16} \cdot \dfrac{x+4}{x+5} = \dfrac{(x-5)\,(x+5)}{(x-4)\,(x+4)} \cdot \dfrac{x+4}{x+5} = \dfrac{x-5}{x-4}$

19. $\dfrac{x^2-x-12}{x^2-9} \cdot \dfrac{3+x}{4-x} = \dfrac{(x-4)\,(x+3)}{(x-3)\,(x+3)} \cdot \dfrac{x+3}{-(x-4)} = \dfrac{x+3}{-(x-3)} = \dfrac{3+x}{3-x}$

20. $\dfrac{x^2+2x-3}{x^2-2x-3} \cdot \dfrac{3-x}{3+x} = \dfrac{(x+3)\,(x-1)}{(x-3)\,(x+1)} \cdot \dfrac{-(x-3)}{x+3} = \dfrac{-(x-1)}{x+1} = \dfrac{-x+1}{x+1} = \dfrac{1-x}{1+x}$

21. $\dfrac{t-3}{t^2+9} \cdot \dfrac{t+3}{t^2-9} = \dfrac{(t-3)\,(t+3)}{(t^2+9)\,(t-3)\,(t+3)} = \dfrac{1}{t^2+9}$

22. $\dfrac{x^2-x-6}{x^2+2x} \cdot \dfrac{x^3+x^2}{x^2-2x-3} = \dfrac{(x-3)\,(x+2)}{x\,(x+2)} \cdot \dfrac{x^2\,(x+1)}{(x-3)\,(x+1)} = x$

23. $\dfrac{x^2+7x+12}{x^2+3x+2} \cdot \dfrac{x^2+5x+6}{x^2+6x+9} = \dfrac{(x+3)\,(x+4)}{(x+1)\,(x+2)} \cdot \dfrac{(x+2)\,(x+3)}{(x+3)\,(x+3)} = \dfrac{x+4}{x+1}$

24. $\dfrac{x^2+2xy+y^2}{x^2-y^2} \cdot \dfrac{2x^2-xy-y^2}{x^2-xy-2y^2} = \dfrac{(x+y)\,(x+y)}{(x-y)\,(x+y)} \cdot \dfrac{(x-y)\,(2x+y)}{(x-2y)\,(x+y)} = \dfrac{2x+y}{x-2y}$

25. $\dfrac{2x^2+3x+1}{x^2+2x-15} \div \dfrac{x^2+6x+5}{2x^2-7x+3} = \dfrac{2x^2+3x+1}{x^2+2x-15} \cdot \dfrac{2x^2-7x+3}{x^2+6x+5} = \dfrac{(2x+1)\,(x+1)}{(x-3)\,(x+5)} \cdot \dfrac{(2x-1)\,(x-3)}{(x+1)\,(x+5)}$

$= \dfrac{(2x+1)\,(2x-1)}{(x+5)\,(x+5)} = \dfrac{(2x+1)\,(2x-1)}{(x+5)^2}$

26. $\dfrac{4y^2-9}{2y^2+9y-18} \div \dfrac{2y^2+y-3}{y^2+5y-6} = \dfrac{4y^2-9}{2y^2+9y-18} \cdot \dfrac{y^2+5y-6}{2y^2+y-3} = \dfrac{(2y-3)\,(2y+3)}{(2y-3)\,(y+6)} \cdot \dfrac{(y-1)\,(y+6)}{(y-1)\,(2y+3)} = 1$

27. $\dfrac{\dfrac{x^3}{x+1}}{\dfrac{x}{x^2+2x+1}} = \dfrac{x^3}{x+1} \cdot \dfrac{x^2+2x+1}{x} = \dfrac{x^3\,(x+1)\,(x+1)}{(x+1)\,x} = x^2\,(x+1)$

28. $\dfrac{\dfrac{2x^2-3x-2}{x^2-1}}{\dfrac{2x^2+5x+2}{x^2+x-2}} = \dfrac{2x^2-3x-2}{x^2-1} \cdot \dfrac{x^2+x-2}{2x^2+5x+2} = \dfrac{(x-2)\,(2x+1)}{(x-1)\,(x+1)} \cdot \dfrac{(x-1)\,(x+2)}{(x+2)\,(2x+1)} = \dfrac{x-2}{x+1}$

29. $\dfrac{x/y}{z} = \dfrac{x}{y} \cdot \dfrac{1}{z} = \dfrac{x}{yz}$

30. $\dfrac{x}{y/z} = x \div \dfrac{y}{z} = \dfrac{x}{1} \cdot \dfrac{z}{y} = \dfrac{xz}{y}$

31. $2 + \dfrac{x}{x+3} = \dfrac{2\,(x+3)}{x+3} + \dfrac{x}{x+3} = \dfrac{2x+6+x}{x+3} = \dfrac{3x+6}{x+3} = \dfrac{3\,(x+2)}{(x+3)}$

32. $\dfrac{2x-1}{x+4} - 1 = \dfrac{2x-1}{x+4} + \dfrac{-(x+4)}{x+4} = \dfrac{2x-1-x-4}{x+4} = \dfrac{x-5}{x+4}$

33. $\dfrac{1}{x+5} + \dfrac{2}{x-3} = \dfrac{x-3}{(x+5)\,(x-3)} + \dfrac{2\,(x+5)}{(x+5)\,(x-3)} = \dfrac{x-3+2x+10}{(x+5)\,(x-3)} = \dfrac{3x+7}{(x+5)\,(x-3)}$

34. $\dfrac{1}{x+1} + \dfrac{1}{x-1} = \dfrac{x-1}{(x+1)\,(x-1)} + \dfrac{x+1}{(x+1)\,(x-1)} = \dfrac{x-1+x+1}{(x+1)\,(x-1)} = \dfrac{2x}{(x+1)\,(x-1)}$

35. $\dfrac{1}{x+1} - \dfrac{1}{x+2} = \dfrac{x+2}{(x+1)(x+2)} + \dfrac{-(x+1)}{(x+1)(x+2)} = \dfrac{x+2-x-1}{(x+1)(x+2)} = \dfrac{1}{(x+1)(x+2)}$

36. $\dfrac{x}{x-4} - \dfrac{3}{x+6} = \dfrac{x(x+6)}{(x-4)(x+6)} + \dfrac{-3(x-4)}{(x-4)(x+6)} = \dfrac{x^2+6x-3x+12}{(x-4)(x+6)} = \dfrac{x^2+3x+12}{(x-4)(x+6)}$

37. $\dfrac{x}{(x+1)^2} + \dfrac{2}{x+1} = \dfrac{x}{(x+1)^2} + \dfrac{2(x+1)}{(x+1)(x+1)} = \dfrac{x+2x+2}{(x+1)^2} = \dfrac{3x+2}{(x+1)^2}$

38. $\dfrac{5}{2x-3} - \dfrac{3}{(2x-3)^2} = \dfrac{5(2x-3)}{(2x-3)^2} - \dfrac{3}{(2x-3)^2} = \dfrac{10x-15-3}{(2x-3)^2} = \dfrac{10x-18}{(2x-3)^2} = \dfrac{2(5x-9)}{(2x-3)^2}$

39. $u+1+\dfrac{u}{u+1} = \dfrac{(u+1)(u+1)}{u+1} + \dfrac{u}{u+1} = \dfrac{u^2+2u+1+u}{u+1} = \dfrac{u^2+3u+1}{u+1}$

40. $\dfrac{2}{a^2} - \dfrac{3}{ab} + \dfrac{4}{b^2} = \dfrac{2b^2}{a^2b^2} - \dfrac{3ab}{a^2b^2} + \dfrac{4a^2}{a^2b^2} = \dfrac{2b^2-3ab+4a^2}{a^2b^2}$

41. $\dfrac{1}{x^2} + \dfrac{1}{x^2+x} = \dfrac{1}{x^2} + \dfrac{1}{x(x+1)} = \dfrac{x+1}{x^2(x+1)} + \dfrac{x}{x^2(x+1)} = \dfrac{2x+1}{x^2(x+1)}$

42. $\dfrac{1}{x} + \dfrac{1}{x^2} + \dfrac{1}{x^3} = \dfrac{x^2}{x^3} + \dfrac{x}{x^3} + \dfrac{1}{x^3} = \dfrac{x^2+x+1}{x^3}$

43. $\dfrac{2}{x+3} - \dfrac{1}{x^2+7x+12} = \dfrac{2}{x+3} - \dfrac{1}{(x+3)(x+4)} = \dfrac{2(x+4)}{(x+3)(x+4)} + \dfrac{-1}{(x+3)(x+4)}$

$= \dfrac{2x+8-1}{(x+3)(x+4)} = \dfrac{2x+7}{(x+3)(x+4)}$

44. $\dfrac{x}{x^2-4} + \dfrac{1}{x-2} = \dfrac{x}{(x-2)(x+2)} + \dfrac{1}{x-2} = \dfrac{x}{(x-2)(x+2)} + \dfrac{x+2}{(x-2)(x+2)}$

$= \dfrac{2x+2}{(x-2)(x+2)} = \dfrac{2(x+1)}{(x-2)(x+2)}$

45. $\dfrac{1}{x+3} + \dfrac{1}{x^2-9} = \dfrac{1}{x+3} + \dfrac{1}{(x-3)(x+3)} = \dfrac{x-3}{(x-3)(x+3)} + \dfrac{1}{(x-3)(x+3)} = \dfrac{x-2}{(x-3)(x+3)}$

46. $\dfrac{x}{x^2+x-2} - \dfrac{2}{x^2-5x+4} = \dfrac{x}{(x-1)(x+2)} + \dfrac{-2}{(x-1)(x-4)}$

$= \dfrac{x(x-4)}{(x-1)(x+2)(x-4)} + \dfrac{-2(x+2)}{(x-1)(x+2)(x-4)} = \dfrac{x^2-4x-2x-4}{(x-1)(x+2)(x-4)} = \dfrac{x^2-6x-4}{(x-1)(x+2)(x-4)}$

47. $\dfrac{2}{x} + \dfrac{3}{x-1} - \dfrac{4}{x^2-x} = \dfrac{2}{x} + \dfrac{3}{x-1} - \dfrac{4}{x(x-1)} = \dfrac{2(x-1)}{x(x-1)} + \dfrac{3x}{x(x-1)} + \dfrac{-4}{x(x-1)} = \dfrac{2x-2+3x-4}{x(x-1)} = \dfrac{5x-6}{x(x-1)}$

48. $\dfrac{x}{x^2-x-6} - \dfrac{1}{x+2} - \dfrac{2}{x-3} = \dfrac{x}{(x-3)(x+2)} + \dfrac{-1}{x+2} + \dfrac{-2}{x-3}$

$= \dfrac{x}{(x-3)(x+2)} + \dfrac{-1(x-3)}{(x-3)(x+2)} + \dfrac{-2(x+2)}{(x-3)(x+2)} = \dfrac{x-x+3-2x-4}{(x-3)(x+2)} = \dfrac{-2x-1}{(x-3)(x+2)}$

49. $\dfrac{1}{x^2+3x+2} - \dfrac{1}{x^2-2x-3} = \dfrac{1}{(x+2)(x+1)} - \dfrac{1}{(x-3)(x+1)}$

$= \dfrac{x-3}{(x-3)(x+2)(x+1)} + \dfrac{-(x+2)}{(x-3)(x+2)(x+1)} = \dfrac{x-3-x-2}{(x-3)(x+2)(x+1)} = \dfrac{-5}{(x-3)(x+2)(x+1)}$

50. $\dfrac{1}{x+1} - \dfrac{2}{(x+1)^2} + \dfrac{3}{x^2-1} = \dfrac{1}{x+1} + \dfrac{-2}{(x+1)^2} + \dfrac{3}{(x-1)(x+1)}$

$= \dfrac{(x+1)(x-1)}{(x-1)(x+1)^2} + \dfrac{-2(x-1)}{(x-1)(x+1)^2} + \dfrac{3(x+1)}{(x-1)(x+1)^2}$

$= \dfrac{x^2-1}{(x-1)(x+1)^2} + \dfrac{-2x+2}{(x-1)(x+1)^2} + \dfrac{3x+3}{(x-1)(x+1)^2} = \dfrac{x^2-1-2x+2+3x+3}{(x-1)(x+1)^2} = \dfrac{x^2+x+4}{(x-1)(x+1)^2}$

51. $\dfrac{\dfrac{x}{y} - \dfrac{y}{x}}{\dfrac{1}{x^2} - \dfrac{1}{y^2}} = \dfrac{\dfrac{x^2 - y^2}{xy}}{\dfrac{y^2 - x^2}{x^2 y^2}} = \dfrac{x^2 - y^2}{xy} \cdot \dfrac{x^2 y^2}{y^2 - x^2} = \dfrac{xy}{-1} = -xy.$ An alternative method is to multiply the

numerator and denominator by the common denominator of both the numerator and denominator, in this case $x^2 y^2$:

$$\dfrac{\dfrac{x}{y} - \dfrac{y}{x}}{\dfrac{1}{x^2} - \dfrac{1}{y^2}} = \dfrac{\left(\dfrac{x}{y} - \dfrac{y}{x}\right)}{\left(\dfrac{1}{x^2} - \dfrac{1}{y^2}\right)} \cdot \dfrac{x^2 y^2}{x^2 y^2} = \dfrac{x^3 y - xy^3}{y^2 - x^2} = \dfrac{xy\left(x^2 - y^2\right)}{y^2 - x^2} = -xy.$$

52. $x - \dfrac{y}{\dfrac{x}{y} + \dfrac{y}{x}} = x - \dfrac{y}{\dfrac{x}{y} + \dfrac{y}{x}} \cdot \dfrac{xy}{xy} = x - \dfrac{xy^2}{x^2 + y^2} = \dfrac{x\left(x^2 + y^2\right)}{x^2 + y^2} - \dfrac{xy^2}{x^2 + y^2} = \dfrac{x^3 + xy^2 - xy^2}{x^2 + y^2} = \dfrac{x^3}{x^2 + y^2}$

53. $\dfrac{1 + \dfrac{1}{c - 1}}{1 - \dfrac{1}{c - 1}} = \dfrac{\dfrac{c - 1}{c - 1} + \dfrac{1}{c - 1}}{\dfrac{c - 1}{c - 1} + \dfrac{-1}{c - 1}} = \dfrac{\dfrac{c}{c - 1}}{\dfrac{c - 2}{c - 1}} = \dfrac{c}{c - 1} \cdot \dfrac{c - 1}{c - 2} = \dfrac{c}{c - 2}.$ Using the alternative method, we obtain

$$\dfrac{1 + \dfrac{1}{c - 1}}{1 - \dfrac{1}{c - 1}} = \dfrac{\left(1 + \dfrac{1}{c - 1}\right)}{\left(1 - \dfrac{1}{c - 1}\right)} \cdot \dfrac{c - 1}{c - 1} = \dfrac{c - 1 + 1}{c - 1 - 1} = \dfrac{c}{c - 2}.$$

54. $1 + \dfrac{1}{1 + \dfrac{1}{1 + x}} = 1 + \dfrac{1}{1 + \dfrac{1}{1 + x}} \cdot \dfrac{1 + x}{1 + x} = 1 + \dfrac{1 + x}{1 + x + 1} = 1 + \dfrac{1 + x}{2 + x} = \dfrac{2 + x}{2 + x} + \dfrac{1 + x}{2 + x} = \dfrac{3 + 2x}{2 + x}$

55. $\dfrac{\dfrac{5}{x - 1} - \dfrac{2}{x + 1}}{\dfrac{x}{x - 1} + \dfrac{1}{x + 1}} = \dfrac{\dfrac{5(x + 1)}{(x - 1)(x + 1)} + \dfrac{-2(x - 1)}{(x - 1)(x + 1)}}{\dfrac{x(x + 1)}{(x - 1)(x + 1)} + \dfrac{x - 1}{(x - 1)(x + 1)}} = \dfrac{\dfrac{5x + 5 - 2x + 2}{(x - 1)(x + 1)}}{\dfrac{x^2 + x + x - 1}{(x - 1)(x + 1)}}$

$$= \dfrac{3x + 7}{(x - 1)(x + 1)} \cdot \dfrac{(x - 1)(x + 1)}{x^2 + 2x - 1} = \dfrac{3x + 7}{x^2 + 2x - 1}$$

Alternatively,

$$\dfrac{\dfrac{5}{x - 1} - \dfrac{2}{x + 1}}{\dfrac{x}{x - 1} + \dfrac{1}{x + 1}} = \dfrac{\left(\dfrac{5}{x - 1} - \dfrac{2}{x + 1}\right)}{\left(\dfrac{x}{x - 1} + \dfrac{1}{x + 1}\right)} \cdot \dfrac{(x - 1)(x + 1)}{(x - 1)(x + 1)} = \dfrac{5(x + 1) - 2(x - 1)}{x(x + 1) + (x - 1)}$$

$$= \dfrac{5x + 5 - 2x + 2}{x^2 + x + x - 1} = \dfrac{3x + 7}{x^2 + 2x - 1}$$

56. $\dfrac{\dfrac{a - b}{a} - \dfrac{a + b}{b}}{\dfrac{a - b}{b} + \dfrac{a + b}{a}} = \dfrac{\dfrac{a - b}{a} - \dfrac{a + b}{b}}{\dfrac{a - b}{b} + \dfrac{a + b}{a}} \cdot \dfrac{ab}{ab} = \dfrac{(a - b)b - (a + b)a}{(a - b)a + (a + b)b} = \dfrac{ab - b^2 - a^2 - ab}{a^2 - ab + ab + b^2}$

$$= \dfrac{-a^2 - b^2}{a^2 + b^2} = \dfrac{-\left(a^2 + b^2\right)}{a^2 + b^2} = -1$$

57. $\dfrac{x^{-2} - y^{-2}}{x^{-1} + y^{-1}} = \dfrac{\dfrac{1}{x^2} - \dfrac{1}{y^2}}{\dfrac{1}{x} + \dfrac{1}{y}} = \dfrac{\dfrac{y^2}{x^2 y^2} - \dfrac{x^2}{x^2 y^2}}{\dfrac{y}{xy} + \dfrac{x}{xy}} = \dfrac{y^2 - x^2}{x^2 y^2} \cdot \dfrac{xy}{y + x} = \dfrac{(y - x)(y + x)xy}{x^2 y^2(y + x)} = \dfrac{y - x}{xy}$

Alternatively, $\dfrac{x^{-2} - y^{-2}}{x^{-1} + y^{-1}} = \dfrac{\left(\dfrac{1}{x^2} - \dfrac{1}{y^2}\right)}{\left(\dfrac{1}{x} + \dfrac{1}{y}\right)} \cdot \dfrac{x^2 y^2}{x^2 y^2} = \dfrac{y^2 - x^2}{xy^2 + x^2 y} = \dfrac{(y - x)(y + x)}{xy(y + x)} = \dfrac{y - x}{xy}.$

58. $\dfrac{x^{-1}+y^{-1}}{(x+y)^{-1}} = \dfrac{\dfrac{1}{x}+\dfrac{1}{y}}{\dfrac{1}{x+y}} = \dfrac{\dfrac{1}{x}+\dfrac{1}{y}}{\dfrac{1}{x+y}} \cdot \dfrac{xy\,(x+y)}{xy\,(x+y)} = \dfrac{y\,(x+y)+x\,(x+y)}{xy}$

$$= \dfrac{xy+y^2+x^2+xy}{xy} = \dfrac{x^2+2xy+y^2}{xy} = \dfrac{(x+y)^2}{xy}$$

59. $\dfrac{1}{1+a^n} + \dfrac{1}{1+a^{-n}} = \dfrac{1}{1+a^n} + \dfrac{1}{1+a^{-n}} \cdot \dfrac{a^n}{a^n} = \dfrac{1}{1+a^n} + \dfrac{a^n}{a^n+1} = \dfrac{1+a^n}{1+a^n} = 1$

60. $\dfrac{\left(a+\dfrac{1}{b}\right)^m \left(a-\dfrac{1}{b}\right)^n}{\left(b+\dfrac{1}{a}\right)^m \left(b-\dfrac{1}{a}\right)^n} = \left(\dfrac{a+\dfrac{1}{b}}{b+\dfrac{1}{a}}\right)^m \left(\dfrac{a-\dfrac{1}{b}}{b-\dfrac{1}{a}}\right)^n = \left(\dfrac{\dfrac{ab+1}{b}}{\dfrac{ab+1}{a}}\right)^m \left(\dfrac{\dfrac{ab-1}{b}}{\dfrac{ab-1}{a}}\right)^n$

$$= \left(\dfrac{a}{b}\right)^m \left(\dfrac{a}{b}\right)^n = \left(\dfrac{a}{b}\right)^{m+n} = \dfrac{a^{m+n}}{b^{m+n}}$$

61. $\dfrac{\dfrac{1}{a+h}-\dfrac{1}{a}}{h} = \dfrac{\dfrac{a}{a\,(a+h)}-\dfrac{a+h}{a\,(a+h)}}{h} = \dfrac{\dfrac{a-a-h}{a\,(a+h)}}{h} = \dfrac{-h}{a\,(a+h)} \cdot \dfrac{1}{h} = \dfrac{-1}{a\,(a+h)}$

62. $\dfrac{(x+h)^{-3}-x^{-3}}{h} = \dfrac{\dfrac{1}{(x+h)^3}-\dfrac{1}{x^3}}{h} = \left(\dfrac{1}{(x+h)^3}-\dfrac{1}{x^3}\right)\cdot\dfrac{1}{h} = \left(\dfrac{x^3}{(x+h)^3\,x^3}+\dfrac{-(x+h)^3}{(x+h)^3\,x^3}\right)\cdot\dfrac{1}{h}$

$$= \dfrac{x^3-(x^3+3x^2h+3xh^2+h^3)}{(x+h)^3\,x^3}\cdot\dfrac{1}{h} = \dfrac{x^3-x^3-3x^2h-3xh^2-h^3}{h\,(x+h)^3\,x^3}$$

$$= \dfrac{-3x^2h-3xh^2-h^3}{h\,(x+h)^3\,x^3} = \dfrac{-h\,(3x^2+3xh+h^2)}{h\,(x+h)^3\,x^3} = \dfrac{-(3x^2+3xh+h^2)}{(x+h)^3\,x^3}$$

63. $\dfrac{\dfrac{1-(x+h)}{2+(x+h)}-\dfrac{1-x}{2+x}}{h} = \dfrac{\dfrac{(2+x)\,(1-x-h)}{(2+x)\,(2+x+h)}-\dfrac{(1-x)\,(2+x+h)}{(2+x)\,(2+x+h)}}{h}$

$$= \dfrac{\dfrac{2-x-x^2-2h-xh}{(2+x)\,(2+x+h)}-\dfrac{2-x-x^2+h-xh}{(2+x)\,(2+x+h)}}{h} = \dfrac{-3h}{(2+x)\,(2+x+h)}\cdot\dfrac{1}{h} = \dfrac{-3}{(2+x)\,(2+x+h)}$$

64. $\dfrac{(x+h)^3-7\,(x+h)-(x^3-7x)}{h} = \dfrac{x^3+3x^2h+3xh^2+h^3-7x-7h-x^3+7x}{h}$

$$= \dfrac{3x^2h+3xh^2+h^3-7h}{h} = \dfrac{h\,(3x^2+3xh+h^2-7)}{h} = 3x^2+3xh+h^2-7$$

65. $\sqrt{1+\left(\dfrac{x}{\sqrt{1-x^2}}\right)^2} = \sqrt{1+\dfrac{x^2}{1-x^2}} = \sqrt{\dfrac{1-x^2}{1-x^2}+\dfrac{x^2}{1-x^2}} = \sqrt{\dfrac{1}{1-x^2}} = \dfrac{1}{\sqrt{1-x^2}}$

66. $\sqrt{1+\left(x^3-\dfrac{1}{4x^3}\right)^2} = \sqrt{1+x^6-\dfrac{2x^3}{4x^3}+\dfrac{1}{16x^6}} = \sqrt{1+x^6-\dfrac{1}{2}+\dfrac{1}{16x^6}} = \sqrt{x^6+\dfrac{1}{2}+\dfrac{1}{16x^6}}$

$$= \sqrt{\left(x^3+\dfrac{1}{4x^3}\right)^2} = \left|x^3+\dfrac{1}{4x^3}\right|$$

67. $\dfrac{3\,(x+2)^2\,(x-3)^2-(x+2)^3\,(2)\,(x-3)}{(x-3)^4} = \dfrac{(x+2)^2\,(x-3)\,[3\,(x-3)-(x+2)\,(2)]}{(x-3)^4}$

$$= \dfrac{(x+2)^2\,(3x-9-2x-4)}{(x-3)^3} = \dfrac{(x+2)^2\,(x-13)}{(x-3)^3}$$

68. $\dfrac{2x\,(x+6)^4-x^2\,(4)\,(x+6)^3}{(x+6)^8} = \dfrac{(x+6)^3\,[2x\,(x+6)-4x^2]}{(x+6)^8} = \dfrac{2x^2+12x-4x^2}{(x+6)^5} = \dfrac{12x-2x^2}{(x+6)^5} = \dfrac{2x\,(6-x)}{(x+6)^5}$

69. $\dfrac{2(1+x)^{1/2}-x(1+x)^{-1/2}}{1+x}=\dfrac{(1+x)^{-1/2}\left[2(1+x)-x\right]}{1+x}=\dfrac{x+2}{(1+x)^{3/2}}$

70. $\dfrac{\left(1-x^2\right)^{1/2}+x^2\left(1-x^2\right)^{-1/2}}{1-x^2}=\dfrac{\left(1-x^2\right)^{-1/2}\left(1-x^2+x^2\right)}{1-x^2}=\dfrac{1}{\left(1-x^2\right)^{3/2}}$

71. $\dfrac{3(1+x)^{1/3}-x(1+x)^{-2/3}}{(1+x)^{2/3}}=\dfrac{(1+x)^{-2/3}\left[3(1+x)-x\right]}{(1+x)^{2/3}}=\dfrac{2x+3}{(1+x)^{4/3}}$

72. $\dfrac{(7-3x)^{1/2}+\frac{3}{2}x(7-3x)^{-1/2}}{7-3x}=\dfrac{(7-3x)^{-1/2}\left(7-3x+\frac{3}{2}x\right)}{7-3x}=\dfrac{7-\frac{3}{2}x}{(7-3x)^{3/2}}$

73. $\dfrac{1}{2-\sqrt{3}}=\dfrac{1}{2-\sqrt{3}}\cdot\dfrac{2+\sqrt{3}}{2+\sqrt{3}}=\dfrac{2+\sqrt{3}}{4-3}=\dfrac{2+\sqrt{3}}{1}=2+\sqrt{3}$

74. $\dfrac{2}{3-\sqrt{5}}=\dfrac{2}{3-\sqrt{5}}\cdot\dfrac{3+\sqrt{5}}{3+\sqrt{5}}=\dfrac{2\left(3+\sqrt{5}\right)}{9-5}=\dfrac{2\left(3+\sqrt{5}\right)}{4}=\dfrac{3+\sqrt{5}}{2}$

75. $\dfrac{2}{\sqrt{2}+\sqrt{7}}=\dfrac{2}{\sqrt{2}+\sqrt{7}}\cdot\dfrac{\sqrt{2}-\sqrt{7}}{\sqrt{2}-\sqrt{7}}=\dfrac{2\left(\sqrt{2}-\sqrt{7}\right)}{2-7}=\dfrac{2\left(\sqrt{2}-\sqrt{7}\right)}{-5}=\dfrac{2\left(\sqrt{7}-\sqrt{2}\right)}{5}$

76. $\dfrac{1}{\sqrt{x}+1}=\dfrac{1}{\sqrt{x}+1}\cdot\dfrac{\sqrt{x}-1}{\sqrt{x}-1}=\dfrac{\sqrt{x}-1}{x-1}$

77. $\dfrac{y}{\sqrt{3}+\sqrt{y}}=\dfrac{y}{\sqrt{3}+\sqrt{y}}\cdot\dfrac{\sqrt{3}-\sqrt{y}}{\sqrt{3}-\sqrt{y}}=\dfrac{y\left(\sqrt{3}-\sqrt{y}\right)}{3-y}=\dfrac{y\sqrt{3}-y\sqrt{y}}{3-y}$

78. $\dfrac{2(x-y)}{\sqrt{x}-\sqrt{y}}=\dfrac{2(x-y)}{\sqrt{x}-\sqrt{y}}\cdot\dfrac{\sqrt{x}+\sqrt{y}}{\sqrt{x}+\sqrt{y}}=\dfrac{2(x-y)\left(\sqrt{x}+\sqrt{y}\right)}{x-y}=2\left(\sqrt{x}+\sqrt{y}\right)=2\sqrt{x}+2\sqrt{y}$

79. $\dfrac{1-\sqrt{5}}{3}=\dfrac{1-\sqrt{5}}{3}\cdot\dfrac{1+\sqrt{5}}{1+\sqrt{5}}=\dfrac{1-5}{3\left(1+\sqrt{5}\right)}=\dfrac{-4}{3\left(1+\sqrt{5}\right)}$

80. $\dfrac{\sqrt{3}+\sqrt{5}}{2}=\dfrac{\sqrt{3}+\sqrt{5}}{2}\cdot\dfrac{\sqrt{3}-\sqrt{5}}{\sqrt{3}-\sqrt{5}}=\dfrac{3-5}{2\left(\sqrt{3}-\sqrt{5}\right)}=\dfrac{-2}{2\left(\sqrt{3}-\sqrt{5}\right)}=\dfrac{-1}{\sqrt{3}-\sqrt{5}}$

81. $\dfrac{\sqrt{r}+\sqrt{2}}{5}=\dfrac{\sqrt{r}+\sqrt{2}}{5}\cdot\dfrac{\sqrt{r}-\sqrt{2}}{\sqrt{r}-\sqrt{2}}=\dfrac{r-2}{5\left(\sqrt{r}-\sqrt{2}\right)}$

82. $\dfrac{\sqrt{x}-\sqrt{x+h}}{h\sqrt{x}\sqrt{x+h}}=\dfrac{\sqrt{x}-\sqrt{x+h}}{h\sqrt{x}\sqrt{x+h}}\cdot\dfrac{\sqrt{x}+\sqrt{x+h}}{\sqrt{x}+\sqrt{x+h}}=\dfrac{x-(x+h)}{h\sqrt{x}\sqrt{x+h}\left(\sqrt{x}+\sqrt{x+h}\right)}$

$\qquad=\dfrac{-h}{h\sqrt{x}\sqrt{x+h}\left(\sqrt{x}+\sqrt{x+h}\right)}=\dfrac{-1}{\sqrt{x}\sqrt{x+h}\left(\sqrt{x}+\sqrt{x+h}\right)}$

83. $\sqrt{x^2+1}-x=\dfrac{\sqrt{x^2+1}-x}{1}\cdot\dfrac{\sqrt{x^2+1}+x}{\sqrt{x^2+1}+x}=\dfrac{x^2+1-x^2}{\sqrt{x^2+1}+x}=\dfrac{1}{\sqrt{x^2+1}+x}$

84. $\sqrt{x+1}-\sqrt{x}=\dfrac{\sqrt{x+1}-\sqrt{x}}{1}\cdot\dfrac{\sqrt{x+1}+\sqrt{x}}{\sqrt{x+1}+\sqrt{x}}=\dfrac{x+1-x}{\sqrt{x+1}+\sqrt{x}}=\dfrac{1}{\sqrt{x+1}+\sqrt{x}}$

85. $\dfrac{16+a}{16}=\dfrac{16}{16}+\dfrac{a}{16}=1+\dfrac{a}{16}$, so the statement is true.

86. This statement is false. For example, take $b=2$ and $c=1$, then LHS $=\dfrac{b}{b-c}=\dfrac{2}{2-1}=2$, while

$\quad$ RHS$=1-\dfrac{b}{c}=1-\frac{2}{1}=-1$, and $2\neq-1$.

87. This statement is false. For example, take $x=2$, then LHS $=\dfrac{2}{4+x}=\dfrac{2}{4+2}=\dfrac{2}{6}=\dfrac{1}{3}$, while

$\quad$ RHS $=\dfrac{1}{2}+\dfrac{2}{x}=\dfrac{1}{2}+\dfrac{2}{2}=\dfrac{3}{2}$, and $\dfrac{1}{3}\neq\dfrac{3}{2}$.

88. This statement is false. For example, take $x = 5$ and $y = 2$. Then substituting into the left hand side we obtain

$$\text{LHS} = \frac{x+1}{y+1} = \frac{5+1}{2+1} = \frac{6}{3} = 2, \text{ while the right hand side yields RHS} = \frac{x}{y} = \frac{5}{2}, \text{ and } 2 \neq \frac{5}{2}.$$

89. This statement is false. For example, take $x = 0$ and $y = 1$. Then substituting into the left side we obtain

$$\text{LHS} = \frac{x}{x+y} = \frac{0}{0+1} = 0, \text{ while the right side yields RHS} = \frac{1}{1+y} = \frac{1}{1+1} = \frac{1}{2}, \text{ and } 0 \neq \frac{1}{2}.$$

90. This statement is false. For example, take $x = 1$ and $y = 1$. Then substituting into the left hand side we obtain

$$\text{LHS} = 2\left(\frac{a}{b}\right) = 2\left(\frac{1}{1}\right) = 2, \text{ while the right hand side yields RHS} = \frac{2a}{2b} = \frac{2}{2} = 1, \text{ and } 2 \neq 1.$$

91. This statement is true: $\dfrac{-a}{b} = (-a)\left(\dfrac{1}{b}\right) = (-1)(a)\left(\dfrac{1}{b}\right) = (-1)\left(\dfrac{a}{b}\right) = -\dfrac{a}{b}.$

92. This statement is true: $\dfrac{1 + x + x^2}{x} = \dfrac{1}{x} + \dfrac{x}{x} + \dfrac{x^2}{x} = \dfrac{1}{x} + 1 + x.$

93. (a) $R = \dfrac{1}{\dfrac{1}{R_1} + \dfrac{1}{R_2}} = \dfrac{1}{\dfrac{1}{R_1} + \dfrac{1}{R_2}} \cdot \dfrac{R_1 R_2}{R_1 R_2} = \dfrac{R_1 R_2}{R_2 + R_1}$

(b) Substituting $R_1 = 10$ ohms and $R_2 = 20$ ohms gives $R = \dfrac{(10)(20)}{(20)+(10)} = \dfrac{200}{30} \approx 6.7$ ohms.

94. (a) The average cost $A = \dfrac{\text{Cost}}{\text{number of shirts}} = \dfrac{500 + 6x + 0.01x^2}{x}.$

(b)

x	10	20	50	100	200	500	1000
Average cost	$56.10	$31.20	$16.50	$12.00	$10.50	$12.00	$16.50

95.

x	2.80	2.90	2.95	2.99	2.999	3	3.001	3.01	3.05	3.10	3.20
$\dfrac{x^2 - 9}{x - 3}$	5.80	5.90	5.95	5.99	5.999	?	6.001	6.01	6.05	6.10	6.20

From the table, we see that the expression $\dfrac{x^2 - 9}{x - 3}$ approaches 6 as x approaches 3. We simplify the expression:

$\dfrac{x^2 - 9}{x - 3} = \dfrac{(x-3)(x+3)}{x-3} = x + 3, x \neq 3.$ Clearly as x approaches 3, $x + 3$ approaches 6. This explains the result in the table.

96. No, squaring $\dfrac{2}{\sqrt{x}}$ changes its value by a factor of $\dfrac{2}{\sqrt{x}}$.

97. Answers will vary.

Algebraic Error	Counterexample
$\dfrac{1}{a} + \dfrac{1}{b} \neq \dfrac{1}{a+b}$	$\dfrac{1}{2} + \dfrac{1}{2} \neq \dfrac{1}{2+2}$
$(a+b)^2 \neq a^2 + b^2$	$(1+3)^2 \neq 1^2 + 3^2$
$\sqrt{a^2 + b^2} \neq a + b$	$\sqrt{5^2 + 12^2} \neq 5 + 12$
$\dfrac{a+b}{a} \neq b$	$\dfrac{2+6}{2} \neq 6$
$(a^3 + b^3)^{1/3} \neq a + b$	$(2^3 + 2^3)^{1/3} \neq 2 + 2$
$\dfrac{a^m}{a^n} \neq a^{m/n}$	$\dfrac{3^5}{3^2} \neq 3^{5/2}$
$a^{-1/n} \neq \dfrac{1}{a^n}$	$64^{-1/3} \neq \dfrac{1}{64^3}$

98. (a) $A + B$ **(b)** AB **(c)** $A^{1/3}$ **(d)** A/B

1.5   Equations

1. (a) When $x = -2$, LHS $= 4(-2) + 7 = -8 + 7 = -1$ and RHS $= 9(-2) - 3 = -18 - 3 = -21$. Since LHS $\neq$ RHS, $x = -2$ is not a solution.

(b) When $x = 2$, LHS $= 4(-2) + 7 = 8 + 7 = 15$ and RHS $= 9(2) - 3 = 18 - 3 = 15$. Since LHS $=$ RHS, $x = 2$ is a solution.

2. (a) When $x = 2$, LHS $= 1 - [2 - (3 - (2))] = 1 - [2 - 1] = 1 - 1 = 0$ and RHS $= 4(2) - (6 + (2)) = 8 - 8 = 0$. Since LHS $=$ RHS, $x = 2$ is a solution.

(b) When $x = 4$ LHS $= 1 - [2 - (3 - (4))] = 1 - [2 - (-1)] = 1 - 3 = -2$ and RHS $= 4(4) - (6 + (4)) = 16 - 10 = 6$. Since LHS $\neq$ RHS, $x = 4$ is not a solution.

3. (a) When $x = 2$, LHS $= \dfrac{1}{2} - \dfrac{1}{2 - 4} = \dfrac{1}{2} - \dfrac{1}{-2} = \dfrac{1}{2} + \dfrac{1}{2} = 1$ and RHS $= 1$. Since LHS $=$ RHS, $x = 2$ is a solution.

(b) When $x = 4$ the expression $\dfrac{1}{4 - 4}$ is not defined, so $x = 4$ is not a solution.

4. (a) When $x = 4$, LHS $= \dfrac{4^{3/2}}{4 - 6} = \dfrac{2^3}{-2} = \dfrac{8}{-2} = -4$ and RHS $= (4) - 8 = -4$. Since LHS $=$ RHS, $x = 4$ is a solution.

(b) When $x = 8$, LHS $= \dfrac{8^{3/2}}{8 - 6} = \dfrac{\left(2^3\right)^{3/2}}{2} = \dfrac{2^{9/2}}{2} = 2^{7/2}$ and RHS $= (8) - 8 = 0$. Since LHS $\neq$ RHS, $x = 8$ is not a solution.

5. $2x + 7 = 31 \quad\Leftrightarrow\quad 2x = 24 \quad\Leftrightarrow\quad x = 12$

6. $5x - 3 = 4 \quad\Leftrightarrow\quad 5x = 7 \quad\Leftrightarrow\quad x = \frac{7}{5}$

7. $\frac{1}{2}x - 8 = 1 \quad\Leftrightarrow\quad \frac{1}{2}x = 9 \quad\Leftrightarrow\quad x = 18$

8. $3 + \frac{1}{3}x = 5 \quad\Leftrightarrow\quad \frac{1}{3}x = 2 \quad\Leftrightarrow\quad x = 6$

9. $-7w = 15 - 2w \quad\Leftrightarrow\quad -5w = 15 \quad\Leftrightarrow\quad w = -3$

10. $5t - 13 = 12 - 5t \quad\Leftrightarrow\quad 10t = 25 \quad\Leftrightarrow\quad t = \frac{5}{2}$

11. $\frac{1}{2}y - 2 = \frac{1}{3}y \quad\Leftrightarrow\quad 3y - 12 = 2y$ (multiply both sides by the LCD, 6) $\quad\Leftrightarrow\quad y = 12$

12. $\frac{z}{5} = \frac{3}{10}z + 7 \quad\Leftrightarrow\quad 2z = 3z + 70 \quad\Leftrightarrow\quad z = -70$

13. $2(1 - x) = 3(1 + 2x) + 5 \quad\Leftrightarrow\quad 2 - 2x = 3 + 6x + 5 \quad\Leftrightarrow\quad 2 - 2x = 8 + 6x \quad\Leftrightarrow\quad -6 = 8x \quad\Leftrightarrow\quad x = -\frac{3}{4}$

14. $\frac{2}{3}y + \frac{1}{2}(y - 3) = \dfrac{y + 1}{4} \quad\Leftrightarrow\quad 8y + 6(y - 3) = 3(y + 1) \quad\Leftrightarrow\quad 8y + 6y - 18 = 3y + 3 \quad\Leftrightarrow\quad 14y - 18 = 3y + 3$
$\quad\Leftrightarrow\quad 11y = 21 \quad\Leftrightarrow\quad y = \frac{21}{11}$

15. $x - \frac{1}{3}x - \frac{1}{2}x - 5 = 0 \quad\Leftrightarrow\quad 6x - 2x - 3x - 30 = 0$ (multiply both sides by the LCD, 6) $\quad\Leftrightarrow\quad x = 30$

16. $2x - \dfrac{x}{2} + \dfrac{x + 1}{4} = 6x \quad\Leftrightarrow\quad 8x - 2x + x + 1 = 24x \quad\Leftrightarrow\quad 7x + 1 = 24x \quad\Leftrightarrow\quad 1 = 17x \quad\Leftrightarrow\quad x = \frac{1}{17}$

17. $\dfrac{1}{x} = \dfrac{4}{3x} + 1 \quad\Rightarrow\quad 3 = 4 + 3x$ (multiply both sides by the LCD, $3x$) $\quad\Leftrightarrow\quad -1 = 3x \quad\Leftrightarrow\quad x = -\frac{1}{3}$

18. $\dfrac{2x - 1}{x + 2} = \frac{4}{5} \quad\Rightarrow\quad 5(2x - 1) = 4(x + 2) \quad\Leftrightarrow\quad 10x - 5 = 4x + 8 \quad\Leftrightarrow\quad 6x = 13 \quad\Leftrightarrow\quad x = \frac{13}{6}$

19. $\dfrac{3}{x + 1} - \frac{1}{2} = \dfrac{1}{3x + 3} \quad\Rightarrow\quad 3(6) - (3x + 3) = 2$ [multiply both sides by the LCD, $6(x + 1)$] $\quad\Leftrightarrow\quad 18 - 3x - 3 = 2$
$\quad\Leftrightarrow\quad -3x + 15 = 2 \quad\Leftrightarrow\quad -3x = -13 \quad\Leftrightarrow\quad x = \frac{13}{3}$

20. $\dfrac{4}{x - 1} + \dfrac{2}{x + 1} = \dfrac{35}{x^2 - 1} \quad\Rightarrow\quad 4(x + 1) + 2(x - 1) = 35 \quad\Leftrightarrow\quad 4x + 4 + 2x - 2 = 35 \quad\Leftrightarrow\quad 6x + 2 = 35$
$\quad\Leftrightarrow\quad 6x = 33 \quad\Leftrightarrow\quad x = \frac{11}{2}$

21. $(t - 4)^2 = (t + 4)^2 + 32 \quad\Leftrightarrow\quad t^2 - 8t + 16 = t^2 + 8t + 16 + 32 \quad\Leftrightarrow\quad -16t = 32 \quad\Leftrightarrow\quad t = -2$

22. $\sqrt{3}x + \sqrt{12} = \dfrac{x+5}{\sqrt{3}}$ $\Leftrightarrow$ $3x + 6 = x + 5$ (multiply both sides by $\sqrt{3}$) $\Leftrightarrow$ $2x = -1$ $\Leftrightarrow$ $x = -\frac{1}{2}$

23. $PV = nRT$ $\Leftrightarrow$ $R = \dfrac{PV}{nT}$

24. $F = G\dfrac{mM}{r^2}$ $\Leftrightarrow$ $m = \dfrac{Fr^2}{GM}$

25. $\dfrac{1}{R} = \dfrac{1}{R_1} + \dfrac{1}{R_2}$ $\Leftrightarrow$ $R_1 R_2 = RR_2 + RR_1$ (multiply both sides by the LCD, $RR_1 R_2$). Thus $R_1 R_2 - RR_1 = RR_2$

$\Leftrightarrow$ $R_1 (R_2 - R) = RR_2$ $\Leftrightarrow$ $R_1 = \dfrac{RR_2}{R_2 - R}$

26. $P = 2l + 2w$ $\Leftrightarrow$ $2w = P - 2l$ $\Leftrightarrow$ $w = \dfrac{P - 2l}{2}$

27. $\dfrac{ax + b}{cx + d} = 2$ $\Leftrightarrow$ $ax + b = 2(cx + d)$ $\Leftrightarrow$ $ax + b = 2cx + 2d$ $\Leftrightarrow$ $ax - 2cx = 2d - b$ $\Leftrightarrow$

$(a - 2c)x = 2d - b$ $\Leftrightarrow$ $x = \dfrac{2d - b}{a - 2c}$

28. $a - 2[b - 3(c - x)] = 6$ $\Leftrightarrow$ $a - 2(b - 3c + 3x) = 6$ $\Leftrightarrow$ $a - 2b + 6c - 6x = 6$ $\Leftrightarrow$ $-6x = 6 - a + 2b - 6c$

$\Leftrightarrow$ $x = \dfrac{6 - a + 2b - 6c}{-6} = -\dfrac{6 - a + 2b - 6c}{6}$

29. $a^2 x + (a - 1) = (a + 1)x$ $\Leftrightarrow$ $a^2 x - (a + 1)x = -(a - 1)$ $\Leftrightarrow$ $(a^2 - (a + 1))x = -a + 1$ $\Leftrightarrow$

$(a^2 - a - 1)x = -a + 1$ $\Leftrightarrow$ $x = \dfrac{-a + 1}{a^2 - a - 1}$

30. $\dfrac{a + 1}{b} = \dfrac{a - 1}{b} + \dfrac{b + 1}{a}$ $\Leftrightarrow$ $a(a + 1) = a(a - 1) + b(b + 1)$ $\Leftrightarrow$ $a^2 + a = a^2 - a + b^2 + b$ $\Leftrightarrow$

$2a = b^2 + b$ $\Leftrightarrow$ $a = \frac{1}{2}(b^2 + b)$

31. $V = \frac{1}{3}\pi r^2 h$ $\Leftrightarrow$ $r^2 = \dfrac{3V}{\pi h}$ $\Rightarrow$ $r = \pm\sqrt{\dfrac{3V}{\pi h}}$

32. $F = G\dfrac{mM}{r^2}$ $\Leftrightarrow$ $r^2 = G\dfrac{mM}{F}$ $\Rightarrow$ $r = \pm\sqrt{G\dfrac{mM}{F}}$

33. $a^2 + b^2 = c^2$ $\Leftrightarrow$ $b^2 = c^2 - a^2$ $\Rightarrow$ $b = \pm\sqrt{c^2 - a^2}$

34. $A = P\left(1 + \dfrac{i}{100}\right)^2$ $\Leftrightarrow$ $\dfrac{A}{P} = \left(1 + \dfrac{i}{100}\right)^2$ $\Rightarrow$ $1 + \dfrac{i}{100} = \pm\sqrt{\dfrac{A}{P}}$ $\Leftrightarrow$ $\dfrac{i}{100} = -1 \pm \sqrt{\dfrac{A}{P}}$ $\Leftrightarrow$

$i = -100 \pm 100\sqrt{\dfrac{A}{P}}$

35. $h = \frac{1}{2}gt^2 + v_0 t$ $\Leftrightarrow$ $\frac{1}{2}gt^2 + v_0 t - h = 0$. Using the quadratic formula,

$t = \dfrac{-(v_0) \pm \sqrt{(v_0)^2 - 4\left(\frac{1}{2}g\right)(-h)}}{2\left(\frac{1}{2}g\right)} = \dfrac{-v_0 \pm \sqrt{v_0^2 + 2gh}}{g}$.

36. $S = \dfrac{n(n + 1)}{2}$ $\Leftrightarrow$ $2S = n^2 + n$ $\Leftrightarrow$ $n^2 + n - 2S = 0$. Using the quadratic formula,

$n = \dfrac{-1 \pm \sqrt{(1)^2 - 4(1)(-2S)}}{2(1)} = \dfrac{-1 \pm \sqrt{1 + 8S}}{2}$.

37. $x^2 + x - 12 = 0$ $\Leftrightarrow$ $(x - 3)(x + 4) = 0$ $\Leftrightarrow$ $x - 3 = 0$ or $x + 4 = 0$. Thus, $x = 3$ or $x = -4$.

38. $x^2 + 3x - 4 = 0$ $\Leftrightarrow$ $(x - 1)(x + 4) = 0$ $\Leftrightarrow$ $x - 1 = 0$ or $x + 4 = 0$. Thus, $x = 1$ or $x = -4$.

39. $x^2 - 7x + 12 = 0$ $\Leftrightarrow$ $(x - 4)(x - 3) = 0$ $\Leftrightarrow$ $x - 4 = 0$ or $x - 3 = 0$. Thus, $x = 4$ or $x = 3$.

40. $x^2 + 8x + 12 = 0$ $\Leftrightarrow$ $(x + 2)(x + 6) = 0$ $\Leftrightarrow$ $x + 2 = 0$ or $x + 6 = 0$. Thus, $x = -2$ or $x = -6$.

41. $4x^2 - 4x - 15 = 0$ $\Leftrightarrow$ $(2x + 3)(2x - 5) = 0$ $\Leftrightarrow$ $2x + 3 = 0$ or $2x - 5 = 0$. Thus, $x = -\frac{3}{2}$ or $x = \frac{5}{2}$.

42. $2y^2 + 7y + 3 = 0$ $\Leftrightarrow$ $(y + 3)(2y + 1) = 0$ $\Leftrightarrow$ $y + 3 = 0$ or $2y + 1 = 0$. Thus, $y = -3$ or $y = -\frac{1}{2}$.

43. $3x^2 + 5x = 2 \iff 3x^2 + 5x - 2 = 0 \iff (3x-1)(x+2) = 0 \iff 3x - 1 = 0$ or $x + 2 = 0$. Thus, $x = \frac{1}{3}$ or $x = -2$.

44. $6x(x-1) = 21 - x \iff 6x^2 - 6x = 21 - x \iff 6x^2 - 5x - 21 = 0 \iff (2x+3)(3x-7) = 0 \iff 2x + 3 = 0$ or $3x - 7 = 0$. If $2x + 3 = 0$, then $x = -\frac{3}{2}$; if $3x - 7 = 0$, then $x = \frac{7}{3}$.

45. $x^2 + 2x - 5 = 0 \iff x^2 + 2x = 5 \iff x^2 + 2x + 1 = 5 + 1 \iff (x+1)^2 = 6 \implies x + 1 = \pm\sqrt{6} \iff x = -1 \pm \sqrt{6}$.

46. $x^2 - 4x + 2 = 0 \iff x^2 - 4x = -2 \iff x^2 - 4x + 4 = -2 + 4 \iff (x-2)^2 = 2 \implies x - 2 = \pm\sqrt{2} \iff x = 2 \pm \sqrt{2}$.

47. $x^2 + 3x - \frac{7}{4} = 0 \iff x^2 + 3x = \frac{7}{4} \iff x^2 + 3x + \frac{9}{4} = \frac{7}{4} + \frac{9}{4} \iff \left(x + \frac{3}{2}\right)^2 = \frac{16}{4} = 4 \implies x + \frac{3}{2} = \pm 2 \iff x = -\frac{3}{2} \pm 2 \iff x = \frac{1}{2}$ or $x = -\frac{7}{2}$.

48. $x^2 = \frac{3}{4}x - \frac{1}{8} \iff x^2 - \frac{3}{4}x = -\frac{1}{8} \iff x^2 - \frac{3}{4}x + \frac{9}{64} = -\frac{1}{8} + \frac{9}{64} \iff \left(x - \frac{3}{8}\right)^2 = \frac{1}{64} \implies x - \frac{3}{8} = \pm\frac{1}{8} \iff x = \frac{3}{8} \pm \frac{1}{8}$, so $x = \frac{1}{2}$ or $x = \frac{1}{4}$.

49. $2x^2 + 8x + 1 = 0 \iff x^2 + 4x + \frac{1}{2} = 0 \iff x^2 + 4x = -\frac{1}{2} \iff x^2 + 4x + 4 = -\frac{1}{2} + 4 \iff (x+2)^2 = \frac{7}{2} \implies x + 2 = \pm\sqrt{\frac{7}{2}} \iff x = -2 \pm \frac{\sqrt{14}}{2}$.

50. $3x^2 - 6x - 1 = 0 \iff x^2 - 2x - \frac{1}{3} = 0 \iff x^2 - 2x = \frac{1}{3} \iff x^2 - 2x + 1 = \frac{1}{3} + 1 \iff (x-1)^2 = \frac{4}{3} \implies x - 1 = \pm\sqrt{\frac{4}{3}} \iff x = 1 \pm \frac{2\sqrt{3}}{3}$.

51. $4x^2 - x = 0 \iff x^2 - \frac{1}{4}x = 0 \iff x^2 - \frac{1}{4}x + \frac{1}{64} = \frac{1}{64} \iff \left(x - \frac{1}{8}\right)^2 = \frac{1}{64} \implies x - \frac{1}{8} = \pm\frac{1}{8} \iff x = \frac{1}{8} \pm \frac{1}{8}$, so $x = \frac{1}{8} - \frac{1}{8} = 0$ or $x = \frac{1}{8} + \frac{1}{8} = \frac{1}{4}$.

52. $-2x^2 + 6x + 3 = 0 \iff x^2 - 3x - \frac{3}{2} = 0 \iff x^2 - 3x + \frac{9}{4} = \frac{3}{2} + \frac{9}{4} \iff \left(x - \frac{3}{2}\right)^2 = \frac{15}{4} \implies x - \frac{3}{2} = \pm\frac{\sqrt{15}}{2} \iff x = \frac{3}{2} \pm \frac{\sqrt{15}}{2}$.

53. $x^2 - 2x - 15 = 0 \iff (x+3)(x-5) = 0 \iff x + 3 = 0$ or $x - 5 = 0$. Thus $x = -3$ or $x = 5$.

54. $x^2 + 30x + 200 = 0 \iff (x+10)(x+20) = 0 \iff x + 10 = 0$ or $x + 20 = 0$. Thus $x = -10$ or $x = -20$.

55. $x^2 + 3x + 1 = 0 \iff x^2 + 3x = -1 \iff x^2 + 3x + \frac{9}{4} = -1 + \frac{9}{4} = \frac{5}{4} \iff \left(x + \frac{3}{2}\right)^2 = \frac{5}{4} \implies x + \frac{3}{2} = \pm\sqrt{\frac{5}{4}} = \pm\frac{\sqrt{5}}{2} \iff x = -\frac{3}{2} \pm \frac{\sqrt{5}}{2}$.

56. $x^2 - 6x + 1 = 0 \implies$
$$x = \frac{-b \pm \sqrt{b^2 - 4ac}}{2a} = \frac{-(-6) \pm \sqrt{(-6)^2 - 4(1)(1)}}{2(1)} = \frac{6 \pm \sqrt{36 - 4}}{2} = \frac{6 \pm \sqrt{32}}{2} = \frac{6 \pm 4\sqrt{2}}{2} = 3 \pm 2\sqrt{2}.$$

57. $2x^2 + x - 3 = 0 \iff (x-1)(2x+3) = 0 \iff x - 1 = 0$ or $2x + 3 = 0$. If $x - 1 = 0$, then $x = 1$; if $2x + 3 = 0$, then $x = -\frac{3}{2}$.

58. $3x^2 + 7x + 4 = 0 \iff (3x+4)(x+1) = 0 \iff 3x + 4 = 0$ or $x + 1 = 0$. Thus $x = -\frac{4}{3}$ or $x = -1$.

59. $2y^2 - y - \frac{1}{2} = 0 \implies y = \frac{-b \pm \sqrt{b^2 - 4ac}}{2a} = \frac{-(-1) \pm \sqrt{(-1)^2 - 4(2)\left(-\frac{1}{2}\right)}}{2(2)} = \frac{1 \pm \sqrt{1 + 4}}{4} = \frac{1 \pm \sqrt{5}}{4}$.

60. $\theta^2 - \frac{3}{2}\theta + \frac{9}{16} = 0 \iff \left(\theta - \frac{3}{4}\right)^2 = 0 \iff \theta - \frac{3}{4} = 0 \iff \theta = \frac{3}{4}$

61. $4x^2 + 16x - 9 = 0 \iff (2x-1)(2x+9) = 0 \iff 2x - 1 = 0$ or $2x + 9 = 0$. If $2x - 1 = 0$, then $x = \frac{1}{2}$; if $2x + 9 = 0$, then $x = -\frac{9}{2}$.

62. $w^2 = 3(w-1) \iff w^2 - 3w + 3 = 0 \implies w = \frac{-(-3) \pm \sqrt{(-3)^2 - 4(1)(3)}}{2(1)} = \frac{3 \pm \sqrt{9 - 12}}{2} = \frac{3 \pm \sqrt{-3}}{2}$.

Since the discriminant is less than 0, the equation has no real solutions.

63. $3 + 5z + z^2 = 0 \quad \Rightarrow \quad z = \dfrac{-b \pm \sqrt{b^2 - 4ac}}{2a} = \dfrac{-(5) \pm \sqrt{(5)^2 - 4(1)(3)}}{2(1)} = \dfrac{-5 \pm \sqrt{25 - 12}}{2} = \dfrac{-5 \pm \sqrt{13}}{2}.$

64. $x^2 - \sqrt{5}x + 1 = 0 \quad \Rightarrow \quad x = \dfrac{-b \pm \sqrt{b^2 - 4ac}}{2a} = \dfrac{-(-\sqrt{5}) \pm \sqrt{(-\sqrt{5})^2 - 4(1)(1)}}{2(1)} = \dfrac{\sqrt{5} \pm \sqrt{5 - 4}}{2} = \dfrac{\sqrt{5} \pm 1}{2}.$

65. *Method 1:* Use the quadratic formula immediately. $\sqrt{6}x^2 + 2x - \sqrt{\frac{3}{2}} = 0 \quad \Rightarrow$

$$x = \dfrac{-b \pm \sqrt{b^2 - 4ac}}{2a} = \dfrac{-(2) \pm \sqrt{(2)^2 - 4(\sqrt{6})\left(-\sqrt{\frac{3}{2}}\right)}}{2(\sqrt{6})} = \dfrac{-2 \pm \sqrt{4 + 12}}{2\sqrt{6}} = \dfrac{-2 \pm \sqrt{16}}{2\sqrt{6}} = \dfrac{-2 \pm 4}{2\sqrt{6}}. \text{ So}$$

$x = -\dfrac{\sqrt{6}}{2}$ or $x = \dfrac{\sqrt{6}}{6}.$

Method 2: Multiply by $\sqrt{6}$ and use the result in the quadratic formula. $\sqrt{6}x^2 + 2x - \sqrt{\frac{3}{2}} = 0 \Leftrightarrow 6x^2 + 2\sqrt{6}x - 3 = 0 \Rightarrow$

$$x = \dfrac{-b \pm \sqrt{b^2 - 4ac}}{2a} = \dfrac{-(2\sqrt{6}) \pm \sqrt{(2\sqrt{6})^2 - 4(6)(-3)}}{2(6)} = \dfrac{-2\sqrt{6} \pm \sqrt{24 + 72}}{12} = \dfrac{-2\sqrt{6} \pm \sqrt{96}}{12} = \dfrac{-2\sqrt{6} \pm 4\sqrt{6}}{12}.$$

So $x = -\dfrac{\sqrt{6}}{2}$ or $x = \dfrac{\sqrt{6}}{6}.$

66. $3x^2 + 2x + 2 = 0 \quad \Rightarrow \quad x = \dfrac{-b \pm \sqrt{b^2 - 4ac}}{2a} = \dfrac{-(2) \pm \sqrt{(2)^2 - 4(3)(2)}}{2(3)} = \dfrac{-2 \pm \sqrt{4 - 24}}{6} = \dfrac{-2 \pm \sqrt{-20}}{6}.$

Since the discriminant is less than 0, the equation has no real solution.

67. $25x^2 + 70x + 49 = 0 \quad \Leftrightarrow \quad (5x + 7)^2 = 0 \quad \Leftrightarrow \quad 5x + 7 = 0 \quad \Leftrightarrow \quad 5x = -7 \quad \Leftrightarrow \quad x = -\frac{7}{5}.$

68. $5x^2 - 7x + 5 \quad \Rightarrow \quad x = \dfrac{-b \pm \sqrt{b^2 - 4ac}}{2a} = \dfrac{-(-7) \pm \sqrt{(-7)^2 - 4(5)(5)}}{2(5)} = \dfrac{7 \pm \sqrt{49 - 100}}{10} = \dfrac{7 \pm \sqrt{-51}}{10}.$

Since the discriminant is less than 0, the equation has no real solution.

69. $D = b^2 - 4ac = (-6)^2 - 4(1)(1) = 32.$ Since D is positive, this equation has two real solutions.

70. $3x^2 = 6x - 9 \quad \Leftrightarrow \quad 3x^2 - 6x + 9 = 0.$ $D = b^2 - 4ac = (-6)^2 - 4(3)(9) = 36 - 108 = -72.$ Since D is negative, this equation has no real solution.

71. $D = b^2 - 4ac = (2.20)^2 - 4(1)(1.21) = 4.84 - 4.84 = 0.$ Since $D = 0$, this equation has one real solution.

72. $D = b^2 - 4ac = (2.21)^2 - 4(1)(1.21) = 4.8841 - 4.84 = 0.0441.$ Since $D \neq 0$, this equation has two real solutions.

73. $D = b^2 - 4ac = (5)^2 - 4(4)\left(\frac{13}{8}\right) = 25 - 26 = -1.$ Since D is negative, this equation has no real solution.

74. $D = b^2 - 4ac = (r)^2 - 4(1)(-s) = r^2 + 4s.$ Since D is positive, this equation has two real solutions.

75. $\dfrac{1}{x - 1} + \dfrac{1}{x + 2} = \frac{5}{4} \quad \Leftrightarrow \quad 4(x - 1)(x + 2)\left(\dfrac{1}{x - 1} + \dfrac{1}{x + 2}\right) = 4(x - 1)(x + 2)\left(\frac{5}{4}\right) \quad \Leftrightarrow$

$4(x + 2) + 4(x - 1) = 5(x - 1)(x + 2) \quad \Leftrightarrow \quad 4x + 8 + 4x - 4 = 5x^2 + 5x - 10 \quad \Leftrightarrow \quad 5x^2 - 3x - 14 = 0 \quad \Leftrightarrow$

$(5x + 7)(x - 2) = 0.$ If $5x + 7 = 0$, then $x = -\frac{7}{5}$; if $x - 2 = 0$, then $x = 2.$ The solutions are $-\frac{7}{5}$ and 2.

76. $\dfrac{10}{x} - \dfrac{12}{x - 3} + 4 = 0 \quad \Leftrightarrow \quad x(x - 3)\left(\dfrac{10}{x} - \dfrac{12}{x - 3} + 4\right) = 0 \quad \Leftrightarrow \quad (x - 3)10 - 12x + 4x(x - 3) = 0 \quad \Leftrightarrow$

$10x - 30 - 12x + 4x^2 - 12x = 0 \quad \Leftrightarrow \quad 4x^2 - 14x - 30 = 0 \quad \Leftrightarrow \quad 2(2x^2 - 7x - 15) = 2(2x + 3)(x - 5) = 0$

$\Leftrightarrow \quad 2x + 3 = 0$ or $x - 5 = 0.$ If $2x + 3 = 0$, then $x = -\frac{3}{2}$; if $x - 5 = 0$, then $x = 5.$

77. $\dfrac{x^2}{x + 100} = 50 \quad \Rightarrow \quad x^2 = 50(x + 100) = 50x + 5000 \quad \Leftrightarrow \quad x^2 - 50x - 5000 = 0 \quad \Leftrightarrow \quad (x - 100)(x + 50) = 0$

$\Leftrightarrow \quad x - 100 = 0$ or $x + 50 = 0.$ Thus $x = 100$ or $x = -50.$ The solutions are 100 and $-50.$

78. $\dfrac{1}{x-1} - \dfrac{2}{x^2} = 0 \iff x^2 - 2(x-1) = 0 \iff x^2 - 2x + 2 = 0 \Rightarrow$

$x = \dfrac{-(-2) \pm \sqrt{(-2)^2 - 4(1)(2)}}{2(1)} = \dfrac{2 \pm \sqrt{4-8}}{2} = \dfrac{2 \pm \sqrt{-4}}{2}$. Since the radicand is negative, there are no real

solution.

79. $\dfrac{x+5}{x-2} = \dfrac{5}{x+2} + \dfrac{28}{x^2-4} \Rightarrow (x+2)(x+5) = 5(x-2) + 28 \iff x^2 + 7x + 10 = 5x - 10 + 28 \iff$

$x^2 + 2x - 8 = 0 \iff (x-2)(x+4) = 0 \iff x - 2 = 0$ or $x + 4 = 0 \iff x = 2$ or $x = -4$. However,

$x = 2$ is inadmissible since we can't divide by 0 in the original equation, so the only solution is -4.

80. $\dfrac{x}{2x+7} - \dfrac{x+1}{x+3} = 1 \iff x(x+3) - (x+1)(2x+7) = (2x+7)(x+3) \iff x^2 + 3x - 2x^2 - 9x -$

$7 = 2x^2 + 13x + 21 \iff 3x^2 + 19x + 28 = 0 \iff (3x+7)(x+4) = 0$. Thus either $3x + 7 = 0$, so $x = -\frac{7}{3}$, or

$x = -4$. The solutions are $-\frac{7}{3}$ and -4.

81. $\sqrt{2x+1} + 1 = x \iff \sqrt{2x+1} = x - 1 \Rightarrow 2x + 1 = (x-1)^2 \iff 2x + 1 = x^2 - 2x + 1 \iff$

$0 = x^2 - 4x = x(x-4)$. Potential solutions are $x = 0$ and $x - 4 \iff x = 4$. These are only potential solutions since

squaring is not a reversible operation. We must check each potential solution in the original equation. Checking $x = 0$:

$\sqrt{2(0)+1} + 1 \stackrel{?}{=} (0), \sqrt{1} + 1 \stackrel{?}{=} 0$, NO! Checking $x = 4$: $\sqrt{2(4)+1} + 1 \stackrel{?}{=} (4), \sqrt{9} + 1 \stackrel{?}{=} 4, 3 + 1 \stackrel{?}{=} 4$, Yes. The only

solution is $x = 4$.

82. $\sqrt{5-x} + 1 = x - 2 \iff \sqrt{5-x} = x - 3 \Rightarrow 5 - x = (x-3)^2 \iff 5 - x = x^2 - 6x + 9 \iff$

$0 = x^2 - 5x + 4 = (x-4)(x-1)$. Potential solutions are $x = 4$ and $x = 1$. We must check each potential solution in

the original equation.

Checking $x = 4$: $\sqrt{5-(4)} + 1 \stackrel{?}{=} (4) - 2, \sqrt{1} + 1 \stackrel{?}{=} 4 - 2, 1 + 1 \stackrel{?}{=} 2$, Yes.

Checking $x = 1$: $\sqrt{5-(1)} + 1 \stackrel{?}{=} (1) - 2, \sqrt{4} + 1 \stackrel{?}{=} -1, 2 + 1 \stackrel{?}{=} -1$, no. The only solution is $x = 4$.

83. $2x + \sqrt{x+1} = 8 \iff \sqrt{x+1} = 8 - 2x \Rightarrow x + 1 = (8-2x)^2 \iff x + 1 = 64 - 32x + 4x^2 \iff$

$0 = 4x^2 - 33x + 63 = (4x-21)(x-3)$. Potential solutions are $x = \frac{21}{4}$ and $x = 3$. Substituting each of these solutions

into the original equation, we see that $x = 3$ is a solution, but $x = \frac{21}{4}$ is not. Thus 3 is the only solution.

84. $\sqrt{\sqrt{x-5}+x} = 5$. Squaring both sides, we get $\sqrt{x-5} + x = 25 \iff \sqrt{x-5} = 25 - x$. Squaring both sides again,

we get $x - 5 = (25-x)^2 \iff x - 5 = 625 - 50x + x^2 \iff 0 = x^2 - 51x + 630 = (x-30)(x-21)$. Potential

solutions are $x = 30$ and $x = 21$. We must check each potential solution in the original equation.

Checking $x = 30$: $\sqrt{\sqrt{(30)-5}+(30)} \stackrel{?}{=} 5, \sqrt{\sqrt{(30)-5}+(30)} = \sqrt{\sqrt{25}+30} = \sqrt{35} > 5$, hence $x = 30$ is not a

solution.

Checking $x = 21$: $\sqrt{\sqrt{(21)-5}+21} \stackrel{?}{=} 5, \sqrt{\sqrt{(21)-5}+21} = \sqrt{\sqrt{16}+21} = \sqrt{25} = 5$, hence $x = 21$ is the only

solution.

85. Let $w = x^2$. Then $x^4 - 13x^2 + 40 = (x^2)^2 - 13x^2 + 40 = 0$ becomes $w^2 - 13w + 40 = 0 \iff (w-5)(w-8) = 0$.

So $w - 5 = 0 \iff w = 5$, and $w - 8 = 0 \iff w = 8$. When $w = 5$, we have $x^2 = 5 \Rightarrow x = \pm\sqrt{5}$. When

$w = 8$, we have $x^2 = 8 \Rightarrow x = \pm\sqrt{8} = \pm 2\sqrt{2}$. The solutions are $\pm\sqrt{5}$ and $\pm 2\sqrt{2}$.

86. $0 = x^4 - 5x^2 + 4 = (x^2-4)(x^2-1) = (x-2)(x+2)(x-1)(x+1)$. So $x = 2$, $x = -2$, or $x = 1$, or $x = -1$.

The solutions are $-2, 2, -1$, and 1.

87. $2x^4 + 4x^2 + 1 = 0$. The LHS is the sum of two nonnegative numbers and a positive number, so $2x^4 + 4x^2 + 1 \geq 1 \neq 0$.

This equation has no real solution.

88. $0 = x^6 - 2x^3 - 3 = (x^3-3)(x^3+1)$. If $x^3 - 3 = 0$, then $x^3 = 3 \iff x = \sqrt[3]{3}$, or if $x^3 = -1 \iff x = -1$.

Thus $x = \sqrt[3]{3}$ or $x = -1$. The solutions are $\sqrt[3]{3}$ and -1.

89. Let $u = x^{2/3}$. Then $0 = x^{4/3} - 5x^{2/3} + 6$ becomes $u^2 - 5u + 6 = 0$ $\Leftrightarrow$ $(u-3)(u-2) = 0$ $\Leftrightarrow$ $u - 3 = 0$ or $u - 2 = 0$. If $u - 3 = 0$, then $x^{2/3} - 3 = 0$ $\Leftrightarrow$ $x^{2/3} = 3$ $\Rightarrow$ $x = \pm 3^{3/2}$. If $u - 2 = 0$, then $x^{2/3} - 2 = 0$ $\Leftrightarrow$ $x^{2/3} = 2$ $\Rightarrow$ $x = \pm 2^{3/2}$. The solutions are $\pm 3^{3/2}$ and $\pm 2^{3/2}$.

90. Let $u = \sqrt[4]{x}$; then $0 = \sqrt{x} - 3\sqrt[4]{x} - 4 = u^2 - 3u - 4 = (u-4)(u+1)$. So $u - 4 = \sqrt[4]{x} - 4 = 0$ $\Leftrightarrow$ $\sqrt[4]{x} = 4$ $\Rightarrow$ $x = 4^4 = 256$, or $u + 1 = \sqrt[4]{x} + 1 = 0$ $\Leftrightarrow$ $\sqrt[4]{x} = -1$. However, $\sqrt[4]{x}$ is the positive fourth root, so this cannot equal -1. The only solution is 256.

91. $4(x+1)^{1/2} - 5(x+1)^{3/2} + (x+1)^{5/2} = 0$ $\Leftrightarrow$ $\sqrt{x+1}\left[4 - 5(x+1) + (x+1)^2\right] = 0$ $\Leftrightarrow$ $\sqrt{x+1}\left(4 - 5x - 5 + x^2 + 2x + 1\right) = 0$ $\Leftrightarrow$ $\sqrt{x+1}\left(x^2 - 3x\right) = 0$ $\Leftrightarrow$ $\sqrt{x+1} \cdot x(x-3) = 0$ $\Leftrightarrow$ $x = -1$ or $x = 0$ or $x = 3$. The solutions are -1, 0, and 3.

92. $x^{1/2} + 3x^{-1/2} = 10x^{-3/2}$ $\Leftrightarrow$ $0 = x^{1/2} + 3x^{-1/2} - 10x^{-3/2} = x^{-3/2}\left(x^2 + 3x - 10\right) = x^{-3/2}(x-2)(x+5)$. Now $x^{-3/2}$ never equals 0, and no solution can be negative, because we cannot take the $\frac{1}{2}$ power of a negative number. Thus 2 is the only solution.

93. Let $u = x^{1/6}$. (We choose the exponent $\frac{1}{6}$ because the LCD of 2, 3, and 6 is 6.) Then $x^{1/2} - 3x^{1/3} = 3x^{1/6} - 9$ $\Leftrightarrow$ $x^{3/6} - 3x^{2/6} = 3x^{1/6} - 9$ $\Leftrightarrow$ $u^3 - 3u^2 = 3u - 9$ $\Leftrightarrow$ $0 = u^3 - 3u^2 - 3u + 9 = u^2(u-3) - 3(u-3) = (u-3)(u^2-3)$. So $u - 3 = 0$ or $u^2 - 3 = 0$. If $u - 3 = 0$, then $x^{1/6} - 3 = 0$ $\Leftrightarrow$ $x^{1/6} = 3$ $\Leftrightarrow$ $x = 3^6 = 729$. If $u^2 - 3 = 0$, then $x^{1/3} - 3 = 0$ $\Leftrightarrow$ $x^{1/3} = 3$ $\Leftrightarrow$ $x = 3^3 = 27$. The solutions are 729 and 27.

94. Let $u = \sqrt{x}$. Then $0 = x - 5\sqrt{x} + 6$ becomes $u^2 - 5u + 6 = (u-3)(u-2) = 0$. If $u - 3 = 0$, then $\sqrt{x} - 3 = 0$ $\Leftrightarrow$ $\sqrt{x} = 3$ $\Rightarrow$ $x = 9$. If $u - 2 = 0$, then $\sqrt{x} - 2 = 0$ $\Leftrightarrow$ $\sqrt{x} = 2$ $\Rightarrow$ $x = 4$. The solutions are 9 and 4.

95. $|2x| = 3$. So $2x = 3$ $\Leftrightarrow$ $x = \frac{3}{2}$ or $2x = -3$ $\Leftrightarrow$ $x = -\frac{3}{2}$.

96. $|3x + 5| = 1$. So $3x + 5 = 1$ $\Leftrightarrow$ $3x = -4$ $\Leftrightarrow$ $x = -\frac{4}{3}$ or $3x + 5 = -1$ $\Leftrightarrow$ $3x = -6$ $\Leftrightarrow$ $x = -2$.

97. $|x - 4| = 0.01$. So $x - 4 = 0.01$ $\Leftrightarrow$ $x = 4.01$ or $x - 4 = -0.01$ $\Leftrightarrow$ $x = 3.99$.

98. $|x - 6| = -1$. Since absolute value is never negative, this equation has no real solution.

99. Using $h_0 = 288$, we solve $0 = -16t^2 + 288$, for $t \geq 0$. So $0 = -16t^2 + 288$ $\Leftrightarrow$ $16t^2 = 288$ $\Leftrightarrow$ $t^2 = 18$ $\Rightarrow$ $t = \pm\sqrt{18} = \pm 3\sqrt{2}$. Thus it takes $3\sqrt{2} \approx 4.24$ seconds for the ball the hit the ground.

100. **(a)** Using $h_0 = 96$, half the distance is 48, so we solve the equation $48 = -16t^2 + 96$ $\Leftrightarrow$ $-48 = -16t^2$ $\Leftrightarrow$ $3 = t^2$ $\Rightarrow$ $t = \pm\sqrt{3}$. Since $t \geq 0$, it takes $\sqrt{3} \approx 1.732$ s.

(b) The ball hits the ground when $h = 0$, so we solve the equation $0 = -16t^2 + 96$ $\Leftrightarrow$ $16t^2 = 96$ $\Leftrightarrow$ $t^2 = 6$ $\Rightarrow$ $t = \pm\sqrt{6}$. Since $t \geq 0$, it takes $\sqrt{6} \approx 2.449$ s.

101. We are given $v_o = 40$ ft/s.

(a) Setting $h = 24$, we have $24 = -16t^2 + 40t$ $\Leftrightarrow$ $16t^2 - 40t + 24 = 0$ $\Leftrightarrow$ $8(2t^2 - 5t + 3) = 0$ $\Leftrightarrow$ $8(2t-3)(t-1) = 0$ $\Leftrightarrow$ $t = 1$ or $t = 1\frac{1}{2}$. Therefore, the ball reaches 24 feet in 1 second (ascending) and again after $1\frac{1}{2}$ seconds (descending).

(b) Setting $h = 48$, we have $48 = -16t^2 + 40t$ $\Leftrightarrow$ $16t^2 - 40t + 48 = 0$ $\Leftrightarrow$ $2t^2 - 5t + 6 = 0$ $\Leftrightarrow$ $t = \dfrac{5 \pm \sqrt{25 - 48}}{4} = \dfrac{5 \pm \sqrt{-23}}{4}$. However, since the discriminant $D < 0$, there are no real solutions, and hence the ball never reaches a height of 48 feet.

(c) The greatest height h is reached only once. So $h = -16t^2 + 40t$ $\Leftrightarrow$ $16t^2 - 40t + h = 0$ has only one solution. Thus $D = (-40)^2 - 4(16)(h) = 0$ $\Leftrightarrow$ $1600 - 64h = 0$ $\Leftrightarrow$ $h = 25$. So the greatest height reached by the ball is 25 feet.

(d) Setting $h = 25$, we have $25 = -16t^2 + 40t$ $\Leftrightarrow$ $16t^2 - 40t + 25 = 0$ $\Leftrightarrow$ $(4t - 5)^2 = 0$ $\Leftrightarrow$ $t = 1\frac{1}{4}$. Thus the ball reaches the highest point of its path after $1\frac{1}{4}$ seconds.

(e) Setting $h = 0$ (ground level), we have $0 = -16t^2 + 40t$ $\Leftrightarrow$ $2t^2 - 5t = 0$ $\Leftrightarrow$ $t(2t - 5) = 0$ $\Leftrightarrow$ $t = 0$ (start) or $t = 2\frac{1}{2}$. So the ball hits the ground in $2\frac{1}{2}$ s.

102. If the maximum height is 100 feet, then the discriminant of the equation, $16t^2 - v_o t + 100 = 0$, must equal zero. So $0 = b^2 - 4ac = (-v_o)^2 - 4\,(16)\,(100)$　$\Leftrightarrow$　$v_o^2 = 6400$　$\Rightarrow$　$v_o = \pm 80$. Since $v_o = -80$ does not make sense, we must have $v_o = 80$ ft/s.

103. (a) The shrinkage factor when $w = 250$ is $S = \dfrac{0.032\,(250) - 2.5}{10{,}000} = \dfrac{8 - 2.5}{10{,}000} = 0.00055$. So the beam shrinks $0.00055 \times 12.025 \approx 0.007$ m, so when it dries it will be $12.025 - 0.007 = 12.018$ m long.

(b) Substituting $S = 0.00050$ we get $0.00050 = \dfrac{0.032w - 2.5}{10{,}000}$　$\Leftrightarrow$　$5 = 0.032w - 2.5$　$\Leftrightarrow$　$7.5 = 0.032w$　$\Leftrightarrow$

$w = \dfrac{7.5}{0.032} \approx 234.375$. So the water content should be 234.375 kg/m^3.

104. Let d be the distance from the lens to the object. Then the distance from the lens to the image is $d - 4$. So substituting $F = 4.8$, $x = d$, and $y = d - 4$, and then solving for x, we have $\dfrac{1}{4.8} = \dfrac{1}{d} + \dfrac{1}{d-4}$. Now we multiply by the LCD, $4.8d\,(d-4)$, to get $d\,(d-4) = 4.8\,(d-4) + 4.8d$　$\Leftrightarrow$　$d^2 - 4d = 9.6d - 19.2$　$\Leftrightarrow$　$0 = d^2 - 13.6d + 19.2$　$\Rightarrow$ $d = \dfrac{13.6 \pm 10.4}{2}$. So $d = 1.6$ or $d = 12$. Since $d - 4$ must also be positive, the object is 12 cm from the lens.

105. (a) The fish population on January 1, 2002 corresponds to $t = 0$, so $F = 1000\,(30 + 17\,(0) - (0)^2) = 30{,}000$. To find when the population will again reach this value, we set $F = 30{,}000$, giving $30000 = 1000\,(30 + 17t - t^2) = 30000 + 17000t - 1000t^2$　$\Leftrightarrow$　$0 = 17000t - 1000t^2 = 1000t\,(17 - t)$　$\Leftrightarrow$ $t = 0$ or $t = 17$. Thus the fish population will again be the same 17 years later, that is, on January 1, 2019.

(b) Setting $F = 0$, we have $0 = 1000\,(30 + 17t - t^2)$　$\Leftrightarrow$　$t^2 - 17t - 30 = 0$　$\Leftrightarrow$ $t = \dfrac{17 \pm \sqrt{289 + 120}}{-2} = \dfrac{17 \pm \sqrt{409}}{-2} = \dfrac{17 \pm 20.22}{2}$. Thus $t \approx -1.612$ or $t \approx 18.612$. Since $t < 0$ is inadmissible, it follows that the fish in the lake will have died out 18.612 years after January 1, 2002, that is on August 12, 2020.

106. We want to solve for t when $P = 500$. Letting $u = \sqrt{t}$ and substituting, we have $500 = 3t + 10\sqrt{t} + 140$　$\Leftrightarrow$ $500 = 3u^2 + 10u + 140$　$\Leftrightarrow$　$0 = 3u^2 + 10u - 360$　$\Rightarrow$　$u = \dfrac{-5 \pm \sqrt{1105}}{3}$. Since $u = \sqrt{t}$, we must have $u \geq 0$. So $\sqrt{t} = u = \dfrac{-5 + \sqrt{1105}}{3} \approx 9.414$　$\Rightarrow$　$t = \approx 88.62$. So it will take 89 days for the fish population to reach 500.

107. Setting $P = 1250$ and solving for x, we have $1250 = \frac{1}{10}x\,(300 - x) = 30x - \frac{1}{10}x^2$　$\Leftrightarrow$　$\frac{1}{10}x^2 - 30x + 1250 = 0$.

Using the quadratic formula, $x = \dfrac{-(-30) \pm \sqrt{(-30)^2 - 4\left(\frac{1}{10}\right)(1250)}}{2\left(\frac{1}{10}\right)} = \dfrac{30 \pm \sqrt{900 - 500}}{0.2} = \dfrac{30 \pm 20}{0.2}$. Thus

$x = \dfrac{30 - 20}{0.2} = 50$ or $x = \dfrac{30 + 20}{0.2} = 250$. Since he must have $0 \leq x \leq 200$, he should make 50 ovens per week.

108. Let x be the distance from the center of the earth to the dead spot (in thousands of miles). Now setting $F = 0$, we have $0 = -\dfrac{K}{x^2} + \dfrac{0.012K}{(239 - x)^2}$　$\Leftrightarrow$　$\dfrac{K}{x^2} = \dfrac{0.012K}{(239 - x)^2}$　$\Leftrightarrow$　$K\,(239 - x)^2 = 0.012Kx^2$　$\Leftrightarrow$ $57121 - 478x + x^2 = 0.012x^2$　$\Leftrightarrow$　$0.988x^2 - 478x + 57121 = 0$. Using the quadratic formula, we obtain $x = \frac{-(-478) \pm \sqrt{(-478)^2 - 4(0.988)(57121)}}{2(0.988)} = \frac{478 \pm \sqrt{228484 - 225742.192}}{1.976} = \frac{478 \pm \sqrt{2741.808}}{1.976} \approx \frac{478 \pm 52.362}{1.976} \approx 241.903 \pm 26.499$. So either $x \approx 241.903 + 26.499 \approx 268$ or $x \approx 241.903 - 26.499 \approx 215$. Since 268 is greater than the distance from the earth to the moon, we reject it; thus $x \approx 215{,}000$ miles.

109. Since the total time is 3 s, we have $3 = \dfrac{\sqrt{d}}{4} + \dfrac{d}{1090}$. Letting $w = \sqrt{d}$, we have $3 = \frac{1}{4}w + \frac{1}{1090}w^2$　$\Leftrightarrow$

$\frac{1}{1090}w^2 + \frac{1}{4}w - 3 = 0$　$\Leftrightarrow$　$2w^2 + 545w - 6540 = 0$　$\Rightarrow$　$w = \dfrac{-545 \pm 591.054}{4}$. Since $w \geq 0$, we have $\sqrt{d} = w \approx 11.51$, so $d = 132.56$. The well is 132.6 ft deep.

110. (a) $3(0) + k - 5 = k(0) - k + 1 \quad \Leftrightarrow \quad k - 5 = -k + 1 \quad \Leftrightarrow \quad 2k = 6 \quad \Leftrightarrow \quad k = 3$

(b) $3(1) + k - 5 = k(1) - k + 1 \quad \Leftrightarrow \quad 3 + k - 5 = k - k + 1 \quad \Leftrightarrow \quad k - 2 = 1 \quad \Leftrightarrow \quad k = 3$

(c) $3(2) + k - 5 = k(2) - k + 1 \quad \Leftrightarrow \quad 6 + k - 5 = 2k - k + 1 \quad \Leftrightarrow \quad k + 1 = k + 1$. Since both sides of this equation are equal, $x = 2$ is a solution for every value of k. That is, $x = 2$ is a solution to every member of this family of equations.

111. When we multiplied by x, we introduced $x = 0$ as a solution. When we divided by $x - 1$, we are really dividing by 0, since $x = 1 \quad \Leftrightarrow \quad x - 1 = 0$.

112. (a) Using the formulas for volume we have: for the sphere, $V = \frac{4}{3}\pi r^3$; for the cylinder, $V = \pi r^2 h_1$; and for the cone, $V = \frac{1}{3}\pi r^2 h_2$. Since these have the same volume we must have $\frac{4}{3}\pi r^3 = \pi r^2 h_1$ and $\frac{4}{3}\pi r^3 = \frac{1}{3}\pi r^2 h_2$.

(b) Setting the volume of the sphere equal to the volume of the cylinder, we have $\frac{4}{3}\pi r^3 = \pi r^2 h_1 \quad \Leftrightarrow \quad \frac{4}{3}r = h_1$. So the height of the cylinder is $h_1 = \frac{4}{3}r$.

Likewise, setting the volume of the sphere equal to the volume of the cone, we have $\frac{4}{3}\pi r^3 = \frac{1}{3}\pi r^2 h_2 \quad \Leftrightarrow \quad 4r = h_2$. So the height of the cone is $h_2 = 4r$.

113. $x^2 - 9x + 20 = (x - 4)(x - 5) = 0$, so $x = 4$ or $x = 5$. The roots are 4 and 5. The product is $4 \cdot 5 = 20$, and the sum is $4 + 5 = 9$. $x^2 - 2x - 8 = (x - 4)(x + 2) = 0$, so $x = 4$ or $x = -2$. The roots are 4 and -2. The product is $4 \cdot (-2) = -8$, and the sum is $4 + (-2) = 2$. $x^2 + 4x + 2 = 0$, so using the quadratic formula,

$$x = \frac{-4 \pm \sqrt{4^2 - 4(1)(2)}}{2(1)} = \frac{-4 \pm \sqrt{8}}{2} = \frac{-4 \pm 2\sqrt{2}}{2} = -2 \pm \sqrt{2}.$$ The roots are $-2 - \sqrt{2}$ and $-2 + \sqrt{2}$. The product

is $(-2 - \sqrt{2}) \cdot (-2 + \sqrt{2}) = 4 - 2 = 2$, and the sum is $(-2 - \sqrt{2}) + (-2 + \sqrt{2}) = -4$. In general, if $x = r_1$ and $x = r_2$ are roots, then $x^2 + bx + c = (x - r_1)(x - r_2) = x^2 - r_1 x - r_2 x + r_1 r_2 = x^2 - (r_1 + r_2)x + r_1 r_2$. Equating the coefficients, we get $c = r_1 r_2$ and $b = -(r_1 + r_2)$.

114. (a) *Method 1:* Let $u = \sqrt{x}$, so $u^2 = x$. Thus $x - \sqrt{x} - 2 = 0$ becomes $u^2 - u - 2 = 0 \quad \Leftrightarrow \quad (u - 2)(u + 1) = 0$. So $u = 2$ or $u = -1$. If $u = 2$, then $\sqrt{x} = 2 \quad \Rightarrow \quad x = 4$. If $u = -1$, then $\sqrt{x} = -1 \quad \Rightarrow \quad x = 1$. So the possible solutions are 4 and 1. Checking $x = 4$ we have $4 - \sqrt{4} - 2 = 4 - 2 - 2 = 0$. Checking $x = 1$ we have $1 - \sqrt{1} - 2 = 1 - 1 - 2 \neq 0$. The only solution is 4.

Method 2: $x - \sqrt{x} - 2 = 0 \quad \Leftrightarrow \quad x - 2 = \sqrt{x} \quad \Rightarrow \quad x^2 - 4x + 4 = x \quad \Leftrightarrow \quad x^2 - 5x + 4 = 0 \quad \Leftrightarrow \quad (x - 4)(x - 1) = 0$. So the possible solutions are 4 and 1. Checking will result in the same solution.

(b) *Method 1:* Let $u = \dfrac{1}{x - 3}$, so $u^2 = \dfrac{1}{(x - 3)^2}$. Thus $\dfrac{12}{(x - 3)^2} + \dfrac{10}{x - 3} + 1 = 0$ becomes $12u^2 + 10u + 1 = 0$. Using

the quadratic formula, we have $u = \frac{-10 \pm \sqrt{10^2 - 4(12)(1)}}{2(12)} = \frac{-10 \pm \sqrt{52}}{24} = \frac{-10 \pm 2\sqrt{13}}{24} = \frac{-5 \pm \sqrt{13}}{12}$. If $u = \frac{-5 - \sqrt{13}}{12}$, then

$\dfrac{1}{x - 3} = \dfrac{-5 - \sqrt{13}}{12} \quad \Leftrightarrow \quad x - 3 = \dfrac{12}{-5 - \sqrt{13}} \cdot \dfrac{-5 + \sqrt{13}}{-5 + \sqrt{13}} = \dfrac{12\left(-5 + \sqrt{13}\right)}{12} = -5 + \sqrt{13}$. So $x = -2 + \sqrt{13}$.

If $u = \frac{-5 + \sqrt{13}}{12}$, then $\dfrac{1}{x - 3} = \dfrac{-5 + \sqrt{13}}{12} \quad \Leftrightarrow \quad x - 3 = \dfrac{12}{-5 + \sqrt{13}} \cdot \dfrac{-5 - \sqrt{13}}{-5 - \sqrt{13}} = \dfrac{12\left(-5 - \sqrt{13}\right)}{12} = -5 - \sqrt{13}$. So

$x = -2 - \sqrt{13}$.

The solutions are $-2 \pm \sqrt{13}$.

Method 2: Multiply by LCD, $(x - 3)^2$, we get $(x - 3)^2 \left(\dfrac{12}{(x - 3)^2} + \dfrac{10}{x - 3} + 1 \right) = 0 \cdot (x - 3)^2 \quad \Leftrightarrow$

$12 + 10(x - 3) + (x - 3)^2 = 0 \quad \Leftrightarrow \quad 12 + 10x - 30 + x^2 - 6x + 9 = 0 \quad \Leftrightarrow \quad x^2 + 4x - 9 = 0$. Using

the quadratic formula, we have $u = \frac{-4 \pm \sqrt{4^2 - 4(1)(-9)}}{2} = \frac{-4 \pm \sqrt{52}}{2} = \frac{-4 \pm 2\sqrt{13}}{22} = -2 \pm \sqrt{13}$. The solutions are $-2 \pm \sqrt{13}$.

1.6 Modeling with Equations

1. If n is the first integer, then $n+1$ is the middle integer, and $n+2$ is the third integer. So the sum of the three consecutive integers is $n+(n+1)+(n+2)=3n+3$.

2. If n is the middle integer, then $n-1$ is the first integer, and $n+1$ is the third integer. So the sum of the three consecutive integers is $(n-1)+n+(n+1)=3n$.

3. If s is the third test score, then since the other test scores are 78 and 82, the average of the three test scores is $\dfrac{78+82+s}{3}=\dfrac{160+s}{3}$.

4. If q is the fourth quiz score, then since the other quiz scores are 8, 8, and 8, the average of the four quiz scores is $\dfrac{8+8+8+q}{4}=\dfrac{24+q}{4}$.

5. If x dollars are invested at $2\frac{1}{2}\%$ simple interest, then the first year you will receive $0.025x$ dollars in interest.

6. If n is the number of months the apartment is rented, and each month the rent is $795, then the total rent paid is $795n$.

7. Since w is the width of the rectangle, the length is three times the width, or $3w$. Then
area = length × width = $3w \times w = 3w^2$ ft^2.

8. Since w is the width of the rectangle, the length is $w+5$. The perimeter is
$$2 \times \text{length} + 2 \times \text{width} = 2\,(w+5) + 2\,(w) = 4w+10$$

9. Since distance = rate × time we have distance $= s \times (45 \text{ min})\,\dfrac{1\text{ h}}{60\text{ min}} = \frac{3}{4}s$ mi.

10. If d is the given distance, in miles, and distance = rate × time, we have time $= \dfrac{\text{distance}}{\text{rate}} = \dfrac{d}{55}$.

11. If x is the quantity of pure water added, the mixture will contain 25 oz of salt and $3+x$ gallons of water. Thus the concentration is $\dfrac{25}{3+x}$.

12. If p is the number of pennies in the purse, then the number of nickels is $2p$, the number of dimes is $4+2p$, and the number of quarters is $(2p)+(4+2p)=4p+4$. Thus the value (in cents) of the change in the purse is
$1 \cdot p + 5 \cdot 2p + 10 \cdot (4+2p) + 25 \cdot (4p+4) = p + 10p + 40 + 20p + 100p + 100 = 131p + 140$.

13. Let x be the first integer. Then $x+1$ and $x+2$ are the next consecutive integers. So $x+(x+1)+(x+2)=156 \quad \Leftrightarrow \quad 3x+3=156 \quad \Leftrightarrow \quad 3x=153 \quad \Leftrightarrow \quad x=51$. Thus the consecutive integers are 51, 52, and 53.

14. Let x be the first consecutive odd integer. Then $x+2$, $x+4$, and $x+6$ are the next consecutive odd integers. So $x+(x+2)+(x+4)+(x+6)=416 \quad \Leftrightarrow \quad 4x+12=416 \quad \Leftrightarrow \quad 4x=404 \quad \Leftrightarrow \quad x=101$. Thus the consecutive odd integers are 101, 103, 105, and 107.

15. Let n be one number. Then the other number must be $55-n$, since $n+(55-n)=55$. Because the product is 684, we have $(n)(55-n)=684 \quad \Leftrightarrow \quad 55n-n^2=684 \quad \Leftrightarrow \quad n^2-55n+684=0 \quad \Rightarrow$
$n=\dfrac{-(-55)\pm\sqrt{(-55)^2-4(1)(684)}}{2(1)} = \dfrac{55\pm\sqrt{3025-2736}}{2} = \dfrac{55\pm\sqrt{289}}{2} = \dfrac{55\pm17}{2}$. So $n=\dfrac{55+17}{2}=\dfrac{72}{2}=36$ or $n=\dfrac{55-17}{2}=\dfrac{38}{2}=19$. In either case, the two numbers are 19 and 36.

16. Let n be one even number. Then the next even number is $n+2$. Thus we get the equation $n^2+(n+2)^2=1252 \quad \Leftrightarrow$
$n^2+n^2+4n+4=1252 \quad \Leftrightarrow \quad 0=2n^2+4n-1248=2\,(n^2+2n-624)=2\,(n-24)\,(n+26)$. So $n=24$ or $n=-26$. Thus the consecutive even integers are 24 and 26 or -26 and -24.

17. Let m be the amount invested at $4\frac{1}{2}\%$. Then $12{,}000-m$ is the amount invested at 4%.
Since the total interest is equal to the interest earned at $4\frac{1}{2}\%$ plus the interest earned at 4%, we have
$525 = 0.045m + 0.04\,(12{,}000-m) \quad \Leftrightarrow \quad 525 = 0.045m + 480 - 0.04m \quad \Leftrightarrow \quad 45 = 0.005m \quad \Leftrightarrow$
$m = \dfrac{45}{0.005} = 9000$. Thus $9000 is invested at $4\frac{1}{2}\%$, and $12{,}000 - 9000 = $3000 is invested at 4%.

18. Let m be amount invested at $5\frac{1}{2}\%$. Then $4000 + m$ is the total amount invested. Thus

$$4\tfrac{1}{2}\% \text{ of the total investment} = \text{interest earned at } 4\% + \text{interest earned at } 5\tfrac{1}{2}\%$$

So $0.045\,(4000 + m) = 0.04\,(4000) + 0.055m$ $\Leftrightarrow$ $180 + 0.045m = 160 + 0.055m$ $\Leftrightarrow$ $20 = 0.01m$ $\Leftrightarrow$ $m = \dfrac{20}{0.01} = 2000$. Thus \$2,000 needs to be invested at $5\frac{1}{2}\%$.

19. Let r be the annual interest rate. Then $3500r = 262.50$ $\Leftrightarrow$ $r = \dfrac{262.50}{3500} = 0.075$. Thus the \$3500 must be invested at 7.5%.

20. Let r be the interest rate at which Jack invests the \$1000. Then $r + 0.005$ is the interest rate at which Jack invest the \$2000. Since total interest= (interest earned at r)+ (interest earned at $r + 0.005$), we have $190 = 1000r + 2000\,(r + 0.005)$ $\Leftrightarrow$ $190 = 1000r + 2000r + 10$ $\Leftrightarrow$ $180 = 3000r$ $\Leftrightarrow$ $r = \frac{180}{3000} = 0.06$. Thus Jack invests \$1,000 is invested at 6%.

21. Let x be her monthly salary. Since her annual salary $= 12 \times$ (monthly salary) + (Christmas bonus) we have $97{,}300 = 12x + 8{,}500$ $\Leftrightarrow$ $88{,}800 = 12x$ $\Leftrightarrow$ $x \approx 7{,}400$. Her monthly salary is \$7,400.

22. Let s be the husband's annual salary. Then her annual salary is $1.15s$. Since husband's annual salary+wife's annual salary $=$ total annual income, we have $s + 1.15s = 69{,}875$ $\Leftrightarrow$ $2.15s = 69{,}875$ $\Leftrightarrow$ $s = 32{,}500$. Thus the husband's annual salary is \$32,500.

23. Let h be the amount that Craig inherits. So $(x + 22{,}000)$ is the amount that he invests and doubles. Thus $2\,(x + 22{,}000) = 134{,}000$ $\Leftrightarrow$ $2x + 44{,}000 = 134{,}000$ $\Leftrightarrow$ $2x = 90{,}000$ $\Leftrightarrow$ $x = 45{,}000$. So Craig inherits \$45,000.

24. Let x be overtime hours Helen works. Since gross pay= regular salary+ overtime pay, we obtain the equation $352.50 = 7.50 \times 35 + 7.50 \times 1.5 \times x$ $\Leftrightarrow$ $352.50 = 262.50 + 11.25x$ $\Leftrightarrow$ $90 = 11.25x$ $\Leftrightarrow$ $x = \dfrac{90}{11.25} = 8$. Thus Helen worked 8 hours of overtime.

25. Let x be the hours the assistant work. Then $2x$ is the hours the plumber worked. Since the labor charge is equal to the plumber's labor plus the assistant's labor, we have $4025 = 45\,(2x) + 25x$ $\Leftrightarrow$ $4025 = 90x + 25x$ $\Leftrightarrow$ $4025 = 115x$ $\Leftrightarrow$ $x = \frac{4025}{115} = 35$. Thus the assistant works for 35 hours, and the plumber works for $2 \times 35 = 70$ hours.

26. Let h be number of home runs Babe Ruth hit. Then $h + 31$ is the number of home runs that Hank Aaron hit. So $1459 = h + h + 31$ $\Leftrightarrow$ $1428 = 2h$ $\Leftrightarrow$ $h = 714$. Thus Babe Ruth hit 714 home runs.

Note: In fact Hank Aaron hit 755 career home runs, not $714 + 31 = 745$.

27. All ages are in terms of the daughter's age 7 years ago. Let y be age of the daughter 7 years ago. Then $11y$ is the age of the movie star 7 years ago. Today, the daughter is $y + 7$, and the movie star is $11y + 7$. But the movie star is also 4 times his daughter's age today. So $4\,(y + 7) = 11y + 7$ $\Leftrightarrow$ $4y + 28 = 11y + 7$ $\Leftrightarrow$ $21 = 7y$ $\Leftrightarrow$ $y = 3$. Thus the movie star's age today is $11\,(3) + 7 = 40$ years.

28. Let a be the daughter's age now. Then her father's age now is $4a$. In 6 years, her age will $a + 6$, and her father's age will be $3\,(a + 6)$. But her father's age in 6 years is also $4a + 6$. So $3\,(a + 6) = 4a + 6$ $\Leftrightarrow$ $3a + 18 = 4a + 6$ $\Leftrightarrow$ $12 = a$. Thus the daughter is 12 years old.

29. Let p be the number of pennies. Then p is the number of nickels and p is the number of dimes. So the value of the coins in the purse is the value of the pennies plus the value of the nickels plus the value of the dimes. Thus $1.44 = 0.01p + 0.05p + 0.10p$ $\Leftrightarrow$ $1.44 = 0.16p$ $\Leftrightarrow$ $p = \frac{1.44}{0.16} = 9$. So the purse contains 9 pennies, 9 nickels, and 9 dimes.

30. Let q be the number of quarters. Then $2q$ is the number of dimes, and $2q + 5$ is the number of nickels. Thus $3.00 =$ value of the nickels+ value of the dimes+ value of the quarters. So $3.00 = 0.05\,(2q + 5) + 0.10\,(2q) + 0.25q$ $\Leftrightarrow$ $3.00 = 0.10q + 0.25 + 0.20q + 0.25q$ $\Leftrightarrow$ $2.75 = 0.55q$ $\Leftrightarrow$ $q = \frac{2.75}{0.55} = 5$. Thus Mary has 5 quarters, $2\,(5) = 10$ dimes, and $2\,(5) + 5 = 15$ nickels.

31. Let x be the distance from the fulcrum to where the mother sits. Then substituting the known values into the formula given, we have $100\,(8) = 125x$ $\Leftrightarrow$ $800 = 125x$ $\Leftrightarrow$ $x = 6.4$. So the mother should sit 6.4 feet from the fulcrum.

32. Let w be the largest weight that can be hung. In this exercise, the edge of the building acts as the fulcrum, so the 240 lb man is sitting 25 feet from the fulcrum. Then substituting the known values into the formula given in Exercise 31, we have $240\,(25) = 5w$ $\Leftrightarrow$ $6000 = 5w$ $\Leftrightarrow$ $w = 1200$. Therefore, 1200 pounds is the largest weight that can be hung.

33. (a) First we write a formula for the area of the figure in terms of x. Region A has dimensions 10 cm and x cm and region B has dimensions 6 cm and x cm. So the shaded region has area $(10 \cdot x) + (6 \cdot x) = 16x$ cm^2. We are given that this is equal to 144 cm^2, so $144 = 16x$ $\Leftrightarrow$ $x = \frac{144}{16} = 9$ cm.

(b) First we write a formula for the area of the figure in terms of x. Region A has dimensions 14 in. and x in. and region B has dimensions $(13 + x)$ in. and x in. So the area of the figure is $(14 \cdot x) + [(13 + x)\,x] = 14x + 13x + x^2 = x^2 + 27x$. We are given that this is equal to 160 in^2, so $160 = x^2 + 27x$ $\Leftrightarrow$ $x^2 + 27x - 160 = 0$ $\Leftrightarrow$ $(x + 32)\,(x - 5)$ $\Leftrightarrow$ $x = -32$ or $x = 5$. x must be positive, so $x = 5$ in.

34. (a) The shaded area is the sum of the area of a square and the area of a triangle. So $A = y^2 + \frac{1}{2}\,(y)\,(y) = \frac{3}{2}y^2$. We are given that the area is 120 in^2, so $120 = \frac{3}{2}y^2$ $\Leftrightarrow$ $y^2 = 80$ $\Leftrightarrow$ $y = \pm\sqrt{80} = \pm 4\sqrt{5}$. y is positive, so $y = 4\sqrt{5} \approx 8.94$ in.

(b) The shaded area is the sum of the area of a rectangle and the area of a triangle. So $A = y\,(1) + \frac{1}{2}\,(y)\,(y) = \frac{1}{2}y^2 + y$. We are given that the area is 1200 cm^2, so $1200 = \frac{1}{2}y^2 + y$ $\Leftrightarrow$ $y^2 + 2y - 2400 = 0$ $\Leftrightarrow$ $(y + 50)\,(y - 48) = 0$. y is positive, so $y = 48$ cm.

35. Let l be the length of the garden. Since area = width $\cdot$ length, we obtain the equation $1125 = 25l$ $\Leftrightarrow$ $l = \frac{1125}{25} = 45$ ft. So the garden is 45 feet long.

36. Let w be the width of the pasture. Then the length of the pasture is $2w$. Since area = length $\times$ width we have $115{,}200 = w\,(2w) = 2w^2$ $\Leftrightarrow$ $w^2 = 57{,}600$ $\Rightarrow$ $w = \pm 240$. Thus the width of the pasture is 240 feet.

37. Let x be the length of a side of the square plot. As shown in the figure, area of the plot = area of the building + area of the parking lot. Thus, $x^2 = 60\,(40) + 12{,}000 = 2{,}400 + 12{,}000 = 14{,}400$ $\Rightarrow$ $x = \pm 120$. So the plot of land measures 120 feet by 120 feet.

38. Let w be the width of the building lot. Then the length of the building lot is $5w$. Since a half-acre is $\frac{1}{2} \cdot 43{,}560 = 21{,}780$ and area is length times width, we have $21{,}780 = w\,(5w) = 5w^2$ $\Leftrightarrow$ $w^2 = 4{,}356$ $\Rightarrow$ $w = \pm 66$. Thus the width of the building lot is 66 feet and the length of the building lot is $5\,(66) = 330$ feet.

39. Let w be the width of the garden in feet. Then the length is $w + 10$. Thus $875 = w\,(w + 10)$ $\Leftrightarrow$ $w^2 + 10w - 875 = 0$ $\Leftrightarrow$ $(w + 35)\,(w - 25) = 0$. So $w + 35 = 0$ in which case $w = -35$, which is not possible, or $w - 25 = 0$ and so $w = 25$. Thus the width is 25 feet and the length is 35 feet.

40. Let w be the width of the bedroom. Then it's length is $w + 7$. Since area is length times width, we have $228 = (w + 7)\,w = w^2 + 7w$ $\Leftrightarrow$ $w^2 + 7w - 228 = 0$ $\Leftrightarrow$ $(w + 19)\,(w - 12) = 0$ $\Leftrightarrow$ $w + 19 = 0$ or $w - 12 = 0$. Thus $w = -19$ or $w = 12$. Since the width must be positive, the width is 12 feet.

41. Let w be the width of the garden in feet. We use the perimeter to express the length l of the garden in terms of width. Since the perimeter is twice the width plus twice the length, we have $200 = 2w + 2l$ $\Leftrightarrow$ $2l = 200 - 2w$ $\Leftrightarrow$ $l = 100 - w$. Using the formula for area, we have $2400 = w(100 - w) = 100w - w^2$ $\Leftrightarrow$ $w^2 - 100w + 2400 = 0$ $\Leftrightarrow$ $(w - 40)(w - 60) = 0$. So $w - 40 = 0$ $\Leftrightarrow$ $w = 40$, or $w - 60 = 0$ $\Leftrightarrow$ $w = 60$. If $w = 40$, then $l = 100 - 40 = 60$. And if $w = 60$, then $l = 100 - 60 = 40$. So the length is 60 feet and the width is 40 feet.

42. Let w be the width of the lot in feet. Then the length is $w + 6$. Using the Pythagorean Theorem, we have $w^2 + (w + 6)^2 = (174)^2$ $\Leftrightarrow$ $w^2 + w^2 + 12w + 36 = 30{,}276$ $\Leftrightarrow$ $2w^2 + 12w - 30240 = 0$ $\Leftrightarrow$ $w^2 + 6w - 15120 = 0$ $\Leftrightarrow$ $(w + 126)(w - 120) = 0$. So either $w + 126 = 0$ in which case $w = -126$, which is not possible, or $w - 120 = 0$ in which case $w = 120$. Thus the width is 120 feet and the length is 126 feet.

43. Let l be the length of the lot in feet. Then the length of the diagonal is $l + 10$. We apply the Pythagorean Theorem with the hypotenuse as the diagonal. So $l^2 + 50^2 = (l + 10)^2$ $\Leftrightarrow$ $l^2 + 2500 = l^2 + 20l + 100$ $\Leftrightarrow$ $20l = 2400$ $\Leftrightarrow$ $l = 120$. Thus the length of the lot is 120 feet.

44. Let r be the radius of the running track. The running track consists of two semicircles and two straight sections 110 yards long, so we get the equation $2\pi r + 220 = 440$ $\Leftrightarrow$ $2\pi r = 220$ $\Leftrightarrow$ $r = \frac{110}{\pi} = 35.03$. Thus the radius of the semicircle is about 35 yards.

45. Let x be the width of the strip. Then the length of the mat is $20 + 2x$, and the width of the mat is $15 + 2x$. Now the perimeter is twice the length plus twice the width, so $102 = 2(20 + 2x) + 2(15 + 2x)$ $\Leftrightarrow$ $102 = 40 + 4x + 30 + 4x$ $\Leftrightarrow$ $102 = 70 + 8x$ $\Leftrightarrow$ $32 = 8x$ $\Leftrightarrow$ $x = 4$. Thus the strip of mat is 4 inches wide.

46. Let w be the uniform width of the lawn. With w cut off each end, the area of the factory is $(240 - 2w)(180 - 2w)$. Since the lawn and the factory are equal in size this area, is $\frac{1}{2} \cdot 240 \cdot 180$. So $21{,}600 = 43{,}200 - 480w - 360w + 4w^2$ $\Leftrightarrow$ $0 = 4w^2 - 840w + 21{,}600 = 4(w^2 - 210w + 5400) = 4(w - 30)(w - 180)$ $\Rightarrow$ $w = 30$ or $w = 180$. Since 180 ft is too wide, the width of the lawn is 30 ft, and the factory is 120 ft by 180 ft.

47. Let h be the height the ladder reaches (in feet). Using the Pythagorean Theorem we have $\left(7\frac{1}{2}\right)^2 + h^2 = \left(19\frac{1}{2}\right)^2$ $\Leftrightarrow$ $\left(\frac{15}{2}\right)^2 + h^2 = \left(\frac{39}{4}\right)^2$ $\Leftrightarrow$ $h^2 = \left(\frac{39}{4}\right)^2 - \left(\frac{15}{2}\right)^2 = \frac{1521}{4} - \frac{225}{4} = \frac{1296}{4} = 324$. So $h = \sqrt{324} = 18$.

48. Let h be the height of the flagpole, in feet. Then the length of each guy wire is $h + 5$. Since the distance between the points where the wires are fixed to the ground is equal to one guy wire, the triangle is equilateral, and the flagpole is the perpendicular bisector of the base. Thus from the Pythagorean Theorem, we get $\left[\frac{1}{2}(h + 5)\right]^2 + h^2 = (h + 5)^2$ $\Leftrightarrow$ $h^2 + 10h + 25 + 4h^2 = 4h^2 + 40h + 100$ $\Leftrightarrow$ $h^2 - 30h - 75 = 0$ $\Rightarrow$ $h = \frac{-(-30) \pm \sqrt{(-30)^2 - 4(1)(-75)}}{2(1)} = \frac{30 \pm \sqrt{900 + 300}}{2} = \frac{30 \pm \sqrt{1200}}{2} = \frac{30 \pm 20\sqrt{3}}{2}$. Since $h = \frac{30 - 20\sqrt{3}}{2} < 0$, we reject it. Thus the height is $h = \frac{30 + 20\sqrt{3}}{2} = 15 + 10\sqrt{3} \approx 32.32$ ft $\approx$ 32 ft 4 in.

49. Let x be the length of the man's shadow, in meters. Using similar triangles, $\frac{10 + x}{6} = \frac{x}{2}$ $\Leftrightarrow$ $20 + 2x = 6x$ $\Leftrightarrow$ $4x = 20$ $\Leftrightarrow$ $x = 5$. Thus the man's shadow is 5 meters long.

50. Let x be the height of the tall tree. Here we use the property that corresponding sides in similar triangles are proportional. The base of the similar triangles starts at eye level of the woodcutter, 5 feet. Thus we obtain the proportion $\frac{x - 5}{15} = \frac{150}{25}$ $\Leftrightarrow$ $25(x - 5) = 15(150)$ $\Leftrightarrow$ $25x - 125 = 2250$ $\Leftrightarrow$ $25x = 2375$ $\Leftrightarrow$ $x = 95$. Thus the tree is 95 feet tall.

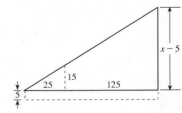

51. Let n be the number of people in the group, so each person now pays $\dfrac{120{,}000}{n}$. If one person joins the group, then there would be $n + 1$ members in the group, and each person would pay $\dfrac{120{,}000}{n} - 6000$. So

$$(n+1)\left(\frac{120{,}000}{n} - 6000\right) = 120{,}000 \quad\Leftrightarrow\quad \left[\left(\frac{n}{6000}\right)\left(\frac{120{,}000}{n} - 6000\right)\right](n+1) = \left(\frac{n}{6000}\right)120{,}000 \quad\Leftrightarrow$$

$(20 - n)(n + 1) = 20n \quad\Leftrightarrow\quad -n^2 + 19n + 20 = 20n \quad\Leftrightarrow\quad 0 = n^2 + n - 20 = (n - 4)(n + 5)$. Thus $n = 4$ or $n = -5$. Since n must be positive, there are now 4 friends in the group.

52. Let x be the amount (in mL) of 60% acid solution to be used. Then $(300 - x)$ mL of 30% solution would have to be used to yield a total of 300 mL of solution.

	60% acid	30% acid	Mixture
mL	x	$300 - x$	300
Rate (% acid)	0.60	0.30	0.50
Value	$0.60x$	$0.30\,(300 - x)$	$0.50\,(300)$

Thus the total amount of pure acid used is $0.60x + 0.30\,(300 - x) = 0.50\,(300) \quad\Leftrightarrow\quad 0.3x + 90 = 150 \quad\Leftrightarrow$ $x = \dfrac{60}{0.3} = 200$. So 200 mL of 60% acid solution must be mixed with 100 mL of 30% solution to get 300 mL of 50% acid solution.

53. Let x be the grams of silver added. The weight of the rings is 5×18 g $= 90$ g.

	5 rings	Pure silver	Mixture
Grams	90	x	$90 + x$
Rate (% gold)	0.90	0	0.75
Value	$0.90\,(90)$	$0x$	$0.75\,(90 + x)$

So $0.90\,(90) + 0x = 0.75\,(90 + x) \quad\Leftrightarrow\quad 81 = 67.5 + 0.75x \quad\Leftrightarrow\quad 0.75x = 13.5 \quad\Leftrightarrow\quad x = \frac{13.5}{0.75} = 18$. Thus 18 grams of silver must be added to get the required mixture.

54. Let x be the number of liters of water to be boiled off. The result will contain $6 - x$ liters.

	Original	Water	Final
Liters	6	$-x$	$6 - x$
Concentration	120	0	200
Amount	$120\,(6)$	0	$200\,(6 - x)$

So $120\,(6) + 0 = 200\,(6 - x) \quad\Leftrightarrow\quad 720 = 1200 - 200x \quad\Leftrightarrow\quad 200x = 480 \quad\Leftrightarrow\quad x = 2.4$. Thus 2.4 liters need to be boiled off.

55. Let x be the liters of coolant removed and replaced by water.

	60% antifreeze	60% antifreeze (removed)	Water	Mixture
Liters	3.6	x	x	3.6
Rate (% antifreeze)	0.60	0.60	0	0.50
Value	$0.60\,(3.6)$	$-0.60x$	$0x$	$0.50\,(3.6)$

so $0.60\,(3.6) - 0.60x + 0x = 0.50\,(3.6) \quad\Leftrightarrow\quad 2.16 - 0.6x = 1.8 \quad\Leftrightarrow\quad -0.6x = -0.36 \quad\Leftrightarrow\quad x = \dfrac{-0.36}{-0.6} = 0.6$. Thus 0.6 liters must be removed and replaced by water.

56. Let x be the number of gallons of 2% bleach removed from the tank. This is also the number of gallons of pure bleach added to make the 5% mixture.

	Original 2%	Pure bleach	5% mixture
Gallons	$100 - x$	x	100
Concentration	0.02	1	0.05
Bleach	$0.02\,(100 - x)$	$1x$	$0.05 \cdot 100$

So $0.02\,(100 - x) + x = 0.05 \cdot 100$ $\Leftrightarrow$ $2 - 0.02x + x = 5$ $\Leftrightarrow$ $0.98x = 3$ $\Leftrightarrow$ $x = 3.06$. Thus 3.06 gallons need to removed and replaced with pure bleach.

57. Let c be the concentration of fruit juice in the cheaper brand. The new mixture that Jill makes will consist of 650 mL of the original fruit punch and 100 ml of the cheaper fruit punch.

	Original Fruit Punch	Cheaper Fruit Punch	Mixture
mL	650	100	750
Concentration	0.50	c	0.48
Juice	$0.50 \cdot 650$	$100c$	$0.48 \cdot 750$

So $0.50 \cdot 650 + 100c = 0.48 \cdot 750$ $\Leftrightarrow$ $325 + 100c = 360$ $\Leftrightarrow$ $100c = 35$ $\Leftrightarrow$ $c = 0.35$. Thus the cheaper brand is only 35% fruit juice.

58. Let x be the number of pounds of \$3.00/lb tea Then $80 - x$ is the number of pounds of \$2.75/lb tea.

	\$3.00 tea	\$2.75 tea	Mixture
Pounds	x	$80 - x$	80
Rate (cost per pound)	3.00	2.75	2.90
Value	$3.00x$	$2.75\,(80 - x)$	$2.90\,(80)$

So $3.00x + 2.75\,(80 - x) = 2.90\,(80)$ $\Leftrightarrow$ $3.00x + 220 - 2.75x = 232$ $\Leftrightarrow$ $0.25x = 12$ $\Leftrightarrow$ $x = 48$. The mixture uses 48 pounds of \$3.00/lb tea and $80 - 48 = 32$ pounds of \$2.75/lb tea.

59. Let t be the time in minutes it would take Candy and Tim if they work together. Candy delivers the papers at a rate of $\frac{1}{70}$ of the job per minute, while Tim delivers the paper at a rate of $\frac{1}{80}$ of the job per minute. The sum of the fractions of the job that each can do individually in one minute equals the fraction of the job they can do working together. So we have $\frac{1}{t} = \frac{1}{70} + \frac{1}{80}$ $\Leftrightarrow$ $560 = 8t + 7t$ $\Leftrightarrow$ $560 = 15t$ $\Leftrightarrow$ $t = 37\frac{1}{3}$ minutes. Since $\frac{1}{3}$ of a minute is 20 seconds, it would take them 37 minutes 20 seconds if they worked together.

60. Let t be the time it takes Hilda, in minutes, to mow the lawn. Since Hilda is twice as fast as Stan, it takes Stan $2t$ minutes to mow the lawn by himself. Thus $40 \cdot \frac{1}{t} + 40 \cdot \frac{1}{2t} = 1$ $\Leftrightarrow$ $40 + 20 = t$ $\Leftrightarrow$ $t = 60$. So it would take Stan $2\,(60) = 120$ minutes to mow the lawn.

61. Let t be the time, in hours, it takes Karen to paint a house alone. Then working together, Karen and Betty can paint a house in $\frac{2}{3}t$ hours. The sum of their individual rates equals their rate working together, so $\frac{1}{t} + \frac{1}{6} = \frac{1}{\frac{2}{3}t}$ $\Leftrightarrow$ $\frac{1}{t} + \frac{1}{6} = \frac{3}{2t}$ $\Leftrightarrow$ $6 + t = 9$ $\Leftrightarrow$ $t = 3$. Thus it would take Karen 3 hours to paint a house alone.

62. Let h be the time, in hours, to fill the swimming pool using Jim's hose alone. Since Bob's hose takes 20% less time, it uses only 80% of the time, or $0.8h$. Thus $18 \cdot \frac{1}{h} + 18 \cdot \frac{1}{0.8h} = 1$ $\Leftrightarrow$ $18 \cdot 0.8 + 18 = 0.8h$ $\Leftrightarrow$ $14.4 + 18 = 0.8h$ $\Leftrightarrow$ $32.4 = 0.8h$ $\Leftrightarrow$ $h = 40.5$. Jim's hose takes 40.5 hours, and Bob's hose takes 32.4 hours to fill the pool alone.

63. Let t be the time, in hours it takes Irene to wash all the windows. Then it takes Henry $t + \frac{3}{2}$ hours to wash all the windows, and the sum of the fraction of the job per hour they can do individually equals the fraction of the job they can do together. Since 1 hour 48 minutes $= 1 + \frac{48}{60} = 1 + \frac{4}{5} = \frac{9}{5}$, we have $\frac{1}{t} + \frac{1}{t + \frac{3}{2}} = \frac{1}{\frac{9}{5}}$ $\Leftrightarrow$ $\frac{1}{t} + \frac{2}{2t + 3} = \frac{5}{9}$

$\Rightarrow$ $9(2t + 3) + 2(9t) = 5t(2t + 3)$ $\Leftrightarrow$ $18t + 27 + 18t = 10t^2 + 15t$ $\Leftrightarrow$ $10t^2 - 21t - 27 = 0$

$\Leftrightarrow$ $t = \dfrac{-(-21) \pm \sqrt{(-21)^2 - 4(10)(-27)}}{2(10)} = \dfrac{21 \pm \sqrt{441 + 1080}}{20} = \dfrac{21 \pm 39}{20}$. So $t = \dfrac{21 - 39}{20} = -\dfrac{9}{10}$

or $t = \dfrac{21 + 39}{20} = 3$. Since $t < 0$ is impossible, all the windows are washed by Irene alone in 3 hours and by Henry alone in $3 + \frac{3}{2} = 4\frac{1}{2}$ hours.

64. Let t be the time, in hours, it takes Kay to deliver all the flyers alone. Then it takes Lynn $t + 1$ hours to deliver all the flyers alone, and it takes the group $0.4t$ hours to do it together. Thus $\frac{1}{4} + \frac{1}{t} + \frac{1}{t + 1} = \frac{1}{0.4t}$ $\Leftrightarrow$

$\frac{1}{4}(0.4t) + \frac{1}{t}(0.4t) + \frac{1}{t + 1}(0.4t) = 1$ $\Leftrightarrow$ $t + 4 + \dfrac{4t}{t + 1} = 10$ $\Leftrightarrow$ $t(t + 1) + 4(t + 1) + 4t = 10(t + 1)$ $\Leftrightarrow$

$t^2 + t + 4t + 4 + 4t = 10t + 10$ $\Leftrightarrow$ $t^2 - t - 6 = 0$ $\Leftrightarrow$ $(t - 3)(t + 2) = 0$. So $t = 3$ or $t = -2$. Since $t = -2$ is impossible, it takes Kay 3 hours to deliver all the flyers alone.

65. Let t be the time in hours that Wendy spent on the train. Then $\frac{11}{2} - t$ is the time in hours that Wendy spent on the bus. We construct a table:

	Rate	Time	Distance
By train	40	t	$40t$
By bus	60	$\frac{11}{2} - t$	$60\left(\frac{11}{2} - t\right)$

The total distance traveled is the sum of the distances traveled by bus and by train, so $300 = 40t + 60\left(\frac{11}{2} - t\right)$ $\Leftrightarrow$ $300 = 40t + 330 - 60t$ $\Leftrightarrow$ $-30 = -20t$ $\Leftrightarrow$ $t = \frac{-30}{-20} = 1.5$ hours. So the time spent on the train is $5.5 - 1.5 = 4$ hours.

66. Let r be the speed of the slower cyclist, in mi/h. Then the speed of the faster cyclist is $2r$.

	Rate	Time	Distance
Slower cyclist	r	2	$2r$
Faster cyclist	$2r$	2	$4r$

When they meet, they will have traveled a total of 90 miles, so $2r + 4r = 90$ $\Leftrightarrow$ $6r = 90$ $\Leftrightarrow$ $r = 15$. The speed of the slower cyclist is 15 mi/h, while the speed of the faster cyclist is $2(15) = 30$ mi/h.

67. Let r be the speed of the plane from Montreal to Los Angeles. Then $r + 0.20r = 1.20r$ is the speed of the plane from Los Angeles to Montreal.

	Rate	Time	Distance
Montreal to L.A.	r	$\dfrac{2500}{r}$	2500
L.A. to Montreal	$1.2r$	$\dfrac{2500}{1.2r}$	2500

The total time is the sum of the times each way, so $9\frac{1}{6} = \dfrac{2500}{r} + \dfrac{2500}{1.2r}$ $\Leftrightarrow$ $\dfrac{55}{6} = \dfrac{2500}{r} + \dfrac{2500}{1.2r}$ $\Leftrightarrow$

$55 \cdot 1.2r = 2500 \cdot 6 \cdot 1.2 + 2500 \cdot 6$ $\Leftrightarrow$ $66r = 18{,}000 + 15{,}000$ $\Leftrightarrow$ $66r = 33{,}000$ $\Leftrightarrow$ $r = \frac{33{,}000}{66} = 500$. Thus the plane flew at a speed of 500 mi/h on the trip from Montreal to Los Angeles.

68. Let x be the speed of the car in mi/h. Since a mile contains 5280 ft and an hour contains 3600 s, 1 mi/h $= \frac{5280 \text{ ft}}{3600 \text{ s}} = \frac{22}{15}$ ft/s. The truck is traveling at $50 \cdot \frac{22}{15} = \frac{220}{3}$ ft/s. So in 6 seconds, the truck travels $6 \cdot \frac{220}{3} = 440$ feet. Thus the back end of the car must travel the length of the car, the length of the truck, and the 440 feet in 6 seconds, so its speed must be $\frac{14+30+440}{6} = \frac{242}{3}$ ft/s. Converting to mi/h, we have that the speed of the car is $\frac{242}{3} \cdot \frac{15}{22} = 55$ mi/h.

69. Let x be the rate, in mi/h, at which the salesman drove between Ajax and Barrington.

Cities	Distance	Rate	Time
Ajax $\rightarrow$ Barrington	120	x	$\dfrac{120}{x}$
Barrington $\rightarrow$ Collins	150	$x + 10$	$\dfrac{150}{x + 10}$

We have used the equation time $= \dfrac{\text{distance}}{\text{rate}}$ to fill in the "Time" column of the table. Since the second part of the trip took 6 minutes (or $\frac{1}{10}$ hour) more than the first, we can use the time column to get the equation $\dfrac{120}{x} + \dfrac{1}{10} = \dfrac{150}{x + 10} \quad \Rightarrow$ $120\,(10)\,(x + 10) + x\,(x + 10) = 150\,(10x) \quad \Leftrightarrow \quad 1200x + 12{,}000 + x^2 + 10x = 1500x \quad \Leftrightarrow \quad x^2 - 290x + 12{,}000 = 0$ $\Leftrightarrow \quad x = \dfrac{-(-290) \pm \sqrt{(-290)^2 - 4(1)(12{,}000)}}{2} = \dfrac{290 \pm \sqrt{84{,}100 - 48{,}000}}{2} = \dfrac{290 \pm \sqrt{36{,}100}}{2} = \dfrac{290 \pm 190}{2} = 145 \pm 95$. Hence, the salesman drove either 50 mi/h or 240 mi/h between Ajax and Barrington. (The first choice seems more likely!)

70. Let x be the rate, in mi/h, at which Kiran drove from Tortula to Cactus.

Cities	Distance	Rate	Time
Tortula $\rightarrow$ Cactus	250	x	$\dfrac{250}{x}$
Cactus $\rightarrow$ Dry Junction	360	$x + 10$	$\dfrac{360}{x + 10}$

We have used time $= \dfrac{\text{distance}}{\text{rate}}$ to fill in the time column of the table. We are given that the sum of the times is 11 hours. Thus we get the equation $\dfrac{250}{x} + \dfrac{360}{x + 10} = 11 \quad \Leftrightarrow \quad 250\,(x + 10) + 360x = 11x\,(x + 10) \quad \Leftrightarrow \quad 250x + 2500 + 360x = 11x^2 + 110x \quad \Leftrightarrow \quad 11x^2 - 500x - 2500 = 0 \quad \Rightarrow$ $x = \dfrac{-(-500) \pm \sqrt{(-500)^2 - 4(11)(-2500)}}{2(11)} = \dfrac{500 \pm \sqrt{250{,}000 + 110{,}000}}{22} = \dfrac{500 \pm \sqrt{360{,}000}}{22} = \dfrac{500 \pm 600}{22}$.

Hence, Kiran drove either -4.54 mi/h (impossible) or 50 mi/h between Tortula and Cactus.

71. Let r be the rowing rate in km/h of the crew in still water. Then their rate upstream was $r - 3$ km/h, and their rate downstream was $r + 3$ km/h.

	Distance	Rate	Time
Upstream	6	$r - 3$	$\dfrac{6}{r - 3}$
Downstream	6	$r + 3$	$\dfrac{6}{r + 3}$

Since the time to row upstream plus the time to row downstream was 2 hours 40 minutes $= \frac{8}{3}$ hour, we get the equation $\dfrac{6}{r - 3} + \dfrac{6}{r + 3} = \dfrac{8}{3} \quad \Leftrightarrow \quad 6\,(3)\,(r + 3) + 6\,(3)\,(r - 3) = 8\,(r - 3)\,(r + 3) \quad \Leftrightarrow \quad 18r + 54 + 18r - 54 = 8r^2 - 72$ $\Leftrightarrow \quad 0 = 8r^2 - 36r - 72 = 4\,(2r^2 - 9r - 18) = 4\,(2r + 3)\,(r - 6)$. Since $2r + 3 = 0 \quad \Leftrightarrow \quad r = -\frac{3}{2}$ is impossible, the solution is $r - 6 = 0 \quad \Leftrightarrow \quad r = 6$. So the rate of the rowing crew in still water is 6 km/h.

72. Let r be the speed of the southbound boat. Then $r + 3$ is the speed of the eastbound boat. In two hours the southbound boat has traveled $2r$ miles and the eastbound boat has traveled $2(r + 3) = 2r + 6$ miles. Since they are traveling is directions with are 90° apart, we can use the Pythagorean Theorem to get $(2r)^2 + (2r + 6)^2 = 30^2$ ⇔ $4r^2 + 4r^2 + 24r + 36 = 900$ ⇔ $8r^2 + 24r - 864 = 0$ ⇔ $8(r^2 + 3r - 108) = 0$ ⇔ $8(r + 12)(r - 9) = 0$. So $r = -12$ or $r = 9$. Since speed is positive, the speed of the southbound boat is 9 mi/h.

73. We have that the volume is 180 ft³, so $x(x - 4)(x + 9) = 180$ ⇔ $x^3 + 5x^2 - 36x = 180$ ⇔ $x^3 + 5x^2 - 36x - 180 = 0$ ⇔ $x^2(x + 5) - 36(x + 5) = 0$ ⇔ $(x + 5)(x^2 - 36) = 0$ ⇔ $(x + 5)(x + 6)(x - 6) = 0$ ⇒ $x = 6$ is the only positive solution. So the box is 2 feet by 6 feet by 15 feet.

74. Let r be the radius of the larger sphere, in mm. Equating the volumes, we have $\frac{4}{3}\pi r^3 = \frac{4}{3}\pi (2^3 + 3^3 + 4^3)$ ⇔ $r^3 = 2^3 + 3^3 + 4^4$ ⇔ $r^3 = 99$ ⇔ $r = \sqrt[3]{99} \approx 4.63$. Therefore, the radius of the larger sphere is about 4.63 mm.

75. Let x be the length of one side of the cardboard, so we start with a piece of cardboard x by x. When 4 inches are removed from each side, the base of the box is $x - 8$ by $x - 8$. Since the volume is 100 in³, we get $4(x - 8)^2 = 100$ ⇔ $x^2 - 16x + 64 = 25$ ⇔ $x^2 - 16x + 39 = 0$ ⇔ $(x - 3)(x - 13) = 0$. So $x = 3$ or $x = 13$. But $x = 3$ is not possible, since then the length of the base would be $3 - 8 = -5$, and all lengths must be positive. Thus $x = 13$, and the piece of cardboard is 13 inches by 13 inches.

76. Let r be the radius of the can. Now using the formula $V = \pi r^2 h$ with $V = 40\pi$ cm³ and $h = 10$, we solve for r. Thus $40\pi = \pi r^2 (10)$ ⇔ $4 = r^2$ ⇒ $r = \pm 2$. Since r represents radius, $r > 0$. Thus $r = 2$, and the diameter is 4 cm.

77. Let r be the radius of the tank, in feet. The volume of the spherical tank is $\frac{4}{3}\pi r^3$ and is also $750 \times 0.1337 = 100.275$. So $\frac{4}{3}\pi r^3 = 100.275$ ⇔ $r^3 = 23.938$ ⇔ $r = 2.88$ feet.

78. Let x be the length of the hypotenuse of the triangle, in feet. Then one of the other sides has length $x - 7$ feet, and since the perimeter is 392 feet, the remaining side must have length $392 - x - (x - 7) = 399 - 2x$. From the Pythagorean Theorem, we get $(x - 7)^2 + (399 - 2x)^2 = x^2$ ⇔ $4x^2 - 1610x + 159250 = 0$. Using the quadratic formula, we get

$x = \frac{1610 \pm \sqrt{1610^2 - 4(4)(159250)}}{2(4)} = \frac{1610 \pm \sqrt{44100}}{8} = \frac{1610 \pm 210}{8}$, and so $x = 227.5$ or $x = 175$. But if $x = 227.5$, then the side of length $x - 7$ combined with the hypotenuse already exceeds the perimeter of 392 feet, and so we must have $x = 175$. Thus the other sides have length $175 - 7 = 168$ and $399 - 2(175) = 49$. The lot has sides of length 49 feet, 168 feet, and 175 feet.

79. Let x be the length, in miles, of the abandoned road to be used. Then the length of the abandoned road not used is $40 - x$, and the length of the new road is $\sqrt{10^2 + (40 - x)^2}$ miles, by the Pythagorean Theorem. Since the cost of the road is cost per mile × number of miles, we have $100{,}000x + 200{,}000\sqrt{x^2 - 80x + 1700} = 6{,}800{,}000$ ⇔ $2\sqrt{x^2 - 80x + 1700} = 68 - x$. Squaring both sides, we get $4x^2 - 320x + 6800 = 4624 - 136x + x^2$ ⇔ $3x^2 - 184x + 2176 = 0$ ⇔ $x = \frac{184 \pm \sqrt{33856 - 26112}}{6} = \frac{184 \pm 88}{6}$ ⇔ $x = \frac{136}{3}$ or $x = 16$. Since $45\frac{1}{3}$ is longer than the existing road, 16 miles of the abandoned road should be used. A completely new road would have length $\sqrt{10^2 + 40^2}$ (let $x = 0$) and would cost $\sqrt{1700} \times 200{,}000 \approx 8.3$ million dollars. So no, it would not be cheaper.

80. Let x be the distance, in feet, that he goes on the boardwalk before veering off onto the sand. The distance along the boardwalk from where he started to the point on the boardwalk closest to the umbrella is $\sqrt{750^2 - 210^2} = 720$ ft. Thus the distance that he walks on the sand is
$$\sqrt{(720 - x)^2 + 210^2} = \sqrt{518,400 - 1440x + x^2 + 44,100} = \sqrt{x^2 - 1440x + 562,500}.$$

	Distance	Rate	Time
Along boardwalk	x	4	$\dfrac{x}{4}$
Across sand	$\sqrt{x^2 - 1440x + 562500}$	2	$\dfrac{\sqrt{x^2 - 1440x + 562,500}}{2}$

Since 4 minutes 45 seconds $= 285$ seconds, we equate the time it takes to walk along the boardwalk and across the sand to the total time to get $285 = \dfrac{x}{4} + \dfrac{\sqrt{x^2 - 1440x + 562,500}}{2}$ $\Leftrightarrow$ $1140 - x = 2\sqrt{x^2 - 1440x + 562,500}$. Squaring both sides, we get $(1140 - x)^2 = 4\left(x^2 - 1440x + 562,500\right)$ $\Leftrightarrow$ $1,299,600 - 2280x + x^2 = 4x^2 - 5760x + 2,250,000$ $\Leftrightarrow$ $0 = 3x^2 - 3480x + 950,400 = 3\left(x^2 - 1160x + 316,800\right) = 3\left(x - 720\right)\left(x - 440\right)$. So $x - 720 = 0$ $\Leftrightarrow$ $x = 720$, and $x - 440 = 0$ $\Leftrightarrow$ $x = 440$. Checking $x = 720$, the distance across the sand is 210 feet. So $\frac{720}{4} + \frac{210}{2} = 180 + 105 = 285$ seconds. Checking $x = 440$, the distance across the sand is $\sqrt{(720 - 440)^2 + 210^2} = 350$ feet. So $\frac{440}{4} + \frac{350}{2} = 110 + 175 = 285$ seconds. Since both solutions are less than or equal to 720 feet, we have two solutions: he walks 440 feet down the boardwalk and then heads towards his umbrella, or he walks 720 feet down the boardwalk and then heads toward his umbrella.

81. Let x be the height of the pile in feet. Then the diameter is $3x$ and the radius is $\frac{3}{2}x$ feet. Since the volume of the cone is 1000 ft^3, we have $\dfrac{\pi}{3}\left(\dfrac{3x}{2}\right)^2 x = 1000$ $\Leftrightarrow$ $\dfrac{3\pi x^3}{4} = 1000$ $\Leftrightarrow$ $x^3 = \dfrac{4000}{3\pi}$ $\Leftrightarrow$ $x = \sqrt[3]{\dfrac{4000}{3\pi}} \approx 7.52$ feet.

82. Let h be the height of the screens in inches. Hence, the width of the smaller screen is $h + 5$ inches, and the width of the bigger screen is $1.8h$ inches. The diagonal measure of the smaller screen is $\sqrt{h^2 + (h + 5)^2}$, and the diagonal measure of the larger screen is $\sqrt{h^2 + (1.8h)^2} = \sqrt{4.24h^2} \approx 2.06h$. Thus $\sqrt{h^2 + (h + 5)^2} + 14 = 2.06h$ $\Leftrightarrow$ $\sqrt{h^2 + (h + 5)^2} = 2.06h - 14$. Squaring both sides yields $h^2 + h^2 + 10h + 25 = 4.24h^2 - 57.68h + 196$ $\Leftrightarrow$ $0 = 2.24h^2 - 67.68h + 171$. Applying the quadratic formula, we obtain $h = \dfrac{67.68 \pm \sqrt{(-67.68)^2 - 4(2.24)(171)}}{2(2.24)} = \dfrac{67.68 \pm \sqrt{3048.4224}}{4.48} = \dfrac{67.68 \pm 55.21}{4.48}$. So $h = 27.4$ or $h = 2.8$. Since high definition television monitors don't come in heights of 2.8 inches, the height of the screens is 27.4 inches.

83. Let h be the height in feet of the structure. The structure is composed of a right cylinder with radius 10 and height $\frac{2}{3}h$ and a cone with base radius 10 and height $\frac{1}{3}h$. Using the formulas for the volume of a cylinder and that of a cone, we obtain the equation $1400\pi = \pi(10)^2\left(\frac{2}{3}h\right) + \frac{1}{3}\pi(10)^2\left(\frac{1}{3}h\right)$ $\Leftrightarrow$ $1400\pi = \frac{200\pi}{3}h + \frac{100\pi}{9}h$ $\Leftrightarrow$ $126 = 6h + h$ (multiply both sides by $\dfrac{9}{100\pi}$) $\Leftrightarrow$ $126 = 7h$ $\Leftrightarrow$ $h = 18$. Thus the height of the structure is 18 feet.

84. Let y be the circumference of the circle, so $360 - y$ is the perimeter of the square. Use the circumference to find the radius, r, in terms of y: $y = 2\pi r$ $\Rightarrow$ $r = y/(2\pi)$. Thus the area of the circle is $\pi\left[y/(2\pi)\right]^2 = y^2/(4\pi)$. Now if the perimeter of the square is $360 - y$, the length of each side is $\frac{1}{4}(360 - y)$, and the area of the square is $\left[\frac{1}{4}(360 - y)\right]^2$. Setting these areas equal, we obtain $y^2/(4\pi) = \left[\frac{1}{4}(360 - y)\right]^2$ $\Leftrightarrow$ $y/(2\sqrt{\pi}) = \frac{1}{4}(360 - y)$ $\Leftrightarrow$ $2y = 360\sqrt{\pi} - \sqrt{\pi}y$ $\Leftrightarrow$ $(2 + \sqrt{\pi})y = 360\sqrt{\pi}$. Therefore, $y = 360\sqrt{\pi}/(2 + \sqrt{\pi}) \approx 169.1$. Thus one wire is 169.1 in. long and the other is 190.9 in. long.

85. Let h be the height of the break, in feet. Then the portion of the bamboo above the break is $10 - h$. Applying the Pythagorean Theorem, we obtain

$$h^2 + 3^2 = (10 - h)^2 \quad \Leftrightarrow \quad h^2 + 9 = 100 - 20h + h^2 \quad \Leftrightarrow \quad -91 = -20h$$

$$\Leftrightarrow \quad h = \frac{91}{20} = 4.55. \text{ Thus the break is } 4.55 \text{ ft above the ground.}$$

86. Pythagoras was born about 569 BC in Samos, Ionia and died about 475 BC.

Euclid was born about 325 BC and died about 265 BC in Alexandria, Egypt.

Archimedes was born in 287 BC in Syracuse, Sicily and died in 212 BC in Syracuse, Sicily.

87. Let x equal the original length of the reed in cubits. Then $x - 1$ is the piece that fits 60 times along the length of the field, that is, the length is $60 (x - 1)$. The width is $30x$. Then converting cubits to ninda, we have

$$375 = 60 (x - 1) \cdot 30x \cdot \frac{1}{12^2} = \frac{25}{2} x (x - 1) \quad \Leftrightarrow \quad 30 = x^2 - x \quad \Leftrightarrow \quad x^2 - x - 30 = 0 \quad \Leftrightarrow \quad (x - 6)(x + 5) = 0.$$

So $x = 6$ or $x = -5$. Since x must be positive, the original length of the reed is 6 cubits.

1.7   Inequalities

1. $x = -2$: $3 - 2(-2) \overset{?}{\le} \frac{1}{2}$. No, $7 \not\le \frac{1}{2}$. $x = -1$: $3 - 2(-1) \overset{?}{\le} \frac{1}{2}$. No, $6 \not\le \frac{1}{2}$. $x = 0$: $3 - 2(0) \overset{?}{\le} \frac{1}{2}$. No, $3 \not\le \frac{1}{2}$.

$x = \frac{1}{2}$: $3 - 2\left(\frac{1}{2}\right) \overset{?}{\le} \frac{1}{2}$. No, $2 \not\le \frac{1}{2}$. $x = 1$: $3 - 2(1) \overset{?}{\le} \frac{1}{2}$. No, $1 \not\le \frac{1}{2}$.

$x = \sqrt{2}$: $3 - 2\left(\sqrt{2}\right) \overset{?}{\le} \frac{1}{2}$. Yes, $3 - 2\sqrt{2} \le \frac{1}{2}$. $x = 2$: $3 - 2(2) \overset{?}{\le} \frac{1}{2}$. Yes, $-1 \le \frac{1}{2}$.

$x = 4$: $3 - 2(4) \overset{?}{\le} \frac{1}{2}$. Yes, $5 \le \frac{1}{2}$.

The elements $\sqrt{2}$, 2, and 4 all satisfy the inequality.

2. $x = -2$: $2(-2) - 1 \overset{?}{\ge} -2$. No, $-5 \not\ge -2$.

$x = -1$: $2(-1) - 1 \overset{?}{\ge} \frac{1}{2}$. No, $6 - 1 \not\ge \frac{1}{2}$. $x = 0$: $2(0) - 1 \overset{?}{\ge} 0$. No, $-1 \not\ge 0$.

$x = \frac{1}{2}$: $2\left(\frac{1}{2}\right) - 1 \overset{?}{\ge} \frac{1}{2}$. No, $0 \not\ge \frac{1}{2}$. $x = 1$: $2(1) - 1 \overset{?}{\ge} 1$. Yes since $1 \ge 1$.

$x = \sqrt{2}$: $2\left(\sqrt{2}\right) - 1 \overset{?}{\ge} \sqrt{2}$. Yes, since $2\sqrt{2} - 1 \approx 1.8$ and $\sqrt{2} \approx 1.4$.

$x = 2$: $2(2) - 1 \overset{?}{\ge} 2$. Yes, $3 \ge 2$.

$x = 4$: $2(4) - 1 \overset{?}{\ge} 4$. Yes, $7 \ge 4$.

The elements 1, $\sqrt{2}$, 2, and 4 all satisfy the inequality.

3. $x = -2$: $1 \overset{?}{<} 2(-2) - 4 \overset{?}{\le} 7$. No, since $2(-2) - 4 = -8$ and $1 \not< -8$.

$x = -1$: $1 \overset{?}{<} 2(-1) - 4 \overset{?}{\le} 7$. No, since $2(-1) - 4 = -6$ and $1 \not< -6$.

$x = 0$: $1 \overset{?}{<} 2(0) - 4 \overset{?}{\le} 7$. No, since $2(0) - 4 = -4$ and $1 \not< -4$.

$x = \frac{1}{2}$: $1 \overset{?}{<} 2\left(\frac{1}{2}\right) - 4 \overset{?}{\le} 7$. No, since $2\left(\frac{1}{2}\right) - 4 = -3$ and $1 \not< -3$.

$x = 1$: $1 \overset{?}{<} 2(1) - 4 \overset{?}{\le} 7$. No, since $2(1) - 4 = -2$ and $1 \not< -2$.

$x = \sqrt{2}$: $1 \overset{?}{<} 2\left(\sqrt{2}\right) - 4 \overset{?}{\le} 7$. No, since $2\sqrt{2} - 4 < 0$ and $1 \not< 0$.

$x = 2$: $1 \overset{?}{<} 2(2) - 4 \overset{?}{\le} 7$. No, since $2(1) - 4 = -2$ and $1 \not< -2$.

$x = 4$: $1 \overset{?}{<} 2(4) - 4 \overset{?}{\le} 7$. Yes, $2(4) - 4 = 4$ and $1 < 4 \le 7$.

Only 4 satisfies the inequality.

4. $x = -2$: $2 \overset{?}{\le} 3 - (-2) \overset{?}{<} 2$. No, since $3 - (-2) = 5$ and $5 \not< 2$.

$x = -1$: $-2 \overset{?}{\le} 3 - (-1) \overset{?}{<} 2$. No, since $3 - (-1) = 4$ and $4 \not< 2$.

$x = 0$: $-2 \overset{?}{\le} 3 - 0 \overset{?}{<} 2$. No, since $3 - (0) = 3$ and $3 \not< 2$.

$x = \frac{1}{2}$: $-2 \overset{?}{\le} 3 - \frac{1}{2} \overset{?}{<} 2$. No, since $3 - \left(\frac{1}{2}\right) = \frac{5}{2}$ and $\frac{5}{2} \not< 2$.

$x = 1$: $-2 \overset{?}{\le} 3 - 1 \overset{?}{<} 2$ No, since $3 - (1) = 2$ and $2 \not< 2$.

$x = \sqrt{2}$: $-2 \overset{?}{\le} 3 - \sqrt{2} \overset{?}{<} 2$. Yes, since $3 - \sqrt{2} \approx 1.5$ and $-2 \le 1.5 < 2$.

$x = 2$: $-2 \overset{?}{\le} 3 - 2 \overset{?}{<} 2$. Yes, since $3 - 2 = 1$ and $-2 \le 1 < 2$.

$x = 4$: $-2 \overset{?}{\le} 3 - 4 \overset{?}{<} 2$. Yes, $3 - 4 = -1$ and $-2 \le -1 < 2$.

The elements $\sqrt{2}$, 2, and 4 all satisfy the inequality.

5. $x = -2$: $\dfrac{1}{(-2)} \overset{?}{\le} \frac{1}{2}$. Yes, $-\frac{1}{2} \le \frac{1}{2}$.

$x = -1$: $\dfrac{1}{(-1)} \overset{?}{\le} \frac{1}{2}$. Yes, $-1 \le \frac{1}{2}$. $x = 0$: $\frac{1}{0} \overset{?}{\le} \frac{1}{2}$. No, $\frac{1}{0}$ is not defined.

$x = \frac{1}{2}$: $\dfrac{1}{1/2} \overset{?}{\le} \frac{1}{2}$. No, $2 \not\le \frac{1}{2}$. $x = 1$: $\frac{1}{1} \overset{?}{\le} \frac{1}{2}$. No, $1 \not\le \frac{1}{2}$.

$x = \sqrt{2}$: $\dfrac{1}{\sqrt{2}} \overset{?}{\le} \frac{1}{2}$. No, $2 \not\le \sqrt{2}$. $x = 2$: $\frac{1}{2} \overset{?}{\le} \frac{1}{2}$. Yes, $\frac{1}{2} \le \frac{1}{2}$.

$x = 4$: $\frac{1}{4} \overset{?}{\le} \frac{1}{2}$. Yes. The elements -2, -1, 2, and 4 all satisfy the inequality.

6. $x = -2$: $(-2)^2 + 2 \overset{?}{<} 4$. No, since $(-2)^2 + 2 = 6$ and $6 \not< 4$.

$x = -1$: $(-1)^2 + 2 \overset{?}{<} 4$. Yes, since $(-1)^2 + 2 = 3$ and $3 < 4$.

$x = 0$: $0^2 + 2 \overset{?}{<} 4$. Yes, since $0^2 + 2 = 2$ and $2 < 4$.

$x = \frac{1}{2}$: $\left(\frac{1}{2}\right)^2 + 2 \overset{?}{<} 4$. Yes, since $\left(\frac{1}{2}\right)^2 + 2 = \frac{9}{4}$ and $\frac{9}{4} < 4$.

$x = 1$: $1^2 + 2 \overset{?}{<} 4$. Yes, since $1^2 + 2 = 3$ and $3 < 4$.

$x = \sqrt{2}$: $\left(\sqrt{2}\right)^2 + 2 \overset{?}{<} 4$. No, since $\left(\sqrt{2}\right)^2 + 2 = 4$ and $4 \not< 4$.

$x = 2$: $2^2 + 2 \overset{?}{<} 4$. No, since $2^2 + 2 = 6$ and $6 \not< 4$.

$x = 4$: $4^2 + 2 \overset{?}{<} 4$. No, $4^2 + 2 = 18$ and $18 \not< 4$.

The elements -1, 0, $\frac{1}{2}$, and 1 all satisfy the inequality.

7. $2x - 5 > 3 \quad \Leftrightarrow \quad 2x > 8 \quad \Leftrightarrow \quad x > 4$
Interval: $(4, \infty)$

Graph:

8. $3x + 11 < 5 \quad \Leftrightarrow \quad 3x < -6 \quad \Leftrightarrow \quad x < -2$
Interval: $(-\infty, -2)$

Graph:

9. $7 - x \geq 5 \quad \Leftrightarrow \quad -x \geq -2 \quad \Leftrightarrow \quad x \leq 2$

Interval: $(-\infty, 2]$

Graph:

10. $5 - 3x \leq -16 \quad \Leftrightarrow \quad -3x \leq -21 \quad \Leftrightarrow \quad x \geq 7$

Interval: $[7, \infty)$

Graph:

11. $2x + 1 < 0 \quad \Leftrightarrow \quad 2x < -1 \quad \Leftrightarrow \quad x < -\frac{1}{2}$

Interval: $\left(-\infty, -\frac{1}{2}\right)$

Graph:

12. $0 < 5 - 2x \quad \Leftrightarrow \quad 2x < 5 \quad \Leftrightarrow \quad x < \frac{5}{2}$

Interval: $\left(-\infty, \frac{5}{2}\right)$

Graph:

13. $3x + 11 \leq 6x + 8 \quad \Leftrightarrow \quad 3 \leq 3x \quad \Leftrightarrow \quad 1 \leq x$

Interval: $[1, \infty)$

Graph:

14. $6 - x \geq 2x + 9 \quad \Leftrightarrow \quad -3 \geq 3x \quad \Leftrightarrow \quad -1 \geq x$

Interval: $(-\infty, -1]$

Graph:

15. $\frac{1}{2}x - \frac{2}{3} > 2 \quad \Leftrightarrow \quad \frac{1}{2}x > \frac{8}{3} \quad \Leftrightarrow \quad x > \frac{16}{3}$

Interval: $\left(\frac{16}{3}, \infty\right)$

Graph:

16. $\frac{2}{5}x + 1 < \frac{1}{5} - 2x \quad \Leftrightarrow \quad \frac{12}{5}x < -\frac{4}{5} \quad \Leftrightarrow \quad x < -\frac{1}{3}$

Interval: $\left(-\infty, -\frac{1}{3}\right)$

Graph:

17. $\frac{1}{3}x + 2 < \frac{1}{6}x - 1 \quad \Leftrightarrow \quad \frac{1}{6}x < -3 \quad \Leftrightarrow \quad x < -18$

Interval: $(-\infty, -18)$

Graph:

18. $\frac{2}{3} - \frac{1}{2}x \geq \frac{1}{6} + x$ (multiply both sides by 6) $\quad \Leftrightarrow$

$4 - 3x \geq 1 + 6x \quad \Leftrightarrow \quad 3 \geq 9x \quad \Leftrightarrow \quad \frac{1}{3} \geq x$

Interval: $\left(-\infty, \frac{1}{3}\right]$

Graph:

19. $4 - 3x \leq -(1 + 8x) \quad \Leftrightarrow \quad 4 - 3x \leq -1 - 8x \quad \Leftrightarrow$

$5x \leq -5 \quad \Leftrightarrow \quad x \leq -1$

Interval: $(-\infty, -1]$

Graph:

20. $2(7x - 3) \leq 12x + 16 \quad \Leftrightarrow \quad 14x - 6 \leq 12x + 16$

$\Leftrightarrow \quad 2x \leq 22 \quad \Leftrightarrow \quad x \leq 11$

Interval: $(-\infty, 11]$

Graph:

21. $2 \leq x + 5 < 4 \quad \Leftrightarrow \quad -3 \leq x < -1$

Interval: $[-3, -1)$

Graph:

22. $5 \leq 3x - 4 \leq 14 \quad \Leftrightarrow \quad 9 \leq 3x \leq 18 \quad \Leftrightarrow$

$3 \leq x \leq 6$

Interval: $[3, 6]$

Graph:

23. $-1 < 2x - 5 < 7 \quad \Leftrightarrow \quad 4 < 2x < 12 \quad \Leftrightarrow$

$2 < x < 6$

Interval: $(2, 6)$

Graph:

24. $1 < 3x + 4 \leq 16 \quad \Leftrightarrow \quad -3 < 3x \leq 12 \quad \Leftrightarrow$

$-1 < x \leq 4$

Interval: $(-1, 4]$

Graph:

25. $-2 < 8 - 2x \le -1$ $\Leftrightarrow$ $-10 < -2x \le -9$ $\Leftrightarrow$ **26.** $-3 \le 3x + 7 \le \frac{1}{2}$ $\Leftrightarrow$ $-10 \le 3x \le -\frac{13}{2}$ $\Leftrightarrow$

$5 > x \ge \frac{9}{2}$ $\Leftrightarrow$ $\frac{9}{2} \le x < 5$ $\qquad\qquad$ $-\frac{10}{3} \le x \le -\frac{13}{6}$

Interval: $\left[\frac{9}{2}, 5\right)$ $\qquad\qquad\qquad\qquad\qquad$ Interval: $\left[-\frac{10}{3}, -\frac{13}{6}\right]$

Graph: $\qquad$ Graph:

27. $\dfrac{1}{6} < \dfrac{2x - 13}{12} \le \dfrac{2}{3}$ $\Leftrightarrow$ $2 < 2x - 13 \le 8$ (multiply each expression by 12) $\Leftrightarrow$ $15 < 2x \le 21$ $\Leftrightarrow$

$\frac{15}{2} < x \le \frac{21}{2}$. Interval: $\left(\frac{15}{2}, \frac{21}{2}\right]$. Graph:

28. $-\dfrac{1}{2} < \dfrac{4 - 3x}{5} \le \dfrac{1}{4}$ $\Leftrightarrow$ (multiply each expression by 20) $-10 < 4(4 - 3x) \le 5$ $\Leftrightarrow$ $-10 < 16 - 12x \le 5$ $\Leftrightarrow$

$-26 < -12x \le -11$ $\Leftrightarrow$ $\frac{13}{6} > x \ge \frac{11}{12}$ $\Leftrightarrow$ $\frac{11}{12} \le x < \frac{13}{6}$. Interval: $\left[\frac{11}{12}, \frac{13}{6}\right)$. Graph:

29. $(x + 2)(x - 3) < 0$. The expression on the left of the inequality changes sign where $x = -2$ and where $x = 3$. Thus we must check the intervals in the following table.

Interval	$(-\infty, -2)$	$(-2, 3)$	$(3, \infty)$
Sign of $x + 2$	$-$	$+$	$+$
Sign of $x - 3$	$-$	$-$	$+$
Sign of $(x + 2)(x - 3)$	$+$	$-$	$+$

From the table, the solution set is $\{x \mid -2 < x < 3\}$. Interval: $(-2, 3)$.

Graph:

30. $(x - 5)(x + 4) \ge 0$. The expression on the left of the inequality changes sign when $x = 5$ and $x = -4$. Thus we must check the intervals in the following table.

Interval	$(-\infty, -4)$	$(-4, 5)$	$(5, \infty)$
Sign of $x - 5$	$-$	$-$	$+$
Sign of $x + 4$	$-$	$+$	$+$
Sign of $(x - 5)(x + 4)$	$+$	$-$	$+$

From the table, the solution set is $\left\{x \mid x \le -\frac{1}{3} \text{ or } 1 \le x\right\}$. Interval: $(-\infty, -4] \cup [5, \infty)$.

Graph:

31. $x(2x + 7) \ge 0$. The expression on the left of the inequality changes sign where $x = 0$ and where $x = -\frac{7}{2}$. Thus we must check the intervals in the following table.

Interval	$\left(-\infty, -\frac{7}{2}\right)$	$\left(-\frac{7}{2}, 0\right)$	$(0, \infty)$
Sign of x	$-$	$-$	$+$
Sign of $2x + 7$	$-$	$+$	$+$
Sign of $x(2x + 7)$	$+$	$-$	$+$

From the table, the solution set is $\left\{x \mid x \le -\frac{7}{2} \text{ or } 0 \le x\right\}$. Interval: $\left(-\infty, -\frac{7}{2}\right] \cup [0, \infty)$.

Graph:

32. $x(2-3x) \le 0$. The expression on the left of the inequality changes sign when $x = 0$ and $x = \frac{2}{3}$. Thus we must check the intervals in the following table.

Interval	$(-\infty, 0)$	$\left(0, \frac{2}{3}\right)$	$\left(\frac{2}{3}, \infty\right)$
Sign of x	$-$	$+$	$+$
Sign of $2 - 3x$	$+$	$+$	$-$
Sign of $x(2 - 3x)$	$-$	$+$	$-$

From the table, the solution set is $\left\{x \mid x \le 0 \text{ or } \frac{2}{3} \le x\right\}$.

Interval: $(-\infty, 0] \cup \left[\frac{2}{3}, \infty\right)$.

Graph:

33. $x^2 - 3x - 18 \le 0 \quad \Leftrightarrow \quad (x+3)(x-6) \le 0$. The expression on the left of the inequality changes sign where $x = 6$ and where $x = -3$. Thus we must check the intervals in the following table.

Interval	$(-\infty, -3)$	$(-3, 6)$	$(6, \infty)$
Sign of $x + 3$	$-$	$+$	$+$
Sign of $x - 6$	$-$	$-$	$+$
Sign of $(x+3)(x-6)$	$+$	$-$	$+$

From the table, the solution set is $\{x \mid -3 \le x \le 6\}$. Interval: $[-3, 6]$.

Graph:

34. $x^2 + 5x + 6 > 0 \quad \Leftrightarrow \quad (x+3)(x+2) > 0$. The expression on the left of the inequality changes sign when $x = -3$ and $x = -2$. Thus we must check the intervals in the following table.

Interval	$(-\infty, -3)$	$(-3, -2)$	$(-2, \infty)$
Sign of $x + 3$	$-$	$+$	$+$
Sign of $x + 2$	$-$	$-$	$+$
Sign of $(x+3)(x+2)$	$+$	$-$	$+$

From the table, the solution set is $\{x \mid x < -3 \text{ or } -2 < x\}$.

Interval: $(-\infty, -3) \cup (-2, \infty)$.

Graph:

35. $2x^2 + x \ge 1 \quad \Leftrightarrow \quad 2x^2 + x - 1 \ge 0 \quad \Leftrightarrow \quad (x+1)(2x-1) \ge 0$. The expression on the left of the inequality changes sign where $x = -1$ and where $x = \frac{1}{2}$. Thus we must check the intervals in the following table.

Interval	$(-\infty, -1)$	$\left(-1, \frac{1}{2}\right)$	$\left(\frac{1}{2}, \infty\right)$
Sign of $x + 1$	$-$	$+$	$+$
Sign of $2x - 1$	$-$	$-$	$+$
Sign of $(x+1)(2x-1)$	$+$	$-$	$+$

From the table, the solution set is $\left\{x \mid x \le -1 \text{ or } \frac{1}{2} \le x\right\}$.

Interval: $(-\infty, -1] \cup \left[\frac{1}{2}, \infty\right)$.

Graph:

36. $x^2 < x + 2 \quad \Leftrightarrow \quad x^2 - x - 2 < 0 \quad \Leftrightarrow \quad (x+1)(x-2) < 0$. The expression on the left of the inequality changes sign when $x = -1$ and $x = 2$. Thus we must check the intervals in the following table.

Interval	$(-\infty, -1)$	$(-1, 2)$	$(2, \infty)$
Sign of $x + 1$	$-$	$+$	$+$
Sign of $x - 2$	$-$	$-$	$+$
Sign of $(x+1)(x-2)$	$+$	$-$	$+$

From the table, the solution set is $\{x \mid -1 < x < 2\}$. Interval: $(-1, 2)$.

Graph:

37. $3x^2 - 3x < 2x^2 + 4$ $\Leftrightarrow$ $x^2 - 3x - 4 < 0$ $\Leftrightarrow$ $(x+1)(x-4) < 0$. The expression on the left of the inequality changes sign where $x = -1$ and where $x = 4$. Thus we must check the intervals in the following table.

Interval	$(-\infty, -1)$	$(-1, 4)$	$(4, \infty)$
Sign of $x + 1$	$-$	$+$	$+$
Sign of $x - 4$	$-$	$-$	$+$
Sign of $(x+1)(x-4)$	$+$	$-$	$+$

From the table, the solution set is $\{x \mid -1 < x < 4\}$. Interval: $(-1, 4)$.

Graph:

38. $5x^2 + 3x \geq 3x^2 + 2$ $\Leftrightarrow$ $2x^2 + 3x - 2 \geq 0$ $\Leftrightarrow$ $(2x - 1)(x + 2) \geq 0$. The expression on the left of the inequality changes sign when $x = \frac{1}{2}$ and $x = -2$. Thus we must check the intervals in the following table.

Interval	$(-\infty, -2)$	$\left(-2, \frac{1}{2}\right)$	$\left(\frac{1}{2}, \infty\right)$
Sign of $2x - 1$	$-$	$-$	$+$
Sign of $x + 2$	$-$	$+$	$+$
Sign of $(2x - 1)(x + 2)$	$+$	$-$	$+$

From the table, the solution set is $\left\{x \mid x \leq -2 \text{ or } \frac{1}{2} \leq x\right\}$.
Interval: $\left(-\infty, -2\right] \cup \left[\frac{1}{2}, \infty\right)$.

Graph:

39. $x^2 > 3(x + 6)$ $\Leftrightarrow$ $x^2 - 3x - 18 > 0$ $\Leftrightarrow$ $(x + 3)(x - 6) > 0$. The expression on the left of the inequality changes sign where $x = 6$ and where $x = -3$. Thus we must check the intervals in the following table.

Interval	$(-\infty, -3)$	$(-3, 6)$	$(6, \infty)$
Sign of $x + 3$	$-$	$+$	$+$
Sign of $x - 6$	$-$	$-$	$+$
Sign of $(x + 3)(x - 6)$	$+$	$-$	$+$

From the table, the solution set is $\{x \mid x < -3 \text{ or } 6 < x\}$.
Interval: $(-\infty, -3) \cup (6, \infty)$.

Graph:

40. $x^2 + 2x > 3$ $\Leftrightarrow$ $x^2 + 2x - 3 > 0$ $\Leftrightarrow$ $(x + 3)(x - 1) > 0$. The expression on the left of the inequality changes sign when $x = -3$ and $x = 1$. Thus we must check the intervals in the following table.

Interval	$(-\infty, -3)$	$(-3, 1)$	$(1, \infty)$
Sign of $x + 3$	$-$	$+$	$+$
Sign of $x - 1$	$-$	$-$	$+$
Sign of $(x + 3)(x - 1)$	$+$	$-$	$+$

From the table, the solution set is $\{x \mid x < -3 \text{ or } 1 < x\}$.
Interval: $(-\infty, -3) \cup (1, \infty)$.

Graph:

41. $x^2 < 4$ $\Leftrightarrow$ $x^2 - 4 < 0$ $\Leftrightarrow$ $(x + 2)(x - 2) < 0$. The expression on the left of the inequality changes sign where $x = -2$ and where $x = 2$. Thus we must check the intervals in the following table.

Interval	$(-\infty, -2)$	$(-2, 2)$	$(2, \infty)$
Sign of $x + 2$	$-$	$+$	$+$
Sign of $x - 2$	$-$	$-$	$+$
Sign of $(x + 2)(x - 2)$	$+$	$-$	$+$

From the table, the solution set is $\{x \mid -2 < x < 2\}$. Interval: $(-2, 2)$.

Graph:

42. $x^2 \geq 9$ $\Leftrightarrow$ $x^2 - 9 \geq 0$ $\Leftrightarrow$ $(x+3)(x-3) \geq 0$. The expression on the left of the inequality changes sign when $x = -3$ and $x = 3$. Thus we must check the intervals in the following table.

Interval	$(-\infty, -3)$	$(-3, 3)$	$(3, \infty)$
Sign of $x + 3$	$-$	$+$	$+$
Sign of $x - 3$	$-$	$-$	$+$
Sign of $(x+3)(x-3)$	$+$	$-$	$+$

From the table, the solution set is $\{x \mid x \leq -3 \text{ or } 3 \leq x\}$. Interval: $(-\infty, -3] \cup [3, \infty)$.

Graph:

43. $-2x^2 \leq 4$ $\Leftrightarrow$ $-2x^2 - 4 \leq 0$ $\Leftrightarrow$ $-2(x^2 + 1) \leq 0$. Since $x^2 + 1 > 0$, $-2(x^2 + 1) \leq 0$ for all x.

Interval: $(-\infty, \infty)$. Graph:

44. $(x+2)(x-1)(x-3) \leq 0$. The expression on the left of the inequality changes sign when $x = -2$, $x = 1$, and $x = 3$. Thus we must check the intervals in the following table.

Interval	$(-\infty, -2)$	$(-2, 1)$	$(1, 3)$	$(3, \infty)$
Sign of $x + 2$	$-$	$+$	$+$	$+$
Sign of $x - 1$	$-$	$-$	$+$	$+$
Sign of $x - 3$	$-$	$-$	$-$	$+$
Sign of $(x+2)(x-1)(x-3)$	$-$	$+$	$-$	$+$

From the table, the solution set is $\{x \mid x \leq -2 \text{ or } 1 \leq x \leq 3\}$. Interval: $(-\infty, -2] \cup [1, 3]$.

Graph:

45. $x^3 - 4x > 0$ $\Leftrightarrow$ $x(x^2 - 4) > 0$ $\Leftrightarrow$ $x(x+2)(x-2) > 0$. The expression on the left of the inequality changes sign where $x = 0$, $x = -2$ and where $x = 4$. Thus we must check the intervals in the following table.

Interval	$(-\infty, -2)$	$(-2, 0)$	$(0, 2)$	$(2, \infty)$
Sign of x	$-$	$-$	$+$	$+$
Sign of $x + 2$	$-$	$+$	$+$	$+$
Sign of $x - 2$	$-$	$-$	$-$	$+$
Sign of $x(x+2)(x-2)$	$-$	$+$	$-$	$+$

From the table, the solution set is $\{x \mid -2 < x < 0 \text{ or } x > 2\}$. Interval: $(-2, 0) \cup (2, \infty)$.

Graph:

46. $16x \leq x^3$ $\Leftrightarrow$ $0 \leq x^3 - 16x = x(x^2 - 16) = x(x-4)(x+4)$. The expression on the left of the inequality changes sign when $x = -4$, $x = 0$, and $x = 4$. Thus we must check the intervals in the following table.

Interval	$(-\infty, -4)$	$(-4, 0)$	$(0, 4)$	$(4, \infty)$
Sign of $x + 4$	$-$	$+$	$+$	$+$
Sign of x	$-$	$-$	$+$	$+$
Sign of $x - 4$	$-$	$-$	$-$	$+$
Sign of $x(x+4)(x-4)$	$-$	$+$	$-$	$+$

From the table, the solution set is $\{x \mid -4 \leq x \leq 0 \text{ or } 4 \leq x\}$. Interval: $[-4, 0] \cup [4, \infty)$. Graph:

47. $\dfrac{x-3}{x+1} \geq 0$. The expression on the left of the inequality changes sign where $x = -1$ and where $x = 3$. Thus we must check the intervals in the following table.

Interval	$(-\infty, -1)$	$(-1, 3)$	$(3, \infty)$
Sign of $x + 1$	$-$	$+$	$+$
Sign of $x - 3$	$-$	$-$	$+$
Sign of $\dfrac{x-3}{x+1}$	$+$	$-$	$+$

From the table, the solution set is $\{x \mid x < -1 \text{ or } x \leq 3\}$. Since the denominator cannot equal 0 we must have $x \neq -1$.

Interval: $(-\infty, -1) \cup [3, \infty)$.

Graph:

48. $\dfrac{2x+6}{x-2} < 0$. The expression on the left of the inequality changes sign when $x = -3$ and $x = 2$. Thus we must check the intervals in the following table.

Interval	$(-\infty, -3)$	$(-3, 2)$	$(2, \infty)$
Sign of $2x + 6$	$-$	$+$	$+$
Sign of $x - 2$	$-$	$-$	$+$
Sign of $\dfrac{2x+6}{x-2}$	$+$	$-$	$+$

From the table, the solution set is $\{x \mid -3 < x < 2\}$. Interval: $(-3, 2)$.

Graph:

49. $\dfrac{4x}{2x+3} > 2 \quad \Leftrightarrow \quad \dfrac{4x}{2x+3} - 2 > 0 \quad \Leftrightarrow \quad \dfrac{4x}{2x+3} - \dfrac{2(2x+3)}{2x+3} > 0 \quad \Leftrightarrow \quad \dfrac{-6}{2x+3} > 0$. The expression on the left of the inequality changes sign where $x = -\frac{3}{2}$. Thus we must check the intervals in the following table.

Interval	$\left(-\infty, -\frac{3}{2}\right)$	$\left(-\frac{3}{2}, \infty\right)$
Sign of -6	$-$	$-$
Sign of $2x + 3$	$-$	$+$
Sign of $\dfrac{-6}{2x+3}$	$+$	$-$

From the table, the solution set is $\left\{x \mid x < -\frac{3}{2}\right\}$.

Interval: $\left(-\infty, -\frac{3}{2}\right)$.

Graph:

50. $-2 < \dfrac{x+1}{x-3} \quad \Leftrightarrow \quad 0 < \dfrac{x+1}{x-3} + 2 \quad \Leftrightarrow \quad 0 < \dfrac{x+1}{x-3} + \dfrac{2(x-3)}{x-3} \quad \Leftrightarrow \quad 0 < \dfrac{3x-5}{x-3}$. The expression on the left of the inequality changes sign when $x = \frac{5}{3}$ and $x = 3$. Thus we must check the intervals in the following table.

Interval	$\left(-\infty, \frac{5}{3}\right)$	$\left(\frac{5}{3}, 3\right)$	$(3, \infty)$
Sign of $3x - 5$	$-$	$+$	$+$
Sign of $x - 3$	$-$	$-$	$+$
Sign of $\dfrac{3x-5}{x-3}$	$+$	$-$	$+$

From the table, the solution set is $\left\{x \mid x < \frac{5}{3} \text{ or } 3 < x < \infty\right\}$.

Interval: $\left(-\infty, \frac{5}{3}\right) \cup (3, \infty)$.

Graph:

51. $\dfrac{2x+1}{x-5} \leq 3 \quad \Leftrightarrow \quad \dfrac{2x+1}{x-5} - 3 \leq 0 \quad \Leftrightarrow \quad \dfrac{2x+1}{x-5} - \dfrac{3(x-5)}{x-5} \leq 0 \quad \Leftrightarrow \quad \dfrac{-x+16}{x-5} \leq 0$. The expression on the left of the inequality changes sign where $x = 16$ and where $x = 5$. Thus we must check the intervals in the following table.

Interval	$(-\infty, 5)$	$(5, 16)$	$(16, \infty)$
Sign of $-x + 16$	$+$	$+$	$-$
Sign of $x - 5$	$-$	$+$	$+$
Sign of $\dfrac{-x+16}{x-5}$	$-$	$+$	$-$

From the table, the solution set is $\{x \mid x < 5 \text{ or } x \geq 16\}$. Since the denominator cannot equal 0, we must have $x \neq 5$.

Interval: $(-\infty, 5) \cup [16, \infty)$.

Graph:

52. $\dfrac{3+x}{3-x} \geq 1 \quad \Leftrightarrow \quad \dfrac{3+x}{3-x} - 1 \geq 0 \quad \Leftrightarrow \quad \dfrac{3+x}{3-x} - \dfrac{3-x}{3-x} \geq 0 \quad \Leftrightarrow \quad \dfrac{2x}{3-x} \geq 0.$ The expression on the left of the

inequality changes sign when $x = 0$ and $x = 3$. Thus we must check the intervals in the following table.

Interval	$(-\infty, 0)$	$(0, 3)$	$(3, \infty)$
Sign of $3 - x$	$+$	$+$	$-$
Sign of $2x$	$-$	$+$	$+$
Sign of $\dfrac{2x}{3-x}$	$-$	$+$	$-$

Since the denominator cannot equal 0, we must have $x \neq 3$. The solution set is $\{x \mid 0 \leq x < 3\}$. Interval: $[0, 3)$.

Graph:

53. $\dfrac{4}{x} < x \quad \Leftrightarrow \quad \dfrac{4}{x} - x < 0 \quad \Leftrightarrow \quad \dfrac{4}{x} - \dfrac{x \cdot x}{x} < 0 \quad \Leftrightarrow \quad \dfrac{4 - x^2}{x} < 0 \quad \Leftrightarrow \quad \dfrac{(2-x)(2+x)}{x} < 0.$ The expression

on the left of the inequality changes sign where $x = 0$, where $x = -2$, and where $x = 2$. Thus we must check the intervals in the following table.

Interval	$(-\infty, -2)$	$(-2, 0)$	$(0, 2)$	$(2, \infty)$
Sign of $2 + x$	$-$	$+$	$+$	$+$
Sign of x	$-$	$-$	$+$	$+$
Sign of $2 - x$	$+$	$+$	$+$	$-$
Sign of $\dfrac{(2-x)(2+x)}{x}$	$+$	$-$	$+$	$-$

From the table, the solution set is $\{x \mid -2 < x < 0 \text{ or } 2 < x\}$.   Interval: $(-2, 0) \cup (2, \infty)$.

Graph:

54. $\dfrac{x}{x+1} > 3x \quad \Leftrightarrow \quad \dfrac{x}{x+1} - 3x > 0 \quad \Leftrightarrow \quad \dfrac{x}{x+1} - \dfrac{3x(x+1)}{x+1} > 0 \quad \Leftrightarrow \quad \dfrac{-2x - 3x^2}{x+1} > 0 \quad \Leftrightarrow$

$\dfrac{-x(2+3x)}{x+1} > 0.$ The expression on the left of the inequality changes sign when $x = 0$, $x = -\frac{2}{3}$, and $x = -1$. Thus we

must check the intervals in the following table.

Interval	$(-\infty, -1)$	$\left(-1, -\frac{2}{3}\right)$	$\left(-\frac{2}{3}, 0\right)$	$(0, \infty)$
Sign of $-x$	$+$	$+$	$+$	$-$
Sign of $2 + 3x$	$-$	$-$	$+$	$+$
Sign of $x + 1$	$-$	$+$	$+$	$+$
Sign of $\dfrac{(2-x)(2+x)}{x}$	$+$	$-$	$+$	$-$

From the table, the solution set is $\left\{x \mid x < -1 \text{ or } -\frac{2}{3} < x < 0\right\}$.   Interval: $(-\infty, -1) \cup \left(-\frac{2}{3}, 0\right)$.

Graph:

55. $1 + \dfrac{2}{x+1} \leq \dfrac{2}{x}$ $\Leftrightarrow$ $1 + \dfrac{2}{x+1} - \dfrac{2}{x} \leq 0$ $\Leftrightarrow$ $\dfrac{x(x+1)}{x(x+1)} + \dfrac{2x}{x(x+1)} - \dfrac{2(x+1)}{x(x+1)} \leq 0$ $\Leftrightarrow$

$\dfrac{x^2 + x + 2x - 2x - 2}{x(x+1)} \leq 0$ $\Leftrightarrow$ $\dfrac{x^2 + x - 2}{x(x+1)} \leq 0$ $\Leftrightarrow$ $\dfrac{(x+2)(x-1)}{x(x+1)} \leq 0$. The expression on the left of the

inequality changes sign where $x = -2$, where $x = -1$, where $x = 0$, and where $x = 1$. Thus we must check the intervals

in the following table.

Interval	$(-\infty, -2)$	$(-2, -1)$	$(-1, 0)$	$(0, 1)$	$(1, \infty)$
Sign of $x + 2$	$-$	$+$	$+$	$+$	$+$
Sign of $x - 1$	$-$	$-$	$-$	$-$	$+$
Sign of x	$-$	$-$	$-$	$+$	$+$
Sign of $x + 1$	$-$	$-$	$+$	$+$	$+$
Sign of $\dfrac{(x+2)(x-1)}{x(x+1)}$	$+$	$-$	$+$	$-$	$+$

Since $x = -1$ and $x = 0$ yield undefined expressions, we cannot include them in the solution. From the table, the solution

set is $\{x \mid -2 \leq x < -1 \text{ or } 0 < x \leq 1\}$. Interval: $[-2, -1) \cup (0, 1]$. Graph:

56. $\dfrac{3}{x-1} - \dfrac{4}{x} \geq 1$ $\Leftrightarrow$ $\dfrac{3}{x-1} - \dfrac{4}{x} - 1 \geq 0$ $\Leftrightarrow$ $\dfrac{3x}{x(x-1)} - \dfrac{4(x-1)}{x(x-1)} - \dfrac{x(x-1)}{x(x-1)} \geq 0$ $\Leftrightarrow$

$\dfrac{3x - 4x + 4 - x^2 + x}{x(x-1)} \geq 0$ $\Leftrightarrow$ $\dfrac{4 - x^2}{x(x-1)} \geq 0$ $\Leftrightarrow$ $\dfrac{(2-x)(2+x)}{x(x-1)} \geq 0$. The expression on the left of the

inequality changes sign when $x = 2$, $x = -2$, $x = 0$, and $x = 1$. Thus we must check the intervals in the following table.

Interval	$(-\infty, -2)$	$(-2, 0)$	$(0, 1)$	$(1, 2)$	$(2, \infty)$
Sign of $2 - x$	$+$	$+$	$+$	$+$	$-$
Sign of $2 + x$	$-$	$+$	$+$	$+$	$+$
Sign of x	$-$	$-$	$+$	$+$	$+$
Sign of $x - 1$	$-$	$-$	$-$	$+$	$+$
Sign of $\dfrac{(2-x)(2+x)}{x(x-1)}$	$-$	$+$	$-$	$+$	$-$

Since $x = 0$ and $x = 1$ give undefined expressions, we cannot include them in the solution. From the table, the solution set

is $\{x \mid -2 \leq x < 0 \text{ or } 1 < x \leq 2\}$. Interval: $[-2, 0) \cup (1, 2]$. Graph:

57. $\dfrac{6}{x-1} - \dfrac{6}{x} \geq 1$ $\Leftrightarrow$ $\dfrac{6}{x-1} - \dfrac{6}{x} - 1 \geq 0$ $\Leftrightarrow$ $\dfrac{6x}{x(x-1)} - \dfrac{6(x-1)}{x(x-1)} - \dfrac{x(x-1)}{x(x-1)} \geq 0$ $\Leftrightarrow$

$\dfrac{6x - 6x + 6 - x^2 + x}{x(x-1)} \geq 0$ $\Leftrightarrow$ $\dfrac{-x^2 + x + 6}{x(x-1)} \geq 0$ $\Leftrightarrow$ $\dfrac{(-x+3)(x+2)}{x(x-1)} \geq 0.$ The

expression on the left of the inequality changes sign where $x = 3$, where $x = -2$, where $x = 0$, and where $x = 1$. Thus we

must check the intervals in the following table.

Interval	$(-\infty, -2)$	$(-2, 0)$	$(0, 1)$	$(1, 3)$	$(3, \infty)$
Sign of $-x + 3$	$+$	$+$	$+$	$+$	$-$
Sign of $x + 2$	$-$	$+$	$+$	$+$	$+$
Sign of x	$-$	$-$	$+$	$+$	$+$
Sign of $x - 1$	$-$	$-$	$-$	$+$	$+$
Sign of $\dfrac{(-x+3)(x+2)}{x(x-1)}$	$-$	$+$	$-$	$+$	$-$

From the table, the solution set is $\{x \mid -2 \leq x < 0 \text{ or } 1 < x \leq 3\}$. The points $x = 0$ and $x = 1$ are excluded from the

solution set because they make the denominator zero. Interval: $[-2, 0) \cup (1, 3]$. Graph:

58. $\dfrac{x}{2} \geq \dfrac{5}{x+1} + 4$ $\Leftrightarrow$ $\dfrac{x}{2} - \dfrac{5}{x+1} - 4 \geq 0$ $\Leftrightarrow$ $\dfrac{x(x+1)}{2(x+1)} - \dfrac{2 \cdot 5}{2(x+1)} - \dfrac{4(2)(x+1)}{2(x+1)} \geq 0$ $\Leftrightarrow$

$\dfrac{x^2 + x - 10 - 8x - 8}{2(x+1)} \geq 0$ $\Leftrightarrow$ $\dfrac{x^2 - 7x - 18}{2(x+1)} \geq 0$ $\Leftrightarrow$ $\dfrac{(x-9)(x+2)}{2(x+1)} \geq 0.$ The expression on the left of the

inequality changes sign when $x = 9$, $x = -2$, and $x = -1$. Thus we must check the intervals in the following table.

Interval	$(-\infty, -2)$	$(-2, -1)$	$(-1, 9)$	$(9, \infty)$
Sign of $x - 9$	$-$	$-$	$-$	$+$
Sign of $x + 2$	$-$	$+$	$+$	$+$
Sign of $x + 1$	$-$	$-$	$+$	$+$
Sign of $\dfrac{(x-9)(x+2)}{2(x+1)}$	$-$	$+$	$-$	$+$

From the table, the solution set is $\{x \mid -2 \leq x < -1 \text{ or } 9 \leq x\}$. The point $x = -1$ is excluded from the solution set

because it makes the expression undefined. Interval: $[-2, -1) \cup [9, \infty)$. Graph:

59. $\dfrac{x+2}{x+3} < \dfrac{x-1}{x-2}$ $\Leftrightarrow$ $\dfrac{x+2}{x+3} - \dfrac{x-1}{x-2} < 0$ $\Leftrightarrow$ $\dfrac{(x+2)(x-2)}{(x+3)(x-2)} - \dfrac{(x-1)(x+3)}{(x-2)(x+3)} < 0$ $\Leftrightarrow$

$\dfrac{x^2 - 4 - x^2 - 2x + 3}{(x+3)(x-2)} < 0$ $\Leftrightarrow$ $\dfrac{-2x - 1}{(x+3)(x-2)} < 0$. The expression on the left of the inequality

changes sign where $x = -\frac{1}{2}$, where $x = -3$, and where $x = 2$. Thus we must check the intervals in the following table.

Interval	$(-\infty, -3)$	$\left(-3, -\frac{1}{2}\right)$	$\left(-\frac{1}{2}, 2\right)$	$(2, \infty)$
Sign of $-2x - 1$	$+$	$+$	$-$	$-$
Sign of $x + 3$	$-$	$+$	$+$	$+$
Sign of $x - 2$	$-$	$-$	$-$	$+$
Sign of $\dfrac{-2x - 1}{(x+3)(x-2)}$	$+$	$-$	$+$	$-$

From the table, the solution set is $\left\{x \mid -3 < x < -\frac{1}{2} \text{ or } 2 < x\right\}$. Interval: $\left(-3, -\frac{1}{2}\right) \cup (2, \infty)$.

Graph:

60. $\dfrac{1}{x+1} + \dfrac{1}{x+2} \le 0$ $\Leftrightarrow$ $\dfrac{x+2}{(x+1)(x+2)} + \dfrac{x+1}{(x+1)(x+2)} \le 0$ $\Leftrightarrow$ $\dfrac{x+2+x+1}{(x+1)(x+2)} \le 0$ $\Leftrightarrow$

$\dfrac{2x+3}{(x+1)(x+2)} \le 0$. The expression on the left of the inequality changes sign when $x = -\frac{3}{2}$, $x = -1$, and $x = -2$. Thus

we must check the intervals in the following table.

Interval	$(-\infty, -2)$	$\left(-2, -\frac{3}{2}\right)$	$\left(-\frac{3}{2}, -1\right)$	$(-1, \infty)$
Sign of $2x + 3$	$-$	$-$	$+$	$+$
Sign of $x + 1$	$-$	$-$	$-$	$+$
Sign of $x + 2$	$-$	$+$	$+$	$+$
Sign of $\dfrac{2x + 3}{(x+1)(x+2)}$	$-$	$+$	$-$	$+$

From the table, the solution set is $\left\{x \mid x < -2 \text{ or } -\frac{3}{2} \le x < -1\right\}$. The points $x = -2$ and $x = -1$ are

excluded from the solution because the expression is undefined at those values. Interval: $(-\infty, -2) \cup \left[-\frac{3}{2}, -1\right)$.

Graph:

61. $x^4 > x^2$ $\Leftrightarrow$ $x^4 - x^2 > 0$ $\Leftrightarrow$ $x^2\left(x^2 - 1\right) > 0$ $\Leftrightarrow$ $x^2\left(x - 1\right)\left(x + 1\right) > 0$. The expression on the left of the inequality changes sign where $x = 0$, where $x = 1$, and where $x = -1$. Thus we must check the intervals in the following table.

Interval	$(-\infty, -1)$	$(-1, 0)$	$(0, 1)$	$(1, \infty)$
Sign of x^2	$+$	$+$	$+$	$+$
Sign of $x - 1$	$-$	$-$	$-$	$+$
Sign of $x + 1$	$-$	$+$	$+$	$+$
Sign of $x^2\left(x - 1\right)\left(x + 1\right)$	$+$	$-$	$-$	$+$

From the table, the solution set is $\{x \mid x < -1 \text{ or } 1 < x\}$. Interval: $(-\infty, -1)\cup(1, \infty)$. Graph:

62. $x^5 > x^2$ $\Leftrightarrow$ $x^5 - x^2 > 0$ $\Leftrightarrow$ $x^2\left(x^3 - 1\right) > 0$ $\Leftrightarrow$ $x^2\left(x - 1\right)\left(x^2 + x + 1\right) > 0$. The expression on the left of the inequality changes sign when $x = 0$ and $x = 1$. But the solution of $x^2 + x + 1 = 0$ are

$$x = \frac{-1 \pm \sqrt{(1)^2 - 4\,(1)\,(1)}}{2\,(1)} = \frac{-1 \pm \sqrt{-3}}{2}.$$ Since these are not real solutions. The expression $x^2 + x + 1$ does not changes signs, so we must check the intervals in the following table.

Interval	$(-\infty, 0)$	$(0, 1)$	$(1, \infty)$
Sign of x^2	$+$	$+$	$+$
Sign of $x - 1$	$-$	$-$	$+$
Sign of $x^2 + x + 1$	$+$	$+$	$+$
Sign of $x^2\left(x - 1\right)\left(x^2 + x + 1\right)$	$-$	$-$	$+$

From the table, the solution set is $\{x \mid 1 < x\}$. Interval: $(1, \infty)$. Graph:

63. $|x| \le 4$ $\Leftrightarrow$ $-4 \le x \le 4$. Interval: $[-4, 4]$.

Graph:

64. $|3x| < 15$ $\Leftrightarrow$ $-15 < 3x < 15$ $\Leftrightarrow$ $-5 < x < 5$. Interval: $(-5, 5)$.

Graph:

65. $|2x| > 7$ is equivalent to $2x > 7$ $\Leftrightarrow$ $x > \frac{7}{2}$; or $2x < 7$ $\Leftrightarrow$ $x < -\frac{7}{2}$.

Interval: $\left(-\infty, -\frac{7}{2}\right) \cup \left(\frac{7}{2}, \infty\right)$.

Graph:

66. $\frac{1}{2}|x| \ge 1$ $\Leftrightarrow$ $|x| \ge 2$ is equivalent to $x \ge 2$ or $x \le -2$.

Interval: $(-\infty, -2] \cup [2, \infty)$.

Graph:

67. $|x - 5| \leq 3$ $\Leftrightarrow$ $-3 \leq x - 5 \leq 3$ $\Leftrightarrow$ $2 \leq x \leq 8$. **68.** $|x + 1| \geq 1$ is equivalent to $x + 1 \geq 1$ $\Leftrightarrow$ $x \geq 0$; or
Interval: $[2, 8]$.

Graph:

68. $|x + 1| \geq 1$ is equivalent to $x + 1 \geq 1$ $\Leftrightarrow$ $x \geq 0$; or
$x + 1 \leq -1$ $\Leftrightarrow$ $x \leq -2$.
Interval: $(-\infty, -2] \cup [0, \infty)$.

Graph:

69. $|2x - 3| \leq 0.4$ $\Leftrightarrow$ $-0.4 \leq 2x - 3 \leq 0.4$ $\Leftrightarrow$
$2.6 \leq 2x \leq 3.4$ $\Leftrightarrow$ $1.3 \leq x \leq 1.7$.
Interval: $[1.3, 1.7]$.

Graph:

70. $|5x - 2| < 6$ $\Leftrightarrow$ $-6 < 5x - 2 < 6$ $\Leftrightarrow$
$-4 < 5x < 8$ $\Leftrightarrow$ $-\frac{4}{5} < x < \frac{8}{5}$.
Interval: $\left(-\frac{4}{5}, \frac{8}{5}\right)$.

Graph:

71. $\left|\dfrac{x - 2}{3}\right| < 2$ $\Leftrightarrow$ $-2 < \dfrac{x - 2}{3} < 2$ $\Leftrightarrow$
$-6 < x - 2 < 6$ $\Leftrightarrow$ $-4 < x < 8$.
Interval: $(-4, 8)$.

Graph:

72. $\left|\dfrac{x + 1}{2}\right| \geq 4$ $\Leftrightarrow$ $\left|\frac{1}{2}(x + 1)\right| \geq 4$ $\Leftrightarrow$
$\frac{1}{2}|x + 1| \geq 4$ $\Leftrightarrow$ $|x + 1| \geq 8$ which is equivalent
either to $x + 1 \geq 8$ $\Leftrightarrow$ $x \geq 7$, or to $x + 1 \leq -8$
$\Leftrightarrow$ $x \leq -9$.
Interval: $(-\infty, -9] \cup [7, \infty)$.

Graph:

73. $|x + 6| < 0.001$ $\Leftrightarrow$ $-0.001 < x + 6 < 0.001$ $\Leftrightarrow$
$-6.001 < x < -5.999$.
Interval: $(-6.001, -5.999)$.

Graph:

74. $3 - |2x + 4| \leq 1$ $\Leftrightarrow$ $-|2x + 4| \leq -2$ $\Leftrightarrow$
$|2x + 4| \geq 2$ which is equivalent to either $2x + 4 \geq 2$
$\Leftrightarrow$ $2x \geq -2$ $\Leftrightarrow$ $x \geq -1$; or $2x + 4 \leq -2$ $\Leftrightarrow$
$2x \leq -6$ $\Leftrightarrow$ $x \leq -3$.
Interval: $(-\infty, -3] \cup [-1, \infty)$.

Graph:

75. $8 - |2x - 1| \geq 6$ $\Leftrightarrow$ $-|2x - 1| \geq -2$ $\Leftrightarrow$
$|2x - 1| \leq 2$ $\Leftrightarrow$ $-2 \leq 2x - 1 \leq 2$ $\Leftrightarrow$
$-1 \leq 2x \leq 3$ $\Leftrightarrow$ $-\frac{1}{2} \leq x \leq \frac{3}{2}$. Interval: $\left[-\frac{1}{2}, \frac{3}{2}\right]$.

Graph:

76. $7|x + 2| + 5 > 4$ $\Leftrightarrow$ $7|x + 2| > -1$ $\Leftrightarrow$
$|x + 2| > -\frac{1}{7}$. Since the absolute value is always
nonnegative, the inequality is true for all real numbers. In
interval notation, this is $(-\infty, \infty)$.

Graph:

77. $|x| < 3$ **78.** $|x| > 2$ **79.** $|x - 7| \geq 5$ **80.** $|x - 2| \leq 4$ **81.** $|x| \leq 2$

82. $|x| \geq 1$ **83.** $|x| > 3$ **84.** $|x| < 4$ **85.** $|x - 1| \leq 3$ **86.** $|x + 2| > 1$

87. For $\sqrt{16 - 9x^2}$ to be defined as a real number we must have $16 - 9x^2 \geq 0$ $\Leftrightarrow$ $(4 - 3x)(4 + 3x) \geq 0$. The expression in the inequality changes sign at $x = \frac{4}{3}$ and $x = -\frac{4}{3}$.

Interval	$\left(-\infty, -\frac{4}{3}\right)$	$\left(-\frac{4}{3}, \frac{4}{3}\right)$	$\left(\frac{4}{3}, \infty\right)$
Sign of $4 - 3x$	$+$	$+$	$-$
Sign of $4 + 3x$	$-$	$+$	$+$
Sign of $(4 - 3x)(4 + 3x)$	$-$	$+$	$-$

Thus $-\frac{4}{3} \leq x \leq \frac{4}{3}$.

88. For $\sqrt{3x^2 - 5x + 2}$ to be defined as a real number, we must have $3x^2 - 5x + 2 \geq 0$ $\Leftrightarrow$ $(3x - 2)(x - 1) \geq 0$. The expression on the left of the inequality changes sign when $x = \frac{2}{3}$ and $x = 1$. Thus we must check the intervals in the following table.

Interval	$\left(-\infty, \frac{2}{3}\right)$	$\left(\frac{2}{3}, 1\right)$	$(1, \infty)$
Sign of $3x - 2$	$-$	$+$	$+$
Sign of $x - 1$	$-$	$-$	$+$
Sign of $(3x - 2)(x - 1)$	$+$	$-$	$+$

Thus $x \leq \frac{2}{3}$ or $1 \leq x$.

89. For $\left(\dfrac{1}{x^2 - 5x - 14}\right)^{1/2}$ to be defined as a real number we must have $x^2 - 5x - 14 > 0$ $\Leftrightarrow$ $(x - 7)(x + 2) > 0$. The expression in the inequality changes sign at $x = 7$ and $x = -2$.

Interval	$(-\infty, -2)$	$(-2, 7)$	$(7, \infty)$
Sign of $x - 7$	$-$	$-$	$+$
Sign of $x + 2$	$-$	$+$	$+$
Sign of $(x - 7)(x + 2)$	$+$	$-$	$+$

Thus $x < -2$ or $7 < x$, and the solution set is $(-\infty, -2) \cup (7, \infty)$.

90. For $\sqrt[4]{\dfrac{1 - x}{2 + x}}$ to be defined as a real number we must have $\dfrac{1 - x}{2 + x} \geq 0$. The expression on the left of the inequality changes sign when $x = 1$ and $x = -2$. Thus we must check the intervals in the following table.

Interval	$(-\infty, -2)$	$(-2, 1)$	$(1, \infty)$
Sign of $1 - x$	$+$	$+$	$-$
Sign of $2 + x$	$-$	$+$	$+$
Sign of $\dfrac{1 - x}{2 + x}$	$-$	$+$	$-$

Thus $-2 < x \leq 1$. Note that $x = -2$ has been excluded from the solution set because the expression is undefined at that value.

91. (a) $a(bx - c) \geq bc$ (where $a, b, c > 0$) $\Leftrightarrow$ $bx - c \geq \dfrac{bc}{a}$ $\Leftrightarrow$ $bx \geq \dfrac{bc}{a} + c$ $\Leftrightarrow$ $x \geq \dfrac{1}{b}\left(\dfrac{bc}{a} + c\right) = \dfrac{c}{a} + \dfrac{c}{b}$

$\Leftrightarrow$ $x \geq \dfrac{c}{a} + \dfrac{c}{b}$.

(b) We have $a \leq bx + c < 2a$, where $a, b, c > 0$ $\Leftrightarrow$ $a - c \leq bx < 2a - c$ $\Leftrightarrow$ $\dfrac{a - c}{b} \leq x < \dfrac{2a - c}{b}$.

92. We are given $\dfrac{a}{b} < \dfrac{c}{d}$, where a, b, c, and d are all positive. So multiplying by d, we get $\dfrac{ad}{b} < c$ and so by Rule 1 for

Inequalities, $a + \dfrac{ad}{b} < a + c \quad \Leftrightarrow \quad \dfrac{ab + ad}{b} < a + c \quad \Leftrightarrow \quad \dfrac{a}{b}\left(b + d\right) < a + c \quad \Leftrightarrow \quad \dfrac{a}{b} < \dfrac{a + c}{b + d}$, since $b + d$ is

positive. Similarly, $\dfrac{a}{b} < \dfrac{c}{d} \quad \Leftrightarrow \quad a < \dfrac{bc}{d} \quad \Leftrightarrow \quad a + c < \dfrac{bc}{d} + c \quad \Leftrightarrow \quad a + c < \dfrac{bc}{d} + \dfrac{dc}{d} \quad \Leftrightarrow \quad a + c < \dfrac{c}{d}\left(b + d\right)$

$\Leftrightarrow \quad \dfrac{a + c}{b + d} < \dfrac{c}{d}$, since $b + d > 0$. Combining the two inequalities, $\dfrac{a}{b} < \dfrac{a + c}{b + d} < \dfrac{c}{d}$.

93. Inserting the relationship $C = \frac{5}{9}\left(F - 32\right)$, we have $20 \le C \le 30 \quad \Leftrightarrow \quad 20 \le \frac{5}{9}\left(F - 32\right) \le 30 \quad \Leftrightarrow$
$36 \le F - 32 \le 54 \quad \Leftrightarrow \quad 68 \le F \le 86$.

94. Inserting the relationship $F = \frac{9}{5}C + 32$, we have $50 \le F \le 95 \quad \Leftrightarrow \quad 50 \le \frac{9}{5}C + 32 \le 95 \quad \Leftrightarrow \quad 18 \le \frac{9}{5}C \le 63$
$\Leftrightarrow \quad 10 \le C \le 35$.

95. Let x be the average number of miles driven per day. Each day the cost of Plan A is $30 + 0.10x$, and the cost of Plan B is
50. Plan B saves money when $50 < 30 + 0.10x \quad \Leftrightarrow \quad 20 < 0.1x \quad \Leftrightarrow \quad 200 < x$. So Plan B saves money when you
average more than 200 miles a day.

96. Let m be the number of minutes of long-distance calls placed per month. Then under Plan A, the cost will be
$25 + 0.05m$, and under Plan B, the cost will be $5 + 0.12m$. To determine when Plan B is advantageous, we must solve
$25 + 0.05m > 5 + 0.12m \quad \Leftrightarrow \quad 20 > 0.07m \quad \Leftrightarrow \quad 285.7 > m$. So Plan B is advantageous if a person places fewer
than 286 minutes of long-distance calls during a month.

97. We need to solve $6400 \le 0.35m + 2200 \le 7100$ for m. So $6400 \le 0.35m + 2200 \le 7100 \quad \Leftrightarrow \quad 4200 \le 0.35m \le 4900$
$\Leftrightarrow \quad 12{,}000 \le m \le 14{,}000$. She plans on driving between 12,000 and 14,000 miles.

98. Solve $30 \le 10 + 0.9v - 0.01v^2$ for $10 \le v \le 75$. We have $30 \le 10 + 0.9v - 0.01v^2 \quad \Leftrightarrow \quad 0.01v^2 - 0.9v + 20 \le 0$
$\Leftrightarrow \quad \left(0.1v - 4\right)\left(0.1v - 5\right) \le 0$. The possible endpoints are $0.1v - 4 = 0 \quad \Leftrightarrow \quad 0.1v = 4 \quad \Leftrightarrow \quad v = 40$ and
$0.1v - 5 = 0 \quad \Leftrightarrow \quad 0.1v = 5 \quad \Leftrightarrow \quad v = 50$.

Interval	$(10, 40)$	$(40, 50)$	$(50, 75)$
Sign of $0.1v - 4$	$-$	$+$	$+$
Sign of $0.1v - 5$	$-$	$-$	$+$
Sign of $(0.1v - 4)(0.1v - 5)$	$+$	$-$	$+$

Thus he must drive between 40 and 50 mi/h.

99. $0.0004 \le \dfrac{4{,}000{,}000}{d^2} \le 0.01$. Since $d^2 \ge 0$ and $d \ne 0$, we can multiply each expression by d^2 to obtain
$0.0004d^2 \le 4{,}000{,}000 \le 0.01d^2$. Solving each pair, we have $0.0004d^2 \le 4{,}000{,}000 \quad \Leftrightarrow \quad d^2 \le 10{,}000{,}000{,}000$
$\Rightarrow \quad d \le 100{,}000$ (recall that d represents distance, so it is always nonnegative). Solving $4{,}000{,}000 \le 0.01d^2 \quad \Leftrightarrow$
$400{,}000{,}000 \le d^2 \Rightarrow 20{,}000 \le d$. Putting these together, we have $20{,}000 \le d \le 100{,}000$.

100. $\dfrac{600{,}000}{x^2 + 300} < 500 \quad \Leftrightarrow \quad 600{,}000 < 500\left(x^2 + 300\right)$ (Note that $x^2 + 300 \ge 300 > 0$, so we can multiply both sides by
the denominator and not worry that we might be multiplying both sides by a negative number or by zero.) $1200 < x^2 + 300$
$\Leftrightarrow \quad 0 < x^2 - 900 \quad \Leftrightarrow \quad 0 < \left(x - 30\right)\left(x + 30\right)$. The expression in the inequality changes sign at $x = 30$ and
$x = -30$. However, since x represents distance, we must have $x > 0$.

Interval	$(0, 30)$	$(30, \infty)$
Sign of $x - 30$	$-$	$+$
Sign of $x + 30$	$+$	$+$
Sign of $(x - 30)(x + 30)$	$-$	$+$

So $x > 30$ and you must stand at least 30 meters from the center of the fire.

101. $240 > v + \dfrac{v^2}{20}$ $\Leftrightarrow$ $\frac{1}{20}v^2 + v - 240 < 0$ $\Leftrightarrow$ $\left(\frac{1}{20}v - 3\right)(v + 80) < 0$. The expression in the inequality changes sign at $v = 60$ and $v = -80$. However, since v represents the speed, we must have $v \geq 0$.

Interval	$(0, 60)$	$(60, \infty)$
Sign of $\frac{1}{20}v - 3$	$-$	$+$
Sign of $v + 80$	$+$	$+$
Sign of $\left(\frac{1}{20}v - 3\right)(v + 80)$	$-$	$+$

So Kerry must drive less than 60 mi/h.

102. Solve $2400 \leq 20x - \left(2000 + 8x + 0.0025x^2\right)$ $\Leftrightarrow$ $2400 \leq 20x - 2000 - 8x - 0.0025x^2$ $\Leftrightarrow$ $0.0025x^2 - 12x + 4400 \leq 0$ $\Leftrightarrow$ $(0.0025x - 1)(x - 4400) \leq 0$. The expression on the left of the inequality changes sign when $x = 400$ and $x = 4400$. Since the manufacturer can only sell positive units, we check the intervals in the following table.

Interval	$(0, 400)$	$(400, 4400)$	$(4400, \infty)$
Sign of $0.0025x - 1$	$-$	$+$	$+$
Sign of $x - 4400$	$-$	$-$	$+$
Sign of $(0.0025x - 1)(x - 4400)$	$+$	$-$	$+$

So the manufacturer must sell between 400 and 4400 units to enjoy a profit of at least $2400.

103. (a) $T = 20 - \dfrac{h}{100}$, where T is the temperature in °C, and h is the height in meters.

(b) Solving the expression in part (a) for h, we get $h = 100(20 - T)$. So $0 \leq h \leq 5000$ $\Leftrightarrow$ $0 \leq 100(20 - T) \leq 5000$ $\Leftrightarrow$ $0 \leq 20 - T \leq 50$ $\Leftrightarrow$ $-20 \leq -T \leq 30$ $\Leftrightarrow$ $20 \geq T \geq -30$. Thus the range of temperature is from $20°$ C down to $-30°$ C.

104. (a) Let x be the number of $3 increases. Then the number of seats sold is $120 - x$. So $P = 200 + 3x$ $\Leftrightarrow$ $3x = P - 200$ $\Leftrightarrow$ $x = \frac{1}{3}(P - 200)$. Substituting for x we have that the number of seats sold is $120 - x = 120 - \frac{1}{3}(P - 200) = -\frac{1}{3}P + \frac{560}{3}$.

(b) $90 \leq -\frac{1}{3}P + \frac{560}{3} \leq 115$ $\Leftrightarrow$ $270 \leq 360 - P + 200 \leq 345$ $\Leftrightarrow$ $270 \leq -P + 560 \leq 345$ $\Leftrightarrow$ $-290 \leq -P \leq -215$ $\Leftrightarrow$ $290 \geq P \geq 215$. Putting this into standard order, we have $215 \leq P \leq 290$. So the ticket prices are between $215 and $290.

105. Let n be the number of people in the group. Then the bus fare is $\dfrac{360}{n}$, and the cost of the theater tickets is $30 - 0.25n$. We want the total cost to be less than $39 per person, that is, $\dfrac{360}{n} + (30 - 0.25n) < 39$. If we multiply this inequality by n, we will not change the direction of the inequality; n is positive since it represents the number of people. So we get $360 + n(30 - 0.25n) < 39n$ $\Leftrightarrow$ $-0.25n^2 + 30n + 360 < 39n$ $\Leftrightarrow$ $-0.25n^2 - 9n + 360 < 0$ $\Leftrightarrow$ $(0.25n + 15)(-n + 24)$. The expression on the left of the inequality changes sign when $n = -60$ and $n = 24$. Since $n > 0$, we check the intervals in the following table.

Interval	$(0, 24)$	$(24, \infty)$
Sign of $0.25n + 15$	$+$	$+$
Sign of $-n + 24$	$+$	$-$
Sign of $(0.25n + 15)(-n + 24)$	$+$	$-$

So the group must have more than 24 people in order that the cost of the theater tour is less than $39.

106. Let x be the length of the garden and w its width. Using the fact that the perimeter is 120 ft, we must have $2x + 2w = 120$ $\Leftrightarrow$ $w = 60 - x$. Now since the area must be at least 800 ft^2, we have $800 < x(60 - x)$ $\Leftrightarrow$ $800 < 60x - x^2$ $\Leftrightarrow$ $x^2 - 60x + 800 < 0$ $\Leftrightarrow$ $(x - 20)(x - 40) < 0$. The expression in the inequality changes sign at $x = 20$ and $x = 40$. However, since x represents length, we must have $x > 0$.

Interval	$(0, 20)$	$(20, 40)$	$(40, \infty)$
Sign of $x - 20$	$-$	$+$	$+$
Sign of $x - 40$	$-$	$-$	$+$
Sign of $(x - 20)(x - 40)$	$+$	$-$	$+$

The length of the garden should be between 20 and 40 feet.

107. (a) Let x be the thickness of the laminate. Then $|x - 0.020| \leq 0.003$.

  (b) $|x - 0.020| \leq 0.003$ $\Leftrightarrow$ $-0.003 \leq x - 0.020 \leq 0.003$ $\Leftrightarrow$ $0.017 \leq x \leq 0.023$.

108. $\left| \dfrac{h - 68.2}{2.9} \right| \leq 2$ $\Leftrightarrow$ $-2 \leq \dfrac{h - 68.2}{2.9} \leq 2$ $\Leftrightarrow$ $-5.8 \leq h - 68.2 \leq 5.8$ $\Leftrightarrow$ $62.4 \leq h \leq 74.0$. Thus 95% of the adult males are between 62.4 in. and 74.0 in.

109. *Case 1:* $a < b < 0$ We have $a \cdot a > a \cdot b$, since $a < 0$, and $b \cdot a > b \cdot b$, since $b < 0$. So $a^2 > a \cdot b > b^2$, that is $a < b < 0$ $\Rightarrow$ $a^2 > b^2$. Continuing, we have $a \cdot a^2 < a \cdot b^2$, since $a < 0$ and $b^2 \cdot a < b^2 \cdot b$, since $b^2 > 0$. So $a^3 < ab^2 < b^3$. Thus $a < b < 0$ $\Rightarrow$ $a^3 > b^3$. So $a < b < 0$ $\Rightarrow$ $a^n > b^n$, if n is even, and $a^n < b$, if n is odd.

  Case 2: $0 < a < b$ We have $a \cdot a < a \cdot b$, since $a > 0$, and $b \cdot a < b \cdot b$, since $b < 0$. So $a^2 < a \cdot b < b^2$. Thus $0 < a < b$ $\Rightarrow$ $a^2 < b^2$. Likewise, $a^2 \cdot a < a^2 \cdot b$ and $b \cdot a^2 < b \cdot b^2$, thus $a^3 < b^3$. So $0 < a < b$ $\Rightarrow$ $a^n < b^n$, for all positive integers n.

  Case 3: $a < 0 < b$ If n is odd, then $a^n < b^n$, because a^n is negative and b^n is positive. If n is even, then we could have either $a^n < b^n$ or $a^n > b^n$. For example, $-1 < 2$ and $(-1)^2 < 2^2$, but $-3 < 2$ and $(-3)^2 > 2^2$.

110. The rule we want to apply here is "$a < b \Rightarrow ac < bc$ if $c > 0$ and $a < b \Rightarrow ac > bc$ if $c < 0$". Thus we cannot simply multiply by x, since we don't yet know if x is positive or negative, so in solving $1 < \dfrac{3}{x}$, we must consider two cases.

  Case 1: $x > 0$ Multiplying both sides by x, we have $x < 3$. Together with our initial condition, we have $0 < x < 3$.

  Case 2: $x < 0$ Multiplying both sides by x, we have $x > 3$. But $x < 0$ and $x > 3$ have no elements in common, so this gives no additional solution. Hence, the only solutions are $0 < x < 3$.

111. $|x - 1|$ is the distance between x and 1; $|x - 3|$ is the distance between x and 3. So $|x - 1| < |x - 3|$ represents those points closer to 1 than to 3, and the solution is $x < 2$, since 2 is the point halfway between 1 and 3. If $a < b$, then the solution to $|x - a| < |x - b|$ is $x < \dfrac{a + b}{2}$.

1.8 Coordinate Geometry

1.

2. $A\,(5,1)$, $B\,(1,2)$, $C\,(-2,6)$, $D\,(-6,2)$, $E\,(-4,-1)$, $F\,(-2,0)$, $G\,(-1,-3)$, $H\,(2,-2)$

3. The two points are $(0,2)$ and $(3,0)$.

(a) $d = \sqrt{(3-0)^2 + (0-(-2))^2} = \sqrt{3^2 + 2^2} = \sqrt{9+4} = \sqrt{13}$

(b) midpoint: $\left(\dfrac{3+0}{2}, \dfrac{0+2}{2}\right) = \left(\tfrac{3}{2}, 1\right)$

4. The two points are $(-2,-1)$ and $(2,2)$.

(a) $d = \sqrt{(-2-2)^2 + (-1-2)^2} = \sqrt{(-4)^2 + (-3)^2} = \sqrt{16+9} = \sqrt{25} = 5$

(b) midpoint: $\left(\dfrac{-2+2}{2}, \dfrac{-1+2}{2}\right) = \left(0, \tfrac{1}{2}\right)$

5. The two points are $(-3,3)$ and $(5,-3)$.

(a) $d = \sqrt{(-3-5)^2 + (3-(-3))^2} = \sqrt{(-8)^2 + 6^2} = \sqrt{64+36} = \sqrt{100} = 10$

(b) midpoint: $\left(\dfrac{-3+5}{2}, \dfrac{3+(-3)}{2}\right) = (1,0)$

6. The two points are $(-2,-3)$ and $(4,-1)$.

(a) $d = \sqrt{(-2-4)^2 + (-3-(-1))^2} = \sqrt{(-6)^2 + (-2)^2} = \sqrt{36+4} = \sqrt{50} = 2\sqrt{10}$

(b) midpoint: $\left(\dfrac{-3+5}{2}, \dfrac{-3+(-1)}{2}\right) = (1,-2)$

7. (a)

(b) $d = \sqrt{(0-6)^2 + (8-16)^2}$

$= \sqrt{(-6)^2 + (-8)^2} = \sqrt{100} = 10$

(c) midpoint: $\left(\dfrac{0+6}{2}, \dfrac{8+16}{2}\right) = (3,12)$

8. (a)

(b) $d = \sqrt{(-2-10)^2 + (5-0)^2}$

$= \sqrt{(-12)^2 + (5)^2} = \sqrt{169} = 13$

(c) midpoint: $\left(\dfrac{-2+10}{2}, \dfrac{5+0}{2}\right) = \left(4, \tfrac{5}{2}\right)$

9. (a)

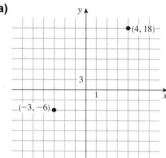

(b) $d = \sqrt{(-3-4)^2 + (-6-18)^2}$

$= \sqrt{(-7)^2 + (-24)^2} = \sqrt{49 + 576} = \sqrt{625} = 25$

(c) midpoint: $\left(\dfrac{-3+4}{2}, \dfrac{-6+18}{2}\right) = \left(\frac{1}{2}, 6\right)$

10. (a)

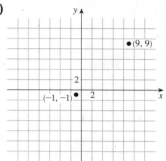

(b) $d = \sqrt{(-1-9)^2 + (-1-9)^2}$

$= \sqrt{(-10)^2 + (-10)^2} = \sqrt{200} = 10\sqrt{2}$

(c) midpoint: $\left(\dfrac{-1+9}{2}, \dfrac{-1+9}{2}\right) = (4,4)$

11. (a)

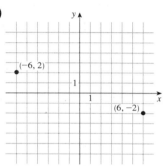

(b) $d = \sqrt{(6-(-6))^2 + (-2-2)^2} = \sqrt{12^2 + (-4)^2}$

$= \sqrt{144 + 16} = \sqrt{160} = 4\sqrt{10}$

(c) midpoint: $\left(\dfrac{6-6}{2}, \dfrac{-2+2}{2}\right) = (0,0)$

12. (a)

(b) $d = \sqrt{(0-5)^2 + (-6-0)^2}$

$= \sqrt{5^2 + (-6)^2} = \sqrt{25 + 36} = \sqrt{61}$

(c) midpoint: $\left(\dfrac{0+5}{2}, \dfrac{-6+0}{2}\right) = \left(\frac{5}{2}, -3\right)$

13. $d(A,B) = \sqrt{(1-5)^2 + (3-3)^2} = \sqrt{(-4)^2} = 4.$

$d(A,C) = \sqrt{(1-1)^2 + (3-(-3))^2} = \sqrt{(6)^2} = 6.$ So the area is $4 \cdot 6 = 24$.

14. The area of a parallelogram is its base times its height. Since two sides are parallel to the x-axis, we use the length of one of these as the base. Thus, the base is $d(A,B) = \sqrt{(1-5)^2 + (2-2)^2} = \sqrt{(-4)^2} = 4.$ The height is the change in the y coordinates, thus, the height is $6 - 2 = 4$. So the area of the parallelogram is base $\cdot$ height $= 4 \cdot 4 = 16$.

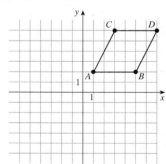

15. From the graph, the quadrilateral $ABCD$ has a pair of parallel sides, so $ABCD$ is a trapezoid. The area is $\left(\dfrac{b_1 + b_2}{2}\right) h$. From the graph we see that

$$b_1 = d(A, B) = \sqrt{(1 - 5)^2 + (0 - 0)^2} = \sqrt{4^2} = 4;$$

$$b_2 = d(C, D) = \sqrt{(4 - 2)^2 + (3 - 3)^2} = \sqrt{2^2} = 2;$$

and h is the difference in y-coordinates is $|3 - 0| = 3$.

Thus the area of the trapezoid is $\left(\dfrac{4 + 2}{2}\right) 3 = 9$.

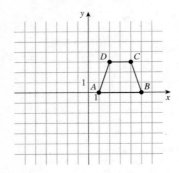

16. The point S must be located at $(0, -4)$. To find the area, we find the length of one side and square it. This gives

$$
\begin{aligned}
d(Q, R) &= \sqrt{(-5 - 0)^2 + (1 - 6)^2} \\
&= \sqrt{(-5)^2 + (-5)^2} \\
&= \sqrt{25 + 25} = \sqrt{50}
\end{aligned}
$$

So the area is $\left(\sqrt{50}\right)^2 = 50$.

17.

18.

19.

20.

21.

22.

23.

24.

25.

26.

27. $d(0, A) = \sqrt{(6-0)^2 + (7-0)^2} = \sqrt{6^2 + 7^2} = \sqrt{36 + 49} = \sqrt{85}$.

$d(0, B) = \sqrt{(-5-0)^2 + (8-0)^2} = \sqrt{(-5)^2 + 8^2} = \sqrt{25 + 64} = \sqrt{89}$.

Thus point $A(6, 7)$ is closer to the origin.

28. $d(E, C) = \sqrt{(-6-(-2))^2 + (3-1)^2} = \sqrt{(-4)^2 + 2^2} = \sqrt{16 + 4} = \sqrt{20}$.

$d(E, D) = \sqrt{(3-(-2))^2 + (0-1)^2} = \sqrt{5^2 + (-1)^2} = \sqrt{25 + 1} = \sqrt{26}$.

Thus point C is closer to point E.

29. $d(P, R) = \sqrt{(-1-3)^2 + (-1-1)^2} = \sqrt{(-4)^2 + (-2)^2} = \sqrt{16 + 4} = \sqrt{20} = 2\sqrt{5}$.

$d(Q, R) = \sqrt{(-1-(-1))^2 + (-1-3)^2} = \sqrt{0 + (-4)^2} = \sqrt{16} = 4$. Thus point $Q(-1, 3)$ is closer to point R.

30. (a) The distance from $(7, 3)$ to the origin is $\sqrt{(7-0)^2 + (3-0)^2} = \sqrt{7^2 + 3^2} = \sqrt{49+9} = \sqrt{58}$. The distance from $(3, 7)$ to the origin is $\sqrt{(3-0)^2 + (7-0)^2} = \sqrt{3^2 + 7^2} = \sqrt{9+49} = \sqrt{58}$. So the points are the same distance from the origin.

(b) The distance from (a, b) to the origin is $\sqrt{(a-0)^2 + (b-0)^2} = \sqrt{a^2 + b^2}$. The distance from (b, a) to the origin is $\sqrt{(b-0)^2 + (a-0)^2} = \sqrt{b^2 + a^2} = \sqrt{a^2 + b^2}$. So the points are the same distance from the origin.

31. Since we do not know which pair are isosceles, we find the length of all three sides.

$d(A, B) = \sqrt{(-3-0)^2 + (-1-2)^2} = \sqrt{(-3)^2 + (-3)^2} = \sqrt{9+9} = \sqrt{18} = 3\sqrt{2}$.

$d(C, B) = \sqrt{(-3-(-4))^2 + (-1-3)^2} = \sqrt{1^2 + (-4)^2} = \sqrt{1+16} = \sqrt{17}$.

$d(A, C) = \sqrt{(0-(-4))^2 + (2-3)^2} = \sqrt{4^2 + (-1)^2} = \sqrt{16+1} = \sqrt{17}$. So sides AC and CB have the same length.

32. Since the side AB is parallel to the x-axis, we use this as the base in the formula area $= \frac{1}{2}$ (base $\cdot$ height). The height is the change in the y-coordinates. Thus, the base is $|-2-4| = 6$ and the height is $|4-1| = 3$. So the area is $\frac{1}{2}(6 \cdot 3) = 9$.

33. (a) Here we have $A = (2, 2)$, $B = (3, -1)$, and $C = (-3, -3)$. So

$d(A, B) = \sqrt{(3-2)^2 + (-1-2)^2} = \sqrt{1^2 + (-3)^2} = \sqrt{1+9} = \sqrt{10}$;

$d(C, B) = \sqrt{(3-(-3))^2 + (-1-(-3))^2} = \sqrt{6^2 + 2^2} = \sqrt{36+4} = \sqrt{40} = 2\sqrt{10}$;

$d(A, C) = \sqrt{(-3-2)^2 + (-3-2)^2} = \sqrt{(-5)^2 + (-5)^2} = \sqrt{25+25} = \sqrt{50} = 5\sqrt{2}$.

Since $[d(A, B)]^2 + [d(C, B)]^2 = [d(A, C)]^2$, we conclude that the triangle is a right triangle.

(b) The area of the triangle is $\frac{1}{2} \cdot d(C, B) \cdot d(A, B) = \frac{1}{2} \cdot \sqrt{10} \cdot 2\sqrt{10} = 10$.

34. $d(A, B) = \sqrt{(11-6)^2 + (-3-(-7))^2} = \sqrt{5^2 + 4^2} = \sqrt{25+16} = \sqrt{41}$;

$d(A, C) = \sqrt{(2-6)^2 + (-2-(-7))^2} = \sqrt{(-4)^2 + 5^2} = \sqrt{16+25} = \sqrt{41}$;

$d(B, C) = \sqrt{(2-11)^2 + (-2-(-3))^2} = \sqrt{(-9)^2 + 1^2} = \sqrt{81+1} = \sqrt{82}$.

Since $[d(A, B)]^2 + [d(A, C)]^2 = [d(B, C)]^2$, we conclude that the triangle is a right triangle. The Area is $\frac{1}{2}\left(\sqrt{41} \cdot \sqrt{41}\right) = \frac{41}{2}$.

35. We show that all sides are the same length (its a rhombus) and then show that the diagonals are equal. Here we have $A = (-2, 9)$, $B = (4, 6)$, $C = (1, 0)$, and $D = (-5, 3)$. So

$d(A, B) = \sqrt{(4-(-2))^2 + (6-9)^2} = \sqrt{6^2 + (-3)^2} = \sqrt{36+9} = \sqrt{45}$;

$d(B, C) = \sqrt{(1-4)^2 + (0-6)^2} = \sqrt{(-3)^2 + (-6)^2} = \sqrt{9+36} = \sqrt{45}$;

$d(C, D) = \sqrt{(-5-1)^2 + (3-0)^2} = \sqrt{(-6)^2 + (-3)^2} = \sqrt{36+9} = \sqrt{45}$;

$d(D, A) = \sqrt{(-2-(-5))^2 + (9-3)^2} = \sqrt{3^2 + 6^2} = \sqrt{9+36} = \sqrt{45}$. So the points form a

rhombus. Also $d(A, C) = \sqrt{(1-(-2))^2 + (0-9)^2} = \sqrt{3^2 + (-9)^2} = \sqrt{9+81} = \sqrt{90} = 3\sqrt{10}$,

and $d(B, D) = \sqrt{(-5-4)^2 + (3-6)^2} = \sqrt{(-9)^2 + (-3)^2} = \sqrt{81+9} = \sqrt{90} = 3\sqrt{10}$. Since the diagonals are equal, the rhombus is a square.

36. $d(A, B) = \sqrt{(3 - (-1))^2 + (11 - 3)^2} = \sqrt{4^2 + 8^2} = \sqrt{16 + 64} = \sqrt{80} = 4\sqrt{5}.$

$d(B, C) = \sqrt{(5 - 3)^2 + (15 - 11)^2} = \sqrt{2^2 + 4^2} = \sqrt{4 + 16} = \sqrt{20} = 2\sqrt{5}.$

$d(A, C) = \sqrt{(5 - (-1))^2 + (15 - 3)^2} = \sqrt{6^2 + 12^2} = \sqrt{36 + 144} = \sqrt{180} = 6\sqrt{5}.$ So

$d(A, B) + d(B, C) = d(A, C)$, and the points are collinear.

37. Let $P = (0, y)$ be such a point. Setting the distances equal we get

$\sqrt{(0 - 5)^2 + (y - (-5))^2} = \sqrt{(0 - 1)^2 + (y - 1)^2} \quad \Leftrightarrow$

$\sqrt{25 + y^2 + 10y + 25} = \sqrt{1 + y^2 - 2y + 1} \quad \Rightarrow \quad y^2 + 10y + 50 = y^2 - 2y + 2 \quad \Leftrightarrow \quad 12y = -48 \quad \Leftrightarrow$

$y = -4$. Thus, the point is $P = (0, -4)$. Check:

$\sqrt{(0 - 5)^2 + (-4 - (-5))^2} = \sqrt{(-5)^2 + 1^2} = \sqrt{25 + 1} = \sqrt{26};$

$\sqrt{(0 - 1)^2 + (-4 - 1)^2} = \sqrt{(-1)^2 + (-5)^2} = \sqrt{25 + 1} = \sqrt{26}.$

38. The midpoint of AB is $C' = \left(\dfrac{1 + 3}{2}, \dfrac{0 + 6}{2}\right) = (2, 3)$. So the length of the median CC' is $d(C, C') =$

$\sqrt{(2 - 8)^2 + (3 - 2)^2} = \sqrt{37}$. The midpoint of AC is $B' = \left(\dfrac{1 + 8}{2}, \dfrac{0 + 2}{2}\right) = \left(\tfrac{9}{2}, 1\right)$. So the length of the median

BB' is $d(B, B') = \sqrt{\left(\tfrac{9}{2} - 3\right)^2 + (1 - 6)^2} = \dfrac{\sqrt{109}}{2}$. The midpoint of BC is $A' = \left(\dfrac{3 + 8}{2}, \dfrac{6 + 2}{2}\right) = \left(\tfrac{11}{2}, 4\right)$. So the

length of the median AA' is $d(A, A') = \sqrt{\left(\tfrac{11}{2} - 1\right)^2 + (4 - 0)^2} = \dfrac{\sqrt{145}}{2}.$

39. As indicated by Example 3, we must find a point $S(x_1, y_1)$ such that the midpoints

of PR and of QS are the same. Thus

$\left(\dfrac{4 + (-1)}{2}, \dfrac{2 + (-4)}{2}\right) = \left(\dfrac{x_1 + 1}{2}, \dfrac{y_1 + 1}{2}\right)$. Setting the x-coordinates equal,

we get $\dfrac{4 + (-1)}{2} = \dfrac{x_1 + 1}{2} \quad \Leftrightarrow \quad 4 - 1 = x_1 + 1 \quad \Leftrightarrow \quad x_1 = 2.$ Setting the

y-coordinates equal, we get $\dfrac{2 + (-4)}{2} = \dfrac{y_1 + 1}{2} \quad \Leftrightarrow \quad 2 - 4 = y_1 + 1 \quad \Leftrightarrow$

$y_1 = -3$. Thus $S = (2, -3)$.

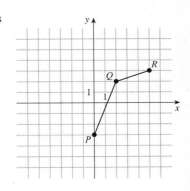

40. We solve the equation $6 = \dfrac{2 + x}{2}$ to find the x coordinate of B. This gives $6 = \dfrac{2 + x}{2} \quad \Leftrightarrow \quad 12 = 2 + x \quad \Leftrightarrow$

$x = 10$. Likewise, $8 = \dfrac{3 + y}{2} \quad \Leftrightarrow \quad 16 = 3 + y \quad \Leftrightarrow \quad y = 13$. Thus, $B = (10, 13).$

41. (a)

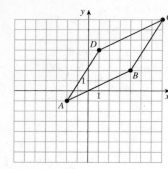

(b) The midpoint of AC is $\left(\dfrac{-2+7}{2}, \dfrac{-1+7}{2}\right) = \left(\dfrac{5}{2}, 3\right)$, the midpoint

of BD is $\left(\dfrac{4+1}{2}, \dfrac{2+4}{2}\right) = \left(\dfrac{5}{2}, 3\right)$.

(c) Since the they have the same midpoint, we conclude that the diagonals bisect each other.

42. We have $M = \left(\dfrac{a+0}{2}, \dfrac{b+0}{2}\right) = \left(\dfrac{a}{2}, \dfrac{b}{2}\right)$. Thus,

$$d\left(C, M\right) = \sqrt{\left(\dfrac{a}{2} - 0\right)^2 + \left(\dfrac{b}{2} - 0\right)^2} = \sqrt{\dfrac{a^2}{4} + \dfrac{b^2}{4}} = \dfrac{\sqrt{a^2 + b^2}}{2};$$

$$d\left(A, M\right) = \sqrt{\left(\dfrac{a}{2} - a\right)^2 + \left(\dfrac{b}{2} - 0\right)^2} = \sqrt{\left(-\dfrac{a}{2}\right)^2 + \left(\dfrac{b}{2}\right)^2} = \sqrt{\dfrac{a^2}{4} + \dfrac{b^2}{4}} = \dfrac{\sqrt{a^2 + b^2}}{2};$$

$$d\left(B, M\right) = \sqrt{\left(\dfrac{a}{2} - 0\right)^2 + \left(\dfrac{b}{2} - b\right)^2} = \sqrt{\left(\dfrac{a}{2}\right)^2 + \left(-\dfrac{b}{2}\right)^2} = \sqrt{\dfrac{a^2}{4} + \dfrac{b^2}{4}} = \dfrac{\sqrt{a^2 + b^2}}{2}.$$

43. $(0, 0)$: $0 - 2\left(0\right) - 1 \overset{?}{=} 0 \quad \Leftrightarrow \quad -1 \overset{?}{=} 0.$ No.

$(1, 0)$: $1 - 2\left(0\right) - 1 \overset{?}{=} 0 \quad \Leftrightarrow \quad -1 + 1 \overset{?}{=} 0.$ Yes.

$(-1, -1)$: $(-1) - 2\left(-1\right) - 1 \overset{?}{=} 0 \quad \Leftrightarrow \quad -1 + 2 - 1 \overset{?}{=} 0.$ Yes.

So $(1, 0)$ and $(-1, -1)$ are points on the graph of this equation.

44. $(1, 1)$: $(1)\left[(1)^2 + 1\right] \overset{?}{=} 1 \quad \Leftrightarrow \quad 1\left(2\right) \overset{?}{=} 1.$ No.

$\left(1, \dfrac{1}{2}\right)$: $\left(\dfrac{1}{2}\right)\left[(1)^2 + 1\right] \overset{?}{=} 1 \quad \Leftrightarrow \quad \dfrac{1}{2}\left(2\right) \overset{?}{=} 1.$ Yes.

$\left(-1, \dfrac{1}{2}\right)$: $\left(\dfrac{1}{2}\right)\left[(-1)^2 + 1\right] \overset{?}{=} 1 \quad \Leftrightarrow \quad \dfrac{1}{2}\left(2\right) \overset{?}{=} 1.$ Yes.

So both $\left(1, \dfrac{1}{2}\right)$ and $\left(-1, \dfrac{1}{2}\right)$ are points on the graph of this equation.

45. $(0, -2)$: $(0)^2 + (0)\left(-2\right) + (-2)^2 \overset{?}{=} 4 \quad \Leftrightarrow \quad 0 + 0 + 4 \overset{?}{=} 4.$ Yes.

$(1, -2)$: $(1)^2 + (1)\left(-2\right) + (-2)^2 \overset{?}{=} 4 \quad \Leftrightarrow \quad 1 - 2 + 4 \overset{?}{=} 4.$ No.

$(2, -2)$: $(2)^2 + (2)\left(-2\right) + (-2)^2 \overset{?}{=} 4 \quad \Leftrightarrow \quad 4 - 4 + 4 \overset{?}{=} 4.$ Yes.

So $(0, -2)$ and $(2, -2)$ are points on the graph of this equation.

46. $(0, 1)$: $(0)^2 + (1)^2 - 1 \overset{?}{=} 0 \quad \Leftrightarrow \quad 0 + 1 - 1 \overset{?}{=} 0.$ Yes.

$\left(\dfrac{1}{\sqrt{2}}, \dfrac{1}{\sqrt{2}}\right)$: $\left(\dfrac{1}{\sqrt{2}}\right)^2 + \left(\dfrac{1}{\sqrt{2}}\right)^2 - 1 \overset{?}{=} 0 \quad \Leftrightarrow \quad \dfrac{1}{2} + \dfrac{1}{2} - 1 \overset{?}{=} 0.$ Yes.

$\left(\dfrac{\sqrt{3}}{\sqrt{2}}, \dfrac{1}{2}\right)$: $\left(\dfrac{\sqrt{3}}{\sqrt{2}}\right)^2 + \left(\dfrac{1}{2}\right)^2 - 1 \overset{?}{=} 0 \quad \Leftrightarrow \quad \dfrac{3}{4} + \dfrac{1}{4} - 1 \overset{?}{=} 0.$ Yes.

So $(0, 1)$, $\left(\dfrac{1}{\sqrt{2}}, \dfrac{1}{\sqrt{2}}\right)$ and $\left(\dfrac{\sqrt{3}}{\sqrt{2}}, \dfrac{1}{2}\right)$, are all points on the graph of this equation.

47. To find x-intercepts, set $y = 0$. This gives $0 = 4x - x^2 \quad \Leftrightarrow \quad 0 = x\left(4 - x\right) \quad \Leftrightarrow \quad 0 = x$ or $x = 4$, so the x-intercept are 0 and 4. To find y-intercepts, set $x = 0$. This gives $y = 4\left(0\right) - 0^2 \quad \Leftrightarrow \quad y = 0$, so the y-intercept is 0.

48. To find x-intercepts, set $y = 0$. This gives $\dfrac{x^2}{9} + \dfrac{0^2}{4} = 1$ $\Leftrightarrow$ $\dfrac{x^2}{9} = 1$ $\Leftrightarrow$ $x^2 = 9$ $\Leftrightarrow$ $x = \pm 3$, so the

x-intercept are -3 and 3.

To find y-intercepts, set $x = 0$. This gives $\dfrac{0^2}{9} + \dfrac{y^2}{4} = 1$ $\Leftrightarrow$ $\dfrac{y^2}{4} = 1$ $\Leftrightarrow$ $y^2 = 4$ $\Leftrightarrow$ $x = \pm 2$, so the

y-intercept are -2 and 2.

49. To find x-intercepts, set $y = 0$. This gives $x^4 + 0^2 - x(0) = 16$ $\Leftrightarrow$ $x^4 = 16$ $\Leftrightarrow$ $x = \pm 2$. So the x-intercept are -2 and 2.

To find y-intercepts, set $x = 0$. This gives $0^4 + y^2 - (0)\,y = 16$ $\Leftrightarrow$ $y^2 = 16$ $\Leftrightarrow$ $y = \pm 4$. So the y-intercept are -4 and 4.

50. To find x-intercepts, set $y = 0$. This gives $x^2 + 0^3 - x^2(0)^2 = 64$ $\Leftrightarrow$ $x^2 = 64$ $\Leftrightarrow$ $x = \pm 8$. So the x-intercept are -8 and 8.

To find y-intercepts, set $x = 0$. This gives $0^2 + y^3 - (0)^2\,y^2 = 64$ $\Leftrightarrow$ $y^3 = 64$ $\Leftrightarrow$ $y = 4$. So the y-intercept is 4.

51. $y = -x + 4$

x	y
-4	8
-2	6
0	4
1	3
2	2
3	1
4	0

When $y = 0$ we get $x = 4$. So the x-intercept is 4, and $x = 0$ $\Rightarrow$ $y = 4$, so the y-intercept is 4.

x-axis symmetry: $(-y) = -x + 4$ $\Leftrightarrow$ $y = x - 4$, which is not the same as $y = -x + 4$, so the graph is not symmetric with respect to the x-axis.

y-axis symmetry: $y = -(-x) + 4$ $\Leftrightarrow$ $y = x + 4$, which is not the same as $y = -x + 4$, so the graph is not symmetric with respect to the y-axis.

Origin symmetry: $(-y) = -(-x) + 4$ $\Leftrightarrow$ $y = -x - 4$, which is not the same as $y = -x + 4$, so the graph is not symmetric with respect to the origin.

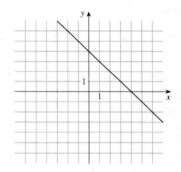

52. $y = -3x + 3$

x	y
-3	-1
-2	1
-1	3
0	5
1	7
2	9
3	11

$y = 0$ $\Rightarrow$ $0 = -3x + 3$ $\Leftrightarrow$ $3x = 3$ $\Leftrightarrow$ $x = 1$, so the x-intercept is 1, and $x = 0$ $\Rightarrow$ $y = -3(0) + 3 = 3$, so the y-intercept is 3.

x-axis symmetry: $(-y) = -3x + 3$ $\Leftrightarrow$ $-y = -3x + 3$, which is not the same as $y = -3x + 3$, so the graph is not symmetric with respect to the x-axis.

y-axis symmetry: $y = -3(-x) + 3$ $\Leftrightarrow$ $y = 3x + 3$, which is not the same as $y = -3x + 3$, so the graph is not symmetric with respect to the y-axis.

Origin symmetry: $(-y) = -3(-x) + 3$ $\Leftrightarrow$ $-y = 3x + 3$, which is not the same as $y = -3x + 3$, so the graph is not symmetric with respect to the origin.

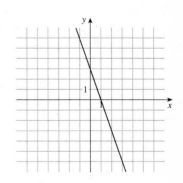

53. $2x - y = 6$

x	y
-1	-8
0	-6
1	-4
2	-2
3	0
4	2
5	4

When $y = 0$ we get $2x = 6$ So the x-intercept is 3. When $x = 0$ we get $-y = 6$ so the y-intercept is -6.

x-axis symmetry: $2x - (-y) = 6$ $\Leftrightarrow$ $2x + y = 6$, which is not the same, so the graph is not symmetric with respect to the x-axis.

y-axis symmetry: $2(-x) - y = 6$ $\Leftrightarrow$ $2x + y = -6$, so the graph is not symmetric with respect to the y-axis.

Origin symmetry: $2(-x) - (-y) = 6$ $\Leftrightarrow$ $-2x + y = 6$, which not he same, so the graph is not symmetric with respect to the origin.

54. Solve for y: $x + y = 3$ $\Leftrightarrow$ $y = -x + 3$.

x	y
-2	5
-1	4
0	3
1	2
2	1
3	0
4	-1

$y = 0$ $\Rightarrow$ $0 = -x + 3$ $\Leftrightarrow$ $x = 3$, so the x-intercept is 3, and $x = 0$ $\Rightarrow$ $y = -(0) + 3 = 3$, so the y-intercept is 3.

x-axis symmetry: $x + (-y) = 3$ $\Leftrightarrow$ $x - y = 3$, which is not the same as $x + y = 3$, so the graph is not symmetric with respect to the x-axis.

y-axis symmetry: $(-x) + y = 5$ $\Leftrightarrow$ $-x + y = 3$, which is not the same as $x + y = 3$, so the graph is not symmetric with respect to the y-axis.

Origin symmetry: $(-x) + (-y) = 3$ $\Leftrightarrow$ $-x - y = 3$, which is not the same as $x + y = 3$, so the graph is not symmetric with respect to the origin.

55. $y = 1 - x^2$

x	y
-3	-8
-2	-3
-1	0
0	1
1	0
2	-3
3	-8

$y = 0$ $\Rightarrow$ $0 = 1 - x^2$ $\Leftrightarrow$ $x^2 = 1$ $\Rightarrow$ $x = \pm 1$, so the x-intercepts are 1 and -1, and $x = 0$ $\Rightarrow$ $y = 1 - (0)^2 = 1$, so the y-intercept is 1.

x-axis symmetry: $(-y) = 1 - x^2$ $\Leftrightarrow$ $-y = 1 - x^2$,which is not the same as $y = 1 - x^2$, so the graph is not symmetric with respect to the x-axis.

y-axis symmetry: $y = 1 - (-x)^2$ $\Leftrightarrow$ $y = 1 - x^2$, so the graph is symmetric with respect to the y-axis.

Origin symmetry: $(-y) = 1 - (-x)^2$ $\Leftrightarrow$ $-y = 1 - x^2$ which is not the same as $y = 1 - x^2$. The graph is not symmetric with respect to the origin.

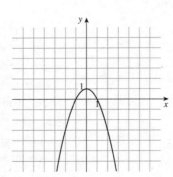

56. $y = x^2 + 2$

x	y
-3	11
-2	6
-1	3
0	2
1	3
2	6
3	11

$y = 0 \Rightarrow 0 = x^2 + 2 \Leftrightarrow -2 = x^2$, since $x^2 \geq 0$, there is no x-intercept, and $x = 0 \Rightarrow y = (0)^2 + 2 = 2$, so the y-intercept is 2.

x-axis symmetry: $(-y) = x^2 + 2 \Leftrightarrow -y = x^2 + 2$, which is not the same, so the graph is not symmetric with respect to the x-axis.

y-axis symmetry: $y = (-x)^2 + 2 = x^2 + 2$, so the graph is symmetric with respect to the y-axis.

Origin symmetry: $(-y) = (-x)^2 + 2 \Leftrightarrow -y = x^2 + 2$, which is not the same, so the graph is not symmetric with respect to the origin.

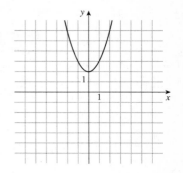

57. $4y = x^2 \Leftrightarrow y = \frac{1}{4}x^2$

x	y
-6	9
-4	4
-2	1
0	0
2	1
4	4
3	2

$y = 0 \Rightarrow 0 = \frac{1}{4}x^2 \Leftrightarrow x^2 = 0 \Rightarrow x = 0$, so the x-intercept is 0, and $x = 0 \Rightarrow y = \frac{1}{4}(0)^2 = 0$, so the y-intercept is 0.

x-axis symmetry: $(-y) = \frac{1}{4}x^2$, which is not the same as $y = \frac{1}{4}x^2$, so the graph is not symmetric with respect to the x-axis.

y-axis symmetry: $y = \frac{1}{4}(-x)^2 \Leftrightarrow y = \frac{1}{4}x^2$, so the graph is symmetric with respect to the y-axis.

Origin symmetry: $(-y) = \frac{1}{4}(-x)^2 \Leftrightarrow -y = \frac{1}{4}x^2$, which is not the same as $y = \frac{1}{4}x^2$, so the graph is not symmetric with respect to the origin.

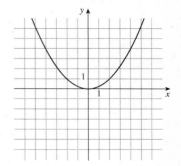

58. $8y = x^3 \Leftrightarrow y = \frac{1}{8}x^3$

x	y
-6	-27
-4	-8
-2	-1
0	0
2	1
4	8
3	27

$y = 0 \Rightarrow 0 = \frac{1}{8}x^3 \Leftrightarrow x^3 = 0 \Rightarrow x = 0$, so the x-intercept is 0, and $x = 0 \Rightarrow y = \frac{1}{8}(0)^3 = 0$, so the y-intercept is 0.

x-axis symmetry: $(-y) = \frac{1}{8}x^3$, which is not the same as $y = \frac{1}{8}x^3$, so the graph is not symmetric with respect to the x-axis.

y-axis symmetry: $y = \frac{1}{8}(-x)^3 = -\frac{1}{8}x^3$, which is not the same as $y = \frac{1}{8}x^3$, so the graph is not symmetric with respect to the y-axis.

Origin symmetry: $(-y) = \frac{1}{8}(-x)^3 \Leftrightarrow -y = -\frac{1}{8}x^3$, which is the same as $y = \frac{1}{8}x^3$, so the graph is symmetric with respect to the origin.

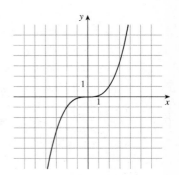

59. $y = x^2 - 9$

x	y
-4	7
-3	0
-2	-5
-1	-8
0	-9
1	-8
2	-5
3	0
4	7

$y = 0 \Rightarrow 0 = x^2 - 9 \Leftrightarrow x^2 = 9 \Rightarrow x = \pm 3$, so the x-intercepts are 3 and -3, and $x = 0 \Rightarrow y = (0)^2 - 9 = -9$, so the y-intercept is -9.

x-axis symmetry: $(-y) = x^2 - 9$, which is not the same as $y = x^2 - 9$, so the graph is not symmetric with respect to the x-axis.

y-axis symmetry: $y = (-x)^2 - 9 \Leftrightarrow y = x^2 - 9$, so the graph is symmetric with respect to the y-axis.

Origin symmetry: $(-y) = (-x)^2 - 9 \Leftrightarrow -y = x^2 - 9$, which is not the same as $y = x^2 - 9$, so the graph is not symmetric with respect to the origin.

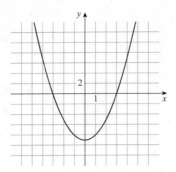

60. $y = 9 - x^2$

x	y
-4	-7
-3	0
-2	5
-1	8
0	9
1	8
2	5
3	0
4	-7

$y = 0 \Rightarrow 0 = 9 - x^2 \Leftrightarrow x^2 = 9 \Rightarrow x = \pm 3$, so the x-intercepts are -3 and 3, and $x = 0 \Rightarrow y = 9 - (0)^2 = 9$, so the y-intercept is 9.

x-axis symmetry: $(-y) = 9 - x^2$, which is not the same as $y = 9 - x^2$, so the graph is not symmetric with respect to the x-axis.

y-axis symmetry: $y = 9 - (-x)^2 = 9 - x^2$, so the graph is symmetric with respect to the y-axis.

Origin symmetry: $(-y) = 9 - (-x)^2 \Leftrightarrow -y = 9 - x^2$, which is not the same as $y = 9 - x^2$, so the graph is not symmetric with respect to the origin.

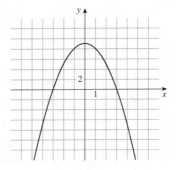

61. $xy = 2 \Leftrightarrow y = \dfrac{2}{x}$

x	y
-4	$-\frac{1}{2}$
-2	-1
-1	-2
$-\frac{1}{2}$	-4
$-\frac{1}{4}$	-8
$\frac{1}{4}$	8
$\frac{1}{2}$	4
1	2
2	1
4	$\frac{1}{2}$

$y = 0$ or $x = 0 \Rightarrow 0 = 2$, which is impossible, so this equation has no x-intercept and no y-intercept.

x-axis symmetry: $x(-y) = 2 \Leftrightarrow -xy = 2$, which is not the same as $xy = 2$, so the graph is not symmetric with respect to the x-axis.

y-axis symmetry: $(-x)y = 2 \Leftrightarrow -xy = 2$, which is not the same as $xy = 2$, so the graph is not symmetric with respect to the y-axis.

Origin symmetry: $(-x)(-y) = 2 \Leftrightarrow xy = 2$, so the graph is symmetric with respect to the origin.

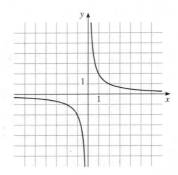

62. $y = \sqrt{x+4}$

x	y
-4	0
$-\frac{15}{4}$	$\frac{1}{2}$
-3	1
-2	$\sqrt{2}$
0	2
5	3
12	4

$y = 0 \ \Rightarrow \ 0 = \sqrt{x+4} \ \Leftrightarrow \ x = -4$. so the x-intercept is -4, and $x = 0 \ \Rightarrow \ y = \sqrt{4} = 2$, so the y-intercept is 2. Since we are graphing real numbers and $\sqrt{x+4}$ is defined to be a nonnegative number, the equation is not symmetric with respect to the x-axis nor with respect to the y-axis. Also, the equation is not symmetric with respect to the origin.

63. $y = \sqrt{4 - x^2}$. Since the radicand (the inside of the square root) cannot be negative, we must have $4 - x^2 \geq 0 \ \Leftrightarrow \ x^2 \leq 4 \ \Leftrightarrow \ |x| \leq 2$.

x	y
-2	0
-1	$\sqrt{3}$
0	4
1	$\sqrt{3}$
2	0

$y = 0 \ \Rightarrow \ 0 = \sqrt{4 - x^2} \ \Leftrightarrow \ 4 - x^2 = 0 \ \Leftrightarrow \ x^2 = 4$ $\Rightarrow \ x = \pm 2$, so the x-intercept are -2 and 2, and $x = 0 \ \Rightarrow$ $y = \sqrt{4 - (0)^2} = \sqrt{4} = 2$, so the y-intercept is 2. Since $y \geq 0$, the graph is not symmetric with respect to the x-axis.

y-axis symmetry: $y = \sqrt{4 - (-x)^2} = \sqrt{4 - x^2}$, so the graph is symmetric with respect to the y-axis. Also, since $y \geq 0$ the graph is not symmetric with respect to the origin.

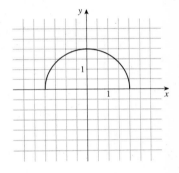

64. Since the radicand (the inside of the square root) cannot be negative, we must have $4 - x^2 \geq 0 \ \Leftrightarrow \ x^2 \leq 4 \ \Leftrightarrow$ $|x| \leq 2$. So $-2 \leq x \leq 2$ is the only portion of the x-axis where this equation is defined.

x	y
-2	0
-1	$-\sqrt{3}$
0	-4
1	$-\sqrt{3}$
2	0

$y = 0 \ \Rightarrow \ 0 = -\sqrt{4 - x^2} \ \Leftrightarrow \ 4 - x^2 = 0 \ \Leftrightarrow \ x^2 = 4$ $\Rightarrow \ x = \pm 2$, so the x-intercepts are -2 and 2, and $x = 0 \ \Rightarrow$ $y = -\sqrt{4 - (0)^2} = -\sqrt{4} = -2$, so the y-intercept is -2.

x-axis symmetry: Since $y \leq 0$, this graph is not symmetric with respect to the x-axis.

y-axis symmetry: $y = -\sqrt{4 - (-x)^2} = -\sqrt{4 - x^2}$, so the graph is symmetric with respect to the y-axis.

Origin symmetry: Since $y \leq 0$, the graph is not symmetric with respect to the origin.

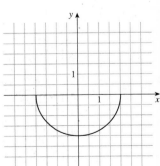

65. Solve for x in terms of y: $x + y^2 = 4$ $\Leftrightarrow$ $x = 4 - y^2$

x	y
-12	-4
-5	-3
0	-2
3	-1
4	0
3	1
0	2
-5	3
-12	4

$y = 0$ $\Rightarrow$ $x + 0^2 = 4$ $\Leftrightarrow$ $x = 4$, so the x-intercept is 4, and $x = 0$ $\Rightarrow$ $0 + y^2 = 4$ $\Rightarrow$ $y = \pm 2$, so the y-intercepts are -2 and 2.

x-axis symmetry: $x + (-y)^2 = 4$ $\Leftrightarrow$ $x + y^2 = 4$, so the graph is symmetric with respect to the x-axis.

y-axis symmetry: $(-x) + y^2 = 4$ $\Leftrightarrow$ $-x + y^2 = 4$, which is not the same, so the graph is not symmetric with respect to the y-axis.

Origin symmetry: $(-x) + (-y)^2 = 4$ $\Leftrightarrow$ $-x + y^2 = 4$, which is not the same as $x + y^2 = 4$, so the graph is not symmetric with respect to the origin.

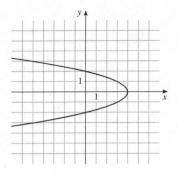

66. Since $x = y^3$ is solved for x in terms of y, we insert values for y and find the corresponding values of x.

x	y
-27	-3
-8	-2
-1	-1
0	0
1	1
8	2
27	3

$y = 0$ $\Rightarrow$ $x = (0)^3 = 0$, so the x-intercept is 0, and $x = 0$ $\Rightarrow$ $0 = y^3$ $\Rightarrow$ $y = 0$, so the y-intercept is 0.

x-axis symmetry: $x = (-y)^3 = -y^3$, which is not the same as $x = y^3$, so the graph is not symmetric with respect to the x-axis.

y-axis symmetry: $(-x) = y^3$ $\Leftrightarrow$ $x = -y^3$, which is not the same as $x = y^3$, so the graph is not symmetric with respect to the y-axis.

Origin symmetry: $(-x) = (-y)^3$ $\Leftrightarrow$ $-x = -y^3$ $\Leftrightarrow$ $x = y^3$, so the graph is symmetric with respect to the origin.

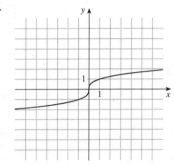

67. $y = 16 - x^4$

x	y
-3	-65
-2	0
-1	15
0	16
1	15
2	0
3	-65

$y = 0$ $\Rightarrow$ $0 = 16 - x^4$ $\Rightarrow$ $x^4 = 16$ $\Rightarrow$ $x^2 = 4 \Rightarrow$ $x = \pm 2$, so the x-intercepts are ± 2, and so $x = 0$ $\Rightarrow$ $y = 16 - 0^4 = 16$, so the y-intercept is 16.

x-axis symmetry: $(-y) = 16 - x^4$ $\Leftrightarrow$ $y = -16 + x^4$, which is not the same as $y = 16 - x^4$, so the graph is not symmetric with respect to the x-axis. y-axis symmetry: $y = 16 - (-x)^4 = 16 - x^4$, so the graph is symmetric with respect to the y-axis.

Origin symmetry: $(-y) = 16 - (-x)^4$ $\Leftrightarrow$ $-y = 16 - x^4$, which is not the same as $y = 16 - x^4$, so the graph is not symmetric with respect to the origin.

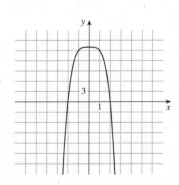

68. $x = |y|$. Here we insert values of y and find the corresponding value of x.

x	y
3	-3
2	-2
1	-1
0	0
1	1
2	2
3	3

$y = 0 \quad \Rightarrow \quad x = |0| = 0$, so the x-intercept is 0, and $x = 0 \Rightarrow$ $0 = |y| \quad \Leftrightarrow \quad y = 0$, so the y-intercept is 0.

x-axis symmetry: $x = |-y| = |y|$, so the graph is symmetric with respect to the x-axis. y-axis symmetry: Since $x \geq 0$, the graph is not symmetric with respect to the y-axis. Origin symmetry: Since $x \geq 0$, the graph is not symmetric with respect to the origin.

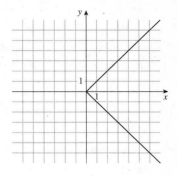

69. $y = 4 - |x|$

x	y
-6	-2
-4	0
-2	2
0	4
2	2
4	0
6	-2

$y = 0 \quad \Rightarrow \quad 0 = 4 - |x| \quad \Leftrightarrow \quad |x| = 4 \quad \Rightarrow \quad x = \pm 4$, so the x-intercepts are -4 and 4, and $x = 0 \quad \Rightarrow \quad y = 4 - |0| = 4$, so the y-intercept is 4.

x-axis symmetry: $(-y) = 4 - |x| \quad \Leftrightarrow \quad y = -4 + |x|$, which is not the same as $y = 4 - |x|$, so the graph is not symmetric with respect to the x-axis.

y-axis symmetry: $y = 4 - |-x| = 4 - |x|$, so the graph is symmetric with respect to the y-axis.

Origin symmetry: $(-y) = 4 - |-x| \quad \Leftrightarrow \quad y = -4 + |x|$, which is not the same as $y = 4 - |x|$, so the graph is not symmetric with respect to the origin.

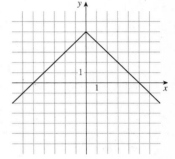

70. $y = |4 - x|$

x	y
-6	10
-4	8
-2	6
0	4
2	2
4	0
6	2
8	4
10	6

$y = 0 \quad \Rightarrow \quad 0 = |4 - x| \quad \Leftrightarrow \quad 4 - x = 0 \quad \Rightarrow \quad x = 4$, so the x-intercept is 4, and $x = 0 \quad \Rightarrow \quad y = |4 - 0| = |4| = 4$, so the y-intercept is 4.

x-axis symmetry: $y = |4 - (-x)| = |4 + x|$, which is not the same as $y = |4 - x|$, so the graph is not symmetric with respect to the x-axis.

y-axis symmetry: $(-y) = |4 - x| \quad \Leftrightarrow \quad -y = |4 - x|$, which is not the same as $y = |4 - x|$, so the graph is not symmetric with respect to the y-axis.

Origin symmetry: $(-y) = |4 - (-x)| \quad \Leftrightarrow \quad -y = |4 + x|$, which is not the same as $y = |4 - x|$, so the graph is not symmetric with respect to the origin.

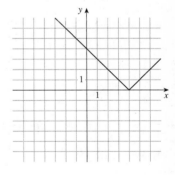

71. x-axis symmetry: $(-y) = x^4 + x^2 \quad \Leftrightarrow \quad y = -x^4 - x^2$, which is not the same as $y = x^4 + x^2$, so the graph is not symmetric with respect to the x-axis.

y-axis symmetry: $y = (-x)^4 + (-x)^2 = x^4 + x^2$, so the graph is symmetric with respect to the y-axis.

Origin symmetry: $(-y) = (-x)^4 + (-x)^2 \quad \Leftrightarrow \quad -y = x^4 + x^2$, which is not the same as $y = x^4 + x^2$, so the graph is not symmetric with respect to the origin.

72. x-axis symmetry: $x = (-y)^4 - (-y)^2 = y^4 - y^2$, so the graph is symmetric with respect to the x-axis.

y-axis symmetry: $(-x) = y^4 - y^2$, which is not the same as $x = y^4 - y^2$, so the graph is not symmetric with respect to the y-axis.

Origin symmetry: $(-x) = (-y)^4 - (-y)^2$ $\Leftrightarrow$ $-x = y^4 - y^2$, which is not the same as $x = y^4 - y^2$, so the graph is not symmetric with respect to the origin.

73. x-axis symmetry: $x^2(-y)^2 + x(-y) = 1$ $\Leftrightarrow$ $x^2 y^2 - xy = 1$, which is not the same as $x^2 y^2 + xy = 1$, so the graph is not symmetric with respect to the x-axis.

y-axis symmetry: $(-x)^2 y^2 + (-x) y = 1$ $\Leftrightarrow$ $x^2 y^2 - xy = 1$, which is not the same as $x^2 y^2 + xy = 1$, so the graph is not symmetric with respect to the y-axis.

Origin symmetry: $(-x)^2(-y)^2 + (-x)(-y) = 1$ $\Leftrightarrow$ $x^2 y^2 + xy = 1$, so the graph is symmetric with respect to the origin.

74. x-axis symmetry: $x^4(-y)^4 + x^2(-y)^2 = 1$ $\Leftrightarrow$ $x^4 y^4 + x^2 y^2 = 1$, so the graph is symmetric with respect to the x-axis.

y-axis symmetry: $(-x)^4 y^4 + (-x)^2 y^2 = 1$ $\Leftrightarrow$ $x^4 y^4 + x^2 y^2 = 1$, so the graph is symmetric with respect to the y-axis.

Origin symmetry: $(-x)^4(-y)^4 + (-x)^2(-y)^2 = 1$ $\Leftrightarrow$ $x^4 y^4 + x^2 y^2 = 1$, so the graph is symmetric with respect to the origin.

75. x-axis symmetry: $(-y) = x^3 + 10x$ $\Leftrightarrow$ $y = -x^3 - 10x$, which is not the same as $y = x^3 + 10x$, so the graph is not symmetric with respect to the x-axis.

y-axis symmetry: $y = (-x)^3 + 10(-x)$ $\Leftrightarrow$ $y = -x^3 - 10x$, which is not the same as $y = x^3 + 10x$, so the graph is not symmetric with respect to the y-axis.

Origin symmetry: $(-y) = (-x)^3 + 10(-x)$ $\Leftrightarrow$ $-y = -x^3 - 10x$ $\Leftrightarrow$ $y = x^3 + 10x$, so the graph is symmetric with respect to the origin.

76. x-axis symmetry: $(-y) = x^2 + |x|$ $\Leftrightarrow$ $y = -x^2 - |x|$, which is not the same as $y = x^2 + |x|$, so the graph is not symmetric with respect to the x-axis.

y-axis symmetry: $y = (-x)^2 + |-x|$ $\Leftrightarrow$ $y = x^2 + |x|$, so the graph is symmetric with respect to the y-axis. Note that $|-x| = |x|$.

Origin symmetry: $(-y) = (-x)^2 + |-x|$ $\Leftrightarrow$ $-y = x^2 + |x|$ $\Leftrightarrow$ $y = -x^2 - |x|$, which is not the same as $y = x^2 + |x|$, so the graph is not symmetric with respect to the origin.

77. Symmetric with respect to the y-axis.

78. Symmetric with respect to the x-axis.

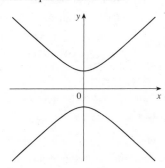

79. Symmetric with respect to the origin.

80. Symmetric with respect to the origin.

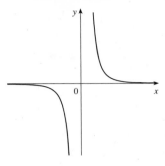

81. Using $h = 2$, $k = -1$, and $r = 3$, we get $(x - 2)^2 + (y - (-1))^2 = 3^2$ $\Leftrightarrow$ $(x - 2)^2 + (y + 1)^2 = 9$.

82. Using $h = -1$, $k = -4$, and $r = 8$ we get $(x - (-1))^2 + (y - (-4))^2 = 8^2$ $\Leftrightarrow$ $(x + 1)^2 + (y + 4)^2 = 64$.

83. The equation of a circle centered at the origin is $x^2 + y^2 = r^2$. Using the point $(4, 7)$ we solve for r^2. This gives
$(4)^2 + (7)^2 = r^2$ $\Leftrightarrow$ $16 + 49 = 65 = r^2$. Thus, the equation of the circle is $x^2 + y^2 = 65$.

84. The center is at the midpoint of the line segment, which is $\left(\dfrac{-1 + 5}{2}, \dfrac{1 + 5}{2} \right) = (2, 3)$. The radius is one half the

diameter, so $r = \frac{1}{2} \sqrt{(-1 - 5)^2 + (1 - 5)^2} = \frac{1}{2} \sqrt{36 + 16} = \frac{1}{2} \sqrt{52} = \sqrt{13}$. Thus, the equation of the circle is

$(x - 2)^2 + (y - 3)^2 = \left(\sqrt{13} \right)^2$ or $(x - 2)^2 + (y - 3)^2 = 13$.

85. Since the circle is tangent to the x-axis, it must contain the point $(7, 0)$, so the radius is the change in the y-coordinates. That
is, $r = |-3 - 0| = 3$. So the equation of the circle is $(x - 7)^2 + (y - (-3))^2 = 3^2$, which is $(x - 7)^2 + (y + 3)^2 = 9$.

86. Since the circle with $r = 5$ lies in the first quadrant and is tangent to both the x-axis and the y-axis, the center of the circle
is at $(5, 5)$. Therefore, the equation of the circle is $(x - 5)^2 + (y - 5)^2 = 25$.

87. From the figure, the center of the circle is at $(-2, 2)$. The radius is the change in the y-coordinates, so $r = |2 - 0| = 2$.
Thus the equation of the circle is $(x - (-2))^2 + (y - 2)^2 = 2^2$, which is $(x + 2)^2 + (y - 2)^2 = 4$.

88. From the figure, the center of the circle is at $(-1, 1)$. The radius is the distance from the center to the point $(2, 0)$. Thus
$r = \sqrt{(-1 - 2)^2 + (1 - 0)^2} = \sqrt{9 + 1} = \sqrt{10}$, and the equation of the circle is $(x + 1)^2 + (y - 1)^2 = 10$.

89. Completing the square gives $x^2 + y^2 - 4x + 10y + 13 = 0$ $\Leftrightarrow$ $x^2 - 4x + \left(\frac{-4}{2} \right)^2 + y^2 + 10y + \left(\frac{10}{2} \right)^2 = -13 + \left(\frac{4}{2} \right)^2 + \left(\frac{10}{2} \right)^2$
$\Leftrightarrow$ $x^2 - 4x + 4 + y^2 + 10y + 25 = -13 + 4 + 25$ $\Leftrightarrow$ $(x - 2)^2 + (y + 5)^2 = 16$.
Thus, the center is $(2, -5)$, and the radius is 4.

90. Completing the square gives $x^2 + y^2 + 6y + 2 = 0$ $\Leftrightarrow$ $x^2 + y^2 + 6y + \left(\frac{6}{2} \right)^2 = -2 + \left(\frac{6}{2} \right)^2$ $\Leftrightarrow$
$x^2 + y^2 + 6y + 9 = -2 + 9$ $\Leftrightarrow$ $x^2 + (y + 3)^2 = 7$. Thus, the circle has center $(0, -3)$, and radius $\sqrt{7}$.

91. Completing the square gives $x^2 + y^2 - \frac{1}{2}x + \frac{1}{2}y = \frac{1}{8}$ $\Leftrightarrow$ $x^2 - \frac{1}{2}x + \left(\frac{-1/2}{2} \right)^2 + y^2 + \frac{1}{2}y + \left(\frac{1/2}{2} \right)^2 = \frac{1}{8} +$

$\left(\frac{-1/2}{2} \right)^2 + \left(\frac{1/2}{2} \right)^2$ $\Leftrightarrow$ $x^2 - \frac{1}{2}x + \frac{1}{16} + y^2 + \frac{1}{2}y + \frac{1}{16} = \frac{1}{8} + \frac{1}{16} + \frac{1}{16} = \frac{2}{8} = \frac{1}{4}$ $\Leftrightarrow$ $\left(x - \frac{1}{4} \right)^2 + \left(y + \frac{1}{4} \right)^2 = \frac{1}{4}$.
Thus, the circle has center $\left(\frac{1}{4}, -\frac{1}{4} \right)$ and radius $\frac{1}{2}$.

92. Completing the square gives $x^2+y^2+\frac{1}{2}x+2y+\frac{1}{16}=0$ $\Leftrightarrow$ $x^2+\frac{1}{2}x+\left(\frac{1/2}{2}\right)^2+y^2+2y+\left(\frac{2}{2}\right)^2=-\frac{1}{16}+\left(\frac{1/2}{2}\right)^2+\left(\frac{2}{2}\right)^2$

$\Leftrightarrow$ $\left(x+\frac{1}{4}\right)^2+(y+1)^2=1$.

Thus, the circle has center $\left(-\frac{1}{4},-1\right)$ and radius 1.

93. Completing the square gives $2x^2+2y^2-3x=0$ $\Leftrightarrow$ $x^2+y^2-\frac{3}{2}x=0$ $\Leftrightarrow$ $\left(x-\frac{3}{4}\right)^2+y^2=\left(\frac{3}{4}\right)^2=\frac{9}{16}$.

Thus, the circle has center $\left(\frac{3}{4},0\right)$ and radius $\frac{3}{4}$.

94. Completing the square gives $3x^2+3y^2+6x-y=0$ $\Leftrightarrow$ $x^2+y^2+2x-\frac{1}{3}y=0$ $\Leftrightarrow$

$(x+1)^2+\left(y-\frac{1}{6}\right)^2=1+\frac{1}{36}=\frac{37}{36}$.

Thus, the circle has center $\left(\frac{3}{4},0\right)$ and radius $\frac{3}{4}$.

95. $\{(x,y)\mid x^2+y^2\le 1\}$. This is the set of points inside (and on) the circle $x^2+y^2=1$.

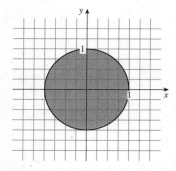

96. $\{(x,y)\mid x^2+y^2>4\}$. This is the set of points outside the circle $x^2+y^2=4$.

97. Completing the square gives $x^2+y^2-4y-12=0$

$\Leftrightarrow$ $x^2+y^2-4y+\left(\frac{-4}{2}\right)^2=12+\left(\frac{-4}{2}\right)^2$ $\Leftrightarrow$

$x^2+(y-2)^2=16$. Thus, the center is $(0,2)$, and the radius is 4. So the circle $x^2+y^2=4$, with center $(0,0)$ and radius 2, sits completely inside the larger circle. Thus, the area is $\pi 4^2-\pi 2^2=16\pi-4\pi=12\pi$.

98. This is the top quarter of the circle of radius 3. Thus, the area is $\frac{1}{4}(9\pi)=\frac{9\pi}{4}$.

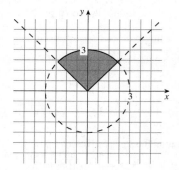

99. (a) $d(A,B)=\sqrt{3^2+4^2}=\sqrt{25}=5$.

(b) We want the distances from $C=(4,2)$ to $D=(11,26)$. The walking distance is $|4-11|+|2-26|=7+24=31$ blocks. Straight-line distance is

$\sqrt{(4-11)^2+(2-26)^2}=\sqrt{7^2+24^2}=\sqrt{625}=25$ blocks.

(c) The two points are on the same avenue or the same street.

100. (a) The midpoint is at $\left(\dfrac{3+27}{2},\dfrac{7+17}{2}\right)=(15,12)$, which is at the intersection of 15th Street and 12th Avenue.

(b) They each must walk $|15-3|+|12-7|=12+5=17$ blocks.

101. (a) Closest: 2 Mm. Farthest: 8 Mm.

(b) When $y = 2$ we have $\dfrac{(x-3)^2}{25} + \dfrac{2^2}{16} = 1$ $\Leftrightarrow$ $\dfrac{(x-3)^2}{25} + \dfrac{1}{4} = 1$ $\Leftrightarrow$ $\dfrac{(x-3)^2}{25} = \dfrac{3}{4}$ $\Leftrightarrow$

$(x-3)^2 = \dfrac{75}{4}$. Taking the square root of both sides we get $x - 3 = \pm\sqrt{\dfrac{75}{4}} = \pm\dfrac{5\sqrt{3}}{2}$ $\Leftrightarrow$ $x = 3 \pm \dfrac{5\sqrt{3}}{2}$.

So $x = 3 - \dfrac{5\sqrt{3}}{2} \approx -1.33$ or $x = 3 + \dfrac{5\sqrt{3}}{2} \approx 7.33$. The distance from $(-1.33, 2)$ to the center $(0, 0)$ is

$d = \sqrt{(-1.33-0)^2 + (2-0)^2} = \sqrt{5.7689} \approx 2.40$. The distance from $(7.33, 2)$ to the center $(0, 0)$ is

$d = \sqrt{(7.33-0)^2 + (2-0)^2} = \sqrt{57.7307} \approx 7.60$.

102. (a) The point $(5, 3)$ is shifted to $(5 + 3, 3 + 2) = (8, 5)$.

(b) The point (a, b) is shifted to $(a + 3, b + 2)$.

(c) Let (x, y) be the point that is shifted to $(3, 4)$. Then $(x + 3, y + 2) = (3, 4)$. Setting the x-coordinates equal, we get $x + 3 = 3$ $\Leftrightarrow$ $x = 0$. Setting the y-coordinates equal, we get $y + 2 = 4$ $\Leftrightarrow$ $y = 2$. So the point is $(0, 2)$.

(d) $A = (-5, -1)$, so $A' = (-5 + 3, -1 + 2) = (-2, 1)$; $B = (-3, 2)$, so $B' = (-3 + 3, 2 + 2) = (0, 4)$; and $C = (2, 1)$, so $C' = (2 + 3, 1 + 2) = (5, 3)$.

103. (a) The point $(3, 7)$ is reflected to the point $(-3, 7)$.

(b) The point (a, b) is reflected to the point $(-a, b)$.

(c) Since the point $(-a, b)$ is the reflection of (a, b), the point $(-4, -1)$ is the reflection of $(4, -1)$.

(d) $A = (3, 3)$, so $A' = (-3, 3)$; $B = (6, 1)$, so $B' = (-6, 1)$; and $C = (1, -4)$, so $C' = (-1, -4)$.

104. We solve the equation $6 = \dfrac{2+x}{2}$ to find the x coordinate of B: $6 = \dfrac{2+x}{2}$ $\Leftrightarrow$ $12 = 2 + x$ $\Leftrightarrow$ $x = 10$.

Likewise, for the y coordinate of B, we have $8 = \dfrac{3+y}{2}$ $\Leftrightarrow$ $16 = 3 + y$ $\Leftrightarrow$ $y = 13$. Thus $B = (10, 13)$.

105. We need to find a point $S(x_1, y_1)$ such that $PQRS$ is a parallelogram. As indicated by Example 3, this will be the case if the diagonals PR and QS bisect each other. So the midpoints of PR and QS are the same. Thus

$\left(\dfrac{0+5}{2}, \dfrac{-3+3}{2}\right) = \left(\dfrac{x_1+2}{2}, \dfrac{y_1+2}{2}\right)$. Setting the x-coordinates equal, we

get $\dfrac{0+5}{2} = \dfrac{x_1+2}{2}$ $\Leftrightarrow$ $0 + 5 = x_1 + 2$ $\Leftrightarrow$ $x_1 = 3$.

Setting the y-coordinates equal, we get $\dfrac{-3+3}{2} = \dfrac{y_1+2}{2}$ $\Leftrightarrow$

$-3 + 3 = y_1 + 2$ $\Leftrightarrow$ $y_1 = -2$. Thus $S = (3, -2)$.

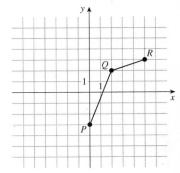

106. Completing the square gives $x^2 + y^2 + ax + by + c = 0$ $\Leftrightarrow$ $x^2 + ax + \left(\dfrac{a}{2}\right)^2 + y^2 + by + \left(\dfrac{b}{2}\right)^2 = -c + \left(\dfrac{a}{2}\right)^2 + \left(\dfrac{b}{2}\right)^2$

$\Leftrightarrow$ $\left(x + \dfrac{a}{2}\right)^2 + \left(y + \dfrac{b}{2}\right)^2 = -c + \dfrac{a^2 + b^2}{4}$. This equation represents a circle only when $-c + \dfrac{a^2 + b^2}{4} > 0$. This

equation represents a point when $-c + \dfrac{a^2 + b^2}{4} = 0$, and this equation represents the empty set when $-c + \dfrac{a^2 + b^2}{4} < 0$.

When the equation represents a circle, the center is $\left(-\dfrac{a}{2}, -\dfrac{b}{2}\right)$, and the radius is $\sqrt{-c + \dfrac{a^2 + b^2}{4}} = \dfrac{1}{2}\sqrt{a^2 + b^2 - 4ac}$.

107. (a) (i) $(x-2)^2 + (y-1)^2 = 9$, the center is at $(2, 1)$, and the radius is 3. $(x-6)^2 +$

$(y-4)^2 = 16$, the center is at $(6, 4)$, and the radius is 4. The distance between centers is

$\sqrt{(2-6)^2 + (1-4)^2} = \sqrt{(-4)^2 + (-3)^2} = \sqrt{16 + 9} = \sqrt{25} = 5$. Since $5 < 3 + 4$, these circles intersect.

(ii) $x^2 + (y-2)^2 = 4$, the center is at $(0,2)$, and the radius is 2. $(x-5)^2 + (y-14)^2 = 9$, the center is at $(5,14)$, and the radius is 3. The distance between centers is

$$\sqrt{(0-5)^2 + (2-14)^2} = \sqrt{(-5)^2 + (-12)^2} = \sqrt{25+144} = \sqrt{169} = 13.$$ Since $13 > 2+3$, these circles do not intersect.

(iii) $(x-3)^2 + (y+1)^2 = 1$, the center is at $(3,-1)$, and the radius is 1. $(x-2)^2 + (y-2)^2 = 25$, the center is at $(2,2)$, and the radius is 5. The distance between centers is

$$\sqrt{(3-2)^2 + (-1-2)^2} = \sqrt{1^2 + (-3)^2} = \sqrt{1+9} = \sqrt{10}.$$ Since $\sqrt{10} < 1+5$, these circles intersect.

(b) As shown in the diagram, if two circles intersect, then the centers of the circles and one point of intersection form a triangle. So because in any triangle each side has length less than the sum of the other two, the two circles will intersect only if the distance between their centers, d, is less than or equal to the sum of the radii, r_1 and r_2. That is, the circles will intersect if $d \le r_1 + r_2$.

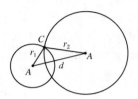

108. (a) Symmetric about the x-axis.   **(b)** Symmetric about the y-axis.   **(c)** Symmetric about the origin.

1.9   Graphing Calculators; Solving Equations and Inequalities Graphically

1. $y = x^4 + 2$

(a) $[-2, 2]$ by $[-2, 2]$

(b) $[0, 4]$ by $[0, 4]$

(c) $[-8, 8]$ by $[-4, 40]$

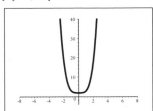

(d) $[-40, 40]$ by $[-80, 800]$

The viewing rectangle in part (c) produces the most appropriate graph of the equation.

2. $y = x^2 + 7x + 6$

(a) $[-5, 5]$ by $[-5, 5]$

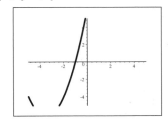

(b) $[0, 10]$ by $[-20, 100]$

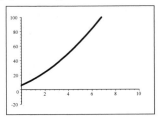

(c) $[-15, 8]$ by $[-20, 100]$

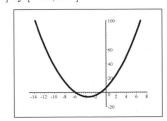

(d) $[-10, 3]$ by $[-100, 20]$

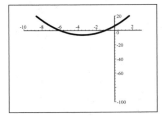

The viewing rectangle in part (c) produces the most appropriate graph of the equation.

3. $y = 100 - x^2$

(a) $[-4, 4]$ by $[-4, 4]$

(b) $[-10, 10]$ by $[-10, 10]$

(c) $[-15, 15]$ by $[-30, 110]$

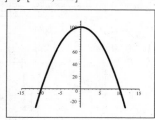

(d) $[-4, 4]$ by $[-30, 110]$

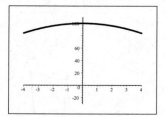

The viewing rectangle in part (c) produces the most appropriate graph of the equation.

4. $y = 2x^2 - 1000$

(a) $[-10, 10]$ by $[-10, 10]$

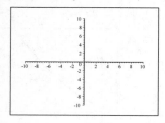

(b) $[-10, 10]$ by $[-100, 100]$

(c) $[-10, 10]$ by $[-1000, 1000]$

(d) $[-25, 25]$ by $[-1200, 200]$

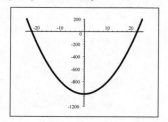

The viewing rectangle in part (d) produces the most appropriate graph of the equation.

5. $y = 10 + 25x - x^3$

(a) $[-4, 4]$ by $[-4, 4]$

(b) $[-10, 10]$ by $[-10, 10]$

(c) $[-20, 20]$ by $[-100, 100]$

(d) $[-100, 100]$ by $[-200, 200]$

The viewing rectangle in part (c) produces the most appropriate graph of the equation.

6. $y = \sqrt{8x - x^2}$

(a) $[-4, 4]$ by $[-4, 4]$

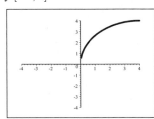

(b) $[-5, 5]$ by $[0, 100]$

(c) $[-10, 10]$ by $[-10, 40]$

(d) $[-2, 10]$ by $[-2, 6]$

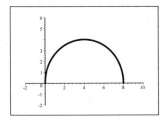

From the graphs we see that the viewing rectangle in (d) produces the most appropriate graph of the equation.

Note: Squaring both sides yields the equation $y^2 = 8x - x^2 \iff (x - 4)^2 + y^2 = 16$. Since this gives a circle, the original equation represents the top half of a circle.

7. $y = 100x^2$, $[-2, 2]$ by $[-10, 400]$

8. $y = -100x^2$, $[-2, 2]$ by $[-400, 10]$

9. $y = 4 + 6x - x^2$, $[-4, 10]$ by $[-10, 20]$

10. $y = 0.3x^2 + 1.7x - 3$, $[-15, 10]$ by $[-10, 20]$

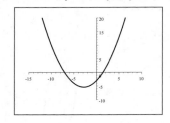

11. $y = \sqrt[4]{256 - x^2}$. We require that $256 - x^2 \geq 0$ $\Rightarrow$ $-16 \leq x \leq 16$, so we graph $y = \sqrt[4]{256 - x^2}$ in the viewing rectangle $[-20, 20]$ by $[-1, 5]$.

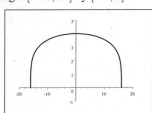

12. $y = \sqrt{12x - 17}$, $[0, 10]$ by $[0, 20]$

13. $y = 0.01x^3 - x^2 + 5$, $[-50, 150]$ by $[-2000, 2000]$

14. $y = x(x + 6)(x - 9)$, $[-10, 10]$ by $[-250, 150]$

15. $y = x^4 - 4x^3$, $[-4, 6]$ by $[-50, 100]$

16. $y = \dfrac{x}{x^2 + 25}$, $[-10, 10]$ by $[-0.2, 0.2]$

17. $y = 1 + |x - 1|$, $[-3, 5]$ by $[-1, 5]$

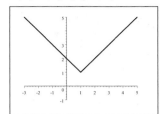

18. $y = 2x - |x^2 - 5|$, $[-10, 10]$ by $[-10, 10]$

19. $x^2 + y^2 = 9$ $\Leftrightarrow$ $y^2 = 9 - x^2$ $\Rightarrow$ $y = \pm\sqrt{9 - x^2}$. So we graph the functions $y_1 = \sqrt{9 - x^2}$ and $y_2 = -\sqrt{9 - x^2}$ in the viewing rectangle $[-6, 6]$ by $[-4, 4]$.

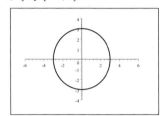

20. $(y - 1)^2 + x^2 = 1$ $\Leftrightarrow$ $(y - 1)^2 = 1 - x^2$ $\Rightarrow$ $y - 1 = \pm\sqrt{1 - x^2}$ $\Leftrightarrow$ $y = 1 \pm \sqrt{1 - x^2}$. So we graph the functions $y_1 = 1 + \sqrt{1 - x^2}$ and $y_2 = 1 - \sqrt{1 - x^2}$ in the viewing rectangle $[-2, 2]$ by $[0, 3]$.

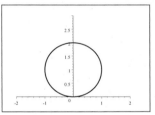

21. $4x^2 + 2y^2 = 1$ $\Leftrightarrow$ $2y^2 = 1 - 4x^2$ $\Leftrightarrow$ $y^2 = \dfrac{1 - 4x^2}{2}$ $\Rightarrow$ $y = \pm\sqrt{\dfrac{1 - 4x^2}{2}}$. So we graph the functions $y_1 = \sqrt{\dfrac{1 - 4x^2}{2}}$ and $y_2 = -\sqrt{\dfrac{1 - 4x^2}{2}}$ in the viewing rectangle $[-1.2, 1.2]$ by $[-0.8, 0.8]$.

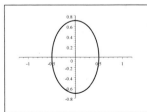

22. $y^2 - 9x^2 = 1$ $\Leftrightarrow$ $y^2 = 1 + 9x^2$ $\Rightarrow$ $y = \pm\sqrt{1 + 9x^2}$. So we graph the functions $y_1 = \sqrt{1 + 9x^2}$ and $y_2 = -\sqrt{1 + 9x^2}$ in the viewing rectangle $[-5, 5]$ by $[-5, 5]$.

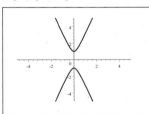

23. Although the graphs of $y = -3x^2 + 6x - \frac{1}{2}$ and
$y = \sqrt{7 - \frac{7}{12}x^2}$ appear to intersect in the viewing
rectangle $[-4, 4]$ by $[-1, 3]$, there is no point of
intersection. You can verify this by zooming in.

24. Although the graphs of $y = \sqrt{49 - x^2}$ and
$y = \frac{1}{5}(41 - 3x)$ appear to intersect in the viewing
rectangle $[-8, 8]$ by $[-1, 8]$, there is no point of
intersection. You can verify this by zooming in.

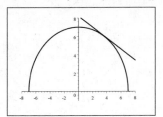

25. The graphs of $y = 6 - 4x - x^2$ and $y = 3x + 18$ appear
to have two points of intersection in the viewing rectangle
$[-6, 2]$ by $[-5, 20]$. You can verify that $x = -4$ and
$x = -3$ are exact solutions.

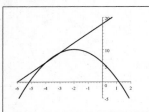

26. The graphs of $y = x^3 - 4x$ and $y = x + 5$ appear to have
one point of intersection in the viewing rectangle $[-4, 4]$
by $[-15, 15]$. The solution is $x \approx 2.627$.

27. Algebraically: $x - 4 = 5x + 12 \quad \Leftrightarrow \quad -16 = 4x \quad \Leftrightarrow$
$x = -4$.
Graphically: We graph the two equations $y_1 = x - 4$ and
$y_2 = 5x + 12$ in the viewing rectangle $[-6, 4]$ by
$[-10, 2]$. Zooming in, we see that the solution is $x = -4$.

28. Algebraically: $\frac{1}{2}x - 3 = 6 + 2x \quad \Leftrightarrow \quad -9 = \frac{3}{2}x \quad \Leftrightarrow$
$x = -6$.
Graphically: We graph the two equations $y_1 = \frac{1}{2}x - 3$
and $y_2 = 6 + 2x$ in the viewing rectangle $[-10, 5]$ by
$[-10, 5]$. Zooming in, we see that the solution is $x = -6$.

29. Algebraically: $\dfrac{2}{x} + \dfrac{1}{2x} = 7 \quad \Leftrightarrow$

$2x\left(\dfrac{2}{x} + \dfrac{1}{2x}\right) = 2x\,(7) \quad \Leftrightarrow \quad 4 + 1 = 14x \quad \Leftrightarrow$

$x = \dfrac{5}{14}$.

Graphically: We graph the two equations $y_1 = \dfrac{2}{x} + \dfrac{1}{2x}$

and $y_2 = 7$ in the viewing rectangle $[-2, 2]$ by $[-2, 8]$.
Zooming in, we see that the solution is $x \approx 0.36$.

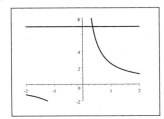

30. Algebraically: $\dfrac{4}{x+2} - \dfrac{6}{2x} = \dfrac{5}{2x+4} \quad \Leftrightarrow$

$2x\,(x+2)\left(\dfrac{4}{x+2} - \dfrac{6}{2x}\right) = 2x\,(x+2)\left(\dfrac{5}{2x+4}\right)$

$\Leftrightarrow \quad 2x\,(4) - (x+2)\,(6) = x\,(5) \quad \Leftrightarrow$

$8x - 6x - 12 = 5x \quad \Leftrightarrow \quad -12 = 3x \quad \Leftrightarrow \quad -4 = x.$

Graphically: We graph the two equations

$y_1 = \dfrac{4}{x+2} - \dfrac{6}{2x}$ and $y_2 = \dfrac{5}{2x+4}$ in the viewing

rectangle $[-5, 5]$ by $[-10, 10]$. Zooming in, we see that
there is only one solution at $x = -4$.

31. Algebraically: $x^2 - 32 = 0 \quad \Leftrightarrow \quad x^2 = 32 \quad \Rightarrow$

$x = \pm\sqrt{32} = \pm 4\sqrt{2}$.

Graphically: We graph the equation $y_1 = x^2 - 32$ and
determine where this curve intersects the x-axis. We use
the viewing rectangle $[-10, 10]$ by $[-5, 5]$. Zooming in,
we see that solutions are $x \approx 5.66$ and $x \approx -5.66$.

32. Algebraically: $x^3 + 16 = 0 \quad \Leftrightarrow \quad x^3 = -16 \quad \Leftrightarrow$

$x = -2\sqrt[3]{2}$.

Graphically: We graph the equation $y = x^3 + 16$ and
determine where this curve intersects the x-axis. We use
the viewing rectangle $[-5, 5]$ by $[-5, 5]$. Zooming in, we
see that the solution is $x \approx -2.52$.

33. Algebraically: $16x^4 = 625 \quad \Leftrightarrow \quad x^4 = \dfrac{625}{16} \quad \Rightarrow$

$x = \pm\dfrac{5}{2} = \pm 2.5$.

Graphically: We graph the two equations $y_1 = 16x^4$ and
$y_2 = 625$ in the viewing rectangle $[-5, 5]$ by $[610, 640]$.
Zooming in, we see that solutions are $x = \pm 2.5$.

34. Algebraically: $2x^5 - 243 = 0 \quad \Leftrightarrow \quad 2x^5 = 243 \quad \Leftrightarrow$

$x^5 = \dfrac{243}{2} \quad \Leftrightarrow \quad x = \sqrt[5]{\dfrac{243}{2}} = \dfrac{3}{2}\sqrt[5]{16}$.

Graphically: We graph the equation $y = 2x^5 - 243$ and
determine where this curve intersects the x-axis. We use
the viewing rectangle $[-5, 10]$ by $[-5, 5]$.
Zooming in, we see that the solution is $x \approx 2.61$.

35. Algebraically: $(x-5)^4 - 80 = 0 \quad \Leftrightarrow \quad (x-5)^4 = 80$ $\Rightarrow \quad x - 5 = \pm\sqrt[4]{80} = \pm 2\sqrt[4]{5} \quad \Leftrightarrow \quad x = 5 \pm 2\sqrt[4]{5}.$ Graphically: We graph the equation $y_1 = (x-5)^4 - 80$ and determine where this curve intersects the x-axis. We use the viewing rectangle $[-1, 9]$ by $[-5, 5]$. Zooming in, we see that solutions are $x \approx 2.01$ and $x \approx 7.99$.

36. Algebraically: $6(x+2)^5 = 64 \quad \Leftrightarrow$ $(x+2)^5 = \frac{64}{6} = \frac{32}{3} \quad \Leftrightarrow \quad x + 2 = \sqrt[5]{\frac{32}{3}} = \frac{2}{3}\sqrt[5]{81}$ $\Leftrightarrow \quad x = -2 + \frac{2}{3}\sqrt[5]{81}.$ Graphically: We graph the two equations $y_1 = 6(x+2)^5$ and $y_2 = 64$ in the viewing rectangle $[-5, 5]$ by $[50, 70]$. Zooming in, we see that the solution is $x \approx -0.39$.

37. We graph $y = x^2 - 7x + 12$ in the viewing rectangle $[0, 6]$ by $[-0.1, 0.1]$. The solutions appear to be exactly $x = 3$ and $x = 4$. [In fact $x^2 - 7x + 12 = (x-3)(x-4)$.]

38. We graph $y = x^2 - 0.75x + 0.125$ in the viewing rectangle $[-2, 2]$ by $[-0.1, 0.1]$. The solutions are $x = 0.25$ and $x = 0.50$.

39. We graph $y = x^3 - 6x^2 + 11x - 6$ in the viewing rectangle $[-1, 4]$ by $[-0.1, 0.1]$. The solutions are $x = 1.00$, $x = 2.00$, and $x = 3.00$.

40. Since $16x^3 + 16x^2 = x + 1 \quad \Leftrightarrow$ $16x^3 + 16x^2 - x - 1 = 0$, we graph $y = 16x^3 + 16x^2 - x - 1$ in the viewing rectangle $[-2, 2]$ by $[-0.1, 0.1]$. The solutions are: $x = -1.00$, $x = -0.25$, and $x = 0.25$.

41. We first graph $y = x - \sqrt{x+1}$ in the viewing rectangle $[-1, 5]$ by $[-0.1, 0.1]$ and find that the solution is near 1.6. Zooming in, we see that solutions is $x \approx 1.62$.

42. $1 + \sqrt{x} = \sqrt{1 + x^2}$ $\Leftrightarrow$

$1 + \sqrt{x} - \sqrt{1 + x^2} = 0$. Since $\sqrt{x}$ is only

defined for $x \geq 0$, we start with the viewing

rectangle $[-1, 5]$ by $[-1, 1]$. In this rectangle,

there appears to be an exact solution at $x = 0$ and

another solution between $x = 2$ and $x = 2.5$. We

then use the viewing rectangle $[2.3, 2.35]$ by

$[-0.01, 0.01]$, and isolate the second solution as

$x \approx 2.314$. Thus the solutions are $x = 0$ and

$x \approx 2.31$.

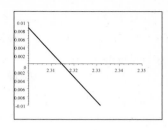

43. We graph $y = x^{1/3} - x$ in the viewing rectangle $[-3, 3]$ by $[-1, 1]$. The solutions

are $x = -1$, $x = 0$, and $x = 1$, as can be verified by substitution.

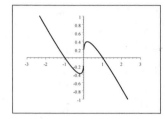

44. Since $x^{1/2}$ is only defined for $x \geq 0$, we start by

graphing $y = x^{1/2} + x^{1/3} - x$ in the viewing

rectangle $[-1, 5]$ by $[-1, 1]$. We see a solution at

$x = 0$ and another one between $x = 3$ and

$x = 3.5$. We then use the viewing rectangle

$[3.3, 3.4]$ by $[-0.01, 0.01]$, and isolate the second

solution as $x \approx 3.31$. Thus, the solutions are

$x = 0$ and $x \approx 3.31$.

45. $x^3 - 2x^2 - x - 1 = 0$, so we start by graphing

the function $y = x^3 - 2x^2 - x - 1$ in the

viewing rectangle $[-10, 10]$ by $[-100, 100]$.

There appear to be two solutions, one near $x = 0$

and another one between $x = 2$ and $x = 3$. We

then use the viewing rectangle $[-1, 5]$ by $[-1, 1]$

and zoom in on the only solution, $x \approx 2.55$.

46. $x^4 - 8x^2 + 2 = 0$. We start by graphing the

function $y = x^4 - 8x^2 + 2$ in the viewing

rectangle $[-10, 10]$ by $[-10, 10]$. There appear to

be four solutions between $x = -3$ and $x = 3$. We

then use the viewing rectangle $[-5, 5]$ by $[-1, 1]$,

and zoom to find the four solutions $x \approx -2.78$,

$x \approx -0.51$, $x \approx 0.51$, and $x \approx 2.78$.

47. $x(x-1)(x+2) = \frac{1}{6}x$ $\Leftrightarrow$

$x(x-1)(x+2) - \frac{1}{6}x = 0$. We start by

graphing the function

$y = x(x-1)(x+2) - \frac{1}{6}x$ in the viewing

rectangle $[-5, 5]$ by $[-10, 10]$. There appear to

be three solutions. We then use the viewing

rectangle $[-2.5, 2.5]$ by $[-1, 1]$ and zoom into

the solutions at $x \approx -2.05$, $x = 0.00$, and

$x \approx 1.05$.

48. $x^4 = 16 - x^3$. We start by graphing the functions $y_1 = x^4$ and $y_2 = 16 - x^3$ in the viewing rectangle $[-10, 10]$ by $[-5, 40]$. There appears to be two solutions, one near $x = -2$ and another one near $x = 2$. We then use the viewing rectangle $[-2.4, -2.2]$ by $[27, 29]$, and zoom in to find the solution at $x \approx -2.31$. We then use the viewing rectangle $[1.7, 1.8]$ by $[9.5, 10.5]$, and zoom in to find the solution at $x \approx 1.79$.

49. We graph $y = x^2 - 3x - 10$ in the viewing rectangle
$[-5, 6]$ by $[-14, 2]$. The the solution to the inequality is
$[-2, 5]$.

50. Since $0.5x^2 + 0.875x \le 0.25$ $\Leftrightarrow$
$0.5x^2 + 0.875x - 0.25 \le 0$, we graph
$y = 0.5x^2 + 0.875x - 0.25$ in the viewing rectangle
$[-3, 1]$ by $[-5, 5]$. Thus the solution to the inequality is
$-2 \le x \le 0.25$.

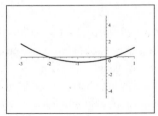

51. Since $x^3 + 11x \le 6x^2 + 6$ $\Leftrightarrow$ $x^3 - 6x^2 + 11x - 6 \le 0$, we graph
$y = x^3 - 6x^2 + 11x - 6$ in the viewing rectangle $[0, 5]$ by $[-5, 5]$. The solution
set is $(-\infty, 1.0] \cup [2.0, 3.0]$.

52. Since $16x^3 + 24x^2 > -9x - 1$ $\Leftrightarrow$ $16x^3 + 24x^2 + 9x + 1 > 0$, we graph $y = 16x^3 + 24x^2 + 9x + 1$ in the viewing rectangle $[-3, 1]$ by $[-5, 5]$. From this rectangle, we see that $x = -1$ is an x-intercept, but it is unclear what is occurring between $x = -0.5$ and

$x = 0$. We then use the viewing rectangle $[-1, 0]$ by $[-0.01, 0.01]$. It shows $y = 0$ at $x = -0.25$. Thus in interval notation, the solution is $(-1, -0.25) \cup (-0.25, \infty)$.

53. Since $x^{1/3} \leq x$ $\Leftrightarrow$ $x^{1/3} - x < 0$, we graph $y = x^{1/3} - x$ in the viewing rectangle $[-3, 3]$ by $[-1, 1]$. From this, we find that the solution set is $(-1, 0) \cup (1, \infty)$.

54. Since $\sqrt{0.5x^2 + 1} \leq 2|x| \Leftrightarrow \sqrt{0.5x^2 + 1} - 2|x| \leq 0$, we graph $y = \sqrt{0.5x^2 + 1} - 2|x|$ in the viewing rectangle $[-1, 1]$ by $[-1, 1]$. We locate the x-intercepts at $x \approx \pm 0.535$. Thus in interval notation, the solution is approximately $(-\infty, -0.535] \cup [0.535, \infty)$.

55. Since $(x + 1)^2 < (x - 1)^2$ $\Leftrightarrow$ $(x + 1)^2 - (x - 1)^2 < 0$, we graph $y = (x + 1)^2 - (x - 1)^2$ in the viewing rectangle $[-2, 2]$ by $[-5, 5]$. The solution set is $(-\infty, 0)$.

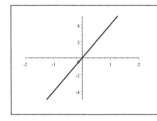

56. Since $(x + 1)^2 \leq x^3$ $\Leftrightarrow$ $(x + 1)^2 - x^3 \leq 0$, we graph $y = (x + 1)^2 - x^3$ in the viewing rectangle $[-4, 4]$ by $[-1, 1]$. The x-intercept is close to $x = 2$. Using a trace function, we obtain $x \approx 2.148$. Thus the solution is $[2.148, \infty)$.

57. As in Example 6, we graph the equation $y = x^3 - 6x^2 + 9x - \sqrt{x}$ in the viewing rectangle $[0, 10]$ by $[-2, 15]$. We see the two solutions found in Example 6 and what appears to be an additional solution at $x = 0$. In the viewing rectangle $[0, 0.05]$ by $[-0.25, 0.25]$, we find yet another solution at $x \approx 0.01$. We can verify that $x = 0$ is an exact solution by substitution.

58. (a)

(b) From the graph, the solution appears to be 100 cooktops. Verifying it by substituting $x = 100$ in $y = 10x + 0.5x^2 - 0.001x^3 - 5000$ we get $y = 0$.

(c) Using a zoom or trace function on a calculator, we find that the company's profits are greater than $15,000 for $280 < x < 400$.

59. (a)

(b) Using a zoom or trace function, we find that $y \geq 10$ for $x \geq 66.7$. We could estimate this since if $x < 100$, then $\left(\dfrac{x}{5280}\right)^2 \leq 0.00036$. So for $x < 100$ we have $\sqrt{1.5x + \left(\dfrac{x}{5280}\right)^2} \approx \sqrt{1.5x}$. Solving $\sqrt{1.5x} > 10$ we get $1.5 > 100$ or $x > \dfrac{100}{1.5} = 66.7$ mi.

60. Answers may vary. Possible answers are given.

(a) Absolute value must be chosen from a menu or written as "abs() ".

(b) Some calculators or computer graphing programs will not take the odd root of a negative number, even though it is defined. Since $\sqrt[5]{-x} = -\sqrt[5]{x}$, you may have to enter two functions: `Y_1=x^(1/5)` and `Y_2=-(-x)^(1/5)`.

(c) Here you must remember to use parentheses and enter $x/(x-1)$.

(d) As in part (b), some graphing devices may not give the entire graph. When this is the case, you will need to determine where the radicand (inside of the radical) is negative. Here you might need to define two functions: `Y_1=x^3+(x+2)^(1/3)` and `Y_2=x^3-(-x-2)^(1/3)`.

61. Calculators perform operations in the following order: exponents are applied before division and division is applied before addition. Therefore, `Y_1=x^1/3` is interpreted as $y = \dfrac{x^1}{3} = \dfrac{x}{3}$, which is the equation of a line. Likewise, `Y_2=x/x+4` is interpreted as $y = \dfrac{x}{x} + 4 = 1 + 4 = 5$. Instead, enter the following: `Y_1=x^(1/3)`, `Y_2=x/(x+4)`.

62. Answers will vary.

63. (a) We graph $y_1 = x^3 - 3x$ and $y_2 = k$ for $k = -4, -2, 0, 2,$ and 4 in the viewing rectangle $[-5, 5]$ by $[-10, 10]$. The number of solutions and the solutions are shown in the table below.

k	Number of solutions	Solutions
-4	1	$x \approx -2.20$
-2	2	$x = -2, x = 1$
0	3	$x \approx \pm 1.73, x = 0$
2	2	$x = -1, x = 2$
4	1	$x \approx 2.20$

(b) The equation $x^3 - 3x = k$ will have one solution for all $k < -2$ or $k > 2$, it will have exactly two solutions when $k = \pm 2$, and it will have three solutions for $-2 < k < 2$.

1.10 Lines

1. $m = \dfrac{y_2 - y_1}{x_2 - x_1} = \dfrac{2 - 0}{4 - 0} = \dfrac{2}{4} = \dfrac{1}{2}$

2. $m = \dfrac{y_2 - y_1}{x_2 - x_1} = \dfrac{0 - (-6)}{0 - (2)} = \dfrac{6}{-2} = -3$

3. $m = \dfrac{y_2 - y_1}{x_2 - x_1} = \dfrac{0 - 2}{-10 - 2} = \dfrac{-2}{-12} = \dfrac{1}{6}$

4. $m = \dfrac{y_2 - y_1}{x_2 - x_1} = \dfrac{2 - (3)}{1 - (3)} = \dfrac{-1}{-2} = \dfrac{1}{2}$

5. $m = \dfrac{y_2 - y_1}{x_2 - x_1} = \dfrac{4 - 3}{2 - 4} = \dfrac{1}{-2} = -\dfrac{1}{2}$

6. $m = \dfrac{y_2 - y_1}{x_2 - x_1} = \dfrac{3 - (-5)}{(-4) - (2)} = \dfrac{8}{-6} = -\dfrac{4}{3}$

7. $m = \dfrac{y_2 - y_1}{x_2 - x_1} = \dfrac{6 - (-3)}{-1 - 1} = \dfrac{9}{-2} = -\dfrac{9}{2}$

8. $m = \dfrac{y_2 - y_1}{x_2 - x_1} = \dfrac{0 - (-4)}{6 - (-1)} = \dfrac{4}{7}$

9. For ℓ_1, we find two points, $(-1, 2)$ and $(0, 0)$ that lie on the line. Thus the slope of ℓ_1 is $m = \dfrac{y_2 - y_1}{x_2 - x_1} = \dfrac{2 - 0}{-1 - 0} = -2$.

For ℓ_2, we find two points $(0, 2)$ and $(2, 3)$. Thus, the slope of ℓ_2 is $m = \dfrac{y_2 - y_1}{x_2 - x_1} = \dfrac{3 - 2}{2 - 0} = \dfrac{1}{2}$. For ℓ_3 we find the points

$(2, -2)$ and $(3, 1)$. Thus, the slope of ℓ_3 is $m = \dfrac{y_2 - y_1}{x_2 - x_1} = \dfrac{1 - (-2)}{3 - 2} = 3$. For ℓ_4, we find the points $(-2, -1)$ and

$(2, -2)$. Thus, the slope of ℓ_4 is $m = \dfrac{y_2 - y_1}{x_2 - x_1} = \dfrac{-2 - (-1)}{2 - (-2)} = \dfrac{-1}{4} = -\dfrac{1}{4}$.

10. (a)

(b)

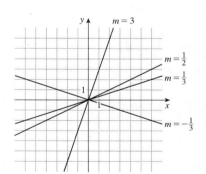

11. First we find two points, $(0, 4)$ and $(4, 0)$ that lie on the line. So the slope is $m = \dfrac{0 - 4}{4 - 0} = -1$. Since the y-intercept is 4, the equation of the line is $y = mx + b = -1x + 4$. So $y = -x + 4$, or $x + y - 4 = 0$.

12. We find two points on the graph, $(0, 4)$ and $(-2, 0)$. So the slope is $m = \dfrac{0 - 4}{-2 - 0} = 2$. Since the y-intercept is 4, the equation of the line is $y = mx + b = 2x + 4$, so $y = 2x + 4 \quad \Leftrightarrow \quad 2x - y + 4 = 0$.

13. We choose the two intercepts as points, $(0, -3)$ and $(2, 0)$. So the slope is $m = \dfrac{0 - (-3)}{2 - 0} = \frac{3}{2}$. Since the y-intercept is -3, the equation of the line is $y = mx + b = \frac{3}{2}x - 3$, or $3x - 2y - 6 = 0$.

14. We choose the two intercepts, $(0, -4)$ and $(-3, 0)$. So the slope is $m = \dfrac{0 - (-4)}{-3 - 0} = -\frac{4}{3}$. Since the y-intercept is -4, the equation of the line is $y = mx + b = -\frac{4}{3}x - 4 \quad \Leftrightarrow \quad 4x + 3y + 12 = 0$.

15. Using the equation $y - y_1 = m(x - x_1)$, we get $y - 3 = 1(x - 2) \quad \Leftrightarrow \quad -x + y = 1 \quad \Leftrightarrow \quad x - y + 1 = 0$.

16. Using the equation $y - y_1 = m(x - x_1)$, we get $y - 4 = -1(x - (-2)) \quad \Leftrightarrow \quad y - 4 = -x - 2 \quad \Leftrightarrow \quad x + y - 2 = 0$.

17. Using the equation $y - y_1 = m(x - x_1)$, we get $y - 7 = \frac{2}{3}(x - 1) \quad \Leftrightarrow \quad 3y - 21 = 2x - 2 \quad \Leftrightarrow \quad -2x + 3y = 19$ $\Leftrightarrow \quad 2x - 3y + 19 = 0$.

18. Using the equation $y - y_1 = m(x - x_1)$, we get $y - (-5) = -\frac{7}{2}(x - (-3)) \quad \Leftrightarrow \quad 2y + 10 = -7x - 21 \quad \Leftrightarrow$ $7x + 2y + 31 = 0$.

19. First we find the slope, which is $m = \dfrac{y_2 - y_1}{x_2 - x_1} = \dfrac{6 - 1}{1 - 2} = \dfrac{5}{-1} = -5$. Substituting into $y - y_1 = m(x - x_1)$, we get $y - 6 = -5(x - 1) \quad \Leftrightarrow \quad y - 6 = -5x + 5 \quad \Leftrightarrow \quad 5x + y - 11 = 0$.

20. First we find the slope, which is $m = \dfrac{y_2 - y_1}{x_2 - x_1} = \dfrac{3 - (-2)}{4 - (-1)} = \frac{5}{5} = 1$. Substituting into $y - y_1 = m(x - x_1)$, we get $y - 3 = 1(x - 4) \quad \Leftrightarrow \quad y - 3 = x - 4 \quad \Leftrightarrow \quad x - y - 1 = 0$.

21. Using $y = mx + b$, we have $y = 3x + (-2)$ or $3x - y - 2 = 0$.

22. Using $y = mx + b$, we have $y = \frac{2}{5}x + 4 \quad \Leftrightarrow \quad 2x - 5y + 20 = 0$.

23. We are given two points, $(1, 0)$ and $(0, -3)$. Thus, the slope is $m = \dfrac{y_2 - y_1}{x_2 - x_1} = \dfrac{-3 - 0}{0 - 1} = \dfrac{-3}{-1} = 3$. Using the y-intercept, we have $y = 3x + (-3)$ or $y = 3x - 3$ or $3x - y - 3 = 0$.

24. We are given two points, $(-8, 0)$ and $(0, 6)$. Thus, the slope is $m = \dfrac{y_2 - y_1}{x_2 - x_1} = \dfrac{6 - 0}{0 - (-8)} = \frac{6}{8} = \frac{3}{4}$. Using the y-intercept we have $y = \frac{3}{4}x + 6 \quad \Leftrightarrow \quad 3x - 4y + 24 = 0$.

25. Since the equation of a horizontal line passing through (a, b) is $y = b$, the equation of the horizontal line passing through $(4, 5)$ is $y = 5$.

26. Any line parallel to the y-axis will have undefined slope and be of the form $x = a$. Since the graph of the line passes through the point $(4, 5)$, the equation of the line is $x = 4$.

27. Since $x + 2y = 6 \quad \Leftrightarrow \quad 2y = -x + 6 \quad \Leftrightarrow \quad y = -\frac{1}{2}x + 3$, the slope of this line is $-\frac{1}{2}$. Thus, the line we seek is given by $y - (-6) = -\frac{1}{2}(x - 1) \quad \Leftrightarrow \quad 2y + 12 = -x + 1 \quad \Leftrightarrow \quad x + 2y + 11 = 0$.

28. Since $2x + 3y + 4 = 0 \quad \Leftrightarrow \quad 3y = -2x - 4 \quad \Leftrightarrow \quad y = -\frac{2}{3}x - \frac{4}{3}$, the slope of this line is $m = -\frac{2}{3}$. Substituting $m = -\frac{2}{3}$ and $b = 6$ into the slope intercept formula, the line we seek is given by $y = -\frac{2}{3}x + 6 \quad \Leftrightarrow \quad 2x + 3y - 18 = 0$.

29. Any line parallel to $x = 5$ will have undefined slope and be of the form $x = a$. Thus the equation of the line is $x = -1$.

30. Any line perpendicular to $y = 1$ has undefined slope and is of the form $x = a$. Since the graph of the line passes through the point $(2, 6)$, the equation of the line is $x = 2$.

31. First find the slope of $2x + 5y + 8 = 0$. This gives $2x + 5y + 8 = 0 \quad \Leftrightarrow \quad 5y = -2x - 8 \quad \Leftrightarrow \quad y = -\frac{2}{5}x - \frac{8}{5}$. So the slope of the line that is perpendicular to $2x + 5y + 8 = 0$ is $m = -\dfrac{1}{-2/5} = \frac{5}{2}$. The equation of the line we seek is $y - (-2) = \frac{5}{2}(x - (-1)) \quad \Leftrightarrow \quad 2y + 4 = 5x + 5 \quad \Leftrightarrow \quad 5x - 2y + 1 = 0$.

32. First find the slope of the line $4x - 8y = 1$. This gives $4x - 8y = 1 \quad \Leftrightarrow \quad -8y = -4x + 1 \quad \Leftrightarrow \quad y = \frac{1}{2}x - \frac{1}{8}$. So the slope of the line that is perpendicular to $4x - 8y = 1$ is $m = -\dfrac{1}{1/2} = -2$. The equation of the line we seek is $y - (-\frac{2}{3}) = -2(x - \frac{1}{2}) \quad \Leftrightarrow \quad y + \frac{2}{3} = -2x + 1 \quad \Leftrightarrow \quad 6x + 3y - 1 = 0$.

33. First find the slope of the line passing through $(2, 5)$ and $(-2, 1)$. This gives $m = \dfrac{1 - 5}{-2 - 2} = \dfrac{-4}{-4} = 1$, and so the equation of the line we seek is $y - 7 = 1\,(x - 1)$ $\quad\Leftrightarrow\quad x - y + 6 = 0$.

34. First find the slope of the line passing through $(1, 1)$ and $(5, -1)$. This gives $m = \dfrac{-1 - 1}{5 - 1} = \dfrac{-2}{4} = -\frac{1}{2}$, and so the slope of the line that is perpendicular is $m = -\dfrac{1}{-1/2} = 2$. Thus the equation of the line we seek is $y + 11 = 2\,(x + 2)$ $\quad\Leftrightarrow\quad$ $2x - y - 7 = 0$.

35. (a)

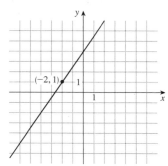

(b) $y - 1 = \frac{3}{2}\,(x - (-2))$ $\quad\Leftrightarrow\quad$ $2y - 2 = 3\,(x + 2)$
$\Leftrightarrow$ $2y - 2 = 3x + 6$ $\quad\Leftrightarrow\quad$ $3x - 2y + 8 = 0$.

36. (a)

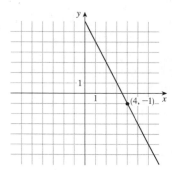

(b) $y - (-1) = -2\,(x - 4)$ $\quad\Leftrightarrow\quad$ $y + 1 = -2x + 8$
$\Leftrightarrow$ $2x + y - 7 = 0$.

37.

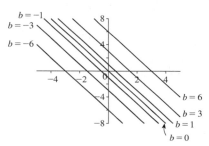

$y = -2x + b$, $b = 0, \pm 1, \pm 3, \pm 6$. They have the same slope, so they are parallel.

38.

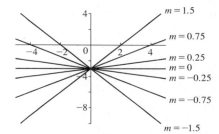

$y = mx - 3$, $m = 0, \pm 0.25, \pm 0.75, \pm 1.5$. Each of the lines contains the point $(0, -3)$ because the point $(0, -3)$ satisfies each equation $y = mx - 3$. Since $(0, -3)$ is on the y-axis, they all have the same y-intercept.

39.

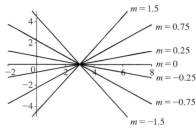

$y = m\,(x - 3)$, $m = 0, \pm 0.25, \pm 0.75, \pm 1.5$. Each of the lines contains the point $(3, 0)$ because the point $(3, 0)$ satisfies each equation $y = m\,(x - 3)$. Since $(3, 0)$ is on the x-axis, we could also say that they all have the same x-intercept.

40.

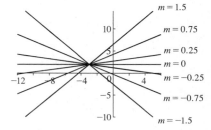

$y = 2 + m\,(x + 3)$, $m = 0, \pm 0.25, \pm 0.75, \pm 1.5$. Each of the lines contains the point $(-3, 2)$ because the point $(-3, 2)$ satisfies each equation $y = 2 + m\,(x + 3)$.

41. $x + y = 3$ $\Leftrightarrow$ $y = -x + 3$. So the slope is -1, and the y-intercept is 3.

42. $3x - 2y = 12$ $\Leftrightarrow$ $-2y = -3x + 12$ $\Leftrightarrow$ $y = \frac{3}{2}x - 6$. So the slope is $\frac{3}{2}$, and the y-intercept is -6.

43. $x + 3y = 0$ $\Leftrightarrow$ $3y = -x$ $\Leftrightarrow$ $y = -\frac{1}{3}x$. So the slope is $-\frac{1}{3}$, and the y-intercept is 0.

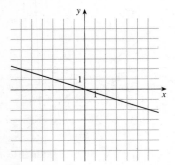

44. $2x - 5y = 0$ $\Leftrightarrow$ $-5y = -2x$ $\Leftrightarrow$ $y = \frac{2}{5}x$. So the slope is $\frac{2}{5}$, and the y-intercept is 0.

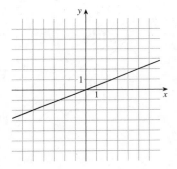

45. $\frac{1}{2}x - \frac{1}{3}y + 1 = 0$ $\Leftrightarrow$ $-\frac{1}{3}y = -\frac{1}{2}x - 1$ $\Leftrightarrow$ $y = \frac{3}{2}x + 3$. So the slope is $\frac{3}{2}$, and the y-intercept is 3.

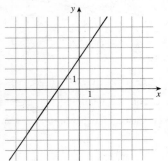

46. $-3x - 5y + 30 = 0$ $\Leftrightarrow$ $-5y = 3x - 30$ $\Leftrightarrow$ $y = -\frac{3}{5}x + 6$. So the slope is $-\frac{3}{5}$, and the y-intercept is 6.

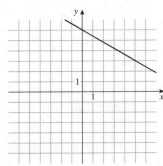

47. $y = 4$ can also be expressed as $y = 0x + 4$. So the slope is 0, and the y-intercept is 4.

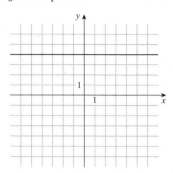

48. $4y + 8 = 0$ $\Leftrightarrow$ $4y = -8$ $\Leftrightarrow$ $y = -2$, which can also be expressed as $y = 0x - 2$. So the slope is 0, and the y-intercept is -2.

49. $3x - 4y = 12$ $\Leftrightarrow$ $-4y = -3x + 12$ $\Leftrightarrow$ $y = \frac{3}{4}x - 3$. So the slope is $\frac{3}{4}$, and the y-intercept is -3.

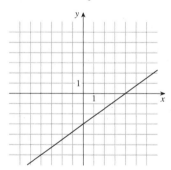

50. $x = -5$ cannot be expressed in the form $y = mx + b$. So the slope is undefined, and there is no y-intercept. This is a vertical line.

51. $3x + 4y - 1 = 0$ $\Leftrightarrow$ $4y = -3x + 1$ $\Leftrightarrow$ $y = -\frac{3}{4}x + \frac{1}{4}$. So the slope is $-\frac{3}{4}$, and the y-intercept is $\frac{1}{4}$.

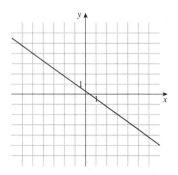

52. $4x + 5y = 10$ $\Leftrightarrow$ $5y = -4x + 10$ $\Leftrightarrow$ $y = -\frac{4}{5}x + 2$. So the slope is $-\frac{4}{5}$, and the y-intercept is 2.

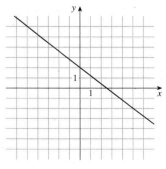

53.   We first plot the points to find the pairs of points that determine each side. Next we find the slopes of opposite sides. The slope of AB is $\dfrac{4-1}{7-1} = \dfrac{3}{6} = \dfrac{1}{2}$, and the slope of DC is $\dfrac{10-7}{5-(-1)} = \dfrac{3}{6} = \dfrac{1}{2}$. Since these slope are equal, these two sides are parallel. The slope of AD is $\dfrac{7-1}{-1-1} = \dfrac{6}{-2} = -3$, and the slope of BC is $\dfrac{10-4}{5-7} = \dfrac{6}{-2} = -3$. Since these slope are equal, these two sides are parallel. Hence $ABCD$ is a parallelogram.

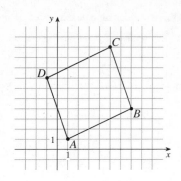

54.   We first plot the points to determine the perpendicular sides. Next find the slopes of the sides. The slope of AB is $\dfrac{3-(-1)}{3-(-3)} = \dfrac{4}{6} = \dfrac{2}{3}$, and the slope of AC is $\dfrac{8-(-1)}{-9-(-3)} = \dfrac{9}{-6} = -\dfrac{3}{2}$. Since (slope of AB) $\times$ (slope of AC) $= \left(\dfrac{2}{3}\right)\left(-\dfrac{3}{2}\right) = -1$, the sides are perpendicular, and ABC is a right triangle.

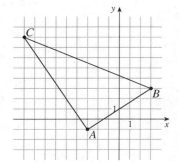

55.   We first plot the points to find the pairs of points that determine each side. Next we find the slopes of opposite sides. The slope of AB is $\dfrac{3-1}{11-1} = \dfrac{2}{10} = \dfrac{1}{5}$ and the slope of DC is $\dfrac{6-8}{0-10} = \dfrac{-2}{-10} = \dfrac{1}{5}$. Since these slope are equal, these two sides are parallel. Slope of AD is $\dfrac{6-1}{0-1} = \dfrac{5}{-1} = -5$, and the slope of BC is $\dfrac{3-8}{11-10} = \dfrac{-5}{1} = -5$. Since these slope are equal, these two sides are parallel. Since (slope of AB) $\times$ (slope of AD) $= \dfrac{1}{5} \times (-5) = -1$, the first two sides are each perpendicular to the second two sides. So the sides form a rectangle.

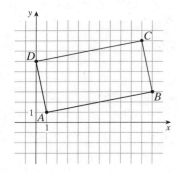

56. (a) The slope of the line passing through $(1,1)$ and $(3,9)$ is $\dfrac{9-1}{3-1} = \dfrac{8}{2} = 4$. The slope of the line passing through $(1,1)$ and $(6,21)$ is $\dfrac{21-1}{6-1} = \dfrac{20}{5} = 4$. Since the slopes are equal, the points are collinear.

(b) The slope of the line passing through $(-1,3)$ and $(1,7)$ is $\dfrac{7-3}{1-(-1)} = \dfrac{4}{2} = 2$. The slope of the line passing through $(-1,3)$ and $(4,15)$ is $\dfrac{15-3}{4-(-1)} = \dfrac{12}{5}$. Since the slopes are not equal, the points are not collinear.

57.   We need the slope and the midpoint of the line AB. The midpoint of AB is $\left(\dfrac{1+7}{2}, \dfrac{4-2}{2}\right) = (4,1)$, and the slope of AB is $m = \dfrac{-2-4}{7-1} = \dfrac{-6}{6} = -1$. The slope of the perpendicular bisector will have slope $\dfrac{-1}{m} = \dfrac{-1}{-1} = 1$. Using the point-slope form, the equation of the perpendicular bisector is $y - 1 = 1\,(x-4)$ or $x - y - 3 = 0$.

58. We find the intercepts (the length of the sides). When $x = 0$, we have $2y + 3(0) - 6 = 0$ ⇔ $2y = 6$ ⇔ $y = 3$, and when $y = 0$, we have $2(0) + 3x - 6 = 0$ ⇔ $3x = 6$ ⇔ $x = 2$. Thus, the area of the triangle is $\frac{1}{2}(3)(2) = 3$.

59. (a) We start with the two points $(a, 0)$ and $(0, b)$. The slope of the line that contains them is $\dfrac{b - 0}{0 - a} = -\dfrac{b}{a}$. So the equation of the line containing them is $y = -\dfrac{b}{a}x + b$ (using the slope-intercept form). Dividing by b (since $b \neq 0$) gives $\dfrac{y}{b} = -\dfrac{x}{a} + 1$ ⇔ $\dfrac{x}{a} + \dfrac{y}{b} = 1$.

(b) Setting $a = 6$ and $b = -8$, we get $\dfrac{x}{6} + \dfrac{y}{-8} = 1$ ⇔ $4x - 3y = 24$ ⇔ $4x - 3y - 24 = 0$.

60. (a) The line tangent at $(3, -4)$ will be perpendicular to the line passing through the points $(0, 0)$ and $(3, -4)$. The slope of this line is $\dfrac{-4 - 0}{3 - 0} = -\dfrac{4}{3}$. Thus, the slope of the tangent line will be $-\dfrac{1}{(-4/3)} = \dfrac{3}{4}$. Then the equation of the tangent line is $y - (-4) = \frac{3}{4}(x - 3)$ ⇔ $4(y + 4) = 3(x - 3)$ ⇔ $3x - 4y - 25 = 0$.

(b) Since diametrically opposite points on the circle have parallel tangent lines, the other point is $(-3, 4)$.

61. Let h be the change in your horizontal distance, in feet. Then $-\frac{6}{100} = \dfrac{-1000}{h}$ ⇔ $h = \dfrac{100{,}000}{6} \approx 16{,}667$. So the change in your horizontal distance is about 16,667 feet.

62. (a) The slope represents the increase in the average surface temperature in degrees in $^\circ$ C per year. The T-intercept is the average surface temperature in 1900, or 8.5° C.

(b) In 2100, $T = 2100 - 1900 = 200$, so $T = 0.02(200) + 8.50 = 12.5^\circ$ C.

63. (a) The slope is $0.0417D = 0.0417(200) = 8.34$. It represents the increase in dosage for each one-year increase in the child's age.

(b) When $a = 0$, $c = 8.34(0 + 1) = 8.34$ mg.

64. (a)

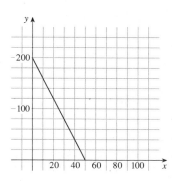

(b) The slope, -4, represents the decline in number of spaces sold for each \$1 increase in rent. The y-intercept is the number of spaces at the flea market, 200, and the x-intercept is the cost per space when the manager rents no spaces, \$50.

65. (a)

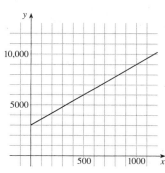

(b) The slope is the cost per toaster oven, \$6. The y-intercept, \$3000, is the monthly fixed cost — the cost that is incurred no matter how many toaster ovens are produced.

66. (a)

C	$-30°$	$-20°$	$-10°$	$0°$	$10°$	$20°$	$30°$
F	$-22°$	$-4°$	$14°$	$32°$	$50°$	$68°$	$86°$

(b) Substituting a for both F and C, we have

$$a = \tfrac{9}{5}a + 32 \quad \Leftrightarrow \quad -\tfrac{4}{5}a = 32 \quad \Leftrightarrow$$

$a = -40°$. Thus both scales agree at $-40°$.

67. (a) Using n in place of x and t in place of y, we find that the slope is $\dfrac{t_2 - t_1}{n_2 - n_1} = \dfrac{80 - 70}{168 - 120} = \tfrac{10}{48} = \tfrac{5}{24}$. So the linear

equation is $t - 80 = \tfrac{5}{24}(n - 168) \quad \Leftrightarrow \quad t - 80 = \tfrac{5}{24}n - 35 \quad \Leftrightarrow \quad t = \tfrac{5}{24}n + 45.$

(b) When $n = 150$, the temperature is approximately given by $t = \tfrac{5}{24}(150) + 45 = 76.25°$ F $\approx 76°$ F.

68. (a) Using t in place of x and V in place of y, we find the slope of the line
using the points $(0, 4000)$ and $(4, 200)$. Thus, the slope is

$$m = \frac{200 - 4000}{4 - 0} = \frac{-3800}{4} = -950.$$ Using the V-intercept, the

linear equation is $V = -950t + 4000$.

(c) The slope represents the rate of depreciation of the computer. The V
-intercept represents the cost of the computer.

(d) When $t = 3$, the value of the computer is given by

$V = -950(3) + 4000 = 1150.$

(b)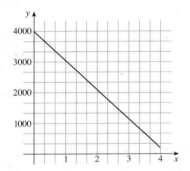

69. (a) We are given $\dfrac{\text{change in pressure}}{\text{10 feet change in depth}} = \dfrac{4.34}{10} = 0.434.$ Using P for

pressure and d for depth, and using the point $P = 15$ when $d = 0$, we

have $P - 15 = 0.434(d - 0) \quad \Leftrightarrow \quad P = 0.434d + 15.$

(c) The slope represents the increase in pressure per foot of descent. The
y-intercept represents the pressure at the surface.

(d) When $P = 100$, then $100 = 0.434d + 15 \quad \Leftrightarrow \quad 0.434d = 85$

$\Leftrightarrow \quad d = 195.9$ ft. Thus the pressure is 100 lb/in^3 at a depth of

approximately 196 ft.

(b)

70. (a) Using rate $= \dfrac{\text{distance}}{\text{time}}$, we have rate $= \dfrac{40}{50/60} = 48$ mi/h. So

$d = 48t.$

(c) The slope of the line is 48 and it represents the speed in mi/h.

(b)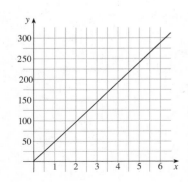

71. (a) Using d in place of x and C in place of y, we find the slope to be

$$\frac{C_2 - C_1}{d_2 - d_1} = \frac{460 - 380}{800 - 480} = \frac{80}{320} = \frac{1}{4}.$$ So the linear equation is

$$C - 460 = \tfrac{1}{4}(d - 800) \quad \Leftrightarrow \quad C - 460 = \tfrac{1}{4}d - 200 \quad \Leftrightarrow$$

$$C = \tfrac{1}{4}d + 260.$$

(b) Substituting $d = 1500$ we get $C = \tfrac{1}{4}(1500) + 260 = 635$. Thus, the
cost of driving 1500 miles is \$635.

(d) The y-intercept represents the fixed cost, \$260.

(e) It is a suitable model because you have fixed monthly costs such as
insurance and car payments, as well as costs that occur as you drive,
such as gasoline, oil, tires, etc., and the cost of these for each
additional mile driven is a constant.

(c)

The slope of the line represents the
cost per mile, \$0.25.

72. (a) Using the points $(100, 2200)$ and $(300, 4800)$, we find that the slope
is $\dfrac{4800 - 2200}{300 - 100} = \dfrac{2600}{200} = 13$. So $y - 2200 = 13(x - 100) \quad \Leftrightarrow$
$y = 13x + 900$.

(b) The slope of the line in part (a) is 13, and it represents the cost of
producing each additional chair.

(c) The y-intercept is 900, and it represents the fixed daily costs of
operating the factory.

73. Slope is the rate of change of one variable per unit change in another variable. So if the slope is positive, then the
temperature is rising. Likewise, if the slope is negative then the temperature is decreasing. If the slope is 0, then the
temperature is not changing.

74. We label the three points A, B, and C. If the slope of the line segment $\overline{AB}$ is equal to the slope of the line segment $\overline{BC}$,
then the points A, B, and C are collinear. Using the distance formula, we find the distance between A and B, between B
and C, and between A and C. If the sum of the two smaller distances equals the largest distance, the points A, B, and C are
collinear.

Another method: Find an equation for the line through A and B. Then check if C satisfies the equation. If so, the points are
collinear.

1.11   Modeling Variation

1. $T = kx$, where k is constant.

2. $P = kw$, where k is constant.

3. $v = \dfrac{k}{z}$, where k is constant.

4. $w = kmn$, where k is constant.

5. $y = \dfrac{ks}{t}$, where k is constant.

6. $P = \dfrac{k}{T}$, where k is constant.

7. $z = k\sqrt{y}$, where k is constant.

8. $A = k\dfrac{t^2}{x^3}$, where k is constant.

9. $V = klwh$, where k is constant.

10. $S = kr^2\theta^2$, where k is constant.

11. $R = \dfrac{ki}{Pt}$, where k is constant.

12. $A = k\sqrt{xy}$, where k is constant.

13. Since y is directly proportional to x, $y = kx$. Since $y = 42$ when $x = 6$, we have $42 = k\,(6)$ $\Leftrightarrow$ $k = 7$. So $y = 7x$.

14. $z = \dfrac{k}{t}$. Since $z = 5$ when $t = 3$, we have $5 = \dfrac{k}{3}$ $\Leftrightarrow$ $k = 15$, so $z = \dfrac{15}{t}$.

15. Since M varies directly as x and inversely as y, $M = \dfrac{kx}{y}$. Since $M = 5$ when $x = 2$ and $y = 6$, we have $5 = \dfrac{k\,(2)}{6}$ $\Leftrightarrow$
$k = 15$. Therefore $M = \dfrac{15x}{y}$.

16. $S = kpq$. Since $S = 180$ when $p = 4$ and $q = 5$, we have $180 = k\,(4)\,(5)$ $\Leftrightarrow$ $180 = 20k$ $\Leftrightarrow$ $k = 9$. So
$S = 9pq$.

17. Since W is inversely proportional to the square of r, $W = \dfrac{k}{r^2}$. Since $W = 10$ when $r = 6$, we have $10 = \dfrac{k}{(6)^2}$ $\Leftrightarrow$
$k = 360$. So $W = \dfrac{360}{r^2}$.

18. $t = k\dfrac{xy}{r}$. Since $t = 25$ when $x = 2$, $y = 3$, and $r = 12$, we have $25 = k\dfrac{(2)\,(3)}{12}$ $\Leftrightarrow$ $k = 50$. So
$t = 50\dfrac{xy}{r}$.

19. Since C is jointly proportional to l, w, and h, we have $C = klwh$. Since $C = 128$ when $l = w = h = 2$, we have
$128 = k\,(2)\,(2)\,(2)$ $\Leftrightarrow$ $128 = 8k$ $\Leftrightarrow$ $k = 16$. Therefore, $C = 16lwh$.

20. $H = kl^2w^2$. Since $H = 36$ when $l = 2$ and $w = \frac{1}{3}$, we have $36 = k\,(2)^2\left(\frac{1}{3}\right)^2$ $\Leftrightarrow$ $36 = \frac{4}{9}k$ $\Leftrightarrow$ $k = 81$. So
$H = 81l^2w^2$.

21. Since s is inversely proportional to the square root of t, we have $s = \dfrac{k}{\sqrt{t}}$. Since $s = 100$ when $t = 25$, we have
$100 = \dfrac{k}{\sqrt{25}}$ $\Leftrightarrow$ $100 = \dfrac{k}{5}$ $\Leftrightarrow$ $k = 500$. So $s = \dfrac{500}{\sqrt{t}}$.

22. $M = k\dfrac{abc}{d}$. Since $M = 128$ when $a = d$ and $b = c = 2$, we have $128 = k\dfrac{a\,(2)\,(2)}{a} = 4k$ $\Leftrightarrow$ $k = 32$. So
$M = 32\dfrac{abc}{d}$.

23. (a) The force F needed is $F = kx$.

(b) Since $F = 40$ when $x = 5$, we have $40 = k\,(5)$ $\Leftrightarrow$ $k = 8$.

(c) From part (b), we have $F = 8x$. Substituting $x = 4$ into $F = 8x$ gives $F = 8\,(4) = 32$ N.

24. (a) Let T and l be the period and the length of the pendulum, respectively. Then $T = k\sqrt{l}$.

(b) $T = k\sqrt{l}$ $\Rightarrow$ $T^2 = k^2l$ $\Leftrightarrow$ $l = \dfrac{T^2}{k^2}$. If the period is doubled, the new length is $\dfrac{(2T)^2}{k^2} = 4\dfrac{T^2}{k^2} = 4l$. So we
would quadruple the length l to double the period T.

25. (a) $C = kpm$

(b) Since $C = 60{,}000$ when $p = 120$ and $m = 4000$, we get $60{,}000 = k\,(120)\,(4000)$ $\Leftrightarrow$ $k = \frac{1}{8}$. So $C = \frac{1}{8}pm$.

(c) Substituting $p = 92$ and $m = 5{,}000$, we get $C = \frac{1}{8}\,(92)\,(5{,}000) = \$57{,}500$ and $k = \frac{1}{8}$.

26. (a) $P = \dfrac{kT}{V}$.

(b) Substituting $P = 33.2$, $T = 400$, and $V = 100$, we get $33.2 = \dfrac{k\,(400)}{100}$ $\Leftrightarrow$ $k = 8.3$. Thus $k = 8.3$ and the
equation is $P = \dfrac{8.3T}{V}$.

(c) Substituting $T = 500$ and $V = 80$, we have $P = \dfrac{8.3\,(500)}{80} = 51.875$ kPa. Hence the pressure of the sample of gas is
about 51.9 kPa.

27. (a) $P = ks^3$.

    (b) Since $P = 96$ when $s = 20$, we get $96 = k \cdot 20^3 \quad \Leftrightarrow \quad k = 0.012$. So $P = 0.012s^3$.

    (c) Substituting $x = 30$, we get $P = 0.012 \cdot 30^3 = 324$ watts.

28. $P = ks^3$. Since $P = 80$ when $s = 10$ we have $80 = k(10)^3$ so $k = 0.08$. Thus $P = 0.08s^3$. When $s = 15$ we have $P = 0.08(15)^3 = 270$. So 270 hp is needed to power the boat at 15 knots.

29. $L = \dfrac{k}{d^2}$. Since $L = 70$ when $d = 10$, we have $70 = \dfrac{k}{10^2}$ so $k = 7,000$. Thus $L = \dfrac{7,000}{d^2}$. When $d = 100$ we get $L = \dfrac{7,000}{100^2} = 0.7$ dB.

30. $D = ks^2$. Since $D = 240$ when $s = 50$ we have $240 = k(50)^2$ so $k = 0.096$. Thus $D = 0.096s^2$. When $D = 160$ then $160 = 0.096s^2 \quad \Leftrightarrow \quad s^2 = 1666.7$ so $s \approx 40$ mi/h (for safety reasons we round down).

31. $P = kAv^3$. If $A = \frac{1}{2}A_0$ and $v = 2v_0$, then $P = k\left(\frac{1}{2}A_0\right)(2v_0)^3 = \frac{1}{2}kA_0\left(8v_0^3\right) = 4kA_0v_0^3$. The power is increased by a factor of 4.

32. $L = ks^2A$. Since $L = 1700$ when $s = 50$ and $A = 500$, we have $1700 = k\left(50^2\right)(500) \quad \Leftrightarrow \quad k = 0.00136$. Thus $L = 0.00136s^2A$. When $A = 600$ and $s = 40$ we get the lift is $L = 0.00136\left(40^2\right)(600) = 1305.6$ lb.

33. $F = kAs^2$. Since $F = 220$ when $A = 40$ and $s = 5$. Solving for k we have $220 = k(40)(5)^2 \quad \Leftrightarrow \quad 220 = 1000k$ $\Leftrightarrow \quad k = 0.22$. Now when $A = 28$ and $F = 175$ we get $175 = 0.220(28)s^2 \quad \Leftrightarrow \quad 28.4090 = s^2$ so $s = \sqrt{28.4090} = 5.33$ mi/h.

34. (a) $F = k\dfrac{ws^2}{r}$

    (b) For the first car we have $w_1 = 1600$ and $s_1 = 60$ and for the second car we have $w_2 = 2500$. Since the forces are equal we have $k\dfrac{1600 \cdot 60^2}{r} = k\dfrac{2500 \cdot s_2^2}{r} \quad \Leftrightarrow \quad \dfrac{16 \cdot 60^2}{25} = s_2^2$, so $s_2 = 48$ mi/h.

35. (a) $R = \dfrac{kL}{d^2}$

    (b) Since $R = 140$ when $L = 1.2$ and $d = 0.005$, we get $140 = \dfrac{k(1.2)}{(0.005)^2} \quad \Leftrightarrow \quad k = \frac{7}{2400} = 0.00291\overline{6}$.

    (c) Substituting $L = 3$ and $d = 0.008$, we have $R = \dfrac{7}{2400} \cdot \dfrac{3}{(0.008)^2} = \dfrac{4375}{32} \approx 137\ \Omega$.

36. (a) $T^2 = kd^3$

    (b) Substituting $T = 365$ and $d = 93 \times 10^6$, we get $365^2 = k \cdot \left(93 \times 10^6\right)^3 \quad \Leftrightarrow \quad k = 1.66 \times 10^{-19}$.

    (c) $T^2 = 1.66 \times 10^{-19}\left(2.79 \times 10^9\right)^3 = 3.60 \times 10^9 \quad \Rightarrow \quad T = 6.00 \times 10^4$. Hence the period of Neptune is 6.00×10^4 days≈ 164 years.

37. (a) $E = kT^4$

    (b) For the sun, $E_S = k6000^4$ and for earth $E_E = k300^4$. Thus $\dfrac{E_S}{E_E} = \dfrac{k6000^4}{k300^4} = \left(\frac{6000}{300}\right)^4 = 20^4 = 160,000$. So the sun produces 160,000 times the radiation energy per unit area than the Earth.

    (c) The surface area of the sun is $4\pi(435,000)^2$ and the surface area of the Earth is $4\pi(3,960)^2$. So the sun has $\dfrac{4\pi(435,000)^2}{4\pi(3,960)^2} = \left(\dfrac{435,000}{3,960}\right)^2$ times the surface area of the Earth. Thus the total radiation emitted by the sun is $160,000 \times \left(\dfrac{435,000}{3,960}\right)^2 = 1,930,670,340$ times the total radiation emitted by the Earth.

38. Let V be the value of a building lot on Galiano Island, A the area of the lot, and q the quantity of the water produced. Since V is jointly proportional to the area and water quantity, we have $V = kAq$. When $A = 200 \cdot 300 = 60,000$ and $q = 10$, we have $V = \$48,000$, so $48,000 = k(60,000)(10)$ $\Leftrightarrow$ $k = 0.08$. Thus $V = 0.08Aq$. Now when $A = 400 \cdot 400 = 160,000$ and $q = 4$, the value is $V = 0.08(160,000)(4) = \$51,200$.

39. Let S be the final size of the cabbage, in pounds, let N be the amount of nutrients it receives, in ounces, and let c be the number of other cabbages around it. Then $S = k\dfrac{N}{c}$. When $N = 20$ and $c = 12$, we have $S = 30$, so substituting, we have $30 = k\frac{20}{12}$ $\Leftrightarrow$ $k = 18$. Thus $S = 18\dfrac{N}{c}$. When $N = 10$ and $c = 5$, the final size is $S = 18\left(\frac{10}{5}\right) = 36$ lb.

40. Let H be the heat experienced by a hiker at a campfire, let A be the amount of wood, and let d be the distance from campfire. So $H = k\dfrac{A}{d^3}$. When the hiker is 20 feet from the fire, the heat experienced is $H = k\dfrac{A}{20^3}$, and when the amount of wood is doubled, the heat experienced is $H = k\dfrac{2A}{d^3}$. So $k\dfrac{A}{8,000} = k\dfrac{2A}{d^3}$ $\Leftrightarrow$ $d^3 = 16,000$ $\Leftrightarrow$ $d = 20\sqrt[3]{2} \approx 25.2$ feet.

41. (a) Since f is inversely proportional to L, we have $f = \dfrac{k}{L}$, where k is a positive constant.

(b) If we replace L by $2L$ we have $\dfrac{k}{2L} = \dfrac{1}{2} \cdot \dfrac{k}{L} = \dfrac{1}{2}f$. So the frequency of the vibration is cut in half.

42. (a) Since r is jointly proportional to x and $P - x$, we have $r = kx(P - x)$, where k is a positive constant.

(b) When 10 people are infected the rate is $r = k10(5000 - 10) = 49,900k$. When 1000 people are infected the rate is $r = k \cdot 1000 \cdot (5000 - 1000) = 4,000,000k$. So the rate is much higher when 1000 people are infected. Comparing these rates, we find that $\dfrac{1000 \text{ people infected}}{10 \text{ people infected}} = \dfrac{4,000,000k}{49,900k} \approx 80$. So the infection rate when 1000 people are infected is about 80 times as large as when 10 people are infected.

(c) When the entire population is infected the rate is $r = k(5000)(5000 - 5000) = 0$. This makes sense since there are no more people who can be infected.

43. Examples include radioactive decay and exponential growth in biology.

Chapter 1 Review

1. Commutative Property for addition.

2. Commutative Law for multiplication.

3. Distributive Property.

4. Distributive Law.

5. $[-2, 6) = \{x \mid -2 \le x < 6\}$

6. $(-\infty, 4] = \{x \mid x \le 4\}$

7. $x \ge 5$ $\Leftrightarrow$ $x \in [5, \infty)$

8. $-1 < x \le 5$ $\Leftrightarrow$ $x \in (-1, 5]$

9. $|3 - |-9|| = |3 - 9| = |-6| = 6$

10. $1 - |1 - |-1|| = 1 - |1 - 1| = 1 - |0| = 1$

11. $2^{-3} - 3^{-2} = \frac{1}{8} - \frac{1}{9} = \frac{9}{72} - \frac{8}{72} = \frac{1}{72}$

12. $\sqrt[3]{-125} = \sqrt[3]{(-5)^3} = -5$

13. $216^{-1/3} = \dfrac{1}{216^{1/3}} = \dfrac{1}{\sqrt[3]{216}} = \frac{1}{6}$

14. $64^{2/3} = \left(4^3\right)^{2/3} = 4^2 = 16$

15. $\dfrac{\sqrt{242}}{\sqrt{2}} = \sqrt{\dfrac{242}{2}} = \sqrt{121} = 11$

16. $\sqrt[4]{4}\sqrt[4]{324} = \sqrt[4]{4}\sqrt[4]{4 \cdot 81} = \sqrt[4]{2^2}\sqrt[4]{2^2 \cdot 3^4} = 2 \cdot 3 = 6$

17. $2^{1/2}8^{1/2} = \sqrt{2} \cdot \sqrt{8} = \sqrt{16} = 4$

18. $\sqrt{2}\sqrt{50} = \sqrt{100} = 10$

19. $\dfrac{x^2 \left(2x\right)^4}{x^3} = \dfrac{x^2 \cdot 16x^4}{x^3} = 16x^{2+4-3} = 16x^3$

20. $\left(a^2\right)^{-3} \left(a^3 b\right)^2 \left(b^3\right)^4 = a^{-6} \cdot a^6 b^2 \cdot b^{12} = a^{-6+6} b^{2+12} = b^{14}$

21. $\left(3xy^2\right)^3 \left(\tfrac{2}{3}x^{-1}y\right)^2 = 27x^3 y^6 \cdot \tfrac{4}{9}x^{-2}y^2 = 27 \cdot \tfrac{4}{9}x^{3-2}y^{6+2} = 12xy^8$

22. $\left(\dfrac{r^2 s^{4/3}}{r^{1/3}s}\right)^6 = \dfrac{r^{12}s^8}{r^2 s^6} = r^{12-2}s^{8-6} = r^{10}s^2$

23. $\sqrt[3]{\left(x^3 y\right)^2 y^4} = \sqrt[3]{x^6 y^4 y^2} = \sqrt[3]{x^6 y^6} = x^2 y^2$

24. $\sqrt{x^2 y^4} = \sqrt{x^2} \cdot \sqrt{\left(y^2\right)^2} = |x|\, y^2$

25. $\left(\dfrac{9x^3 y}{y^{-3}}\right)^{1/2} = \left(9x^3 y^4\right)^{1/2} = 3x^{3/2}y^2$

26. $\left(\dfrac{x^{-2}y^3}{x^2 y}\right)^{-1/2} \left(\dfrac{x^3 y}{y^{1/2}}\right)^2 = \left(\dfrac{y^2}{x^4}\right)^{-1/2} \left(x^3 y^{1/2}\right)^2 = \dfrac{x^2}{y} \cdot x^6 y = x^8$

27. $\dfrac{8r^{1/2}s^{-3}}{2r^{-2}s^4} = 4r^{(1/2)-(-2)}s^{-3-4} = 4r^{5/2}s^{-7} = \dfrac{4r^{5/2}}{s^7}$

28. $\left(\dfrac{ab^2 c^{-3}}{2a^3 b^{-4}}\right)^{-2} = \dfrac{a^{-2}b^{-4}c^6}{2^{-2}a^{-6}b^8} = 2^2 a^{-2-(-6)}b^{-4-8}c^6 = 4a^4 b^{-12}c^6 = \dfrac{4a^4 c^6}{b^{12}}$

29. $78{,}250{,}000{,}000 = 7.825 \times 10^{10}$

30. $2.08 \times 10^{-8} = 0.0000000208$

31. $\dfrac{ab}{c} \approx \dfrac{\left(0.00000293\right)\left(1.582 \times 10^{-14}\right)}{2.8064 \times 10^{12}} = \dfrac{\left(2.93 \times 10^{-6}\right)\left(1.582 \times 10^{-14}\right)}{2.8064 \times 10^{12}} = \dfrac{2.93 \cdot 1.582}{2.8064} \times 10^{-6-14-12}$

$\approx 1.65 \times 10^{-32}$

32. $80\ \dfrac{\text{times}}{\text{minute}} \cdot \dfrac{60\ \text{minutes}}{\text{hour}} \cdot \dfrac{24\ \text{hours}}{\text{day}} \cdot \dfrac{365\ \text{days}}{\text{year}} \cdot 90\ \text{years} \approx 3.8 \times 10^9\ \text{times}$

33. $12x^2 y^4 - 3xy^5 + 9x^3 y^2 = 3xy^2 \left(4xy^2 - y^3 + 3x^2\right)$

34. $x^2 - 9x + 18 = (x - 6)(x - 3)$

35. $x^2 + 3x - 10 = (x + 5)(x - 2)$

36. $6x^2 + x - 12 = (3x - 4)(2x + 3)$

37. $4t^2 - 13t - 12 = (4t + 3)(t - 4)$

38. $x^4 - 2x^2 + 1 = \left(x^2 - 1\right)^2 = \left[(x - 1)(x + 1)\right]^2 = (x - 1)^2 (x + 1)^2$

39. $25 - 16t^2 = (5 - 4t)(5 + 4t)$

40. $2y^6 - 32y^2 = 2y^2 \left(y^4 - 16\right) = 2y^2 \left(y^2 + 4\right)\left(y^2 - 4\right) = 2y^2 \left(y^2 + 4\right)(y + 2)(y - 2)$

41. $x^6 - 1 = \left(x^3 - 1\right)\left(x^3 + 1\right) = (x - 1)\left(x^2 + x + 1\right)(x + 1)\left(x^2 - x + 1\right)$

42. $y^3 - 2y^2 - y + 2 = y^2 (y - 2) - 1(y - 2) = (y - 2)\left(y^2 - 1\right) = (y - 2)(y - 1)(y + 1)$

43. $x^{-1/2} - 2x^{1/2} + x^{3/2} = x^{-1/2}\left(1 - 2x + x^2\right) = x^{-1/2}(1 - x)^2 = x^{-1/2}(x - 1)^2$

44. $a^4 b^2 + ab^5 = ab^2 \left(a^3 + b^3\right) = ab^2 (a + b)\left(a^2 - ab + b^2\right)$

45. $4x^3 - 8x^2 + 3x - 6 = 4x^2 (x - 2) + 3(x - 2) = \left(4x^2 + 3\right)(x - 2)$

46. $8x^3 + y^6 = (2x)^3 + \left(y^2\right)^3 = \left(2x + y^2\right)\left(4x^2 - 2xy^2 + y^4\right)$

47. $\left(x^2+2\right)^{5/2}+2x\left(x^2+2\right)^{3/2}+x^2\sqrt{x^2+2}=\left(x^2+2\right)^{1/2}\left(\left(x^2+2\right)^2+2x\left(x^2+2\right)+x^2\right)$

$\quad=\sqrt{x^2+2}\left(x^4+4x^2+4+2x^3+4x+x^2\right)=\sqrt{x^2+2}\left(x^4+2x^3+5x^2+4x+4\right)=\sqrt{x^2+2}\left(x^2+x+2\right)^2$

48. $3x^3-2x^2+18x-12=x^2\left(3x-2\right)+6\left(3x-2\right)=\left(3x-2\right)\left(x^2+6\right)$

49. $\left(2x+1\right)\left(3x-2\right)-5\left(4x-1\right)=6x^2-4x+3x-2-20x+5=6x^2-21x+3$

50. $\left(2y-7\right)\left(2y+7\right)=4y^2-49$

51. $\left(1+x\right)\left(2-x\right)-\left(3-x\right)\left(3+x\right)=2+x-x^2-\left(9-x^2\right)=2+x-x^2-9+x^2=-7+x$

52. $\sqrt{x}\left(\sqrt{x}+1\right)\left(2\sqrt{x}-1\right)=\left(x+\sqrt{x}\right)\left(2\sqrt{x}-1\right)=2x\sqrt{x}-x+2x-\sqrt{x}=2x^{3/2}+x-x^{1/2}$

53. $x^2\left(x-2\right)+x\left(x-2\right)^2=x^3-2x^2+x\left(x^2-4x+4\right)=x^3-2x^2+x^3-4x^2+4x=2x^3-6x^2+4x$

54. $\dfrac{x^2-2x-3}{2x^2+5x+3}=\dfrac{\left(x-3\right)\left(x+1\right)}{\left(2x+3\right)\left(x+1\right)}=\dfrac{x-3}{2x+3}$

55. $\dfrac{x^2+2x-3}{x^2+8x+16}\cdot\dfrac{3x+12}{x-1}=\dfrac{\left(x+3\right)\left(x-1\right)}{\left(x+4\right)\left(x+4\right)}\cdot\dfrac{3\left(x+4\right)}{\left(x-1\right)}=\dfrac{3\left(x+3\right)}{x+4}$

56. $\dfrac{t^3-1}{t^2-1}=\dfrac{\left(t-1\right)\left(t^2+t+1\right)}{\left(t-1\right)\left(t+1\right)}=\dfrac{t^2+t+1}{t+1}$

57. $\dfrac{x^2-2x-15}{x^2-6x+5}\div\dfrac{x^2-x-12}{x^2-1}=\dfrac{\left(x-5\right)\left(x+3\right)}{\left(x-5\right)\left(x-1\right)}\cdot\dfrac{\left(x-1\right)\left(x+1\right)}{\left(x-4\right)\left(x+3\right)}=\dfrac{x+1}{x-4}$

58. $\dfrac{2}{x}+\dfrac{1}{x-2}+\dfrac{3}{\left(x-2\right)^2}=\dfrac{2\left(x-2\right)^2}{x\left(x-2\right)^2}+\dfrac{x\left(x-2\right)}{x\left(x-2\right)^2}+\dfrac{3x}{x\left(x-2\right)^2}$

$\quad=\dfrac{2\left(x^2-4x+4\right)+x^2-2x+3x}{x\left(x-2\right)^2}=\dfrac{2x^2-8x+8+x^2-2x+3x}{x\left(x-2\right)^2}=\dfrac{3x^2-7x+8}{x\left(x-2\right)^2}$

59. $\dfrac{1}{x-1}-\dfrac{2}{x^2-1}=\dfrac{1}{x-1}-\dfrac{2}{\left(x-1\right)\left(x+1\right)}=\dfrac{x+1}{\left(x-1\right)\left(x+1\right)}-\dfrac{2}{\left(x-1\right)\left(x+1\right)}$

$\quad=\dfrac{x+1-2}{\left(x-1\right)\left(x+1\right)}=\dfrac{x-1}{\left(x-1\right)\left(x+1\right)}=\dfrac{1}{x+1}$

60. $\dfrac{1}{x+2}+\dfrac{1}{x^2-4}-\dfrac{2}{x^2-x-2}=\dfrac{1}{x+2}+\dfrac{1}{\left(x-2\right)\left(x+2\right)}-\dfrac{2}{\left(x-2\right)\left(x+1\right)}$

$\quad=\dfrac{\left(x-2\right)\left(x+1\right)}{\left(x-2\right)\left(x+1\right)\left(x+2\right)}+\dfrac{x+1}{\left(x-2\right)\left(x+1\right)\left(x+2\right)}-\dfrac{2\left(x+2\right)}{\left(x-2\right)\left(x+1\right)\left(x+2\right)}$

$\quad=\dfrac{x^2-x-2+x+1-2x-4}{\left(x-2\right)\left(x+1\right)\left(x+2\right)}=\dfrac{x^2-2x-5}{\left(x-2\right)\left(x+1\right)\left(x+2\right)}$

61. $\dfrac{\frac{1}{x}-\frac{1}{2}}{x-2}=\dfrac{\frac{2}{2x}-\frac{x}{2x}}{x-2}=\dfrac{2-x}{2x}\cdot\dfrac{1}{x-2}=\dfrac{-1\left(x-2\right)}{2x}\cdot\dfrac{1}{x-2}=\dfrac{-1}{2x}$

62. $\dfrac{\frac{1}{x}-\frac{1}{x+1}}{\frac{1}{x}+\frac{1}{x+1}}=\dfrac{\frac{1}{x}-\frac{1}{x+1}}{\frac{1}{x}+\frac{1}{x+1}}\cdot\dfrac{x\left(x+1\right)}{x\left(x+1\right)}=\dfrac{\left(x+1\right)-x}{\left(x+1\right)+x}=\dfrac{1}{2x+1}$

63. $\dfrac{\sqrt{6}}{\sqrt{3}+\sqrt{2}}=\dfrac{\sqrt{6}}{\sqrt{3}+\sqrt{2}}\cdot\dfrac{\sqrt{3}-\sqrt{2}}{\sqrt{3}-\sqrt{2}}=\dfrac{3\sqrt{2}-2\sqrt{3}}{3-2}=3\sqrt{2}-2\sqrt{3}$

64. $\dfrac{\sqrt{x+h}-\sqrt{x}}{h}=\dfrac{\sqrt{x+h}-\sqrt{x}}{h}\cdot\dfrac{\sqrt{x+h}+\sqrt{x}}{\sqrt{x+h}+\sqrt{x}}=\dfrac{\left(x+h\right)-x}{h\left(\sqrt{x+h}+\sqrt{x}\right)}=\dfrac{h}{h\left(\sqrt{x+h}+\sqrt{x}\right)}=\dfrac{1}{\sqrt{x+h}+\sqrt{x}}$

65. $7x-6=4x+9\quad\Leftrightarrow\quad3x=15\quad\Leftrightarrow\quad x=5$

66. $8-2x=14+x\quad\Leftrightarrow\quad-3x=6\quad\Leftrightarrow\quad x=-2.$

67. $\dfrac{x+1}{x-1}=\dfrac{3x}{3x-6}=\dfrac{3x}{3\left(x-2\right)}=\dfrac{x}{x-2}\quad\Leftrightarrow\quad\left(x+1\right)\left(x-2\right)=x\left(x-1\right)\quad\Leftrightarrow\quad x^2-x-2=x^2-x\quad\Leftrightarrow$

$-2=0.$ Since this last equation is never true, there is no real solution to the original equation.

68. $(x+2)^2 = (x-4)^2$ $\Leftrightarrow$ $(x+2)^2 - (x-4)^2 = 0$ $\Leftrightarrow$ $[(x+2) - (x-4)][(x+2) + (x-4)] = 0$ $\Leftrightarrow$ $[x+2-x+4][x+2+x-4] = 6(2x-2) = 0$ $\Leftrightarrow$ $2x-2 = 0$ $\Leftrightarrow$ $x = 1$.

69. $x^2 - 9x + 14 = 0$ $\Leftrightarrow$ $(x-7)(x-2) = 0$ $\Leftrightarrow$ $x = 7$ or $x = 2$.

70. $x^2 + 24x + 144 = 0$ $\Leftrightarrow$ $(x+12)^2 = 0$ $\Leftrightarrow$ $x + 12 = 0$ $\Leftrightarrow$ $x = -12$.

71. $2x^2 + x = 1$ $\Leftrightarrow$ $2x^2 + x - 1 = 0$ $\Leftrightarrow$ $(2x-1)(x+1) = 0$. So either $2x - 1 = 0$ $\Leftrightarrow$ $2x = 1$ $\Leftrightarrow$ $x = \frac{1}{2}$; or $x + 1 = 0$ $\Leftrightarrow$ $x = -1$.

72. $3x^2 + 5x - 2 = 0$ $\Leftrightarrow$ $(3x-1)(x+2) = 0$ $\Leftrightarrow$ $x = \frac{1}{3}$ or $x = -2$.

73. $0 = 4x^3 - 25x = x\left(4x^2 - 25\right) = x(2x-5)(2x+5) = 0$. So either $x = 0$; or $2x - 5 = 0$ $\Leftrightarrow$ $2x = 5$ $\Leftrightarrow$ $x = \frac{5}{2}$; or $2x + 5 = 0$ $\Leftrightarrow$ $2x = -5$ $\Leftrightarrow$ $x = -\frac{5}{2}$.

74. $x^3 - 2x^2 - 5x + 10 = 0$ $\Leftrightarrow$ $x^2(x-2) - 5(x-2) = 0$ $\Leftrightarrow$ $(x-2)\left(x^2 - 5\right) = 0$ $\Leftrightarrow$ $x = 2$ or $x = \pm\sqrt{5}$.

75. $3x^2 + 4x - 1 = 0 \Rightarrow$
$x = \frac{-b \pm \sqrt{b^2 - 4ac}}{2a} = \frac{-(4) \pm \sqrt{(4)^2 - 4(3)(-1)}}{2(-3)} = \frac{-4 \pm \sqrt{16+12}}{-6} = \frac{-4 \pm \sqrt{28}}{-6} = \frac{-4 \pm 2\sqrt{7}}{6} = \frac{2\left(-2\pm\sqrt{7}\right)}{-6} = \frac{-2\pm\sqrt{7}}{3}$.

76. $\frac{1}{x} + \frac{2}{x-1} = 3$ $\Leftrightarrow$ $(x-1) + 2(x) = 3(x)(x-1)$ $\Leftrightarrow$ $x - 1 + 2x = 3x^2 - 3x$ $\Leftrightarrow$ $0 = 3x^2 - 6x + 1$
$\Rightarrow$ $x = \frac{-b \pm \sqrt{b^2 - 4ac}}{2a} = \frac{-(-6) \pm \sqrt{(-6)^2 - 4(3)(1)}}{2(3)} = \frac{6 \pm \sqrt{36-12}}{6} = \frac{6 \pm \sqrt{24}}{6} = \frac{6 \pm 2\sqrt{6}}{6} = \frac{2\left(3\pm\sqrt{6}\right)}{6} = \frac{3\pm\sqrt{6}}{3}$.

77. $\frac{x}{x-2} + \frac{1}{x+2} = \frac{8}{x^2 - 4}$ $\Leftrightarrow$ $x(x+2) + (x-2) = 8$ $\Leftrightarrow$ $x^2 + 2x + x - 2 = 8$ $\Leftrightarrow$ $x^2 + 3x - 10 = 0$ $\Leftrightarrow$ $(x-2)(x+5) = 0$ $\Leftrightarrow$ $x = 2$ or $x = -5$. However, since $x = 2$ makes the expression undefined, we reject this solution. Hence the only solution is $x = -5$.

78. $x^4 - 8x^2 - 9 = 0$ $\Leftrightarrow$ $\left(x^2 - 9\right)\left(x^2 + 1\right) = 0$ $\Leftrightarrow$ $(x-3)(x+3)\left(x^2+1\right) = 0$ $\Rightarrow$ $x - 3 = 0$ $\Leftrightarrow$ $x = 3$, or $x + 3 = 0$ $\Leftrightarrow$ $x = -3$, however $x^2 + 1 = 0$ has no real solution. The solutions are $x = \pm 3$.

79. $|x - 7| = 4$ $\Leftrightarrow$ $x - 7 = \pm 4$ $\Leftrightarrow$ $x = 7 \pm 4$, so $x = 11$ or $x = 3$.

80. $|2x - 5| = 9$ is equivalent to $2x - 5 = \pm 9$ $\Leftrightarrow$ $2x = 5 \pm 9$ $\Leftrightarrow$ $x = \frac{5 \pm 9}{2}$. So $x = -2$ or $x = 7$.

81. Let x be the number of pounds of raisins. Then the number of pounds of nuts is $50 - x$.

	Raisins	Nuts	Mixture
Pounds	x	$50 - x$	50
Rate (cost per pound)	3.20	2.40	2.72

So $3.20x + 2.40(50 - x) = 2.72(50)$ $\Leftrightarrow$ $3.20x + 120 - 2.40x = 136$ $\Leftrightarrow$ $0.8x = 16$ $\Leftrightarrow$ $x = 20$. Thus the mixture uses 20 pounds of raisins and $50 - 20 = 30$ pounds of nuts.

82. Let t be the number of hours that Anthony drives. Then Helen drives for $t - \frac{1}{4}$ hours.

	Rate	Time	Distance
Anthony	45	t	$45t$
Helen	40	$t - \frac{1}{4}$	$40\left(t - \frac{1}{4}\right)$

When they pass each other, they will have traveled a total of 160 miles. So $45t + 40\left(t - \frac{1}{4}\right) = 160$ $\Leftrightarrow$ $45t + 40t - 10 = 160$ $\Leftrightarrow$ $85t = 170$ $\Leftrightarrow$ $t = 2$. Since Anthony leaves at 2:00 P.M. and travels for 2 hours, they pass each other at 4:00 P.M.

83. Let r be the rate the woman runs in mi/h. Then she cycles at $r + 8$ mi/h.

	Rate	Time	Distance
Cycle	$r+8$	$\dfrac{4}{r+8}$	4
Run	r	$\dfrac{2.5}{r}$	2.5

Since the total time of the workout is 1 hour, we have $\dfrac{4}{r+8} + \dfrac{2.5}{r} = 1$. Multiplying by $2r(r+8)$, we get

$4(2r) + 2.5(2)(r+8) = 2r(r+8) \quad\Leftrightarrow\quad 8r + 5r + 40 = 2r^2 + 16r \quad\Leftrightarrow\quad 0 = 2r^2 + 3r - 40 \quad\Rightarrow$

$r = \dfrac{-3 \pm \sqrt{(3)^2 - 4(2)(-40)}}{2(2)} = \dfrac{-3 \pm \sqrt{9+320}}{4} = \dfrac{-3 \pm \sqrt{329}}{4}$. Since $r \geq 0$, we reject the negative value. She runs at

$r = \dfrac{-3 + \sqrt{329}}{4} \approx 3.78$ mi/h.

84. Let x be the length of one side in cm. Then $28 - x$ is the length of the other side. Using the Pythagorean Theorem, we have $x^2 + (28 - x)^2 = 20^2 \quad\Leftrightarrow\quad x^2 + 784 - 56x + x^2 = 400 \quad\Leftrightarrow\quad 2x^2 - 56x + 384 = 0 \quad\Leftrightarrow\quad 2(x^2 - 28x + 192) = 0 \quad\Leftrightarrow\quad 2(x-12)(x-16) = 0$. So $x = 12$ or $x = 16$. If $x = 12$, then the other side is $28 - 12 = 16$. Similarly, if $x = 16$, then the other side is 12. The sides are 12 cm and 16 cm.

85. Let t be the time it would take Abbie to paint a living room if she works alone. It would take Beth $2t$ hours to paint the living room alone, and it would take $3t$ hours for Cathie to paint the living room. Thus Abbie does $\dfrac{1}{t}$ of the job per hour, Beth does $\dfrac{1}{2t}$ of the job per hour, and Cathie does $\dfrac{1}{3t}$ of the job per hour. So $\dfrac{1}{t} + \dfrac{1}{2t} + \dfrac{1}{3t} = 1 \quad\Leftrightarrow\quad 6 + 3 + 2 = 6t$ $\Leftrightarrow\quad 6t = 11 \quad\Leftrightarrow\quad t = \frac{11}{6}$. So it would Abbie 1 hour 50 minutes to paint the living room alone.

86. Let l be length of each garden plot. The width of each plot is then $\dfrac{80}{l}$ and the total amount of fencing material is $4(l) + 6\left(\dfrac{80}{l}\right) = 88$. Thus $4l + \dfrac{480}{l} = 88 \quad\Leftrightarrow\quad 4l^2 + 480 = 88l \quad\Leftrightarrow\quad 4l^2 - 88l + 480 = 0 \quad\Leftrightarrow\quad 4(l^2 - 22l + 120) = 0 \quad\Leftrightarrow\quad 4(l - 10)(l - 12) = 0$. So $l = 10$ or $l = 12$. If $l = 10$ ft, then the width of each plot is $\frac{80}{10} = 8$ ft. If $l = 12$ ft, then the width of each plot is $\frac{80}{12} = 6.67$ ft. Both solutions are possible.

87. $3x - 2 > -11 \quad\Leftrightarrow\quad 3x > -9 \quad\Leftrightarrow\quad x > -3$.
Interval: $(-3, \infty)$.

Graph:

88. $-1 < 2x + 5 \leq 3 \quad\Leftrightarrow\quad -6 < 2x \leq -2 \quad\Leftrightarrow$
$-3 < x \leq -1$
Interval: $(-3, -1]$.

Graph:

89. $x^2 + 4x - 12 > 0 \quad\Leftrightarrow\quad (x - 2)(x + 6) > 0$. The expression on the left of the inequality changes sign where $x = 2$ and where $x = -6$. Thus we must check the intervals in the following table.

Interval	$(-\infty, -6)$	$(-6, 2)$	$(2, \infty)$
Sign of $x - 2$	$-$	$-$	$+$
Sign of $x + 6$	$-$	$+$	$+$
Sign of $(x-2)(x+6)$	$+$	$-$	$+$

Interval: $(-\infty, -6) \cup (2, \infty)$.

Graph:

90. $x^2 \leq 1 \quad \Leftrightarrow \quad x^2 - 1 \leq 0 \quad \Leftrightarrow \quad (x-1)(x+1) \leq 0$. The expression on the left of the inequality changes sign when $x = -1$ and $x = 1$. Thus we must check the intervals in the following table.

Interval	$(-\infty, -1)$	$(-1, 1)$	$(1, \infty)$
Sign of $x - 1$	$-$	$-$	$+$
Sign of $x + 1$	$-$	$+$	$+$
Sign of $(x-1)(x+1)$	$+$	$-$	$+$

Interval: $[-1, 1]$

Graph:

91. $\dfrac{x-4}{x^2-4} \leq 0 \quad \Leftrightarrow \quad \dfrac{x-4}{(x-2)(x+2)} \leq 0$. The expression on the left of the inequality changes sign where $x = -2$, where $x = 2$, and where $x = 4$. Thus we must check the intervals in the following table.

Interval	$(-\infty, -2)$	$(-2, 2)$	$(2, 4)$	$(4, \infty)$
Sign of $x - 4$	$-$	$-$	$-$	$+$
Sign of $x - 2$	$-$	$-$	$+$	$+$
Sign of $x + 2$	$-$	$+$	$+$	$+$
Sign of $\dfrac{x-4}{(x-2)(x+2)}$	$-$	$+$	$-$	$+$

Since the expression is not defined when $x = \pm 2$, we exclude these values and the solution is $(-\infty, -2) \cup (2, 4]$.

Graph:

92. $\dfrac{5}{x^3 - x^2 - 4x + 4} < 0 \quad \Leftrightarrow \quad \dfrac{5}{x^2(x-1) - 4(x-1)} < 0 \quad \Leftrightarrow \quad \dfrac{5}{(x-1)(x^2-4)} < 0 \quad \Leftrightarrow$

$\dfrac{5}{(x-1)(x-2)(x+2)} < 0$. The expression on the left of the inequality changes sign when $-2, 1,$ and 2. Thus we must check the intervals in the following table.

Interval	$(-\infty, -2)$	$(-2, 1)$	$(1, 2)$	$(2, \infty)$
Sign of $x - 1$	$-$	$-$	$+$	$+$
Sign of $x - 2$	$-$	$-$	$-$	$+$
Sign of $x + 2$	$-$	$+$	$+$	$+$
Sign of $\dfrac{5}{(x-1)(x-2)(x+2)}$	$-$	$+$	$-$	$+$

Interval: $(-\infty, -2) \cup (1, 2)$

Graph:

93. $|x - 5| \leq 3 \quad \Leftrightarrow \quad -3 \leq x - 5 \leq 3 \quad \Leftrightarrow \quad 2 \leq x \leq 8$. **94.** $|x - 4| < 0.02 \quad \Leftrightarrow \quad -0.02 < x - 4 < 0.02 \quad \Leftrightarrow$

Interval: $[2, 8]$

Graph:

$3.98 < x < 4.02$

Interval: $(3.98, 4.02)$

Graph:

95. $x^2 - 4x = 2x + 7$. We graph the equations $y_1 = x^2 - 4x$ and $y_2 = 2x + 7$ in the viewing rectangle rectangle $[-10, 10]$ by $[-5, 25]$. Using a zoom or trace function, we get the solutions $x = -1$ and $x = 7$.

96. $\sqrt{x + 4} = x^2 - 5$. We graph the equations $y_1 = \sqrt{x + 4}$ and $y_2 = x^2 - 5$ in the viewing rectangle $[-4, 5]$ by $[0, 10]$. Using a zoom or trace function, we get the solutions $x \approx -2.50$ and $x \approx 2.76$.

97. $4x - 3 \geq x^2$. We graph the equations $y_1 = 4x - 3$ and $y_2 = x^2$ in the viewing rectangle $[-5, 5]$ by $[0, 15]$. Using a zoom or trace function, we find the points of intersection are at $x = 1$ and $x = 3$. Since we want $4x - 3 \geq x^2$, the solution is the interval $[1, 3]$.

98. $x^3 - 4x^2 - 5x > 2$. We graph the equations $y_1 = x^3 - 4x^2 - 5x$ and $y_2 = 2$ in the viewing rectangle $[-10, 10]$ by $[-5, 5]$. We find that the point of intersection is at $x \approx 5.07$. Since we want $x^3 - 4x^2 - 5x > 2$, the solution is the interval $(5.07, \infty)$.

99. (a)

(d) The line has slope $m = \dfrac{12 - 0}{-5 - 2} = -\dfrac{12}{7}$, and has equation $y - 0 = -\dfrac{12}{7}(x - 2)$ $\Leftrightarrow$ $y = -\dfrac{12}{7}x + \dfrac{24}{7}$ $\Leftrightarrow$ $12x + 7y - 24 = 0$.

(b) The distance from P to Q is
$$d(P, Q) = \sqrt{(-5 - 2)^2 + (12 - 0)^2}$$
$$= \sqrt{49 + 144} = \sqrt{193}$$

(c) The midpoint is $\left(\dfrac{-5 + 2}{2}, \dfrac{12 + 0}{2}\right) = \left(-\dfrac{3}{2}, 6\right)$.

(e) The radius of this circle was found in part (b). It is $r = d(P, Q) = \sqrt{193}$. So an equation is
$$(x - 2)^2 + (y - 0)^2 = \left(\sqrt{193}\right)^2   \Leftrightarrow$$
$$(x - 2)^2 + y^2 = 193.$$

100. (a)

(b) The distance from P to Q is

$$d(P, Q) = \sqrt{(2-7)^2 + (-11+1)^2}$$
$$= \sqrt{25 + 100} = \sqrt{125} = 5\sqrt{5}$$

(c) The midpoint is $\left(\dfrac{2+7}{2}, \dfrac{-11-1}{2} \right) = \left(\dfrac{9}{2}, -6 \right)$.

(d) The line has slope $m = \dfrac{-11+1}{2-7} = \dfrac{-10}{-5} = 2$, and its equation is $y + 11 = 2(x-2)$ $\Leftrightarrow$ $y + 11 = 2x - 4$ $\Leftrightarrow$ $y = 2x - 15$.

(e) The radius of this circle was found in part (b). It is $r = d(P, Q) = 5\sqrt{5}$. So an equation is
$$(x-7)^2 + (y+1)^2 = \left(5\sqrt{5}\right)^2 \quad \Leftrightarrow$$
$$(x-7)^2 + (y+1)^2 = 125.$$

101.

102. $\{(x, y) \mid x \geq 4 \text{ or } y \geq 2\}$

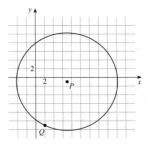

103. $d(A, C) = \sqrt{(4-(-1))^2 + (4-(-3))^2} = \sqrt{(4+1)^2 + (4+3)^2} = \sqrt{74}$ and

$d(B, C) = \sqrt{(5-(-1))^2 + (3-(-3))^2} = \sqrt{(5+1)^2 + (3+3)^2} = \sqrt{72}$. Therefore, B is closer to C.

104. The circle with center at $(2, -5)$ and radius $\sqrt{2}$ has equation $(x-2)^2 + (y+5)^2 = \left(\sqrt{2}\right)^2$ $\Leftrightarrow$ $(x-2)^2 + (y+5)^2 = 2$.

105. The center is $C = (-5, -1)$, and the point $P = (0, 0)$ is on the circle. The radius of the circle is

$r = d(P, C) = \sqrt{(0-(-5))^2 + (0-(-1))^2} = \sqrt{(0+5)^2 + (0+1)^2} = \sqrt{26}$. Thus, the equation of the circle is

$(x+5)^2 + (y+1)^2 = 26$.

106. The midpoint of segment PQ is $\left(\dfrac{2-1}{2}, \dfrac{3+8}{2}\right) = \left(\dfrac{1}{2}, \dfrac{11}{2}\right)$, and the radius is $\frac{1}{2}$ of the distance from P to Q, or

$r = \frac{1}{2} \cdot d(P,Q) = \frac{1}{2}\sqrt{(2-(-1))^2 + (3-8)^2} = \frac{1}{2}\sqrt{(2+1)^2 + (3-8)^2} \quad \Leftrightarrow \quad r = \frac{1}{2}\sqrt{34}$. Thus the equation is

$\left(x - \frac{1}{2}\right)^2 + \left(y - \frac{11}{2}\right)^2 = \frac{17}{2}$.

107. $x^2 + y^2 + 2x - 6y + 9 = 0 \quad \Leftrightarrow \quad (x^2 + 2x) + (y^2 - 6y) = -9 \quad \Leftrightarrow \quad (x^2 + 2x + 1) + (y^2 - 6y + 9) = -9 + 1 + 9$

$\Leftrightarrow \quad (x+1)^2 + (y-3)^2 = 1$. This equation represents a circle with center at $(-1, 3)$ and radius 1.

108. $2x^2 + 2y^2 - 2x + 8y = \frac{1}{2} \quad \Leftrightarrow \quad x^2 - x + y^2 + 4y = \frac{1}{4} \quad \Leftrightarrow \quad \left(x^2 - x + \frac{1}{4}\right) + (y^2 + 4y + 4) = \frac{1}{4} + \frac{1}{4} + 4 \quad \Leftrightarrow$

$\left(x - \frac{1}{2}\right)^2 + (y+2)^2 = \frac{9}{2}$. This is the equation of a circle whose center is $\left(\frac{1}{2}, -2\right)$ and radius is $\dfrac{3}{\sqrt{2}}$.

109. $x^2 + y^2 + 72 = 12x \quad \Leftrightarrow \quad (x^2 - 12x) + y^2 = -72 \quad \Leftrightarrow \quad (x^2 - 12x + 36) + y^2 = -72 + 36 \quad \Leftrightarrow$

$(x-6)^2 + y^2 = -36$. Since the left side of this equation must be greater than or equal to zero, this equation has no graph.

110. $x^2 + y^2 - 6x - 10y + 34 = 0 \quad \Leftrightarrow \quad x^2 - 6x + y^2 - 10y = -34 \quad \Leftrightarrow \quad (x^2 - 6x + 9) + (y^2 - 10y + 25) = -34 + 9 + 25$

$\Leftrightarrow \quad (x-3)^2 + (y-5)^2 = 0$. This is the equation of the point $(3, 5)$.

111. $y = 2 - 3x$

x	y
-2	8
0	2
$\frac{2}{3}$	0

x-axis symmetry: $(-y) = 2 - 3x \quad \Leftrightarrow \quad y = -2 + 3x$, which is not the same as the original equation, so the graph is not symmetric with respect to the x-axis.

y-axis symmetry: $y = 2 - 3(-x) \quad \Leftrightarrow \quad y = 2 + 3x$, which is not the same as the original equation, so the graph is not symmetric with respect to the y-axis.

Origin symmetry: $(-y) = 2 - 3(-x) \quad \Leftrightarrow \quad -y = 2 + 3x \quad \Leftrightarrow$ $y = -2 - 3x$, which is not the same as the original equation, so the graph is not symmetric with respect to the origin.

Hence the graph has no symmetry.

112. $2x - y + 1 = 0 \quad \Leftrightarrow \quad y = 2x + 1$

x	y
-2	-3
0	1
$-\frac{1}{2}$	0

x-axis symmetry: $(-y) = 2x + 1 \quad \Leftrightarrow \quad y = -2x - 1$, which is not the same as the original equation, so the graph is not symmetric with respect to the x-axis.

y-axis symmetry: $y = 2(-x) + 1 \quad \Leftrightarrow \quad y = -2x + 1$, which is not the same as the original equation, so the graph is not symmetric with respect to the y-axis.

Origin symmetry: $(-y) = 2(-x) + 1 \quad \Leftrightarrow \quad -y = -2x + 1$ $\Leftrightarrow \quad y = 2x - 1$, which is not the same as the original equation, so the graph is not symmetric with respect to the origin.

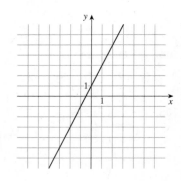

113. $x + 3y = 21 \quad \Leftrightarrow \quad y = -\frac{1}{3}x + 7$

x	y
-3	8
0	7
21	0

x-axis symmetry: $x + 3(-y) = 21 \quad \Leftrightarrow \quad x - 3y = 21$, which is not the same as the original equation, so the graph is not symmetric with respect to the x-axis.

y-axis symmetry: $(-x) + 3y = 21 \quad \Leftrightarrow \quad x - 3y = -21$, which is not the same as the original equation, so the graph is not symmetric with respect to the y-axis.

Origin symmetry: $(-x) + 3(-y) = 21 \quad \Leftrightarrow \quad x + 3y = -21$, which is not the same as the original equation, so the graph is not symmetric with respect to the origin. Hence the graph has no symmetry.

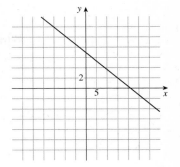

114. $x = 2y + 12 \quad \Leftrightarrow \quad 2y = x - 12 \quad \Leftrightarrow \quad y = \frac{1}{2}x - 6$

x	y
-4	-8
0	-6
12	0

x-axis symmetry: $(-y) = \frac{1}{2}x - 6 \quad \Leftrightarrow \quad y = -\frac{1}{2}x + 6$, which is not the same as the original equation, so the graph is not symmetric with respect to the x-axis.

y-axis symmetry: $y = \frac{1}{2}(-x) - 6 \quad \Leftrightarrow \quad y = -\frac{1}{2}x - 6$, which is not the same as the original equation, so the graph is not symmetric with respect to the y-axis.

Origin symmetry: $(-y) = \frac{1}{2}(-x) - 6 \quad \Leftrightarrow \quad y = \frac{1}{2}x + 6$, which is not the same as the original equation, so the graph is not symmetric with respect to the origin.

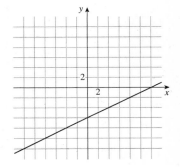

115. $y = 16 - x^2$

x	y
-3	7
-1	15
0	16
1	15
3	7

x-axis symmetry: $(-y) = 16 - x^2 \quad \Leftrightarrow \quad y = -16 + x^2$, which is not the same as the original equation, so the graph is not symmetric with respect to the x-axis.

y-axis symmetry: $y = 16 - (-x)^2 \quad \Leftrightarrow \quad y = 16 - x^2$, which is the same as the original equation, so its is symmetric with respect to the y-axis.

Origin symmetry: $(-y) = 16 - (-x)^2 \quad \Leftrightarrow \quad y = -16 + x^2$, which is not the same as the original equation, so the graph is not symmetric with respect to the origin. Hence, the graph is symmetric with respect to the y-axis.

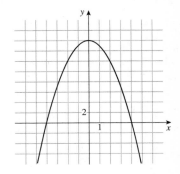

116. $8x + y^2 = 0$ $\Leftrightarrow$ $y^2 = -8x$

x	y
-8	± 8
-2	± 4
0	0

x-axis symmetry: $(-y)^2 = -8x$ $\Leftrightarrow$ $y^2 = -8x$, which is the same as the original equation, so the graph is symmetric with respect to the x-axis.

y-axis symmetry: $y^2 = -8(-x)$ $\Leftrightarrow$ $y^2 = 8x$, which is not the same as the original equation, so the graph is not symmetric with respect to the y-axis.

Origin symmetry: $(-y)^2 = -8(-x)$ $\Leftrightarrow$ $y^2 = 8x$, which is not the same as the original equation, so the graph is not symmetric with respect to the origin.

117. $x = \sqrt{y}$

x	y
0	0
1	1
2	4
3	9

x-axis symmetry: $x = \sqrt{-y}$, which is not the same as the original equation, so the graph is not symmetric with respect to the x-axis.

y-axis symmetry: $(-x) = \sqrt{y}$ $\Leftrightarrow$ $x = -\sqrt{y}$, which is not the same as the original equation, so the graph is not symmetric with respect to the y-axis.

Origin symmetry: $(-x) = \sqrt{-y}$, which is not the same as the original equation, so the graph is not symmetric with respect to the origin. Hence, the graph has no symmetry.

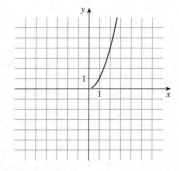

118. $y = -\sqrt{1 - x^2}$

x	y
-1	0
$\frac{1}{2}$	$-\frac{\sqrt{3}}{2}$
0	-1
1	0

x-axis symmetry: $(-y) = -\sqrt{1 - x^2}$ $\Leftrightarrow$ $y = \sqrt{1 - x^2}$, which is not the same as the original equation, so the graph is not symmetric with respect to the x-axis.

y-axis symmetry: $y = -\sqrt{1 - (-x)^2}$ $\Leftrightarrow$ $y = -\sqrt{1 - x^2}$, which is the same as the original equation, so the graph is symmetric with respect to the y-axis.

Origin symmetry: $(-y) = -\sqrt{1 - (-x)^2}$ $\Leftrightarrow$ $y = \sqrt{1 - x^2}$, which is not the same as the original equation, so the graph is not symmetric with respect to the origin.

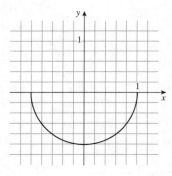

119. $y = x^2 - 6x$. Viewing rectangle $[-10, 10]$ by $[-10, 10]$.   **120.** $y = \sqrt{5 - x}$; Viewing rectangle $[-10, 6]$ by $[-1, 5]$.

121. $y = x^3 - 4x^2 - 5$. Viewing rectangle $[-4, 10]$ by $[-30, 20]$.

122. $\dfrac{x^2}{4} + y^2 = 1 \quad \Leftrightarrow \quad y^2 = 1 - \dfrac{x^2}{4} \quad \Rightarrow$

$y = \pm\sqrt{1 - \dfrac{x^2}{4}}$. Viewing rectangle $[-3, 3]$ by $[-2, 2]$.

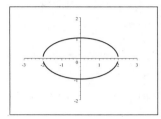

123. The line has slope $m = \dfrac{-4 + 6}{2 + 1} = \dfrac{2}{3}$, and so, by the point-slope formula, the equation is $y + 4 = \frac{2}{3}(x - 2) \quad \Leftrightarrow$

$y = \frac{2}{3}x - \frac{16}{3} \quad \Leftrightarrow \quad 2x - 3y - 16 = 0$.

124. Using the point slope formula, the equation is $y + 3 = -\frac{1}{2}(x - 6) \quad \Leftrightarrow \quad y + 3 = -\frac{1}{2}x + 3 \quad \Leftrightarrow \quad y = -\frac{1}{2}x$ or $x + 2y = 0$.

125. The x-intercept is 4, and the y-intercept is 12, so the slope is $m = \dfrac{12 - 0}{0 - 4} = -3$. Therefore, by the slope-intercept formula, the equation of the line is $y = -3x + 12 \quad \Leftrightarrow \quad 3x + y - 12 = 0$.

126. $x - 3y + 16 = 0 \quad \Leftrightarrow \quad -3y = -x - 16 \quad \Leftrightarrow \quad y = \frac{1}{3}x + \frac{16}{3}$. So the slope of the perpendicular line we seek is $m = -\dfrac{1}{(1/3)} = -3$. Then the equation of the perpendicular line passing through the point $(1, 7)$ is $y - 7 = -3(x - 1)$ $\Leftrightarrow \quad y = -3x + 10$ or $3x + y - 10 = 0$.

127. We first find the slope of the line $3x + 15y = 22$. This gives $3x + 15y = 22 \quad \Leftrightarrow \quad 15y = -3x + 22 \quad \Leftrightarrow$ $y = -\frac{1}{5}x + \frac{22}{15}$. So this line has slope $m = -\frac{1}{5}$, as does any line parallel to it. Then the parallel line passing through the origin has equation $y - 0 = -\frac{1}{5}(x - 0) \quad \Leftrightarrow \quad x + 5y = 0$.

128. The line passing through the points $(-1, -3)$ and $(3, 2)$ has slope $m = \dfrac{2 + 3}{3 + 1} = \dfrac{5}{4}$. Therefore the equation of the parallel line passing through the point $(5, 2)$ is $y - 2 = \frac{5}{4}(x - 5) \quad \Leftrightarrow \quad 4y - 8 = 5x - 25 \quad \Leftrightarrow \quad 5x - 4y - 17 = 0$.

129. Here the center is at $(0, 0)$, and the circle passes through the point $(-5, 12)$, so the radius is

$r = \sqrt{(-5 - 0)^2 + (12 - 0)^2} = \sqrt{25 + 144} = \sqrt{169} = 13$. The equation of the circle is $x^2 + y^2 = 13^2 \quad \Leftrightarrow$

$x^2 + y^2 = 169$. The line shown is the tangent that passes through the point $(-5, 12)$, so it is perpendicular to the line

through the points $(0, 0)$ and $(-5, 12)$. This line has slope $m_1 = \dfrac{12 - 0}{-5 - 0} = -\dfrac{12}{5}$. The slope of the line we seek is

$m_2 = -\dfrac{1}{m_1} = -\dfrac{1}{-12/5} = \dfrac{5}{12}$. Thus, the equation of the tangent line is $y - 12 = \frac{5}{12}(x + 5) \quad \Leftrightarrow \quad y - 12 = \frac{5}{12}x + \frac{25}{12}$

$\Leftrightarrow \quad y = \frac{5}{12}x + \frac{169}{12} \quad \Leftrightarrow \quad 5x - 12y + 169 = 0$.

130. Since the circle is tangent to the x-axis at the point $(5, 0)$ and tangent to the y-axis at the point $(0, 5)$, the center is at $(5, 5)$

and the radius is 5. Thus the equation is $(x - 5)^2 + (y - 5)^2 = 5^2 \quad \Leftrightarrow \quad (x - 5)^2 + (y - 5)^2 = 25$. The slope of

the line passing through the points $(8, 1)$ and $(5, 5)$ is $m = \dfrac{5 - 1}{5 - 8} = \dfrac{4}{-3} = -\dfrac{4}{3}$, so the equation of the line we seek is

$y - 8 = -\frac{4}{3}(x - 1) \quad \Leftrightarrow \quad 4x + 3y - 28 = 0$.

131. (a) The slope, 0.3, represents the increase in length of the spring for each unit increase in weight w. The S-intercept is the resting or natural length of the spring.

(b) When $w = 5$, $S = 0.3\,(5) + 2.5 = 1.5 + 2.5 = 4.0$ inches.

132. (a) We use the information to find two points, $(0, 60000)$ and $(3, 70500)$. Then the slope is
$$m = \frac{70500 - 60000}{3 - 0} = \frac{10500}{3} = 3{,}500. \text{ So } s = 3{,}500t + 60{,}000.$$

(b) The slope represents her annual increase, $3,500, and the S-intercept represents her initial salary, $60,000.

(c) When $t = 12$, her salary will be $S = 3{,}500\,(12) + 60{,}000 = 42{,}000 + 60{,}000 = \$102{,}000$.

133. Since M varies directly as z we have $M = kz$. Substituting $M = 120$ when $z = 15$, we find $120 = k\,(15) \quad \Leftrightarrow \quad k = 8$. Therefore, $M = 8z$.

134. Since z is inversely proportional to y, we have $z = \dfrac{k}{y}$. Substituting $z = 12$ when $y = 16$, we find $12 = \dfrac{k}{16} \quad \Leftrightarrow$ $k = 192$. Therefore $z = \dfrac{192}{y}$.

135. (a) The intensity I varies inversely as the square of the distance d, so $I = \dfrac{k}{d^2}$.

(b) Substituting $I = 1000$ when $d = 8$, we get $1000 = \dfrac{k}{(8)^2} \quad \Leftrightarrow \quad k = 64{,}000$.

(c) From parts (a) and (b), we have $I = \dfrac{64{,}000}{d^2}$. Substituting $d = 20$, we get $I = \dfrac{64{,}000}{(20)^2} = 160$ candles.

136. Let f be the frequency of the string and l be the length of the string. Since the frequency is inversely proportional to the length, we have $f = \dfrac{k}{l}$. Substituting $l = 12$ when $k = 440$, we find $440 = \dfrac{k}{12} \quad \Leftrightarrow \quad k = 5280$. Therefore $f = \dfrac{5280}{l}$. For $f = 660$, we must have $660 = \dfrac{5280}{l} \quad \Leftrightarrow \quad l = \frac{5280}{660} = 8$. So the string needs to be shortened to 8 inches.

137. Let v be the terminal velocity of the parachutist in mi/h and w be his weight in pounds. Since the terminal velocity is directly proportional to the square root of the weight, we have $v = k\sqrt{w}$. Substituting $v = 9$ when $w = 160$, we solve for k. This gives $9 = k\sqrt{160} \quad \Leftrightarrow \quad k = \dfrac{9}{\sqrt{160}} \approx 0.712$. Thus $v = 0.712\sqrt{w}$. When $w = 240$, the terminal velocity is $v = 0.712\sqrt{240} \approx 11$ mi/h.

138. Let r be the maximum range of the baseball and v be the velocity of the baseball. Since the maximum range is directly proportional to the square of the velocity, we have $r = lv^2$. Substituting $v = 60$ and $r = 242$, we find $242 = k\,(60)^2 \quad \Leftrightarrow$ $k \approx 0.0672$. If $v = 70$, then we have a maximum range of $r = 0.0672\,(70)^2 = 329.4$ feet.

Chapter 1 Test

1. (a)

$$(-5, 3]$$ $$(-5, \infty)$$

(b) $x \le 3 \iff x \in (-\infty, 3]; -1 \le x < 4 \iff x \in [-1, 4)$ **(c)** Distance $= |-12 - 39| = |-51| = 51$

2. (a) $(-3)^4 = 81$ **(b)** $-3^4 = -81$ **(c)** $3^{-4} = \dfrac{1}{3^4} = \dfrac{1}{81}$

(d) $\dfrac{5^{23}}{5^{21}} = 5^{23-21} = 5^2 = 25$ **(e)** $\left(\dfrac{2}{3}\right)^{-2} = \dfrac{3^2}{2^2} = \dfrac{9}{4}$ **(f)** $16^{-3/4} = \left(2^4\right)^{-3/4} = 2^{-3} = \dfrac{1}{8}$

3. (a) $186{,}000{,}000{,}000 = 1.86 \times 10^{11}$

(b) $0.0000003965 = 3.965 \times 10^{-7}$

4. (a) $\sqrt{200} - \sqrt{32} = 10\sqrt{2} - 4\sqrt{2} = 6\sqrt{2}$

(b) $\left(3a^2b^3\right)\left(4ab^2\right)^2 = 3a^2b^3 \cdot 4^2 a^2 b^4 = 48a^4b^7$

(c) $\left(\dfrac{3x^{3/2}y^3}{x^2y^{-1/2}}\right)^{-2} = \dfrac{3^{-2}x^{-3}y^{-6}}{x^{-4}y^1} = \tfrac{1}{9}x^{-3-(-4)}y^{-6-1} = \tfrac{1}{9}xy^{-7} = \dfrac{x}{9y^7}$

(d) $\dfrac{x^2 + 3x + 2}{x^2 - x - 2} = \dfrac{(x+1)(x+2)}{(x+1)(x-2)} = \dfrac{x+2}{x-2}$

(e) $\dfrac{x^2}{x^2 - 4} - \dfrac{x+1}{x+2} = \dfrac{x^2}{(x-2)(x+2)} - \dfrac{x+1}{x+2} = \dfrac{x^2}{(x-2)(x+2)} + \dfrac{-(x+1)(x-2)}{(x-2)(x+2)}$

$$= \dfrac{x^2 - (x^2 - x - 2)}{(x-2)(x+2)} = \dfrac{x+2}{(x-2)(x+2)} = \dfrac{1}{x-2}$$

(f) $\dfrac{\dfrac{y}{x} - \dfrac{x}{y}}{\dfrac{1}{y} - \dfrac{1}{x}} = \dfrac{\dfrac{y}{x} - \dfrac{x}{y}}{\dfrac{1}{y} - \dfrac{1}{x}} \cdot \dfrac{xy}{xy} = \dfrac{y^2 - x^2}{x - y} = \dfrac{(y-x)(y+x)}{x-y} = \dfrac{-(x-y)(y+x)}{x-y} = -(y+x)$

5. $\dfrac{\sqrt{10}}{\sqrt{5}-2} = \dfrac{\sqrt{10}}{\sqrt{5}-2} \cdot \dfrac{\sqrt{5}+2}{\sqrt{5}+2} = \dfrac{\sqrt{50}+2\sqrt{10}}{5-4} = \dfrac{5\sqrt{2}+2\sqrt{10}}{1} = 5\sqrt{2}+2\sqrt{10}$

6. (a) $3(x+6) + 4(2x-5) = 3x + 18 + 8x - 20 = 11x - 2$

(b) $(x+3)(4x-5) = 4x^2 - 5x + 12x - 15 = 4x^2 + 7x - 15$

(c) $\left(\sqrt{a}+\sqrt{b}\right)\left(\sqrt{a}-\sqrt{b}\right) = \left(\sqrt{a}\right)^2 - \left(\sqrt{b}\right)^2 = a - b$

(d) $(2x+3)^2 = (2x)^2 + 2(2x)(3) + (3)^2 = 4x^2 + 12x + 9$

(e) $(x+2)^3 = (x)^3 + 3(x)^2(2) + 3(x)(2)^2 + (2)^3 = x^3 + 6x^2 + 12x + 8$

7. (a) $4x^2 - 25 = (2x-5)(2x+5)$

(b) $2x^2 + 5x - 12 = (2x-3)(x+4)$

(c) $x^3 - 3x^2 - 4x + 12 = x^2(x-3) - 4(x-3) = (x-3)(x^2-4) = (x-3)(x-2)(x+2)$

(d) $x^4 + 27x = x\left(x^3 + 27\right) = x(x+3)(x^2 - 3x + 9)$

(e) $3x^{3/2} - 9x^{1/2} + 6x^{-1/2} = 3x^{-1/2}\left(x^2 - 3x + 2\right) = 3x^{-1/2}(x-2)(x-1)$

(f) $x^3y - 4xy = xy\left(x^2 - 4\right) = xy(x-2)(x+2)$

8. (a) $x + 5 = 14 - \tfrac{1}{2}x \iff 2x + 10 = 28 - x \iff 3x = 18 \iff x = 6$

(b) $\dfrac{2x}{x+1} = \dfrac{2x-1}{x}$ $\Leftrightarrow$ $(2x)(x) = (2x-1)(x+1)\ (x \neq -1, x \neq 0)$ $\Leftrightarrow$ $2x^2 = 2x^2 + x - 1$ $\Leftrightarrow$
$0 = x - 1$ $\Leftrightarrow$ $x = 1$

(c) $x^2 - x - 12 = 0$ $\Leftrightarrow$ $(x-4)(x+3) = 0$. So $x = 4$ or $x = -3$.

(d) $2x^2 + 4x + 1 = 0$ $\Rightarrow$ $x = \dfrac{-4 \pm \sqrt{4^2 - 4(2)(1)}}{2(2)} = \dfrac{-4 \pm \sqrt{16-8}}{4} = \dfrac{-4 \pm \sqrt{8}}{4} = \dfrac{-4 \pm 2\sqrt{2}}{4} = \dfrac{-2 \pm \sqrt{2}}{2}$.

(e) $\sqrt{3 - \sqrt{x+5}} = 2$ $\Rightarrow$ $3 - \sqrt{x+5} = 4$ $\Leftrightarrow$ $-1 = \sqrt{x+5}$. (Note that this is impossible, so there can be no solution.) Squaring both sides again, we get $1 = x + 5$ $\Leftrightarrow$ $x = -4$. But this does not satisfy the original equation, so there is no solution. (You must always check your final answers if you have squared both sides when solving an equation, since extraneous answers may be introduced, as here.)

(f) $x^4 - 3x^2 + 2 = 0$ $\Leftrightarrow$ $(x^2 - 1)(x^2 - 2) = 0$. So $x^2 - 1 = 0$ $\Leftrightarrow$ $x = \pm 1$ or $x^2 - 2 = 0$ $\Leftrightarrow$ $x = \pm\sqrt{2}$. Thus the solutions are $x = -1$, $x = 1$, $x = -\sqrt{2}$, and $x = \sqrt{2}$.

(g) $3|x-4| - 10 = 0$ $\Leftrightarrow$ $3|x-4| = 10$ $\Leftrightarrow$ $|x-4| = \frac{10}{3}$ $\Leftrightarrow$ $x - 4 = \pm\frac{10}{3}$ $\Leftrightarrow$ $x = 4 \pm \frac{10}{3}$. So $x = 4 - \frac{10}{3} = \frac{2}{3}$ or $x = 4 + \frac{10}{3} = \frac{22}{3}$. Thus the solutions are $x = \frac{2}{3}$ and $x = \frac{22}{3}$.

9. Let t be the time (in hours) it took Mary to drive from Amity to Belleville. Then $4.4 - t$ is the time it took Mary to drive from Belleville to Amity. Since then distance from Amity to Belleville equals the distance from Belleville to Amity we have $50t = 60(4.4 - t)$ $\Leftrightarrow$ $50t = 264 - 60t$ $\Leftrightarrow$ $110t = 264$ $\Leftrightarrow$ $t = 2.4$ hours. Thus the distance is $50(2.4) = 120$ mi.

10. Let w be the width of the parcel of land. Then $w + 70$ is the length of the parcel of land. Then $w^2 + (w+70)^2 = 130^2$ $\Leftrightarrow$ $w^2 + w^2 + 140w + 4900 = 16{,}900$ $\Leftrightarrow$ $2w^2 + 140w - 12000 = 0$ $\Leftrightarrow$ $w^2 + 70w - 6000 = 0$ $\Leftrightarrow$ $(w-50)(w+120) = 0$. So $w = 50$ or $w = -120$. Since $w \geq 0$, the width is $w = 50$ ft and the length is $w + 70 = 120$ ft.

11. (a) $-4 < 5 - 3x \leq 17$ $\Leftrightarrow$ $-9 < -3x \leq 12$ $\Leftrightarrow$ $3 > x \geq -4$. Expressing in standard form we have:

$-4 \leq x < 3$. Interval: $[-4, 3)$. Graph:

(b) $x(x-1)(x+2) > 0$. The expression on the left of the inequality changes sign when $x = 0$, $x = 1$, and $x = -2$. Thus we must check the intervals in the following table.

Interval	$(-\infty, -2)$	$(-2, 0)$	$(0, 1)$	$(1, \infty)$
Sign of x	$-$	$-$	$+$	$+$
Sign of $x - 1$	$-$	$-$	$-$	$+$
Sign of $x + 2$	$-$	$+$	$+$	$+$
Sign of $x(x-1)(x-2)$	$-$	$+$	$-$	$+$

From the table, the solution set is $\{x \mid -2 < x < 0 \text{ or } 1 < x\}$. Interval: $(-2, 0) \cup (1, \infty)$.

Graph:

(c) $|x - 4| < 3$ is equivalent to $-3 < x - 4 < 3$ $\Leftrightarrow$ $1 < x < 7$. Interval: $(1, 7)$. Graph:

(d) $\dfrac{2x - 3}{x + 1} \le 1$ $\Leftrightarrow$ $\dfrac{2x - 3}{x + 1} - 1 \le 0$ $\Leftrightarrow$ $\dfrac{2x - 3}{x + 1} - \dfrac{x + 1}{x + 1} \le 0$ $\Leftrightarrow$ $\dfrac{x - 4}{x + 1} \le 0$. The expression on the left
of the inequality changes sign where $x = -4$ and where $x = -1$. Thus we must check the intervals in the following
table.

Interval	$(-\infty, -1)$	$(-1, 4)$	$(4, \infty)$
Sign of $x - 4$	$-$	$-$	$+$
Sign of $x + 1$	$-$	$+$	$+$
Sign of $\dfrac{x - 4}{x + 1}$	$+$	$-$	$+$

Since $x = -1$ makes the expression in the inequality undefined, we exclude this value. Interval: $(-1, 4]$.

Graph:
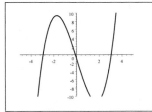

12. $5 \le \frac{5}{9}(F - 32) \le 10$ $\Leftrightarrow$ $9 \le F - 32 \le 18$ $\Leftrightarrow$ $41 \le F \le 50$. Thus the medicine is to be stored at a temperature
between $41°$ F and $50°$ F.

13. For $\sqrt{6x - x^2}$ to be defined as a real number $6x - x^2 \ge 0$ $\Leftrightarrow$ $x(6 - x) \ge 0$. The expression on the left of the
inequality changes sign when $x = 0$ and $x = 6$. Thus we must check the intervals in the following table.

Interval	$(-\infty, 0)$	$(0, 6)$	$(6, \infty)$
Sign of x	$-$	$+$	$+$
Sign of $6 - x$	$+$	$+$	$-$
Sign of $x(6 - x)$	$-$	$+$	$-$

From the table, we see that $\sqrt{6x - x^2}$ is defined when $0 \le x \le 6$.

14. (a) $x^3 - 9x - 1 = 0$. We graph the equation
$y = x^3 - 9x - 1$ in the viewing rectangle $[-5, 5]$
by $[-10, 10]$. We find that the points of
intersection occur at $x \approx -2.94, -0.11, 3.05$.

(b) $x^2 - 1 \le |x + 1|$. We graph the equations
$y_1 = x^2 - 1$ and $y_2 = |x + 1|$ in the viewing
rectangle $[-5, 5]$ by $[-5, 10]$. We find that the
points of intersection occur at $x = -1$ and $x = 2$.
Since we want $x^2 - 1 \le |x + 1|$, the solution is
the interval $[-1, 2]$.

15. (a)

There are several ways to determine the coordinates of S. The
diagonals of a square have equal length and are perpendicular. The
diagonal PR is horizontal and has length is 6 units. So the diagonal
QS is vertical and also has length 6. Thus, the coordinates of S are
$(3, 6)$.

(b) The length of PQ is $\sqrt{(0 - 3)^2 + (3 - 0)^2} = \sqrt{18} = 3\sqrt{2}$. So the
area of $PQRS$ is $\left(3\sqrt{2}\right)^2 = 18$.

16. (a)

(b) The x-intercept occurs when $y = 0$, so $0 = x^2 - 4$ $\Leftrightarrow$ $x^2 = 4$ $\Rightarrow$ $x = \pm 2$. The y-intercept occurs when $x = 0$, so $y = -4$.

(c) x-axis symmetry: $(-y) = x^2 - 4$ $\Leftrightarrow$ $y = -x^2 + 4$, which is not the same as the original equation, so the graph is not symmetric with respect to the x-axis.

y-axis symmetry: $y = (-x)^2 - 4$ $\Leftrightarrow$ $y = x^2 - 4$, which is the same as the original equation, so the graph is symmetric with respect to the y-axis.

Origin symmetry: $(-y) = (-x)^2 - 4$ $\Leftrightarrow$ $-y = x^2 - 4$, which is not the same as the original equation, so the graph is not symmetric with respect to the origin.

17. (a)

(b) The distance between P and Q is
$$d(P, Q) = \sqrt{(-3 - 5)^2 + (1 - 6)^2} = \sqrt{64 + 25} = \sqrt{89}.$$

(c) The midpoint is $\left(\dfrac{-3 + 5}{2}, \dfrac{1 + 6}{2} \right) = \left(1, \frac{7}{2} \right)$.

(d) The slope of the line is $\dfrac{1 - 6}{-3 - 5} = \dfrac{-5}{-8} = \dfrac{5}{8}$.

(e) The perpendicular bisector of PQ contains the midpoint, $\left(1, \frac{7}{2} \right)$, and it slope is the negative reciprocal of $\frac{5}{8}$. Thus the slope is $-\frac{1}{5/8} = -\frac{8}{5}$. Hence the equation is $y - \frac{7}{2} = -\frac{8}{5}(x - 1)$ $\Leftrightarrow$ $y = -\frac{8}{5}x + \frac{8}{5} + \frac{7}{2} = -\frac{8}{5}x + \frac{51}{10}$. That is, $y = -\frac{8}{5}x + \frac{51}{10}$.

(f) The center of the circle is the midpoint, $\left(1, \frac{7}{2} \right)$, and the length of the radius is $\frac{1}{2}\sqrt{89}$. Thus the equation of the circle whose diameter is PQ is $(x - 1)^2 + \left(y - \frac{7}{2} \right)^2 = \left(\frac{1}{2}\sqrt{89} \right)^2$ $\Leftrightarrow$ $(x - 1)^2 + \left(y - \frac{7}{2} \right)^2 = \frac{89}{4}$.

18. (a) $x^2 + y^2 = 25 = 5^2$ has center $(0, 0)$ and radius 5.

(b) $(x - 2)^2 + (y + 1)^2 = 9 = 3^2$ has center $(2, -1)$ and radius 3.

(c) $x^2 + 6x + y^2 - 2y + 6 = 0$ $\Leftrightarrow$ $x^2 + 6x + 9 + y^2 - 2y + 1 = 4$ $\Leftrightarrow$ $(x + 3)^2 + (y - 1)^2 = 4 = 2^2$ has center $(-3, 1)$ and radius 2.

19. $2x - 3y = 15$ $\Leftrightarrow$

$-3y = -2x + 15$ $\Leftrightarrow$ $y = \frac{2}{3}x - 5$.

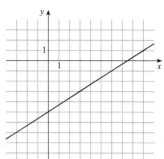

20. (a) $3x + y - 10 = 0$ $\Leftrightarrow$ $y = -3x + 10$, so the slope of the line we seek is -3. Using the point-slope, $y - (-6) = -3(x - 3)$ $\Leftrightarrow$

$y + 6 = -3x + 9$ $\Leftrightarrow$ $3x + y - 3 = 0$.

(b) Using the intercept form we get $\dfrac{x}{6} + \dfrac{y}{4} = 1$ $\Leftrightarrow$ $2x + 3y = 12$

$\Leftrightarrow$ $2x + 3y - 12 = 0$.

21. (a) When $x = 100$ we have $T = 0.08(100) - 4 = 8 - 4 = 4$, so the temperature at one meter is $4°$ C.

(c) The slope represents the raise in temperature as the depth increase. The T-intercept is the surface temperature of the soil and the x-intercept represents the depth of the "frost line", where the soil below is not frozen.

(b)

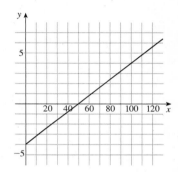

22. (a) $M = k\dfrac{wh^2}{L}$.

(b) Substituting $w = 4$, $h = 6$, $L = 12$, and $M = 4800$, we have $4800 = k\dfrac{(4)\left(6^2\right)}{12}$ $\Leftrightarrow$ $k = 400$. Thus

$M = 400\dfrac{wh^2}{L}$.

(c) Now if $L = 10$, $w = 3$, and $h = 10$, then $M = 400\dfrac{(3)\left(10^2\right)}{10} = 12,000$. So the beam can support $12,000$ pounds.

Focus on Problem Solving: General Principles

1. Let d be the distance traveled to and from work. Let t_1 and t_2 be the times for the trip from home to work and the trip from work to home, respectively. Using time$=\dfrac{\text{distance}}{\text{rate}}$, we get $t_1 = \dfrac{d}{50}$ and $t_2 = \dfrac{d}{30}$. Since average speed $=\dfrac{\text{distance traveled}}{\text{total time}}$, we have average speed $=\dfrac{2d}{t_1 + t_2} = \dfrac{2d}{\dfrac{d}{50} + \dfrac{d}{30}} \Leftrightarrow$

average speed $=\dfrac{150\,(2d)}{150\left(\dfrac{d}{50} + \dfrac{d}{30}\right)} = \dfrac{300d}{3d + 5d} = \dfrac{300}{8} = 37.5$ mi/h.

2. Let r be the rate of the descent. We use the formula time $=\dfrac{\text{distance}}{\text{rate}}$; the ascent takes $\frac{1}{15}$ h, the descent takes $\dfrac{1}{r}$ h, and the total trip should take $\dfrac{2}{30} = \dfrac{1}{15}$ h. Thus we have $\dfrac{1}{15} + \dfrac{1}{r} = \dfrac{1}{15} \Leftrightarrow \dfrac{1}{r} = 0$, which is impossible. So the car cannot go fast enough to average 30 mi/h for the 2-mile trip.

3. We use the formula $d = rt$. Since the car and the van each travel at a speed of 40 mi/h, they approach each other at a combined speed of 80 mi/h. (The distance between them decreases at a rate of 80 mi/h.) So the time spent driving till they meet is $t = \dfrac{d}{r} = \dfrac{120}{80} = 1.5$ hours. Thus, the fly flies at a speed of 100 mi/h for 1.5 hours, and therefore travels a distance of $d = rt = (100)\,(1.5) = 150$ miles.

4. Let us start with a given price P. After a discount of 40%, the price decreases to $0.6P$. After a discount of 20%, the price decreases to $0.8P$, and after another 20% discount, it becomes $0.8\,(0.8P) = 0.64P$. Since $0.6P < 0.64P$, a 40% discount is better.

5. We continue the pattern. Three parallel cuts produce 10 pieces. Thus, each new cut produces an additional 3 pieces. Since the first cut produces 4 pieces, we get the formula $f\,(n) = 4 + 3\,(n - 1)$, $n \ge 1$. Since $f\,(142) = 4 + 3\,(141) = 427$, we see that 142 parallel cuts produce 427 pieces.

6. By placing two amoebas into the vessel, we skip the first simple division which took 3 minutes. Thus when we place two amoebas into the vessel, it will take $60 - 3 = 57$ minutes for the vessel to be full of amoebas.

7. George's speed is $\frac{1}{50}$ lap/s, and Sue's is $\frac{1}{30}$ lap/s. So after t seconds, George has run $\dfrac{t}{50}$ laps, and Sue has run $\dfrac{t}{30}$ laps. They will next be side by side when Sue has run exactly one more lap than George, that is, when $\dfrac{t}{30} = \dfrac{t}{50} + 1$. We solve for t by first multiplying by 150, so $50t = 30t + 150 \Leftrightarrow 20t = 150 \Leftrightarrow t = 75$. Therefore, they will be even after 75 s.

8. The statement is false. Here is one particular counterexample:

	Player A	Player B
First half	1 hit in 99 at-bats: average $= \frac{1}{99}$	0 hit in 1 at-bat: average $= \frac{0}{1}$
Second half	1 hit in 1 at-bat: average $= \frac{1}{1}$	98 hits in 99 at-bats: average $= \frac{98}{99}$
Entire season	2 hits in 100 at-bats: average $= \frac{2}{100}$	99 hits in 100 at-bats: average $= \frac{99}{100}$

9. *Method 1:* After the exchanges, the volume of liquid in the pitcher and in the cup is the same as it was to begin with. Thus, any coffee in the pitcher of cream must be replacing an equal amount of cream that has ended up in the coffee cup.

Method 2: Alternatively, look at the drawing of the spoonful of coffee and cream mixture being returned to the pitcher of cream. Suppose it is possible to separate the cream and the coffee, as shown. Then you can see that the coffee going into the cream occupies the same volume as the cream that was left in the coffee.

Method 3 (an algebraic approach): Suppose the cup of coffee has y spoonfuls of coffee. When one spoonful of cream is added to the coffee cup, the resulting mixture has the following ratios: $\dfrac{\text{cream}}{\text{mixture}} = \dfrac{1}{y+1}$ and $\dfrac{\text{coffee}}{\text{mixture}} = \dfrac{y}{y+1}$.

So, when we remove a spoonful of the mixture and put it into the pitcher of cream, we are really removing $\dfrac{1}{y+1}$ of a spoonful of cream and $\dfrac{y}{y+1}$ spoonful of coffee. Thus the amount of cream left in the mixture (cream in the coffee) is $1 - \dfrac{1}{y+1} = \dfrac{y}{y+1}$ of a spoonful. This is the same as the amount of coffee we added to the cream.

10. It remains the same. The weight of the ice cube is the same as the weight of the volume of water it displaces. Thus as the ice cube melts, it becomes water that fits exactly into the space displaced by the floating ice cube.

11. Let r be the radius of the earth in feet. Then the circumference (length of the ribbon) is $2\pi r$. When we increase the radius by 1 foot, the new radius is $r + 1$, so the new circumference is $2\pi (r + 1)$. Thus you need $2\pi (r + 1) - 2\pi r = 2\pi$ extra feet of ribbon.

12. We know that $\sqrt{2}$ is irrational. Now $\sqrt{2}^{\sqrt{2}}$ is either rational or irrational. If $\sqrt{2}^{\sqrt{2}}$ is rational, we would be done because we would have found an irrational number raised to an irrational number which is rational. If $\sqrt{2}^{\sqrt{2}}$ is not rational, then consider $\left(\sqrt{2}^{\sqrt{2}}\right)^{\sqrt{2}} = \sqrt{2}^{\sqrt{2}\cdot\sqrt{2}} = \sqrt{2}^{2} = 2$. So, again we would have found an irrational number (namely $\sqrt{2}^{\sqrt{2}}$) raised to an irrational number (namely $\sqrt{2}$) which is rational (namely 2).

13. Let $r_1 = 8$. $r_2 = \frac{1}{2}\left(8 + \frac{72}{8}\right) = \frac{1}{2}(8+9) = 8.5$, $r_3 = \frac{1}{2}\left(8.5 + \dfrac{72}{8.5}\right) = \frac{1}{2}(8.5 + 8.471) = 8.485$, and

$r_4 = \frac{1}{2}\left(8.485 + \dfrac{72}{8.485}\right) = \frac{1}{2}(8.485 + 8.486) = 8.485$. Thus $\sqrt{72} \approx 8.49$.

14. Let n, $n + 1$, and $n + 2$ be three consecutive integers. Then the product of three consecutive integers plus the middle is
$$n(n+1)(n+2) + (n+1) = n^3 + 3n^2 + 2n + n + 1 = n^3 + 3n^2 + 3n + 1 = (n+1)^3.$$

15. The first few powers of 3 are $3^1 = 3$, $3^2 = 9$, $3^3 = 27$, $3^4 = 81$, $3^5 = 243$, $3^6 = 729$. It appears that the final digit cycles in a pattern, namely $3 \to 9 \to 7 \to 1 \to 3 \to 9 \to 7 \to 1$, of length 4. Since $459 = 4 \times 114 + 3$, the final digit is the third in the cycle, namely 7.

16. Let us see what happens when we square similar numbers with fewer 9 's: $39^2 = 1521$, $399^2 = 159201$, $3999^2 = 15992001$, $39999^2 = 1599920001$.

The pattern is that the square always seems to start with 15 and end with 1, and if $39\cdots 9$ has n 9 's, then the 2 in the middle of its square is preceded by $(n-1)$ 9 's and followed by $(n-1)$ 0 's. From this pattern, we make the guess that
$$3{,}999{,}999{,}999{,}999^2 = 15{,}999{,}999{,}999{,}992{,}000{,}000{,}000{,}001$$
This can be verified by writing the number as follows:

$$3{,}999{,}999{,}999{,}999^2 = (4{,}000{,}000{,}000{,}000 - 1)^2 = 4{,}000{,}000{,}000{,}000^2 - 2 \cdot 4{,}000{,}000{,}000{,}000 + 1$$
$$= 16{,}000{,}000{,}000{,}000{,}000{,}000{,}000{,}000 - 8{,}000{,}000{,}000{,}000 + 1$$
$$= 15{,}999{,}999{,}999{,}992{,}000{,}000{,}000{,}001$$

17. Let p be an odd prime and label the other integer sides of the triangle as shown.

Then $p^2 + b^2 = c^2 \iff p^2 = c^2 - b^2 \iff p^2 = (c - b)(c + b)$. Now $c - b$ and $c + b$ are integer factors of p^2 where p is a prime.

Case 1: $c - b = p$ and $c + b = p$ Subtracting gives $b = 0$ which contradicts that b is the length of a side of a triangle.

Case 2: $c - b = 1$ and $c + b = p^2$ Adding gives $2c = 1 + p^2 \iff c = \dfrac{1 + p^2}{2}$ and $b = \dfrac{p^2 - 1}{2}$. Since p is odd, p^2 is odd. Thus $\dfrac{1 + p^2}{2}$ and $\dfrac{p^2 - 1}{2}$ both define integers and are the only solutions. (For example, if we choose $p = 3$, then $c = 5$ and $b = 4$.)

18. $x^2 + y^2 = 4z + 3$. We consider all possible cases for x and y even or odd.

Case 1: x and y are both odd   Since the square of an odd number is odd, and the sum of two odd numbers is even, the left hand side is even but the right hand side is odd. Thus the left hand side cannot equal the right hand side.

Case 2: x and y are both even   Since the square of an even number is even, and the sum of two even numbers is even, the left hand side is even but the right hand side is odd. Thus the left hand side cannot equal the right hand side.

Case 3: x is odd and y is even   Let $x = 2n + 1$ and let $y = 2m$ for some integers n and m. Then $(2n + 1)^2 + (2m)^2 = 4z + 3 \iff 4n^2 + 4n + 1 + 4m^2 = 4z + 3 \iff 4(n^2 + n + m^2) + 1 = 4z + 3$. However, when the left hand side is divided by 4 the remainder is 1, but when the right hand side is divided by 4 the remainder is 3. Thus the left hand side cannot equal the right hand side.

Case 4: x is even and y is odd   This is handled in the same way as Case 3.

Thus, there is no integer solution to $x^2 + y^2 = 4z + 3$.

19. The north pole is such a point. And there are others: Consider a point a_1 near the south pole such that the parallel passing through a_1 forms a circle C_1 with circumference exactly one mile. Any point P_1 exactly one mile north of the circle C_1 along a meridian is a point satisfying the conditions in the problem: starting at P_1 she walks one mile south to the point a_1 on the circle C_1, then one mile east along C_1 returning to the point a_1, then north for one mile to P_1. That's not all. If a point a_2 (or a_3, a_4, a_5, ...) is chosen near the south pole so that the parallel passing through it forms a circle C_2 (C_3, C_4, C_5, ...) with a circumference of exactly $\frac{1}{2}$ mile ($\frac{1}{3}$ mi, $\frac{1}{4}$ mi, $\frac{1}{5}$ mi, ...), then the point P_2 (P_3, P_4, P_5, ...) one mile north of a_2 (a_3, a_4, a_5, ...) along a meridian satisfies the conditions of the problem: she walks one mile south from P_2 (P_3, P_4, P_5, ...) arriving at a_2 (a_3, a_4, a_5, ...) along the circle C_2 (C_3, C_4, C_5, ...), walks east along the circle for one mile thus traversing the circle twice (three times, four times, five times, ...) returning to a_2 (a_3, a_4, a_5, ...), and then walks north one mile to P_2 (P_3, P_4, P_5, ...).

20. Let h_1 be the height of the pyramid whose square base length is a. Then $h_1 - h$ is the height of the pyramid whose square base length is b. Thus the volume of the truncated pyramid is $V = \frac{1}{3}h_1 a^2 - \frac{1}{3}(h_1 - h)b^2 = \frac{1}{3}h_1 a^2 - \frac{1}{3}h_1 b^2 + \frac{1}{3}hb^2 = \frac{1}{3}h_1(a^2 - b^2) + \frac{1}{3}hb^2$. Next we must find a relationship between h_1 and the other variables. Using geometry, the ratio of the height to the base of the two pyramids must be the same. Thus $\dfrac{h_1}{a} = \dfrac{h_1 - h}{b} \iff bh_1 = ah_1 - ah \iff ah = ah_1 - bh_1 = (a - b)h_1 \iff \dfrac{ah}{a - b} = h_1$. Substituting for h_1 we have $V = \frac{1}{3}\left(\dfrac{ah}{a - b}\right)(a^2 - b^2) + \frac{1}{3}hb^2 = \frac{1}{3}(ah)(a + b) + \frac{1}{3}hb^2 = \frac{1}{3}ha^2 + \frac{1}{3}hab + \frac{1}{3}hb^2 = \frac{1}{3}h(a^2 + ab + b^2)$.

21. Let r and R be the radius of the smaller circle and larger circle, respectively. Since the line is tangent to the smaller circle, using the Pythagorean Theorem, we get the following relationship between the radii: $R^2 = 1^2 + r^2$. Thus the area of the shaded region is $\pi R^2 - \pi r^2 = \pi \left(1 + r^2\right) - \pi r^2 = \pi$.

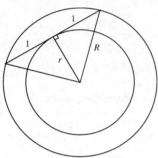

22. Label the figures as shown. The unshaded area is c^2 in the first figure and $a^2 + b^2$ in the second figure. These unshaded areas are equal, since in each case they equal the area of the large square minus the areas of the four shaded triangles. Thus $a^2 + b^2 = c^2$. Finally, note that a, b, and c are the legs and hypotenuse of the shaded triangle.

 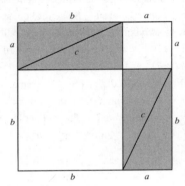

23. Since $\sqrt[3]{1729} \approx 12.0023$, we start with $n = 12$ and find the other perfect cube.

n	$1729 - n^3$
12	$1729 - (12)^3 = 1$
11	$1729 - (11)^3 = 398$
10	$1729 - (10)^3 = 729$

Since 1 and 729 are perfect cubes, the two representations we seek are $1^3 + 12^3 = 1729$ and $9^3 + 10^3 = 1729$.

24. (a) $\left(\sqrt{3 + 2\sqrt{2}} - \sqrt{3 - 2\sqrt{2}}\right)^2 = 3 + 2\sqrt{2} - 2 \cdot \sqrt{\left(3 + 2\sqrt{2}\right)\left(3 - 2\sqrt{2}\right)} + 3 - 2\sqrt{2} = 6 - 2 \cdot \sqrt{9 - 8} = 6 - 2 = 4$.

Therefore, $\sqrt{3 + 2\sqrt{2}} - \sqrt{3 - 2\sqrt{2}} = \sqrt{4} = 2$.

(b) $\dfrac{\sqrt{2} + \sqrt{6}}{\sqrt{2 + \sqrt{3}}} = \sqrt{\dfrac{\left(\sqrt{2} + \sqrt{6}\right)^2}{2 + \sqrt{3}}} = \sqrt{\dfrac{2 + 2\sqrt{12} + 6}{2 + \sqrt{3}}} = \sqrt{\dfrac{8 + 4\sqrt{3}}{2 + \sqrt{3}}} = \sqrt{\dfrac{4\left(2 + \sqrt{3}\right)}{2 + \sqrt{3}}} = 2$

25. (a) Imagine that the rooms are colored alternately black and white (like a checkerboard) with the entrance being a white room. So there are 18 black rooms and 18 white rooms. If a tourist is in a white room, he must next go to a black room, and if he is in a black room, the must next go to a white room.

(b) Since the entrance is white, any path that the tourist takes must be of the form W, B, W, B, W, B, ... Since the museum contains an even number of rooms and the tourist starts in a white room, he must end his tour in a black room. But the exit is in a white room, so the proposed tour is impossible.

26. Consider any three points that are exactly one unit apart, as shown in the figure. Since only two colors are available, it must be that at least two of these points have the same color, and this proves that there are at least two points exactly one unit apart with the same color.

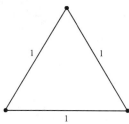

27. You can see infinitely far in this forest, because if your vision is blocked by a tree [at the rational point (a, b), say], then the slope of the line of sight from you to this tree is $\dfrac{b - 0}{a - 0} = \dfrac{b}{a}$, which is a rational number. Thus if you look along a line of irrational slope, you will see infinitely far.

28. Label the points $P_1, P_2, \ldots, P_{1000}$ and consider all possible pairs of points. Each such pair (P_i, P_j) determines a slope $m_{i,j}$ (which may be infinite). There are only a finite number of slopes $m_{i,j}$, so let m be a number not equal to any of these. Move a line of slope m through the 1000 points (from bottom to top, say). Since $m \neq m_{i,j}$, the line will cross one point at a time. Stop after it has crossed 500 points. Then 500 points will be below the line and 500 above.

29. We consider four cases corresponding to the four quadrants.

Case 1: $x \geq 0$ and $y \geq 0$ $|x| + |y| \leq 1$ becomes $x + y \leq 1$.
Case 2: $x \leq 0$ and $y \geq 0$ $|x| + |y| \leq 1$ becomes $-x + y \leq 1$.
Case 3: $x \geq 0$ and $y \leq 0$ $|x| + |y| \leq 1$ becomes $x - y \leq 1$.
Case 4: $x \leq 0$ and $y \leq 0$ $|x| + |y| \leq 1$ becomes $-x - y \leq 1$ $\Leftrightarrow$ $x + y \geq -1$.

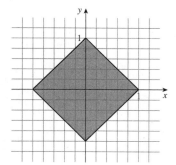

30. $x^2 y - y^3 - 5x^2 + 5y^2 = 0$ $\Leftrightarrow$ $y\left(x^2 - y^2\right) - 5\left(x^2 - y^2\right) = 0$ $\Leftrightarrow$ $(y - 5)\left(x^2 - y^2\right) = 0$ $\Leftrightarrow$
$(y - 5)(x - y)(x + y) = 0$. So $y = 5$, $x = y$ or $x = -y$. The graph consists of 3 lines.

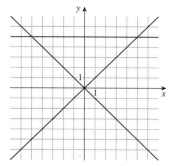

2 Functions

2.1 What is a Function?

1. $f(x) = 2(x + 3)$

2. $f(x) = \dfrac{x}{7} - 4$

3. $f(x) = (x - 5)^2$

4. $f(x) = \frac{1}{3}(\sqrt{x} + 8)$

5. Subtract 4, then divide by 3.

6. Divide by 3, then subtract 4.

7. Square, then add 2.

8. Add 2, then take the square root.

9. Machine diagram for $f(x) = \sqrt{x - 1}$.

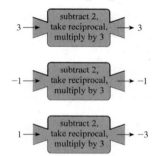

10. Machine diagram for $f(x) = \dfrac{3}{x - 2}$.

11. $f(x) = 2(x - 1)^2$

x	$f(x)$
-1	$2(-1 - 1)^2 = 8$
0	$2(-1)^2 = 2$
1	$2(1 - 1)^2 = 0$
2	$2(2 - 1)^2 = 2$
3	$2(3 - 1)^2 = 8$

12. $g(x) = |2x + 3|$

x	$g(x)$
-3	$|2(-3) + 3| = 3$
-2	$|2(-2) + 3| = 1$
0	$|2(0) + 3| = 3$
1	$|2(1) + 3| = 5$
3	$|2(3) + 3| = 9$

13. $f(1) = 2(1) + 1 = 3$; $f(-2) = 2(-2) + 1 = -3$; $f\left(\frac{1}{2}\right) = 2\left(\frac{1}{2}\right) + 1 = 2$; $f(a) = 2(a) + 1 = 2a + 1$; $f(-a) = 2(-a) + 1 = -2a + 1$; $f(a + b) = 2(a + b) + 1 = 2a + 2b + 1$.

14. $f(0) = 0^2 + 2(0) = 0$; $f(3) = 3^2 + 2(3) = 9 + 6 = 15$; $f(-3) = (-3)^2 + 2(-3) = 9 - 6 = 3$;

$f(a) = a^2 + 2(a) = a^2 + 2a$; $f(-x) = (-x)^2 + 2(-x) = x^2 - 2x$; $f\left(\dfrac{1}{a}\right) = \left(\dfrac{1}{a}\right)^2 + 2\left(\dfrac{1}{a}\right) = \dfrac{1}{a^2} + \dfrac{2}{a}$.

15. $g(2) = \dfrac{1 - (2)}{1 + (2)} = \dfrac{-1}{3} = -\dfrac{1}{3}$; $g(-2) = \dfrac{1 - (-2)}{1 + (-2)} = \dfrac{3}{-1} = -3$; $g\left(\dfrac{1}{2}\right) = \dfrac{1 - \left(\frac{1}{2}\right)}{1 + \left(\frac{1}{2}\right)} = \dfrac{\frac{1}{2}}{\frac{3}{2}} = \dfrac{1}{3}$;

$g(a) = \dfrac{1 - (a)}{1 + (a)} = \dfrac{1 - a}{1 + a}$; $g(a - 1) = \dfrac{1 - (a - 1)}{1 + (a - 1)} = \dfrac{1 - a + 1}{1 + a - 1} = \dfrac{2 - a}{a}$; $g(-1) = \dfrac{1 - (-1)}{1 + (-1)} = \dfrac{2}{0}$, so $g(-1)$ is not defined.

16. $h(1) = (1) + \frac{1}{(1)} = 2$; $h(-1) = (-1) + \frac{1}{-1} = -1 - 1 = -2$; $h(2) = 2 + \frac{1}{2} = \frac{5}{2}$; $h\left(\frac{1}{2}\right) = \frac{1}{2} + \frac{1}{\frac{1}{2}} = \frac{1}{2} + 2 = \frac{5}{2}$;

$h(x) = x + \frac{1}{x}$; $h\left(\frac{1}{x}\right) = \frac{1}{x} + \frac{1}{\frac{1}{x}} = \frac{1}{x} + x$.

17. $f(0) = 2(0)^2 + 3(0) - 4 = -4$; $f(2) = 2(2)^2 + 3(2) - 4 = 8 + 6 - 4 = 10$;

$f(-2) = 2(-2)^2 + 3(-2) - 4 = 8 - 6 - 4 = -2$; $f(\sqrt{2}) = 2(\sqrt{2})^2 + 3(\sqrt{2}) - 4 = 4 + 3\sqrt{2} - 4 = 3\sqrt{2}$;

$f(x+1) = 2(x+1)^2 + 3(x+1) - 4 = 2x^2 + 4x + 2 + 3x + 3 - 4 = 2x^2 + 7x + 1$;

$f(-x) = 2(-x)^2 + 3(-x) - 4 = 2x^2 - 3x - 4$.

18. $f(0) = 0^3 - 4(0)^2 = 0 + 0 = 0$; $f(1) = 1^3 - 4(1)^2 = 1 - 4 = -3$; $f(-1) = (-1)^3 - 4(-1)^2 = -1 - 4 = -5$;

$f\left(\frac{3}{2}\right) = \left(\frac{3}{2}\right)^3 - 4\left(\frac{3}{2}\right)^2 = \frac{27}{8} - 9 = -\frac{45}{8}$; $f\left(\frac{x}{2}\right) = \left(\frac{x}{2}\right)^3 - 4\left(\frac{x}{2}\right)^2 = \frac{x^3}{8} - x^2$; $f(x^2) = (x^2)^3 - 4(x^2)^2 = x^6 - 4x^4$.

19. $f(-2) = 2|-2-1| = 2(3) = 6$; $f(0) = 2|0-1| = 2(1) = 2$;

$f\left(\frac{1}{2}\right) = 2\left|\frac{1}{2} - 1\right| = 2\left(\frac{1}{2}\right) = 1$; $f(2) = 2|2-1| = 2(1) = 2$; $f(x+1) = 2|(x+1) - 1| = 2|x|$;

$f(x^2 + 2) = 2|(x^2 + 2) - 1| = 2|x^2 + 1| = 2x^2 + 2$ (since $x^2 + 1 > 0$).

20. $f(-2) = \frac{|-2|}{-2} = \frac{2}{-2} = -1$; $f(-1) = \frac{|-1|}{-1} = \frac{1}{-1} = -1$; $f(x)$ is not defined at $x = 0$; $f(5) = \frac{|5|}{5} = \frac{5}{5} = 1$;

$f(x^2) = \frac{|x^2|}{x^2} = \frac{x^2}{x^2} = 1$ since $x^2 > 0$, $x \neq 0$; $f\left(\frac{1}{x}\right) = \frac{|1/x|}{1/x} = \frac{x}{|x|}$.

21. Since $-2 < 0$, we have $f(-2) = (-2)^2 = 4$. Since $-1 < 0$, we have $f(-1) = (-1)^2 = 1$. Since $0 \geq 0$, we have $f(0) = 0 + 1 = 1$. Since $1 \geq 0$, we have $f(1) = 1 + 1 = 2$. Since $2 \geq 0$, we have $f(2) = 2 + 1 = 3$.

22. Since $-3 \leq 2$, we have $f(-3) = 5$. Since $0 \leq 2$, we have $f(0) = 5$. Since $2 \leq 2$, we have $f(2) = 5$. Since $3 > 2$, we have $f(3) = 2(3) - 3 = 3$. Since $5 > 2$, we have $f(5) = 2(5) - 3 = 7$.

23. Since $-4 \leq -1$, we have $f(-4) = (-4)^2 + 2(-4) = 16 - 8 = 8$. Since $-\frac{3}{2} \leq -1$, we have $f\left(-\frac{3}{2}\right) = \left(-\frac{3}{2}\right)^2 + 2\left(-\frac{3}{2}\right) = \frac{9}{4} - 3 = -\frac{3}{4}$. Since $-1 \leq -1$, we have $f(-1) = (-1)^2 + 2(-1) = 1 - 2 = -1$. Since $-1 < 0 \leq 1$, we have $f(0) = 0$. Since $25 > 1$, we have $f(25) = -1$.

24. Since $-5 < 0$, we have $f(-5) = 3(-5) = -15$. Since $0 \leq 0 \leq 2$, we have $f(0) = 0 + 1 = 1$. Since $0 \leq 1 \leq 2$, we have $f(1) = 1 + 1 = 2$. Since $0 \leq 2 \leq 2$, we have $f(2) = 2 + 1 = 3$. Since $5 > 2$, we have $f(5) = (5 - 2)^2 = 9$.

25. $f(x+2) = (x+2)^2 + 1 = x^2 + 4x + 4 + 1 = x^2 + 4x + 5$; $f(x) + f(2) = x^2 + 1 + (2)^2 + 1 = x^2 + 1 + 4 + 1 = x^2 + 6$.

26. $f(2x) = 3(2x) - 1 = 6x - 1$; $2f(x) = 2(3x - 1) = 6x - 2$.

27. $f(x^2) = x^2 + 4$; $[f(x)]^2 = [x + 4]^2 = x^2 + 8x + 16$.

28. $f\left(\frac{x}{3}\right) = 6\left(\frac{x}{3}\right) - 18 = 2x - 18$; $\frac{f(x)}{3} = \frac{6x - 18}{3} = \frac{3(2x - 6)}{3} = 2x - 6$.

29. $f(a) = 3(a) + 2 = 3a + 2$; $f(a+h) = 3(a+h) + 2 = 3a + 3h + 2$;

$\frac{f(a+h) - f(a)}{h} = \frac{(3a + 3h + 2) - (3a + 2)}{h} = \frac{3a + 3h + 2 - 3a - 2}{h} = \frac{3h}{h} = 3$.

30. $f(a) = (a)^2 + 1 = a^2 + 1$; $f(a+h) = (a+h)^2 + 1 = a^2 + 2ah + h^2 + 1$;

$\frac{f(a+h) - f(a)}{h} = \frac{(a^2 + 2ah + h^2 + 1) - (a^2 + 1)}{h} = \frac{a^2 + 2ah + h^2 + 1 - a^2 - 1}{h}$

$= \frac{2ah + h^2}{h} = \frac{h(2a + h)}{h} = 2a + h$.

31. $f(a) = 5$; $f(a+h) = 5$; $\frac{f(a+h) - f(a)}{h} = \frac{5 - 5}{h} = 0$.

32. $f(a) = \dfrac{1}{a+1}$; $f(a+h) = \dfrac{1}{a+h+1}$;

$$\dfrac{f(a+h) - f(a)}{h} = \dfrac{\dfrac{1}{a+h+1} - \dfrac{1}{a+1}}{h} = \dfrac{\dfrac{a+1}{(a+1)(a+h+1)} - \dfrac{a+h+1}{(a+1)(a+h+1)}}{h}$$

$$= \dfrac{\dfrac{-h}{(a+1)(a+h+1)}}{h} = \dfrac{-1}{(a+1)(a+h+1)}.$$

33. $f(a) = \dfrac{a}{a+1}$; $f(a+h) = \dfrac{a+h}{a+h+1}$;

$$\dfrac{f(a+h) - f(a)}{h} = \dfrac{\dfrac{a+h}{a+h+1} - \dfrac{a}{a+1}}{h} = \dfrac{\dfrac{(a+h)(a+1)}{(a+h+1)(a+1)} - \dfrac{a(a+h+1)}{(a+h+1)(a+1)}}{h}$$

$$= \dfrac{\dfrac{(a+h)(a+1) - a(a+h+1)}{(a+h+1)(a+1)}}{h} = \dfrac{a^2 + a + ah + h - (a^2 + ah + a)}{h(a+h-1)(a+1)}$$

$$= \dfrac{1}{(a+h-1)(a+1)}$$

34. $f(a) = \dfrac{2a}{a-1}$; $f(a+h) = \dfrac{2(a+h)}{a+h-1}$;

$$\dfrac{f(a+h) - f(a)}{h} = \dfrac{\dfrac{2a+h}{a+h-1} - \dfrac{2a}{a-1}}{h} = \dfrac{\dfrac{(2a+h)(a-1)}{(a+h-1)(a-1)} - \dfrac{2a(a+h-1)}{(a+h-1)(a-1)}}{h}$$

$$= \dfrac{\dfrac{(2a+h)(a-1) - 2a(a+h-1)}{(a+h-1)(a-1)}}{h} = \dfrac{2a^2 + ah - 2a - h - (2a^2 + 2ah - 2a)}{h(a+h-1)(a-1)}$$

$$= \dfrac{-ah - h}{h(a+h-1)(a-1)} = -\dfrac{a+1}{(a+h-1)(a-1)}$$

35. $f(a) = 3 - 5a + 4a^2$;

$$f(a+h) = 3 - 5(a+h) + 4(a+h)^2 = 3 - 5a - 5h + 4(a^2 + 2ah + h^2)$$

$$= 3 - 5a - 5h + 4a^2 + 8ah + 4h^2;$$

$$\dfrac{f(a+h) - f(a)}{h} = \dfrac{(3 - 5a - 5h + 4a^2 + 8ah + 4h^2) - (3 - 5a + 4a^2)}{h}$$

$$= \dfrac{3 - 5a - 5h + 4a^2 + 8ah + 4h^2 - 3 + 5a - 4a^2}{h} = \dfrac{-5h + 8ah + 4h^2}{h}$$

$$= \dfrac{h(-5 + 8a + 4h)}{h} = -5 + 8a + 4h.$$

36. $f(a) = a^3$; $f(a+h) = (a+h)^3 = a^3 + 3a^2h + 3ah^2 + h^3$;

$$\dfrac{f(a+h) - f(a)}{h} = \dfrac{(a^3 + 3a^2h + 3ah^2 + h^3) - (a^3)}{h} = \dfrac{3a^2h + 3ah^2 + h^3}{h}$$

$$= \dfrac{h(3a^2 + 3ah + h^2)}{h} = 3a^2 + 3ah + h^2.$$

37. $f(x) = 2x$. Since there is no restrictions, the domain is the set of real numbers, $(-\infty, \infty)$.

38. $f(x) = x^2 + 1$. Since there is no restrictions, the domain is all real numbers, $(-\infty, \infty)$.

39. $f(x) = 2x$. The domain is restricted by the exercise to $[-1, 5]$.

40. $f(x) = x^2 + 1$. The domain is restricted by the exercise to $[0, 5]$.

41. $f(x) = \dfrac{1}{x-3}$. Since the denominator cannot equal 0 we have $x - 3 \neq 0 \quad \Leftrightarrow \quad x \neq 3$. Thus the domain is $\{x \mid x \neq 3\}$. In interval notation, the domain is $(-\infty, 3) \cup (3, \infty)$.

42. $f(x) = \dfrac{1}{3x - 6}$. Since the denominator cannot equal 0, we have $3x - 6 \neq 0$ $\Leftrightarrow$ $3x \neq 6$ $\Leftrightarrow$ $x \neq 2$. In interval notation, the domain is $(-\infty, 2) \cup (2, \infty)$.

43. $f(x) = \dfrac{x + 2}{x^2 - 1}$. Since the denominator cannot equal 0 we have $x^2 - 1 \neq 0$ $\Leftrightarrow$ $x^2 \neq 1$ $\Rightarrow$ $x \neq \pm 1$. Thus the domain is $\{x \mid x \neq \pm 1\}$. In interval notation, the domain is $(-\infty, -1) \cup (-1, 1) \cup (1, \infty)$.

44. $f(x) = \dfrac{x^4}{x^2 + x - 6}$. Since the denominator cannot equal 0, $x^2 + x - 6 \neq 0$ $\Leftrightarrow$ $(x + 3)(x - 2) \neq 0$ $\Rightarrow$ $x \neq -3$ or $x \neq 2$. In interval notation, the domain is $(-\infty, -3) \cup (-3, 2) \cup (2, \infty)$.

45. $f(x) = \sqrt{x - 5}$. We require $x - 5 \geq 0$ $\Leftrightarrow$ $x \geq 5$. Thus the domain is $\{x \mid x \geq 5\}$. The domain can also be expressed in interval notation as $[5, \infty)$.

46. $f(x) = \sqrt[4]{x + 9}$. Since even roots are only defined for nonnegative numbers, we must have $x + 9 \geq 0$ $\Leftrightarrow$ $x \geq -9$, so the domain is $[-9, \infty)$.

47. $f(t) = \sqrt[3]{t - 1}$. Since the odd root is defined for all real numbers, the domain is the set of real numbers, $(-\infty, \infty)$.

48. $g(x) = \sqrt{7 - 3x}$. For the square root to be defined, we must have $7 - 3x \geq 0$ $\Leftrightarrow$ $7 \geq 3x$ $\Leftrightarrow$ $\frac{7}{3} \geq x$. Thus the domain is $\left(-\infty, \frac{7}{3}\right]$.

49. $h(x) = \sqrt{2x - 5}$. Since the square root is defined as a real number only for nonnegative numbers, we require that $2x - 5 \geq 0$ $\Leftrightarrow$ $2x \geq 5$ $\Leftrightarrow$ $x \geq \frac{5}{2}$. So the domain is $\{x \mid x \geq \frac{5}{2}\}$. In interval notation, the domain is $\left[\frac{5}{2}, \infty\right)$.

50. $G(x) = \sqrt{x^2 - 9}$. We must have $x^2 - 9 \geq 0$ $\Leftrightarrow$ $x^2 \geq 9$ $\Leftrightarrow$ $|x| \geq 3$ $\Rightarrow$ $x \geq 3$ or $x \leq -3$. Thus the domain is $(-\infty, -3] \cup [3, \infty)$.

51. $g(x) = \dfrac{\sqrt{2 + x}}{3 - x}$. We require $2 + x \geq 0$, and the denominator cannot equal 0. Now $2 + x \geq 0$ $\Leftrightarrow$ $x \geq -2$, and $3 - x \neq 0$ $\Leftrightarrow$ $x \neq 3$. Thus the domain is $\{x \mid x \geq -2 \text{ and } x \neq 3\}$, which can be expressed in interval notation as $[-2, 3) \cup (3, \infty)$.

52. $g(x) = \dfrac{\sqrt{x}}{2x^2 + x - 1}$. We must have $x \geq 0$ for the numerator and $2x^2 + x - 1 \neq 0$ for the denominator. So $2x^2 + x - 1 \neq 0$ $\Leftrightarrow$ $(2x - 1)(x + 1) \neq 0$ $\Rightarrow$ $2x - 1 \neq 0$ or $x + 1 \neq 0$ $\Leftrightarrow$ $x \neq \frac{1}{2}$ or $x \neq -1$. Thus the domain is $\left[0, \frac{1}{2}\right) \cup \left(\frac{1}{2}, \infty\right)$.

53. $g(x) = \sqrt[4]{x^2 - 6x}$. Since the input to an even root must be nonnegative, we have $x^2 - 6x \geq 0$ $\Leftrightarrow$ $x(x - 6) \geq 0$. We make a table:

	$(-\infty, 0)$	$(0, 6)$	$(6, \infty)$
Sign of x	$-$	$+$	$+$
Sign of $x - 6$	$-$	$-$	$+$
Sign of $x(x - 6)$	$+$	$-$	$+$

Thus the domain is $(-\infty, 0] \cup [6, \infty)$.

54. $g(x) = \sqrt{x^2 - 2x - 8}$. We must have $x^2 - 2x - 8 \geq 0$ $\Leftrightarrow$ $(x - 4)(x + 2) \geq 0$. We make a table:

	$(-\infty, -2)$	$(-2, 4)$	$(4, \infty)$
Sign of $x - 4$	$-$	$-$	$+$
Sign of $x + 2$	$-$	$+$	$+$
Sign of $(x - 4)(x + 2)$	$+$	$-$	$+$

Thus the domain is $(-\infty, -2] \cup [4, \infty)$.

55. $f(x) = \dfrac{3}{\sqrt{x-4}}$. Since the input to an even root must be nonnegative and the denominator cannot equal 0, we have

$x - 4 > 0 \quad \Leftrightarrow \quad x > 4$. Thus the domain is $(4, \infty)$.

56. $f(x) = \dfrac{x^2}{\sqrt{6-x}}$. Since the input to an even root must be nonnegative and the denominator cannot equal 0, we have

$6 - x > 0 \quad \Leftrightarrow \quad 6 > x$. Thus the domain is $(-\infty, 6)$.

57. $f(x) = \dfrac{(x+1)^2}{\sqrt{2x-1}}$. Since the input to an even root must be nonnegative and the denominator cannot equal 0, we have

$2x - 1 > 0 \quad \Leftrightarrow \quad x > \frac{1}{2}$. Thus the domain is $\left(\frac{1}{2}, \infty\right)$.

58. $f(x) = \dfrac{x}{\sqrt[4]{9-x^2}}$. Since the input to an even root must be nonnegative and the denominator cannot equal 0, we have

$9 - x^2 > 0 \quad \Leftrightarrow \quad (3-x)(3+x) > 0$. We make a table:

Interval	$(-\infty, -3)$	$(-3, 3)$	$(3, \infty)$
Sign of $3 - x$	$+$	$+$	$-$
Sign of $3 + x$	$-$	$+$	$+$
Sign of $(x-4)(x+2)$	$-$	$+$	$-$

Thus the domain is $(-3, 3)$.

59. (a) $C(10) = 1500 + 3(10) + 0.02(10)^2 + 0.0001(10)^3 = 1500 + 30 + 2 + 0.1 = 1532.1$

$C(100) = 1500 + 3(100) + 0.02(100)^2 + 0.0001(100)^3 = 1500 + 300 + 200 + 100 = 2100$

(b) $C(10)$ represents the cost of producing 10 yards of fabric and $C(100)$ represents the cost of producing 100 yards of fabric.

(c) $C(0) = 1500 + 3(0) + 0.02(0)^2 + 0.0001(0)^3 = 1500$

60. (a) $S(2) = 4\pi(2)^2 = 16\pi \approx 50.27$, $S(3) = 4\pi(3)^2 = 36\pi \approx 113.10$.

(b) $S(2)$ represents the surface area of a sphere of radius 2, and $S(3)$ represents the surface area of a sphere of radius 3.

61. (a) $D(0.1) = \sqrt{2(3960)(0.1) + (0.1)^2} = \sqrt{792.01} \approx 28.1$ miles

$D(0.2) = \sqrt{2(3960)(0.2) + (0.2)^2} = \sqrt{1584.04} \approx 39.8$ miles

(b) 1135 feet $= \frac{1135}{5280}$ miles ≈ 0.215 miles. $D(0.215) = \sqrt{2(3960)(0.215) + (0.215)^2} = \sqrt{1702.846} \approx 41.3$ miles

(c) $D(7) = \sqrt{2(3960)(7) + (7)^2} = \sqrt{55489} \approx 235.6$ miles

62. (a) $V(0) = 50\left(1 - \frac{0}{20}\right)^2 = 50$ and $V(20) = 50\left(1 - \frac{20}{20}\right)^2 = 0$.

(b) $V(0) = 50$ represents the volume of the full tank at time $t = 0$, and $V(20) = 0$ represents the volume of the empty tank twenty minutes later.

(c)

x	$V(x)$
0	50
5	28.125
10	12.5
15	3.125
20	0

63. (a) $v(0.1) = 18500 \left(0.25 - 0.1^2\right) = 4440$,

$v(0.4) = 18500 \left(0.25 - 0.4^2\right) = 1665$.

(b) They tell us that the blood flows much faster (about 2.75 times faster) 0.1 cm from the center than 0.1 cm from the edge.

(c)

r	$v(r)$
0	4625
0.1	4440
0.2	3885
0.3	2960
0.4	1665
0.5	0

64. (a) $R(1) = \sqrt{\dfrac{13 + 7(1)^{0.4}}{1 + 4(1)^{0.4}}} = \sqrt{\dfrac{20}{5}} = 2$,

$R(10) = \sqrt{\dfrac{13 + 7(10)^{0.4}}{1 + 4(10)^{0.4}}} \approx 1.66$, and

$R(100) = \sqrt{\dfrac{13 + 7(100)^{0.4}}{1 + 4(100)^{0.4}}} \approx 1.48$.

(b)

x	$R(x)$
1	2
10	1.66
100	1.48
200	1.44
500	1.41
1000	1.39

65. (a) $L(0.5c) = 10\sqrt{1 - \dfrac{(0.5c)^2}{c^2}} \approx 8.66$ m, $L(0.75c) = 10\sqrt{1 - \dfrac{(0.75c)^2}{c^2}} \approx 6.61$ m, and

$L(0.9c) = 10\sqrt{1 - \dfrac{(0.9c)^2}{c^2}} \approx 4.36$ m.

(b) It will appear to get shorter.

66. (a) Since $0 \le 5{,}000 \le 10{,}000$ we have $T(5{,}000) = 0$. Since $10{,}000 < 12{,}000 \le 20{,}000$ we have $T(12{,}000) = 0.08(12{,}000) = 960$. Since $20{,}000 < 25{,}000$ we have $T(25{,}000) = 1600 + 0.15(25{,}000) = 5350$.

(b) There is no tax on $5000, a tax of $960 on $12,000 income, and a tax of $5350 on $25,000.

67. (a) $C(75) = 75 + 15 = \$90$; $C(90) = 90 + 15 = \$105$; $C(100) = \$100$; and $C(105) = \$105$.

(b) The total price of the books purchased, including shipping.

68. (a) $T(x) = \begin{cases} 75x & \text{if } 0 \le x \le 2 \\ 50x + 50 & \text{if } x > 2 \end{cases}$

(b) $T(2) = 75(2) = 150$; $T(3) = 50(3) + 50 = 200$; and $T(5) = 5(50) + 50 = 300$.

(c) The total cost of the lodgings.

69. (a) $F(x) = \begin{cases} 15(40 - x) & \text{if } 0 < x < 40 \\ 0 & \text{if } 40 \le x \le 65 \\ 15(x - 65) & \text{if } x > 65 \end{cases}$.

(b) $F(30) = 15(40 - 10) = 15 \cdot 10 = \$150$; $F(50) = \$0$;

and $F(75) = 15(75 - 65) \, 15 \cdot 10 = \$150$.

(c) The fines for violating the speed limits on the freeway.

70. We assume the grass grows linearly.

71.

72.

73.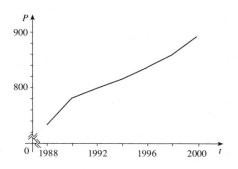

74. Answers will vary.

75. Answers will vary.

2.2   **Graphs of Functions**

1.

x	$f(x) = 2$
-9	2
-6	2
-3	2
0	2
3	2
6	2

2.

x	$f(x) = -3$
-4	-3
-2	-3
0	-3
2	-3
4	-3
6	-3

3.

x	$f(x) = 2x - 4$
-1	-6
0	-4
1	-2
2	0
3	2
4	4
5	6

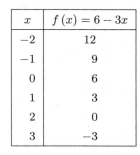

4.

x	$f(x) = 6 - 3x$
-2	12
-1	9
0	6
1	3
2	0
3	-3

5.

x	$f(x) = -x + 3,$ $-3 \leq x \leq 3$
-3	6
-2	5
0	3
1	2
2	1
3	0

6.

x	$f(x) = \dfrac{x-3}{2},$ $0 \leq x \leq 5$
0	-1.5
1	-1
2	-0.5
3	0
4	0.5
5	1

7.

x	$f(x) = -x^2$
± 4	-16
± 3	-9
± 2	-4
± 1	-1
0	0

8.

x	$f(x) = x^2 - 4$
± 5	21
± 4	12
± 3	5
± 2	0
± 1	-3
0	-4

9.

x	$g(x) = x^3 - 8$
-2	-16
-1	-9
0	-8
1	-7
2	0
3	19

10.

x	$g(x) = 4x^2 - x^4$
± 4	-64
± 3	-45
± 2	0
± 1	3
0	0

11.

x	$g(x) = \sqrt{x+4}$
-4	0
-3	1
-2	1.414
-1	1.732
0	2
1	2.236

12.

x	$g(x) = \sqrt{-x}$
-9	3
-5	2.236
-4	2
-2	1.414
-1	1
0	0

13.

x	$F\left(x\right) = \dfrac{1}{x}$
-5	-0.2
-1	-1
-0.1	-10
0.1	10
1	1
5	0.2

14.

x	$F\left(x\right) = \dfrac{1}{x+4}$
-6	-0.5
-5	-1
-4.5	-2
-4.1	-10
-3.9	10
-3.5	2
-3	1
-2	0.5

15.

x	$H\left(x\right) = |2x|$
± 5	10
± 4	8
± 3	6
± 2	4
± 1	2
0	0

16.

x	$H\left(x\right) = |x+1|$
-5	4
-4	3
-3	2
-2	1
-1	0
0	1
1	2

17.

x	$G\left(x\right) = |x| + x$
-5	0
-2	0
0	0
1	2
2	4
5	10

18.

x	$G\left(x\right) = |x| - x$
-5	10
-2	4
-1	2
0	0
1	0
3	0

19.

x	$f\left(x\right) = |2x - 2|$
-5	12
-2	8
0	2
1	0
2	2
5	8

20.

x	$f\left(x\right) = \dfrac{x}{|x|}$
-3	-1
-2	-1
-1	-1
0	undefined
1	0
2	0
3	0

21.

x	$g(x) = \dfrac{2}{x^2}$
± 5	0.08
± 4	0.125
± 3	0.2
± 2	0.5
± 1	2
± 0.5	8

22.

x	$g(x) = \dfrac{|x|}{x^2}$
± 4	0.25
± 2	0.5
± 1	1
± 0.5	2
± 0.25	4
± 0.10	10

23. (a) $h(-2) = 1$; $h(0) = -1$; $h(2) = 3$; $h(3) = 4$.

(b) Domain: $[-3, 4]$. Range: $[-1, 4]$.

24. (a) $g(-4) = 3$; $g(-2) = 2$; $g(0) = -2$; $g(2) = 1$; $g(4) = 0$.

(b) Domain: $[-4, 4]$. Range: $[-2, 3]$.

25. (a) $f(0) = 3 > \frac{1}{2} = g(0)$. So $f(0)$ is larger.

(b) $f(-3) \approx -\frac{3}{2} < 2 = g(-3)$. So $g(-3)$ is larger.

(c) For $x = -2$ and $x = 2$.

26. (a) $f(0.5) \approx 1.2$

(b) $f(3) \approx 2.1$

(c) $x = 0.4$ and $x = 3.6$ are the only solutions to the equation $f(x) = 1$.

27. (a)

(b) Domain: $(-\infty, \infty)$; Range: $(-\infty, \infty)$

28. (a)

(b) Domain: $(-\infty, \infty)$; Range: $(-\infty, \infty)$

29. (a)

(b) Domain: $(-\infty, \infty)$; Range: $\{4\}$

30. (a)

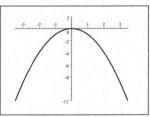

(b) Domain: $(-\infty, \infty)$; Range: $(-\infty, 0]$

31. (a)

(b) Domain: $(-\infty, \infty)$; Range: $(-\infty, 4]$

32. (a)

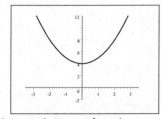

(b) Domain: $(-\infty, \infty)$; Range: $[4, \infty)$

33. (a)

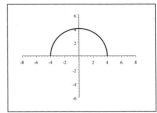

(b) Domain: $[-4, 4]$; Range: $[0, 4]$

34. (a)

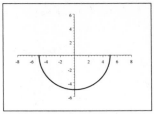

(b) Domain: $[-5, 5]$; Range: $[-5, 0]$

35. (a)

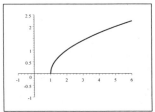

(b) Domain: $[1, \infty)$; Range: $[0, \infty)$

36. (a)

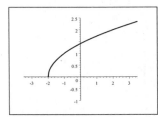

(b) Domain: $[-2, \infty)$; Range: $[0, \infty)$

37. $f(x) = \begin{cases} 0 & \text{if } x < 2 \\ 1 & \text{if } x \geq 2 \end{cases}$

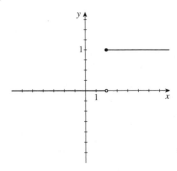

38. $f(x) = \begin{cases} 1 & \text{if } x \leq 1 \\ x + 1 & \text{if } x > 1 \end{cases}$

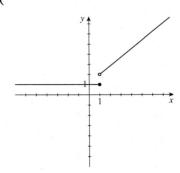

39. $f(x) = \begin{cases} 3 & \text{if } x < 2 \\ x - 1 & \text{if } x \geq 2 \end{cases}$

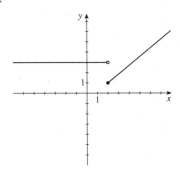

40. $f(x) = \begin{cases} 1 - x & \text{if } x < -2 \\ 5 & \text{if } x \geq -2 \end{cases}$

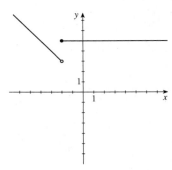

41. $f(x) = \begin{cases} x & \text{if } x \le 0 \\ x+1 & \text{if } x > 0 \end{cases}$

42. $f(x) = \begin{cases} 2x+3 & \text{if } x < -1 \\ 3-x & \text{if } x \ge -1 \end{cases}$

43. $f(x) = \begin{cases} -1 & \text{if } x < -1 \\ 1 & \text{if } -1 \le x \le 1 \\ -1 & \text{if } x > 1 \end{cases}$

44. $f(x) = \begin{cases} -1 & \text{if } x < -1 \\ x & \text{if } -1 \le x \le 1 \\ 1 & \text{if } x > 1 \end{cases}$

45. $f(x) = \begin{cases} 2 & \text{if } x \le -1 \\ x^2 & \text{if } x > -1 \end{cases}$

46. $f(x) = \begin{cases} 1 - x^2 & \text{if } x \le 2 \\ x & \text{if } x > 2 \end{cases}$

47. $f(x) = \begin{cases} 0 & \text{if } |x| \le 2 \\ 3 & \text{if } |x| > 2 \end{cases}$

48. $f(x) = \begin{cases} x^2 & \text{if } |x| \le 1 \\ 1 & \text{if } |x| > 1 \end{cases}$

49. $f(x) = \begin{cases} 4 & \text{if } x < -2 \\ x^2 & \text{if } -2 \leq x \leq 2 \\ -x+6 & \text{if } x > 2 \end{cases}$

50. $f(x) = \begin{cases} -x & \text{if } x \leq 0 \\ 9-x^2 & \text{if } 0 < x \leq 3 \\ x-3 & \text{if } x > 3 \end{cases}$

51. $f(x) = \begin{cases} x+2 & \text{if } x \leq -1 \\ x^2 & \text{if } x > -1 \end{cases}$

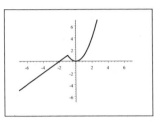

52. $f(x) = \begin{cases} 2x - x^2 & \text{if } x > 1 \\ (x-1)^3 & \text{if } x \leq 1 \end{cases}$ The first graph shows the output of a typical graphing device. However, the actual graph of this function is also shown, and its difference from the graphing device's version should be noted.

53. $f(x) = \begin{cases} -2 & \text{if } x < -2 \\ x & \text{if } -2 \leq x \leq 2 \\ 2 & \text{if } x > 2 \end{cases}$

54. $f(x) = \begin{cases} 1 & \text{if } x \leq -1 \\ 1-x & \text{if } -1 < x \leq 2 \\ -2 & \text{if } x > 2 \end{cases}$

55. The curves in parts (a) and (c) are graphs of a function of x, by the Vertical Line Test.

56. The curves in parts (b) and (c) are graphs of functions of x.

57. The given curve is the graph of a function of x. Domain: $[-3, 2]$. Range: $[-2, 2]$.

58. No, the given curve is not the graph of a function of x.

59. No, the given curve is not the graph of a function of x, by the Vertical Line Test.

60. The given curve is the graph of a function of x. Domain: $[-3, 2]$. Range: $\{-2\} \cup (0, 3]$.

61. Solving for y in terms of x gives $x^2 + 2y = 4 \quad \Leftrightarrow \quad 2y = 4 - x^2 \quad \Leftrightarrow \quad y = 2 - \frac{1}{2}x^2$. This defines y as a function of x.

62. Solving for y in terms of x gives $3x + 7y = 21 \quad \Leftrightarrow \quad 7y = -3x + 21 \quad \Leftrightarrow \quad y = -\frac{3}{7}x + 3$. This defines y as a function of x.

63. Solving for y in terms of x gives $x = y^2$ $\Leftrightarrow$ $y = \pm\sqrt{x}$. The last equation gives two values of y for a given value of x. Thus, this equation does not define y as a function of x.

64. Solving for y in terms of x gives $x^2 + (y - 1)^2 = 4$ $\Leftrightarrow$ $(y - 1)^2 = 4 - x^2$ $\Leftrightarrow$ $y - 1 = \pm\sqrt{4 - x^2}$ $\Leftrightarrow$ $y = 1 \pm \sqrt{4 - x^2}$. The last equation gives two values of y for a given value of x. Thus, this equation does not define y as a function of x.

65. Solving for y in terms of x gives $x + y^2 = 9$ $\Leftrightarrow$ $y^2 = 9 - x$ $\Leftrightarrow$ $y = \pm\sqrt{9 - x}$. The last equation gives two values of y for a given value of x. Thus, this equation does not define y as a function of x.

66. Solving for y in terms of x gives $x^2 + y = 9$ $\Leftrightarrow$ $y = 9 - x^2$. This defines y as a function of x.

67. Solving for y in terms of x gives $x^2 y + y = 1$ $\Leftrightarrow$ $y(x^2 + 1) = 1$ $\Leftrightarrow$ $y = \dfrac{1}{x^2 + 1}$. This defines y as a function of x.

68. Solving for y in terms of x gives $\sqrt{x} + y = 12$ $\Leftrightarrow$ $y = 12 - \sqrt{x}$. This defines y as a function of x.

69. Solving for y in terms of x gives $2|x| + y = 0$ $\Leftrightarrow$ $y = -2|x|$. This defines y as a function of x.

70. Solving for y in terms of x gives $2x + |y| = 0$ $\Leftrightarrow$ $|y| = -2x$. Since $|a| = |-a|$, the last equation gives two values of y for a given value of x. Thus, this equation does not define y as a function of x.

71. Solving for y in terms of x gives $x = y^3$ $\Leftrightarrow$ $y = \sqrt[3]{x}$. This defines y as a function of x.

72. Solving for y in terms of x gives $x = y^4$ $\Leftrightarrow$ $y = \pm\sqrt[4]{x}$. The last equation gives two values of y for a given value of x. Thus, this equation does not define y as a function of x.

73. (a) $f(x) = x^2 + c$, for $c = 0, 2, 4$, and 6.

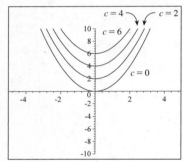

(b) $f(x) = x^2 + c$, for $c = 0, -2, -4$, and -6.

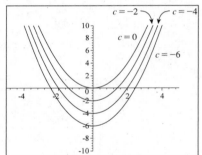

(c) The graphs in part (a) are obtained by shifting the graph of $f(x) = x^2$ upward c units, $c > 0$. The graphs in part (b) are obtained by shifting the graph of $f(x) = x^2$ downward c units.

74. (a) $f(x) = (x - c)^2$, for $c = 0, 1, 2$, and 3.

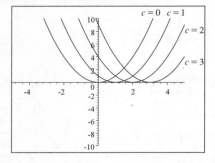

(b) $f(x) = (x - c)^2$, for $c = 0, -1, -2$, and -3.

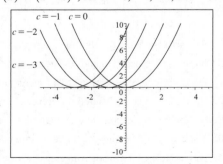

(c) The graphs in part (a) are obtained by shifting the graph of $y = x^2$ to the right $1, 2$, and 3 units, while the graphs in part (b) are obtained by shifting the graph of $y = x^2$ to the left $1, 2$, and 3 units.

75. (a) $f(x) = (x - c)^3$, for $c = 0, 2, 4$, and 6.

(b) $f(x) = (x - c)^3$, for $c = 0, -2, -4$, and -6.

(c) The graphs in part (a) are obtained by shifting the graph of $f(x) = x^3$ to the right c units, $c > 0$. The graphs in part (b) are obtained by shifting the graph of $f(x) = x^3$ to the left $|c|$ units, $c < 0$.

76. (a) $f(x) = cx^2$, for $c = 1, \frac{1}{2}, 2$, and 4.

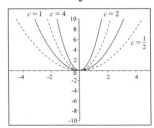

(b) $f(x) = cx^2$, for $c = 1, -1, -\frac{1}{2}$, and -2.

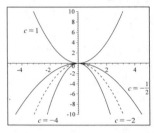

(c) As $|c|$ increases, the graph of $f(x) = cx^2$ is stretched vertically. As $|c|$ decreases, the graph of f is flattened. When $c < 0$, the graph is reflected about the x-axis.

77. (a) $f(x) = x^c$, for $c = \frac{1}{2}, \frac{1}{4}$, and $\frac{1}{6}$.

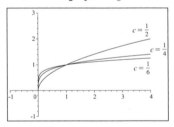

(b) $f(x) = x^c$, for $c = 1, \frac{1}{3}$, and $\frac{1}{5}$.

(c) Graphs of even roots are similar to $y = \sqrt{x}$, graphs of odd roots are similar to $y = \sqrt[3]{x}$. As c increases, the graph of $y = \sqrt[c]{x}$ becomes steeper near $x = 0$ and flatter when $x > 1$.

78. (a) $f(x) = \dfrac{1}{x^n}$, for $n = 1$ and 3.

(b) $f(x) = \dfrac{1}{x^n}$, for $n = 2$ and 4.

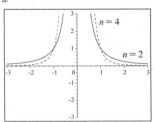

(c) As n increases, the graphs of $y = 1/x^n$ go to zero faster for x large. Also, as n increases and x goes to 0, the graphs of $y = 1/x^n$ go to infinity faster. The graphs of $y = 1/x^n$ for n odd are similar to each other. Likewise, the graphs for n even are similar to each other.

79. The slope of the line segment joining the points $(-2, 1)$ and $(4, -6)$ is $m = \dfrac{-6-1}{4-(-2)} = -\dfrac{7}{6}$. Using the point-slope form,

we have $y - 1 = -\dfrac{7}{6}(x+2)$ $\Leftrightarrow$ $y = -\dfrac{7}{6}x - \dfrac{7}{3} + 1$ $\Leftrightarrow$ $y = -\dfrac{7}{6}x - \dfrac{4}{3}$. Thus the function is $f(x) = -\dfrac{7}{6}x - \dfrac{4}{3}$

for $-2 \le x \le 4$.

80. The slope of the line containing the points $(-3, -2)$ and $(6, 3)$ is $m = \dfrac{-2-3}{-3-6} = \dfrac{-5}{-9} = \dfrac{5}{9}$. Using the point-slope equation

of the line, we have $y - 3 = \dfrac{5}{9}(x-6)$ $\Leftrightarrow$ $y = \dfrac{5}{9}x - \dfrac{10}{3} + 3 = \dfrac{5}{9}x - \dfrac{1}{3}$. Thus the function is $f(x) = \dfrac{5}{9}x - \dfrac{1}{3}$, for

$-3 \le x \le 6$.

81. First solve the circle for y: $x^2 + y^2 = 9$ $\Leftrightarrow$ $y^2 = 9 - x^2$ $\Rightarrow$ $y = \pm\sqrt{9 - x^2}$. Since we seek the top half of the

circle, we choose $y = \sqrt{9 - x^2}$. So the function is $f(x) = \sqrt{9 - x^2}$, $-3 \le x \le 3$.

82. First solve the circle for y: $x^2 + y^2 = 9$ $\Leftrightarrow$ $y^2 = 9 - x^2$ $\Rightarrow$ $y = \pm\sqrt{9 - x^2}$. Since we seek the bottom half of

the circle, we choose $y = -\sqrt{9 - x^2}$. So the function is $f(x) = -\sqrt{9 - x^2}$, $-3 \le x \le 3$.

83. This person appears to gain weight steadily until the age of 21 when this person's weight gain slows down. At age 30, this person experiences a sudden weight loss, but recovers, and by about age 40, this person's weight seems to level off at around 200 pounds. It then appears that the person dies at about age 68. The sudden weight loss could be due to a number of reasons, among them major illness, a weight loss program, etc.

84. The salesman travels away from home and stops to make a sales call between 9 A.M. and 10 A.M., and then travels further from home for a sales call between 12 noon and 1 P.M.. Next he travels along a route that takes him closer to home before taking him further away from home. He then makes a final sales call between 5 P.M. and 6 P.M. and then returns home.

85. Runner A won the race. All runners finished the race. Runner B fell, but got up and finished the race.

86. (a) At 6 A.M. the graph shows that the power consumption is about 500 megawatts. Since $t = 18$ represents 6 P.M., the graph shows that the power consumption at 6 P.M. is about 725 megawatts.

(b) The power consumption is lowest between 3 A.M. and 4 A.M..

(c) The power consumption is highest just before 12 noon.

87. (a) The first noticeable movements occurred at time $t = 5$ seconds.

(b) It seemed to end at time $t = 30$ seconds.

(c) Maximum intensity was reached at $t = 17$ seconds.

88. (a) $E(x) = \begin{cases} 6.00 + 0.10x & \text{if } 0 \le x \le 300 \\ 36.00 + 0.06(x - 300) & \text{if } 300 < x \end{cases}$

(b)

89. $C(x) = \begin{cases} 2.00 & \text{if } 0 < x \le 1 \\ 2.20 & \text{if } 1 < x \le 1.1 \\ 2.40 & \text{if } 1.1 < x \le 1.2 \\ \vdots \\ 4.00 & \text{if } 1.9 < x < 2 \end{cases}$

90. $P(x) = \begin{cases} 0.37 & \text{if } 0 < x \le 1 \\ 0.60 & \text{if } 1 < x \le 2 \\ 0.83 & \text{if } 2 < x \le 3 \\ \vdots \\ 2.90 & \text{if } 11 < x \le 12 \end{cases}$

91. The graph of $x = y^2$ is not the graph of a function because both $(1, 1)$ and $(-1, 1)$ satisfy the equation $x = y^2$. The graph of $x = y^3$ is the graph of a function because $x = y^3 \Leftrightarrow x^{1/3} = y$. If n is even, then both $(1, 1)$ and $(-1, 1)$ satisfies the equation $x = y^n$, so the graph of $x = y^n$ is not the graph of a function. When n is odd, $y = x^{1/n}$ is defined for all real numbers, and since $y = x^{1/n} \Leftrightarrow x = y^n$, the graph of $x = y^n$ is the graph of a function.

92. Answers vary. Some examples are almost anything we purchase based on weight, volume, length, or time, for example gasoline. Although the amount delivered by the pump is continuous, the amount we pay is rounded to the penny. An example involving time would be the cost of a telephone call.

93.

$f(x) = [\![x]\!]$ $g(x) = [\![2x]\!]$ $h(x) = [\![3x]\!]$

The graph of $k(x) = [\![nx]\!]$ is a step function whose steps are each $\dfrac{1}{n}$ wide.

94. (a) The graphs of $f(x) = x^2 + x - 6$ and $g(x) = |x^2 + x - 6|$ are shown in the viewing rectangle $[-10, 10]$ by $[-10, 10]$.

 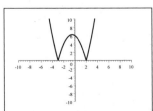

For those values of x where $f(x) \ge 0$, the graphs of f and g coincide, and for those values of x where $f(x) < 0$, the graph of g is obtained from that of f by reflecting the part below the x-axis about the x-axis.

(b) The graphs of $f(x) = x^4 - 6x^2$ and $g(x) = |x^4 - 6x^2|$ are shown in the viewing rectangle $[-5, 5]$ by $[-10, 15]$.

For those values of x where $f(x) \geq 0$, the graphs of f and g coincide, and for those values of x where $f(x) < 0$, the graph of g is obtained from that of f by reflecting the part below the x-axis above the x-axis.

(c) In general, if $g(x) = |f(x)|$, then for those values of x where $f(x) \geq 0$, the graphs of f and g coincide, and for those values of x where $f(x) < 0$, the graph of g is obtained from that of f by reflecting the part below the x-axis above the x-axis.

$y = f(x)$ $y = g(x)$

2.3   Increasing and Decreasing Functions; Average Rate of Change

1. The function is increasing on $[-1, 1]$ and $[2, 4]$. It is decreasing on $[1, 2]$.

2. The function is increasing on $[0, 1]$. It is decreasing on $[-2, 0]$ and $[1, 3]$.

3. The function is increasing on $[-2, -1]$ and $[1, 2]$. It is decreasing on $[-3, -2]$, $[-1, 1]$, and $[2, 3]$.

4. The function is increasing on $[-1, 1]$. It is decreasing on $[-2, -1]$ and $[1, 2]$.

5. (a) $f(x) = x^{2/5}$ is graphed in the viewing rectangle $[-10, 10]$ by $[-5, 5]$.

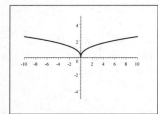

(b) The function is increasing on $[0, \infty)$. It is decreasing on $(-\infty, 0]$.

6. (a) $f(x) = 4 - x^{2/3}$ is graphed in the viewing rectangle $[-10, 10]$ by $[-10, 10]$.

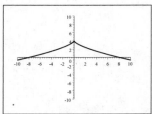

(b) The function is increasing on $(-\infty, 0]$. It is decreasing on $[0, \infty)$.

7. (a) $f(x) = x^2 - 5x$ is graphed in the viewing rectangle $[-2, 7]$ by $[-10, 10]$.

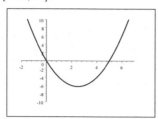

(b) The function is increasing on $[2.5, \infty)$. It is decreasing on $(-\infty, 2.5]$.

8. (a) $f(x) = x^3 - 4x$ is graphed in the viewing rectangle $[-10, 10]$ by $[-10, 10]$.

(b) The function is increasing on $(-\infty, -1.15]$ and $[1.15, \infty)$. It is decreasing on $[-1.15, 1.15]$.

9. (a) $f(x) = 2x^3 - 3x^2 - 12x$ is graphed in the viewing rectangle $[-3, 5]$ by $[-25, 20]$.

(b) The function is increasing on $(-\infty, -1]$ and $[2, \infty)$. It is decreasing on $[-1, 2]$.

10. (a) $f(x) = x^4 - 16x^2$ is graphed in the viewing rectangle $[-10, 10]$ by $[-70, 10]$.

(b) The function is increasing on $[-2.83, 0]$ and $[2.83, \infty)$. It is decreasing on $(-\infty, -2.83]$ and $[0, 2.83]$.

11. (a) $f(x) = x^3 + 2x^2 - x - 2$ is graphed in the viewing rectangle $[-5, 5]$ by $[-3, 3]$.

(b) The function is increasing on $(-\infty, -1.55]$ and $[0.22, \infty)$. It is decreasing on $[-1.55, 0.22]$.

12. (a) $f(x) = x^4 - 4x^3 + 2x^2 + 4x - 3$ is graphed in the viewing rectangle $[-3, 5]$ by $[-5, 5]$.

(b) The function is increasing on $(-0.4, 1]$ and $[2.4, \infty)$. It is decreasing on $[-\infty, -0.4]$ and $[1, 2.4]$.

13. We use the points $(1, 3)$ and $(4, 5)$, so the average rate of change is $\dfrac{5 - 3}{4 - 1} = \dfrac{2}{3}$.

14. We use the points $(1, 4)$ and $(5, 2)$, so the average rate of change is $\dfrac{2 - 4}{5 - 1} = \dfrac{-2}{4} = -\dfrac{1}{2}$.

15. We use the points $(0, 6)$ and $(5, 2)$, so the average rate of change is $\dfrac{2 - 6}{5 - 0} = \dfrac{-4}{5}$.

16. We use the points $(-1, 0)$ and $(5, 4)$, so the average rate of change is $\dfrac{4 - 0}{5 - (-1)} = \dfrac{4}{6} = \dfrac{2}{3}$.

17. The average rate of change is $\dfrac{f(3) - f(2)}{3 - 2} = \dfrac{[3(3) - 2] - [3(2) - 2]}{1} = 7 - 4 = 3$.

18. The average rate of change is $\dfrac{g\,(5)-g\,(1)}{5-1}=\dfrac{\left[5+\frac12\,(5)\right]-\left[5+\frac12\,(1)\right]}{4}=\dfrac{\frac{15}{2}-\frac{11}{2}}{4}=\dfrac24=\dfrac12$.

19. The average rate of change is $\dfrac{h\,(4)-h\,(-1)}{4-(-1)}=\dfrac{\left[4^2+2\,(4)\right]-\left[(-1)^2+2\,(-1)\right]}{5}=\dfrac{24-(-1)}{5}=5$.

20. The average rate of change is $\dfrac{f\,(0)-f\,(-2)}{0-(-2)}=\dfrac{\left[1-3\,(0)^2\right]-\left[1-3\,(-2)^2\right]}{2}=\dfrac{1-(-11)}{2}=\dfrac{12}{2}=6$.

21. The average rate of change is $\dfrac{f\,(10)-f\,(0)}{10-0}=\dfrac{\left[10^3-4\,(10^2)\right]-\left[0^3-4\,(0^2)\right]}{10-0}=\dfrac{600-0}{10}=60$.

22. The average rate of change is $\dfrac{f\,(3)-f\,(-1)}{3-(-1)}=\dfrac{\left[3+3^4\right]-\left[(-1)+(-1)^4\right]}{4}=\dfrac{3+81}{4}=\dfrac{84}{4}=21$.

23. The   average   rate   of   change   is
$$\dfrac{f\,(2+h)-f\,(2)}{(2+h)-2}=\dfrac{\left[3\,(2+h)^2\right]-\left[3\,(2^2)\right]}{h}=\dfrac{12+12h+3h^2-12}{h}=\dfrac{12h+3h^2}{h}=\dfrac{h\,(12+3h)}{h}=12+3h.$$

24. The   average   rate   of   change   is
$$\dfrac{f\,(1+h)-f\,(1)}{(1+h)-1}=\dfrac{\left[4-(1+h)^2\right]-\left[4-1^2\right]}{h}=\dfrac{3-2h-h^2-3}{h}=\dfrac{-2h-h^2}{h}=\dfrac{h\,(-2-h)}{h}=-2-h.$$

25. The average rate of change is $\dfrac{g\,(1)-g\,(a)}{1-a}=\dfrac{\frac11-\frac1a}{1-a}\cdot\dfrac{a}{a}=\dfrac{a-1}{a\,(1-a)}=\dfrac{-1\,(1-a)}{a\,(1-a)}=\dfrac{-1}{a}$.

26. The average rate of change is $\dfrac{g\,(h)-g\,(0)}{h-0}=\dfrac{\frac{2}{h+1}-\frac{2}{0+1}}{h}\cdot\dfrac{h+1}{h+1}=\dfrac{2-2\,(h+1)}{h\,(h+1)}=\dfrac{-2h}{h\,(h+1)}=\dfrac{-2}{h+1}$.

27. The average rate of change is
$$\dfrac{f\,(a+h)-f\,(a)}{(a+h)-a}=\dfrac{\frac{2}{a+h}-\frac{2}{a}}{h}\cdot\dfrac{a\,(a+h)}{a\,(a+h)}=\dfrac{2a-2\,(a+h)}{ah\,(a+h)}=\dfrac{-2h}{ah\,(a+h)}=\dfrac{-2}{a\,(a+h)}.$$

28. The average rate of change is
$$\dfrac{f\,(a+h)-f\,(a)}{(a+h)-a}=\dfrac{\sqrt{a+h}-\sqrt{a}}{h}\cdot\dfrac{\sqrt{a+h}+\sqrt{a}}{\sqrt{a+h}+\sqrt{a}}=\dfrac{(a+h)-a}{h\,(\sqrt{a+h}+\sqrt{a})}=\dfrac{h}{h\,(\sqrt{a+h}+\sqrt{a})}=\dfrac{1}{\sqrt{a+h}+\sqrt{a}}.$$

29. (a) The average rate of change is
$$\dfrac{f\,(a+h)-f\,(a)}{(a+h)-a}=\dfrac{\left[\frac12\,(a+h)+3\right]-\left[\frac12a+3\right]}{h}=\dfrac{\frac12a+\frac12h+3-\frac12a-3}{h}=\dfrac{\frac12h}{h}=\dfrac12.$$

(b) The slope of the line $f\,(x)=\frac12x+3$ is $\frac12$, which is also the average rate of change.

30. (a) The average rate of change is
$$\dfrac{g\,(a+h)-g\,(a)}{(a+h)-a}=\dfrac{\left[-4\,(a+h)+2\right]-\left[-4a+2\right]}{h}=\dfrac{-4a-4h+2+4a-2}{h}=\dfrac{-4h}{h}=-4.$$

(b) The slope of the line $g\,(x)=-4x+2$ is -4, which is also the average rate of change.

31. (a) The function P is increasing on $[0,150]$ and $[300,365]$ and decreasing on $[150,300]$.

(b) The average rate of change is $\dfrac{W\,(200)-W\,(100)}{200-100}=\dfrac{50-75}{200-100}=\dfrac{-25}{100}=-\dfrac14$ ft/day.

32. (a) The function P is increasing on $[0,25]$ and decreasing on $[25,50]$.

(b) The average rate of change is $\dfrac{P\,(40)-P\,(20)}{40-20}=\dfrac{40-40}{40-20}=\dfrac{0}{20}=0$.

(c) The population increased and decreased the same amount during the 20 years.

33. (a) The average rate of change of population is $\dfrac{1,591 - 856}{2001 - 1998} = \dfrac{735}{3} = 245$ persons/yr.

(b) The average rate of change of population is $\dfrac{826 - 1,483}{2004 - 2002} = \dfrac{-657}{2} = -328.5$ persons/yr.

(c) The population was increasing from 1997 to 2001.

(d) The population was decreasing from 2001 to 2006.

34. (a) The average speed is $\dfrac{800 - 400}{152 - 68} = \dfrac{400}{84} = \dfrac{100}{21} \approx 4.76$ m/s.

(b) The average speed is $\dfrac{1,600 - 1,200}{412 - 263} = \dfrac{400}{149} \approx 2.68$ m/s.

(c)

Lap	Length of time to run lap	Average speed of lap.
1	32	6.25 m/s
2	36	5.56 m/s
3	40	5.00 m/s
4	44	4.55 m/s
5	51	3.92 m/s
6	60	3.33 m/s
7	72	2.78 m/s
8	77	2.60 m/s

The man is slowing down throughout the run.

35. (a) The average rate of change of sales is $\dfrac{584 - 512}{2003 - 1993} = \frac{72}{10} = 7.2$ units/yr.

(b) The average rate of change of sales is $\dfrac{520 - 512}{1994 - 1993} = \frac{8}{1} = 8$ units/yr.

(c) The average rate of change of sales is $\dfrac{410 - 520}{1996 - 1994} = \dfrac{-110}{2} = -55$ units/yr.

(d)

Year	CD players sold	Change in sales from previous year
1993	512	—
1994	520	8
1995	413	−107
1996	410	−3
1997	468	58
1998	510	42
1999	590	80
2000	607	17
2001	732	125
2002	612	−120
2003	584	−28

Sales increased most quickly between 2000 and 2001. Sales decreased most quickly between 2001 and 2002.

36.

Year	Number of books
1980	420
1981	460
1982	500
1985	620
1990	820
1992	900
1995	1020
1997	1100
1998	1140
1999	1180
2000	1220

37. (a) For all three runners, the average rate of change is $\dfrac{d(10) - d(0)}{10 - 0} = \dfrac{100}{10} = 10.$

(b) Runner A gets a great jump out of the blocks but tires at the end of the race. Runner B runs a steady race. Runner C is slow at the beginning but accelerates down the track.

38. (a)

Time (s)	Average speed (ft/s)
0–2	17
2–4	18
4–6	63
6–8	147
8–10	237

The average speed is increasing, so the car is accelerating. From the shape of the graph, we see that the slope continues to get steeper.

(b)

Time (s)	Average speed (ft/s)
30–32	263
32–34	144
34–36	91
36–38	74
38–40	48

The average speed is decreasing, so the car is decelerating. From the shape of the graph, we see that the slope continues to get flatter.

39. (a) $f(x)$ is always increasing, and $f(x) > 0$ for all x.

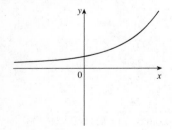

(b) $f(x)$ is always decreasing, and $f(x) > 0$ for all x.

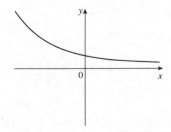

(c) $f(x)$ is always increasing, and $f(x) < 0$ for all x.

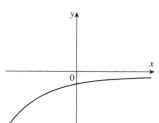

(d) $f(x)$ is always decreasing, and $f(x) < 0$ for all x.

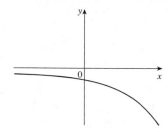

2.4   Transformations of Functions

1. (a) Shift the graph of $y = f(x)$ downward 5 units.

   (b) Shift the graph of $y = f(x)$ to the right 5 units.

2. (a) Shift the graph of $y = f(x)$ to the left 7 units.

   (b) Shift the graph of $y = f(x)$ upward 7 units.

3. (a) Shift the graph of f to the left $\frac{1}{2}$ unit.

   (b) Shift the graph of f upward $\frac{1}{2}$ unit.

4. (a) Reflect the graph of $y = f(x)$ about the x-axis.

   (b) Reflect the graph of $y = f(x)$ about the y-axis.

5. (a) Reflect the graph of $y = f(x)$ about the x-axis, and stretch vertically by a factor of 2.

   (b) Reflect the graph of $y = f(x)$ about the x-axis, and shrink vertically by a factor of $\frac{1}{2}$.

6. (a) Reflect the graph of $y = f(x)$ about the x-axis, and then shift upward 5 units.

   (b) Stretch the graph of $y = f(x)$ vertically by a factor of 3, and then shift downward 5 units.

7. (a) Shift the graph of $y = f(x)$ to the right 4 units, and then upward $\frac{3}{4}$ of a unit.

   (b) Shift the graph of $y = f(x)$ to the left 4 units, and then downward $\frac{3}{4}$ of a unit.

8. (a) Shift the graph of $y = f(x)$ to the left 2 units, stretch vertically by a factor of 2, and then shift downward 2 units.

   (b) Shift the graph of $y = f(x)$ to the right 2 units, stretch vertically by a factor of 2, and then shift upward 2 units.

9. (a) Shrink the graph of $y = f(x)$ horizontally by a factor of $\frac{1}{4}$.

   (b) Stretch the graph of $y = f(x)$ horizontally by a factor of 4.

10. (a) Shrink the graph of $y = f(x)$ horizontally by a factor of $\frac{1}{2}$, and then reflect the resulting graph about the x-axis.

   (b) Shrink the graph of $y = f(x)$ horizontally by a factor of $\frac{1}{2}$ and then shift downward 1 unit.

11. $g(x) = f(x - 2) = (x - 2)^2 = x^2 - 4x + 4$

12. $g(x) = f(x) + 3 = x^3 + 3$

13. $g(x) = f(x + 1) + 2 = |x + 1| + 2$

14. $g(x) = 2f(x) = 2|x|$

15. $g(x) = -f(x + 2) = -\sqrt{x + 2}$

16. $g(x) = -f(x - 2) + 1 = -(x - 2)^2 + 1 = -x^2 + 4x - 3$

17. (a) $y = f(x - 4)$ is graph #3.

   (b) $y = f(x) + 3$ is graph #1.

   (c) $y = 2f(x + 6)$ is graph #2.

   (d) $y = -f(2x)$ is graph #4.

18. (a) $y = \frac{1}{3}f(x)$ is graph #2.

   (b) $y = -f(x + 4)$ is graph #3.

   (c) $y = f(x - 5) + 3$ is graph #1.

   (d) $y = f(-x)$ is graph #4.

19. (a) $y = f(x - 2)$

(b) $y = f(x) - 2$

(c) $y = 2f(x)$

(d) $y = -f(x) + 3$

(e) $y = f(-x)$

(f) $y = \frac{1}{2} f(x - 1)$

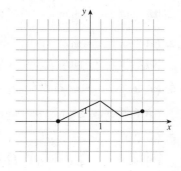

20. (a) $y = g(x + 1)$

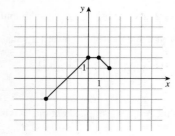

(b) $y = -g(x + 1)$

(c) $y = g(x - 2)$

(d) $y = g(x) - 2$

(e) $y = -g(x) + 2$

(f) $y = 2g(x)$

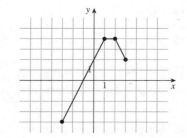

21. (a) $f(x) = \dfrac{1}{x}$

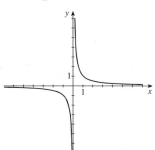

(b) (i) $y = -\dfrac{1}{x}$. Reflect the graph of f about the x-axis.

(ii) $y = \dfrac{1}{x-1}$. Shift the graph of f to the right 1 unit.

(iii) $y = \dfrac{2}{x+2}$. Shift the graph of f to the left 2 units and stretch vertically by a factor of 2.

(iv) $y = 1 + \dfrac{1}{x-3}$. Shift the graph of f to the right 3 units and upward 1 unit.

22. (a) $f(x) = \sqrt[3]{x}$

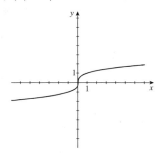

(b) (i) $\sqrt[3]{x-2}$. Shift the graph of $f(x) = \sqrt[3]{x}$ to the right 2 units.

(ii) $y = \sqrt[3]{x+2} + 2$. Shift the graph of $f(x) = \sqrt[3]{x}$ to the left 2 units and upward 2 units.

(iii) $y = 1 - \sqrt[3]{x}$. Reflect the graph of $f(x) = \sqrt[3]{x}$ about the x-axis, and then shift it upward 1 unit.

(iv) $y = 2\sqrt[3]{x}$. Stretch the graph of $f(x) = \sqrt[3]{x}$ vertically by a factor of 2.

23. (a) The graph of $g(x) = (x+2)^2$ is obtained by shifting the graph of $f(x)$ to the left 2 units.

(b) The graph of $g(x) = x^2 + 2$ is obtained by shifting the graph of $f(x)$ upward 2 units.

24. (a) The graph of $g(x) = (x-4)^3$ is obtained by shifting the graph of $f(x)$ to the right 4 units.

(b) The graph of $g(x) = x^3 - 4$ is obtained by shifting the graph of $f(x)$ downward 4 units.

25. (a) The graph of $g(x) = 2\sqrt{x}$ is obtained by stretching the graph of $f(x)$ vertically by a factor of 2.

(b) The graph of $g(x) = \frac{1}{2}\sqrt{x-2}$ is obtained by shifting the graph of $f(x)$ to the right 2 units, and then shrinking the graph vertically by a factor of $\frac{1}{2}$.

26. (a) The graph of $g(x) = 3|x| + 1$ is obtained by stretching the graph of $f(x)$ vertically by a factor of 3, then shifting the graph upward 1 unit.

(b) The graph of $g(x) = -|x+1|$ is obtained by shifting the graph of $f(x)$ left 1 unit, then reflecting the graph about the x-axis.

27. $y = f(x-2) + 3$. When $f(x) = x^2$, we get $y = (x-2)^2 + 3 = x^2 - 4x + 4 + 3 = x^2 - 4x + 7$.

28. $y = f(x+4) - 1$. When $f(x) = x^3$, we get $y = (x+4)^3 - 1 = x^3 + 12x^2 + 48x + 64 - 1 = x^3 + 12x^2 + 48x + 63$.

29. $y = -5f(x+3)$. When $f(x) = \sqrt{x}$, we get $y = -5\sqrt{x+3}$

30. $y = \frac{1}{2}f(-x) + \frac{3}{5}$. When $f(x) = \sqrt[3]{x}$, we get $y = \frac{1}{2}\sqrt[3]{-x} + \frac{3}{5}$.

31. $y = 0.1f\left(x - \frac{1}{2}\right) - 2$. When $f(x) = |x|$, we get $y = 0.1\left|x - \frac{1}{2}\right| - 2$

32. $y = 3f(x+1) + 10$. When $f(x) = |x|$, we get $y = 3|x+1| + 10$

33. $f(x) = (x-2)^2$. Shift the graph of $y = x^2$ to the right 2 units.

34. $f(x) = (x+7)^2$. Shift the graph of $y = x^2$ to the left 7 units.

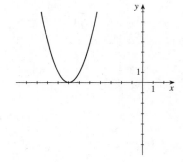

35. $f(x) = -(x+1)^2$. Shift the graph of $y = x^2$ to the left 1 unit, then reflect about the x-axis.

36. $f(x) = 1 - x^2$. Reflect the graph of $y = x^2$ about the x-axis, then shift it upward 1 unit.

37. $f(x) = x^3 + 2$. Shift the graph of $y = x^3$ upward 2 units.

38. $f(x) = -x^3$. Reflect the graph of $y = x^3$ about the x-axis.

39. $y = 1 + \sqrt{x}$. Shift the graph of $y = \sqrt{x}$ upward 1 unit.

40. $y = 2 - \sqrt{x+1}$. Shift the graph of $y = \sqrt{x}$ to the left 1 unit, reflect it about the x-axis, and finally shift it upward 2 units.

41. $y = \frac{1}{2}\sqrt{x+4} - 3$. Shift the graph of $y = \sqrt{x}$ to the left 4 units, shrink vertically by a factor of $\frac{1}{2}$, and then shift it downward 3 units.

42. $y = 3 - 2(x-1)^2$. Shift the graph of $y = x^2$ to the right 1 unit, reflect it about the x-axis, stretch it vertically by a factor of 2, and then shift it upward 3 units.

43. $y = 5 + (x+3)^2$. Shift the graph of $y = x^2$ to the left 3 units, then upward 5 units.

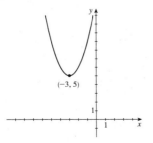

44. $y = \frac{1}{3}x^3 - 1$. Shrink the graph of $y = x^3$ vertically by a factor of $\frac{1}{3}$, then shift it downward 1 unit.

45. $y = |x| - 1$. Shift the graph of $y = |x|$ downward 1 unit.

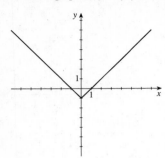

46. $y = |x - 1|$. Shift the graph of $y = |x|$ to the right 1 unit.

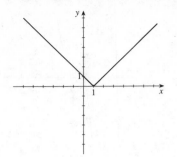

47. $y = |x + 2| + 2$. Shift the graph of $y = |x|$ to the left 2 units and upward 2 units.

48. $y = 2 - |x|$. Reflect the graph of $y = |x|$ about the x-axis, and then shift it upward 2 units.

49.

For part (b), shift the graph in (a) to the left 5 units; for part (c), shift the graph in (a) to the left 5 units, and stretch it vertically by a factor of 2; for part (d), shift the graph in (a) to the left 5 units, stretch it vertically by a factor of 2, and then shift it upward 4 units.

50.

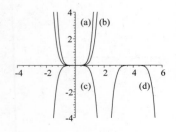

For (b), reflect the graph in (a) about the x-axis; for (c), stretch the graph in (a) vertically by a factor of 3 and reflect about the x-axis; for (d), shift the graph in (a) to the right 5 units, stretch it vertically by a factor of 3, and reflect it about the x-axis. The order in which each operation is applied to the graph in (a) is not important to obtain the graphs in part (c) and (d).

51.

For part (b), shrink the graph in (a) vertically by a factor of $\frac{1}{3}$; for part (c), shrink the graph in (a) vertically by a factor of $\frac{1}{3}$, and reflect it about the x-axis; for part (d), shift the graph in (a) to the right 4 units, shrink vertically by a factor of $\frac{1}{3}$, and then reflect it about the x-axis.

52.

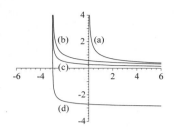

For (b), shift the graph in (a) to the left 3 units; for (c), shift the graph in (a) to the left 3 units and shrink it vertically by a factor of $\frac{1}{2}$; for (d), shift the graph in (a) to the left 3 units, shrink it vertically by a factor of $\frac{1}{2}$, and then shift it downward 3 units. The order in which each operation is applied to the graph in (a) is not important to sketch (c), while it is important in (d).

53. (a) $y = g\left(2x\right)$

(b) $y = g\left(\frac{1}{2}x\right)$

54. (a) $y = h\left(3x\right)$

(b) $y = h\left(\frac{1}{3}x\right)$

55. (a) Even

(b) Odd

56. (a) Even

(b) Odd

57. $y = [\![2x]\!]$

58. $y = [\![\frac{1}{4}x]\!]$

59. (a) $y = f(x) = \sqrt{2x - x^2}$ **(b)** $y = f(2x) = \sqrt{2(2x) - (2x)^2}$ **(c)** $y = f\left(\frac{1}{2}x\right) = \sqrt{2\left(\frac{1}{2}x\right) - \left(\frac{1}{2}x\right)^2}$

$$= \sqrt{4x - 4x^2}$$

$$= \sqrt{x - \frac{1}{4}x^2}$$

  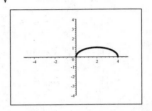

The graph in part (b) is obtained by horizontally shrinking the graph in part (a) by a factor of 2 (so the graph is half as wide). The graph in part (c) is obtained by horizontally stretching the graph in part (a) by a factor of 2 (so the graph is twice as wide).

60. (a) $y = f(x) = \sqrt{2x - x^2}$ **(b)** $y = f(-x) = \sqrt{2(-x) - (-x)^2}$ **(c)** $y = -f(-x) = -\sqrt{2(-x) - (-x)^2}$

$$= \sqrt{-2x - x^2}$$

$$= -\sqrt{-2x} = x^2$$

(d) $y = f(-2x) = \sqrt{2(-2x) - (-2x)^2}$

$$= -\sqrt{-2x - x^2} = \sqrt{-4x - 4x^2}$$

(e) $y = f\left(-\frac{1}{2}x\right) = \sqrt{2\left(-\frac{1}{2}x\right) - \left(-\frac{1}{2}x\right)^2}$

$$= \sqrt{-x - \frac{1}{4}x^2}$$

The graph in part (b) is obtained by reflecting the graph in part (a) about the y-axis. The graph in part (c) is obtained by reflecting the graph in part (a) about the origin. The graph in part (d) is obtained by reflecting the graph in part (a) about the y-axis and then horizontally shrinking the graph by a factor of 2 (so the graph is $\frac{1}{2}$ as wide). The graph in part (e) is obtained by reflecting the graph is part (a) about the y-axis and then horizontally stretching the graph by a factor of 2 (so the graph is twice as wide).

61. $f(x) = x^{-2}$. $f(-x) = (-x)^{-2} = x^{-2} = f(x)$. Thus $f(x)$ is even.

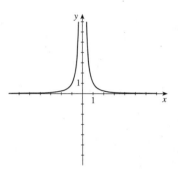

62. $f(x) = x^{-3}$. $f(-x) = (-x)^{-3} = -x^{-3} = -f(x)$. Thus $f(x)$ is odd.

63. $f(x) = x^2 + x$. $f(-x) = (-x)^2 + (-x) = x^2 - x$. Thus $f(-x) \neq f(x)$. Also, $f(-x) \neq -f(x)$, so $f(x)$ is neither odd nor even.

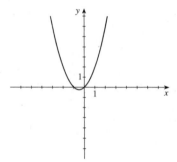

64. $f(x) = x^4 - 4x^2$.

$f(-x) = (-x)^4 - 4(-x)^2 = x^4 - 4x^2 = f(x)$. Thus $f(x)$ is even.

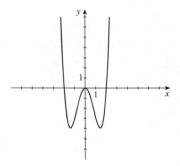

65. $f(x) = x^3 - x$.

$$f(-x) = (-x)^3 - (-x) = -x^3 + x$$
$$= -(x^3 - x) = -f(x).$$

Thus $f(x)$ is odd.

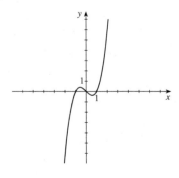

66. $f(x) = 3x^3 + 2x^2 + 1$.

$f(-x) = 3(-x)^3 + 2(-x)^2 + 1 = -3x^3 + 2x^2 + 1$. Thus $f(-x) \neq f(x)$. Also $f(-x) \neq -f(x)$, so $f(x)$ is neither odd nor even.

67. $f(x) = 1 - \sqrt[3]{x}$. $f(-x) = 1 - \sqrt[3]{(-x)} = 1 + \sqrt[3]{x}$.

Thus $f(-x) \neq f(x)$. Also $f(-x) \neq -f(x)$, so $f(x)$ is neither odd nor even.

68. $f(x) = x + 1/x$.

$$f(-x) = (-x) + 1/(-x) = -x - 1/x$$
$$= -(x + 1/x) = -f(x).$$

Thus $f(x)$ is odd.

69. Since $f(x) = x^2 - 4 < 0$, for $-2 < x < 2$, the graph of $y = g(x)$ is found by sketching the graph of $y = f(x)$ for $x \leq -2$ and $x \geq 2$, then reflecting about the x-axis the part of the graph of $y = f(x)$ for $-2 < x < 2$.

70. $g(x) = |x^4 - 4x^2|$

71. (a) $f(x) = 4x - x^2$

(b) $f(x) = |4x - x^2|$

72. (a) $f(x) = x^3$

(b) $g(x) = |x^3|$

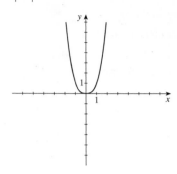

73. (a) The graph of $y = t^2$ must be shrunk vertically by a factor of 0.01 and shifted vertically 4 units up to obtain the graph of $y = f(t)$.

(b) The graph of $y = f(t)$ must be shifted horizontally 10 units to the right to obtain the graph of $y = g(t)$. So $g(t) = f(t - 10) = 4 + 0.01(t - 10)^2 = 5 - 0.02t + 0.01t^2$.

74. (a) The graph of $y = t^2$ must be shrunk vertically by a factor of $\frac{1}{2}$ and shifted up 2 units to obtain the graph of $y = C(t)$.

(b) The graph of $y = C(t)$ must be stretched vertically by a factor of $\frac{9}{5}$ and shifted up 32 units to obtain the graph of $y = F(t)$. So $F(t) = \frac{9}{5}C(t) + 32 = \frac{9}{5}\left(\frac{1}{2}t^2 + 2\right) + 32 = \frac{9}{10}t^2 + \frac{178}{5}$.

75. f even implies $f(-x) = f(x)$; g even implies $g(-x) = g(x)$; f odd implies $f(-x) = -f(x)$; and g odd implies $g(-x) = -g(x)$

If f and g are both even, then $(f + g)(-x) = f(-x) + g(-x) = f(x) + g(x) = (f + g)(x)$ and $f + g$ is even.

If f and g are both odd, then $(f + g)(-x) = f(-x) + g(-x) = -f(x) - g(x) = -(f + g)(x)$ and $f + g$ is odd.

If f odd and g even, then $(f + g)(-x) = f(-x) + g(-x) = -f(x) + g(x)$, which is neither odd nor even.

76. f even implies $f(-x) = f(x)$; g even implies $g(-x) = g(x)$; f odd implies $f(-x) = -f(x)$; and g odd implies $g(-x) = -g(x)$.

If f and g are both even, then $(fg)(-x) = f(-x) \cdot g(-x) = f(x) \cdot g(x) = (fg)(x)$. Thus fg is even.

If f and g are both odd, then $(fg)(-x) = f(-x) \cdot g(-x) = -f(x) \cdot (-g(x)) = f(x) \cdot g(x) = (fg)(x)$. Thus fg is even

If f if odd and g is even, then $(fg)(-x) = f(-x) \cdot g(-x) = f(x) \cdot (-g(x)) = -f(x) \cdot g(x) = -(fg)(x)$. Thus fg is odd.

77. $f(x) = x^n$ is even when n is an even integer and $f(x) = x^n$ is odd when n is an odd integer.

These names were chosen because polynomials with only terms with odd powers are odd functions, and polynomials with only terms with even powers are even functions.

2.5 Quadratic Functions; Maxima and Minima

1. (a) Vertex: $(3, 4)$

(b) Maximum value of f: 4.

2. (a) Vertex: $(-2, 8)$

(b) Maximum value of f: 8.

3. (a) Vertex: $(1, -3)$

(b) Minimum value of f: -3.

4. (a) Vertex: $(-1, -4)$

(b) Minimum value of f: -4.

5. (a) $f(x) = x^2 - 6x = (x-3)^2 - 9$

(b) Vertex: $y = x^2 - 6x = x^2 - 6x + 9 - 9 = (x-3)^2 - 9$. So the
vertex is at $(3, -9)$.

x-intercepts: $y = 0 \Rightarrow 0 = x^2 - 6x = x(x-6)$. So $x = 0$ or
$x = 6$. The x-intercepts are $x = 0$ and $x = 6$.

y-intercept: $x = 0 \Rightarrow y = 0$. The y-intercept is $y = 0$.

(c)

6. (a) $f(x) = x^2 + 8x = (x+4)^2 - 16$

(b) The vertex is $(-4, -16)$. x-intercepts: $y = 0 \Rightarrow$
$0 = x^2 + 8x = x(x+8)$. So $x = 0$ or $x = -8$. The x-intercepts are
$x = 0$ and $x = -8$. y-intercept: $x = 0 \Rightarrow y = 0$. The
y-intercept is $y = 0$.

(c)

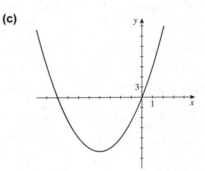

7. (a) $f(x) = 2x^2 + 6x = 2\left(x + \frac{3}{2}\right)^2 - \frac{9}{2}$

(b) The vertex is $\left(-\frac{3}{2}, -\frac{9}{2}\right)$.

x-intercepts: $y = 0 \Rightarrow 0 = 2x^2 + 6x = 2x(x+3) \Rightarrow$
$x = 0$ or $x = -3$. The x-intercepts are $x = 0$ and $x = -3$.

y-intercept: $x = 0 \Rightarrow y = 0$. The y-intercept is $y = 0$.

(c)

8. (a) $f(x) = -x^2 + 10x = -(x-5)^2 + 25$

(b) The vertex is $(5, 25)$.

x-intercepts: $y = 0 \Rightarrow 0 = -x^2 + 10x = -x(x-10) = 0$
$\Rightarrow x = 0$ or $x = 10$. The x-intercepts are $x = 0$ and $x = 10$.

y-intercept: $x = 0 \Rightarrow y = 0$. The y-intercept is $y = 0$.

(c)

9. **(a)** $f(x) = x^2 + 4x + 3 = (x+2)^2 - 1$

(b) The vertex is $(-2, -1)$.

x-intercepts: $y = 0 \quad \Rightarrow \quad 0 = x^2 + 4x + 3 = (x+1)(x+3)$. So $x = -1$ or $x = -3$. The x-intercepts are $x = -1$ and $x = -3$.

y-intercept: $x = 0 \quad \Rightarrow \quad y = 3$. The y-intercept is $y = 3$.

(c)

10. **(a)** $f(x) = x^2 - 2x + 2 = (x-1)^2 + 1$

(b) The vertex is $(1, 1)$.

x-intercepts: $y = 0 \quad \Rightarrow \quad (x-1)^2 + 1 = 0 \quad \Leftrightarrow \quad (x-1)^2 = -1$. Since this last equation has no real solution, there is no x-intercept.

y-intercept: $x = 0 \quad \Rightarrow \quad y = 2$. The y-intercept is $y = 2$.

(c)

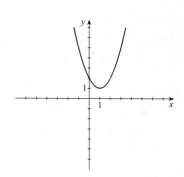

11. **(a)** $f(x) = -x^2 + 6x + 4 = -(x-3)^2 + 13$

(b) The vertex is $(3, 13)$.

x-intercepts: $y = 0 \quad \Rightarrow \quad 0 = -(x-3)^2 + 13 \quad \Leftrightarrow \quad (x-3)^2 = 13 \Rightarrow x - 3 = \pm\sqrt{13} \quad \Leftrightarrow \quad x = 3 \pm \sqrt{13}$. The x-intercepts are $x = 3 - \sqrt{13}$ and $x = 3 + \sqrt{13}$.

y-intercept: $x = 0 \quad \Rightarrow \quad y = 4$. The y-intercept is $y = 4$.

(c)

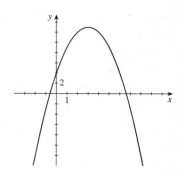

12. **(a)** $f(x) = -x^2 - 4x + 4 = -(x+2)^2 + 8$

(b) The vertex is $(-2, 8)$.

x-intercepts: $y = 0 \quad \Rightarrow \quad 0 = -x^2 - 4x + 4 \Leftrightarrow 0 = x^2 + 4x - 4$. Using the quadratic formula,

$$x = \frac{-4 \pm \sqrt{(4)^2 - 4(1)(-4)}}{2(1)} = \frac{-4 \pm \sqrt{32}}{2} = \frac{2(-2 \pm 2\sqrt{2})}{2} = -2 \pm 2\sqrt{2}.$$

The x-intercepts are $x = -2 + 2\sqrt{2}$ and $x = -2 - 2\sqrt{2}$.

y-intercept: $x = 0 \quad \Rightarrow \quad y = 4$. The y-intercept is $y = 4$.

(c)

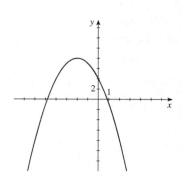

13. (a) $f(x) = 2x^2 + 4x + 3 = 2(x+1)^2 + 1$

(c)

(b) The vertex is $(-1, 1)$.

x-intercepts: $y = 0 \Rightarrow 0 = 2x^2 + 4x + 3 = 2(x+1)^2 + 1$

$\Leftrightarrow 2(x+1)^2 = -1$. Since this last equation has no real solution, there is no x-intercept.

y-intercept: $x = 0 \Rightarrow y = 3$. The y-intercept is $y = 3$.

14. (a) $f(x) = -3x^2 + 6x - 2 = -3(x-1)^2 + 1$

(c)

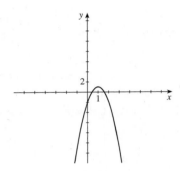

(b) The vertex is $(1, 1)$.

x-intercepts: $y = 0 \Rightarrow 0 = -3(x-1)^2 + 1 = 0$

$\Leftrightarrow (x-1)^2 = \frac{1}{3} \Rightarrow x - 1 = \pm\sqrt{\frac{1}{3}} \Leftrightarrow x = 1 \pm \sqrt{\frac{1}{3}}$. The

x-intercepts are $x = 1 + \sqrt{\frac{1}{3}}$ and $x = 1 - \sqrt{\frac{1}{3}}$.

y-intercept: $x = 0 \Rightarrow y = -2$. The y-intercept is $y = -2$.

15. (a) $f(x) = 2x^2 - 20x + 57 = 2(x-5)^2 + 7$

(c)

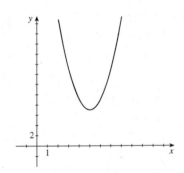

(b) The vertex is $(5, 7)$.

x-intercepts: $y = 0 \Rightarrow$

$0 = 2x^2 - 20x + 57 = 2(x-5)^2 + 7 \Leftrightarrow 2(x-5)^2 = -7$. Since this last equation has no real solution, there is no x-intercept.

y-intercept: $x = 0 \Rightarrow y = 57$. The y-intercept is $y = 57$.

16. (a) $f(x) = 2x^2 + x - 6 = 2\left(x + \frac{1}{4}\right)^2 - \frac{49}{8}$

(c)

(b) The vertex is $\left(-\frac{1}{4}, -\frac{49}{8}\right)$.

x-intercepts: $y = 0 \Rightarrow 0 = 2x^2 + x - 6 = (2x - 3)(x + 2)$

$\Rightarrow x = \frac{3}{2}$ or $x = -2$. The x-intercepts are $x = \frac{3}{2}$ and $x = -2$.

y-intercept: $x = 0 \Rightarrow y = -6$. The y-intercept is $y = -6$.

17. (a) $f(x) = -4x^2 - 16x + 3 = -4(x+2)^2 + 19$

(b) The vertex is $(-2, 19)$.

x-intercepts: $y = 0 \quad \Rightarrow$

$0 = -4x^2 - 16x + 3 = -4(x+2)^2 + 19 \Leftrightarrow 4(x+2)^2 = 19$

$\Leftrightarrow \quad (x+2)^2 = \frac{19}{4} \Rightarrow x + 2 = \pm\sqrt{\frac{19}{4}} = \pm\frac{\sqrt{19}}{2} \quad \Leftrightarrow$

$x = -2 \pm \frac{\sqrt{19}}{2}$. The x-intercepts are $x = -2 - \frac{\sqrt{19}}{2}$ and

$x = -2 + \frac{\sqrt{19}}{2}$.

y-intercept: $x = 0 \quad \Rightarrow \quad y = 3$. The y-intercept is $y = 3$.

(c)

18. (a) $f(x) = 6x^2 + 12x - 5 = 6(x+1)^2 - 11$

(b) The vertex is $(-1, -11)$.

x-intercepts: $y = 0 \quad \Rightarrow \quad 0 = 6x^2 + 12x - 5$. Using the quadratic

formula, $x = \frac{-12 \pm \sqrt{(12)^2 - 4(6)(-5)}}{2(6)} = \frac{-12 \pm \sqrt{264}}{12} = \frac{-6 \pm \sqrt{66}}{6}$. The

x-intercepts are $x = \frac{-6 \pm \sqrt{66}}{6}$.

y-intercept: $x = 0 \quad \Rightarrow \quad y = -5$. The y-intercept is $y = -5$.

(c)

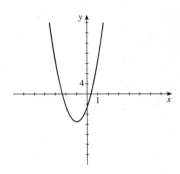

19. (a) $f(x) = 2x - x^2 = -(x^2 - 2x)$

$= -(x^2 - 2x + 1) + 1 = -(x-1)^2 + 1$

(b)

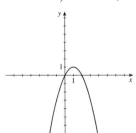

(c) The maximum value is $f(1) = 1$.

20. (a) $f(x) = x + x^2 = (x^2 + x + \frac{1}{4}) - \frac{1}{4}$

$= (x + \frac{1}{2})^2 - \frac{1}{4}$

(b)

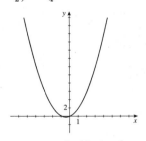

(c) The minimum value is $f(-\frac{1}{2}) = -\frac{1}{4}$.

21. (a) $f(x) = x^2 + 2x - 1 = (x^2 + 2x) - 1$

$= (x^2 + 2x + 1) - 1 - 1 = (x+1)^2 - 2$

(b)

(c) The minimum value is $f(-1) = -2$.

22. (a) $f(x) = x^2 - 8x + 8 = (x^2 - 8x + 16) + 8 - 16$

$= (x-4)^2 - 8$

(b)

(c) The minimum value is $f(4) = -8$.

23. (a) $f(x) = -x^2 - 3x + 3 = -\left(x^2 + 3x\right) + 3$

$\qquad = -\left(x^2 + 3x + \frac{9}{4}\right) + 3 + \frac{9}{4}$

$\qquad = -\left(x + \frac{3}{2}\right)^2 + \frac{21}{4}$

(b)

(c) The maximum value is $f\left(-\frac{3}{2}\right) = \frac{21}{4}$.

24. (a) $f(x) = 1 - 6x - x^2 = -\left(x^2 + 6x\right) + 1$

$\qquad = -\left(x^2 + 6x + 9\right) + 1 + 9$

$\qquad = -\left(x + 3\right)^2 + 10$

(b)

(c) The maximum value is $f(-3) = 10$.

25. (a) $g(x) = 3x^2 - 12x + 13 = 3\left(x^2 - 4x\right) + 13$

$\qquad = 3\left(x^2 - 4x + 4\right) + 13 - 12$

$\qquad = 3\left(x - 2\right)^2 + 1$

(b)

(c) The minimum value is $g(2) = 1$.

26. (a) $g(x) = 2x^2 + 8x + 11 = 2\left(x^2 + 4x\right) + 11$

$\qquad = 2\left(x^2 + 4x + 4\right) + 11 - 8$

$\qquad = 2\left(x + 2\right)^2 + 3$

(b)

(c) The minimum value is $g(-2) = 3$.

27. (a) $h(x) = 1 - x - x^2 = -\left(x^2 + x\right) + 1$

$\qquad = -\left(x^2 + x + \frac{1}{4}\right) + 1 + \frac{1}{4}$

$\qquad = -\left(x + \frac{1}{2}\right)^2 + \frac{5}{4}$

(b)

(c) The maximum value is $h\left(-\frac{1}{2}\right) = \frac{5}{4}$.

28. (a) $h(x) = 3 - 4x - 4x^2 = -4\left(x^2 + x\right) + 3$

$\qquad = -4\left(x^2 + x + \frac{1}{4}\right) + 3 + 1$

$\qquad = -4\left(x + \frac{1}{2}\right)^2 + 4$

(b)

(c) The maximum value is $h\left(-\frac{1}{2}\right) = 4$.

29. $f(x) = x^2 + x + 1 = \left(x^2 + x\right) + 1 = \left(x^2 + x + \frac{1}{4}\right) + 1 + \frac{1}{4} = \left(x + \frac{1}{2}\right)^2 + \frac{3}{4}$.

Therefore, the minimum value is $f\left(-\frac{1}{2}\right) = \frac{3}{4}$.

30. $f(x) = 1 + 3x - x^2 = -\left(x^2 - 3x\right) + 1 = -\left(x^2 - 3x + \frac{9}{4}\right) + 1 + \frac{9}{4} = -\left(x - \frac{3}{2}\right)^2 + \frac{13}{4}$. Therefore, the maximum

value is $f\left(\frac{3}{2}\right) = \frac{13}{4}$.

31. $f(t) = 100 - 49t - 7t^2 = -7\left(t^2 + 7t\right) + 100 = -7\left(t^2 + 7t + \frac{49}{4}\right) + 100 + \frac{343}{4} = -7\left(t + \frac{7}{2}\right)^2 + \frac{743}{4}$.

Therefore, the maximum value is $f\left(-\frac{7}{2}\right) = \frac{743}{4} = 185.75$.

32. $f(t) = 10t^2 + 40t + 113 = 10\left(t^2 + 4t\right) + 113 = 10\left(t^2 + 4t + 4\right) + 113 - 40 = 10\left(t + 2\right)^2 + 73.$ Therefore, the minimum value is $f(-2) = 73$.

33. $f(s) = s^2 - 1.2s + 16 = \left(s^2 - 1.2s\right) + 16 = \left(s^2 - 1.2s + 0.36\right) + 16 - 0.36 = \left(s - 0.6\right)^2 + 15.64.$ Therefore, the minimum value is $f(0.6) = 15.64$.

34. $g(x) = 100x^2 - 1500x = 100\left(x^2 - 15x\right) = 100\left(x^2 - 15x + \frac{225}{4}\right) - 5625 = 10\left(x - \frac{15}{2}\right)^2 - 5625.$ Therefore, the minimum value is $g\left(\frac{15}{2}\right) = -5625$.

35. $h(x) = \frac{1}{2}x^2 + 2x - 6 = \frac{1}{2}\left(x^2 + 4x\right) - 6 = \frac{1}{2}\left(x^2 + 4x + 4\right) - 6 - 2 = \frac{1}{2}\left(x + 2\right)^2 - 8.$ Therefore, the minimum value is $h(-2) = -8$.

36. $f(x) = -\dfrac{x^2}{3} + 2x + 7 = -\frac{1}{3}\left(x^2 + 6x\right) + 7 = -\frac{1}{3}\left(x^2 + 6x + 9\right) + 7 + 3 = -\frac{1}{3}\left(x + 3\right)^2 + 10.$ Therefore, the maximum value is $f(-3) = 10$.

37. $f(x) = 3 - x - \frac{1}{2}x^2 = -\frac{1}{2}\left(x^2 + 2x\right) + 3 = -\frac{1}{2}\left(x^2 + 2x + 1\right) + 3 + \frac{1}{2} = -\frac{1}{2}\left(x + 1\right) + \frac{7}{2}.$ Therefore, the maximum value is $f(-1) = \frac{7}{2}$.

38. $g(x) = 2x\left(x - 4\right) + 7 = 2x^2 - 8x + 7 = 2\left(x^2 - 4x\right) + 7 = 2\left(x^2 - 4x + 4\right) + 7 - 8 = 2\left(x - 2\right)^2 - 1.$ Therefore, the minimum value is $g(2) = -1$.

39. Since the vertex is at $(1, -2)$, the function is of the form $f(x) = a\left(x - 1\right)^2 - 2$. Substituting the point $(4, 16)$, we get $16 = a\left(4 - 1\right)^2 - 2 \Leftrightarrow 16 = 9a - 2 \Leftrightarrow 9a = 18 \Leftrightarrow a = 2$. So the function is $f(x) = 2\left(x - 1\right)^2 - 2 = 2x^2 - 4x$.

40. Since the vertex is $(3, 4)$, the function is of the form $y = a\left(x - 3\right)^2 + 4$. Since the parabola passes through the point $(1, -8)$, it must satisfy $-8 = a\left(1 - 3\right)^2 + 4 \Leftrightarrow -8 = 4a + 4 \Leftrightarrow 4a = -12 \Leftrightarrow a = -3$. So the function is $y = -3\left(x - 3\right)^2 + 4 = -3x^2 + 18x - 23$.

41. $f(x) = -x^2 + 4x - 3 = -\left(x^2 - 4x\right) - 3 = -\left(x^2 - 4x + 4\right) - 3 + 4 = -\left(x - 2\right)^2 + 1$. So the domain of $f(x)$ is $(-\infty, \infty)$. Since $f(x)$ has a maximum value of 1, the range is $(-\infty, 1]$.

42. $f(x) = x^2 - 2x - 3 = \left(x^2 - 2x + 1\right) - 3 - 1 = \left(x - 1\right)^2 - 4$. Then the domain of the function is all real numbers, and since the minimum value of the function is $f(1) = -4$, the range of the function is $[-4, \infty)$.

43. $f(x) = 2x^2 + 6x - 7 = 2\left(x + 3\right)^2 - 7 - 9 = 2\left(x + 3\right)^2 - 16$. The domain of the function is all real numbers, and since the minimum value of the function is $f(-3) = -16$, the range of the function is $[-16, \infty)$.

44. $f(x) = -3x^2 + 6x + 4 = -3\left(x - 1\right)^2 + 4 + 3 = -3\left(x - 1\right)^2 + 7$. The domain of the function is all real numbers, and since the maximum value of the function is $f(1) = 7$, the range of the function is $(-\infty, 7]$.

45. (a) The graph of $f(x) = x^2 + 1.79x - 3.21$ is shown. The minimum value is $f(x) \approx -4.01$.

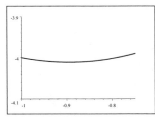

(b) $f(x) = x^2 + 1.79x - 3.21$
$= \left[x^2 + 1.79x + \left(\frac{1.79}{2}\right)^2\right] - 3.21 - \left(\frac{1.79}{2}\right)^2$
$= \left(x + 0.895\right)^2 - 4.011025$

Therefore, the exact minimum of $f(x)$ is -4.011025.

46. (a) The graph of $f(x) = 1 + x - \sqrt{2}x^2$ is shown. The maximum value is $f(x) \approx 1.18$.

(b) $f(x) = 1 + x - \sqrt{2}\,x^2 = -\sqrt{2}\left(x^2 - \frac{\sqrt{2}}{2}x\right) + 1$

$ = -\sqrt{2}\left[x^2 - \frac{\sqrt{2}}{2}x + \left(\frac{\sqrt{2}}{4}\right)^2\right] + 1 + \frac{\sqrt{2}}{8}$

$ = -\sqrt{2}\left(x - \frac{\sqrt{2}}{4}\right)^2 + \frac{8 + \sqrt{2}}{8}$

Therefore, the exact maximum of $f(x)$ is $\frac{8+\sqrt{2}}{8}$.

47. Local maximum: 2 at $x = 0$. Local minimum: -1 at $x = -2$ and 0 at $x = 2$.

48. Local maximum: 2 at $x = -2$ and $x = 1$ at $x = 2$. Local minimum: -1 at $x = 0$.

49. Local maximum: 0 at $x = 0$ and 1 at $x = 3$. Local minimum: -2 at $x = -2$ and -1 at $x = 1$.

50. Local maximum: 3 at $x = -2$ and 2 at $x = 1$. Local minimum: 0 at $x = -1$ and -1 at $x = 2$.

51. In the first graph, we see that $f(x) = x^3 - x$ has a local minimum and a local maximum. Smaller x- and y-ranges show that $f(x)$ has a local maximum of about 0.38 when $x \approx -0.58$ and a local minimum of about -0.38 when $x \approx 0.58$.

52. In the first graph, we see that $f(x) = 3 + x + x^2 - x^3$ has a local minimum and a local maximum. Smaller x- and y-ranges show that $f(x)$ has a local maximum of about 4.00 when $x \approx 1.00$ and a local minimum of about 2.81 when $x \approx -0.33$.

53. In the first graph, we see that $g(x) = x^4 - 2x^3 - 11x^2$ has two local minimums and a local maximum. The local maximum is $g(x) = 0$ when $x = 0$. Smaller x- and y-ranges show that local minima are $g(x) \approx -13.61$ when $x \approx -1.71$ and $g(x) \approx -73.32$ when $x \approx 3.21$.

54. In the first graph, we see that $g(x) = x^5 - 8x^3 + 20x$ has two local minimums and two local maximums. The local maximums are $g(x) \approx -7.87$ when $x \approx -1.93$ and $g(x) \approx 13.02$ when $x = 1.04$. Smaller x- and y-ranges show that local minimums are $g(x) \approx -13.02$ when $x = -1.04$ and $g(x) \approx 7.87$ when $x \approx 1.93$. Notice that since $g(x)$ is odd, the local maxima and minima are related.

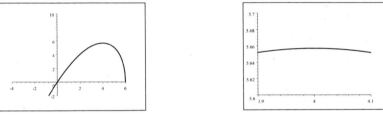

55. In the first graph, we see that $U(x) = x\sqrt{6 - x}$ only has a local maximum. Smaller x- and y-ranges show that $U(x)$ has a local maximum of about 5.66 when $x \approx 4.00$.

56. In the first viewing rectangle below, we see that $U(x) = x\sqrt{x - x^2}$ has only a local maximum. Smaller x- and y-ranges show that $U(x)$ has a local maximum of about 0.32 when $x \approx 0.75$.

57. In the first graph, we see that $V(x) = \dfrac{1 - x^2}{x^3}$ has a local minimum and a local maximum. Smaller x- and y-ranges show that $V(x)$ has a local maximum of about 0.38 when $x \approx -1.73$ and a local minimum of about -0.38 when $x \approx 1.73$.

58. In the first viewing rectangle below, we see that $V(x) = \dfrac{1}{x^2 + x + 1}$ only has a local maximum. Smaller x- and y-ranges show that $V(x)$ has a local maximum of about 1.33 when $x \approx -0.50$.

59. $y = f(t) = 40t - 16t^2 = -16\left(t^2 - \frac{5}{2}\right) = -16\left[t^2 - \frac{5}{2}t + \left(\frac{5}{4}\right)^2\right] + 16\left(\frac{5}{4}\right)^2 = -16\left(t - \frac{5}{4}\right)^2 + 25$. Thus the maximum height attained by the ball is $f\left(\frac{5}{4}\right) = 25$ feet.

60. (a) $y = -0.005x^2 + x + 5 = -0.005\left(x^2 - 200x\right) + 5 = -0.005\left(x^2 - 200x + 10,000\right) + 5 + 50 = -0.005\left(x - 100\right)^2 + 55$. Thus the maximum height attained by the football is 55 ft.

(b) We solve for $y = 0$: $0 = -0.005x^2 + x + 5$. Using the quadratic formula, we have
$x = \dfrac{-1 \pm \sqrt{1^2 - (4)(-0.005)(5)}}{2(-0.005)} = \dfrac{-1 \pm \sqrt{1.1}}{-0.01} = 100 \pm 100\sqrt{1.1}$. Since he throws the football downfield, we take the positive root, so $x = 100 + 100\sqrt{1.1} \approx 204.9$ feet.

61. $R(x) = 80x - 0.4x^2 = -0.4\left(x^2 - 200x\right) = -0.4\left(x^2 - 200x + 10,000\right) + 4,000 = -0.4\left(x - 100\right)^2 + 4,000$. So revenue is maximized at \$4,000 when 100 units are sold.

62. $P(x) = -0.001x^2 + 3x - 1800 = -0.001\left(x^2 - 3000x\right) - 1800 = -0.001\left(x^2 - 3000x + 2,250,000\right) - 1800 + 2250 = -0.001\left(x - 1500\right)^2 + 450$. The vendor's maximum profit occurs when he sells 1500 cans and the profit is \$450.

63. $E(n) = \frac{2}{3}n - \frac{1}{90}n^2 = -\frac{1}{90}\left(n^2 - 60n\right) = -\frac{1}{90}\left(n^2 - 60n + 900\right) + 10 = -\dfrac{1}{90}\left(n - 30\right)^2 + 10$. Since the maximum of the function occurs when $n = 30$, the viewer should watch the commercial 30 times for maximum effectiveness.

64. $C(t) = 0.06t - 0.0002t^2 = -0.0002\left(t^2 - 300t\right) = -0.0002\left(t^2 - 300t + 22,500\right) + 4.5 = -0.0002\left(t - 150\right)^2 + 4.5$. The maximum concentration of 4.5 mg/L occurs after 150 minutes.

65. Graphing $A(n) = n(900 - 9n)$ in the viewing rectangle $[0, 100]$ by $[0, 25000]$, we see that maximum yield of apples occurs when there are 50 trees per acre.

66. In the first graph, we see the general location of the minimum of $E(v) = 2.73v^3 \dfrac{10}{v - 5}$. In the second graph, we isolate the minimum, and from this graph, we see that energy is minimized when $v \approx 7.5$ mi/h.

67. In the first graph, we see the general location of the maximum of $N(s) = \dfrac{88s}{17 + 17\left(\dfrac{s}{20}\right)^2}$. In the second graph we isolate

the maximum, and from this graph we see that at the speed of 20 mi/h the largest number of cars that can use the highway safely is 52.

68. In the first graph, we see the general location of the minimum of $V = 999.87 - 0.06426T + 0.0085043T^2 - 0.0000679T^3$ is around $T = 4$. In the second graph, we isolate the minimum, and from this graph, we see that the minimum volume of 1 kg of water occurs at $T \approx 3.96°$ C.

69. In the first graph, we see the general location of the maximum of $v(r) = 3.2(1 - r)r^2$ is around $r = 0.7$ cm. In the second graph, we isolate the maximum, and from this graph we see that at the maximum velocity is 0.47 when $r \approx 0.67$ cm.

70. Numerous answers are possible.

71. (a) If $x = a$ is a local maximum of $f(x)$ then

$f(a) \geq f(x) \geq 0$ for all x around $x = a$. So

$[g(a)]^2 \geq [g(x)]^2$ and thus $g(a) \geq g(x)$.

Similarly, if $x = b$ is a local minimum of $f(x)$,

then $f(x) \geq f(b) \geq 0$ for all x around $x = b$.

So $[g(x)]^2 \geq [g(b)]^2$ and thus $g(x) \geq g(b)$.

(b) Using the distance formula,

$$g(x) = \sqrt{(x - 3)^2 + (x^2 - 0)^2}$$
$$= \sqrt{x^4 + x^2 - 6x + 9}$$

(c) Let $f(x) = x^4 + x^2 - 6x + 9$. From the graph, we see that $f(x)$ has a minimum at $x = 1$. Thus $g(x)$ also has a minimum at $x = 1$ and this minimum value is

$$g(1) = \sqrt{1^4 + 1^2 - 6(1) + 9} = \sqrt{5}.$$

72. $f(x) = 3 + 4x^2 - x^4$. Substituting $t = x^2$, we have $f(\sqrt{t}) = 3 + 4t - t^2 = -(t^2 - 4t) + 3 = -(t^2 - 4t + 4) + 3 + 4 = -(t - 2)^2 + 7$. Therefore, the function $f(\sqrt{t}) = f(x)$ has a maximum value of 7.

2.6　Modeling with Functions

1. Let w be the width of the building lot. Then the length of the lot is $3w$. So the area of the building lot is $A(w) = 3w^2$, $w > 0$.

2. Let w be the width of the poster. Then the length of the poster is $w + 10$. So the area of the poster is
$A(w) = w(w + 10) = w^2 + 10w$.

3. Let w be the width of the base of the rectangle. Then the height of the rectangle is $\frac{1}{2}w$. Thus the volume of the box is given by the function $V(w) = \frac{1}{2}w^3$, $w > 0$.

4. Let r be the radius of the cylinder. Then the height of the cylinder is $4r$. Since for a cylinder $V = \pi r^2 h$, the volume of the cylinder is given by the function $V(r) = \pi r^2 (4r) = 4\pi r^3$.

5. Let P be the perimeter of the rectangle and y be the length of the other side. Since $P = 2x + 2y$ and the perimeter is 20, we have $2x + 2y = 20 \quad \Leftrightarrow \quad x + y = 10 \quad \Leftrightarrow \quad y = 10 - x$. Since area is $A = xy$, substituting gives $A(x) = x(10 - x) = 10x - x^2$, and since A must be positive, the domain is $0 < x < 10$.

6. Let A be the area and y be the length of the other side. Then $A = xy = 16 \quad \Leftrightarrow \quad y = \dfrac{16}{x}$. Substituting into $P = 2x + 2y$ gives $P = 2x + 2 \cdot \dfrac{16}{x} = 2x + \dfrac{32}{x}$, where $x > 0$.

7.

Let h be the height of an altitude of the equilateral triangle whose side has length x, as shown in the diagram. Thus the area is given by $A = \frac{1}{2}xh$. By the Pythagorean Theorem, $h^2 + \left(\frac{1}{2}x\right)^2 = x^2 \quad \Leftrightarrow \quad h^2 + \frac{1}{4}x^2 = x^2 \quad \Leftrightarrow \quad h^2 = \frac{3}{4}x^2 \Leftrightarrow h = \frac{\sqrt{3}}{2}x$. Substituting into the area of a triangle, we get $A(x) = \frac{1}{2}xh = \frac{1}{2}x\left(\frac{\sqrt{3}}{2}x\right) = \frac{\sqrt{3}}{4}x^2$, $x > 0$.

8. Let d represent the length of any side of a cube. Then the surface area is $S = 6d^2$, and the volume is $V = d^3 \quad \Leftrightarrow \quad d = \sqrt[3]{V}$. Substituting for d gives $S(V) = 6\left(\sqrt[3]{V}\right)^2 = 6V^{2/3}$, $V > 0$.

9. We solve for r in the formula for the area of a circle. This gives $A = \pi r^2 \quad \Leftrightarrow \quad r^2 = \dfrac{A}{\pi} \quad \Rightarrow \quad r = \sqrt{\dfrac{A}{\pi}}$, so the model is $r(A) = \sqrt{\dfrac{A}{\pi}}$, $A > 0$.

10. Let r be the radius of a circle. Then the area is $A = \pi r^2$, and the circumference is $C = 2\pi r \quad \Leftrightarrow \quad r = \dfrac{C}{2\pi}$. Substituting for r gives $A(C) = \pi\left(\dfrac{C}{2\pi}\right)^2 = \dfrac{C^2}{4\pi}$, $C > 0$.

11. Let h be the height of the box in feet. The volume of the box is $V = 60$. Then $x^2 h = 60 \quad \Leftrightarrow \quad h = \dfrac{60}{x^2}$. The surface area, S, of the box is the sum of the area of the 4 sides and the area of the base and top. Thus $S = 4xh + 2x^2 = 4x\left(\dfrac{60}{x^2}\right) + 2x^2 = \dfrac{240}{x} + 2x^2$, so the model is $S(x) = \dfrac{240}{x} + 2x^2$, $x > 0$.

12. By similar triangles, $\dfrac{5}{L} = \dfrac{12}{L + d} \quad \Leftrightarrow \quad 5(L + d) = 12L \quad \Leftrightarrow \quad 5d = 7L \quad \Leftrightarrow \quad L = \dfrac{5d}{7}$. The model is $L(d) = \frac{5}{7}d$.

13.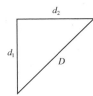

Let d_1 be the distance traveled south by the first ship and d_2 be the distance traveled east by the second ship. The first ship travels south for t hours at 5 mi/h, so $d_1 = 15t$ and, similarly, $d_2 = 20t$. Since the ships are traveling at right angles to each other, we can apply the Pythagorean Theorem to get

$$D^2 = d_1^2 + d_2^2 = (15t)^2 + (20t)^2 = 225t^2 + 400t^2 = 625t^2.$$

14. Let n be one of the numbers. Then the other number is $60 - n$, so the product is given by the function
$P(n) = n(60 - n) = 60n - n^2.$

15.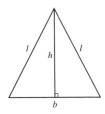

Let b be the length of the base, l be the length of the equal sides, and h be the height in centimeters. Since the perimeter is 8, $2l + b = 8 \quad \Leftrightarrow \quad 2l = 8 - b$
$\Leftrightarrow \quad l = \frac{1}{2}(8 - b)$. By the Pythagorean Theorem, $h^2 + \left(\frac{1}{2}b\right)^2 = l^2 \quad \Leftrightarrow$
$h = \sqrt{l^2 - \frac{1}{4}b^2}$. Therefore the area of the triangle is

$$A = \frac{1}{2} \cdot b \cdot h = \frac{1}{2} \cdot b\sqrt{l^2 - \frac{1}{4}b^2} = \frac{b}{2}\sqrt{\frac{1}{4}(8 - b)^2 - \frac{1}{4}b^2}$$
$$= \frac{b}{4}\sqrt{64 - 16b + b^2 - b^2} = \frac{b}{4}\sqrt{64 - 16b} = \frac{b}{4} \cdot 4\sqrt{4 - b} = b\sqrt{4 - b}$$

so the model is $A(b) = b\sqrt{4 - b}, 0 < b < 4.$

16. Let x be the length of the shorter leg of the right triangle. Then the length of the other triangle is $2x$. Since it is a right triangle, the length of the hypotenuse is $\sqrt{x^2 + (2x)^2} = \sqrt{5x^2} = \sqrt{5}\,x$ (since $x \geq 0$). Thus the perimeter of the triangle is $P(x) = x + 2x + \sqrt{5}\,x = \left(3 + \sqrt{5}\right)x.$

17. Let w be the length of the rectangle. By the Pythagorean Theorem, $\left(\frac{1}{2}w\right)^2 + h^2 = 10^2 \quad \Leftrightarrow \quad \dfrac{w^2}{4} + h^2 = 10^2$
$\Leftrightarrow \quad w^2 = 4\left(100 - h^2\right) \quad \Leftrightarrow \quad w = 2\sqrt{100 - h^2}$ (since $w > 0$). Therefore, the area of the rectangle is
$A = wh = 2h\sqrt{100 - h^2}$, so the model is $A(h) = 2h\sqrt{100 - h^2}, 0 < h < 10.$

18. Using the formula for the volume of a cone, $V = \frac{1}{3}\pi r^2 h$, we substitute $V = 100$ and solve for h. Thus $100 = \frac{1}{3}\pi r^2 h$
$\Leftrightarrow \quad h(r) = \dfrac{300}{\pi r^2}.$

19. (a) We complete the table.

First number	Second number	Product
1	18	18
2	17	34
3	16	48
4	15	60
5	14	70
6	13	78
7	12	84
8	11	88
9	10	90
10	9	90
11	8	88

From the table we conclude that the numbers is still increasing, the numbers whose product is a maximum should both be 9.5.

(b) Let x be one number: then $19 - x$ is the other number, and so the product, p, is
$$p(x) = x(19 - x) = 19x - x^2.$$
(c) $p(x) = 19x - x^2 = -\left(x^2 - 19x\right)$
$$= -\left[x^2 - 19x + \left(\frac{19}{2}\right)^2\right] + \left(\frac{19}{2}\right)^2$$
$$= -(x - 9.5)^2 + 90.25$$

So the product is maximized when the numbers are both 9.5.

20. Let the positive numbers be x and y. Since their sum is 100, we have $x+y = 100 \quad \Leftrightarrow \quad y = 100-x$. We wish to minimize the sum of squares, which is $S = x^2 + y^2 = x^2 + (100 - x)^2$. So $S(x) = x^2 + (100 - x)^2 = x^2 + 10{,}000 - 200x + x^2 = 2x^2 - 200x + 10{,}000 = 2\left(x^2 - 100x\right) + 10{,}000 = 2\left(x^2 - 100x + 2500\right) + 10{,}000 - 5000 = 2\left(x - 50\right)^2 + 5000$. Thus the minimum sum of squares occurs when $x = 50$. Then $y = 100 - 50 = 50$. Therefore both numbers are 50.

21. Let x and y be the two numbers. Since their sum is -24, we have $x + y = -24 \quad \Leftrightarrow \quad y = -x - 24$. The product of the two numbers is $P = xy = x\left(-x - 24\right) = -x^2 - 24x$, which we wish to maximize. So $P = -x^2 - 24x = -\left(x^2 + 24x\right) = -\left(x^2 + 24x + 144\right) + 144 = -\left(x + 12\right)^2 + 144$. Thus the maximum product is 144, and it occurs when $x = -12$ and $y = -(-12) - 24 = -12$. Thus the two numbers are -12 and -12.

22. Let w and l be the width and the length of the rectangle in feet. We want all rectangles with perimeter equal to 20, so we have $2w + 2l = 20 \quad \Leftrightarrow \quad l = 10 - w$. The area of a rectangle is given by $A(w) = l \cdot w = (10 - w)w = 10w - w^2 = -\left(w^2 - 10w\right) = -\left(w^2 - 10w + 25\right) + 25 = -\left(w - 5\right)^2 + 25$. So the area is maximized when $w = 5$, and hence the largest rectangle is a square where the dimension of each side is 5 feet.

23. (a) Let x be the width of the field (in feet) and l be the length of the field (in feet). Since the farmer has 2400 ft of fencing we must have $2x + l = 2400$.

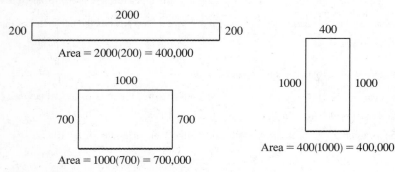

Width	Length	Area
200	2000	400,000
300	1800	540,000
400	1600	640,000
500	1400	700,000
600	1200	720,000
700	1000	700,000
800	800	640,000

It appears that the field of largest area is about 600 ft × 1200 ft.

(b) Let x be the width of the field (in feet) and l be the length of the field (in feet). Since the farmer has 2400 ft of fencing we must have $2x + l = 2400 \quad \Leftrightarrow \quad l = 2400 - 2x$. The area of the fenced-in field is given by $A(x) = l \cdot x = (2400 - 2x)x = -2x^2 + 2400x = -2\left(x^2 - 1200x\right)$.

(c) The area is $A(x) = -2\left(x^2 - 1200x + 600^2\right) + 2\left(600^2\right) = -2\left(x - 600\right)^2 + 720000$. So the maximum area occurs when $x = 600$ feet and $l = 2400 - 2(600) = 1200$ feet.

24. (a) Let w be the width of the rectangular area (in feet) and l be the length of the field (in feet). Since the farmer has 750 feet of fencing, we must have $5w + 2l = 750 \quad \Leftrightarrow \quad 2l = 750 - 5w \quad \Leftrightarrow \quad l = \frac{5}{2}(150 - w)$. Thus the total area of the four pens is $A(w) = l \cdot w = \frac{5}{2}w(150 - w) = -\frac{5}{2}\left(w^2 - 150w\right)$.

(b) We complete the square to get $A(w) = -\frac{5}{2}\left(w^2 - 150w\right) = -\frac{5}{2}\left(w^2 - 150w + 75^2\right) + \left(\frac{5}{2}\right) \cdot 75^2 = -\frac{5}{2}\left(w - 75\right)^2 + 14062.5$. Therefore, the largest possible total area of the four pens is 14,062.5 square feet.

25. (a) Let x be the length of the fence along the road. If the area is 1200, we have $1200 = x \cdot$ width, so the width of the garden is $\dfrac{1200}{x}$. Then the cost of the fence is given by the function $C(x) = 5(x) + 3\left[x + 2 \cdot \dfrac{1200}{x}\right] = 8x + \dfrac{7200}{x}$.

(b) We graph the function $y = C(x)$ in the viewing rectangle $[0, 75] \times [0, 800]$. From this we get the cost is minimized when $x = 30$ ft. Then the width is $\frac{1200}{30} = 40$ ft. So the length is 30 ft and the width is 40 ft.

(c) We graph the function $y = C(x)$ and $y = 600$ in the viewing rectangle $[10, 65] \times [450, 650]$. From this we get that the cost is at most $600 when $15 \le x \le 60$. So the range of lengths he can fence along the road is 15 feet to 60 feet.

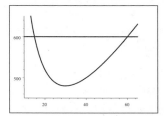

26. (a) Let x be the length of wire in cm that is bent into a square. So $10 - x$ is the length of wire in cm that is bent into the second square. The width of each square is $\dfrac{x}{4}$ and $\dfrac{10-x}{4}$, and the area of each square is $\left(\dfrac{x}{4}\right)^2 = \dfrac{x^2}{16}$ and $\left(\dfrac{10-x}{4}\right)^2 = \dfrac{100 - 20x + x^2}{16}$. Thus the sum of the areas is

$$A(x) = \dfrac{x^2}{16} + \dfrac{100 - 20x + x^2}{16} = \dfrac{100 - 20x + 2x^2}{16} = \tfrac{1}{8}x^2 - \tfrac{5}{4}x + \tfrac{25}{4}.$$

(b) We complete the square. $A(x) = \tfrac{1}{8}x^2 - \tfrac{5}{4}x + \tfrac{25}{4} = \tfrac{1}{8}\left(x^2 - 10x\right) + \tfrac{25}{4} = \tfrac{1}{8}\left(x^2 - 10x + 25\right) + \dfrac{25}{4} - \tfrac{25}{8} = \tfrac{1}{8}(x - 5)^2 + \tfrac{25}{8}$ So the minimum area is $\tfrac{25}{8}$ cm^2 when each piece is 5 cm long.

27. (a) Let p be the price of the ticket. So $10 - p$ is the difference in ticket price and therefore the number of tickets sold is $27{,}000 + 3000(10 - p) = 57{,}000 - 3000p$. Thus the revenue is $R(p) = p(57{,}000 - 3000p) = 57{,}000p - 3000p^2$.

(b) $R(p) = 0 = p(57{,}000 - 3000p)$. So $p = 0 \; or = \dfrac{57{,}000}{3000} = 19$. So at $19 no one will come.

(c) We complete the square:

$$\begin{aligned} R(p) &= 57{,}000p - 3000p^2 = -3000\left(p^2 - 19p\right) = -3000\left(p^2 - 19p + \tfrac{19^2}{4}\right) + 270{,}750 \\ &= -3000\left(p - \tfrac{19}{2}\right)^2 + 270{,}750 \end{aligned}$$

The revenue is maximized when $p = \tfrac{19}{2}$, and so the price should be set at $9.50.

28. (a) Let x be the number of one dollar increases in the price of a bird feeder. So the selling price will be $10 + x$ dollars, and the number of bird feeders sold will be $20 - 2x$. The revenue from the sales will be $(10 + x)(20 - 2x)$, and the cost will be $6(20 - 2x)$. The profits will be $P(x) = (10 + x)(20 - 2x) - 6(20 - 2x) = (4 + x)(20 - 2x) = 80 + 12x - 2x^2$.

(b) Completing the square we get $P(x) = 80 + 12x - 2x^2 = -2\left(x^2 - 6x\right) + 80 = -2\left(x^2 - 6x + 9\right) + 80 + 18 = -2(x - 3)^2 + 98$. Thus the profit would be maximized at $98 when $x = 3$. So the bird society should set the selling price at $10 + x = 13$.

29. (a) Let h be the height in feet of the straight portion of the window. The circumference of the semicircle is $C = \frac{1}{2}\pi x$. Since the perimeter of the window is 30 feet, we have $x + 2h + \frac{1}{2}\pi x = 30$. Solving for h, we get $2h = 30 - x - \frac{1}{2}\pi x \quad \Leftrightarrow \quad h = 15 - \frac{1}{2}x - \frac{1}{4}\pi x$. The area of the window is

$$A(x) = xh + \frac{1}{2}\pi\left(\frac{1}{2}x\right)^2 = x\left(15 - \frac{1}{2}x - \frac{1}{4}\pi x\right) + \frac{1}{8}\pi x^2 = 15x - \frac{1}{2}x^2 - \frac{1}{8}\pi x^2.$$

(b) $A(x) = 15x - \frac{1}{2}x^2 - \frac{1}{8}\pi x^2 = 15x - \frac{1}{8}(\pi + 4)x^2 = -\frac{1}{8}(\pi + 4)\left[x^2 - \frac{120}{\pi + 4}x\right]$

$$= -\frac{1}{8}(\pi + 4)\left[x^2 - \frac{120}{\pi + 4}x + \left(\frac{60}{\pi + 4}\right)^2\right] + \frac{450}{\pi + 4} = -\frac{1}{8}(\pi + 4)\left(x - \frac{60}{\pi + 4}\right)^2 + \frac{450}{\pi + 4}$$

The area is maximized when $x = \dfrac{60}{\pi + 4} \approx 8.40$, and hence $h \approx 15 - \frac{1}{2}(8.40) - \frac{1}{4}\pi(8.40) \approx 4.20$.

30. (a) The height of the box is x, the width of the box is $12 - 2x$, and the length of the box is $20 - 2x$. Therefore, the volume of the box is

$$\begin{aligned} V(x) &= x(12 - 2x)(20 - 2x) \\ &= 4x^3 - 64x^2 + 240x, 0 < x < 6 \end{aligned}$$

(b) We graph the function $y = V(x)$ in the viewing rectangle $[0, 6] \times [200, 270]$.

From the calculator we get that the volume of the box is greater than 200 in^3 for $1.174 \le x \le 3.898$ (accurate to 3 decimal places).

(c) From the graph, the volume of the box with the largest volume is 262.682 in^3 when $x \approx 2.427$.

31. (a) Let x be the length of one side of the base and let h be the height of the box in feet. Since the volume of the box is $V = x^2 h = 12$, we have $x^2 h = 12 \quad \Leftrightarrow \quad h = \dfrac{12}{x^2}$. The surface area, A, of the box is sum of the area of the four sides and the area of the base. Thus the surface area of the box is given by the formula

$$A(x) = 4xh + x^2 = 4x\left(\frac{12}{x^2}\right) + x^2 = \frac{48}{x} + x^2, x > 0.$$

(b) The function $y = A(x)$ is shown in the first viewing rectangle below. In the second viewing rectangle, we isolate the minimum, and we see that the amount of material is minimized when x (the length and width) is 2.88 ft. Then the height is $h = \dfrac{12}{x^2} \approx 1.44$ ft.

32. Let A, B, C, and D be the vertices of a rectangle with base AB on the x-axis and its other two vertices C and D above the x-axis and lying on the parabola $y = 8 - x^2$. Let C have the coordinates (x, y), $x > 0$. By symmetry, the coordinates of D must be $(-x, y)$. So the width of the rectangle is $2x$, and the length is $y = 8 - x^2$. Thus the area of the rectangle is $A(x) = \text{length} \cdot \text{width} = 2x\left(8 - x^2\right) = 16x - 2x^3$. The graphs of $A(x)$ below show that the area is maximized when $x \approx 1.63$. Hence the maximum area occurs when the width is 3.26 and the length is 5.33.

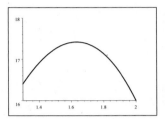

33. (a) Let w be the width of the pen and l be the length in meters. We use the area to establish a relationship between w and l. Since the area is 100 m^2, we have $l \cdot w = 100 \quad \Leftrightarrow \quad l = \dfrac{100}{w}$. So the amount of fencing used is

$$F = 2l + 2w = 2\left(\frac{100}{w}\right) + 2w = \frac{200 + 2w^2}{w}.$$

(b) Using a graphing device, we first graph F in the viewing rectangle $[0, 40]$ by $[0, 100]$, and locate the approximate location of the minimum value. In the second viewing rectangle, $[8, 12]$ by $[39, 41]$, we see that the minimum value of F occurs when $w = 10$. Therefore the pen should be a square with side 10 m.

34. (a) Let t_1 represent the time, in hours, spent walking, and let t_2 represent the time spent rowing. Since the distance walked is x and the walking speed is 5 mi/h, the time spent walking is $t_1 = \frac{1}{5}x$. By the Pythagorean Theorem, the distance rowed is

$$d = \sqrt{2^2 + (7 - x)^2} = \sqrt{x^2 - 14x + 53},$$ and so the time spent

rowing is $t_2 = \frac{1}{2} \cdot \sqrt{x^2 - 14x + 53}$. Thus the total time is

$$T(x) = \frac{1}{2}\sqrt{x^2 - 14x + 53} + \frac{1}{5}x.$$

(b) We graph $y = T(x)$. Using the zoom function, we see that T is minimized when $x \approx 6.13$. He should land at a point 6.13 miles from point B.

35. (a) Let x be the distance from point B to C, in miles. Then the distance from A to C is $\sqrt{x^2 + 25}$, and the energy used in flying from A to C then C to D is $f(x) = 14\sqrt{x^2 + 25} + 10(12 - x)$.

(b) By using a graphing device, the energy expenditure is minimized when the distance from B to C is about 5.1 miles.

36. (a) Using the Pythagorean Theorem, we have that the height of the upper triangles is $\sqrt{25 - x^2}$ and the height of the lower triangles is $\sqrt{144 - x^2}$. So the area of the each of the upper triangles is $\frac{1}{2}x\sqrt{25 - x^2}$, and the area of the each of the lower triangles is $\frac{1}{2}x\sqrt{144 - x^2}$. Since there are two upper triangles and two lower triangles, we get that the total area is $A(x) = 2 \cdot \left[\frac{1}{2}x\sqrt{25 - x^2}\right] + 2 \cdot \left[\frac{1}{2}x\sqrt{144 - x^2}\right] = x\left(\sqrt{25 - x^2} + \sqrt{144 - x^2}\right)$.

(b) The function $y = A(x) = x\left(\sqrt{25 - x^2} + \sqrt{144 - x^2}\right)$ is shown in the first viewing rectangle below. In the second viewing rectangle, we isolate the maximum, and we see that the area of the kite is maximized when $x \approx 4.615$. So the length of the horizontal crosspiece must be $2 \cdot 4.615 = 9.23$. The length of the vertical crosspiece is
$$\sqrt{5^2 - (4.615)^2} + \sqrt{12^2 - (4.615)^2} \approx 13.00.$$

2.7   Combining Functions

1. $f(x) = x - 3$ has domain $(-\infty, \infty)$. $g(x) = x^2$ has domain $(-\infty, \infty)$. The intersection of the domains of f and g is $(-\infty, \infty)$.

$(f + g)(x) = (x - 3) + (x^2) = x^2 + x - 3$, and the domain is $(-\infty, \infty)$.

$(f - g)(x) = (x - 3) - (x^2) = -x^2 + x - 3$, and the domain is $(-\infty, \infty)$.

$(fg)(x) = (x - 3)(x^2) = x^3 - 3x^2$, and the domain is $(-\infty, \infty)$.

$\left(\dfrac{f}{g}\right)(x) = \dfrac{x - 3}{x^2}$, and the domain is $\{x \mid x \neq 0\}$.

2. $f(x) = x^2 + 2x$ has domain $(-\infty, \infty)$. $g(x) = 3x^2 - 1$ has domain $(-\infty, \infty)$. The intersection of the domains of f and g is $(-\infty, \infty)$.

$(f + g)(x) = x^2 + 2x + (3x^2 - 1) = 4x^2 + 2x - 1$, and the domain is $(-\infty, \infty)$.

$(f - g)(x) = x^2 + 2x - (3x^2 - 1) = -2x^2 + 2x + 1$, and the domain is $(-\infty, \infty)$.

$(fg)(x) = (x^2 + 2x)(3x^2 - 1) = 3x^4 + 6x^3 - x^2 - 2x$, and the domain is $(-\infty, \infty)$.

$\left(\dfrac{f}{g}\right)(x) = \dfrac{x^2 + 2x}{3x^2 - 1}$, $3x^2 - 1 \neq 0 \quad \Rightarrow \quad x \neq \pm\frac{\sqrt{3}}{3}$, and the domain is $\left\{x \mid x \neq \pm\frac{\sqrt{3}}{3}\right\}$.

3. $f(x) = \sqrt{4 - x^2}$, has domain $[-2, 2]$. $g(x) = \sqrt{1 + x}$, has domain $[-1, \infty)$. The intersection of the domains of f and g is $[-1, 2]$.

$(f + g)(x) = \sqrt{4 - x^2} + \sqrt{1 + x}$, and the domain is $[-1, 2]$.

$(f - g)(x) = \sqrt{4 - x^2} - \sqrt{1 + x}$, and the domain is $[-1, 2]$.

$(fg)(x) = \sqrt{4 - x^2}\sqrt{1 + x} = \sqrt{-x^3 - x^2 + 4x + 4}$, and the domain is $[-1, 2]$.

$\left(\dfrac{f}{g}\right)(x) = \dfrac{\sqrt{4 - x^2}}{\sqrt{1 + x}} = \sqrt{\dfrac{4 - x^2}{1 + x}}$, and the domain is $(-1, 2]$.

4. $f(x) = \sqrt{9 - x^2}$ has domain $[-3, 3]$. $g(x) = \sqrt{x^2 - 4}$ has domain $(-\infty, -2] \cup [2, \infty)$. The intersection of the domains of f and g is $[-3, -2] \cup [2, 3]$.

$(f + g)(x) = \sqrt{9 - x^2} + \sqrt{x^2 - 4}$, and the domain is $[-3, -2] \cup [2, 3]$.

$(f - g)(x) = \sqrt{9 - x^2} - \sqrt{x^2 - 4}$, and the domain is $[-3, -2] \cup [2, 3]$.

$(fg)(x) = \sqrt{9 - x^2} \cdot \sqrt{x^2 - 4} = \sqrt{-x^4 + 13x^2 - 36}$, and the domain is $[-3, -2] \cup [2, 3]$.

$\left(\dfrac{f}{g}\right)(x) = \dfrac{\sqrt{9 - x^2}}{\sqrt{x^2 - 4}} = \sqrt{\dfrac{9 - x^2}{x^2 - 4}}$, and the domain is $[-3, -2) \cup (2, 3]$.

5. $f(x) = \dfrac{2}{x}$ has domain $x \neq 0$. $g(x) = \dfrac{4}{x + 4}$, has domain $x \neq -4$. The intersection of the domains of f and g is $\{x \mid x \neq 0, -4\}$; in interval notation, this is $(-\infty, -4) \cup (-4, 0) \cup (0, \infty)$.

$(f + g)(x) = \dfrac{2}{x} + \dfrac{4}{x + 4} = \dfrac{2}{x} + \dfrac{4}{x + 4} = \dfrac{2(3x + 4)}{x(x + 4)}$, and the domain is $(-\infty, -4) \cup (-4, 0) \cup (0, \infty)$.

$(f - g)(x) = \dfrac{2}{x} - \dfrac{4}{x + 4} = -\dfrac{2(x - 4)}{x(x + 4)}$, and the domain is $(-\infty, -4) \cup (-4, 0) \cup (0, \infty)$.

$(fg)(x) = \dfrac{2}{x} \cdot \dfrac{4}{x + 4} = \dfrac{8}{x(x + 4)}$, and the domain is $(-\infty, -4) \cup (-4, 0) \cup (0, \infty)$.

$\left(\dfrac{f}{g}\right)(x) = \dfrac{\dfrac{2}{x}}{\dfrac{4}{x + 4}} = \dfrac{x + 4}{2x}$, and the domain is $(-\infty, -4) \cup (-4, 0) \cup (0, \infty)$.

6. $f(x) = \dfrac{2}{x + 1}$ has domain $x \neq -1$. $g(x) = \dfrac{x}{x + 1}$ has domain $x \neq -1$. The intersection of the domains of f and g is $\{x \mid x \neq -1\}$; in interval notation, this is $(-\infty, -1) \cup (-1, \infty)$.

$(f + g)(x) = \dfrac{2}{x + 1} + \dfrac{x}{x + 1} = \dfrac{x + 2}{x + 1}$, and the domain is $(-\infty, -1) \cup (-1, \infty)$.

$(f - g)(x) = \dfrac{2}{x + 1} - \dfrac{x}{x + 1} = \dfrac{2 - x}{x + 1}$, and the domain is $(-\infty, -1) \cup (-1, \infty)$.

$(fg)(x) = \dfrac{2}{x + 1} \cdot \dfrac{x}{x + 1} = \dfrac{2x}{(x + 1)^2}$, and the domain is $(-\infty, -1) \cup (-1, \infty)$.

$\left(\dfrac{f}{g}\right)(x) = \dfrac{\dfrac{2}{x + 1}}{\dfrac{x}{x + 1}} = \dfrac{2}{x}$, so $x \neq 0$ as well. Thus the domain is $(-\infty, -1) \cup (-1, 0) \cup (0, \infty)$.

7. $f(x) = \sqrt{x} + \sqrt{1 - x}$. The domain of $\sqrt{x}$ is $[0, \infty)$, and the domain of $\sqrt{1 - x}$ is $(-\infty, 1]$. Thus the domain is $(-\infty, 1] \cap [0, \infty) = [0, 1]$.

8. $g(x) = \sqrt{x + 1} + \dfrac{1}{x}$. The domain of $\sqrt{x + 1}$ is $[-1, \infty)$, and the domain of $\dfrac{1}{x}$ is $x \neq 0$. Since $x \neq 0$ is $(-\infty, 0) \cup (0, \infty)$, the domain is $[-1, \infty) \cap \{(-\infty, 0) \cup (0, \infty)\} = [-1, 0) \cup (0, \infty)$.

9. $h(x) = (x - 3)^{-1/4} = \dfrac{1}{(x - 3)^{1/4}}$. Since $1/4$ is an even root and the denominator can not equal 0, $x - 3 > 0$ $\Leftrightarrow$ $x > 3$. So the domain is $(3, \infty)$.

10. $k(x) = \dfrac{\sqrt{x+3}}{x-1}$. The domain of $\sqrt{x+3}$ is $[-3, \infty)$, and the domain of $\dfrac{1}{x-1}$ is $x \neq 1$. Since $x \neq 1$ is $(-\infty, 1) \cup (1, \infty)$, the domain is $[-3, \infty) \cap \{(-\infty, 1) \cup (1, \infty)\} = [-3, 1) \cup (1, \infty)$.

11.

12.

13.

14.

15.

16.

17. (a) $f(g(0)) = f(2 - (0)^2) = f(2) = 3(2) - 5 = 1$

(b) $g(f(0)) = g(3(0) - 5) = g(-5) = 2 - (-5)^2 = -23$

18. (a) $f(f(4)) = f(3(4) - 5) = f(7) = 3(7) - 5 = 16$

(b) $g(g(3)) = g(2 - (3)^2) = g(-7) = 2 - (-7)^2 = -47$

19. (a) $(f \circ g)(-2) = f(g(-2)) = f(2 - (-2)^2) = f(-2) = 3(-2) - 5 = -11$

(b) $(g \circ f)(-2) = g(f(-2)) = g(3(-2) - 5) = g(-11) = 2 - (-11)^2 = -119$

20. (a) $(f \circ f)(-1) = f(f(-1)) = f(3(-1) - 5) = f(-8) = 3(-8) - 5 = -29$

(b) $(g \circ g)(2) = g(g(2)) = g(2 - (2)^2) = g(-2) = 2 - (-2)^2 = -2$

21. (a) $(f \circ g)(x) = f(g(x)) = f(2 - x^2) = 3(2 - x^2) - 5 = 6 - 3x^2 - 5 = 1 - 3x^2$

(b) $(g \circ f)(x) = g(f(x)) = g(3x - 5) = 2 - (3x - 5)^2 = 2 - (9x^2 - 30x + 25) = -9x^2 + 30x - 23$

22. (a) $(f \circ f)(x) = f(f(x)) = f(3x - 5) = 3(3x - 5) - 5 = 9x - 15 - 5 = 9x - 20$

(b) $(g \circ g)(x) = g(g(x)) = g(2 - x^2) = 2 - (2 - x^2)^2 = 2 - (4 - 4x^2 + x^4) = -x^4 + 4x^2 - 2$

23. $f(g(2)) = f(5) = 4$

24. $f(0) = 0$, so $g(f(0)) = g(0) = 3$.

25. $(g \circ f)(4) = g(f(4)) = g(2) = 5$

26. $g(0) = 3$, so $(f \circ g)(0) = f(3) = 0$.

27. $(g \circ g)(-2) = g(g(-2)) = g(1) = 4$

28. $f(4) = 2$, so $(f \circ f)(4) = f(2) = -2$.

29. $f(x) = 2x + 3$, has domain $(-\infty, \infty)$; $g(x) = 4x - 1$, has domain $(-\infty, \infty)$.

$(f \circ g)(x) = f(4x - 1) = 2(4x - 1) + 3 = 8x + 1$, and the domain is $(-\infty, \infty)$.

$(g \circ f)(x) = g(2x + 3) = 4(2x + 3) - 1 = 8x + 11$, and the domain is $(-\infty, \infty)$.

$(f \circ f)(x) = f(2x + 3) = 2(2x + 3) + 3 = 4x + 9$, and the domain is $(-\infty, \infty)$.

$(g \circ g)(x) = g(4x - 1) = 4(4x - 1) - 1 = 16x - 5$, and the domain is $(-\infty, \infty)$.

30. $f(x) = 6x - 5$ has domain $(-\infty, \infty)$. $g(x) = \dfrac{x}{2}$ has domain $(-\infty, \infty)$.

$(f \circ g)(x) = f\left(\dfrac{x}{2}\right) = 6\left(\dfrac{x}{2}\right) - 5 = 3x - 5$, and the domain is $(-\infty, \infty)$.

$(g \circ f)(x) = g(6x - 5) = \dfrac{6x - 5}{2} = 3x - \frac{5}{2}$, and the domain is $(-\infty, \infty)$.

$(f \circ f)(x) = f(6x - 5) = 6(6x - 5) - 5 = 36x - 35$, and the domain is $(-\infty, \infty)$.

$(g \circ g)(x) = g\left(\dfrac{x}{2}\right) = \dfrac{\frac{x}{2}}{2} = \dfrac{x}{4}$, and the domain is $(-\infty, \infty)$.

31. $f(x) = x^2$, has domain $(-\infty, \infty)$; $g(x) = x + 1$, has domain $(-\infty, \infty)$.

$(f \circ g)(x) = f(x + 1) = (x + 1)^2 = x^2 + 2x + 1$, and the domain is $(-\infty, \infty)$.

$(g \circ f)(x) = g(x^2) = (x^2) + 1 = x^2 + 1$, and the domain is $(-\infty, \infty)$.

$(f \circ f)(x) = f(x^2) = (x^2)^2 = x^4$, and the domain is $(-\infty, \infty)$.

$(g \circ g)(x) = g(x + 1) = (x + 1) + 1 = x + 2$, and the domain is $(-\infty, \infty)$.

32. $f(x) = x^3 + 2$ has domain $(-\infty, \infty)$. $g(x) = \sqrt[3]{x}$ has domain $(-\infty, \infty)$.

$(f \circ g)(x) = f(\sqrt[3]{x}) = (\sqrt[3]{x})^3 + 2 = x + 2$, and the domain is $(-\infty, \infty)$.

$(g \circ f)(x) = g(x^3 + 2) = \sqrt[3]{x^3 + 2}$ and the domain is $(-\infty, \infty)$.

$(f \circ f)(x) = f(x^3 + 2) = (x^3 + 2)^3 + 2 = x^9 + 6x^6 + 12x^3 + 8 + 2 = x^9 + 6x^6 + 12x^3 + 10$, and the domain is $(-\infty, \infty)$.

$(g \circ g)(x) = g(\sqrt[3]{x}) = \sqrt[3]{\sqrt[3]{x}} = \left(x^{1/3}\right)^{1/3} = x^{1/9}$, and the domain is $(-\infty, \infty)$.

33. $f(x) = \dfrac{1}{x}$, has domain $\{x \mid x \neq 0\}$; $g(x) = 2x + 4$, has domain $(-\infty, \infty)$.

$(f \circ g)(x) = f(2x + 4) = \dfrac{1}{2x + 4}$. $(f \circ g)(x)$ is defined for $2x + 4 \neq 0 \quad \Leftrightarrow \quad x \neq -2$. So the domain is $\{x \mid x \neq -2\} = (-\infty, -2) \cup (-2, \infty)$.

$(g \circ f)(x) = g\left(\dfrac{1}{x}\right) = 2\left(\dfrac{1}{x}\right) + 4 = \dfrac{2}{x} + 4$, the domain is $\{x \mid x \neq 0\} = (-\infty, 0) \cup (0, \infty)$.

$(f \circ f)(x) = f\left(\dfrac{1}{x}\right) = \dfrac{1}{\left(\dfrac{1}{x}\right)} = x$. $(f \circ f)(x)$ is defined whenever both $f(x)$ and $f(f(x))$ are defined; that is,

whenever $\{x \mid x \neq 0\} = (-\infty, 0) \cup (0, \infty)$.

$(g \circ g)(x) = g(2x + 4) = 2(2x + 4) + 4 = 4x + 8 + 4 = 4x + 12$, and the domain is $(-\infty, \infty)$.

34. $f(x) = x^2$ has domain $(-\infty, \infty)$. $g(x) = \sqrt{x - 3}$ has domain $[3, \infty)$.

$(f \circ g)(x) = f(\sqrt{x - 3}) = (\sqrt{x - 3})^2 = x - 3$, and the domain is $[3, \infty)$.

$(g \circ f)(x) = g(x^2) = \sqrt{x^2 - 3}$. For the domain we must have $x^2 \geq 3 \quad \Rightarrow \quad x \leq -\sqrt{3}$ or $x \geq \sqrt{3}$. Thus the domain is $(-\infty, -\sqrt{3}] \cup [\sqrt{3}, \infty)$.

$(f \circ f)(x) = f(x^2) = (x^2)^2 = x^4$, and the domain is $(-\infty, \infty)$.

$(g \circ g)(x) = g(\sqrt{x - 3}) = \sqrt{\sqrt{x - 3} - 3}$. For the domain we must have $\sqrt{x - 3} \geq 3 \quad \Rightarrow \quad x - 3 \geq 9 \quad \Rightarrow \quad x \geq 12$, so the domain is $[12, \infty)$.

35. $f(x) = |x|$, has domain $(-\infty, \infty)$; $g(x) = 2x + 3$, has domain $(-\infty, \infty)$

$(f \circ g)(x) = f(2x + 4) = |2x + 3|$, and the domain is $(-\infty, \infty)$.

$(g \circ f)(x) = g(|x|) = 2|x| + 3$, and the domain is $(-\infty, \infty)$.

$(f \circ f)(x) = f(|x|) = ||x|| = |x|$, and the domain is $(-\infty, \infty)$.

$(g \circ g)(x) = g(2x + 3) = 2(2x + 3) + 3 = 4x + 6 + 3 = 4x + 9$. Domain is $(-\infty, \infty)$.

36. $f(x) = x - 4$ has domain $(-\infty, \infty)$. $g(x) = |x + 4|$ has domain $(-\infty, \infty)$.

$(f \circ g)(x) = f(|x + 4|) = |x + 4| - 4$, and the domain is $(-\infty, \infty)$.

$(g \circ f)(x) = g(x - 4) = |(x - 4) + 4| = |x|$, and the domain is $(-\infty, \infty)$.

$(f \circ f)(x) = f(x - 4) = (x - 4) - 4 = x - 8$, and the domain is $(-\infty, \infty)$.

$(g \circ g)(x) = g(|x + 4|) = ||x + 4| + 4| = |x + 4| + 4$ ($|x + 4| + 4$ is always positive). The domain is $(-\infty, \infty)$.

37. $f(x) = \dfrac{x}{x + 1}$, has domain $\{x \mid x \neq -1\}$; $g(x) = 2x - 1$, has domain $(-\infty, \infty)$

$(f \circ g)(x) = f(2x - 1) = \dfrac{2x - 1}{(2x - 1) + 1} = \dfrac{2x - 1}{2x}$, and the domain is $\{x \mid x \neq 0\} = (-\infty, 0) \cup (0, \infty)$.

$(g \circ f)(x) = g\left(\dfrac{x}{x + 1}\right) = 2\left(\dfrac{x}{x + 1}\right) - 1 = \dfrac{2x}{x + 1} - 1$, and the domain is $\{x \mid x \neq -1\} = (-\infty, -1) \cup (-1, \infty)$

$(f \circ f)(x) = f\left(\dfrac{x}{x + 1}\right) = \dfrac{\dfrac{x}{x + 1}}{\dfrac{x}{x + 1} + 1} = \dfrac{x}{x + 1} \cdot \dfrac{x + 1}{x + 1} = \dfrac{x}{x + x + 1} = \dfrac{x}{2x + 1}$. $(f \circ f)(x)$ is defined whenever

both $f(x)$ and $f(f(x))$ are defined; that is, whenever $x \neq -1$ and $2x + 1 \neq 0 \quad \Rightarrow \quad x \neq -\frac{1}{2}$, which is

$(-\infty, -1) \cup \left(-1, -\frac{1}{2}\right) \cup \left(-\frac{1}{2}, \infty\right)$.

$(g \circ g)(x) = g(2x - 1) = 2(2x - 1) - 1 = 4x - 2 - 1 = 4x - 3$, and the domain is $(-\infty, \infty)$.

38. $f(x) = \dfrac{1}{\sqrt{x}}$ has domain $\{x \mid x > 0\}$; $g(x) = x^2 - 4x$ has domain $(-\infty, \infty)$.

$(f \circ g)(x) = f(x^2 - 4x) = \dfrac{1}{\sqrt{x^2 - 4x}}$. $(f \circ g)(x)$ is defined whenever $0 < x^2 - 4x = x(x - 4)$. The product of two

numbers is positive either when both numbers are negative or when both numbers are positive. So the domain of $f \circ g$ is

$\{x \mid x < 0 \text{ and } x < 4\} \cup \{x \mid x > 0 \text{ and } x > 4\}$ which is $(-\infty, 0) \cup (4, \infty)$.

$(g \circ f)(x) = g\left(\dfrac{1}{\sqrt{x}}\right) = \left(\dfrac{1}{\sqrt{x}}\right)^2 - 4\left(\dfrac{1}{\sqrt{x}}\right) = \dfrac{1}{x} - \dfrac{4}{\sqrt{x}}$. $(g \circ f)(x)$ is defined whenever both $f(x)$ and $g(f(x))$

are defined, that is, whenever $x > 0$. So the domain of $g \circ f$ is $(0, \infty)$.

$(f \circ f)(x) = f\left(\dfrac{1}{\sqrt{x}}\right) = \dfrac{1}{\sqrt{\dfrac{1}{\sqrt{x}}}} = x^{1/4}$. $(f \circ f)(x)$ is defined whenever both $f(x)$ and $f(f(x))$ are defined, that is,

whenever $x > 0$. So the domain of $f \circ f$ is $(0, \infty)$.

$(g \circ g)(x) = g(x^2 - 4x) = (x^2 - 4x)^2 - 4(x^2 - 4x) = x^4 - 8x^3 + 16x^2 - 4x^2 + 16x = x^4 - 8x^3 + 12x^2 + 16x$,

and the domain is $(-\infty, \infty)$.

39. $f(x) = \sqrt[3]{x}$, has domain $(-\infty, \infty)$; $g(x) = \sqrt[4]{x}$, has domain $[0, \infty)$.

$(f \circ g)(x) = f(\sqrt[4]{x}) = \sqrt[3]{\sqrt[4]{x}} = \sqrt[12]{x}$. $(f \circ g)(x)$ is defined whenever both $g(x)$ and $f(g(x))$ are defined. Since $f(x)$

has no restriction, the domain is $[0, \infty)$.

$(g \circ f)(x) = g(\sqrt[3]{x}) = \sqrt[4]{\sqrt[3]{x}} = \sqrt[12]{x}$. $(g \circ f)(x)$ is defined whenever both $f(x)$ and $g(f(x))$ are defined; that is,

whenever $x \geq 0$. So the domain is $[0, \infty)$.

$(f \circ f)(x) = f(\sqrt[3]{x}) = \sqrt[3]{\sqrt[3]{x}} = \sqrt[9]{x}$. $(f \circ f)(x)$ is defined whenever both $f(x)$ and $f(f(x))$ are defined. Since $f(x)$

is defined everywhere, the domain is $(-\infty, \infty)$.

$(g \circ g)(x) = g(\sqrt[4]{x}) = \sqrt[4]{\sqrt[4]{x}} = \sqrt[16]{x}$. $(g \circ g)(x)$ is defined whenever both $g(x)$ and $g(g(x))$ are defined; that is,

whenever $x \geq 0$. So the domain is $[0, \infty)$.

40. $f(x) = \dfrac{2}{x}$ has domain $\{x \mid x \neq 0\}$ $g(x) = \dfrac{x}{x+2}$ has domain $\{x \mid x \neq -2\}$.

$(f \circ g)(x) = f\left(\dfrac{x}{x+2}\right) = \dfrac{2}{\dfrac{x}{x+2}} = \dfrac{2x+4}{x}$. $(f \circ g)(x)$ is defined whenever both $g(x)$ and $f(g(x))$ are defined; that

is, whenever $x \neq 0$ and $x \neq -2$. So the domain is $\{x \mid x \neq 0, -2\}$.

$(g \circ f)(x) = g\left(\dfrac{2}{x}\right) = \dfrac{\dfrac{2}{x}}{\dfrac{2}{x}+2} = \dfrac{2}{2+2x} = \dfrac{1}{1+x}$. $(g \circ f)(x)$ is defined whenever both $f(x)$ and $g(f(x))$ are

defined; that is, whenever $x \neq 0$ and $x \neq -1$. So the domain is $\{x \mid x \neq 0, -1\}$.

$(f \circ f)(x) = f\left(\dfrac{2}{x}\right) = \dfrac{2}{\dfrac{2}{x}} = x$. $(f \circ f)(x)$ is defined whenever both $f(x)$ and $f(f(x))$ are defined; that is, whenever

$x \neq 0$. So the domain is $\{x \mid x \neq 0\}$.

$(g \circ g)(x) = g\left(\dfrac{x}{x+2}\right) = \dfrac{\dfrac{x}{x+2}}{\dfrac{x}{x+2}+2} = \dfrac{x}{x+2(x+2)} = \dfrac{x}{3x+4}$. $(g \circ g)(x)$ is defined whenever both $g(x)$ and

$g(g(x))$ are defined; that is whenever $x \neq -2$ and $x \neq -\frac{4}{3}$. So the domain is $\{x \mid x \neq -2, -\frac{4}{3}\}$.

41. $(f \circ g \circ h)(x) = f(g(h(x))) = f(g(x-1)) = f(\sqrt{x-1}) = \sqrt{x-1} - 1$

42. $(g \circ h)(x) = g(x^2 + 2) = (x^2 + 2)^3 = x^6 + 6x^4 + 12x^2 + 8$.

$(f \circ g \circ h)(x) = f(x^6 + 6x^4 + 12x^2 + 8) = \dfrac{1}{x^6 + 6x^4 + 12x^2 + 8}$.

43. $(f \circ g \circ h)(x) = f(g(h(x))) = f(g(\sqrt{x})) = f(\sqrt{x} - 5) = (\sqrt{x} - 5)^4 + 1$

44. $(g \circ h)(x) = g(\sqrt[3]{x}) = \dfrac{\sqrt[3]{x}}{\sqrt[3]{x}-1}$. $(f \circ g \circ h)(x) = f\left(\dfrac{\sqrt[3]{x}}{\sqrt[3]{x}-1}\right) = \sqrt{\dfrac{\sqrt[3]{x}}{\sqrt[3]{x}-1}}$.

45. $F(x) = (x-9)^5$. Let $f(x) = x^5$ and $g(x) = x - 9$, then $F(x) = (f \circ g)(x)$.

46. $F(x) = \sqrt{x} + 1$. If $f(x) = x + 1$ and $g(x) = \sqrt{x}$, then $F(x) = (f \circ g)(x)$.

47. $G(x) = \dfrac{x^2}{x^2 + 4}$. Let $f(x) = \dfrac{x}{x+4}$ and $g(x) = x^2$, then $G(x) = (f \circ g)(x)$.

48. $G(x) = \dfrac{1}{x+3}$. If $f(x) = \dfrac{1}{x}$ and $g(x) = x + 3$, then $G(x) = (f \circ g)(x)$.

49. $H(x) = |1 - x^3|$. Let $f(x) = |x|$ and $g(x) = 1 - x^3$, then $H(x) = (f \circ g)(x)$. For Exercises 51 and 53 there are several possible solutions, only one of which is shown.

50. $H(x) = \sqrt{1 + \sqrt{x}}$. If $f(x) = \sqrt{1+x}$ and $g(x) = \sqrt{x}$, then $H(x) = (f \circ g)(x)$. For Exercises 52 and 54 there are several possible solutions only one of which is shown.

51. $F(x) = \dfrac{1}{x^2 + 1}$. Let $f(x) = \dfrac{1}{x}$, $g(x) = x + 1$, and $h(x) = x^2$, then $F(x) = (f \circ g \circ h)(x)$.

52. $F(x) = \sqrt[3]{\sqrt{x} - 1}$. If $g(x) = x - 1$ and $h(x) = \sqrt{x}$, then $(g \circ h)(x) = \sqrt{x} - 1$, and if $f(x) = \sqrt[3]{x}$, then $F(x) = (f \circ g \circ h)(x)$.

53. $G(x) = (4 + \sqrt[3]{x})^9$. Let $f(x) = x^9$, $g(x) = 4 + x$, and $h(x) = \sqrt[3]{x}$, then $G(x) = (f \circ g \circ h)(x)$.

54. $G(x) = \dfrac{2}{(3 + \sqrt{x})^2}$. If $g(x) = 3 + x$ and $h(x) = \sqrt{x}$, then $(g \circ h)(x) = 3 + \sqrt{x}$, and if $f(x) = \dfrac{2}{x^2}$, then $G(x) = (f \circ g \circ h)(x)$.

55. The price per sticker is $0.15 - 0.000002x$ and the number sold is x, so the revenue is

$R(x) = (0.15 - 0.000002x)x = 0.15x - 0.000002x^2$.

56. As found in Exercise 55, the revenue is $R(x) = 0.15x - 0.000002x^2$, and the cost is $0.095x - 0.0000005x^2$, so the profit is $P(x) = 0.15x - 0.000002x^2 - (0.095x - 0.0000005x^2) = 0.055x - 0.0000015x^2$.

57. (a) Since the ripple travels at a speed of 60 cm/s, the distance traveled in t seconds is the radius, so $g(t) = 60t$.

(b) The area of a circle is πr^2, so $f(r) = \pi r^2$.

(c) $f \circ g = \pi (g(t))^2 = \pi (60t)^2 = 3600\pi t^2$ cm^2. This function represents the area of the ripple as a function of time.

58. (a) Let $f(t)$ be the radius of the spherical balloon in centimeters. Since the radius is increasing at a rate of 1 cm/s, the radius is $f(t) = t$ after t seconds.

(b) The volume of the balloon can be written as $g(r) = \frac{4}{3}\pi r^3$.

(c) $g \circ f = \frac{4}{3}\pi (t)^3 = \frac{4}{3}\pi t^3$. $g \circ f$ represents the volume as a function of time.

59. Let r be the radius of the spherical balloon in centimeters. Since the radius is increasing at a rate of 2 cm/s, the radius is $r = 2t$ after t seconds. Therefore, the surface area of the balloon can be written as $S = 4\pi r^2 = 4\pi (2t)^2 = 4\pi (4t^2) = 16\pi t^2$.

60. (a) $f(x) = 0.80x$

(b) $g(x) = x - 50$

(c) $f \circ g = f(x - 50) = 0.80(x - 50) = 0.80x - 40$. $f \circ g$ represents applying the $50 coupon, then the 20% discount. $g \circ f = g(0.80x) = 0.80x - 50$. $g \circ f$ represents applying the 20% discount, then the $50 coupon. So applying the 20% discount, then the $50 coupon gives the lower price.

61. (a) $f(x) = 0.90x$

(b) $g(x) = x - 100$

(c) $f \circ g = f(x - 100) = 0.90(x - 100) = 0.90x - 90$. $f \circ g$ represents applying the $100 coupon, then the 10% discount. $g \circ f = g(0.90x) = 0.90x - 100$. $g \circ f$ represents applying the 10% discount, then the $100 coupon. So applying the 10% discount, then the $100 coupon gives the lower price.

62. Let t be the time since the plane flew over the radar station.

(a) Let s be the distance in miles between the plane and the radar station, and let d be the horizontal distance that the plane has flown. Using the Pythagorean theorem, $s = f(d) = \sqrt{1 + d^2}$.

(b) Since distance=rate$\times$ time we have $d = g(t) = 350t$.

(c) $s(t) = (f \circ g)(t) = f(350t) = \sqrt{1 + (350t)^2} = \sqrt{1 + 122{,}500t^2}$.

63. $A(x) = 1.05x$. $(A \circ A)(x) = A(A(x)) = A(1.05x) = 1.05(1.05x) = (1.05)^2 x$.
$(A \circ A \circ A)(x) = A(A \circ A(x)) = A((1.05)^2 x) = 1.05[(1.05)^2 x] = (1.05)^3 x$.
$(A \circ A \circ A \circ A)(x) = A(A \circ A \circ A(x)) = A((1.05)^3 x) = 1.05[(1.05)^3 x] = (1.05)^4 x$. A represents the amount in the account after 1 year; $A \circ A$ represents the amount in the account after 2 years; $A \circ A \circ A$ represents the amount in the account after 3 years; and $A \circ A \circ A \circ A$ represents the amount in the account after 4 years. We can see that if we compose n copies of A, we get $(1.05)^n x$.

64. Yes. If $f(x) = m_1 x + b_1$ and $g(x) = m_2 x + b_2$, then
$(f \circ g)(x) = f(m_2 x + b_2) = m_1(m_2 x + b_2) + b_1 = m_1 m_2 x + m_1 b_2 + b_1$, which is a linear function, because it is of the form $y = mx + b$. The slope is $m_1 m_2$.

65. $g(x) = 2x + 1$ and $h(x) = 4x^2 + 4x + 7$.

Method 1: Notice that $(2x + 1)^2 = 4x^2 + 4x + 1$. We see that adding 6 to this quantity gives $(2x + 1)^2 + 6 = 4x^2 + 4x + 1 + 6 = 4x^2 + 4x + 7$, which is $h(x)$. So let $f(x) = x^2 + 6$, and we have $(f \circ g)(x) = (2x + 1)^2 + 6 = h(x)$.

Method 2: Since $g(x)$ is linear and $h(x)$ is a second degree polynomial, $f(x)$ must be a second degree polynomial, that is, $f(x) = ax^2 + bx + c$ for some a, b, and c. Thus $f(g(x)) = f(2x + 1) = a(2x + 1)^2 + b(2x + 1) + c$ $\Leftrightarrow$ $4ax^2 + 4ax + a + 2bx + b + c = 4ax^2 + (4a + 2b)x + (a + b + c) = 4x^2 + 4x + 7$. Comparing this with $f(g(x))$, we have $4a = 4$ (the x^2 coefficients), $4a + 2b = 4$ (the x coefficients), and $a + b + c = 7$ (the constant terms) $\Leftrightarrow$ $a = 1$ and $2a + b = 2$ and $a + b + c = 7$ $\Leftrightarrow$ $a = 1, b = 0, c = 6$. Thus $f(x) = x^2 + 6$.

$f(x) = 3x + 5$ and $h(x) = 3x^2 + 3x + 2$.

Note since $f(x)$ is linear and $h(x)$ is quadratic, $g(x)$ must also be quadratic. We can then use trial and error to find $g(x)$. Another method is the following: We wish to find g so that $(f \circ g)(x) = h(x)$. Thus $f(g(x)) = 3x^2 + 3x + 2$ $\Leftrightarrow$ $3(g(x)) + 5 = 3x^2 + 3x + 2$ $\Leftrightarrow$ $3(g(x)) = 3x^2 + 3x - 3$ $\Leftrightarrow$ $g(x) = x^2 + x - 1$.

66. If $g(x)$ is even, then $h(-x) = f(g(-x)) = f(g(x)) = h(x)$. So yes, h is always an even function.

If $g(x)$ is odd, then h is not necessarily an odd function. For example, if we let $f(x) = x - 1$ and $g(x) = x^3$, g is an odd function, but $h(x) = (f \circ g)(x) = f(x^3) = x^3 - 1$ is not an odd function.

If $g(x)$ is odd and f is also odd, then $h(-x) = (f \circ g)(-x) = f(g(-x)) = f(-g(x)) = -f(g(x)) = -(f \circ g)(x) = -h(x)$. So in this case, h is also an odd function.

If $g(x)$ is odd and f is even, then $h(-x) = (f \circ g)(-x) = f(g(-x)) = f(-g(x)) = f(g(x)) = (f \circ g)(x) = h(x)$, so in this case, h is an even function.

2.8   One-to-One Functions and Their Inverses

1. By the Horizontal Line Test, f is not one-to-one.

2. By the Horizontal Line Test, f is one-to-one.

3. By the Horizontal Line Test, f is one-to-one.

4. By the Horizontal Line Test, f is not one-to-one.

5. By the Horizontal Line Test, f is not one-to-one.

6. By the Horizontal Line Test, f is one-to-one.

7. $f(x) = -2x + 4$. If $x_1 \neq x_2$, then $-2x_1 \neq -2x_2$ and $-2x_1 + 4 \neq -2x_2 + 4$. So f is a one-to-one function.

8. $f(x) = 3x - 2$. If $x_1 \neq x_2$, then $3x_1 \neq 3x_2$ and $3x_1 - 2 \neq 3x_2 - 2$. So f is a one-to-one function.

9. $g(x) = \sqrt{x}$. If $x_1 \neq x_2$, then $\sqrt{x_1} \neq \sqrt{x_2}$ because two different numbers cannot have the same square root. Therefore, g is a one-to-one function.

10. $g(x) = |x|$. Since every number and its negative have the same absolute value, that is, $|-1| = 1 = |1|$, g is not a one-to-one function.

11. $h(x) = x^2 - 2x$. Since $h(0) = 0$ and $h(2) = (2) - 2(2) = 0$ we have $h(0) = h(2)$. So f is not a one-to-one function.

12. $h(x) = x^3 + 8$. If $x_1 \neq x_2$, then $x_1^3 \neq x_2^3$ and $x_1^3 + 8 \neq x_2^3 + 8$. So f is a one-to-one function.

13. $f(x) = x^4 + 5$. Every nonzero number and its negative have the same fourth power. For example, $(-1)^4 = 1 = (1)^4$, so $f(-1) = f(1)$. Thus f is not a one-to-one function.

14. $f(x) = x^4 + 5$, $0 \leq x \leq 2$. If $x_1 \neq x_2$, then $x_1^4 \neq x_2^4$ because two different positive numbers cannot have the same fourth power. Thus, $x_1^4 + 5 \neq x_2^4 + 5$. So f is a one-to-one function.

15. $f(x) = \dfrac{1}{x^2}$. Every nonzero number and its negative have the same square. For example, $\dfrac{1}{(-1)^2} = 1 = \dfrac{1}{(1)^2}$, so $f(-1) = f(1)$. Thus f is not a one-to-one function.

16. $f(x) = \dfrac{1}{x}$. If $x_1 \neq x_2$, then $\dfrac{1}{x_1} \neq \dfrac{1}{x_2}$. So f is a one-to-one function.

17. (a) $f(2) = 7$. Since f is one-to-one, $f^{-1}(7) = 2$.

   (b) $f^{-1}(3) = -1$. Since f is one-to-one, $f(-1) = 3$.

18. (a) $f(5) = 18$. Since f is one-to-one, $f^{-1}(18) = 5$.

   (b) $f^{-1}(4) = 2$. Since f is one-to-one, $f(2) = 4$.

19. $f(x) = 5 - 2x$. Since f is one-to-one and $f(1) = 5 - 2(1) = 3$, then $f^{-1}(3) = 1$. (Find 1 by solving the equation $5 - 2x = 3$.)

20. To find $g^{-1}(5)$, we find the x value such that $g(x) = 5$; that is, we solve the equation $g(x) = x^2 + 4x = 5$. Now
$x^2 + 4x = 5 \quad \Leftrightarrow \quad x^2 + 4x - 5 = 0 \quad \Leftrightarrow \quad (x-1)(x+5) = 0 \quad \Leftrightarrow \quad x = 1 \text{ or } x = -5$. Since the domain of g is $[-2, \infty)$, $x = 1$ is the only value where $g(x) = 5$. Therefore, $g^{-1}(5) = 1$.

21. $f(g(x)) = f(x+6) = (x+6) - 6 = x$ for all x.

$g(f(x)) = g(x-6) = (x-6) + 6 = x$ for all x. Thus f and g are inverses of each other.

22. $f(g(x)) = f\left(\dfrac{x}{3}\right) = 3\left(\dfrac{x}{3}\right) = x$ for all x.

$g(f(x)) = g(3x) = \dfrac{3x}{3} = x$ for all x. Thus f and g are inverses of each other.

23. $f(g(x)) = f\left(\dfrac{x+5}{2}\right) = 2\left(\dfrac{x+5}{2}\right) - 5 = x + 5 - 5 = x$ for all x.

$g(f(x)) = g(2x - 5) = \dfrac{(2x-5) + 5}{2} = x$ for all x. Thus f and g are inverses of each other.

24. $f(g(x)) = f(3 - 4x) = \dfrac{3 - (3 - 4x)}{4} = \dfrac{3 - 3 + 4x}{4} = x$ for all x.

$g(f(x)) = g\left(\dfrac{3-x}{4}\right) = 3 - 4\left(\dfrac{3-x}{4}\right) = 3 - 3 + x = x$ for all x. Thus f and g are inverses of each other.

25. $f(g(x)) = f\left(\dfrac{1}{x}\right) = \dfrac{1}{1/x} = x$ for all x. Since $f(x) = g(x)$, we also have $g(f(x)) = x$. Thus f and g are inverses of each other.

26. $f(g(x)) = f(\sqrt[5]{x}) = (\sqrt[5]{x})^5 = x$ for all x.

$g(f(x)) = g(x^5) = \sqrt[5]{x^5} = x$ for all x. Thus f and g are inverses of each other.

27. $f(g(x)) = f(\sqrt{x+4}) = (\sqrt{x+4})^2 - 4 = x + 4 - 4 = x$ for all $x \geq -4$.

$g(f(x)) = g(x^2 - 4) = \sqrt{(x^2 - 4) + 4} = \sqrt{x^2} = x$ for all $x \geq 0$. Thus f and g are inverses of each other.

28. $f(g(x)) = f\left((x-1)^{1/3}\right) = \left((x-1)^{1/3}\right)^3 + 1 = x - 1 + 1 = x$ for all x.

$g(f(x)) = g(x^3 + 1) = \left[(x-1)^{1/3}\right]^3 + 1 = x - 1 + 1 = x$ for all x. Thus f and g are inverses of each other.

29. $f(g(x)) = f\left(\dfrac{1}{x} + 1\right) = \dfrac{1}{\left(\dfrac{1}{x} + 1\right) - 1} = x$ for all $x \neq 0$.

$g(f(x)) = g\left(\dfrac{1}{x-1}\right) = \dfrac{1}{\left(\dfrac{1}{x-1}\right)} + 1 = (x - 1) + 1 = x$ for all $x \neq 1$. Thus f and g are inverses of each other.

30. $f(g(x)) = f(\sqrt{4 - x^2}) = \sqrt{4 - (\sqrt{4 - x^2})^2} = \sqrt{4 - 4 + x^2} = \sqrt{x^2} = x$, for all $0 \leq x \leq 2$. (Note that the last equality is possible since $x \geq 0$.)

$g(f(x)) = g(\sqrt{4 - x^2}) = \sqrt{4 - (\sqrt{4 - x^2})^2} = \sqrt{4 - 4 + x^2} = \sqrt{x^2} = x$, for all $0 \leq x \leq 2$. (Again, the last equality is possible since $x \geq 0$.) Thus f and g are inverses of each other.

31. $f(x) = 2x + 1$. $y = 2x + 1$ $\Leftrightarrow$ $2x = y - 1$ $\Leftrightarrow$ $x = \frac{1}{2}(y - 1)$. So $f^{-1}(x) = \frac{1}{2}(x - 1)$.

32. $f(x) = 6 - x$. $y = 6 - x$ $\Leftrightarrow$ $x = 6 - y$. So $f^{-1}(x) = 6 - x$.

33. $f(x) = 4x + 7$. $y = 4x + 7$ $\Leftrightarrow$ $4x = y - 7$ $\Leftrightarrow$ $x = \frac{1}{4}(y - 7)$. So $f^{-1}(x) = \frac{1}{4}(x - 7)$.

34. $f(x) = 3 - 5x$. $y = 3 - 5x$ $\Leftrightarrow$ $-5x = y - 3$ $\Leftrightarrow$ $x = -\frac{1}{5}(y - 3) = \frac{1}{5}(3 - y)$. So $f^{-1}(x) = \frac{1}{5}(3 - x)$.

35. $f(x) = \frac{x}{2}$. $y = \frac{x}{2}$ $\Leftrightarrow$ $x = 2y$. So $f^{-1}(x) = 2x$.

36. $f(x) = \frac{1}{x^2}$, $x > 0$. Since the function f is restricted to positive values, f is one-to-one. So $y = \frac{1}{x^2}$ $\Leftrightarrow$ $\sqrt{y} = \frac{1}{x}$

$\Leftrightarrow$ $x = \frac{1}{\sqrt{y}}$. Thus $f^{-1}(x) = \frac{1}{\sqrt{x}}$, $x > 0$.

37. $f(x) = \frac{1}{x + 2}$. $y = \frac{1}{x + 2}$ $\Leftrightarrow$ $x + 2 = \frac{1}{y}$ $\Leftrightarrow$ $x = \frac{1}{y} - 2$. So $f^{-1}(x) = \frac{1}{x} - 2$.

38. $f(x) = \frac{x - 2}{x + 2}$. $y = \frac{x - 2}{x + 2}$ $\Leftrightarrow$ $y(x + 2) = x - 2$ $\Leftrightarrow$ $xy + 2y = x - 2$ $\Leftrightarrow$ $xy - x = -2 - 2y$ $\Leftrightarrow$

$x(y - 1) = -2(y + 1)$ $\Leftrightarrow$ $x = \frac{-2(y + 1)}{y - 1}$. So $f^{-1}(x) = \frac{-2(x + 1)}{x - 1}$.

39. $f(x) = \frac{1 + 3x}{5 - 2x}$. $y = \frac{1 + 3x}{5 - 2x}$ $\Leftrightarrow$ $y(5 - 2x) = 1 + 3x$ $\Leftrightarrow$ $5y - 2xy = 1 + 3x$ $\Leftrightarrow$ $3x + 2xy = 5y - 1$

$\Leftrightarrow$ $x(3 + 2y) = 5y - 1$ $\Leftrightarrow$ $x = \frac{5y - 1}{2y + 3}$. So $f^{-1}(x) = \frac{5x - 1}{2x + 3}$.

40. $f(x) = 5 - 4x^3$. $y = 5 - 4x^3$ $\Leftrightarrow$ $4x^3 = 5 - y$ $\Leftrightarrow$ $x^3 = \frac{1}{4}(5 - y)$ $\Leftrightarrow$ $x = \sqrt[3]{\frac{1}{4}(5 - y)}$. So

$f^{-1}(x) = \sqrt[3]{\frac{1}{4}(5 - x)}$.

41. $f(x) = \sqrt{2 + 5x}$, $x \geq -\frac{2}{5}$. $y = \sqrt{2 + 5x}$, $y \geq 0$ $\Leftrightarrow$ $y^2 = 2 + 5x$ $\Leftrightarrow$ $5x = y^2 - 2$ $\Leftrightarrow$ $x = \frac{1}{5}(y^2 - 2)$
and $y \geq 0$. So $f^{-1}(x) = \frac{1}{5}(x^2 - 2)$, $x \geq 0$.

42. $f(x) = x^2 + x = \left(x^2 + x + \frac{1}{4}\right) - \frac{1}{4} = \left(x + \frac{1}{2}\right)^2 - \frac{1}{4}$, $x \geq -\frac{1}{2}$. $y = \left(x + \frac{1}{2}\right)^2 - \frac{1}{4}$ $\Leftrightarrow$ $\left(x + \frac{1}{2}\right)^2 = y + \frac{1}{4}$ $\Leftrightarrow$

$x + \frac{1}{2} = \sqrt{y + \frac{1}{4}}$ $\Leftrightarrow$ $x = \sqrt{y + \frac{1}{4}} - \frac{1}{2}$, $y \geq -\frac{1}{4}$. So $f^{-1}(x) = \sqrt{x + \frac{1}{4}} - \frac{1}{2}$, $x \geq -\frac{1}{4}$. (Note that $x \geq -\frac{1}{2}$, so that

$x + \frac{1}{2} \geq 0$, and hence $\left(x + \frac{1}{2}\right)^2 = y + \frac{1}{4}$ $\Leftrightarrow$ $x + \frac{1}{2} = \sqrt{y + \frac{1}{4}}$. Also, since $x \geq -\frac{1}{2}$, $y = \left(x + \frac{1}{2}\right)^2 - \frac{1}{4} \geq -\frac{1}{4}$ so

that $y + \frac{1}{4} \geq 0$, and hence $\sqrt{y + \frac{1}{4}}$ is defined.)

43. $f(x) = 4 - x^2$, $x \geq 0$. $y = 4 - x^2$ $\Leftrightarrow$ $x^2 = 4 - y$ $\Leftrightarrow$ $x = \sqrt{4 - y}$. So $f^{-1}(x) = \sqrt{4 - x}$. Note: $x \geq 0$ $\Rightarrow$
$f(x) \leq 4$.

44. $f(x) = \sqrt{2x - 1}$. $y = \sqrt{2x - 1}$ $\Leftrightarrow$ $2x - 1 = y^2$ $\Leftrightarrow$ $x = \frac{1}{2}(y^2 + 1)$. Since the range of f is $f(x) \geq 0$ so
$f^{-1}(x) = \frac{1}{2}(x^2 + 1)$ for $x \geq 0$.

45. $f(x) = 4 + \sqrt[3]{x}$. $y = 4 + \sqrt[3]{x}$ $\Leftrightarrow$ $\sqrt[3]{x} = y - 4$ $\Leftrightarrow$ $x = (y - 4)^3$. So $f^{-1}(x) = (x - 4)^3$.

46. $f(x) = \left(2 - x^3\right)^5$. $y = \left(2 - x^3\right)^5$ $\Leftrightarrow$ $2 - x^3 = \sqrt[5]{y}$ $\Leftrightarrow$ $x^3 = 2 - \sqrt[5]{y}$ $\Leftrightarrow$ $x = \sqrt[3]{2 - \sqrt[5]{y}}$. So
$f^{-1}(x) = \sqrt[3]{2 - \sqrt[5]{x}}$.

47. $f(x) = 1 + \sqrt{1 + x}$. $y = 1 + \sqrt{1 + x}$, $y \geq 1$ $\Leftrightarrow$ $\sqrt{1 + x} = y - 1$ $\Leftrightarrow$ $1 + x = (y - 1)^2$
$\Leftrightarrow x = (y - 1)^2 - 1 = y^2 - 2y$. So $f^{-1}(x) = x^2 - 2x$, $x \geq 1$.

48. $f(x) = \sqrt{9 - x^2}$, $0 \leq x \leq 3$. $y = \sqrt{9 - x^2}$ $\Leftrightarrow$ $y^2 = 9 - x^2$ $\Leftrightarrow$ $x^2 = 9 - y^2$ $\Rightarrow$ $x = \sqrt{9 - y^2}$ (since we
must have $x \geq 0$). So $f^{-1}(x) = \sqrt{9 - x^2}$, $0 \leq x \leq 3$.

49. $f(x) = x^4$, $x \geq 0$. $y = x^4$, $y \geq 0$ $\Leftrightarrow$ $x = \sqrt[4]{y}$. So $f^{-1}(x) = \sqrt[4]{x}$, $x \geq 0$.

50. $f(x) = 1 - x^3$. $y = 1 - x^3$ $\Leftrightarrow$ $x^3 = 1 - y$ $\Leftrightarrow$ $x = \sqrt[3]{1 - y}$. So $f^{-1}(x) = \sqrt[3]{1 - x}$.

51. (a), (b) $f(x) = 3x - 6$

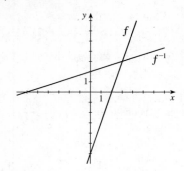

(c) $f(x) = 3x - 6$. $y = 3x - 6$ $\Leftrightarrow$

$3x = y + 6$ $\Leftrightarrow$ $x = \frac{1}{3}(y + 6)$. So

$f^{-1}(x) = \frac{1}{3}(x + 6)$.

52. (a), (b) $f(x) = 16 - x^2$, $x \geq 0$

(c) $f(x) = 16 - x^2$, $x \geq 0$. $y = 16 - x^2$ $\Leftrightarrow$

$x^2 = 16 - y$ $\Leftrightarrow$ $x = \sqrt{16 - y}$. So

$f^{-1}(x) = \sqrt{16 - x}$, $x \leq 16$. (*Note:* $x \geq 0$

$\Rightarrow$ $f(x) = 16 - x^2 \leq 16$.)

53. (a), (b) $f(x) = \sqrt{x + 1}$

(c) $f(x) = \sqrt{x + 1}$, $x \geq -1$.

$y = \sqrt{x + 1}$, $y \geq 0$ $\Leftrightarrow$ $y^2 = x + 1$ $\Leftrightarrow$

$x = y^2 - 1$ and $y \geq 0$. So $f^{-1}(x) = x^2 - 1$,

$x \geq 0$.

54. (a), (b) $f(x) = x^3 - 1$

(c) $f(x) = x^3 - 1$ $\Leftrightarrow$ $y = x^3 - 1$ $\Leftrightarrow$

$x^3 = y + 1$ $\Leftrightarrow$ $x = \sqrt[3]{y + 1}$. So

$f^{-1}(x) = \sqrt[3]{x + 1}$.

55. $f(x) = x^3 - x$. Using a graphing device and the Horizontal Line Test, we see that f is not a one-to-one function. For example, $f(0) = 0 = f(-1)$.

56. $f(x) = x^3 + x$. Using a graphing device and the Horizontal Line Test, we see that f is a one-to-one function.

57. $f(x) = \dfrac{x+12}{x-6}$. Using a graphing device and the Horizontal Line Test, we see that f is a one-to-one function.

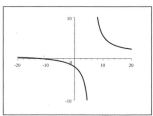

58. $f(x) = \sqrt{x^3 - 4x + 1}$. Using a graphing device and the Horizontal Line Test, we see that f is not a one-to-one function. For example, $f(0) = 1 = f(2)$.

59. $f(x) = |x| - |x-6|$. Using a graphing device and the Horizontal Line Test, we see that f is not a one-to-one function. For example $f(0) = -6 = f(-2)$.

60. $f(x) = x \cdot |x|$. Using a graphing device and the Horizontal Line Test, we see that f is a one-to-one function.

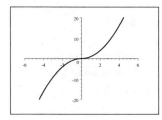

61. (a) $y = f(x) = 2 + x \quad \Leftrightarrow \quad x = y - 2$. So $f^{-1}(x) = x - 2$.

(b)

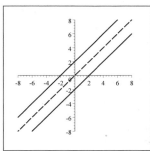

62. (a) $y = f(x) = 2 - \frac{1}{2}x \quad \Leftrightarrow \quad \frac{1}{2}x = 2 - y \quad \Leftrightarrow$ $x = 4 - 2y$. So $f^{-1}(x) = 4 - 2x$.

(b)

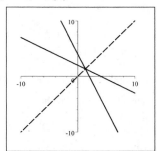

63. (a) $y = g(x) = \sqrt{x+3}, y \ge 0 \quad \Leftrightarrow \quad x + 3 = y^2,$ $y \ge 0 \quad \Leftrightarrow \quad x = y^2 - 3, y \ge 0$. So $g^{-1}(x) = x^2 - 3, x \ge 0$.

(b)

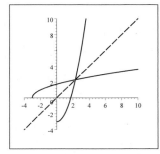

64. (a) $y = g(x) = x^2 + 1, x \ge 0 \quad \Leftrightarrow \quad x^2 = y - 1,$ $x \ge 0 \quad \Leftrightarrow \quad x = \sqrt{y-1}$. So $g^{-1}(x) = \sqrt{x-1}$.

(b)

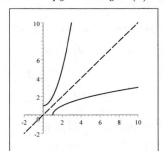

65. If we restrict the domain of $f(x)$ to $[0, \infty)$, then $y = 4 - x^2$ $\Leftrightarrow$ $x^2 = 4 - y$ $\Rightarrow$ $x = \sqrt{4 - y}$ (since $x \geq 0$, we take the positive square root). So $f^{-1}(x) = \sqrt{4 - x}$.

If we restrict the domain of $f(x)$ to $(-\infty, 0]$, then $y = 4 - x^2$ $\Leftrightarrow$ $x^2 = 4 - y$ $\Rightarrow$ $x = -\sqrt{4 - y}$ (since $x \leq 0$, we take the negative square root). So $f^{-1}(x) = -\sqrt{4 - x}$.

66. If we restrict the domain of $g(x)$ to $[1, \infty)$, then $y = (x - 1)^2$ $\Rightarrow$ $x - 1 = \sqrt{y}$ (since $x \geq 1$ we take the positive square root) $\Leftrightarrow x = 1 + \sqrt{y}$. So $g^{-1}(x) = 1 + \sqrt{x}$.

If we restrict the domain of $g(x)$ to $(-\infty, 1]$, then $y = (x - 1)^2$ $\Rightarrow$ $x - 1 = -\sqrt{y}$ (since $x \leq 1$ we take the negative square root) $\Leftrightarrow x = 1 - \sqrt{y}$. So $g^{-1}(x) = 1 - \sqrt{x}$.

67. If we restrict the domain of $h(x)$ to $[-2, \infty)$, then $y = (x + 2)^2$ $\Rightarrow$ $x + 2 = \sqrt{y}$ (since $x \geq -2$, we take the positive square root) $\Leftrightarrow x = -2 + \sqrt{y}$. So $h^{-1}(x) = -2 + \sqrt{x}$.

If we restrict the domain of $h(x)$ to $(-\infty, -2]$, then $y = (x + 2)^2$ $\Rightarrow$ $x + 2 = -\sqrt{y}$ (since $x \leq -2$, we take the negative square root) $\Leftrightarrow x = -2 - \sqrt{y}$. So $h^{-1}(x) = -2 - \sqrt{x}$.

68. $k(x) = |x - 3| = \begin{cases} -(x - 3) & \text{if } x - 3 < 0 \quad \Leftrightarrow \quad x < 3 \\ x - 3 & \text{if } x - 3 \geq 0 \quad \Leftrightarrow \quad x \geq 3 \end{cases}$

If we restrict the domain of $k(x)$ to $[3, \infty)$, then $y = x - 3$ $\Leftrightarrow$ $x = 3 + y$. So $k^{-1}(x) = 3 + x$.

If we restrict the domain of $k(x)$ to $(-\infty, 3]$, then $y = -(x - 3)$ $\Leftrightarrow$ $y = -x + 3$ $\Leftrightarrow$ $x = 3 - y$. So $k^{-1}(x) = 3 - x$.

69.

70.

71. (a) $f(x) = 500 + 80x$.

(b) $f(x) = 500 + 80x$. $y = 500 + 80x$ $\Leftrightarrow$ $80x = y - 500$ $\Leftrightarrow$ $x = \dfrac{y - 500}{80}$. So $f^{-1}(x) = \dfrac{x - 500}{80}$. f^{-1} represents the number of hours of investigation the investigate spends on a case for x dollars.

(c) $f^{-1}(1220) = \dfrac{1220 - 500}{80} = \dfrac{720}{80} = 9$. The investigator spent 9 hours investigating this case.

72. (a) $V(t) = 100\left(1 - \dfrac{t}{40}\right)^2$, $0 \leq t \leq 40$. $y = 100\left(1 - \dfrac{t}{40}\right)^2$ $\Leftrightarrow$ $\dfrac{y}{100} = \left(1 - \dfrac{t}{40}\right)^2$ $\Rightarrow$ $1 - \dfrac{t}{40} = \pm\sqrt{\dfrac{y}{100}}$ $\Leftrightarrow$ $\dfrac{t}{40} = 1 \pm \dfrac{\sqrt{y}}{10}$ $\Leftrightarrow$ $t = 40 \pm 4\sqrt{y}$. Since $t \leq 40$ we must have $V^{-1}(t) = 40 - 4\sqrt{t}$.

V^{-1} represents time that has elapsed since the tank started to leak.

(b) $V^{-1}(15) = 40 - 4\sqrt{15} \approx 24.5$ minutes. In 24.5 minutes the tank has drained to just 15 gallons of water.

73. (a) $v(r) = 18{,}500\,(0.25 - r^2)$. $t = 18{,}500\,(0.25 - r^2)$ $\Leftrightarrow$ $t = 4625 - 18{,}500r^2$ $\Leftrightarrow$ $18500r^2 = 4625 - t$ $\Leftrightarrow$ $r^2 = \dfrac{4625 - t}{18{,}500}$ $\Rightarrow$ $r = \pm\sqrt{\dfrac{4625 - t}{18{,}500}}$. Since r represents a distance, $r \geq 0$, so $v^{-1}(t) = \sqrt{\dfrac{4625 - t}{18{,}500}}$.

v^{-1} represents the radius in the vein that has the velocity v.

(b) $v^{-1}(30) = \sqrt{\dfrac{4625 - 30}{18{,}500}} \approx 0.498$ cm. The velocity is 30 at 0.498 cm from the center of the artery or vein.

74. (a) $D(p) = -3p + 150$. $y = -3p + 150$ $\Leftrightarrow$ $3p = 150 - y \Leftrightarrow p = 50 - \frac{1}{3}y$. So $D^{-1}(p) = 50 - \frac{1}{3}p$. D^{-1} represents the price that is associated with demand D.

(b) $D^{-1}(30) = 50 - \frac{1}{3}(30) = 40$. So when the demand is 30 units the price per unit is $40.

75. (a) $F(x) = \frac{9}{5}x + 32$. $y = \frac{9}{5}x + 32$ $\Leftrightarrow$ $\frac{9}{5}x = y - 32$ $\Leftrightarrow$ $x = \frac{5}{9}(y - 32)$. So $F^{-1}(x) = \frac{5}{9}(x - 32)$. F^{-1} represents the Celsius temperature that corresponds to the Fahrenheit temperature of F.

(b) $F^{-1}(86) = \frac{5}{9}(86 - 32) = \frac{5}{9}(54) = 30$. So $86°$ Fahrenheit is the same as $30°$ Celsius.

76. (a) $f(x) = 0.8159x$.

(b) $f(x) = 0.8159x$. $y = 0.8159x$ $\Leftrightarrow$ $x = 1.2256y$. So $f^{-1}(x) = 1.2256x$. f^{-1} represents the exchange rate from US dollars to Canadian dollars.

(c) $f^{-1}(12,250) = 1.2256(12,250) = 15,013.60$. So $12,250 in US currency is worth $15,013.60 in Canadian currency.

77. (a) $f(x) = \begin{cases} 0.1x, & \text{if } 0 \le x \le 20{,}000 \\ 2000 + 0.2(x - 20{,}000) & \text{if } x > 20{,}000 \end{cases}$

(b) We will find the inverse of each piece of the function f.

$f_1(x) = 0.1x$. $y = 0.1x$ $\Leftrightarrow$ $x = 10y$. So $f_1^{-1}(x) = 10x$.

$f_2(x) = 2000 + 0.2(x - 20{,}000) = 0.2x - 2000$. $y = 0.2x - 2000$ $\Leftrightarrow$ $0.2x = y + 2000$ $\Leftrightarrow$ $x = 5y + 10{,}000$. So $f_2^{-1}(x) = 5x + 10{,}000$.

Since $f(0) = 0$ and $f(20{,}000) = 2000$ we have $f^{-1}(x) = \begin{cases} 10x, & \text{if } 0 \le x \le 2000 \\ 5x + 10{,}000 & \text{if } x > 2000 \end{cases}$ It represents the taxpayer's income.

(b) $f^{-1}(10{,}000) = 5(10{,}000) + 10{,}000 = 60{,}000$. The required income is $60,000.

78. (a) $f(x) = 0.85x$.

(b) $g(x) = x - 1000$.

(c) $H = f \circ g = f(x - 1000) = 0.85(x - 1000) = 0.85x - 850$.

(d) $H(x) = 0.85x - 850$. $y = 0.85x - 850$ $\Leftrightarrow$ $0.85x = y + 850$ $\Leftrightarrow$ $x = 1.176y + 1000$. So $H^{-1}(x) = 1.176x + 1000$. The function H^{-1} represents the original sticker price for a given discounted price.

(e) $H^{-1}(13{,}000) = 1.176(13{,}000) + 1000 = 16{,}266$. So the original price of the car is $16,288 when the discounted price ($1000 rebate, then 15% off) is $13,000.

79. $f(x) = 7 + 2x$. $y = 7 + 2x$ $\Leftrightarrow$ $2x = y - 7$ $\Leftrightarrow$ $x = \dfrac{y - 7}{2}$. So $f^{-1}(x) = \dfrac{x - 7}{2}$. f^{-1} is the number of toppings on a pizza that costs x dollars.

80. $f(x) = mx + b$. Notice that $f(x_1) = f(x_2)$ $\Leftrightarrow$ $mx_1 + b = mx_2 + b$ $\Leftrightarrow$ $mx_1 = mx_2$. We can conclude that $x_1 = x_2$ if and only if $m \ne 0$. Therefore f is one-to-one if and only if $m \ne 0$. If $m \ne 0$, $f(x) = mx + b$ $\Leftrightarrow$ $y = mx + b$ $\Leftrightarrow$ $mx = y - b$ $\Leftrightarrow$ $x = \dfrac{y - b}{m}$. So, $f^{-1}(x) = \dfrac{x - b}{m}$.

81. (a) $f(x) = \dfrac{2x + 1}{5}$ is "multiply by 2, add 1, and then divide by 5". So the reverse is "multiply by 5, subtract 1, and then divide by 2" or $f^{-1}(x) = \dfrac{5x - 1}{2}$. Check: $f \circ f^{-1}(x) = f\left(\dfrac{5x - 1}{2}\right) = \dfrac{2\left(\dfrac{5x - 1}{2}\right) + 1}{5} = \dfrac{5x - 1 + 1}{5} = \dfrac{5x}{5} = x$

and $f^{-1} \circ f(x) = f^{-1}\left(\dfrac{2x + 1}{5}\right) = \dfrac{5\left(\dfrac{2x + 1}{5}\right) - 1}{2} = \dfrac{2x + 1 - 1}{2} = \dfrac{2x}{2} = x$.

(b) $f(x) = 3 - \dfrac{1}{x} = \dfrac{-1}{x} + 3$ is "take the negative reciprocal and add 3". Since the reverse of "take the negative reciprocal" is "take the negative reciprocal", $f^{-1}(x)$ is "subtract 3 and take the negative reciprocal", that is,

$f^{-1}(x) = \dfrac{-1}{x-3}$. Check: $f \circ f^{-1}(x) = f\left(\dfrac{-1}{x-3}\right) = 3 - \dfrac{1}{\frac{-1}{x-3}} = 3 - \left(1 \cdot \dfrac{x-3}{-1}\right) = 3 + x - 3 = x$ and

$f^{-1} \circ f(x) = f^{-1}\left(3 - \dfrac{1}{x}\right) = \dfrac{-1}{\left(3 - \frac{1}{x}\right) - 3} = \dfrac{-1}{-\frac{1}{x}} = -1 \cdot \dfrac{x}{-1} = x.$

(c) $f(x) = \sqrt{x^3 + 2}$ is "cube, add 2, and then take the square root". So the reverse is "square, subtract 2, then take the cube root" or $f^{-1}(x) = \sqrt[3]{x^2 - 2}$. Domain for $f(x)$ is $\left[-\sqrt[3]{2}, \infty\right)$; domain for $f^{-1}(x)$ is $[0, \infty)$. Check:

$f \circ f^{-1}(x) = f\left(\sqrt[3]{x^2 - 2}\right) = \sqrt{\left(\sqrt[3]{x^2 - 2}\right)^3 + 2} = \sqrt{x^2 - 2 + 2} = \sqrt{x^2} = x$ (on the appropriate domain) and

$f^{-1} \circ f(x) = f^{-1}\left(\sqrt{x^3 + 2}\right) = \sqrt[3]{\left(\sqrt{x^3 + 2}\right)^2 - 2} = \sqrt[3]{x^3 + 2 - 2} = \sqrt[3]{x^3} = x$ (on the appropriate domain).

(d) $f(x) = (2x - 5)^3$ is "double, subtract 5, and then cube". So the reverse is "take the cube root, add

5, and divide by 2" or $f^{-1}(x) = \dfrac{\sqrt[3]{x} + 5}{2}$ Domain for both $f(x)$ and $f^{-1}(x)$ is $(-\infty, \infty)$. Check:

$f \circ f^{-1}(x) = f\left(\dfrac{\sqrt[3]{x} + 5}{2}\right) = \left[2\left(\dfrac{\sqrt[3]{x} + 5}{2}\right) - 5\right]^3 = (\sqrt[3]{x} + 5 - 5)^3 = (\sqrt[3]{x})^3 = \sqrt[3]{x^3} = x$ and

$f^{-1} \circ f(x) = f^{-1}\left((2x - 5)^3\right) = \dfrac{\sqrt[x]{(2x-5)^3} + 5}{2} = \dfrac{(2x - 5) + 5}{2} = \dfrac{2x}{2} = x.$

In a function like $f(x) = 3x - 2$, the variable occurs only once and it easy to see how to reverse the operations step by step. But in $f(x) = x^3 + 2x + 6$, you apply two different operations to the variable x (cubing and multiplying by 2) and then add 6, so it is not possible to reverse the operations step by step.

82. $f(I(x)) = f(x)$; therefore $f \circ I = f$. $I(f(x)) = f(x)$; therefore $I \circ f = f$.

By definition, $f \circ f^{-1}(x) = x = I(x)$; therefore $f \circ f^{-1} = I$. Similarly, $f^{-1} \circ f(x) = x = I(x)$; therefore $f^{-1} \circ f = I$.

83. (a) We find $g^{-1}(x)$: $y = 2x + 1 \iff 2x = y - 1 \iff x = \frac{1}{2}(y - 1)$. So $g^{-1}(x) = \frac{1}{2}(x - 1)$. Thus

$f(x) = h \circ g^{-1}(x) = h\left(\frac{1}{2}(x - 1)\right) = 4\left[\frac{1}{2}(x - 1)\right]^2 + 4\left[\frac{1}{2}(x - 1)\right] + 7 = x^2 - 2x + 1 + 2x - 2 + 7 = x^2 + 6.$

(b) $f \circ g = h \iff f^{-1} \circ f \circ g = f^{-1} \circ h \iff I \circ g = f^{-1} \circ h \iff g = f^{-1} \circ h.$

Note that we compose with f^{-1} on the left on each side of the equation. We find f^{-1}:

$y = 3x + 5 \iff 3x = y - 5 \iff x = \dfrac{1}{3}(y - 5)$. So $f^{-1}(x) = \frac{1}{3}(x - 5)$. Thus

$g(x) = f^{-1} \circ h(x) = f^{-1}(3x^2 + 3x + 2) = \frac{1}{3}\left[(3x^2 + 3x + 2) - 5\right] = \frac{1}{3}\left[3x^2 + 3x - 3\right] = x^2 + x - 1.$

Chapter 2 Review

1. $f(x) = x^2 - 4x + 6$; $f(0) = (0)^2 - 4(0) + 6 = 6$; $f(2) = (2)^2 - 4(2) + 6 = 2$;
$f(-2) = (-2)^2 - 4(-2) + 6 = 18$; $f(a) = (a)^2 - 4(a) + 6 = a^2 - 4a + 6$; $f(-a) = (-a)^2 - 4(-a) + 6 = a^2 + 4a + 6$;
$f(x + 1) = (x + 1)^2 - 4(x + 1) + 6 = x^2 + 2x + 1 - 4x - 4 + 6 = x^2 - 2x + 3$; $f(2x) = (2x)^2 - 4(2x) + 6 = 4x^2 - 8x + 6$;
$2f(x) - 2 = 2(x^2 - 4x + 6) - 2 = 2x^2 - 8x + 12 - 2 = 2x^2 - 8x + 10.$

2. $f(x) = 4 - \sqrt{3x - 6}$; $f(5) = 4 - \sqrt{15 - 6} = 3$; $f(9) = 4 - \sqrt{27 - 6} = 4 - \sqrt{21}$;
$f(a + 2) = 4 - \sqrt{3a + 6 - 6} = 4 - \sqrt{3a}$; $f(-x) = 4 - \sqrt{3(-x) - 6} = 4 - \sqrt{-3x - 6}$; $f(x^2) = 4 - \sqrt{3x^2 - 6}$.
$[f(x)]^2 = (4 - \sqrt{3x - 6})^2 = 4 - 8\sqrt{3x - 6} + 3x - 6 = -2 - 8\sqrt{3x - 6} + 3x.$

3. **(a)** $f(-2) = -1$. $f(2) = 2$.

(b) The domain of f is $[-4, 5]$.

(b) The range of f is $[-4, 4]$.

(d) f is increasing on $[-4, -2]$ and $[-1, 4]$; f is decreasing on $[-2, -1]$ and $[4, 5]$.

(e) f is not a one-to-one, for example, $f(-2) = -1 = f(0)$. There are many more examples.

4. By the Vertical Line Test, figures (b) and (c) are graphs of functions. By the Horizontal Line Test, figure (c) is the graph of a one-to-one function.

5. Domain: We must have $x + 3 \geq 0 \quad \Leftrightarrow \quad x \geq -3$. In interval notation, the domain is $[-3, \infty)$.

Range: For x in the domain of f, we have $x \geq -3 \quad \Leftrightarrow \quad x + 3 \geq 0 \quad \Leftrightarrow \quad \sqrt{x + 3} \geq 0 \quad \Leftrightarrow \quad f(x) \geq 0$. So the range is $[0, \infty)$.

6. $F(t) = t^2 + 2t + 5 = (t^2 + 2t + 1) + 5 - 1 = (t + 1)^2 + 4$. Therefore $F(t) \geq 4$ for all t. Since there are no restrictions on t, the domain of F is $(-\infty, \infty)$, and the range is $[4, \infty)$.

7. $f(x) = 7x + 15$. The domain is all real numbers, $(-\infty, \infty)$.

8. $f(x) = \dfrac{2x + 1}{2x - 1}$. Then $2x - 1 \neq 0 \quad \Leftrightarrow \quad x \neq \frac{1}{2}$. So the domain of f is $\left\{ x \mid x \neq \frac{1}{2} \right\}$.

9. $f(x) = \sqrt{x + 4}$. We require $x + 4 \geq 0 \quad \Leftrightarrow \quad x \geq -4$. Thus the domain is $[-4, \infty)$.

10. $f(x) = 3x - \dfrac{2}{\sqrt{x + 1}}$. The domain of f is the set of x where $x + 1 > 0 \quad \Leftrightarrow \quad x > -1$. So the domain is $(-1, \infty)$.

11. $f(x) = \dfrac{1}{x} + \dfrac{1}{x + 1} + \dfrac{1}{x + 2}$. The denominators cannot equal 0, therefore the domain is $\{ x \mid x \neq 0, -1, -2 \}$.

12. $g(x) = \dfrac{2x^2 + 5x + 3}{2x^2 - 5x - 3} = \dfrac{2x^2 + 5x + 3}{(2x + 1)(x - 3)}$. The domain of g is the set of all x where the denominator is not 0. So the domain is $\{ x \mid 2x + 1 \neq 0 \text{ and } x - 3 \neq 0 \} = \left\{ x \mid x \neq -\frac{1}{2} \text{ and } x \neq 3 \right\}$.

13. $h(x) = \sqrt{4 - x} + \sqrt{x^2 - 1}$. We require the expression inside the radicals be nonnegative. So $4 - x \geq 0 \quad \Leftrightarrow \quad 4 \geq x$; also $x^2 - 1 \geq 0 \quad \Leftrightarrow \quad (x - 1)(x + 1) \geq 0$. We make a table:

Interval	$(-\infty, -1)$	$(-1, 1)$	$(1, \infty)$
Sign of $x - 1$	$-$	$-$	$+$
Sign of $x + 1$	$-$	$+$	$+$
Sign of $(x - 1)(x + 1)$	$+$	$-$	$+$

Thus the domain is $(-\infty, 4] \cap \{ (-\infty, -1] \cup [1, \infty) \} = (-\infty, -1] \cup [1, 4]$.

14. $f(x) = \dfrac{\sqrt[3]{2x + 1}}{\sqrt[3]{2x + 2}}$. Since we have an odd root, the domain is the set of all x where the denominator is not 0. Now $\sqrt[3]{2x + 2} \neq 0 \quad \Leftrightarrow \quad \sqrt[3]{2x} \neq -2 \quad \Leftrightarrow \quad 2x \neq -8 \quad \Leftrightarrow \quad x \neq -4$. Thus the domain of f is $\{ x \mid x \neq -4 \}$.

15. $f(x) = 1 - 2x$

16. $f(x) = \frac{1}{3}(x - 5)$, $2 \leq x \leq 8$

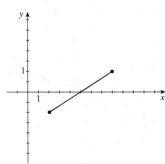

17. $f(t) = 1 - \frac{1}{2}t^2$

18. $g(t) = t^2 - 2t = (t-1)^2 - 1$

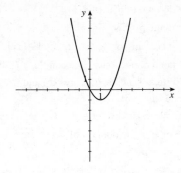

19. $f(x) = x^2 - 6x + 6$

20. $f(x) = 3 - 8x - 2x^2 = -2(x-2)^2 + 11$

21. $g(x) = 1 - \sqrt{x}$

22. $g(x) = -|x|$

23. $h(x) = \frac{1}{2}x^3$

24. $h(x) = \sqrt{x+3}$

25. $h(x) = \sqrt[3]{x}$

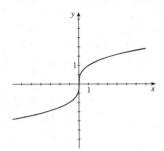

26. $H(x) = x^3 - 3x^2 = x^2(x-3)$

27. $g(x) = \dfrac{1}{x^2}$

28. $G(x) = \dfrac{1}{(x-3)^2}$

29. $f(x) = \begin{cases} 1-x & \text{if } x < 0 \\ 1 & \text{if } x \geq 0 \end{cases}$

30. $f(x) = \begin{cases} 1-2x & \text{if } x \leq 0 \\ 2x-1 & \text{if } x > 0 \end{cases}$

31. $f(x) = \begin{cases} x+6 & \text{if } x < -2 \\ x^2 & \text{if } x \geq -2 \end{cases}$

32. $f(x) = \begin{cases} -x & \text{if } x < 0 \\ x^2 & \text{if } 0 \leq x < 2 \\ 1 & \text{if } x \geq 2 \end{cases}$

33. $f(x) = 6x^3 - 15x^2 + 4x - 1$

(i) $[-2, 2]$ by $[-2, 2]$

(ii) $[-8, 8]$ by $[-8, 8]$

(iii) $[-4, 4]$ by $[-12, 12]$

(iv) $[-100, 100]$ by $[-100, 100]$

From the graphs, we see that the viewing rectangle in (iii) produces the most appropriate graph.

34. $f(x) = \sqrt{100 - x^3}$

(i) $[-4, 4]$ by $[-4, 4]$

(ii) $[-10, 10]$ by $[-10, 10]$

(iii) $[-10, 10]$ by $[-10, 40]$

(iv) $[-100, 100]$ by $[-100, 100]$

From the graphs, we see that the viewing rectangle in (iii) produces the most appropriate graph of f.

35. $f(x) = x^2 + 25x + 173$
$$= \left(x^2 + 25x + \tfrac{625}{4}\right) + 173 - \tfrac{625}{4}$$
$$= \left(x + \tfrac{25}{2}\right)^2 + \tfrac{67}{4}$$

We use the viewing rectangle $[-30, 5]$ by $[-20, 250]$.

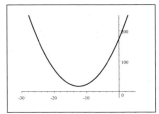

36. $f(x) = 1.1x^3 - 9.6x^2 - 1.4x + 3.2$. Here we experiment to find an appropriate viewing rectangle. The viewing rectangle shown is $[-10, 10]$ by $[-125, 10]$.

37. $f(x) = \dfrac{x}{\sqrt{x^2 + 16}}$. Since $\sqrt{x^2 + 16} \geq \sqrt{x^2} = |x|$, it follows that y should behave like $\dfrac{x}{|x|}$. Thus we use the viewing rectangle $[-20, 20]$ by $[-2, 2]$.

38. $f(x) = |x(x+2)(x+4)|$. Here, the interesting parts of the function occur near $y = 0$. Thus we choose a viewing rectangle that includes $x = -4, -2,$ and 0, where $f(x)$ is close to 0. So we choose the viewing rectangle $[-5, 5]$ by $[-1, 15]$.

39. $f(x) = \sqrt{x^3 - 4x + 1}$. The domain consists of all x where $x^3 - 4x + 1 \geq 0$. Using a graphing device, we see that the domain is approximately $[-2.1, 0.2] \cup [1.9, \infty)$.

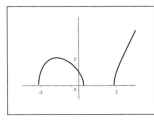

40. We find that the range of $f(x) = x^4 - x^3 + x^2 + 3x - 6$ is about $[-7.10, \infty)$.

41. The average rate of change is $\dfrac{f(2) - f(0)}{2 - 0} = \dfrac{\left[(2)^2 + 3(2)\right] - \left[0^2 + 3(0)\right]}{2} = \dfrac{4 + 6 - 0}{2} = 5.$

42. The average rate of change is $\dfrac{f(8) - f(4)}{8 - 4} = \dfrac{\frac{1}{8-2} - \frac{1}{4-2}}{4} = \dfrac{\frac{1}{6} - \frac{1}{2}}{4} \cdot \dfrac{6}{6} = \dfrac{1 - 3}{24} = -\dfrac{1}{12}.$

43. The average rate of change is $\dfrac{f(3+h) - f(3)}{(3+h) - 3} = \dfrac{\frac{1}{3+h} - \frac{1}{3}}{h} \cdot \dfrac{3(3+h)}{3(3+h)} = \dfrac{3 - (3+h)}{3h(3+h)} = \dfrac{-h}{3h(3+h)} = -\dfrac{1}{3(3+h)}.$

44. The average rate of change is

$$\frac{f(a+h) - f(a)}{(a+h) - a} = \frac{(a+h+1)^2 - (a+1)^2}{h} = \frac{a^2 + 2ah + h^2 + 2a + 2h + 1 - a^2 - 2a - 1}{h}$$

$$= \frac{2ah + h^2 + 2h}{h} = \frac{h(2a + h + 2)}{h} = 2a + h + 2.$$

45. $f(x) = x^3 - 4x^2$ is graphed in the viewing rectangle $[-5, 5]$ by $[-20, 10]$. $f(x)$ is increasing on $(-\infty, 0]$ and $[2.67, \infty)$. It is decreasing on $[0, 2.67]$.

46. $f(x) = |x^4 - 16|$ is graphed in the viewing rectangle $[-5, 5]$ by $[-5, 20]$. $f(x)$ is increasing on $[-2, 0]$ and $[2, \infty)$. It is decreasing on $(-\infty, -2]$ and $[0, 2]$.

47. (a) $y = f(x) + 8$. Shift the graph of $f(x)$ upward 8 units.

(b) $y = f(x + 8)$. Shift the graph of $f(x)$ to the left 8 units.

(c) $y = 1 + 2f(x)$. Stretch the graph of $f(x)$ vertically by a factor of 2, then shift it upward 1 unit.

(d) $y = f(x - 2) - 2$. Shift the graph of $f(x)$ to the right 2 units, then downward 2 units.

(e) $y = f(-x)$. Reflect the graph of $f(x)$ about the y-axis.

(f) $y = -f(-x)$. Reflect the graph of $f(x)$ first about the y-axis, then reflect about the x-axis.

(g) $y = -f(x)$. Reflect the graph of $f(x)$ about the x-axis.

(h) $y = f^{-1}(x)$. Reflect the graph of $f(x)$ about the line $y = x$.

48. (a) $y = f(x - 2)$ **(b)** $y = -f(x)$ **(c)** $y = 3 - f(x)$

(d) $y = \frac{1}{2}f(x) - 1$ **(e)** $y = f^{-1}(x)$ **(f)** $y = f(-x)$

49. (a) $f(x) = 2x^5 - 3x^2 + 2$. $f(-x) = 2(-x)^5 - 3(-x)^2 + 2 = -2x^5 - 3x^2 + 2$. Since $f(x) \neq f(-x)$, f is not even.
$-f(x) = -2x^5 + 3x^2 - 2$. Since $-f(x) \neq f(-x)$, f is not odd.

(b) $f(x) = x^3 - x^7$. $f(-x) = (-x)^3 - (-x)^7 = -(x^3 - x^7) = -f(x)$, hence f is odd.

(c) $f(x) = \dfrac{1-x^2}{1+x^2}$. $f(-x) = \dfrac{1-(-x)^2}{1+(-x)^2} = \dfrac{1-x^2}{1+x^2} = f(x)$. Since $f(x) = f(-x)$, f is even.

(d) $f(x) = \dfrac{1}{x+2}$. $f(-x) = \dfrac{1}{(-x)+2} = \dfrac{1}{2-x}$. $-f(x) = -\dfrac{1}{x+2}$. Since $f(x) \neq f(-x)$, f is not even, and since
$f(-x) \neq -f(x)$, f is not odd.

50. (a) This function is odd.

(b) This function is neither even nor odd.

(c) This function is even.

(d) This function is neither even nor odd.

51. $f(x) = x^2 + 4x + 1 = (x^2 + 4x + 4) + 1 - 4 = (x+2)^2 - 3$.

52. $f(x) = -2x^2 + 12x + 12 = -2(x^2 - 6x) + 12 = -2(x^2 - 6x + 9) + 12 + 18 = -2(x-3)^2 + 30$

53. $g(x) = 2x^2 + 4x - 5 = 2(x^2 + 2x) - 5 = 2(x^2 + 2x + 1) - 5 - 2 = 2(x+1)^2 - 7$. So the minimum value is
$g(-1) = -7$.

54. $f(x) = 1 - x - x^2 = -(x^2 + x) + 1 = -(x^2 + x + \frac{1}{4}) + 1 + \frac{1}{4} = -(x+\frac{1}{2})^2 + \frac{5}{4}$. So the maximum value of f is $\frac{5}{4}$.

55. $h(t) = -16t^2 + 48t + 32 = -16(t^2 - 3t) + 32 = -16(t^2 - 3t + \frac{9}{4}) + 32 + 36$
$= -16(t^2 - 3t + \frac{9}{4}) + 68 = -16(t - \frac{3}{2})^2 + 68$

The stone reaches a maximum height of 68 feet.

56. $P(x) = -1500 + 12x - 0.0004x^2 = -0.0004(x^2 - 30{,}000x) -$
$1500 = -0.0004(x^2 - 30{,}000x + 225{,}000{,}000) - 1500 + 90{,}000 = -0.0004(x - 15{,}000)^2 + 88{,}500$
The maximum profit occurs when 15,000 units are sold, and the maximum profit is \$88,500.

57. $f(x) = 3.3 + 1.6x - 2.5x^3$. In the first viewing rectangle, $[-2, 2]$ by $[-4, 8]$, we see that $f(x)$ has a local maximum
and a local minimum. In the next viewing rectangle, $[0.4, 0.5]$ by $[3.78, 3.80]$, we isolate the local maximum value as
approximately 3.79 when $x \approx 0.46$. In the last viewing rectangle, $[-0.5, -0.4]$ by $[2.80, 2.82]$, we isolate the local
minimum value as 2.81 when $x \approx -0.46$.

58. $f(x) = x^{2/3}(6-x)^{1/3}$. In the first viewing rectangle, $[-10, 10]$ by $[-10, 10]$, we see that $f(x)$ has a local maximum and
a local minimum. The local minimum is 0 at $x = 0$ (and is easily verified). In the next viewing rectangle, $[3.95, 4.05]$ by
$[3.16, 3.18]$, we isolate the local maximum value as approximately 3.175 when $x \approx 4.00$.

59. The sales of air conditioners will start to increase in May as it gets hot, peaking in July and decreasing afterward.

60.

Let b be the length of the base, l be the length of the equal sides, and h be the height in cm. Since the perimeter is 8, $2l + b = 8$ $\Leftrightarrow$ $2l = 8 - b$ $\Leftrightarrow$ $l = \frac{1}{2}(8 - b)$. By the Pythagorean Theorem, $h^2 + \left(\frac{1}{2}b\right)^2 = l^2$ $\Leftrightarrow$ $h^2 = l^2 - \left(\frac{1}{2}b\right)^2$ $\Leftrightarrow$ $h = \sqrt{l^2 - \frac{1}{4}b^2}$. Therefore the area of the triangle is

$$A = \frac{1}{2} \cdot b \cdot h = \frac{1}{2} \cdot b\sqrt{l^2 - \frac{1}{4}b^2} = \frac{b}{2}\sqrt{\frac{1}{4}(8 - b)^2 - \frac{1}{4}b^2}$$

$$= \frac{b}{4}\sqrt{64 - 16b + b^2 - b^2} = \frac{b}{4} \cdot 4\sqrt{4 - b} = b\sqrt{4 - b}$$

61.

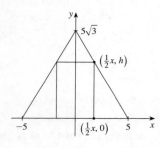

Let x be the width of the rectangle in cm and h be the height of the rectangle. If we orient the triangle on the xy-plane with the center of the base at the origin, then the coordinates of the vertices are $(-5, 0)$, $(5, 0)$, and $(0, 5\sqrt{3})$ (applying the Pythagorean Theorem). The point $\left(\frac{1}{2}x, h\right)$ must lie on the line segment joining the points $(5, 0)$ and $(0, 5\sqrt{3})$. This line segment has slope $-\sqrt{3}$ and y-intercept $5\sqrt{3}$, so its equation is $y = -\sqrt{3}x + 5\sqrt{3}$. Thus

$$h = -\sqrt{3}\left(\frac{1}{2}x\right) + 5\sqrt{3} = -\frac{\sqrt{3}}{2}x + 5\sqrt{3} = \sqrt{3}\left(5 - \frac{1}{2}x\right)$$

(a) The area of the rectangle is $A = xh = x \cdot \sqrt{3}\left(5 - \frac{1}{2}x\right) = \sqrt{3}x\left(5 - \frac{1}{2}x\right)$.

(b) $A = \sqrt{3}x\left(5 - \frac{1}{2}x\right) = -\frac{\sqrt{3}}{2}\left(x^2 - 10x\right) = -\frac{\sqrt{3}}{2}\left(x^2 - 10x + 25\right) + \frac{25\sqrt{3}}{2} = -\frac{\sqrt{3}}{2}(x - 5)^2 + \frac{25\sqrt{3}}{2}$. Therefore the area is maximum when $x = 5$ and by substitution $h = \sqrt{3}\left(5 - \frac{5}{2}\right) = \frac{5\sqrt{3}}{2}$. Hence the dimensions of the rectangle with the largest area are 5 cm by $\frac{5\sqrt{3}}{2}$ cm.

62. Let x be the length of wire in cm that is bent into a square. So $10 - x$ is the length of wire in cm that is bent into an equilateral triangle. The area of the square is $A_1 = \left(\frac{x}{4}\right)^2 = \frac{x^2}{16}$ and the area of the triangle is $A_2 = \frac{1}{2} \cdot b \cdot h = \frac{1}{2} \cdot \frac{10 - x}{3} \cdot \frac{\sqrt{3}(10 - x)}{6}$, where the height is found by using the Pythagorean Theorem. So $A_2 = \frac{\sqrt{3}(10 - x)^2}{36}$.

(a) The total area is $A(x) = A_1 + A_2 = \frac{x^2}{16} + \frac{\sqrt{3}(10 - x)^2}{36}$, $0 \le x \le 10$.

(b) $A(x) = \frac{x^2}{16} + \frac{\sqrt{3}(10 - x)^2}{36} = \frac{9x^2}{144} + \frac{4\sqrt{3}(10 - x)^2}{144} = \frac{1}{144}\left(9x^2 + 400\sqrt{3} - 80\sqrt{3}x + 4\sqrt{3}x^2\right)$

$= \frac{1}{144}\left(9x^2 + 4\sqrt{3}x^2 - 80\sqrt{3}x\right) + \frac{25\sqrt{3}}{9} = \frac{9 + 4\sqrt{3}}{144}\left(x^2 - \frac{80\sqrt{3}x}{9 + 4\sqrt{3}}\right) + \frac{25\sqrt{3}}{9}$

$= \frac{9 + 4\sqrt{3}}{144}\left(x - \frac{40\sqrt{3}}{9 + 4\sqrt{3}}\right)^2 + \frac{25\sqrt{3}}{9} - \frac{4800}{144(9 + 4\sqrt{3})}$

Therefore the area is a minimum when $x = \frac{40\sqrt{3}}{9 + 4\sqrt{3}} \approx 4.35$ m.

63. $f(x) = x^2 - 3x + 2$ and $g(x) = 4 - 3x$.

(a) $(f + g)(x) = (x^2 - 3x + 2) + (4 - 3x) = x^2 - 6x + 6$

(b) $(f - g)(x) = (x^2 - 3x + 2) - (4 - 3x) = x^2 - 2$

(c) $(fg)(x) = (x^2 - 3x + 2)(4 - 3x) = 4x^2 - 12x + 8 - 3x^3 + 9x^2 - 6x = -3x^3 + 13x^2 - 18x + 8$

(d) $\left(\dfrac{f}{g}\right)(x) = \dfrac{x^2 - 3x + 2}{4 - 3x}$, $x \neq \frac{4}{3}$

(e) $(f \circ g)(x) = f(4 - 3x) = (4 - 3x)^2 - 3(4 - 3x) + 2 = 16 - 24x + 9x^2 - 12 + 9x + 2 = 9x^2 - 15x + 6$

(f) $(g \circ f)(x) = g(x^2 - 3x + 2) = 4 - 3(x^2 - 3x + 2) = -3x^2 + 9x - 2$

64. $f(x) = 1 + x^2$ and $g(x) = \sqrt{x - 1}$. (Remember that the proper domains must apply.)

(a) $(f \circ g)(x) = f(\sqrt{x - 1}) = 1 + (\sqrt{x - 1})^2 = 1 + x - 1 = x$

(b) $(g \circ f)(x) = g(1 + x^2) = \sqrt{(1 + x^2) - 1} = \sqrt{x^2} = |x|$

(c) $(f \circ g)(2) = f(g(2)) = f\left(\sqrt{(2) - 1}\right) = f(1) = 1 + (1)^2 = 2$.

(d) $(f \circ f)(2) = f(f(2)) = f(1 + (2)^2) = f(5) = 1 + (5)^2 = 26$.

(e) $(f \circ g \circ f)(x) = f((g \circ f)(x)) = f(|x|) = 1 + (|x|)^2 = 1 + x^2$. Note that $(g \circ f)(x) = |x|$ by part (b).

(f) $(g \circ f \circ g)(x) = g((f \circ g)(x)) = g(x) = \sqrt{x - 1}$. Note that $(f \circ g)(x) = x$ by part (a).

65. $f(x) = 3x - 1$ and $g(x) = 2x - x^2$.

$(f \circ g)(x) = f(2x - x^2) = 3(2x - x^2) - 1 = -3x^2 + 6x - 1$, and the domain is $(-\infty, \infty)$.

$(g \circ f)(x) = g(3x - 1) = 2(3x - 1) - (3x - 1)^2 = 6x - 2 - 9x^2 + 6x - 1 = -9x^2 + 12x - 3$, and the domain is $(-\infty, \infty)$

$(f \circ f)(x) = f(3x - 1) = 3(3x - 1) - 1 = 9x - 4$, and the domain is $(-\infty, \infty)$.

$(g \circ g)(x) = g(2x - x^2) = 2(2x - x^2) - (2x - x^2)^2 = 4x - 2x^2 - 4x^2 + 4x^3 - x^4 = -x^4 + 4x^3 - 6x^2 + 4x$, and domain is $(-\infty, \infty)$.

66. $f(x) = \sqrt{x}$, has domain $\{x \mid x \geq 0\}$. $g(x) = \dfrac{2}{x - 4}$, has domain $\{x \mid x \neq 4\}$.

$(f \circ g)(x) = f\left(\dfrac{2}{x - 4}\right) = \sqrt{\dfrac{2}{x - 4}}$. $(f \circ g)(x)$ is defined whenever both $g(x)$ and $f(g(x))$ are defined; that is,

whenever $x \neq 4$ and $\dfrac{2}{x - 4} \geq 0$. Now $\dfrac{2}{x - 4} \geq 0 \quad \Leftrightarrow \quad x - 4 > 0 \quad \Leftrightarrow \quad x > 4$. So the domain of $f \circ g$ is $(4, \infty)$.

$(g \circ f)(x) = g(\sqrt{x}) = \dfrac{2}{\sqrt{x} - 4}$. $(g \circ f)(x)$ is defined whenever both $f(x)$ and $g(f(x))$ are defined; that is, whenever

$x \geq 0$ and $\sqrt{x} - 4 \neq 0$. Now $\sqrt{x} - 4 \neq 0 \quad \Leftrightarrow \quad x \neq 16$. So the domain of $g \circ f$ is $[0, 16) \cup (16, \infty)$.

$(f \circ f)(x) = f(\sqrt{x}) = \sqrt{\sqrt{x}} = x^{1/4}$. $(f \circ f)(x)$ is defined whenever both $f(x)$ and $f(f(x))$ are defined; that is, whenever $x \geq 0$. So the domain of $f \circ f$ is $[0, \infty)$.

$(g \circ g)(x) = g\left(\dfrac{2}{x - 4}\right) = \dfrac{2}{\dfrac{2}{x - 4} - 4} = \dfrac{2(x - 4)}{2 - 4(x - 4)} = \dfrac{x - 4}{9 - 2x}$. $(g \circ g)(x)$ is defined whenever both $g(x)$ and

$g(g(x))$ are defined; that is, whenever $x \neq 4$ and $9 - 2x \neq 0$. Now $9 - 2x \neq 0 \quad \Leftrightarrow \quad 2x \neq 9 \quad \Leftrightarrow \quad x \neq \frac{9}{2}$. So the

domain of $g \circ g$ is $\left\{x \mid x \neq \frac{9}{2}, 4\right\}$.

67. $f(x) = \sqrt{1 - x}$, $g(x) = 1 - x^2$ and $h(x) = 1 + \sqrt{x}$.

$(f \circ g \circ h)(x) = f(g(h(x))) = f(g(1 + \sqrt{x})) = f\left(1 - (1 + \sqrt{x})^2\right) = f(1 - (1 + 2\sqrt{x} + x))$

$ = f(-x - 2\sqrt{x}) = \sqrt{1 - (-x - 2\sqrt{x})} = \sqrt{1 + 2\sqrt{x} + x} = \sqrt{(1 + \sqrt{x})^2} = 1 + \sqrt{x}$

68. If $h(x) = \sqrt{x}$ and $g(x) = 1 + x$, then $(g \circ h)(x) = g(\sqrt{x}) = 1 + \sqrt{x}$. If $f(x) = \dfrac{1}{\sqrt{x}}$, then

$$(f \circ g \circ h)(x) = f(1 + \sqrt{x}) = \frac{1}{\sqrt{1 + \sqrt{x}}} = T(x).$$

69. $f(x) = 3 + x^3$. If $x_1 \neq x_2$, then $x_1^3 \neq x_2^3$ (unequal numbers have unequal cubes), and therefore $3 + x_1^3 \neq 3 + x_2^3$. Thus f is a one-to-one function.

70. $g(x) = 2 - 2x + x^2 = (x^2 - 2x + 1) + 1 = (x - 1)^2 + 1$. Since $g(0) = 2 = g(2)$, as is true for all pairs of numbers equidistant from 1, g is not a one-to-one function.

71. $h(x) = \dfrac{1}{x^4}$. Since the fourth powers of a number and its negative are equal, h is not one-to-one. For example,

$h(-1) = \dfrac{1}{(-1)^4} = 1$ and $h(1) = \dfrac{1}{(1)^4} = 1$, so $h(-1) = h(1)$.

72. $r(x) = 2 + \sqrt{x + 3}$. If $x_1 \neq x_2$, then $x_1 + 3 \neq x_2 + 3$, so $\sqrt{x_1 + 3} \neq \sqrt{x_2 + 3}$ and $2 + \sqrt{x_1 + 3} \neq 2 + \sqrt{x_2 + 3}$. Thus r is one-to-one.

73. $p(x) = 3.3 + 1.6x - 2.5x^3$. Using a graphing device and the Horizontal Line Test, we see that p is not a one-to-one function.

74. $q(x) = 3.3 + 1.6x + 2.5x^3$. Using a graphing device and the Horizontal Line Test, we see that q is a one-to-one function.

75. $f(x) = 3x - 2 \Leftrightarrow y = 3x - 2 \Leftrightarrow 3x = y + 2 \Leftrightarrow x = \frac{1}{3}(y + 2)$. So $f^{-1}(x) = \frac{1}{3}(x + 2)$.

76. $f(x) = \dfrac{2x + 1}{3}$. $y = \dfrac{2x + 1}{3} \Leftrightarrow 2x + 1 = 3y \Leftrightarrow 2x = 3y - 1 \Leftrightarrow x = \frac{1}{2}(3y - 1)$. So $f^{-1}(x) = \frac{1}{2}(3x - 1)$.

77. $f(x) = (x + 1)^3 \Leftrightarrow y = (x + 1)^3 \Leftrightarrow x + 1 = \sqrt[3]{y} \Leftrightarrow x = \sqrt[3]{y} - 1$. So $f^{-1}(x) = \sqrt[3]{x} - 1$.

78. $f(x) = 1 + \sqrt[5]{x - 2}$. $y = 1 + \sqrt[5]{x - 2} \Leftrightarrow y - 1 = \sqrt[5]{x - 2} \Leftrightarrow x - 2 = (y - 1)^5 \Leftrightarrow x = 2 + (y - 1)^5$. So $f^{-1}(x) = 2 + (x - 1)^5$.

79. (a), (b) $f(x) = x^2 - 4$, $x \ge 0$

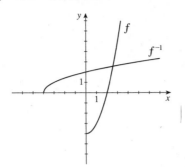

(c) $f(x) = x^2 - 4$, $x \ge 0$ $\Leftrightarrow$ $y = x^2 - 4$,

$y \ge -4$ $\Leftrightarrow$ $x^2 = y + 4$ $\Leftrightarrow$

$x = \sqrt{y + 4}$. So $f^{-1}(x) = \sqrt{x + 4}$,

$x \ge -4$.

80. $f(x) = 1 + \sqrt[4]{x}$

(a) If $x_1 \ne x_2$, then $\sqrt[4]{x_1} \ne \sqrt[4]{x_2}$, and so $1 + \sqrt[4]{x_1} \ne 1 + \sqrt[4]{x_2}$. Therefore, f is a one-to-one function.

(b), (c)

(d) $f(x) = 1 + \sqrt[4]{x}$. $y = 1 + \sqrt[4]{x}$ $\Leftrightarrow$ $\sqrt[4]{x} = y - 1$ $\Leftrightarrow$ $x = (y - 1)^4$. So $f^{-1}(x) = (x - 1)^4$, $x \ge 1$. Note that the domain of f is $[0, \infty)$, so $y = 1 + \sqrt[4]{x} \ge 1$. Hence, the domain of f^{-1} is $[1, \infty)$.

Chapter 2 Test

1. By the Vertical Line Test, figures (a) and (b) are graphs of functions. By the Horizontal Line Test, only figure (a) is the graph of a one-to-one function.

2. (a) $f(3) = \dfrac{\sqrt{3 + 1}}{3} = \dfrac{\sqrt{4}}{3} = \dfrac{2}{3}$; $f(5) = \dfrac{\sqrt{5 + 1}}{5} = \dfrac{\sqrt{6}}{5}$; $f(a - +1) = \dfrac{\sqrt{(a - 1) + 1}}{a - 1} = \dfrac{\sqrt{a}}{a - 1}$.

(b) $f(x) = \dfrac{\sqrt{x + 1}}{x}$. Our restrictions are that the input to the radical is nonnegative, and the denominator must not be equal to zero. Thus $x + 1 \ge 0$ $\Leftrightarrow$ $x \ge -1$ and $x \ne 0$. In interval notation, the domain is $[-1, 0) \cup (0, \infty)$.

3. The average rate of change is $\dfrac{f(2) - f(5)}{2 - 5} = \dfrac{[2^2 - 2(2)] - [5^2 - 2(5)]}{-3} = \dfrac{4 - 4 - (25 - 10)}{-3} = \dfrac{-15}{-3} = 5$.

4. (a) $f(x) = x^3$

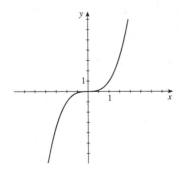

(b) $g(x) = (x - 1)^3 - 2$. To obtain the graph of g, shift the graph of f to the right 1 unit and downward 2 units.

5. (a) $y = f(x - 3) + 2$. Shift the graph of $f(x)$ to the right 3 units, then shift the graph upward 2 units.

   (b) $y = f(-x)$. Reflect the graph of $f(x)$ about the y-axis.

6. (a) $f(x) = 2x^2 - 8x + 13$

$$= 2(x^2 - 4x) + 13$$

$$= 2(x^2 - 4x + 4) + 13 - 8$$

$$= 2(x - 2)^2 + 5$$

(b)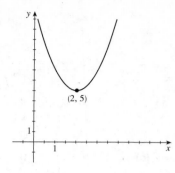

   (c) Since $f(x) = 2(x - 2)^2 + 5$ is in standard form, the minimum value of f is $f(2) = 5$.

7. (a) $f(-2) = 1 - (-2)^2 = 1 - 4 = -3$ (since $-2 \le 0$).

$f(1) = 2(1) + 1 = 2 + 1 = 3$ (since $1 > 0$).

(b)

8. (a) Since 1800 ft of fencing are available, $6x + 2y = 1800 \quad \Leftrightarrow \quad 2y = 1800 - 6x \quad \Leftrightarrow \quad y = 900 - 3x$. Thus the area of the pens is $A = xy = x(900 - 3x) = 900x - 3x^2$.

   (b) $A = 900x - 3x^2 = -3(x^2 - 300x) = -3(x^2 - 300x + 150^2) + 67{,}500 = -3(x - 150)^2 + 67{,}500$. The total area is maximized if $x = 150$ ft.

9. $f(x) = x^2 + 1$; $g(x) = x - 3$.

   (a) $(f \circ g)(x) = f(g(x)) = f(x - 3) = (x - 3)^2 + 1 = x^2 - 6x + 9 + 1 = x^2 - 6x + 10$

   (b) $(g \circ f)(x) = g(f(x)) = g(x^2 + 1) = (x^2 + 1) - 3 = x^2 - 2$

   (c) $f(g(2)) = f(-1) = (-1)^2 + 1 = 2$. (We have used the fact that $g(2) = (2) - 3 = -1$.)

   (d) $g(f(2)) = g(5) = 5 - 3 = 2$. (We have used the fact that $f(2) = 2^2 + 1 = 5$.)

   (e) $(g \circ g \circ g)(x) = g(g(g(x))) = g(g(x - 3)) = g(x - 6) = (x - 6) - 3 = x - 9$. (We have used the fact that $g(x - 3) = (x - 3) - 3 = x - 6$.)

10. (a) $f(x) = \sqrt{3 - x}$, $x \le 3 \quad \Leftrightarrow \quad y = \sqrt{3 - x}$

$\Leftrightarrow \quad y^2 = 3 - x \quad \Leftrightarrow \quad x = 3 - y^2$. Thus

$f^{-1}(x) = 3 - x^2$, $x \ge 0$.

(b) $f(x) = \sqrt{3 - x}$, $x \le 3$ and $f^{-1}(x) = 3 - x^2$, $x \ge 0$

11. **(a)** The domain of f is $[0, 6]$, and the range of f is $[1, 7]$.

(c) The average rate of change is $\dfrac{f(6) - f(2)}{6 - 2} = \dfrac{7 - 2}{4} = \dfrac{5}{4}$.

(b)

12. **(a)** $f(x) = 3x^4 - 14x^2 + 5x - 3$. The graph is shown in the viewing rectangle $[-10, 10]$ by $[-30, 10]$.

(b) No, by the Horizontal Line Test.

(c) The local maximum is approximately -2.55 when $x \approx 0.18$, as shown in the first viewing rectangle $[0.15, 0.25]$ by $[-2.6, -2.5]$. One local minimum is approximately -27.18 when $x \approx -1.61$, as shown in the second viewing rectangle $[-1.65, -1.55]$ by $[-27.5, -27]$. The other local minimum is approximately -11.93 when $x \approx 1.43$, as shown is the viewing rectangle $[1.4, 1.5]$ by $[-12, -11.9]$.

(d) Using the graph in part (a) and the local minimum, -27.18, found in part (c), we see that the range is $[-27.18, \infty)$.

(e) Using the information from part (c) and the graph in part (a), $f(x)$ is increasing on the intervals $[-1.61, 0.18]$ and $[1.43, \infty)$ and decreasing on the intervals $(-\infty, -1.61]$ and $[0.18, 1.43]$.

Focus on Modeling: Fitting Lines to Data

1. (a)

Femur length (cm)

(b) Using a graphing calculator, we obtain the regression line $y = 1.8807x + 82.65$.

(c) Using $x = 58$ in the equation $y = 1.8807x + 82.65$, we get $y = 1.8807\,(58) + 82.65 \approx 191.7$ cm.

2. (a)

High temperature (°F)

(b) Using a graphing calculator, we obtain the regression line $y = 16.4163x - 621.83$.

(c) Using $x = 95$ in the equation $y = 16.4163x - 621.83$, we get $y = 16.4163\,(95) - 621.83 \approx 938$ cans.

3. (a)

Diameter (in.)

(b) Using a graphing calculator, we obtain the regression line $y = 6.451x - 0.1523$.

(c) Using $x = 18$ in the equation $y = 6.451x - 0.1523$, we get $y = 6.451\,(18) - 0.1523 \approx 116$ years.

4. (a)

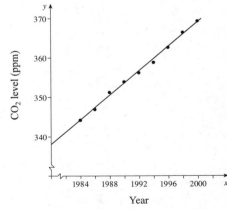

Year

(b) Using a graphing calculator, we obtain the regression line $y = 1.555x - 2740.8$.

(c) Using $x = 2001$ in the equation $y = 1.555x - 2740.8$, we get $y = 1.555\,(2001) - 2740.8 \approx 370.8$ ppm CO_2.

5. (a)

Temperature (°F)

(b) Using a graphing calculator, we obtain the regression line $y = 4.857x - 220.97$.

(c) Using $x = 100°$ F in the equation $y = 4.857x - 220.97$, we get $y \approx 265$ chirps per minute.

6. (a)

Income ($\times \$1000$)

(b) Using a graphing calculator, we obtain the regression line $y = -0.0995x + 13.9$, where x is measured in thousands of dollars.

(c) Using the regression line equation, $y = -0.0995x + 13.9$, we get an estimated $y = 11.4$ ulcers per 100 population when $x = \$25,000$.

(d) Again using $y = -0.0995x + 13.9$, we get an estimated $y = 5.8$ ulcers per 100 population when $x = \$80,000$.

7. (a)

Flow rate (%)

(b) Using a graphing calculator, we obtain the regression line $y = -0.168x + 19.89$.

(c) Using the regression line equation $y = -0.168x + 19.89$, we get $y \approx 8.13\%$ when $x = 70\%$.

8. (a)

Noise level (dB)

(b) Using a graphing calculator, we obtain $y = -3.9018x + 419.7$.

(c) The correlation coefficient is $r = -0.98$, so linear model is appropriate for x between 80 dB and 104 dB.

(d) Substituting $x = 94$ into the regression equation, we get $y = -3.9018\,(94) + 419.7 \approx 53$. So the intelligibility is about 53%.

9. (a)

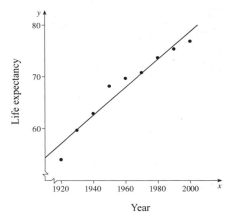

Year

(b) Using a graphing calculator, we obtain

$y = 0.27083x - 462.9$.

(c) We substitute $x = 2004$ in the model
$y = 0.27083x - 462.9$ to get $y = 79.8$, that is, a life
expectancy of 79.8 years.

(d) As of this writing, data for 2004 are not yet available.
The life expectancy of a child born in the US in 2003
is 77.6 years.

11. (a) If we take $x = 0$ in 1900 for both men and
women, then the regression equation for the
men's data is $y = -0.173x + 64.72$ and the
regression equation for the women's data is
$y = -0.269x + 78.67$.

10. (a)

Height (ft)

(b) Using a graphing calculator, we obtain the regression
line $y = 0.0669x - 0.23$.

(c) The slope is 0.0789. It indicates the fraction of a
storey represented by one foot of height in the
building. Since $\dfrac{1}{0.0669} \approx 14.94$, each storey is about
15 feet.

(b)

Years since 1900

These lines predict that the women will overtake
the men in this event when
$-0.173x + 64.72 = -0.269x + 78.67 \quad \Leftrightarrow$
$0.096x = 13.95 \quad \Leftrightarrow \quad x = 145.31$, or in
2045. This seems unlikely, but who knows?

12. (a) Using a graphing calculator, we obtain the regression line $y = 0.7804x + 15.5$.

 (b) Answers will vary.

13. The students should find a fairly strong correlation between shoe size and height.

14. Results will depend on student surveys in each class.

3 Polynomial and Rational Functions

3.1 Polynomial Functions and Their Graphs

1. (a) $P(x) = x^2 - 4$

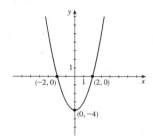

(b) $Q(x) = (x - 4)^2$

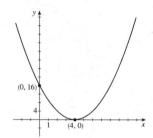

(c) $R(x) = 2x^2 - 2$

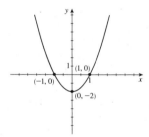

(d) $S(x) = 2(x - 2)^2$

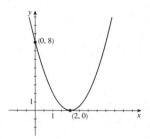

2. (a) $P(x) = x^4 - 16$

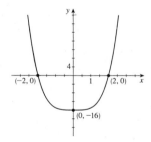

(b) $Q(x) = (x + 2)^4$

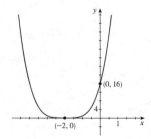

(c) $R(x) = (x + 2)^4 - 16$

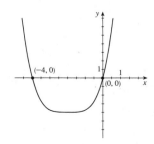

(d) $S(x) = -2(x + 2)^4$

3. (a) $P(x) = x^3 - 8$

(b) $Q(x) = -x^3 + 27$

(c) $R(x) = -(x+2)^3$

(d) $S(x) = \frac{1}{2}(x-1)^3 + 4$

4. (a) $P(x) = (x+3)^5$

(b) $Q(x) = 2(x+3)^5 - 64$

(c) $R(x) = -\frac{1}{2}(x-2)^5$

(d) $S(x) = -\frac{1}{2}(x-2)^5 + 16$

5. III   **6.** I   **7.** V   **8.** II   **9.** VI   **10.** IV

11. $P(x) = (x-1)(x+2)$

12. $P(x) = (x-1)(x+1)(x-2)$

13. $P(x) = x(x-3)(x+2)$

14. $P(x) = (2x-1)(x+1)(x+3)$

15. $P(x) = (x-3)(x+2)(3x-2)$

16. $P(x) = \frac{1}{5}x(x-5)^2$

17. $P(x) = (x-1)^2(x-3)$

18. $P(x) = \frac{1}{4}(x+1)^3(x-3)$

19. $P(x) = \frac{1}{12}(x+2)^2(x-3)^2$

20. $P(x) = (x-1)^2(x+2)^3$

21. $P(x) = x^3(x+2)(x-3)^2$

22. $P(x) = (x-3)^2(x+1)^2$

23. $P(x) = x^3 - x^2 - 6x = x(x+2)(x-3)$

24. $P(x) = x^3 + 2x^2 - 8x = x(x-2)(x+4)$

25. $P(x) = -x^3 + x^2 + 12x = -x(x+3)(x-4)$

26. $P(x) = -2x^3 - x^2 + x = -x(2x^2 + x - 1)$
   $= -x(2x-1)(x+1)$

27. $P(x) = x^4 - 3x^3 + 2x^2 = x^2(x-1)(x-2)$

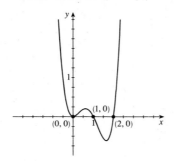

28. $P(x) = x^5 - 9x^3 = x^3(x+3)(x-3)$

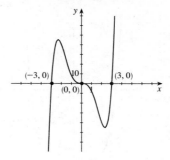

29. $P(x) = x^3 + x^2 - x - 1 = (x-1)(x+1)^2$

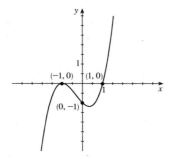

30. $P(x) = x^3 + 3x^2 - 4x - 12 = (x+3)(x-2)(x+2)$

31. $P(x) = 2x^3 - x^2 - 18x + 9$
$= (x-3)(2x-1)(x+3)$

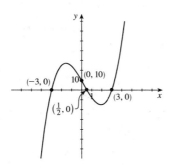

32. $P(x) = \frac{1}{8}(2x^4 + 3x^3 - 16x - 24)^2$
$= \frac{1}{8}(x-2)^2(2x+3)^2(x^2+2x+4)^2$

33. $P(x) = x^4 - 2x^3 - 8x + 16$
$= (x-2)^2(x^2+2x+4)$

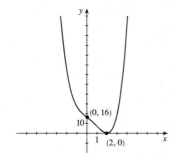

34. $P(x) = x^4 - 2x^3 + 8x - 16$
$= (x+2)(x-2)(x^2-2x+4)$

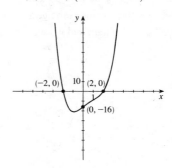

35. $P(x) = x^4 - 3x^2 - 4 = (x - 2)(x + 2)(x^2 + 1)$

36. $P(x) = x^6 - 2x^3 +$
$$1 = (x^3 - 1)^2 = (x - 1)^2 (x^2 + x + 1)^2$$

37. $P(x) = 3x^3 - x^2 + 5x + 1$; $Q(x) = 3x^3$. Since P has odd degree and positive leading coefficient, it has the following end behavior: $y \to \infty$ as $x \to \infty$ and $y \to -\infty$ as $x \to -\infty$.

On a large viewing rectangle, the graphs of P and Q look almost the same. On a small viewing rectangle, we see that the graphs of P and Q have different intercepts.

38. $P(x) = -\frac{1}{8}x^3 + \frac{1}{4}x^2 + 12x$; $Q(x) = -\frac{1}{8}x^3$. Since P has odd degree and negative leading coefficient, it has the following end behavior: $y \to -\infty$ as $x \to \infty$ and $y \to \infty$ as $x \to -\infty$.

On a large viewing rectangle, the graphs of P and Q look almost the same. On a small viewing rectangle, the graphs of P and Q look very different and seem (wrongly) to have different end behavior.

39. $P(x) = x^4 - 7x^2 + 5x + 5$; $Q(x) = x^4$. Since P has even degree and positive leading coefficient, it has the following end behavior: $y \to \infty$ as $x \to \infty$ and $y \to \infty$ as $x \to -\infty$.

On a large viewing rectangle, the graphs of P and Q look almost the same. On a small viewing rectangle, the graphs of P and Q look very different and we see that they have different intercepts.

40. $P(x) = -x^5 + 2x^2 + x$; $Q(x) = -x^5$. Since P has odd degree and negative leading coefficient, it has the following end behavior: $y \to -\infty$ as $x \to \infty$ and $y \to \infty$ as $x \to -\infty$.

On a large viewing rectangle, the graphs of P and Q look almost the same. On a small viewing rectangle, the graphs of P and Q look very different.

41. $P(x) = x^{11} - 9x^9$; $Q(x) = x^{11}$. Since P has odd degree and positive leading coefficient, it has the following end behavior: $y \to \infty$ as $x \to \infty$ and $y \to -\infty$ as $x \to -\infty$.

On a large viewing rectangle, the graphs of P and Q look like they have the same end behavior. On a small viewing rectangle, the graphs of P and Q look very different and seem (wrongly) to have different end behavior.

42. $P(x) = 2x^2 - x^{12}$; $Q(x) = -x^{12}$. Since P has even degree and negative leading coefficient, it has the following end behavior: $y \to -\infty$ as $x \to \infty$ and $y \to -\infty$ as $x \to -\infty$.

On a large viewing rectangle, the graphs of P and Q look almost the same. On a small viewing rectangle, the graphs of P and Q look very different.

43. (a) x-intercepts at 0 and 4, y-intercept at 0.

    (b) Local maximum at $(2, 4)$, no local minimum.

44. (a) x-intercepts at 0 and 4.5, y-intercept at 0.

    (b) Local maximum at $(0, 0)$, local minimum at $(3, -3)$.

45. (a) x-intercepts at -2 and 1, y-intercept at -1.

    (b) Local maximum at $(1, 0)$, local minimum at $(-1, -2)$.

46. (a) x-intercepts at 0 and 4, y-intercept at 0.

    (b) No local maximum, local minimum at $(3, -3)$.

47. $y = -x^2 + 8x$, $[-4, 12]$ by $[-50, 30]$

No local minimum. Local maximum at $(4, 16)$.

48. $y = x^3 - 3x^2$, $[-2, 5]$ by $[-10, 10]$

Local minimum at $(2, -4)$. Local maximum at $(0, 0)$.

49. $y = x^3 - 12x + 9$, $[-5, 5]$ by $[-30, 30]$

Local minimum at $(-2, 25)$, Local maximum at $(2, -7)$.

50. $y = 2x^3 - 3x^2 - 12x - 32$, $[-5, 5]$ by $[-60, 30]$

Local minimum at $(2, -52)$. Local maximum at $(-1, -25)$.

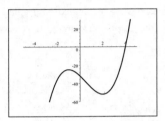

51. $y = x^4 + 4x^3$, $[-5, 5]$ by $[-30, 30]$

Local minimum at $(-3, -27)$. No local maximum.

52. $y = x^4 - 18x^2 + 32$, $[-5, 5]$ by $[-100, 100]$

Local minima at $(-3, -49)$ and $(3, -49)$. Local maximum at $(0, 32)$.

53. $y = 3x^5 - 5x^3 + 3$, $[-3, 3]$ by $[-5, 10]$

Local maximum at $(-1, 5)$. Local minimum at $(1, 1)$.

54. $y = x^5 - 5x^2 + 6$, $[-3, 3]$ by $[-5, 10]$

Local minimum at $(1.26, 1.24)$. Local maximum at $(0, 6)$.

55. $y = -2x^2 + 3x + 5$ has one local maximum at $(0.75, 6.13)$.

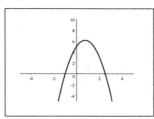

56. $y = x^3 + 12x$ has no local maximum or minimum.

57. $y = x^3 - x^2 - x$ has one local maximum at $(-0.33, 0.19)$ and one local minimum at $(1.00, -1.00)$.

58. $y = 6x^3 + 3x + 1$ has no local maximum or minimum.

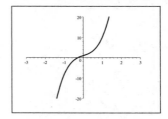

59. $y = x^4 - 5x^2 + 4$ has one local maximum at $(0, 4)$ and two local minima at $(-1.58, -2.25)$ and $(1.58, -2.25)$.

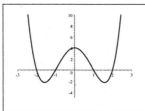

60. $y = 1.2x^5 + 3.75x^4 - 7x^3 - 15x^2 + 18x$ has two local maxima at $(0.50, 4.65)$ and $(-2.97, 12.10)$ and two local minima at $(-1.40, -27.44)$ and $(1.40, -2.54)$.

61. $y = (x - 2)^5 + 32$ has no maximum or minimum.

62. $y = (x^2 - 2)^3$ has one local minimum at $(0, -8)$.

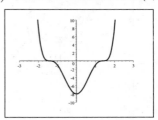

63. $y = x^8 - 3x^4 + x$ has one local maximum at $(0.44, 0.33)$
and two local minima at $(1.09, -1.15)$ and
$(-1.12, -3.36)$.

64. $y = \frac{1}{3}x^7 - 17x^2 + 7$ has one local maximum at $(0, 7)$ and
one local minimum at $(1.71, -28.46)$.

65. $y = cx^3$; $c = 1, 2, 5, \frac{1}{2}$. Increasing the value of c stretches
the graph vertically.

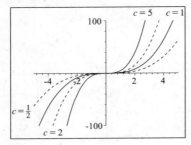

66. $P(x) = (x - c)^4$; $c = -1, 0, 1, 2$. Increasing the value
of c shifts the graph to the right.

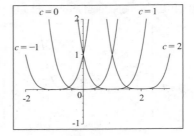

67. $P(x) = x^4 + c$; $c = -1, 0, 1,$ and 2. Increasing the value
of c moves the graph up.

68. $P(x) = x^3 + cx$; $c = 2, 0, -2, -4$. Increasing the value
of c makes the "bumps" in the graph flatter.

69. $P(x) = x^4 - cx$; $c = 0, 1, 8,$ and 27. Increasing the
value of c causes a deeper dip in the graph, in the fourth
quadrant, and moves the positive x-intercept to the right.

70. $P(x) = x^c$; $c = 1, 3, 5, 7$. The larger c gets, the flatter the
graph is near the origin, and the steeper it is away from the
origin.

71. (a)

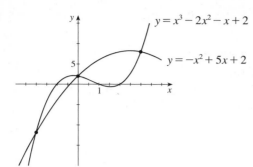

$y = x^3 - 2x^2 - x + 2$

$y = -x^2 + 5x + 2$

(b) The two graphs appear to intersect at 3 points.

(c) $x^3 - 2x^2 - x + 2 = -x^2 + 5x + 2 \quad \Leftrightarrow$
$x^3 - x^2 - 6x = 0 \quad \Leftrightarrow \quad x\left(x^2 - x - 6\right) = 0 \Leftrightarrow$
$x(x-3)(x+2) = 0$. Then either $x = 0$, $x = 3$, or
$x = -2$. If $x = 0$, then $y = 2$; if $x = 3$ then $y = 8$; if
$x = -2$, then $y = -12$. Hence the points where the two
graphs intersect are $(0, 2)$, $(3, 8)$, and $(-2, -12)$.

72. Graph 1 belongs to $y = x^4$. Graph 2 belongs to $y = x^2$. Graph 3 belongs to $y = x^6$. Graph 4 belongs to $y = x^3$. Graph 5 belongs to $y = x^5$.

73. (a) Let $P(x)$ be a polynomial containing only odd powers of x. Then each term of $P(x)$ can be written as Cx^{2n+1}, for some constant C and integer n. Since $C(-x)^{2n+1} = -Cx^{2n+1}$, each term of $P(x)$ is an odd function. Thus by part (a), $P(x)$ is an odd function.

(b) Let $P(x)$ be a polynomial containing only even powers of x. Then each term of $P(x)$ can be written as Cx^{2n}, for some constant C and integer n. Since $C(-x)^{2n} = Cx^{2n}$, each term of $P(x)$ is an even function. Thus by part (b), $P(x)$ is an even function.

(c) Since $P(x)$ contains both even and odd powers of x, we can write it in the form $P(x) = R(x) + Q(x)$, where $R(x)$ contains all the even-powered terms in $P(x)$ and $Q(x)$ contains all the odd-powered terms. By part (d), $Q(x)$ is an odd function, and by part (e), $R(x)$ is an even function. Thus, since neither $Q(x)$ nor $R(x)$ are constantly 0 (by assumption), by part (c), $P(x) = R(x) + Q(x)$ is neither even nor odd.

(d) $P(x) = x^5 + 6x^3 - x^2 - 2x + 5 = \left(x^5 + 6x^3 - 2x\right) + \left(-x^2 + 5\right) = P_O(x) + P_E(x)$ where
$P_O(x) = x^5 + 6x^3 - 2x$ and $P_E(x) = -x^2 + 5$. Since $P_O(x)$ contains only odd powers of x, it is an odd function, and since $P_E(x)$ contains only even powers of x, it is an even function.

74. (a) $P(x) = (x-1)(x-3)(x-4)$. Local maximum at $(1.8, 2.1)$. Local minimum at $(3.6, -0.6)$.

(b) Since $Q(x) = P(x) + 5$, each point on the graph of Q has y-coordinate 5 units more than the corresponding point on the graph of P. Thus Q has a local maximum at $(1.8, 7.1)$ and a local minimum at $(3.5, 4.4)$.

75. (a) $P(x) = (x - 2)(x - 4)(x - 5)$ has one local maximum and one local minimum.

(b) Since $P(a) = P(b) = 0$, and $P(x) > 0$ for $a < x < b$ (see the table below), the graph of P must first rise and then fall on the interval (a, b), and so P must have at least one local maximum between a and b. Using similar reasoning, the fact that $P(b) = P(c) = 0$ and $P(x) < 0$ for $b < x < c$ shows that P must have at least one local minimum between b and c. Thus P has at least two local extrema.

Interval	$(-\infty, a)$	(a, b)	(b, c)	(c, ∞)
Sign of $x - a$	$-$	$+$	$+$	$+$
Sign of $x - b$	$-$	$-$	$+$	$+$
Sign of $x - c$	$-$	$-$	$-$	$+$
Sign of $(x - a)(x - b)(x - c)$	$-$	$+$	$-$	$+$

76. (a) From the graph,
$P(x) = x^3 - 4x = x(x - 2)(x + 2)$ has three x-intercepts, one local maximum, and one local minimum.

(b) From the graph, $Q(x) = x^3 + 4x = x(x^2 + 4)$ has one x-intercept and no local maximum or minimum.

(c) For the x-intercepts of $P(x) = x^3 - ax$, we solve $x^3 - ax = 0$. Then we have $x(x^2 - a) = 0 \Leftrightarrow x = 0$ or $x^2 = a$. If $x^2 = a$, then $x = \pm\sqrt{a}$. So P has 3 x-intercepts. Since $P(x) = x(x^2 - a) = x(x + \sqrt{a})(x - \sqrt{a})$, by part (c) of problem 67, P has 2 local extrema. For the x-intercepts of $Q(x) = x^3 + ax$, we solve $x^3 + ax = 0$. Then we have $x(x^2 + a) = 0 \Leftrightarrow x = 0$ or $x^2 = -a$. The equation $x^2 = -a$ has no real solutions because $a > 0$. So Q has 1 x-intercept. We now show that Q is always increasing and hence has no extrema. If $x_1 < x_2$, then $ax_1 < ax_2$ (because $a > 0$) and $x_1^3 < x_2^3$. So we have $x_1^3 + ax_1 < x_2^3 + ax_2$, and hence $Q(x_1) < Q(x_2)$. Thus Q is increasing, that is, its graph always rises, and so it has no local extrema.

77. $P(x) = 8x + 0.3x^2 - 0.0013x^3 - 372$

(b) For the firm to break even, $P(x) = 0$. From the graph, we see that $P(x) = 0$ when $x \approx 25.2$. Of course, the firm cannot produce fractions of a blender, so the manufacturer must produce at least 26 blenders a year.

(c) No, the profit does not increase indefinitely. The largest profit is approximately $ 3276.22, which occurs when the firm produces 166 blenders per year.

78. $P(t) = 120t - 0.4t^4 + 1000$

(b) A maximum population of approximately 1380 is attained after 4.22 months.

(c) The rabbit population disappears after approximately 8.42 months.

79. **(a)** The length of the bottom is $40 - 2x$, the width of the bottom is $20 - 2x$, and the height is x, so the volume of the box is
$$V = x(20 - 2x)(40 - 2x) = 4x^3 - 120x^2 + 800x.$$

(b) Since the height and width must be positive, we must have $x > 0$ and $20 - 2x > 0$, and so the domain of V is $0 < x < 10$.

(c) Using the domain from part (b), we graph V in the viewing rectangle $[0, 10]$ by $[0, 1600]$. The maximum volume is $V \approx 1539.6$ when $x = 4.23$.

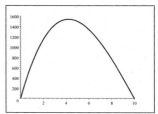

80. **(a)** Let h be the height of the box. Then the total length of all 12 edges is $8x + 4h = 144$ in. Thus, $8x + 4h = 144 \quad \Leftrightarrow \quad 2x + h = 36 \quad \Leftrightarrow \quad h = 36 - 2x$. The volume of the box is equal to (area of base) $\times$ (height) $= (x^2) \times (36 - 2x) = -2x^3 + 36x^2$. Therefore, the volume of the box is $V(x) = -2x^3 + 36x^2 = 2x^2(18 - x)$.

(b) Since the length of the base is x, we must have $x > 0$. Likewise, the height must be positive so $36 - 2x > 0 \quad \Leftrightarrow \quad x < 18$. Putting these together, we get that the domain of V is $0 < x < 18$.

(c) Using the domain from part (b), we graph V in the viewing rectangle $[0, 18]$ by $[0, 2000]$. The maximum volume is $V = 1728$ in^3 when $x = 12$ in.

81.

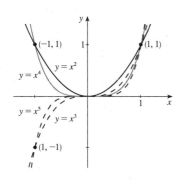

The graph of $y = x^{100}$ is close to the x-axis for $|x| < 1$, but passes through the points $(1, 1)$ and $(-1, 1)$. The graph of $y = x^{101}$ behaves similarly except that the y-values are negative for negative values of x, and it passes through $(-1, -1)$ instead of $(-1, 1)$.

82. Since the polynomial shown has five zeros, it has at least five factors, and so the degree of the polynomial is greater than or equal to 5.

83. No, it is impossible. The end behavior of a third degree polynomial is the same as that of $y = kx^3$, and for this function, the values of y go off in opposite directions as $x \to \infty$ and $x \to -\infty$. But for a function with just one extremum, the values of y would head off in the same direction (either both up or both down) on either side of the extremum. An nth-degree polynomial can have $n - 1$ extrema or $n - 3$ extrema or $n - 5$ extrema, and so on (decreasing by 2). A polynomial that has six local extrema must be of degree 7 or higher. For example, $P(x) = (x - 1)(x - 2)(x - 3)(x - 4)(x - 5)(x - 6)(x - 7)$ has six local extrema.

84. No, it is not possible. Clearly a polynomial must have a local minimum between any two local maxima.

3.2   Dividing Polynomials

1.

$$
\begin{array}{r}
3x-\ 4 \\
x+3 \enclose{longdiv}{3x^2+5x-4} \\
\underline{3x^2+9x} \\
-4x-4 \\
\underline{-4x-12} \\
8
\end{array}
$$

Thus the quotient is $3x - 4$ and the remainder is 8, so
$P(x) = 3x^2 + 5x - 4 = (x + 3) \cdot (3x - 4) + 8$.

2. *Long division:*

$$
\begin{array}{r}
x^2 +\ 5x\ -\ 1 \\
x-1 \enclose{longdiv}{x^3 + 4x^2 - 6x + 1} \\
\underline{x^3 -\ x^2} \\
5x^2 - 6x \\
\underline{5x^2 - 5x} \\
-x + 1 \\
\underline{-x + 1} \\
0
\end{array}
$$

Thus
$$P(x) = x^3 + 4x^2 - 6x + 1 = (x - 1) \cdot (x^2 + 5x - 1).$$
Synthetic division:

$$
\begin{array}{r|rrrr}
1 & 1 & 4 & -6 & 1 \\
  &   & 1 & 5 & -1 \\
\hline
  & 1 & 5 & -1 & 0
\end{array}
$$

Thus the quotient is $x^2 + 5x - 1$ and the remainder is 0, as above.

3.

$$
\begin{array}{r}
x^2 \qquad\ -\ 1 \\
2x-3 \enclose{longdiv}{2x^3 - 3x^2 - 2x} \\
\underline{2x^3 - 3x^2} \\
-2x \\
\underline{-2x + 3} \\
-3
\end{array}
$$

Thus the quotient is $x^2 - 1$ and the remainder is -3, and
$P(x) = 2x^3 - 3x^2 - 2x = (x^2 - 1)(2x - 3) - 3$.

4.

$$
\begin{array}{r}
2x^2 -\ x\ +\ 4 \\
2x+1 \enclose{longdiv}{4x^3 \qquad\ + 7x + 9} \\
\underline{4x^3 + 2x^2} \\
-2x^2 + 7x \\
\underline{-2x^2 -\ x} \\
8x + 9 \\
\underline{8x + 4} \\
5
\end{array}
$$

Thus
$$P(x) = 4x^3 + 7x + 9 = (2x^2 - x + 4)(2x + 1) + 5.$$

5.

$$
\begin{array}{r}
x^2 - x - 3 \\
x^2 + 3 \enclose{longdiv}{x^4 - x^3 + 0x^2 + 4x + 2} \\
\underline{x^4 + 3x^2} \\
-x^3 - 3x^2 + 4x \\
\underline{-x^2 - 3x} \\
-3x^2 + 7x + 2 \\
\underline{-3x^2 - 9} \\
7x + 11
\end{array}
$$

Thus the quotient is $x^2 - x - 3$ and the remainder is $7x + 11$, and

$$P(x) = x^3 + 4x^2 - 6x + 1$$
$$= (x^2 + 3) \cdot (x^2 - x - 3) + (7x + 11)$$

6.

$$
\begin{array}{r}
2x^3 + 4x^2 + 8 \\
x^2 - 2 \enclose{longdiv}{x^5 + 4x^4 - 4x^3 + 0x^2 - x - 3} \\
\underline{x^5 - 4x^3} \\
4x^4 + 0x^2 \\
\underline{4x^4 - 8x^2} \\
8x^2 - x - 3 \\
\underline{8x^2 - 16} \\
-x + 13
\end{array}
$$

Thus

$$P(x) = 2x^5 + 4x^4 - 4x^3 - x - 3$$
$$= (x^2 - 2) \cdot (2x^3 + 4x^2 + 8) + (-x + 13)$$

7.

$$
\begin{array}{r|rrr}
-3 & 1 & 4 & -8 \\
& & -3 & -3 \\
\hline
& 1 & 1 & -11
\end{array}
$$

Thus the quotient is $x + 1$ and the remainder is -11, and

$$\frac{P(x)}{D(x)} = \frac{x^2 + 4x - 8}{x + 3} = (x + 1) + \frac{-11}{x + 3}.$$

8.

$$
\begin{array}{r|rrrr}
4 & 1 & 0 & 6 & 5 \\
& & 4 & 16 & 88 \\
\hline
& 1 & 4 & 22 & 93
\end{array}
$$

Thus the quotient is $x^2 + 4x + 22$ and the remainder is 93, and $\dfrac{P(x)}{D(x)} = \dfrac{x^3 + 6x + 5}{x - 4} = (x^2 + 4x + 22) + \dfrac{93}{x - 4}.$

9.

$$
\begin{array}{r}
2x - \tfrac{1}{2} \\
2x - 1 \enclose{longdiv}{4x^2 - 3x - 7} \\
\underline{4x^2 - 2x} \\
-x - 7 \\
\underline{-x + \tfrac{1}{2}} \\
-\tfrac{15}{2}
\end{array}
$$

Thus the quotient is $2x - \tfrac{1}{2}$ and the remainder is $-\tfrac{15}{2}$, and

$$\frac{P(x)}{D(x)} = \frac{4x^2 - 3x - 7}{2x - 1} = \left(2x - \tfrac{1}{2}\right) + \frac{-\tfrac{15}{2}}{2x - 1}.$$

10.

$$
\begin{array}{r}
2x^2 + 3x \\
3x - 4 \enclose{longdiv}{6x^3 + x^2 - 12x + 5} \\
\underline{6x^3 - 8x^2} \\
9x^2 - 12x \\
\underline{9x^2 - 12x} \\
5
\end{array}
$$

Thus the quotient is $2x^2 + 3x$ and the remainder is 5, and

$$\frac{P(x)}{D(x)} = \frac{6x^3 + x^2 - 12x + 5}{3x - 4} = (2x^2 + 3x) + \frac{5}{3x - 4}.$$

11.

$$
\begin{array}{r}
2x^2 - x + 1 \\
x^2 + 4 \enclose{longdiv}{2x^4 - x^3 + 9x^2} \\
\underline{2x^4 + 8x^2} \\
-x^3 + x^2 \\
\underline{-x^3 - 4x} \\
x^2 + 4x \\
\underline{x^2 + 4} \\
4x - 4
\end{array}
$$

Thus the quotient is $2x^2 - x + 1$ and the remainder is $4x - 4$, and

$$\frac{P(x)}{D(x)} = \frac{2x^4 - x^3 + 9x^2}{x^2 + 4} = (2x^2 - x + 1) + \frac{4x - 4}{x^2 + 4}.$$

12.

$$
\begin{array}{r}
x^3 - x + 1 \\
x^2 + x - 1 \enclose{longdiv}{x^5 + x^4 - 2x^3 + 0x^2 + x + 1} \\
\underline{x^5 + x^4 - x^3} \\
-x^3 + x \\
\underline{-x^3 - x^2 + x} \\
x^2 + 1 \\
\underline{x^2 + x - 1} \\
-x + 2
\end{array}
$$

Thus the quotient is $x^3 - x + 1$ and the remainder is $-x + 2$, and

$$\frac{P(x)}{D(x)} = \frac{x^5 + x^4 - 2x^3 + x + 1}{x^2 + x - 1}$$
$$= (x^3 - x + 1) + \frac{-x + 2}{x^2 + x - 1}$$

13.

$$
\begin{array}{r}
x - 2 \\
x - 4 \enclose{longdiv}{x^2 - 6x - 8} \\
\underline{x^2 - 4x} \\
-2x - 8 \\
\underline{-2x + 8} \\
-16
\end{array}
$$

Thus the quotient is $x - 2$ and the remainder is -16.

14.

$$
\begin{array}{r}
x^2 + x \\
x - 2 \enclose{longdiv}{x^3 - x^2 - 2x + 6} \\
\underline{x^3 - 2x^2} \\
x^2 - 2x \\
\underline{x^2 - 2x} \\
6
\end{array}
$$

Thus the quotient is $x^2 + x$, and the remainder is 6.

15.

$$
\begin{array}{r}
2x^2 \qquad - 1 \\
2x + 1 \enclose{longdiv}{4x^3 + 2x^2 - 2x - 3} \\
\underline{4x^3 + 2x^2} \\
-2x - 3 \\
\underline{-2x - 1} \\
- 2
\end{array}
$$

Thus the quotient is $2x^2 - 1$ and the remainder is -2.

16.

$$
\begin{array}{r}
\frac{1}{3}x^2 + \frac{1}{3}x + \frac{2}{3} \\
3x + 6 \enclose{longdiv}{x^3 + 3x^2 + 4x + 3} \\
\underline{x^3 + 2x^2} \\
x^2 + 4x \\
\underline{x^2 + 2x} \\
2x + 3 \\
\underline{2x + 4} \\
-1
\end{array}
$$

Thus the quotient is $\frac{1}{3}x^2 + \frac{1}{3}x + \frac{2}{3}$, and the remainder is -1.

17.

$$
\begin{array}{r}
x + 2 \\
x^2 - 2x + 2 \enclose{longdiv}{x^3 + 0x^2 + 6x + 3} \\
\underline{x^3 - 2x^2 + 2x} \\
2x^2 + 4x + 3 \\
\underline{2x^2 - 4x + 4} \\
8x - 1
\end{array}
$$

Thus the quotient is $x + 2$, and the remainder is $8x - 1$.

18.

$$
\begin{array}{r}
3x^2 - 8x - 1 \\
x^2 + x + 3 \enclose{longdiv}{3x^4 - 5x^3 + 0x^2 - 20x - 5} \\
\underline{3x^4 + 3x^3 + 9x^2} \\
-8x^3 - 9x^2 - 20x \\
\underline{-8x^3 - 8x^2 - 24x} \\
-x^2 + 4x - 5 \\
\underline{-x^2 - x - 3} \\
5x - 2
\end{array}
$$

Thus the quotient is $3x^2 - 8x - 1$, and the remainder is $5x - 2$.

19.

$$
\begin{array}{r}
3x + 1 \\
2x^2 + 0x + 5 \enclose{longdiv}{6x^3 + 2x^2 + 22x + 0} \\
\underline{6x^3 \qquad + 15x} \\
2x^2 + 7x + 0 \\
\underline{2x^2 \qquad + 5} \\
7x - 5
\end{array}
$$

Thus the quotient is $3x + 1$, and the remainder is $7x - 5$.

20.

$$
\begin{array}{r}
3 \\
3x^2 - 7x \enclose{longdiv}{9x^2 - x + 5} \\
\underline{9x^2 - 21x} \\
20x + 5
\end{array}
$$

Thus the quotient is 3, and the remainder is $20x + 5$.

21.

$$
\begin{array}{r}
x^4 \qquad\qquad\qquad\quad + 1 \\
x^2 + 1 \enclose{longdiv}{x^6 + 0x^5 + x^4 + 0x^3 + x^2 + 0x + 1} \\
\underline{x^6 \qquad\quad + x^4} \\
0 \qquad\qquad + x^2 \qquad + 1 \\
\underline{x^2 \qquad + 1} \\
0
\end{array}
$$

Thus the quotient is $x^4 + 1$, and the remainder is 0.

22.

$$
\begin{array}{r}
\frac{1}{2}x^3 - x^2 - \frac{5}{2}x - \frac{7}{4} \\
4x^2 - 6x + 8 \enclose{longdiv}{2x^5 - 7x^4 + 0x^3 + 0x^2 + 0x - 13} \\
\underline{2x^5 - 3x^4 + 4x^3} \\
-4x^4 - 4x^3 + 0x^2 \\
\underline{-4x^4 + 6x^3 - 8x^2} \\
-10x^3 + 8x^2 + 0x \\
\underline{-10x^3 + 15x^2 - 20x} \\
-7x^2 + 20x - 13 \\
\underline{-7x^2 + \frac{21}{2}x - 14} \\
\frac{19}{2}x + 1
\end{array}
$$

Thus the quotient is $\frac{1}{2}x^3 - x^2 - \frac{5}{2}x - \frac{7}{4}$, and the remainder is $\frac{19}{2}x + 1$.

23. The synthetic division table for this problem takes the following form.

$$
\begin{array}{r|rrr}
3 & 1 & -5 & 4 \\
  &   & 3 & -6 \\
\hline
  & 1 & -2 & -2
\end{array}
$$

Thus the quotient is $x - 2$, and the remainder is -2.

24. The synthetic division table for this problem takes the following form.

$$
\begin{array}{r|rrr}
1 & 1 & -5 & 4 \\
  &   & 1 & -4 \\
\hline
  & 1 & -4 & 0
\end{array}
$$

Thus the quotient is $x - 4$, and the remainder is 0.

25. The synthetic division table for this problem takes the following form.

$$
\begin{array}{r|rrr}
6 & 3 & 5 & 0 \\
  &   & 18 & 138 \\
\hline
  & 3 & 23 & 138
\end{array}
$$

Thus the quotient is $3x + 23$, and the remainder is 138.

26. The synthetic division table for this problem takes the following form.

$$
\begin{array}{r|rrr}
-5 & 4 & 0 & -3 \\
   &   & -20 & 100 \\
\hline
   & 4 & -20 & 97
\end{array}
$$

Thus the quotient is $4x - 20$, and the remainder is 97.

27. Since $x + 2 = x - (-2)$, the synthetic division table for this problem takes the following form.

$$
\begin{array}{r|rrrr}
-2 & 1 & 2 & 2 & 1 \\
   &   & -2 & 0 & -4 \\
\hline
   & 1 & 0 & 2 & -3
\end{array}
$$

Thus the quotient is $x^2 + 2$, and the remainder is -3.

28. The synthetic division table for this problem takes the following form.

$$
\begin{array}{r|rrrr}
5 & 3 & -12 & -9 & 1 \\
  &   & 15 & 15 & 30 \\
\hline
  & 3 & 3 & 6 & 31
\end{array}
$$

Thus the quotient is $3x^2 + 3x + 6$, and the remainder is 31.

29. Since $x + 3 = x - (-3)$ and $x^3 - 8x + 2 = x^3 + 0x^2 - 8x + 2$, the synthetic division table for this problem takes the following form.

$$
\begin{array}{r|rrrr}
-3 & 1 & 0 & -8 & 2 \\
   &   & -3 & 9 & -3 \\
\hline
   & 1 & -3 & 1 & -1
\end{array}
$$

Thus the quotient is $x^2 - 3x + 1$, and the remainder is -1.

30. The synthetic division table for this problem takes the following form.

$$
\begin{array}{r|rrrrr}
2 & 1 & -1 & 1 & -1 & 2 \\
  &   & 2 & 2 & 6 & 10 \\
\hline
  & 1 & 1 & 3 & 5 & 12
\end{array}
$$

Thus the quotient is $x^3 + x^2 + 3x + 5$, and the remainder is 12.

31. Since $x^5 + 3x^3 - 6 = x^5 + 0x^4 + 3x^3 + 0x^2 + 0x - 6$, the synthetic division table for this problem takes the following form.

$$
\begin{array}{r|rrrrrr}
1 & 1 & 0 & 3 & 0 & 0 & -6 \\
  &   & 1 & 1 & 4 & 4 & 4 \\
\hline
  & 1 & 1 & 4 & 4 & 4 & -2
\end{array}
$$

Thus the quotient is $x^4 + x^3 + 4x^2 + 4x + 4$, and the remainder is -2.

32. The synthetic division table for this problem takes the following form.

$$
\begin{array}{r|rrrr}
3 & 1 & -9 & 27 & -27 \\
  &   & 3 & -18 & 27 \\
\hline
  & 1 & -6 & 9 & 0
\end{array}
$$

Thus the quotient is $x^2 - 6x + 9$, and the remainder is 0.

33. The synthetic division table for this problem takes the following form.

$$
\begin{array}{r|rrrr}
\frac{1}{2} & 2 & 3 & -2 & 1 \\
  &   & 1 & 2 & 0 \\
\hline
  & 2 & 4 & 0 & 1
\end{array}
$$

Thus the quotient is $2x^2 + 4x$, and the remainder is 1.

34. The synthetic division table for this problem takes the following form.

$$
\begin{array}{r|rrrrr}
-\frac{2}{3} & 6 & 10 & 5 & 1 & 1 \\
  &   & -4 & -4 & -\frac{2}{3} & -\frac{2}{9} \\
\hline
  & 6 & 6 & 1 & \frac{1}{3} & \frac{7}{9}
\end{array}
$$

Thus the quotient is $6x^3 + 6x^2 + x + \frac{1}{3}$, and the remainder is $\frac{7}{9}$.

35. Since $x^3 - 27 = x^3 + 0x^2 + 0x - 27$, the synthetic division table for this problem takes the following form.

$$
\begin{array}{r|rrrr}
3 & 1 & 0 & 0 & -27 \\
  &   & 3 & 9 & 27 \\
\hline
  & 1 & 3 & 9 & 0
\end{array}
$$

Thus the quotient is $x^2 + 3x + 9$, and the remainder is 0.

36. The synthetic division table for this problem takes the following form.

$$
\begin{array}{r|rrrrr}
-2 & 1 & 0 & 0 & 0 & -16 \\
  &   & -2 & 4 & -8 & 16 \\
\hline
  & 1 & -2 & 4 & -8 & 0
\end{array}
$$

Thus the quotient is $x^3 - 2x^2 + 4x - 8$, and the remainder is 0.

37. $P(x) = 4x^2 + 12x + 5$, $c = -1$

$$
\begin{array}{r|rrr}
-1 & 4 & 12 & 5 \\
  &   & -4 & -8 \\
\hline
  & 4 & 8 & -3
\end{array}
$$

Therefore, by the Remainder Theorem, $P(-1) = -3$.

38. $P(x) = 2x^2 + 9x + 1$, $c = \frac{1}{2}$

$$
\begin{array}{r|rrr}
\frac{1}{2} & 2 & 9 & 1 \\
  &   & 1 & 5 \\
\hline
  & 2 & 10 & 6
\end{array}
$$

Therefore, by the Remainder Theorem, $P\left(\frac{1}{2}\right) = 6$.

39. $P(x) = x^3 + 3x^2 - 7x + 6$, $c = 2$

$$
\begin{array}{r|rrrr}
2 & 1 & 3 & -7 & 6 \\
  &   & 2 & 10 & 6 \\
\hline
  & 1 & 5 & 3 & 12
\end{array}
$$

Therefore, by the Remainder Theorem, $P(2) = 12$.

40. $P(x) = x^3 - x^2 + x + 5$, $c = -1$

$$
\begin{array}{r|rrrr}
-1 & 1 & -1 & 1 & 5 \\
  &   & -1 & 2 & -3 \\
\hline
  & 1 & -2 & 3 & 2
\end{array}
$$

Therefore, by the Remainder Theorem, $P(-1) = 2$.

41. $P(x) = x^3 + 2x^2 - 7$, $c = -2$

$$
\begin{array}{r|rrrr}
-2 & 1 & 2 & 0 & -7 \\
   &   & -2 & 0 & 0 \\
\hline
   & 1 & 0 & 0 & -7
\end{array}
$$

Therefore, by the Remainder Theorem, $P(-2) = -7$.

42. $P(x) = 2x^3 - 21x^2 + 9x - 200$, $c = 11$

$$
\begin{array}{r|rrrr}
11 & 2 & -21 & 9 & -200 \\
   &   & 22 & 11 & 220 \\
\hline
   & 2 & 1 & 20 & 20
\end{array}
$$

Therefore, by the Remainder Theorem, $P(11) = 20$.

43. $P(x) = 5x^4 + 30x^3 - 40x^2 + 36x + 14$, $c = -7$

$$
\begin{array}{r|rrrrr}
-7 & 5 & 30 & -40 & 36 & 14 \\
   &   & -35 & 35 & 35 & -497 \\
\hline
   & 5 & -5 & -5 & 71 & -483
\end{array}
$$

Therefore, by the Remainder Theorem, $P(-7) = -483$.

44. $P(x) = 6x^5 + 10x^3 + x + 1$, $c = -2$

$$
\begin{array}{r|rrrrrr}
-2 & 6 & 0 & 10 & 0 & 1 & 1 \\
   &   & -12 & 24 & -68 & 136 & -274 \\
\hline
   & 6 & -12 & 34 & -68 & 137 & -273
\end{array}
$$

Therefore, by the Remainder Theorem, $P(-2) = -273$.

45. $P(x) = x^7 - 3x^2 - 1$
$\qquad = x^7 + 0x^6 + 0x^5 + 0x^4 + 0x^3 - 3x^2 + 0x - 1$

$c = 3$

$$
\begin{array}{r|rrrrrrrr}
3 & 1 & 0 & 0 & 0 & 0 & -3 & 0 & -1 \\
  &   & 3 & 9 & 27 & 81 & 243 & 720 & 2160 \\
\hline
  & 1 & 3 & 9 & 27 & 81 & 240 & 720 & 2159
\end{array}
$$

Therefore by the Remainder Theorem, $P(3) = 2159$.

46. $P(x) = -2x^6 + 7x^5 + 40x^4 - 7x^2 + 10x + 112$, $c = -3$

$$
\begin{array}{r|rrrrrrr}
-3 & -2 & 7 & 40 & 0 & -7 & 10 & 112 \\
   &   & 6 & -39 & -3 & 9 & -6 & -12 \\
\hline
   & -2 & 13 & 1 & -3 & 2 & 4 & 100
\end{array}
$$

Therefore, by the Remainder Theorem, $P(-3) = 100$.

47. $P(x) = 3x^3 + 4x^2 - 2x + 1$, $c = \frac{2}{3}$

$$
\begin{array}{r|rrrr}
\frac{2}{3} & 3 & 4 & -2 & 1 \\
            &   & 2 & 4 & \frac{4}{3} \\
\hline
            & 3 & 6 & 2 & \frac{7}{3}
\end{array}
$$

Therefore, by the Remainder Theorem, $P\left(\frac{2}{3}\right) = \frac{7}{3}$.

48. $P(x) = x^3 - x + 1$, $c = \frac{1}{4}$

$$
\begin{array}{r|rrrr}
\frac{1}{4} & 1 & 0 & -1 & 1 \\
            &   & \frac{1}{4} & \frac{1}{16} & -\frac{15}{64} \\
\hline
            & 1 & \frac{1}{4} & -\frac{15}{16} & \frac{49}{64}
\end{array}
$$

Therefore, by the Remainder Theorem, $P\left(\frac{1}{4}\right) = \frac{49}{64}$.

49. $P(x) = x^3 + 2x^2 - 3x - 8$, $c = 0.1$

$$
\begin{array}{r|rrrr}
0.1 & 1 & 2 & -3 & -8 \\
    &   & 0.1 & 0.21 & -0.279 \\
\hline
    & 1 & 2.1 & -2.79 & -8.279
\end{array}
$$

Therefore, by the Remainder Theorem, $P(0.1) = -8.279$.

50. (a) $P(x) = 6x^7 - 40x^6 + 16x^5 - 200x^4 - 60x^3 - 69x^2 + 13x - 139$, $c = 7$

$$
\begin{array}{r|rrrrrrrr}
7 & 6 & -40 & 16 & -200 & -60 & -69 & 13 & -139 \\
  &   & 42 & 14 & 210 & 70 & 70 & 7 & 140 \\
\hline
  & 6 & 2 & 30 & 10 & 10 & 1 & 20 & 1
\end{array}
$$

Therefore, by the Remainder Theorem, $P(7) = 1$.

(b) $P(7) = 6(7)^7 - 40(7)^6 + 16(7)^5 - 200(7)^4 - 60(7)^3 - 69(7)^2 + 13(7) - 139$
$\qquad = 6(823{,}543) - 40(117{,}649) + 16(16{,}807) - 200(2401) - 60(343) - 69(49) + 13(7) - 139 = 1$

which agrees with the value obtained by synthetic division, but requires more work.

51. $P(x) = x^3 - 3x^2 + 3x - 1, c = 1$

$$
\begin{array}{r|rrrr}
1 & 1 & -3 & 3 & -1 \\
  &   & 1 & -2 & 1 \\
\hline
  & 1 & -2 & 1 & 0
\end{array}
$$

Since the remainder is 0, $x - 1$ is a factor.

52. $P(x) = x^3 + 2x^2 - 3x - 10, c = 2$

$$
\begin{array}{r|rrrr}
2 & 1 & 2 & -3 & -10 \\
  &   & 2 & 8 & 10 \\
\hline
  & 1 & 4 & 5 & 0
\end{array}
$$

Since the remainder is 0, $x - 2$ is a factor.

53. $P(x) = 2x^3 + 7x^2 + 6x - 5, c = \frac{1}{2}$

$$
\begin{array}{r|rrrr}
\frac{1}{2} & 2 & 7 & 6 & -5 \\
            &   & 1 & 4 & 5 \\
\hline
            & 2 & 8 & 10 & 0
\end{array}
$$

Since the remainder is 0, $x - \frac{1}{2}$ is a factor.

54. $P(x) = x^4 + 3x^3 - 16x^2 - 27x + 63, c = 3, -3$

$$
\begin{array}{r|rrrrr}
3 & 1 & 3 & -16 & -27 & 63 \\
  &   & 3 & 18 & 6 & -63 \\
\hline
  & 1 & 6 & 2 & -21 & 0
\end{array}
$$

Since the remainder is 0, $x - 3$ is a factor. We next show that $x + 3$ is also a factor by using synthetic division on the quotient of the above synthetic division,
$x^3 + 6x^2 - 2x - 21$.

$$
\begin{array}{r|rrrr}
-3 & 1 & 6 & 2 & -21 \\
   &   & -3 & -9 & 21 \\
\hline
   & 1 & 3 & -7 & 0
\end{array}
$$

Since the remainder is 0, $x + 3$ is a factor.

55. $P(x) = x^3 - x^2 - 11x + 15, c = 3$

$$
\begin{array}{r|rrrr}
3 & 1 & -1 & -11 & 15 \\
  &   & 3 & 6 & -15 \\
\hline
  & 1 & 2 & -5 & 0
\end{array}
$$

Since the remainder is 0, we know that 3 is a zero
$x^3 - x^2 - 11x + 15 = (x - 3)(x^2 + 2x - 5)$. Now
$x^2 + 2x - 5 = 0$ when $x = \frac{-2 \pm \sqrt{2^2 + 4(1)(5)}}{2} = -1 \pm \sqrt{6}$.
Hence, the zeros are $-1 - \sqrt{6}, -1 + \sqrt{6}$, and 3.

56. $P(x) = 3x^4 - x^3 - 21x^2 - 11x + 6, c = \frac{1}{3}, -2$.

$$
\begin{array}{r|rrrrr}
\frac{1}{3} & 3 & -1 & -21 & -11 & 6 \\
            &   & 1 & 0 & -7 & -6 \\
\hline
            & 3 & 0 & -21 & -18 & 0
\end{array}
$$

Since the remainder is 0, it follows that $\frac{1}{3}$ is a zero. Thus
$P(x) = \left(x - \frac{1}{3}\right)(3x^3 - 21x - 18)$. Next, we use
synthetic division on the quotient.

$$
\begin{array}{r|rrrr}
-2 & 3 & 0 & -21 & -18 \\
   &   & -6 & 12 & 18 \\
\hline
   & 3 & -6 & -9 & 0
\end{array}
$$

Since the remainder is 0, it follows that 2 is a zero. So

$$
\begin{aligned}
P(x) &= \left(x - \tfrac{1}{3}\right)(x + 2)(3x^2 - 6x - 9) \\
&= 3\left(x - \tfrac{1}{3}\right)(x + 2)(x^2 - 2x - 3) \\
&= 3\left(x - \tfrac{1}{3}\right)(x + 2)(x - 3)(x + 1)
\end{aligned}
$$

Hence, the zeros are $\frac{1}{3}, -2, -1$, and 3.

57. Since the zeros are $x = -1$, $x = 1$, and $x = 3$, the factors are $x + 1$, $x - 1$, and $x - 3$. Thus
$P(x) = (x + 1)(x - 1)(x - 3) = x^3 - 3x^2 - x + 3$.

58. Since the zeros are $x = -2$, $x = 0$, $x = 2$, and $x = 4$, the factors are $x + 2$, x, $x - 2$, and $x - 4$. Thus
$P(x) = c(x + 2)x(x - 2)(x - 4)$. If we let $c = 1$, then $P(x) = x^4 - 4x^3 - 4x^2 + 16x$.

59. Since the zeros are $x = -1$, $x = 1$, $x = 3$, and $x = 5$, the factors are $x + 1$, $x - 1$, $x - 3$, and $x - 5$. Thus
$P(x) = (x + 1)(x - 1)(x - 3)(x - 5) = x^4 - 8x^3 + 14x^2 + 8x - 15$.

60. Since the zeros are $x = -2$, $x = -1$, $x = 0$, $x = 1$, and $x = 2$, the factors are $x + 2$, $x + 1$, x, $x - 1$, and $x - 2$. Thus $P(x) = c(x + 2)(x + 1)x(x - 1)(x - 2)$. If we let $c = 1$, then $P(x) = x^5 - 5x^3 + 4x$.

61. Since the zeros of the polynomial are 1, -2, and 3, it follows that
$$P(x) = C(x - 1)(x + 2)(x - 3) = C(x^3 - 2x^2 - 5x + 6) = Cx^3 - 2Cx^2 - 5Cx + 6C.$$ Since the coefficient of x^2 is to be 3, $-2C = 3$ so $C = -\frac{3}{2}$. Therefore, $P(x) = -\frac{3}{2}(x^3 - 2x^2 - 5x + 6) = -\frac{3}{2}x^3 + 3x^2 + \frac{15}{2}x - 9$ is the polynomial.

62. Since the zeros of the polynomial are 1, -1, 2, and $\frac{1}{2}$, it follows that
$P(x) = C(x - 1)(x + 1)(x - 2)\left(x - \frac{1}{2}\right) = C(x^2 - 1)\left(x^2 - \frac{5}{2}x + 1\right)$. To ensure integer coefficients, we choose C to be any nonzero multiple of 2. When $C = 2$, we have
$P(x) = 2(x^2 - 1)\left(x^2 - \frac{5}{2}x + 1\right) = (x^2 - 1)(2x^2 - 5x + 2) = 2x^4 - 5x^3 + 5x - 2$. (Note: This is just one of many polynomials with the desired zeros and integer coefficients. We can choose C to be any even integer.)

63. The y-intercept is 2 and the zeros of the polynomial are -1, 1, and 2. It follows that
$P(x) = C(x + 1)(x - 1)(x - 2) = C(x^3 - 2x^2 - x + 2)$. Since $P(0) = 2$ we have $2 = C\left[(0)^3 - 2(0)^2 - (0) + 2\right]$
$\Leftrightarrow \quad 2 = 2C \Leftrightarrow C = 1$ and $P(x) = (x + 1)(x - 1)(x - 2) = x^3 - 2x^2 - x + 2$.

64. The y-intercept is 4 and the zeros of the polynomial are -1 and 2 with 2 being degree two. It follows that
$P(x) = C(x + 1)(x - 2)^2 = C(x^3 - 3x^2 + 4)$. Since $P(0) = 4$ we have $4 = C\left[(0)^3 - 3(0)^2 + 4\right] \quad \Leftrightarrow \quad 4 = 4C$
$\Leftrightarrow \quad C = 1$ and $P(x) = x^3 - 3x^2 + 4$.

65. The y-intercept is 4 and the zeros of the polynomial are -2 and 1 both being degree two. It follows that $P(x) = C(x + 2)^2(x - 1)^2 = C(x^4 + 2x^3 - 3x^2 - 4x + 4)$. Since $P(0) = 4$ we have $4 = C\left[(0)^4 + 2(0)^3 - 3(0)^2 - 4(0) + 4\right] \quad \Leftrightarrow \quad 4 = 4C \Leftrightarrow C = 1$. Thus $P(x) = (x + 2)^2(x - 1)^2 = x^4 + 2x^3 - 3x^2 - 4x + 4$.

66. The y-intercept is 2 and the zeros of the polynomial are -2, -1, and 1 with 1 being degree two. It follows that $P(x) = C(x + 2)(x + 1)(x - 1)^2 = C(x^4 + x^3 - 3x^2 - x + 2)$. Since $P(0) = 2$ we have $4 = C\left[(0)^4 + (0)^3 - 3(0)^2 - (0) + 2\right] \quad \Leftrightarrow \quad 2 = 2C$ so $C = 1$ and $P(x) = x^4 + x^3 - 3x^2 - x + 2$.

67. **A.** By the Remainder Theorem, the remainder when $P(x) = 6x^{1000} - 17x^{562} + 12x + 26$ is divided by $x + 1$ is $P(-1) = 6(-1)^{1000} - 17(-1)^{562} + 12(-1) + 26 = 6 - 17 - 12 + 26 = 3$.
B. If $x - 1$ is a factor of $Q(x) = x^{567} - 3x^{400} + x^9 + 2$, then $Q(1)$ must equal 0.
$Q(1) = (1)^{567} - 3(1)^{400} + (1)^9 + 2 = 1 - 3 + 1 + 2 = 1 \neq 0$, so $x - 1$ is not a factor.

68. $R(x) = x^5 - 2x^4 + 3x^3 - 2x^2 + 3x + 4 = (x^4 - 2x^3 + 3x^2 - 2x + 3)x + 4 = ((x^3 - 2x^2 + 3x - 2)x + 3)x + 4 = (((x^2 - 2x + 3)x - 2)x + 3)x + 4 = ((((x - 2)x + 3)x - 2)x + 3)x + 4$
So to calculate $R(3)$, we start with 3, then subtract 2, multiply by 3, add 3, multiply by 3, subtract 2, multiply by 3, add 3, multiply by 3, and add 4, to get 157.

3.3   **Real Zeros of Polynomials**

1. $P(x) = x^3 - 4x^2 + 3$ has possible rational zeros ± 1 and ± 3.

2. $Q(x) = x^4 - 3x^3 - 6x + 8$ has possible rational zeros ± 1, ± 2, ± 4, ± 8.

3. $R(x) = 2x^5 + 3x^3 + 4x^2 - 8$ has possible rational zeros ± 1, ± 2, ± 4, ± 8, $\pm \frac{1}{2}$.

4. $S(x) = 6x^4 - x^2 + 2x + 12$ has possible rational zeros ± 1, ± 2, ± 3, ± 4, ± 6, ± 12, $\pm \frac{1}{2}$, $\pm \frac{3}{2}$, $\pm \frac{1}{3}$, $\pm \frac{2}{3}$, $\pm \frac{4}{3}$, $\pm \frac{1}{6}$.

5. $T(x) = 4x^4 - 2x^2 - 7$ has possible rational zeros ± 1, ± 7, $\pm \frac{1}{2}$, $\pm \frac{7}{2}$, $\pm \frac{1}{4}$, $\pm \frac{7}{4}$.

6. $U(x) = 12x^5 + 6x^3 - 2x - 8$ has possible rational zeros ± 1, ± 2, ± 4, ± 8, $\pm \frac{1}{2}$, $\pm \frac{1}{3}$, $\pm \frac{2}{3}$, $\pm \frac{4}{3}$, $\pm \frac{8}{3}$, $\pm \frac{1}{4}$, $\pm \frac{1}{6}$, $\pm \frac{1}{12}$.

7. (a) $P(x) = 5x^3 - x^2 - 5x + 1$ has possible rational zeros $\pm 1, \pm \frac{1}{5}$.

(b) From the graph, the actual zeroes are -1, $\frac{1}{5}$, and 1.

8. (a) $P(x) = 3x^3 + 4x^2 - x - 2$ has possible rational zeros $\pm 1, \pm 2, \pm \frac{1}{3}, \pm \frac{2}{3}$.

(b) From the graph, the actual zeroes are -1 and $\frac{2}{3}$.

9. (a) $P(x) = 2x^4 - 9x^3 + 9x^2 + x - 3$ has possible rational zeros $\pm 1, \pm 3, \pm \frac{1}{2}, \pm \frac{3}{2}$.

(b) From the graph, the actual zeroes are $-\frac{1}{2}$, 1, and 3.

10. (a) $P(x) = 4x^4 - x^3 - 4x + 1$ has possible rational zeros $\pm 1, \pm \frac{1}{2}, \pm \frac{1}{4}$.

(b) From the graph, the actual zeroes are $\frac{1}{4}$ and 1.

11. $P(x) = x^3 + 3x^2 - 4$. The possible rational zeros are $\pm 1, \pm 2, \pm 4$. $P(x)$ has 1 variation in sign and hence 1 positive real zero. $P(-x) = -x^3 + 3x^2 - 4$ has 2 variations in sign and hence 0 or 2 negative real zeros.

$$
\begin{array}{r|rrr}
1 & 1 & 3 & 0 & -4 \\
  &   & 1 & 4 & 4 \\
\hline
  & 1 & 4 & 4 & 0
\end{array}
\Rightarrow x = 1 \text{ is a zero.}
$$

$P(x) = x^3 + 3x^2 - 4 = (x - 1)(x^2 + 4x + 4)$
$= (x - 1)(x + 2)^2$

Therefore, the zeros are $x = -2, 1$.

12. $P(x) = x^3 - 7x^2 + 14x - 8$. The possible rational zeros are $\pm 1, \pm 2, \pm 4, \pm 8$. $P(x)$ has 3 variations in sign and hence 1 or 3 positive real zeros.

$P(-x) = -x^3 - 7x^2 - 14x - 8$ has 0 variations in sign and hence no negative real zeros.

$$
\begin{array}{r|rrr}
1 & 1 & -7 & 14 & -8 \\
  &   & 1 & -6 & 8 \\
\hline
  & 1 & -6 & 8 & 0
\end{array}
\Rightarrow x = 1 \text{ is a zero.}
$$

So

$P(x) = x^3 - 7x^2 + 14x - 8 = (x - 1)(x^2 - 6x + 8)$
$= (x - 1)(x - 2)(x - 4)$

Therefore, the zeros are $x = 1, 2, 4$.

13. $P(x) = x^3 - 3x - 2$. The possible rational zeros are $\pm 1, \pm 2$. $P(x)$ has 1 variation in sign and hence 1 positive real zero. $P(-x) = -x^3 + 3x - 2$ has 2 variations in sign and hence 0 or 2 negative real zeros.

$$
\begin{array}{r|rrrr}
1 & 1 & 0 & -3 & -2 \\
  &   & 1 & 1 & -2 \\
\hline
  & 1 & 1 & -2 & -4
\end{array}
\Rightarrow x = 1 \text{ is not a zero.}
\qquad
\begin{array}{r|rrrr}
2 & 1 & 0 & -3 & -2 \\
  &   & 2 & 4 & 2 \\
\hline
  & 1 & 2 & 1 & 0
\end{array}
\Rightarrow x = 2 \text{ is a zero.}
$$

$P(x) = x^3 - 3x - 2 = (x - 2)(x^2 + 2x + 1) = (x - 2)(x + 1)^2$. Therefore, the zeros are $x = 2, -1$.

14. $P(x) = x^3 + 4x^2 - 3x - 18$. The possible rational zeros are $\pm 1, \pm 2, \pm 3, \pm 6, \pm 9, \pm 18$. $P(x)$ has 1 variation in sign and hence 1 positive real zero. $P(-x) = -x^3 + 4x^2 + 3x - 18$ has 2 variations in sign and hence 0 or 2 negative real zeros.

$$
\begin{array}{r|rrrr}
1 & 1 & 4 & -3 & -18 \\
  &   & 1 & 5 & 2 \\
\hline
  & 1 & 5 & 2 & -16
\end{array}
\qquad
\begin{array}{r|rrrr}
2 & 1 & 4 & -3 & -18 \\
  &   & 2 & 12 & 18 \\
\hline
  & 1 & 6 & 9 & 0
\end{array}
\Rightarrow x = 2 \text{ is a zero.}
$$

$P(x) = x^3 + 4x^2 - 3x - 18 = (x - 2)(x^2 + 6x + 9) = (x - 2)(x + 3)^2$. Therefore, the zeros are $x = -3, 2$.

15. $P(x) = x^3 - 6x^2 + 12x - 8$. The possible rational zeros are $\pm 1, \pm 2, \pm 4, \pm 8$. $P(x)$ has 3 variations in sign and hence 1 or 3 positive real zeros. $P(-x) = -x^3 - 6x^2 - 12x - 8$ has no variations in sign and hence 0 negative real zeros.

$$
\begin{array}{r|rrrr}
1 & 1 & -6 & 12 & -8 \\
  &   & 1 & -5 & 7 \\
\hline
  & 1 & -5 & 7 & -1
\end{array}
\Rightarrow x = 1 \text{ is not a zero.}
\qquad
\begin{array}{r|rrrr}
2 & 1 & -6 & 12 & -8 \\
  &   & 2 & -8 & 8 \\
\hline
  & 1 & -4 & 4 & 0
\end{array}
\Rightarrow x = 2 \text{ is a zero.}
$$

$P(x) = x^3 - 6x^2 + 12x - 8 = (x - 2)(x^2 - 4x + 4) = (x - 2)^3$. Therefore, the zero is $x = 2$.

16. $P(x) = x^3 - x^2 - 8x + 12$. The possible rational zeros are ± 1, ± 2, ± 3, ± 4, ± 6, ± 12. $P(x)$ has 2 variations in sign and hence 0 or 2 positive real zeros. $P(-x) = -x^3 - x^2 + 8x + 12$ has 1 variation in sign and hence 1 negative real zero.

$$
\begin{array}{r|rrrr}
1 & 1 & -1 & -8 & 12 \\
  &   & 1 & 0 & -8 \\
\hline
  & 1 & 0 & -8 & 4
\end{array}
\qquad
\begin{array}{r|rrrr}
2 & 1 & -1 & -8 & 12 \\
  &   & 2 & 2 & -12 \\
\hline
  & 1 & 1 & -6 & 0 \quad \Rightarrow x = 2 \text{ is a zero.}
\end{array}
$$

$P(x) = x^3 - x^2 - 8x + 12 = (x - 2)(x^2 + x - 6) = (x - 2)(x + 3)(x - 2)$. Therefore, the zeros are $x = -3, 2$.

17. $P(x) = x^3 - 4x^2 + x + 6$. The possible rational zeros are ± 1, ± 2, ± 3, ± 6. $P(x)$ has 2 variations in sign and hence 0 or 2 positive real zeros. $P(-x) = -x^3 - 4x^2 - x + 6$ has 1 variation in sign and hence 1 negative real zeros.

$$
\begin{array}{r|rrrr}
-1 & 1 & -4 & 1 & 6 \\
   &   & -1 & 5 & -6 \\
\hline
   & 1 & -5 & 6 & 0 \quad \Rightarrow x + 1 \text{ is a factor.}
\end{array}
$$

So

$P(x) = x^3 - 4x^2 + x + 6 = (x + 1)(x^2 - 5x + 6)$
$\qquad = (x + 1)(x - 3)(x - 2)$

Therefore, the zeros are $x = -1, 2, 3$.

18. $P(x) = x^3 - 4x^2 - 7x + 10$. The possible rational zeros are ± 1, ± 2, ± 5, ± 10. $P(x)$ has 2 variations in sign and hence 0 or 2 positive real zeros.

$P(-x) = -x^3 - 4x^2 + 7x + 10$ has 1 variation in sign and hence 1 negative real zero.

$$
\begin{array}{r|rrrr}
1 & 1 & -4 & -7 & 10 \\
  &   & 1 & -3 & -10 \\
\hline
  & 1 & -3 & -10 & 0 \quad \Rightarrow x = 1 \text{ is a zero.}
\end{array}
$$

So

$P(x) = x^3 - 4x^2 - 7x + 10 = (x - 1)(x^2 - 3x - 10)$
$\qquad = (x - 1)(x - 5)(x + 2)$

Therefore, the zeros are $x = -2, 1, 5$.

19. $P(x) = x^3 + 3x^2 + 6x + 4$. The possible rational zeros are ± 1, ± 2, ± 4. $P(x)$ has no variation in sign and hence no positive real zeros. $P(-x) = -x^3 + 3x^2 - 6x + 4$ has 3 variations in sign and hence 1 or 3 negative real zeros.

$$
\begin{array}{r|rrrr}
-1 & 1 & 3 & 6 & 4 \\
   &   & -1 & -2 & -4 \\
\hline
   & 1 & 2 & 4 & 0 \quad \Rightarrow x + 1 \text{ is a factor.}
\end{array}
$$

So $P(x) = x^3 + 3x^2 + 6x + 4 = (x + 1)(x^2 + 2x + 4)$. Now, $Q(x) = x^2 + 2x + 4$ has no real zeros, since the discriminant of this quadratic is $b^2 - 4ac = (2)^2 - 4(1)(4) = -12 < 0$. Thus, the only real zero is $x = -1$.

20. $P(x) = x^3 - 2x^2 - 2x - 3$. The possible rational zeros are ± 1, ± 3. $P(x)$ has 1 variation in sign and hence 1 positive real zero. $P(-x) = -x^3 - 2x^2 + 2x - 3$ has 2 variations in sign and hence 0 or 2 negative real zeros.

$$
\begin{array}{r|rrrr}
1 & 1 & -2 & -2 & -3 \\
  &   & 1 & -1 & -3 \\
\hline
  & 1 & -1 & -3 & -6
\end{array}
\qquad
\begin{array}{r|rrrr}
3 & 1 & -2 & -2 & -3 \\
  &   & 3 & 3 & 3 \\
\hline
  & 1 & 1 & 1 & 0 \quad \Rightarrow x = 3 \text{ is a zero.}
\end{array}
$$

So $P(x) = x^3 - 2x^2 - 2x - 3 = (x - 3)(x^2 + x + 1)$. Now, $Q(x) = x^2 + x + 1$ has no real zeros, since the discriminant is $b^2 - 4ac = (1)^2 - 4(1)(1) = -3 < 0$. Thus, the only real zero is $x = 3$.

21. *Method 1:* $P(x) = x^4 - 5x^2 + 4$. The possible rational zeros are ± 1, ± 2, ± 4. $P(x)$ has 1 variation in sign and hence 1 positive real zero. $P(-x) = x^4 - 5x^2 + 4$ has 2 variations in sign and hence 0 or 2 negative real zeros.

$$
\begin{array}{r|rrrrr}
1 & 1 & 0 & -5 & 0 & 4 \\
  &   & 1 & 1 & -4 & -4 \\
\hline
  & 1 & 1 & -4 & -4 & 0
\end{array} \Rightarrow x = 1 \text{ is a zero.}
$$

Thus $P(x) = x^4 - 5x^2 + 4 = (x-1)(x^3 + x^2 - 4x - 4)$. Continuing with the quotient we have:

$$
\begin{array}{r|rrrr}
-1 & 1 & 1 & -4 & -4 \\
   &   & -1 & 0 & 4 \\
\hline
   & 1 & 0 & -4 & 0
\end{array} \Rightarrow x = -1 \text{ is a zero.}
$$

$P(x) = x^4 - 5x^2 + 4 = (x-1)(x+1)(x^2 - 4) = (x-1)(x+1)(x-2)(x+2)$. Therefore, the zeros are $x = \pm 1$, ± 2.

Method 2: Substituting $u = x^2$, the polynomial becomes $P(u) = u^2 - 5u + 4$, which factors: $u^2 - 5u + 4 = (u-1)(u-4) = (x^2-1)(x^2-4)$, so either $x^2 = 1$ or $x^2 = 4$. If $x^2 = 1$, then $x = \pm 1$; if $x^2 = 4$, then $x = \pm 2$. Therefore, the zeros are $x = \pm 1$, ± 2.

22. $P(x) = x^4 - 2x^3 - 3x^2 + 8x - 4$. Using synthetic division, we see that $(x-1)$ is a factor of $P(x)$:

$$
\begin{array}{r|rrrrr}
1 & 1 & -2 & -3 & 8 & -4 \\
  &   & 1 & -1 & -4 & 4 \\
\hline
  & 1 & -1 & -4 & 4 & 0
\end{array} \Rightarrow x = 1 \text{ is a zero.}
$$

We continue by factoring the quotient, and we see that $(x-1)$ is again a factor:

$$
\begin{array}{r|rrrr}
1 & 1 & -1 & -4 & 4 \\
  &   & 1 & 0 & -4 \\
\hline
  & 1 & 0 & -4 & 0
\end{array} \Rightarrow x = 1 \text{ is a zero.}
$$

$P(x) = x^4 - 2x^3 - 3x^2 + 8x - 4 = (x-1)(x-1)(x^2 - 4) = (x-1)^2 (x-2)(x+2)$

Therefore, the zeros are $x = 1$, ± 2.

23. $P(x) = x^4 + 6x^3 + 7x^2 - 6x - 8$. The possible rational zeros are ± 1, ± 2, ± 4, ± 8. $P(x)$ has 1 variation in sign and hence 1 positive real zero. $P(-x) = x^4 - 6x^3 + 7x^2 + 6x - 8$ has 3 variations in sign and hence 1 or 3 negative real zeros.

$$
\begin{array}{r|rrrrr}
1 & 1 & 6 & 7 & -6 & -8 \\
  &   & 1 & 7 & 14 & 8 \\
\hline
  & 1 & 7 & 14 & 8 & 0
\end{array} \Rightarrow x = 1 \text{ is a zero}
$$

and there are no other positive zeros. Thus $P(x) = x^4 + 6x^3 + 7x^2 - 6x - 8 = (x-1)(x^3 + 7x^2 + 14x + 8)$. Continuing by factoring the quotient, we have:

$$
\begin{array}{r|rrrr}
-1 & 1 & 7 & 14 & 8 \\
   &   & -1 & -6 & -8 \\
\hline
   & 1 & 6 & 8 & 0
\end{array} \Rightarrow x = -1 \text{ is a zero.}
$$

So $P(x) = x^4 + 6x^3 + 7x^2 - 6x - 8 = (x-1)(x+1)(x^2 + 6x + 8) = (x-1)(x+1)(x+2)(x+4)$. Therefore, the zeros are $x = -4, -2, \pm 1$.

24. $P(x) = x^4 - x^3 - 23x^2 - 3x + 90$. The possible rational zeros are ± 1, ± 2, ± 3, ± 5, ± 6, ± 9, ± 10, ± 15, ± 18, ± 30, ± 45, ± 90. Since $P(x)$ has 2 variations in sign, P has 0 or 2 positive real zeros. Since $P(-x) = x^4 + x^3 - 23x^2 + 3x + 90$ has 2 variations in sign, P has 0 or 2 negative real zeros.

1	1	−1	−23	−3	90
		1	0	−23	−26
	1	0	−23	−26	64

2	1	−1	−23	−3	90
		2	2	−42	−90
	1	1	−21	−45	0	$\Rightarrow x = 2$ is a zero.

$P(x) = (x-2)(x^3 + x^2 - 21x - 45)$. Continuing with the quotient we have:

3	1	1	−21	−45
		3	12	−27
	1	4	−9	−72

5	1	1	−21	−45
		5	30	45
	1	6	9	0	$\Rightarrow x = 5$ is a zero.

$P(x) = (x-2)(x-5)(x^2 + 6x + 9) = (x-2)(x-5)(x+3)^2$. Therefore, the zeros are $x = -3, 2, 5$.

25. $P(x) = 4x^4 - 25x^2 + 36$ has possible rational zeros ± 1, ± 2, ± 3, ± 4, ± 6, ± 9, ± 12, ± 18, ± 36, $\pm \frac{1}{2}$, $\pm \frac{1}{4}$, $\pm \frac{3}{2}$, $\pm \frac{3}{4}$, $\pm \frac{9}{2}$, $\pm \frac{9}{4}$. Since $P(x)$ has 2 variations in sign, there are 0 or 2 positive real zeros. Since $P(-x) = 4x^4 - 25x^2 + 36$ has 2 variations in sign, there are 0 or 2 negative real zeros.

1	4	0	−25	0	36
		4	4	−21	−21
	4	4	−21	−21	15

2	4	0	−25	0	36
		8	16	−18	−36
	4	8	−9	−18	0	$\Rightarrow x = 2$ is a zero.

$P(x) = (x-2)(4x^3 + 8x^2 - 9x - 18)$

2	4	8	−9	−18
		8	32	46
	4	16	23	28	$\Rightarrow$ all positive, $x = 2$ is an upper bound.

$\frac{1}{2}$	4	8	−9	−18
		2	5	−2
	4	10	−4	−20

$\frac{1}{4}$	4	8	−9	−18
		1	$\frac{9}{4}$	$-\frac{27}{16}$
	4	9	$-\frac{27}{4}$	$-\frac{315}{16}$

$\frac{3}{2}$	4	8	−9	−18
		6	21	18
	4	14	12	0	$\Rightarrow x = \frac{3}{2}$ is a zero.

$P(x) = (x-2)(2x-3)(2x^2 + 7x + 6) = (x-2)(2x-3)(2x+3)(x+2)$. Therefore, the zeros are $x = \pm 2$, $\pm \frac{3}{2}$.

Note: Since $P(x)$ has only even terms, factoring by substitution also works. Let $x^2 = u$; then $P(u) = 4u^2 - 25u + 36 = (u-4)(4u-9) = (x^2 - 4)(4x^2 - 9)$, which gives the same results.

26. $P(x) = x^4 - x^3 - 5x^2 + 3x + 6$. The possible rational zeros are ± 1, ± 2, ± 3, ± 6. Since $P(x)$ has 2 variations in sign, P has 0 or 2 positive real zeros. Since $P(-x) = x^4 + x^3 - 5x^2 - 3x + 6$ has 2 variations in sign, P has 0 or 2 negative real zeros.

1	1	−1	−5	3	6
		1	0	−5	−2
	1	0	−5	−2	4

2	1	−1	−5	3	6
		2	2	−6	−6
	1	1	−3	−3	0	$\Rightarrow x = 2$ is a zero.

$P(x) = (x-2)(x^3 + x^2 - 3x - 3)$. Continuing with the quotient we have:

3	1	1	−3	−3
		3	12	27
	1	4	9	24	$\Rightarrow x = 3$ is an upper bound.

−1	1	1	−3	−3
		−1	0	3
	1	0	−3	0	$\Rightarrow x = -1$ is a zero.

$P(x) = (x-2)(x+1)(x^2 - 3)$. Therefore, the rational zeros are $x = -1, 2$.

27. $P(x) = x^4 + 8x^3 + 24x^2 + 32x + 16$. The possible rational zeros are $\pm 1, \pm 2, \pm 4, \pm 8, \pm 16$. $P(x)$ has no variations in sign and hence no positive real zero. $P(-x) = x^4 - 8x^3 + 24x^2 - 32x + 16$ has 4 variations in sign and hence 0 or 2 or 4 negative real zeros.

$$
\begin{array}{r|rrrrr}
-1 & 1 & 8 & 24 & 32 & 16 \\
   &   & -1 & -7 & -17 & -15 \\
\hline
   & 1 & 7 & 17 & 15 & 1
\end{array}
\Rightarrow x = -1 \text{ is not a zero.}
$$

$$
\begin{array}{r|rrrrr}
-2 & 1 & 8 & 24 & 32 & 16 \\
   &   & -2 & -12 & -24 & -16 \\
\hline
   & 1 & 6 & 12 & 8 & 0
\end{array}
\Rightarrow x = -2 \text{ is a zero.}
$$

Thus $P(x) = x^4 + 8x^3 + 24x^2 + 32x + 16 = (x + 2)(x^3 + 6x^2 + 12x + 8)$. Continuing by factoring the quotient, we have

$$
\begin{array}{r|rrrr}
-2 & 1 & 6 & 12 & 8 \\
   &   & -2 & -8 & -8 \\
\hline
   & 1 & 4 & 4 & 0
\end{array}
\Rightarrow x = -2 \text{ is a zero.}
$$

Thus $P(x) = (x + 2)^2(x^2 + 4x + 4) = (x + 2)^4$. Therefore, the zero is $x = -2$

28. $P(x) = 2x^3 + 7x^2 + 4x - 4$. The possible rational zeros are $\pm 1, \pm 2, \pm 4, \pm \frac{1}{2}$. Since $P(x)$ has 1 variation in sign, P has 1 positive real zero. Since $P(-x) = -2x^3 + 7x^2 - 4x - 4$ has 2 variations in sign, P has 0 or 2 negative real zeros.

$$
\begin{array}{r|rrrr}
1 & 2 & 7 & 4 & -4 \\
  &   & 2 & 9 & 13 \\
\hline
  & 2 & 9 & 13 & 9
\end{array}
\Rightarrow x = 1 \text{ is an upper bound.}
$$

$$
\begin{array}{r|rrrr}
\frac{1}{2} & 2 & 7 & 4 & -4 \\
  &   & 1 & 4 & 4 \\
\hline
  & 2 & 8 & 8 & 0
\end{array}
\Rightarrow x = \frac{1}{2} \text{ is a zero.}
$$

$P(x) = \left(x - \frac{1}{2}\right)(2x^2 + 8x + 8) = 2\left(x - \frac{1}{2}\right)(x^2 + 4x + 4) = 2\left(x - \frac{1}{2}\right)(x + 2)^2$. Therefore, the zeros are $x = -2$, $\frac{1}{2}$.

29. Factoring by grouping can be applied to this exercise. $4x^3 + 4x^2 - x - 1 = 4x^2(x + 1) - (x + 1) = (x + 1)(4x^2 - 1) = (x + 1)(2x + 1)(2x - 1)$. Therefore, the zeros are $x = -1, \pm \frac{1}{2}$.

30. We use factoring by grouping: $P(x) = 2x^3 - 3x^2 - 2x + 3 = 2x(x^2 - 1) - 3(x^2 - 1) = (x^2 - 1)(2x - 3) = (x - 1)(x + 1)(2x - 3)$. Therefore, the zeros are $x = \frac{3}{2}, \pm 1$.

31. $P(x) = 4x^3 - 7x + 3$. The possible rational zeros are $\pm 1, \pm 3, \pm \frac{1}{2}, \pm \frac{3}{2}, \pm \frac{1}{4}, \pm \frac{3}{4}$. Since $P(x)$ has 2 variations in sign, there are 0 or 2 positive zeros. Since $P(-x) = -4x^3 + 7x + 3$ has 1 variation in sign, there is 1 negative zero.

$$
\begin{array}{r|rrrr}
\frac{1}{2} & 4 & 0 & -7 & 3 \\
  &   & 2 & 1 & -3 \\
\hline
  & 4 & 2 & -6 & 0
\end{array}
\Rightarrow x = \frac{1}{2} \text{ is a zero.}
$$

$P(x) = \left(x - \frac{1}{2}\right)(4x^2 + 2x - 6) = (2x - 1)(2x^2 + x - 3) = (2x - 1)(x - 1)(2x + 3) = 0$. Thus, the zeros are $x = -\frac{3}{2}, \frac{1}{2}, 1$.

32. $P(x) = 8x^3 + 10x^2 - x - 3$. The possible rational zeros are $\pm 1, \pm 3, \pm \frac{1}{2}, \pm \frac{3}{2}, \pm \frac{1}{4}, \pm \frac{3}{4}, \pm \frac{1}{8}, \pm \frac{3}{8}$. Since $P(x)$ has 1 variation in sign, P has 1 positive real zero. Since $P(-x) = -8x^3 + 10x^2 + x - 3$ has 2 variations in sign, P has 0 or 2 negative real zeros.

$$
\begin{array}{r|rrrr}
1 & 8 & 10 & -1 & -3 \\
  &   & 8 & 18 & 17 \\
\hline
  & 8 & 18 & 17 & 14
\end{array}
\Rightarrow x = 1 \text{ is an upper bound.}
$$

$$
\begin{array}{r|rrrr}
\frac{1}{2} & 8 & 10 & -1 & -3 \\
  &   & 4 & 7 & 3 \\
\hline
  & 8 & 14 & 6 & 0
\end{array}
\Rightarrow x = \frac{1}{2} \text{ is a zero.}
$$

$$
\begin{aligned}
P(x) &= 8x^3 + 10x^2 - x - 3 = \left(x - \tfrac{1}{2}\right)(8x^2 + 14x + 6) \\
&= 2\left(x - \tfrac{1}{2}\right)(4x^2 + 7x + 3) = (2x - 1)(x + 1)(4x + 3) = 0
\end{aligned}
$$

Therefore, the zeros are $x = -1, -\frac{3}{4}, \frac{1}{2}$.

33. $P(x) = 4x^3 + 8x^2 - 11x - 15$. The possible rational zeros are $\pm 1, \pm 3, \pm 5, \pm\frac{1}{2}, \pm\frac{1}{4}, \pm\frac{3}{2}, \pm\frac{3}{4}, \pm\frac{5}{2}, \pm\frac{5}{4}$. $P(x)$ has 1 variation in sign and hence 1 positive real zero. $P(-x) = -4x^3 + 8x^2 + 11x - 15$ has 2 variations in sign, so P has 0 or 2 negative real zeros.

$$
\begin{array}{r|rrrr}
1 & 4 & 8 & -11 & -15 \\
  &   & 4 & 12 & 1 \\
\hline
  & 4 & 12 & 1 & -14
\end{array}
\Rightarrow x = 1 \text{ is not a zero.}
\qquad
\begin{array}{r|rrrr}
3 & 4 & 8 & -11 & -15 \\
  &   & 12 & 60 & 147 \\
\hline
  & 4 & 20 & 49 & 132
\end{array}
\Rightarrow x = 3 \text{ is not a zero.}
$$

$$
\begin{array}{r|rrrr}
5 & 4 & 8 & -11 & -15 \\
  &   & 20 & 140 & 645 \\
\hline
  & 4 & 28 & 129 & 630
\end{array}
\Rightarrow x = 5 \text{ is not a zero.}
\qquad
\begin{array}{r|rrrr}
3 & 4 & 8 & -11 & -15 \\
  &   & 12 & 60 & 147 \\
\hline
  & 4 & 20 & 49 & 132
\end{array}
\Rightarrow x = 3 \text{ is not a zero.}
$$

$$
\begin{array}{r|rrrr}
\frac{1}{2} & 4 & 8 & -11 & -15 \\
  &   & 2 & 5 & -3 \\
\hline
  & 4 & 10 & -6 & -18
\end{array}
\Rightarrow x = \tfrac{1}{2} \text{ is not a zero.}
\qquad
\begin{array}{r|rrrr}
\frac{1}{4} & 4 & 8 & -11 & -15 \\
  &   & 1 & \frac{9}{4} & -\frac{35}{16} \\
\hline
  & 4 & 9 & -\frac{35}{4} & -\frac{275}{16}
\end{array}
\Rightarrow x = \tfrac{1}{4} \text{ is not a zero.}
$$

$$
\begin{array}{r|rrrr}
\frac{3}{2} & 4 & 8 & -11 & -15 \\
  &   & 6 & 21 & 15 \\
\hline
  & 4 & 14 & 10 & 0
\end{array}
\Rightarrow x = \tfrac{3}{2} \text{ is a zero.}
$$

Thus $P(x) = 4x^3 + 8x^2 - 11x - 15 = \left(x - \frac{3}{2}\right)\left(4x^2 + 14x + 10\right)$. Continuing by factoring the quotient, whose possible rational zeros are $-1, -5, -\frac{1}{2}, -\frac{1}{4}, -\frac{5}{2},$ and $-\frac{5}{4}$, we have

$$
\begin{array}{r|rrr}
-1 & 4 & 14 & 10 \\
   &   & -4 & -10 \\
\hline
   & 4 & 10 & 0
\end{array}
\Rightarrow x = -1 \text{ is a zero.}
$$

Thus $P(x) = \left(x - \frac{3}{2}\right)(x + 1)(4x + 10)$ has zeros $\frac{3}{2}, -1$, and $-\frac{5}{2}$.

34. $P(x) = 6x^3 + 11x^2 - 3x - 2$. The possible rational zeros are $\pm 1, \pm 2, \pm\frac{1}{2}, \pm\frac{1}{3}, \pm\frac{1}{6}, \pm\frac{2}{3}$. $P(x)$ has 1 variation in sign and hence 1 positive real zero. $P(-x) = -6x^3 + 11x^2 + 3x - 2$ has 2 variations in sign and hence 0 or 2 negative real zeros.

$$
\begin{array}{r|rrrr}
1 & 6 & 11 & -3 & -2 \\
  &   & 6 & 17 & 14 \\
\hline
  & 6 & 17 & 14 & 12
\end{array}
\Rightarrow x = 1 \text{ is not a zero.}
\qquad
\begin{array}{r|rrrr}
2 & 6 & 11 & -3 & -2 \\
  &   & 12 & 46 & 86 \\
\hline
  & 6 & 23 & 43 & 84
\end{array}
\Rightarrow x = 2 \text{ is not a zero.}
$$

$$
\begin{array}{r|rrrr}
\frac{1}{2} & 6 & 11 & -3 & -2 \\
  &   & 3 & 7 & 2 \\
\hline
  & 6 & 14 & 4 & 0
\end{array}
\Rightarrow x = \tfrac{1}{2} \text{ is a zero.}
$$

Thus, $P(x) = 6x^3 + 11x^2 - 3x - 2 = \left(x - \frac{1}{2}\right)\left(6x^2 + 14x + 4\right)$. Continuing:

$$
\begin{array}{r|rrr}
-1 & 6 & 14 & 4 \\
   &   & -6 & -8 \\
\hline
   & 6 & 8 & -4
\end{array}
\Rightarrow x = -1 \text{ is not a zero.}
\qquad
\begin{array}{r|rrr}
-2 & 6 & 14 & 4 \\
   &   & -12 & -4 \\
\hline
   & 6 & 2 & 0
\end{array}
\Rightarrow x = -2 \text{ is a zero.}
$$

Thus, $P(x) = \left(x - \frac{1}{2}\right)(x + 2)(6x + 2)$ has zeros $\frac{1}{2}, -2$, and $-\frac{1}{3}$.

35. $P(x) = 2x^4 - 7x^3 + 3x^2 + 8x - 4$. The possible rational zeros are $\pm 1, \pm 2, \pm 4, \pm \frac{1}{2}$. $P(x)$ has 3 variations in sign and hence 1 or 3 positive real zeros. $P(-x) = 2x^4 + 7x^3 + 3x^2 - 8x - 4$ has 1 variation in sign and hence 1 negative real zero.

$$
\begin{array}{r|rrrrr}
1 & 2 & -7 & 3 & 8 & -4 \\
  &   & 2 & -5 & -2 & 6 \\
\hline
  & 2 & -5 & -2 & 6 & 2
\end{array}
\Rightarrow x = 1 \text{ is not a zero.}
\qquad
\begin{array}{r|rrrrr}
\frac{1}{2} & 2 & -7 & 3 & 8 & -4 \\
  &   & 1 & -3 & 0 & 4 \\
\hline
  & 2 & -6 & 0 & 8 & 0
\end{array}
\Rightarrow x = \frac{1}{2} \text{ is a zero.}
$$

Thus $P(x) = 2x^4 - 7x^3 + 3x^2 + 8x - 4 = \left(x - \frac{1}{2}\right)\left(2x^3 - 6x^2 + 8\right)$. Continuing by factoring the quotient, we have:

$$
\begin{array}{r|rrrr}
2 & 2 & -6 & 0 & 8 \\
  &   & 4 & -4 & -8 \\
\hline
  & 2 & -2 & -4 & 0
\end{array}
\Rightarrow x = 2 \text{ is a zero.}
$$

$P(x) = \left(x - \frac{1}{2}\right)(x - 2)\left(2x^2 - 2x - 4\right) = 2\left(x - \frac{1}{2}\right)(x - 2)\left(x^2 - x - 2\right) = 2\left(x - \frac{1}{2}\right)(x - 2)^2(x + 1)$. Thus, the zeros are $x = \frac{1}{2}, 2, -1$.

36. $P(x) = 6x^4 - 7x^3 - 12x^2 + 3x + 2$. The possible rational zeros are $\pm 1, \pm 2, \pm \frac{1}{2}, \pm \frac{1}{3}, \pm \frac{2}{3}, \pm \frac{1}{6}$. Since $P(x)$ has 2 variations in sign, P has 0 or 2 positive real zeros. Since $P(-x) = 6x^4 + 7x^3 - 12x^2 - 3x + 2$ has 2 variations in sign, P has 0 or 2 negative real zeros.

$$
\begin{array}{r|rrrrr}
1 & 6 & -7 & -12 & 3 & 2 \\
  &   & 6 & -1 & -13 & -10 \\
\hline
  & 6 & -1 & -13 & -10 & -8
\end{array}
\qquad
\begin{array}{r|rrrrr}
2 & 6 & -7 & -12 & 3 & 2 \\
  &   & 12 & 10 & -4 & -2 \\
\hline
  & 6 & 5 & -2 & -1 & 0
\end{array}
\Rightarrow x = 2 \text{ is a zero.}
$$

$P(x) = 6x^4 - 7x^3 - 12x^2 + 3x + 2 = (x - 2)\left(6x^3 + 5x^2 - 2x - 1\right)$. Continuing by factoring the quotient, we first note that the possible rational zeros are $-1, \pm \frac{1}{2}, \pm \frac{1}{3}, \pm \frac{1}{6}$. We have:

$$
\begin{array}{r|rrrr}
\frac{1}{2} & 6 & 5 & -2 & -1 \\
  &   & 3 & 4 & 1 \\
\hline
  & 6 & 8 & 2 & 0
\end{array}
\Rightarrow x = \frac{1}{2} \text{ is a zero.}
$$

$P(x) = (x - 2)\left(x - \frac{1}{2}\right)\left(6x^2 + 8x + 2\right) = 2(x - 2)\left(x - \frac{1}{2}\right)\left(3x^2 + 4x + 1\right) = (x - 2)\left(x - \frac{1}{2}\right)(x + 1)(3x + 1)$. Therefore, the zeros are $x = -1, -\frac{1}{3}, \frac{1}{2}, 2$.

37. $P(x) = x^5 + 3x^4 - 9x^3 - 31x^2 + 36$. The possible rational zeros are $\pm 1, \pm 2, \pm 3, \pm 4, \pm 6, \pm 8, \pm 9, \pm 12, \pm 18$. $P(x)$ has 2 variations in sign and hence 0 or 2 positive real zeros. $P(-x) = -x^5 + 3x^4 + 9x^3 - 31x^2 + 36$ has 3 variations in sign and hence 1 or 3 negative real zeros.

$$
\begin{array}{r|rrrrrr}
1 & 1 & 3 & -9 & -31 & 0 & 36 \\
  &   & 1 & 4 & -5 & -36 & -36 \\
\hline
  & 1 & 4 & -5 & -36 & -36 & 0
\end{array}
\Rightarrow x = 1 \text{ is a zero.}
$$

So $P(x) = x^5 + 3x^4 - 9x^3 - 31x^2 + 36 = (x - 1)\left(x^4 + 4x^3 - 5x^2 - 36x - 36\right)$. Continuing by factoring the quotient, we have:

$$
\begin{array}{r|rrrrr}
1 & 1 & 4 & -5 & -36 & -36 \\
  &   & 1 & 5 & 0 & -36 \\
\hline
  & 1 & 1 & 0 & -36 & -72
\end{array}
\qquad
\begin{array}{r|rrrrr}
2 & 1 & 4 & -5 & -36 & -36 \\
  &   & 2 & 12 & 14 & -44 \\
\hline
  & 1 & 6 & 7 & -22 & -80
\end{array}
$$

$$
\begin{array}{r|rrrrr}
3 & 1 & 4 & -5 & -36 & -36 \\
  &   & 3 & 21 & 48 & 36 \\
\hline
  & 1 & 7 & 16 & 12 & 0
\end{array}
\Rightarrow x = 3 \text{ is a zero.}
$$

So $P(x) = (x-1)(x-3)(x^3 + 7x^2 + 16x + 12)$. Since we have 2 positive zeros, there are no more positive zeros, so we continue by factoring the quotient with possible negative zeros.

$$
\begin{array}{r|rrrr}
-1 & 1 & 7 & 16 & 12 \\
   &   & -1 & -6 & -10 \\
\hline
   & 1 & 6 & 10 & 2
\end{array}
\qquad
\begin{array}{r|rrrr}
-2 & 1 & 7 & 16 & 12 \\
   &   & -2 & -10 & -12 \\
\hline
   & 1 & 5 & 6 & 0
\end{array}
\;\Rightarrow x = -2 \text{ is a zero.}
$$

Then $P(x) = (x-1)(x-3)(x+2)(x^2 + 5x + 6) = (x-1)(x-3)(x+2)^2(x+3)$. Thus, the zeros are $x = 1, 3, -2, -3$.

38. $P(x) = x^5 - 4x^4 - 3x^3 + 22x^2 - 4x - 24$ has possible rational zeros $\pm 1, \pm 2, \pm 3, \pm 4, \pm 6, \pm 8, \pm 12, \pm 24$. Since $P(x)$ has 3 variations in sign, there are 1 or 3 positive real zeros. Since $P(-x) = -x^5 - 4x^4 + 3x^3 + 22x^2 + 4x - 24$ has 2 variations in sign, there are 0 or 2 negative real zeros.

$$
\begin{array}{r|rrrrrr}
1 & 1 & -4 & -3 & 22 & -4 & -24 \\
  &   & 1 & -3 & -6 & 16 & 12 \\
\hline
  & 1 & -3 & -6 & 16 & 12 & -12
\end{array}
\qquad
\begin{array}{r|rrrrrr}
2 & 1 & -4 & -3 & 22 & -4 & -24 \\
  &   & 2 & -4 & -14 & 16 & 24 \\
\hline
  & 1 & -2 & -7 & 8 & 12 & 0
\end{array}
\;\Rightarrow x = 2 \text{ is a zero.}
$$

$P(x) = (x-2)(x^4 - 2x^3 - 7x^2 + 8x + 12)$

$$
\begin{array}{r|rrrrr}
2 & 1 & -2 & -7 & 8 & 12 \\
  &   & 2 & 0 & -14 & -12 \\
\hline
  & 1 & 0 & -7 & -6 & 0
\end{array}
\;\Rightarrow x = 2 \text{ is a zero again.}
$$

$P(x) = (x-2)^2(x^3 - 7x - 6)$

$$
\begin{array}{r|rrrr}
2 & 1 & 0 & -7 & -6 \\
  &   & 2 & 4 & -6 \\
\hline
  & 1 & 2 & -3 & -12
\end{array}
\qquad
\begin{array}{r|rrrr}
3 & 1 & 0 & -7 & -6 \\
  &   & 3 & 9 & 6 \\
\hline
  & 1 & 3 & 2 & 0
\end{array}
\;\Rightarrow x = 3 \text{ is a zero.}
$$

$P(x) = (x-2)^2(x-3)(x^2 + 3x + 2) = (x-2)^2(x-3)(x+1)(x+2) = 0$. Therefore, the zeros are $x = -1, \pm 2, 3$.

39. $P(x) = 3x^5 - 14x^4 - 14x^3 + 36x^2 + 43x + 10$ has possible rational zeros $\pm 1, \pm 2, \pm 5, \pm 10, \pm \frac{1}{3}, \pm \frac{2}{3}, \pm \frac{5}{3}, \pm \frac{10}{3}$. Since $P(x)$ has 2 variations in sign, there are 0 or 2 positive real zeros. Since $P(-x) = -3x^5 - 14x^4 + 14x^3 + 36x^2 - 43x + 10$ has 3 variations in sign, there are 1 or 3 negative real zeros.

$$
\begin{array}{r|rrrrrr}
1 & 3 & -14 & -14 & 36 & 43 & 10 \\
  &   & 3 & -11 & -25 & 11 & 54 \\
\hline
  & 3 & -11 & -25 & 11 & 54 & 64
\end{array}
\qquad
\begin{array}{r|rrrrrr}
2 & 3 & -14 & -14 & 36 & 43 & 10 \\
  &   & 6 & -16 & -60 & -48 & -10 \\
\hline
  & 3 & -8 & -30 & -24 & -5 & 0
\end{array}
\;\Rightarrow x = 2 \text{ is a zero.}
$$

$P(x) = (x-2)(3x^4 - 8x^3 - 30x^2 - 24x - 5)$

$$
\begin{array}{r|rrrrr}
2 & 3 & -8 & -30 & -24 & -5 \\
  &   & 6 & -4 & -68 & -184 \\
\hline
  & 3 & -2 & -34 & -92 & -189
\end{array}
\qquad
\begin{array}{r|rrrrr}
5 & 3 & -8 & -30 & -24 & -5 \\
  &   & 15 & 35 & 25 & 5 \\
\hline
  & 3 & 7 & 5 & 1 & 0
\end{array}
\;\Rightarrow x = 5 \text{ is a zero.}
$$

$P(x) = (x-2)(x-5)(3x^3 + 7x^2 + 5x + 1)$. Since $3x^3 + 7x^2 + 5x + 1$ has no variation in sign, there are no more positive zeros.

$$
\begin{array}{r|rrrr}
-1 & 3 & 7 & 5 & 1 \\
   &   & -3 & -4 & -1 \\
\hline
   & 3 & 4 & 1 & 0
\end{array}
\;\Rightarrow x = -1 \text{ is a zero.}
$$

$P(x) = (x-2)(x-5)(x+1)(3x^2 + 4x + 1) = (x-2)(x-5)(x+1)(x+1)(3x+1)$. Therefore, the zeros are $x = -1, -\frac{1}{3}, 2, 5$.

40. $P(x) = 2x^6 - 3x^5 - 13x^4 + 29x^3 - 27x^2 + 32x - 12$ has possible rational zeros ± 1, ± 2, ± 3, ± 4, ± 6, ± 12, $\pm\frac{1}{2}$, $\pm\frac{3}{2}$. Since $P(x)$ has 5 variations in sign, there are 1 or 3 or 5 positive real zeros. Since $P(-x) = 2x^6 + 3x^5 - 13x^4 - 29x^3 + 27x^2 - 32x - 12$ has 3 variations in sign, there are 1 or 3 negative real zeros.

$$
\begin{array}{r|rrrrrrr}
1 & 2 & -3 & -13 & 29 & -27 & 32 & -12 \\
  &   & 2 & -1 & -14 & 15 & -12 & 20 \\
\hline
  & 2 & -1 & -14 & 15 & -12 & 20 & 8 \\
\end{array}
$$

$$
\begin{array}{r|rrrrrrr}
2 & 2 & -3 & -13 & 29 & -27 & 32 & -12 \\
  &   & 4 & 2   & -22 & 14 & -26 & 12 \\
\hline
  & 2 & 1 & -11 & 7 & -13 & 6 & 0 \\
\end{array}
\Rightarrow x = 2 \text{ is a zero.}
$$

$P(x) = (x-2)(2x^5 + x^4 - 11x^3 + 7x^2 - 13x + 6)$. We continue with the quotient:

$$
\begin{array}{r|rrrrrr}
2 & 2 & 1 & -11 & 7 & -13 & 6 \\
  &   & 4 & 10 & -2 & 10 & -6 \\
\hline
  & 2 & 5 & -1 & 5 & -3 & 0 \\
\end{array}
\Rightarrow x = 2 \text{ is a zero again.}
$$

$P(x) = (x-2)^2(2x^4 + 5x^3 - x^2 + 5x - 3)$. We continue with the quotient, first noting 2 is no longer a possible rational solution:

$$
\begin{array}{r|rrrrr}
3 & 2 & 5 & -1 & 5 & -3 \\
  &   & 6 & 22 & 42 & 94 \\
\hline
  & 2 & 11 & 21 & 47 & 91 \\
\end{array}
\Rightarrow x = 3 \text{ is an upper bound.}
$$

We know that there is at least 1 more positive zero.

$$
\begin{array}{r|rrrrr}
\frac{1}{2} & 2 & 5 & -1 & 5 & -3 \\
  &   & 1 & 2 & 1 & 3 \\
\hline
  & 2 & 6 & 2 & 6 & 0 \\
\end{array}
\Rightarrow x = \frac{1}{2} \text{ is a zero.}
$$

$P(x) = (x-2)^2\left(x - \frac{1}{2}\right)(2x^3 + 6x^2 + 2x + 6)$. We can factor $2x^3 + 6x^2 + 2x + 6$ by grouping; $2x^3 + 6x^2 + 2x + 6 = (2x^3 + 6x^2) + (2x + 6) = (2x + 6)(x^2 + 1)$. So $P(x) = 2(x-2)^2\left(x - \frac{1}{2}\right)(x + 3)(x^2 + 1)$. Since $x^2 + 1$ has no real zeros, the zeros of P are $x = -3, 2, \frac{1}{2}$.

41. $P(x) = x^3 + 4x^2 + 3x - 2$. The possible rational zeros are ± 1, ± 2. $P(x)$ has 1 variation in sign and hence 1 positive real zero. $P(-x) = -x^3 + 4x^2 - 3x - 2$ has 2 variations in sign and hence 0 or 2 negative real zeros.

$$
\begin{array}{r|rrrr}
1 & 1 & 4 & 3 & -2 \\
  &   & 1 & 5 & 8 \\
\hline
  & 1 & 5 & 8 & 6 \\
\end{array}
\Rightarrow x = 1 \text{ is an upper bound.}
\qquad
\begin{array}{r|rrrr}
-1 & 1 & 4 & 3 & -2 \\
   &   & -1 & -3 & 0 \\
\hline
   & 1 & 3 & 0 & -2 \\
\end{array}
$$

$$
\begin{array}{r|rrrr}
-2 & 1 & 4 & 3 & -2 \\
   &   & -2 & -4 & 2 \\
\hline
   & 1 & 2 & -1 & 0 \\
\end{array}
\Rightarrow x = -2 \text{ is a zero.}
$$

So $P(x) = (x+2)(x^2 + 2x - 1)$. Using the quadratic formula on the second factor, we have:

$x = \frac{-2 \pm \sqrt{2^2 - 4(1)(-1)}}{2(1)} = \frac{-2 \pm \sqrt{8}}{2} = \frac{-2 \pm 2\sqrt{2}}{2} = -1 \pm \sqrt{2}$. Therefore, the zeros are $x = -2, -1 + \sqrt{2}, -1 - \sqrt{2}$.

42. $P(x) = x^3 - 5x^2 + 2x + 12$. The possible rational zeros are $\pm 1, \pm 2, \pm 3, \pm 4, \pm 6, \pm 12$. $P(x)$ has 2 variations in sign and hence 0 or 2 positive real zeros. $P(-x) = -x^3 - 5x^2 - 2x + 12$ has 1 variation in sign and hence 1 negative real zero.

$$
\begin{array}{r|rrrr}
1 & 1 & -5 & 2 & 12 \\
  &   & 1 & -4 & -2 \\
\hline
  & 1 & -4 & -2 & 10
\end{array}
\qquad
\begin{array}{r|rrrr}
2 & 1 & -5 & 2 & 12 \\
  &   & 2 & -6 & -8 \\
\hline
  & 1 & -3 & -4 & 4
\end{array}
$$

$$
\begin{array}{r|rrrr}
3 & 1 & -5 & 2 & 12 \\
  &   & 3 & -6 & -12 \\
\hline
  & 1 & -2 & -4 & 0
\end{array}
\Rightarrow x = 3 \text{ is a zero.}
$$

So $P(x) = (x - 3)(x^2 - 2x - 4)$. Using the quadratic formula on the second factor, we have:

$x = \dfrac{-(-2) \pm \sqrt{(-2)^2 - 4(1)(-4)}}{2(1)} = \dfrac{2 \pm \sqrt{20}}{2} = \dfrac{2 \pm 2\sqrt{5}}{2} = 1 \pm \sqrt{5}$. Therefore, the zeros are $x = 3, 1 \pm \sqrt{5}$.

43. $P(x) = x^4 - 6x^3 + 4x^2 + 15x + 4$. The possible rational zeros are $\pm 1, \pm 2, \pm 4$. $P(x)$ has 2 variations in sign and hence 0 or 2 positive real zeros. $P(-x) = x^4 + 6x^3 + 4x^2 - 15x + 4$ has 2 variations in sign and hence 0 or 2 negative real zeros.

$$
\begin{array}{r|rrrrr}
1 & 1 & -6 & 4 & 15 & 4 \\
  &   & 1 & -5 & -1 & 14 \\
\hline
  & 1 & -5 & -1 & 14 & 18
\end{array}
\qquad
\begin{array}{r|rrrrr}
2 & 1 & -6 & 4 & 15 & 4 \\
  &   & 2 & -8 & -8 & 14 \\
\hline
  & 1 & -4 & -4 & 7 & 18
\end{array}
$$

$$
\begin{array}{r|rrrrr}
4 & 1 & -6 & 4 & 15 & 4 \\
  &   & 4 & -8 & -16 & -4 \\
\hline
  & 1 & -2 & -4 & -1 & 0
\end{array}
\Rightarrow x = 4 \text{ is a zero.}
$$

So $P(x) = (x - 4)(x^3 - 2x^2 - 4x - 1)$. Continuing by factoring the quotient, we have:

$$
\begin{array}{r|rrrr}
4 & 1 & -2 & -4 & -1 \\
  &   & 4 & 8 & 16 \\
\hline
  & 1 & 2 & 4 & 15
\end{array}
\Rightarrow x = 4 \text{ is an upper bound.}
\qquad
\begin{array}{r|rrrr}
-1 & 1 & -2 & -4 & -1 \\
   &   & -1 & 3 & 1 \\
\hline
   & 1 & -3 & -1 & 0
\end{array}
\Rightarrow x = -1 \text{ is a zero.}
$$

So $P(x) = (x - 4)(x + 1)(x^2 - 3x - 1)$. Using the quadratic formula on the third factor, we have:

$x = \dfrac{-(-3) \pm \sqrt{(-3)^2 - 4(1)(-1)}}{2(1)} = \dfrac{3 \pm \sqrt{13}}{2}$. Therefore, the zeros are $x = 4, -1, \dfrac{3 \pm \sqrt{13}}{2}$.

44. $P(x) = x^4 + 2x^3 - 2x^2 - 3x + 2$. The possible rational zeros are $\pm 1, \pm 2$. $P(x)$ has 2 variations in sign and hence 0 or 2 positive real zeros. $P(-x) = x^4 - 2x^3 - 2x^2 + 3x + 2$ has 2 variations in sign and hence 0 or 2 negative real zeros.

$$
\begin{array}{r|rrrrr}
1 & 1 & 2 & -2 & -3 & 2 \\
  &   & 1 & 3 & 1 & -2 \\
\hline
  & 1 & 3 & 1 & -2 & 0
\end{array}
\Rightarrow x = 1 \text{ is a zero.}
$$

$P(x) = (x - 1)(x^3 + 3x^2 + x - 2)$. Continuing with the quotient:

$$
\begin{array}{r|rrrr}
1 & 1 & 3 & 1 & -2 \\
  &   & 1 & 4 & 5 \\
\hline
  & 1 & 4 & 5 & 3
\end{array}
\Rightarrow x = 1 \text{ is an upper bound.}
\qquad
\begin{array}{r|rrrr}
-1 & 1 & 3 & 1 & -2 \\
   &   & -1 & -2 & 1 \\
\hline
   & 1 & 2 & -1 & -1
\end{array}
\qquad
\begin{array}{r|rrrr}
-2 & 1 & 3 & 1 & -2 \\
   &   & -2 & -2 & 2 \\
\hline
   & 1 & 1 & -1 & 0
\end{array}
\Rightarrow x = -2 \text{ is a zero.}
$$

So $P(x) = (x - 1)(x + 2)(x^2 + x - 1)$. Using the quadratic formula on the third factor, we have:

$x = \dfrac{-1 \pm \sqrt{1^2 - 4(1)(-1)}}{2(1)} = \dfrac{1 \pm \sqrt{5}}{2}$. Therefore, the zeros are $x = 1, -2, \dfrac{1 \pm \sqrt{5}}{2}$.

45. $P(x) = x^4 - 7x^3 + 14x^2 - 3x - 9$. The possible rational zeros are $\pm 1, \pm 3, \pm 9$. $P(x)$ has 3 variations in sign and hence 1 or 3 positive real zeros. $P(-x) = x^4 + 7x^3 + 14x^2 + 3x - 4$ has 1 variation in sign and hence 1 negative real zero.

1	1	−7	14	−3	−9
		1	−6	8	5
	1	−6	8	5	4

3	1	−7	14	−3	−9
		3	−12	6	9
	1	−4	2	3	0	$\Rightarrow x = 3$ is a zero.

So $P(x) = (x - 3)(x^3 - 4x^2 + 2x + 3)$. Since the constant term of the second term is 3, ± 9 are no longer possible zeros. Continuing by factoring the quotient, we have:

3	1	−4	2	3
		3	−3	−3
	1	−1	−1	0	$\Rightarrow x = 3$ is a zero again.

So $P(x) = (x - 3)^2 (x^2 - x - 1)$. Using the quadratic formula on the second factor, we have: $x = \frac{-(-1) \pm \sqrt{(-1)^2 - 4(1)(-1)}}{2(1)} = \frac{1 \pm \sqrt{5}}{2}$. Therefore, the zeros are $x = 3, \frac{1 \pm \sqrt{5}}{2}$.

46. $P(x) = x^5 - 4x^4 - x^3 + 10x^2 + 2x - 4$. The possible rational zeros are $\pm 1, \pm 2, \pm 4$. $P(x)$ has 3 variations in sign and hence 1 or 3 positive real zeros. $P(-x) = -x^5 - 4x^4 + x^3 + 10x^2 - 2x - 4$ has 2 variations in sign and hence 0 or 2 negative real zeros.

1	1	−4	−1	10	2	−4
		1	−3	−4	6	8
	1	−3	−4	6	8	4

2	1	−4	−1	10	2	−4
		2	−4	−10	0	4
	1	−2	−5	0	2	0	$\Rightarrow x = 2$ is a zero.

So $P(x) = (x - 2)(x^4 - 2x^3 - 5x^2 + 2)$. Since the constant term of the second factor is 2, ± 4 are no longer possible zeros. Continuing by factoring the quotient, we have:

2	1	−2	−5	0	2
		2	0	−10	−20
	1	0	−5	−10	18

−1	1	−2	−5	0	2
		−1	3	2	−2
	1	−3	−2	2	0	$\Rightarrow x = -1$ is a zero.

So $P(x) = (x - 2)(x + 1)(x^3 - 3x^2 - 2x - 2)$. Continuing by factoring the quotient, we have:

−1	1	−3	−2	2
		−1	4	−2
	1	−4	2	0	$\Rightarrow x = -1$ is a zero again.

So $P(x) = (x - 2)(x + 1)^2 (x^2 - 4x + 2)$. Using the quadratic formula on the second factor, we have: $x = \frac{-(-4) \pm \sqrt{(-4)^2 - 4(1)(2)}}{2(1)} = \frac{4 \pm \sqrt{8}}{2} = \frac{4 \pm 2\sqrt{2}}{2} = 2 \pm \sqrt{2}$. Therefore, the zeros are $x = -1, 2, 2 \pm \sqrt{2}$.

47. $P(x) = 4x^3 - 6x^2 + 1$. The possible rational zeros are $\pm 1, \pm \frac{1}{2}, \pm \frac{1}{4}$. $P(x)$ has 2 variations in sign and hence 0 or 2 positive real zeros. $P(-x) = -4x^3 - 6x^2 + 1$ has 1 variation in sign and hence 1 negative real zero.

1	4	−6	0	1
		4	−2	−2
	4	−2	−2	−1

$\frac{1}{2}$	4	−6	0	1
		2	−2	−1
	4	−4	−2	0	$\Rightarrow x = \frac{1}{2}$ is a zero.

So $P(x) = \left(x - \frac{1}{2}\right)(4x^2 - 4x - 2)$. Using the quadratic formula on the second factor, we have: $x = \frac{-(-4) \pm \sqrt{(-4)^2 - 4(4)(-2)}}{2(4)} = \frac{4 \pm \sqrt{48}}{8} = \frac{4 \pm 4\sqrt{3}}{8} = \frac{1 \pm \sqrt{3}}{2}$. Therefore, the zeros are $x = \frac{1}{2}, \frac{1 \pm \sqrt{3}}{2}$.

48. $P(x) = 3x^3 - 5x^2 - 8x - 2$. The possible rational zeros are $\pm 1, \pm 2, \pm \frac{1}{3}, \pm \frac{2}{3}$. $P(x)$ has 1 variation in sign and hence 1 positive real zero. $P(-x) = -3x^3 - 5x^2 + 8x - 2$ has 2 variations in sign and hence 0 or 2 negative real zeros.

$$
\begin{array}{r|rrrr}
1 & 3 & -5 & -8 & -2 \\
  &   & 3 & -2 & -10 \\
\hline
  & 3 & -2 & -10 & -12
\end{array}
\qquad
\begin{array}{r|rrrr}
2 & 3 & -5 & -8 & -2 \\
  &   & 6 & 2 & -12 \\
\hline
  & 3 & 1 & -6 & -14
\end{array}
$$

$$
\begin{array}{r|rrrr}
\frac{1}{3} & 3 & -5 & -8 & -2 \\
  &   & 1 & -\frac{4}{3} & -\frac{28}{9} \\
\hline
  & 3 & -4 & -\frac{28}{3} & -\frac{46}{9}
\end{array}
\qquad
\begin{array}{r|rrrr}
\frac{2}{3} & 3 & -5 & -8 & -2 \\
  &   & 2 & -2 & -\frac{20}{3} \\
\hline
  & 3 & -3 & -10 & -\frac{26}{3}
\end{array}
$$

Thus we have tried all the positive rational zeros, so we try the negative zeros.

$$
\begin{array}{r|rrrr}
-1 & 3 & -5 & -8 & -2 \\
  &   & -3 & 8 & 0 \\
\hline
  & 3 & -8 & 0 & -2
\end{array}
\qquad
\begin{array}{r|rrrr}
-2 & 3 & -5 & -8 & -2 \\
  &   & -6 & 22 & -28 \\
\hline
  & 3 & -11 & 14 & -30
\end{array}
$$

$$
\begin{array}{r|rrrr}
-\frac{1}{3} & 3 & -5 & -8 & -2 \\
  &   & -1 & 2 & 2 \\
\hline
  & 3 & -6 & -6 & 0
\end{array}
\quad \Rightarrow x = -\tfrac{1}{3} \text{ is a zero.}
$$

So $P(x) = \left(x + \frac{1}{3}\right)\left(3x^2 - 6x - 6\right) = 3\left(x + \frac{1}{3}\right)\left(x^2 - 2x - 2\right)$. Using the quadratic formula on the second factor, we have: $x = \frac{-(-2) \pm \sqrt{(-2)^2 - 4(1)(-2)}}{2(1)} = \frac{2 \pm \sqrt{12}}{2} = \frac{2 \pm 2\sqrt{3}}{2} = 1 \pm \sqrt{3}$. Therefore, the zeros are $x = -\frac{1}{3}, 1 \pm \sqrt{3}$.

49. $P(x) = 2x^4 + 15x^3 + 17x^2 + 3x - 1$. The possible rational zeros are $\pm 1, \pm \frac{1}{2}$. $P(x)$ has 1 variation in sign and hence 1 positive real zero. $P(-x) = 2x^4 - 15x^3 + 17x^2 - 3x - 1$ has 3 variations in sign and hence 1 or 3 negative real zeros.

$$
\begin{array}{r|rrrrr}
\frac{1}{2} & 2 & 15 & 17 & 3 & -1 \\
  &   & 1 & 8 & \frac{25}{2} & \frac{31}{4} \\
\hline
  & 2 & 16 & 25 & \frac{31}{2} & \frac{27}{4}
\end{array}
\quad \Rightarrow x = \tfrac{1}{2} \text{ is an upper bound.}
$$

$$
\begin{array}{r|rrrrr}
-\frac{1}{2} & 2 & 15 & 17 & 3 & -1 \\
  &   & -1 & -7 & -5 & 1 \\
\hline
  & 2 & 14 & 10 & -2 & 0
\end{array}
\quad \Rightarrow x = -\tfrac{1}{2} \text{ is a zero.}
$$

So $P(x) = \left(x + \frac{1}{2}\right)\left(2x^3 + 14x^2 + 10x - 2\right) = 2\left(x + \frac{1}{2}\right)\left(x^3 + 7x^2 + 5x - 1\right)$.

$$
\begin{array}{r|rrrr}
-1 & 1 & 7 & 5 & -1 \\
  &   & -1 & -6 & 1 \\
\hline
  & 1 & 6 & -1 & 0
\end{array}
\quad \Rightarrow x = -1 \text{ is a zero.}
$$

So $P(x) = \left(x + \frac{1}{2}\right)\left(2x^3 + 14x^2 + 10x - 2\right) = 2\left(x + \frac{1}{2}\right)(x + 1)\left(x^2 + 6x - 1\right)$ Using the quadratic formula on the third factor, we have $x = \frac{-(6) \pm \sqrt{(6)^2 - 4(1)(-1)}}{2(1)} = \frac{-6 \pm \sqrt{40}}{2} = \frac{-6 \pm 2\sqrt{10}}{2} = -3 \pm \sqrt{10}$. Therefore, the zeros are $x = -1, -\frac{1}{2}, -3 \pm \sqrt{10}$.

50. $P(x) = 4x^5 - 18x^4 - 6x^3 + 91x^2 - 60x + 9$. The possible rational zeros are $\pm 1, \pm 3, \pm 9, \pm \frac{1}{2}, \pm \frac{3}{2}, \pm \frac{9}{2}, \pm \frac{1}{4}, \pm \frac{3}{4}, \pm \frac{9}{4}$. $P(x)$ has 4 variations in sign and hence 0 or 2 or 4 positive real zeros. $P(-x) = -4x^5 - 18x^4 + 6x^3 + 91x^2 + 60x + 9$ has 1 variation in sign and hence 1 negative real zero.

1	4	−18	−6	91	−60	9
		4	−14	−20	71	1
	4	−14	−20	71	11	10

3	4	−18	−6	91	−60	9
		12	−18	−72	57	−9
	4	−6	−24	19	−3	0	$\Rightarrow x = 3$ is a zero.

So $P(x) = (x - 3)\left(4x^4 - 6x^3 - 24x^2 + 19x - 3\right)$. Continuing by factoring the quotient, we have:

3	4	−6	−24	19	−3
		12	18	−18	3
	4	6	−6	1	0	$\Rightarrow x = 3$ is a zero again.

So $P(x) = (x - 3)^2 \left(4x^3 + 6x^2 - 6x + 1\right)$. Continuing by factoring the quotient, we have:

3	4	6	−6	1
		12	54	144
	4	18	48	1445	$\Rightarrow x = 3$ is an upper bound.

$\frac{1}{2}$	4	6	−6	1
		2	4	−1
	4	8	−2	0	$\Rightarrow x = \frac{1}{2}$ is a zero.

So $P(x) = (x - 3)^2 \left(x - \frac{1}{2}\right)\left(4x^2 + 8x - 2\right) = 2(x - 3)^2 \left(x - \frac{1}{2}\right)\left(2x^2 + 4x - 1\right)$. Using the quadratic formula on the second factor, we have $x = \frac{-4 \pm \sqrt{4^2 - 4(2)(-1)}}{2(2)} = \frac{-4 \pm \sqrt{24}}{4} = -1 \pm \frac{\sqrt{6}}{2}$. Therefore, the zeros are $x = \frac{1}{2}, 3, -1 \pm \frac{\sqrt{6}}{2}$.

51. (a) $P(x) = x^3 - 3x^2 - 4x + 12$ has possible rational zeros $\pm 1, \pm 2, \pm 3, \pm 4, \pm 6, \pm 12$.

(b)

1	1	−3	−4	12
		1	−2	−6
	1	−2	−6	6

2	1	−3	−4	12
		2	−2	−12
	1	−1	−6	0	$\Rightarrow x = 2$ is a zero.

So $P(x) = (x - 2)\left(x^2 - x - 6\right) = (x - 2)(x + 2)(x - 3)$. The real zeros of P are $-2, 2, 3$.

52. (a) $P(x) = -x^3 - 2x^2 + 5x + 6$ has possible rational zeros $\pm 1, \pm 2, \pm 3, \pm 6$.

(b)

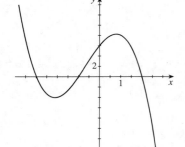

1	−1	−2	5	6
		−1	−3	2
	−1	−3	2	8

2	−1	−2	5	6
		−2	−8	−6
	−1	−4	−3	0	$\Rightarrow x = 2$ is a zero.

So $P(x) = (x - 2)\left(-x^2 - 4x - 3\right) = -(x - 2)\left(x^2 + 4x + 3\right) = -(x - 2)(x + 1)(x + 3)$. The real zeros of P are $2, -1, -3$.

53. (a) $P(x) = 2x^3 - 7x^2 + 4x + 4$ has possible rational zeros $\pm 1, \pm 2,$ $\pm 4, \pm \frac{1}{2}$.

(b)

$$
\begin{array}{r|rrrr}
1 & 2 & -7 & 4 & 4 \\
  &   & 2 & -5 & -1 \\
\hline
  & 2 & -5 & -1 & -3
\end{array}
\qquad
\begin{array}{r|rrrr}
2 & 2 & -7 & 4 & 4 \\
  &   & 4 & -6 & -4 \\
\hline
  & 2 & -3 & -2 & 0
\end{array}
\Rightarrow x = 2 \text{ is a zero.}
$$

So $P(x) = (x - 2)(2x^2 - 3x - 2)$. Continuing:

$$
\begin{array}{r|rrr}
2 & 2 & -3 & -2 \\
  &   & 4 & 2 \\
\hline
  & 2 & 1 & 0
\end{array}
\Rightarrow x = 2 \text{ is a zero again.}
$$

Thus $P(x) = (x - 2)^2(2x + 1)$. The real zeros of P are 2 and $-\frac{1}{2}$.

54. (a) $P(x) = 3x^3 + 17x^2 + 21x - 9$ has possible rational zeros $\pm 1, \pm 3,$ $\pm 9, \pm \frac{1}{3}, \pm \frac{2}{3}$.

(b)

$$
\begin{array}{r|rrrr}
1 & 3 & 17 & 21 & -9 \\
  &   & 3 & 20 & 41 \\
\hline
  & 3 & 20 & 41 & 32
\end{array}
\Rightarrow x = 1 \text{ is an upper bound.}
$$

$$
\begin{array}{r|rrrr}
\frac{1}{3} & 3 & 17 & 21 & -9 \\
  &   & 1 & 6 & 9 \\
\hline
  & 3 & 18 & 27 & 0
\end{array}
\Rightarrow x = \frac{1}{3} \text{ is a zero.}
$$

So $P(x) = \left(x - \frac{1}{3}\right)(3x^2 + 18x + 27) = 3\left(x - \frac{1}{3}\right)(x^2 + 6x + 9) = 3\left(x - \frac{1}{3}\right)(x + 3)^2$. The real zeros of P are $-3, \frac{1}{3}$.

55. (a) $P(x) = x^4 - 5x^3 + 6x^2 + 4x - 8$ has possible rational zeros $\pm 1,$ $\pm 2, \pm 4, \pm 8$.

(b)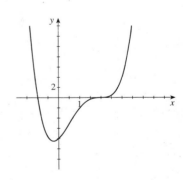

$$
\begin{array}{r|rrrrr}
1 & 1 & -5 & 6 & 4 & -8 \\
  &   & 1 & -4 & 2 & 6 \\
\hline
  & 1 & -4 & 2 & 6 & -2
\end{array}
$$

$$
\begin{array}{r|rrrrr}
2 & 1 & -5 & 6 & 4 & -8 \\
  &   & 2 & -6 & 0 & 8 \\
\hline
  & 1 & -3 & 0 & 4 & 0
\end{array}
\Rightarrow x = 2 \text{ is a zero.}
$$

So $P(x) = (x - 2)(x^3 - 3x^2 + 4)$ and the possible rational zeros are restricted to $-1, \pm 2, \pm 4$.

$$
\begin{array}{r|rrrr}
2 & 1 & -3 & 0 & 4 \\
  &   & 2 & -2 & -4 \\
\hline
  & 1 & -1 & -2 & 0
\end{array}
\Rightarrow x = 2 \text{ is a zero again.}
$$

$P(x) = (x - 2)^2(x^2 - x - 2) = (x - 2)^2(x - 2)(x + 1) = (x - 2)^3(x + 1)$. So the real zeros of P are -1 and 2.

56. (a) $P(x) = -x^4 + 10x^2 + 8x - 8$ has possible rational zeros $\pm 1, \pm 2,$ **(b)**
$\pm 4, \pm 8.$

$$\begin{array}{r|rrrrr} 1 & -1 & 0 & 10 & 8 & -8 \\ & & -1 & -1 & 9 & 17 \\ \hline & -1 & -1 & 9 & 17 & 9 \end{array} \qquad \begin{array}{r|rrrrr} 2 & -1 & 0 & 10 & 8 & -8 \\ & & -2 & -4 & 12 & 40 \\ \hline & -1 & -2 & 6 & 20 & 32 \end{array}$$

$$\begin{array}{r|rrrrr} 4 & -1 & 0 & 10 & 8 & -8 \\ & & -4 & -16 & -24 & -64 \\ \hline & -1 & -4 & -6 & -16 & -72 \end{array} \Rightarrow x = 4 \text{ is an upper bound.}$$

$$\begin{array}{r|rrrrr} -1 & -1 & 0 & 10 & 8 & -8 \\ & & 1 & -1 & -9 & 1 \\ \hline & -1 & 1 & 9 & -1 & -7 \end{array} \qquad \begin{array}{r|rrrrr} -2 & -1 & 0 & 10 & 8 & -8 \\ & & 2 & -4 & -12 & 8 \\ \hline & -1 & 2 & 6 & -4 & 0 \end{array} \Rightarrow x = -2 \text{ is a zero.}$$

So $P(x) = (x + 2)(-x^3 + 2x^2 + 6x - 4)$. Continuing, we have:

$$\begin{array}{r|rrrr} -2 & -1 & 2 & 6 & -4 \\ & & 2 & -8 & 4 \\ \hline & -1 & 4 & -2 & 0 \end{array} \Rightarrow x = -2 \text{ is a zero again.}$$

$P(x) = (x + 2)^2(-x^2 + 4x - 2)$. Using the quadratic formula on the second factor, we have

$x = \frac{-4 \pm \sqrt{4^2 - 4(-1)(-2)}}{2(-1)} = \frac{-4 \pm \sqrt{8}}{-2} = \frac{-4 \pm 2\sqrt{2}}{-2} = 2 \pm \sqrt{2}$. So the real zeros of P are $-2, 2 \pm \sqrt{2}$.

57. (a) $P(x) = x^5 - x^4 - 5x^3 + x^2 + 8x + 4$ has possible rational zeros **(b)**
$\pm 1, \pm 2, \pm 4.$

$$\begin{array}{r|rrrrrr} 1 & 1 & -1 & -5 & 1 & 8 & 4 \\ & & 1 & 0 & -5 & -4 & 4 \\ \hline & 1 & 0 & -5 & -4 & 4 & 8 \end{array}$$

$$\begin{array}{r|rrrrrr} 2 & 1 & -1 & -5 & 1 & 8 & 4 \\ & & 2 & 2 & -6 & -10 & -4 \\ \hline & 1 & 1 & -3 & -5 & -2 & 0 \end{array} \Rightarrow x = 2 \text{ is a zero.}$$

So $P(x) = (x - 2)(x^4 + x^3 - 3x^2 - 5x - 2)$, and the possible
rational zeros are restricted to $-1, \pm 2.$

$$\begin{array}{r|rrrrr} 2 & 1 & 1 & -3 & -5 & -2 \\ & & 2 & 6 & 6 & 2 \\ \hline & 1 & 3 & 3 & 1 & 0 \end{array} \Rightarrow x = 2 \text{ is a zero again.}$$

So $P(x) = (x - 2)^2(x^3 + 3x^2 + 3x + 1)$, and the possible rational zeros are restricted to $-1.$

$$\begin{array}{r|rrrr} -1 & 1 & 3 & 3 & 1 \\ & & -1 & -2 & -1 \\ \hline & 1 & 2 & 1 & 0 \end{array} \Rightarrow x = -1 \text{ is a zero.}$$

So $P(x) = (x - 2)^2(x + 1)(x^2 + 2x + 1) = (x - 2)^2(x + 1)^3$., and the real zeros of P are -1 and 2.

58. (a) $P(x) = x^5 - x^4 - 6x^3 + 14x^2 - 11x + 3$ has possible rational zeros $\pm 1, \pm 3$.

$$
\begin{array}{r|rrrrrr}
1 & 1 & -1 & -6 & 14 & -11 & 3 \\
  &   & 1 & 0 & -6 & 8 & -3 \\
\hline
  & 1 & 0 & -6 & 8 & -3 & 0
\end{array}
\Rightarrow x = 1 \text{ is a zero.}
$$

So $P(x) = (x - 1)\left(x^4 - 6x^2 + 8x - 3\right)$:

$$
\begin{array}{r|rrrrr}
1 & 1 & 0 & -6 & 8 & -3 \\
  &   & 1 & 1 & -5 & 3 \\
\hline
  & 1 & 1 & -5 & 3 & 0
\end{array}
\Rightarrow x = 1 \text{ is a zero again.}
$$

So $P(x) = (x - 1)^2 \left(x^3 + x^2 - 5x + 3\right)$:

$$
\begin{array}{r|rrrr}
1 & 1 & 1 & -5 & 3 \\
  &   & 1 & 2 & -3 \\
\hline
  & 1 & 2 & -3 & 0
\end{array}
\Rightarrow x = 1 \text{ is a zero again.}
$$

So $P(x) = (x - 1)^3 \left(x^2 + 2x - 3\right) = (x - 1)^4 (x + 3)$, and the real zeros of P are 1 and -3.

(b)

59. $P(x) = x^3 - x^2 - x - 3$. Since $P(x)$ has 1 variation in sign, P has 1 positive real zero. Since $P(-x) = -x^3 - x^2 + x - 3$ has 2 variations in sign, P has 2 or 0 negative real zeros. Thus, P has 1 or 3 real zeros.

60. $P(x) = 2x^3 - x^2 + 4x - 7$. Since $P(x)$ has 3 variations in signs, P has 3 or 1 positive real zeros. Since $P(-x) = -2x^3 - x^2 - 4x - 7$ has no variation in sign, there is no negative real zero. Thus, P has 1 or 3 real zeros.

61. $P(x) = 2x^6 + 5x^4 - x^3 - 5x - 1$. Since $P(x)$ has 1 variation in sign, P has 1 positive real zero. Since $P(-x) = 2x^6 + 5x^4 + x^3 + 5x - 1$ has 1 variation in sign, P has 1 negative real zero. Therefore, P has 2 real zeros.

62. $P(x) = x^4 + x^3 + x^2 + x + 12$. Since $P(x)$ has no variations in sign, P has no positive real zeros. Since $P(-x) = x^4 - x^3 + x^2 - x + 12$ has 4 variations in sign, P has 4, 2, or 0 negative real zeros. Therefore, $P(x)$ has 0, 2, or 4 real zeros.

63. $P(x) = x^5 + 4x^3 - x^2 + 6x$. Since $P(x)$ has 2 variations in sign, P has 2 or 0 positive real zeros. Since $P(-x) = -x^5 - 4x^3 - x^2 - 6x$ has no variation in sign, P has no negative real zero. Therefore, P has a total of 1 or 3 real zeros (since $x = 0$ is a zero, but is neither positive nor negative).

64. $P(x) = x^8 - x^5 + x^4 - x^3 + x^2 - x + 1$. Since $P(x)$ has 6 variations in sign, the polynomial has 6, 4, 2, or 0 positive real zeros. Since $P(-x)$ has no variation in sign, the polynomial has no negative real zeros. Therefore, P has 6, 4, 2, or 0 real zeros.

65. $P(x) = 2x^3 + 5x^2 + x - 2$; $a = -3, b = 1$

$$
\begin{array}{r|rrrr}
-3 & 2 & 5 & 1 & -2 \\
   &   & -6 & 3 & -12 \\
\hline
   & 2 & -1 & 4 & -14
\end{array}
\quad \text{alternating signs} \quad \Rightarrow \quad \text{lower bound.}
$$

$$
\begin{array}{r|rrrr}
1 & 2 & 5 & 1 & -2 \\
  &   & 2 & 7 & 8 \\
\hline
  & 2 & 7 & 8 & 6
\end{array}
\quad \text{all nonnegative} \quad \Rightarrow \quad \text{upper bound.}
$$

Therefore $a = -3$ and $b = 1$ are lower and upper bounds.

66. $P(x) = x^4 - 2x^3 - 9x^2 + 2x + 8$; $a = -3, b = 5$

$$
\begin{array}{r|rrrrr}
-3 & 1 & -2 & -9 & 2 & 8 \\
   &   & -3 & 15 & -18 & 48 \\
\hline
   & 1 & -5 & 6 & -16 & 56
\end{array}
\quad \text{Alternating signs} \quad \Rightarrow \quad \text{lower bound.}
$$

$$
\begin{array}{r|rrrrr}
5 & 1 & -2 & -9 & 2 & 8 \\
  &   & 5 & 15 & 30 & 160 \\
\hline
  & 1 & 3 & 6 & 32 & 168
\end{array}
\quad \text{All nonnegative} \quad \Rightarrow \quad \text{upper bound.}
$$

Therefore $a = -3$ and $b = 5$ are lower and upper bounds.

67. $P(x) = 8x^3 + 10x^2 - 39x + 9$; $a = -3, b = 2$

$$
\begin{array}{r|rrrr}
-3 & 8 & 10 & -39 & 9 \\
   &   & -24 & 42 & -9 \\
\hline
   & 8 & -14 & 3 & 0
\end{array}
\quad \text{alternating signs} \quad \Rightarrow \quad \text{lower bound.}
$$

$$
\begin{array}{r|rrrr}
2 & 8 & 10 & -39 & 9 \\
  &   & 16 & 52 & 26 \\
\hline
  & 8 & 26 & 13 & 35
\end{array}
\quad \text{all nonnegative} \quad \Rightarrow \quad \text{upper bound.}
$$

Therefore $a = -3$ and $b = 2$ are lower and upper bounds. Note that $x = -3$ is also a zero.

68. $P(x) = 3x^4 - 17x^3 + 24x^2 - 9x + 1$; $a = 0, b = 6$

$$
\begin{array}{r|rrrrr}
0 & 3 & -17 & 24 & -9 & 1 \\
  &   & 0 & 0 & 0 & 0 \\
\hline
  & 3 & -17 & 24 & -9 & 1
\end{array}
\quad \text{Alternating signs} \quad \Rightarrow \quad \text{lower bound.}
$$

$$
\begin{array}{r|rrrrr}
6 & 3 & -17 & 24 & -9 & 1 \\
  &   & 18 & 6 & 180 & 1026 \\
\hline
  & 3 & 1 & 30 & 171 & 1027
\end{array}
\quad \text{All nonnegative} \quad \Rightarrow \quad \text{upper bound.}
$$

Therefore $a = 0$, $b = 6$ are lower and upper bounds, respectively. Note, since $P(x)$ alternates in sign, by Descartes' Rule of Signs, 0 is automatically a lower bound.

69. $P(x) = x^3 - 3x^2 + 4$ and use the Upper and Lower Bounds Theorem:

$$
\begin{array}{r|rrrr}
-1 & 1 & -3 & 0 & 4 \\
   &   & -1 & 4 & -4 \\
\hline
   & 1 & -4 & 4 & 0
\end{array}
\quad \text{alternating signs} \quad \Rightarrow \quad \text{lower bound.}
$$

$$
\begin{array}{r|rrrr}
3 & 1 & -3 & 0 & 4 \\
  &   & 3 & 0 & 0 \\
\hline
  & 1 & 0 & 0 & 4
\end{array}
\quad \text{all nonnegative} \quad \Rightarrow \quad \text{upper bound.}
$$

Therefore -1 is a lower bound (and a zero) and 3 is an upper bound. (There are many possible solutions.)

70. $P(x) = 2x^3 - 3x^2 - 8x + 12$ and using the Upper and Lower Bounds Theorem:

$$\begin{array}{r|rrrr} -2 & 2 & -3 & -8 & 12 \\ & & -4 & 14 & -12 \\ \hline & 2 & -7 & 6 & 0 \end{array}$$

Alternating signs $\Rightarrow$ $x = -2$ is a lower bound (and a zero).

$$\begin{array}{r|rrrr} 3 & 2 & -3 & -8 & 12 \\ & & 6 & 9 & 3 \\ \hline & 2 & 3 & 1 & 15 \end{array}$$

All nonnegative $\Rightarrow$ $x = 3$ is an upper bound.

(There are many possible solutions.)

71. $P(x) = x^4 - 2x^3 + x^2 - 9x + 2$.

$$\begin{array}{r|rrrrr} 1 & 1 & -2 & 1 & -9 & 2 \\ & & 1 & -1 & 0 & -9 \\ \hline & 1 & -1 & 0 & -9 & -7 \end{array} \qquad \begin{array}{r|rrrrr} 2 & 1 & -2 & 1 & -9 & 2 \\ & & 2 & 0 & 2 & -14 \\ \hline & 1 & 0 & 1 & -7 & -12 \end{array}$$

$$\begin{array}{r|rrrrr} 3 & 1 & -2 & 1 & -9 & 2 \\ & & 3 & 3 & 12 & 9 \\ \hline & 1 & 1 & 4 & 3 & 11 \end{array}$$

all positive $\Rightarrow$ upper bound.

$$\begin{array}{r|rrrrr} -1 & 1 & -2 & 1 & -9 & 2 \\ & & -1 & 3 & -4 & 13 \\ \hline & 1 & -3 & 4 & -13 & 15 \end{array}$$

alternating signs $\Rightarrow$ lower bound.

Therefore -1 is a lower bound and 3 is an upper bound. (There are many possible solutions.)

72. Set $P(x) = x^5 - x^4 + 1$.

$$\begin{array}{r|rrrrrr} 1 & 1 & -1 & 0 & 0 & 0 & 1 \\ & & 1 & 0 & 0 & 0 & 0 \\ \hline & 1 & 0 & 0 & 0 & 0 & 1 \end{array}$$

All nonnegative $\Rightarrow$ $x = 1$ is an upper bound.

$$\begin{array}{r|rrrrrr} -1 & 1 & -1 & 0 & 0 & 0 & 1 \\ & & -1 & 2 & -2 & 2 & -2 \\ \hline & 1 & -2 & 2 & -2 & 2 & -1 \end{array}$$

Alternating signs $\Rightarrow$ $x = -1$ is a lower bound.

(There are many possible solutions.)

73. $P(x) = 2x^4 + 3x^3 - 4x^2 - 3x + 2$.

$$\begin{array}{r|rrrrr} 1 & 2 & 3 & -4 & -3 & 2 \\ & & 2 & 5 & 1 & -2 \\ \hline & 2 & 5 & 1 & -2 & 0 \end{array} \Rightarrow x = 1 \text{ is a zero.}$$

$P(x) = (x - 1)(2x^3 + 5x^2 + x - 2)$

$$\begin{array}{r|rrrr} -1 & 2 & 5 & 1 & -2 \\ & & -2 & -3 & 2 \\ \hline & 2 & 3 & -2 & 0 \end{array} \Rightarrow x = -1 \text{ is a zero.}$$

$P(x) = (x - 1)(x + 1)(2x^2 + 3x - 2) = (x - 1)(x + 1)(2x - 1)(x + 2)$. Therefore, the zeros are $x = -2, \frac{1}{2}, \pm 1$.

74. $P(x) = 2x^4 + 15x^3 + 31x^2 + 20x + 4$. The possible rational zeros are ± 1, ± 2, ± 4, $\pm\frac{1}{2}$. Since all of the coefficients are positive, there are no positive zeros. Since $P(-x) = 2x^4 - 15x^3 + 31x^2 - 20x + 4$ has 4 variations in sign, there are 0, 2, or 4 negative real zeros.

$$
\begin{array}{r|rrrrr}
-1 & 2 & 15 & 31 & 20 & 4 \\
   &   & -2 & -13 & -18 & -2 \\
\hline
   & 2 & 13 & 18 & 2 & 2
\end{array}
\qquad
\begin{array}{r|rrrrr}
-2 & 2 & 15 & 31 & 20 & 4 \\
   &   & -4 & -22 & -18 & -4 \\
\hline
   & 2 & 11 & 9 & 2 & 0
\end{array} \Rightarrow x = -2 \text{ is a zero.}
$$

$P(x) = (x+2)\left(2x^3 + 11x^2 + 9x + 2\right)$:

$$
\begin{array}{r|rrrr}
-2 & 2 & 11 & 9 & 2 \\
   &   & -4 & -14 & 10 \\
\hline
   & 2 & 7 & -5 & 12
\end{array}
\quad
\begin{array}{r|rrrr}
-4 & 2 & 11 & 9 & 2 \\
   &   & -8 & -12 & 12 \\
\hline
   & 2 & 3 & -3 & 14
\end{array}
\quad
\begin{array}{r|rrrr}
-\frac{1}{2} & 2 & 11 & 9 & 2 \\
   &   & -1 & -5 & -2 \\
\hline
   & 2 & 10 & 4 & 0
\end{array} \; x = -\tfrac{1}{2} \text{ is a zero.}
$$

$P(x) = (x+2)(2x+1)\left(x^2 + 5x + 2\right)$. Now if $x^2 + 5x + 2 = 0$, then $x = \frac{-5\pm\sqrt{25-4(1)(2)}}{2} = \frac{-5\pm\sqrt{17}}{2}$. Thus, the zeros are -2, $-\frac{1}{2}$, and $\frac{-5\pm\sqrt{17}}{2}$.

75. *Method 1:* $P(x) = 4x^4 - 21x^2 + 5$ has 2 variations in sign, so by Descartes' rule of signs there are either 2 or 0 positive zeros. If we replace x with $(-x)$, the function does not change, so there are either 2 or 0 negative zeros. Possible rational zeros are ± 1, $\pm\frac{1}{2}$, $\pm\frac{1}{4}$, ± 5, $\pm\frac{5}{2}$, $\pm\frac{5}{4}$. By inspection, ± 1 and ± 5 are not zeros, so we must look for non-integer solutions:

$$
\begin{array}{r|rrrrr}
\frac{1}{2} & 4 & 0 & -21 & 0 & 5 \\
   &   & 2 & 1 & -10 & -5 \\
\hline
   & 4 & 2 & -20 & -10 & 0
\end{array} \Rightarrow x = \tfrac{1}{2} \text{ is a zero.}
$$

$P(x) = \left(x - \frac{1}{2}\right)\left(4x^3 + 2x^2 - 20x - 10\right)$, continuing with the quotient, we have:

$$
\begin{array}{r|rrrr}
-\frac{1}{2} & 4 & 2 & -20 & -10 \\
   &   & -2 & 0 & 10 \\
\hline
   & 4 & 0 & -20 & 0
\end{array} \Rightarrow x = -\tfrac{1}{2} \text{ is a zero.}
$$

$P(x) = \left(x - \frac{1}{2}\right)\left(x + \frac{1}{2}\right)\left(4x^2 - 20\right) = 0$. If $4x^2 - 20 = 0$, then $x = \pm\sqrt{5}$. Thus the zeros are $x = \pm\frac{1}{2}, \pm\sqrt{5}$.

Method 2: Substituting $u = x^2$, the equation becomes $4u^2 - 21u + 5 = 0$, which factors:
$4u^2 - 21u + 5 = (4u - 1)(u - 5) = \left(4x^2 - 1\right)\left(x^2 - 5\right)$. Then either we have $x^2 = 5$, so that $x = \pm\sqrt{5}$, or we have $x^2 = \frac{1}{4}$, so that $x = \pm\sqrt{\frac{1}{4}} = \pm\frac{1}{2}$. Thus the zeros are $x = \pm\frac{1}{2}, \pm\sqrt{5}$.

76. $P(x) = 6x^4 - 7x^3 - 8x^2 + 5x = x\left(6x^3 - 7x^2 - 8x + 5\right)$. So $x = 0$ is a zero. Continuing with the quotient, $Q(x) = 6x^3 - 7x^2 - 8x + 5$. The possible rational zeros are ± 1, ± 5, $\pm\frac{1}{2}$, $\pm\frac{5}{2}$, $\pm\frac{1}{3}$, $\pm\frac{5}{3}$, $\pm\frac{1}{6}$, $\pm\frac{5}{6}$. Since $Q(x)$ has 2 variations in sign, there are 0 or 2 positive real zeros. Since $Q(-x) = 6x^4 + 7x^3 - 8x^2 - 5x$ has 1 variation in sign, there is 1 negative real zero.

$$
\begin{array}{r|rrrr}
1 & 6 & -7 & -8 & 5 \\
  &   & 6 & -1 & -9 \\
\hline
  & 6 & -1 & -9 & -4
\end{array}
\qquad
\begin{array}{r|rrrr}
5 & 6 & -7 & -8 & 5 \\
  &   & 30 & 115 & 535 \\
\hline
  & 6 & 23 & 107 & 540
\end{array} \text{ All positive } \Rightarrow \text{ upper bound.}
$$

$$
\begin{array}{r|rrrr}
\frac{1}{2} & 6 & -7 & -8 & 5 \\
  &   & 3 & -2 & -5 \\
\hline
  & 6 & -4 & -10 & 0
\end{array} \Rightarrow x = \tfrac{1}{2} \text{ is a zero.}
$$

$P(x) = x(2x - 1)\left(3x^2 - 2x - 5\right) = x(2x - 1)(3x - 5)(x + 1)$. Therefore, the zeros are 0, -1, $\frac{1}{2}$ and $\frac{5}{3}$.

77. $P(x) = x^5 - 7x^4 + 9x^3 + 23x^2 - 50x + 24$. The possible rational zeros are $\pm 1, \pm 2, \pm 3, \pm 4, \pm 6, \pm 8, \pm 12, \pm 24$. $P(x)$ has 4 variations in sign and hence 0, 2, or 4 positive real zeros. $P(-x) = -x^5 - 7x^4 - 9x^3 + 23x^2 + 50x + 24$ has 1 variation in sign, and hence 1 negative real zero.

$$
\begin{array}{r|rrrrrr}
1 & 1 & -7 & 9 & 23 & -50 & 24 \\
  &   & 1 & -6 & 3 & 26 & -24 \\
\hline
  & 1 & -6 & 3 & 26 & -24 & 0
\end{array} \Rightarrow x = 1 \text{ is a zero.}
$$

$P(x) = (x - 1)\left(x^4 - 6x^3 + 3x^2 + 26x - 24\right)$; continuing with the quotient, we try 1 again.

$$
\begin{array}{r|rrrrr}
1 & 1 & -6 & 3 & 26 & -24 \\
  &   & 1 & -5 & -2 & 24 \\
\hline
  & 1 & -5 & -2 & 24 & 0
\end{array} \Rightarrow x = 1 \text{ is a zero again.}
$$

$P(x) = (x - 1)^2\left(x^3 - 5x^2 - 2x + 24\right)$; continuing with the quotient, we start by trying 1 again.

$$
\begin{array}{r|rrrr}
1 & 1 & -5 & -2 & 24 \\
  &   & 1 & -4 & -6 \\
\hline
  & 1 & -4 & -6 & 18
\end{array}
\quad
\begin{array}{r|rrrr}
2 & 1 & -5 & -2 & 24 \\
  &   & 2 & -6 & -16 \\
\hline
  & 1 & -3 & -8 & 8
\end{array}
\quad
\begin{array}{r|rrrr}
3 & 1 & -5 & -2 & 24 \\
  &   & 3 & -6 & -24 \\
\hline
  & 1 & -2 & -8 & 0
\end{array} \Rightarrow x = 3 \text{ is a zero.}
$$

$P(x) = (x - 1)^2 (x - 3)\left(x^2 - 2x - 8\right) = (x - 1)^2 (x - 3)(x - 4)(x + 2)$. Therefore, the zeros are $x = -2, 1, 3, 4$.

78. $P(x) = 8x^5 - 14x^4 - 22x^3 + 57x^2 - 35x + 6$. The possible rational zeros are $\pm 1, \pm 2, \pm 3, \pm 6, \pm \dfrac{1}{2}$, $\pm \dfrac{3}{2}, \pm \dfrac{1}{4}, \pm \dfrac{3}{4}, \pm \dfrac{1}{8}, \pm \dfrac{3}{8}$. Since $P(x)$ has 4 variations in sign, there are 0, 2, or 4 positive real zeros. Since $P(-x) = -8x^5 - 14x^4 + 22x^3 + 57x^2 + 35x + 6$ has 1 variation in sign, there is 1 negative real zero.

$$
\begin{array}{r|rrrrrr}
-1 & 8 & -14 & -22 & 57 & -35 & 6 \\
   &   & -8 & 22 & 0 & -57 & 92 \\
\hline
   & 8 & -22 & 0 & 57 & -92 & 98
\end{array}
\quad
\begin{array}{r|rrrrrr}
-2 & 8 & -14 & -22 & 57 & -35 & 6 \\
   &   & -16 & 60 & -76 & 38 & -6 \\
\hline
   & 8 & -30 & 38 & -19 & 3 & 0
\end{array} \Rightarrow x = -2 \text{ is a zero.}
$$

$P(x) = (x + 2)\left(8x^4 - 30x^3 + 38x^2 - 19x + 3\right)$. All the other real zeros are positive.

$$
\begin{array}{r|rrrrr}
1 & 8 & -30 & 38 & -19 & 3 \\
  &   & 8 & -22 & 16 & -3 \\
\hline
  & 8 & -22 & 16 & -3 & 0
\end{array} \Rightarrow x = 1 \text{ is a zero.}
$$

$P(x) = (x + 2)(x - 1)\left(8x^3 - 22x^2 + 16x - 3\right)$.

$$
\begin{array}{r|rrrr}
1 & 8 & -22 & 16 & -3 \\
  &   & 8 & -14 & 2 \\
\hline
  & 8 & -14 & 2 & -1
\end{array}
\qquad
\begin{array}{r|rrrr}
\frac{1}{2} & 8 & -22 & 16 & -3 \\
  &   & 4 & -9 & \frac{7}{2} \\
\hline
  & 8 & -18 & 7 & \frac{1}{2}
\end{array}
$$

Since $f\left(\frac{1}{2}\right) > 0 > f(1)$, there must be a zero between $\frac{1}{2}$ and 1. We try $\frac{3}{4}$:

$$
\begin{array}{r|rrrr}
\frac{3}{4} & 8 & -22 & 16 & -3 \\
  &   & 6 & -12 & 3 \\
\hline
  & 8 & -16 & 4 & 0
\end{array} \Rightarrow x = \frac{3}{4} \text{ is a zero.}
$$

$P(x) = (x + 2)(x - 1)(4x - 3)\left(2x^2 - 4x + 1\right)$. Now, $2x^2 - 4x + 1 = 0$ when $x = \dfrac{4 \pm \sqrt{16 - 4(2)(1)}}{2(2)} = \dfrac{2 \pm \sqrt{2}}{2}$. Thus, the zeros are $1, \frac{3}{4}, -2$, and $\dfrac{2 \pm \sqrt{2}}{2}$.

79. $P(x) = x^3 - x - 2$. The only possible rational zeros of $P(x)$ are ± 1 and ± 2.

$$
\begin{array}{r|rrrr}
1 & 1 & 0 & -1 & -2 \\
  &   & 1 & 1 & 0 \\
\hline
  & 1 & 1 & 0 & -2
\end{array}
\qquad
\begin{array}{r|rrrr}
2 & 1 & 0 & -1 & -2 \\
  &   & 2 & 4 & 6 \\
\hline
  & 1 & 2 & 3 & 4
\end{array}
\qquad
\begin{array}{r|rrrr}
-1 & 1 & 0 & -1 & -2 \\
   &   & -1 & 1 & 0 \\
\hline
   & 1 & -1 & 0 & -2
\end{array}
$$

Since the row that contains -1 alternates between nonnegative and nonpositive, -1 is a lower bound and there is no need to try -2. Therefore, $P(x)$ does not have any rational zeros.

80. $P(x) = 2x^4 - x^3 + x + 2$. The only possible rational zeros of $P(x)$ are ± 1, ± 2, $\pm \frac{1}{2}$.

$$
\begin{array}{r|rrrrr}
\frac{1}{2} & 2 & -1 & 0 & 1 & 2 \\
            &   & 1 & 0 & 0 & \frac{1}{2} \\
\hline
            & 2 & 0 & 0 & 1 & \frac{5}{2}
\end{array}
\quad \text{All nonnegative} \quad \Rightarrow \quad x = \tfrac{1}{2} \text{ is an upper bound.}
$$

$$
\begin{array}{r|rrrrr}
-1 & 2 & -1 & 0 & 1 & 2 \\
   &   & -2 & 3 & -3 & 2 \\
\hline
   & 2 & -3 & 3 & -2 & 4
\end{array}
\quad \text{Alternating signs} \quad \Rightarrow \quad x = -1 \text{ is a lower bound.}
$$

$$
\begin{array}{r|rrrrr}
-\frac{1}{2} & 2 & -1 & 0 & 1 & 2 \\
             &   & -1 & 1 & -\frac{1}{2} & -\frac{1}{4} \\
\hline
             & 2 & -2 & 1 & \frac{1}{2} & \frac{7}{4}
\end{array}
$$

Therefore, there is no rational zero.

81. $P(x) = 3x^3 - x^2 - 6x + 12$ has possible rational zeros ± 1, ± 2, ± 3, ± 4, ± 6, ± 12, $\pm \frac{1}{3}$, $\pm \frac{2}{3}$, $\pm \frac{4}{3}$.

$$
\begin{array}{c|rrrr}
 & 3 & -1 & -6 & 12 \\
\hline
1 & 3 & 2 & -4 & 8 \\
2 & 3 & 5 & 4 & 20 \\
-1 & 3 & -4 & -2 & 14 \\
-2 & 3 & -7 & 8 & -4 \\
\end{array}
$$

2: all positive $\Rightarrow$ $x = 2$ is an upper bound

-2: alternating signs $\Rightarrow$ $x = -2$ is a lower bound

$$
\begin{array}{c|rrrr}
 & 3 & -1 & -6 & 12 \\
\hline
\frac{1}{3} & 3 & 0 & -6 & 10 \\
\frac{2}{3} & 3 & 1 & -\frac{16}{3} & \frac{76}{9} \\
\frac{4}{3} & 3 & 3 & -2 & \frac{28}{3} \\
-\frac{1}{3} & 3 & -2 & -\frac{16}{3} & \frac{124}{9} \\
-\frac{2}{3} & 3 & -3 & -4 & \frac{44}{3} \\
-\frac{4}{3} & 3 & -5 & \frac{2}{3} & \frac{100}{9} \\
\end{array}
$$

Therefore, there is no rational zero.

82. $P(x) = x^{50} - 5x^{25} + x^2 - 1$. The only possible rational zeros of $P(x)$ are ± 1. Since $P(1) = (1)^{50} - 5(1)^{25} + (1)^2 - 1 = -4$ and $P(-1) = (-1)^{50} - 5(-1)^{25} + (-1)^2 - 1 = 6$, $P(x)$ does not have a rational zero.

83. $P(x) = x^3 - 3x^2 - 4x + 12$, $[-4, 4]$ by $[-15, 15]$. The possible rational zeros are ± 1, ± 2, ± 3, ± 4, ± 6, ± 12. By observing the graph of P, the rational zeros are $x = -2$, 2, 3.

84. $P(x) = x^4 - 5x^2 + 4$, $[-4, 4]$ by $[-30, 30]$. The possible rational solutions are ± 1, ± 2, ± 4. By observing the graph of the equation, the solutions of the given equation are $x = \pm 1$, ± 2.

85. $P(x) = 2x^4 - 5x^3 - 14x^2 + 5x + 12$, $[-2, 5]$ by $[-40, 40]$. The possible rational zeros are $\pm 1, \pm 2, \pm 3, \pm 4, \pm 6, \pm 12, \pm \frac{1}{2}, \pm \frac{3}{2}$. By observing the graph of P, the zeros are $x = -\frac{3}{2}, -1, 1, 4$.

86. $P(x) = 3x^3 + 8x^2 + 5x + 2$, $[-3, 3]$ by $[-10, 10]$ The possible rational solutions are $\pm 1, \pm 2, \pm \frac{1}{3}, \pm \frac{2}{3}$. By observing the graph of the equation, the only real solution of the given equation is $x = -2$.

87. $x^4 - x - 4 = 0$. Possible rational solutions are $\pm 1, \pm 2, \pm 4$.

1	1	0	0	-1	-4
		1	1	1	0
	1	1	1	0	-4

2	1	0	0	-1	-4
		2	4	8	14
	1	2	4	7	10	$\Rightarrow x = 2$ is an upper bound.

-1	1	0	0	-1	-4
		-1	1	-1	2
	1	-1	1	-2	-2

-2	1	0	0	-1	-4
		-2	4	-8	18
	1	-2	4	-9	14	$\Rightarrow x = -2$ is a lower bound.

Therefore, we graph the function $P(x) = x^4 - x - 4$ in the viewing rectangle $[-2, 2]$ by $[-5, 20]$ and see there are two solutions. In the viewing rectangle $[-1.3, -1.25]$ by $[-0.1, 0.1]$, we find the solution $x \approx -1.28$. In the viewing rectangle $[1.5.1.6]$ by $[-0.1, 0.1]$, we find the solution $x \approx 1.53$. Thus the solutions are $x \approx -1.28, 1.53$.

88. $2x^3 - 8x^2 + 9x - 9 = 0$. Possible rational solutions are $\pm 1, \pm 3, \pm 9, \pm \frac{1}{2}, \pm \frac{3}{2}, \pm \frac{9}{2}$.

1	2	-8	9	-9
		2	-6	3
	2	-6	3	-6

3	2	-8	9	-9
		6	-6	9
	2	-2	3	0	$\Rightarrow x = 3$ is a zero.

We graph $P(x) = 2x^3 - 8x^2 + 9x - 9$ in the viewing rectangle $[-4, 6]$ by $[-40, 40]$. It appears that the equation has no other real solution. We can factor $2x^3 - 8x^2 + 9x - 9 = (x - 3)(2x^2 - 2x + 3)$. Since the quotient is a quadratic expression, we can use the quadratic formula to locate the other possible solutions:
$x = \frac{2 \pm \sqrt{2^2 - 4(2)(3)}}{2(2)}$, which are not real. So the only solution is $x = 3$.

89. $4.00x^4 + 4.00x^3 - 10.96x^2 - 5.88x + 9.09 = 0$.

1	4	4	−10.96	−5.88	9.09
		4	8	−2.96	−8.84
	4	8	−2.96	−8.84	0.25

2	4	4	−10.96	−5.88	9.09
		8	24	26.08	40.40
	4	12	13.04	20.2	49.49 $\Rightarrow x = 2$ is an upper bound.

−2	4	4	−10.96	−5.88	9.09
		−8	8	5.92	−0.08
	4	−4	−2.96	0.04	9.01

−3	4	4	−10.96	−5.88	9.09
		−12	24	−39.12	135
	4	−8	13.04	−45	144.09 $\Rightarrow x = -3$ is a lower bound.

Therefore, we graph the function $P(x) = 4.00x^4 + 4.00x^3 - 10.96x^2 - 5.88x + 9.09$ in the viewing rectangle $[-3, 2]$ by $[-10, 40]$. There appear to be two solutions. In the viewing rectangle $[-1.6, -1.4]$ by $[-0.1, 0.1]$, we find the solution $x \approx -1.50$. In the viewing rectangle $[0.8, 1.2]$ by $[0, 1]$, we see that the graph comes close but does not go through the x-axis. Thus there is no solution here. Therefore, the only solution is $x \approx -1.50$.

  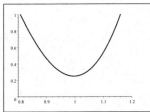

90. $x^5 + 2x^4 + 0.96x^3 + 5x^2 + 10x + 4.8 = 0$. Since all the coefficients are positive, there is no positive solution. So $x = 0$ is an upper bound.

−2	1	2	0.96	5	10	4.8
		−2	0	−1.92	−6.16	−7.68
	1	0	0.96	3.08	3.84	−2.88

−3	1	2	0.96	5	10	4.8
		−3	3	−11.88	20.64	−91.92
	1	−1	3.96	−6.88	30.64	−87.12 $\Rightarrow x = -3$ is a lower bound.

Therefore, we graph $P(x) = x^5 + 2x^4 + 0.96x^3 + 5x^2 + 10x + 4.8$ in the viewing rectangle $[-3, 0]$ by $[-10, 5]$ and see that there are three possible solutions. In the viewing rectangle $[-1.75, -1.7]$ by $[-0.1, 0.1]$, we find the solution $x \approx -1.71$. In the viewing rectangle $[-1.25, -1.15]$ by $[-0.1, 0.1]$, we find the solution $x \approx -1.20$. In the viewing rectangle $[-0.85, -0.75]$ by $[-0.1, 0.1]$, we find the solution $x \approx -0.80$. So the solutions are $x \approx -1.71, -1.20, -0.80$.

91. (a) Since $z > b$, we have $z - b > 0$. Since all the coefficients of $Q(x)$ are nonnegative, and since $z > 0$, we have $Q(z) > 0$ (being a sum of positive terms). Thus, $P(z) = (z - b) \cdot Q(z) + r > 0$, since the sum of a positive number and a nonnegative number.

(b) In part (a), we showed that if b satisfies the conditions of the first part of the Upper and Lower Bounds Theorem and $z > b$, then $P(z) > 0$. This means that no real zero of P can be larger than b, so b is an upper bound for the real zeros.

(c) Suppose $-b$ is a negative lower bound for the real zeros of $P(x)$. Then clearly b is an upper bound for $P_1(x) = P(-x)$. Thus, as in Part (a), we can write $P_1(x) = (x - b) \cdot Q(x) + r$, where $r > 0$ and the coefficients of Q are all nonnegative, and $P(x) = P_1(-x) = (-x - b) \cdot Q(-x) + r = (x + b) \cdot [-Q(-x)] + r$. Since the coefficients of $Q(x)$ are all nonnegative, the coefficients of $-Q(-x)$ will be alternately nonpositive and nonnegative, which proves the second part of the Upper and Lower Bounds Theorem.

92. $P(x) = x^5 - x^4 - x^3 - 5x^2 - 12x - 6$ has possible rational zeros $\pm 1, \pm 2, \pm 3, \pm 6$. Since $P(x)$ has 1 variation in sign, there is 1 positive real zero. Since $P(-x) = -x^5 - x^4 + x^3 - 5x^2 + 12x - 6$ has 4 variations in sign, there are 0, 2, or 4 negative real zeros.

$$
\begin{array}{r|rrrrrr}
1 & 1 & -1 & -1 & -5 & -12 & -6 \\
  &   & 1 & 0 & -1 & -6 & -18 \\
\hline
  & 1 & 0 & -1 & -6 & -18 & -24
\end{array}
\qquad
\begin{array}{r|rrrrrr}
2 & 1 & -1 & -1 & -5 & -12 & -6 \\
  &   & 2 & 2 & 2 & -6 & -36 \\
\hline
  & 1 & 1 & 1 & -3 & -18 & -42
\end{array}
$$

$$
\begin{array}{r|rrrrrr}
3 & 1 & -1 & -1 & -5 & -12 & -6 \\
  &   & 3 & 6 & 15 & 30 & 54 \\
\hline
  & 1 & 2 & 5 & 10 & 18 & 48 \quad \Rightarrow 3 \text{ is an upper bound.}
\end{array}
$$

$$
\begin{array}{r|rrrrrr}
-1 & 1 & -1 & -1 & -5 & -12 & -6 \\
   &   & -1 & 2 & -1 & 6   & 6 \\
\hline
   & 1 & -2 & 1 & -6 & -6 & 0 \quad \Rightarrow x = -1 \text{ is a zero.}
\end{array}
$$

$P(x) = (x+1)\left(x^4 - 2x^3 + x^2 - 6x - 6\right)$, continuing with the quotient we have

$$
\begin{array}{r|rrrrr}
-1 & 1 & -2 & 1 & -6 & -6 \\
   &   & -1 & 3 & -4 & 10 \\
\hline
   & 1 & -3 & 4 & -10 & 4 \quad \Rightarrow -1 \text{ is a lower bound.}
\end{array}
$$

Therefore, there is 1 rational zero, namely -1. Since there are 1, 3 or 5 real zeros, and we found 1 rational zero, there must be 0, 2 or 4 irrational zeros. However, since 1 zero must be positive, there cannot be 0 irrational zeros. Therefore, there is exactly 1 rational zero and 2 or 4 irrational zeros.

93. Let r be the radius of the silo. The volume of the hemispherical roof is $\frac{1}{2}\left(\frac{4}{3}\pi r^3\right) = \frac{2}{3}\pi r^3$. The volume of the cylindrical section is $\pi\left(r^2\right)(30) = 30\pi r^2$. Because the total volume of the silo is 15,000 ft^3, we get the following equation: $\frac{2}{3}\pi r^3 + 30\pi r^2 = 15000 \quad \Leftrightarrow \quad \frac{2}{3}\pi r^3 + 30\pi r^2 - 15000 = 0 \Leftrightarrow \pi r^3 + 45\pi r^2 - 22500 = 0$. Using a graphing device, we first graph the polynomial in the viewing rectangle $[0, 15]$ by $[-10000, 10000]$. The solution, $r \approx 11.28$ ft., is shown in the viewing rectangle $[11.2, 11.4]$ by $[-1, 1]$.

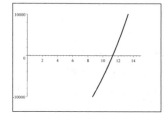

94. Given that x is the length of a side of the rectangle, we have that the length of the diagonal is $x+10$, and the length of the other side of the rectangle is $\sqrt{(x+10)^2 - x^2}$. Hence $x\sqrt{(x+10)^2 - x^2} = 5000 \quad \Rightarrow \quad x^2(20x + 100) = 25{,}000{,}000$ $\Leftrightarrow \quad 2x^3 + 10x^2 - 2{,}500{,}000 = 0 \quad \Leftrightarrow \quad x^3 + 5x^2 - 1{,}250{,}000 = 0$. The first viewing rectangle, $[0, 120]$ by $[-100, 500]$, shows there is one solution. The second viewing rectangle, $[106, 106.1]$ by $[-0.1, 0.1]$, shows the solution is $x = 106.08$. Therefore, the dimensions of the rectangle are 47 ft by 106 ft.

95. $h(t) = 11.60t - 12.41t^2 + 6.20t^3$
$- 1.58t^4 + 0.20t^5 - 0.01t^6$

is shown in the viewing rectangle

$[0, 10]$ by $[0, 6]$.

(a) It started to snow again.

(b) No, $h(t) \leq 4$.

(c) The function $h(t)$ is shown in the viewing rectangle $[6, 6.5]$ by $[0, 0.5]$. The x-intercept of the function is a little less than 6.5, which means that the snow melted just before midnight on Saturday night.

96. The volume of the box is $V = 1500 = x(20 - 2x)(40 - 2x) = 4x^3 - 120x^2 + 800x \quad \Leftrightarrow$
$4x^3 - 120x^2 + 800x - 1500 = 4(x^3 - 30x^2 + 200x - 375) = 0$. Clearly, we must have $20 - 2x > 0$, and so
$0 < x < 10$.

$$
\begin{array}{r|rrrr}
5 & 1 & -30 & 200 & -375 \\
& & 5 & -125 & 375 \\
\hline
& 1 & -25 & 75 & 0 \quad \Rightarrow x = 5 \text{ is a zero.}
\end{array}
$$

$x^3 - 30x^2 + 200x - 375 = (x - 5)(x^2 - 25x + 75) = 0$. Using the quadratic formula, we find the

other zeros: $x = \frac{25 \pm \sqrt{625 - 4(1)(75)}}{2} = \frac{25 \pm \sqrt{325}}{2} = \frac{25 \pm 5\sqrt{13}}{2}$. Since $\frac{25 + 5\sqrt{13}}{2} > 10$, the two answers are:

$x = $ height $= 5$ cm, width $= 20 - 2(5) = 10$ cm, and length $= 40 - 2(5) = 30$ cm; and $x = \frac{25 - 5\sqrt{13}}{2}$,

width $= 20 - (25 - 5\sqrt{13}) = 5\sqrt{13} - 5$ cm, and length $= 40 - (25 - 5\sqrt{13}) = 15 + 5\sqrt{13}$ cm.

97. Let r be the radius of the cone and cylinder and let h be the height of the cone.
Since the height and diameter are equal, we get $h = 2r$. So the volume of the
cylinder is $V_1 = \pi r^2 \cdot$ (cylinder height) $= 20\pi r^2$, and the volume of the cone is

$V_2 = \frac{1}{3}\pi r^2 h = \frac{1}{3}\pi r^2 (2r) = \frac{2}{3}\pi r^3$. Since the total volume is $\frac{500\pi}{3}$, it follows

that $\frac{2}{3}\pi r^3 + 20\pi r^2 = \frac{500\pi}{3} \quad \Leftrightarrow \quad r^3 + 30r^2 - 250 = 0$. By Descartes' Rule

of Signs, there is 1 positive zero. Since r is between 2.76 and 2.765 (see the table),
the radius should be 2.76 m (correct to two decimals).

r	$r^3 + 30r^2 - 250$
1	-219
2	-122
3	47
2.7	-11.62
2.76	-2.33
2.77	1.44
2.765	1.44
2.8	7.15

98. (a) Let x be the length, in ft, of each side of the base and let h be the height. The volume of the box is $V = 2\sqrt{2} = hx^2$,
and so $hx^2 = 2\sqrt{2}$. The length of the diagonal on the base is $\sqrt{x^2 + x^2} = \sqrt{2x^2}$, and hence the length of the diagonal
between opposite corners is $\sqrt{2x^2 + h^2} = x + 1$. Squaring both sides of the equation, we have $2x^2 + h^2 = x^2 + 2x + 1$
$\Leftrightarrow \quad h^2 = -x^2 + 2x + 1 \quad \Leftrightarrow \quad h = \sqrt{-x^2 + 2x + 1}$. Therefore, $2\sqrt{2} = hx^2 = \left(\sqrt{-x^2 + 2x + 1}\right)x^2 \quad \Leftrightarrow$
$\left(-x^2 + 2x + 1\right)x^4 = 8 \quad \Leftrightarrow \quad x^6 - 2x^5 - x^4 + 8 = 0$.

(b) We graph $y = x^6 - 2x^5 - x^4 + 8$ in the viewing rectangle $[0, 5]$ by $[-10, 10]$, and we see that there are two solutions. In the second viewing rectangle, $[1.4, 1.5]$ by $[-1, 1]$, we see the solution $x \approx 1.45$. The third viewing rectangle, $[2.25, 2.35]$ by $[-1, 1]$, shows the solution $x \approx 2.31$.

If $x = $ width $= $ length $= 1.45$ ft, then height $= \sqrt{-x^2 + 2x + 1} = 1.34$ ft, and if $x = $ width $= $ length $= 2.31$ ft, then height $= \sqrt{-x^2 + 2x + 1} = 0.53$ ft.

99. Let b be the width of the base, and let l be the length of the box. Then the length plus girth is $l + 4b = 108$, and the volume is $V = lb^2 = 2200$. Solving the first equation for l and substituting this value into the second equation yields $l = 108 - 4b \Rightarrow V = (108 - 4b)\, b^2 = 2200 \quad \Leftrightarrow \quad 4b^3 - 108b^2 + 2200 = 0 \Leftrightarrow 4\left(b^3 - 27b^2 + 550\right) = 0$. Now $P(b) = b^3 - 27b^2 + 550$ has two variations in sign, so there are 0 or 2 positive real zeros. We also observe that since $l > 0, b < 27$, so $b = 27$ is an upper bound. Thus the possible positive rational real zeros are $1, 2, 3, 10, 11, 22, 25$.

$$
\begin{array}{r|rrrr}
1 & 1 & -27 & 0 & 550 \\
  &   & 1 & -26 & -26 \\
\hline
  & 1 & -26 & -26 & 524 \\
\end{array}
\qquad
\begin{array}{r|rrrr}
2 & 1 & -27 & 0 & 550 \\
  &   & 2 & -50 & -100 \\
\hline
  & 1 & -25 & -50 & 450 \\
\end{array}
$$

$$
\begin{array}{r|rrrr}
5 & 1 & -27 & 0 & 550 \\
  &   & 5 & -110 & -550 \\
\hline
  & 1 & -22 & -110 & 0 \quad \Rightarrow b = 5 \text{ is a zero.}
\end{array}
$$

$P(b) = (b - 5)\left(b^2 - 22b - 110\right)$. The other zeros are $b = \dfrac{22 \pm \sqrt{484 - 4(1)(-110)}}{2} = \dfrac{22 \pm \sqrt{924}}{2} = \dfrac{22 \pm 30.397}{2}$. The positive answer from this factor is $b \approx 26.20$. Thus we have two possible solutions, $b = 5$ or $b \approx 26.20$. If $b = 5$, then $l = 108 - 4(5) = 88$; if $b \approx 26.20$, then $l = 108 - 4(26.20) = 3.20$. Thus the length of the box is either 88 in. or 3.20 in.

100. (a) An odd-degree polynomial must have a real zero. The end behavior of such a polynomial requires that the graph of the polynomial heads off in opposite directions as $x \to \infty$ and $x \to -\infty$. Thus the graph must cross the x-axis.

(b) There are many possibilities one of which is $P(x) = x^4 + 1$.

(c) $P(x) = x\left(x - \sqrt{2}\right)\left(x + \sqrt{2}\right) = x^3 - 2x$.

(d) $P(x) = \left(x - \sqrt{2}\right)\left(x + \sqrt{2}\right)\left(x - \sqrt{3}\right)\left(x + \sqrt{3}\right) = x^4 - 5x^2 + 6$. If a polynomial with integer coefficients has no real zeroes, then the polynomial must have even degree.

101. (a) Substituting $X - \dfrac{a}{3}$ for x we have

$$
\begin{aligned}
x^3 + ax^2 + bx + c &= \left(X - \frac{a}{3}\right)^3 + a\left(X - \frac{a}{3}\right)^2 + b\left(X - \frac{a}{3}\right) + c \\
&= X^3 - aX^2 + \frac{a^2}{3}X + \frac{a^3}{27} + a\left(X^2 - \frac{2a}{3}X + \frac{a^2}{9}\right) + bX - \frac{ab}{3} + c \\
&= X^3 - aX^2 + \frac{a^2}{3}X + \frac{a^3}{27} + aX^2 - \frac{2a^2}{3}X + \frac{a^3}{9} + bX - \frac{ab}{3} + c \\
&= X^3 + (-a + a)X^2 + \left(-\frac{a^2}{3} - \frac{2a^2}{3} + b\right)X + \left(\frac{a^3}{27} + \frac{a^3}{9} - \frac{ab}{3} + c\right) \\
&= X^3 + (b - a^2)X + \left(\frac{4a^3}{27} - \frac{ab}{3} + c\right)
\end{aligned}
$$

(b) $x^3 + 6x^2 + 9x + 4 = 0$. Setting $a = 6$, $b = 9$, and $c = 4$, we have: $X^3 + (9 - 6^2)X + (32 - 18 + 4) = X^3 - 27X + 18$.

102. (a) Using the cubic formula, $x = \sqrt[3]{\dfrac{-2}{2} + \sqrt{\dfrac{2^2}{4} + \dfrac{(-3)^3}{27}}} + \sqrt[3]{\dfrac{-2}{2} - \sqrt{\dfrac{2^2}{4} + \dfrac{(-3)^3}{27}}} = \sqrt[3]{-1} + \sqrt[3]{-1} = -1 - 1 = -2.$

$$
\begin{array}{r|rrr}
-2 & 1 & 0 & -3 & 2 \\
   &   & -2 & 4 & -2 \\
\hline
   & 1 & -2 & 1 & 0
\end{array}
$$

So $(x + 2)(x^2 - 2x + 1) = (x + 2)(x - 1)^2 = 0 \quad \Rightarrow \quad x = -2, 1$. Using the methods from this section, we have

$$
\begin{array}{r|rrr}
1 & 1 & 0 & -3 & 2 \\
  &   & 1 & 1 & -2 \\
\hline
  & 1 & 1 & -2 & 0
\end{array}
$$

So $x^3 - 3x + 2 = (x - 1)(x^2 + x - 2) = (x - 1)^2(x + 2) = 0 \quad \Leftrightarrow \quad x = -2, 1$.
Since this factors easily, the factoring method was easier.

(b) Using the cubic formula,

$$
\begin{aligned}
x &= \sqrt[3]{\frac{-(-54)}{2} + \sqrt{\frac{(-54)^2}{4} + \frac{(-27)^3}{27}}} + \sqrt[3]{\frac{-(-54)}{2} - \sqrt{\frac{(-54)^2}{4} + \frac{(-27)^3}{27}}} \\
&= \sqrt[3]{\frac{54}{2} + \sqrt{27^2 - 27^2}} + \sqrt[3]{\frac{54}{2} - \sqrt{27^2 - 27^2}} = \sqrt[3]{27} + \sqrt[3]{27} = 3 + 3 = 6
\end{aligned}
$$

$$
\begin{array}{r|rrr}
6 & 1 & 0 & -27 & -54 \\
  &   & 6 & 36 & 54 \\
\hline
  & 1 & 6 & 9 & 0
\end{array}
$$

$x^3 - 27x - 54 = (x - 6)(x^2 + 6x + 9) = (x - 6)(x + 3)^2 = 0 \quad \Rightarrow \quad x = -3, 6$.
Using methods from this section,

$$
\begin{array}{r|rrr}
-1 & 1 & 0 & -27 & -54 \\
   &   & -1 & 1 & 26 \\
\hline
   & 1 & -1 & -26 & -28
\end{array}
\qquad
\begin{array}{r|rrr}
-2 & 1 & 0 & -27 & -54 \\
   &   & -2 & 4 & 46 \\
\hline
   & 1 & -2 & -23 & -8
\end{array}
\qquad
\begin{array}{r|rrr}
-3 & 1 & 0 & -27 & -54 \\
   &   & -3 & 9 & 54 \\
\hline
   & 1 & -3 & -18 & 0
\end{array}
$$

So $x^3 - 27x - 54 = (x + 3)(x^2 - 3x - 18) = (x - 6)(x + 3)^2 = 0 \quad \Leftrightarrow \quad x = -3, 6$.
Since this factors easily, the factoring method was easier.

(c) Using the cubic formula,

$$x = \sqrt[3]{\frac{-4}{2} + \sqrt{\frac{4^2}{4} + \frac{3^3}{27}}} + \sqrt[3]{\frac{-4}{2} - \sqrt{\frac{4^2}{4} + \frac{3^3}{27}}}$$

$$= \sqrt[3]{-2 + \sqrt{4+1}} + \sqrt[3]{-2 - \sqrt{4+1}} = \sqrt[3]{-2 + \sqrt{5}} + \sqrt[3]{-2 - \sqrt{5}}$$

From the graphing calculator, we see that $P(x) = x^3 + 3x + 4$ has one zero.

Using methods from this section, $P(x)$ has possible rational zeros $\pm 1, \pm 2, \pm 4$.

$$\begin{array}{r|rrrr} 1 & 1 & 0 & 3 & 4 \\ & & 1 & 1 & 4 \\ \hline & 1 & 1 & 4 & 4 \end{array} \Rightarrow 1 \text{ is an upper bound.}$$

$$\begin{array}{r|rrrr} -1 & 1 & 0 & 3 & 4 \\ & & -1 & 1 & -4 \\ \hline & 1 & -1 & 4 & 0 \end{array} \Rightarrow x = -1 \text{ is a zero.}$$

$P(x) = x^3 + 3x + 4 = (x+1)(x^2 - x + 4)$. Using the quadratic formula we have:

$x = \frac{-(-1) \pm \sqrt{(-1)^2 - 4(1)(4)}}{2} = \frac{1 \pm \sqrt{-15}}{2}$ which is not a real number. Since it is not easy to see that

$\sqrt[3]{-2 + \sqrt{5}} + \sqrt[3]{-2 - \sqrt{5}} = -1$, we see that the factoring method was much easier.

3.4   Complex Numbers

1. $5 - 7i$: real part 5, imaginary part -7.

2. $-6 + 4i$: real part -6, imaginary part 4.

3. $\frac{-2 - 5i}{3} = -\frac{2}{3} - \frac{5}{3}i$: real part $-\frac{2}{3}$, imaginary part $-\frac{5}{3}$.

4. $\frac{4 + 7i}{2} = 2 + \frac{7}{2}i$: real part 2, imaginary part $\frac{7}{2}$.

5. 3: real part 3, imaginary part 0.

6. $-\frac{1}{2}$: real part $-\frac{1}{2}$, imaginary part 0.

7. $-\frac{2}{3}i$: real part 0, imaginary part $-\frac{2}{3}$.

8. $i\sqrt{3}$: real part 0, imaginary part $\sqrt{3}$.

9. $\sqrt{3} + \sqrt{-4} = \sqrt{3} + 2i$: real part $\sqrt{3}$, imaginary part 2.

10. $2 - \sqrt{-5} = 2 - i\sqrt{5}$: real part 2, imaginary part $-\sqrt{5}$.

11. $(2 - 5i) + (3 + 4i) = (2 + 3) + (-5 + 4)i = 5 - i$

12. $(2 + 5i) + (4 - 6i) = (2 + 4) + (5 - 6)i = 6 - i$

13. $(-6 + 6i) + (9 - i) = (-6 + 9) + (6 - 1)i = 3 + 5i$

14. $(3 - 2i) + \left(-5 - \frac{1}{3}i\right) = (3 - 5) + \left(-2 - \frac{1}{3}\right)i = -2 - \frac{7}{3}i$

15. $3i + (6 - 4i) = 6 + (3i - 4i) = 6 - 7i$

16. $\left(\frac{1}{2} - \frac{1}{3}i\right) + \left(\frac{1}{2} + \frac{1}{3}i\right) = \left(\frac{1}{2} + \frac{1}{2}\right) + \left(-\frac{1}{3} + \frac{1}{3}\right)i = 1$

17. $\left(7 - \frac{1}{2}i\right) - \left(5 + \frac{3}{2}i\right) = (7 - 5) + \left(-\frac{1}{2} - \frac{3}{2}\right)i = 2 - 2i$

18. $(-4 + i) - (2 - 5i) = -4 + i - 2 + 5i = (-4 - 2) + (1 + 5)i = -6 + 6i$

19. $(-12 + 8i) - (7 + 4i) = -12 + 8i - 7 - 4i = (-12 - 7) + (8 - 4)i = -19 + 4i$

20. $6i - (4 - i) = 6i - 4 + i = (-4) + (6 + 1)i = -4 + 7i$

21. $\frac{1}{3}i - \left(\frac{1}{4} - \frac{1}{6}i\right) = -\frac{1}{4} + \left[\frac{1}{3} - \left(-\frac{1}{6}\right)\right]i = -\frac{1}{4} + \frac{1}{2}i$

22. $(0.1 - 1.1i) - (1.2 - 3.6i) = (0.1 - 1.2) + [-1.1 - (-3.6)]i = -1.1 + 2.5i$

23. $4(-1 + 2i) = -4 + 8i$

24. $2i\left(\frac{1}{2} - i\right) = i - 2i^2 = 2 + i$

25. $(7 - i)(4 + 2i) = 28 + 14i - 4i - 2i^2 = (28 + 2) + (14 - 4)i = 30 + 10i$

26. $(5 - 3i)(1 + i) = 5 + 5i - 3i - 3i^2 = (5 + 3) + (5 - 3)i = 8 + 2i$

27. $(3 - 4i)(5 - 12i) = 15 - 36i - 20i + 48i^2 = (15 - 48) + (-36 - 20)i = -33 - 56i$

28. $\left(\frac{2}{3} + 12i\right)\left(\frac{1}{6} + 24i\right) = \frac{1}{9} + 16i + 2i + 288i^2 = \left(\frac{1}{9} - 288\right) + (16 + 2)i = -\frac{2591}{9} + 18i$

29. $(6 + 5i)(2 - 3i) = 12 - 18i + 10i - 15i^2 = (12 + 15) + (-18 + 10)i = 27 - 8i$

30. $(-2 + i)(3 - 7i) = -6 + 14i + 3i - 7i^2 = (-6 + 7) + (14 + 3)i = 1 + 17i$

31. $\dfrac{1}{i} = \dfrac{1}{i} \cdot \dfrac{i}{i} = \dfrac{i}{i^2} = \dfrac{i}{-1} = -i$

32. $\dfrac{1}{1 + i} = \dfrac{1}{1 + i} \cdot \dfrac{1 - i}{1 - i} = \dfrac{1 - i}{1 - i^2} = \dfrac{1 - i}{1 + 1} = \dfrac{1 - i}{2} = \frac{1}{2} - \frac{1}{2}i$

33. $\dfrac{2 - 3i}{1 - 2i} = \dfrac{2 - 3i}{1 - 2i} \cdot \dfrac{1 + 2i}{1 + 2i} = \dfrac{2 + 4i - 3i - 6i^2}{1 - 4i^2} = \dfrac{(2 + 6) + (4 - 3)i}{1 + 4} = \dfrac{8 + i}{5}$ or $\frac{8}{5} + \frac{1}{5}i$

34. $\dfrac{5 - i}{3 + 4i} = \dfrac{5 - i}{3 + 4i} \cdot \dfrac{3 - 4i}{3 - 4i} = \dfrac{15 - 20i - 3i + 4i^2}{9 - 16i^2} = \dfrac{(15 - 4) + (-20 - 3)i}{9 + 16} = \dfrac{11 - 23i}{25} = \frac{11}{25} - \frac{23}{25}i$

35. $\dfrac{26 + 39i}{2 - 3i} = \dfrac{26 + 39i}{2 - 3i} \cdot \dfrac{2 + 3i}{2 + 3i} = \dfrac{52 + 78i + 78i + 117i^2}{4 - 9i^2} = \dfrac{(52 - 117) + (78 + 78)i}{4 + 9} = \dfrac{-65 + 156i}{13}$

$\qquad = \dfrac{13(-5 + 12i)}{13} = -5 + 12i$

36. $\dfrac{25}{4 - 3i} = \dfrac{25}{4 - 3i} \cdot \dfrac{4 + 3i}{4 + 3i} = \dfrac{100 + 75i}{16 - 9i^2} = \dfrac{100 + 75i}{16 + 9} = \dfrac{100 + 75i}{25} = \dfrac{25(4 + 3i)}{25} = 4 + 3i$

37. $\dfrac{10i}{1 - 2i} = \dfrac{10i}{1 - 2i} \cdot \dfrac{1 + 2i}{1 + 2i} = \dfrac{10i + 20i^2}{1 - 4i^2} = \dfrac{-20 + 10i}{1 + 4} = \dfrac{5(-4 + 2i)}{5} = -4 + 2i$

38. $(2 - 3i)^{-1} = \dfrac{1}{2 - 3i} = \dfrac{1}{2 - 3i} \cdot \dfrac{2 + 3i}{2 + 3i} = \dfrac{2 + 3i}{4 - 9i^2} = \dfrac{2 + 3i}{4 + 9} = \dfrac{2 + 3i}{13} = \frac{2}{13} + \frac{3}{13}i$

39. $\dfrac{4 + 6i}{3i} = \dfrac{4 + 6i}{3i} \cdot \dfrac{i}{i} = \dfrac{4i + 6i^2}{3i^2} = \dfrac{-6 + 4i}{-3} = \dfrac{-6}{-3} + \dfrac{4}{-3}i = 2 - \frac{4}{3}i$

40. $\dfrac{-3 + 5i}{15i} = \dfrac{-3 + 5i}{15i} \cdot \dfrac{i}{i} = \dfrac{-3i + 5i^2}{15i^2} = \dfrac{-5 - 3i}{-15} = \dfrac{-5}{-15} + \dfrac{-3}{-15}i = \frac{1}{3} + \frac{1}{5}i$

41. $\dfrac{1}{1 + i} - \dfrac{1}{1 - i} = \dfrac{1}{1 + i} \cdot \dfrac{1 - i}{1 - i} - \dfrac{1}{1 - i} \cdot \dfrac{1 + i}{1 + i} = \dfrac{1 - i}{1 - i^2} - \dfrac{1 + i}{1 - i^2} = \dfrac{1 - i}{2} + \dfrac{-1 - i}{2} = -i$

42. $\dfrac{(1 + 2i)(3 - i)}{2 + i} = \dfrac{3 - i + 6i - 2i^2}{2 + i} = \dfrac{5 + 5i}{2 + i} \cdot \dfrac{2 - i}{2 - i} = \dfrac{10 - 5i + 10i - 5i^2}{4 - i^2} = \dfrac{(10 + 5) + (-5 + 10)i}{5}$

$\qquad = \dfrac{15 + 5i}{5} = \frac{15}{5} + \frac{5}{5}i = 3 + i$

43. $i^3 = i^2 \cdot i = -1 \cdot i = -i$

44. $(2i)^4 = 2^4 \cdot i^4 = 16 \cdot (1) = 16$

45. $i^{100} = (i^4)^{25} = (1)^{25} = 1$

46. $i^{1002} = (i^4)^{250} \cdot i^2 = (1)^{250} \cdot (-1) = -1$

47. $\sqrt{-25} = 5i$

48. $\sqrt{-\frac{9}{4}} = \frac{3}{2}i$

49. $\sqrt{-3}\sqrt{-12} = i\sqrt{3} \cdot 2i\sqrt{3} = 6i^2 = -6$

50. $\sqrt{\frac{1}{3}}\sqrt{-27} = \sqrt{\frac{1}{3}} \cdot 3\sqrt{3}i = 3i$

51. $\left(3 - \sqrt{-5}\right)\left(1 + \sqrt{-1}\right) = \left(3 - i\sqrt{5}\right)(1 + i) = 3 + 3i - i\sqrt{5} - i^2\sqrt{5} = (3 + \sqrt{5}) + (3 - \sqrt{5})i$

52. $\dfrac{1 - \sqrt{-1}}{1 + \sqrt{-1}} = \dfrac{1 - i}{1 + i} = \dfrac{1 - i}{1 + i} \cdot \dfrac{1 - i}{1 - i} = \dfrac{1 - i - i + i^2}{1 - i^2} = \dfrac{(1 - 1) + (-1 - 1)i}{1 + 1} = \dfrac{-2i}{2} = -i$

53. $\dfrac{2 + \sqrt{-8}}{1 + \sqrt{-2}} = \dfrac{2 + 2i\sqrt{2}}{1 + i\sqrt{2}} = \dfrac{2 + 2i\sqrt{2}}{1 + i\sqrt{2}} \cdot \dfrac{1 - i\sqrt{2}}{1 - i\sqrt{2}} = \dfrac{2 - 2i\sqrt{2} + 2i\sqrt{2} - 4i^2}{1 - 2i^2} = \dfrac{(2 + 4) + (-2\sqrt{2} + 2\sqrt{2})i}{1 + 2} = \frac{6}{3} = 2$

54. $\left(\sqrt{3} - \sqrt{-4}\right)\left(\sqrt{6} - \sqrt{-8}\right) = \left(\sqrt{3} - 2i\right)\left(\sqrt{6} - 2\sqrt{2}i\right) = \sqrt{18} - 2\sqrt{6}i - 2\sqrt{6}i + 4\sqrt{2}i^2$

$\qquad = \left(3\sqrt{2} - 4\sqrt{2}\right) + \left(-2\sqrt{6} - 2\sqrt{6}\right)i = -\sqrt{2} - 4\sqrt{6}i$

55. $\dfrac{\sqrt{-36}}{\sqrt{-2}\sqrt{-9}} = \dfrac{6i}{i\sqrt{2}\cdot 3i} = \dfrac{2}{i\sqrt{2}}\cdot\dfrac{i\sqrt{2}}{i\sqrt{2}} = \dfrac{2i\sqrt{2}}{2i^2} = \dfrac{i\sqrt{2}}{-1} = -i\sqrt{2}$

56. $\dfrac{\sqrt{-7}\sqrt{-49}}{\sqrt{28}} = \dfrac{\left(\sqrt{7}i\right)\left(7i\right)}{2\sqrt{7}} = \dfrac{7i^2}{2} = -\dfrac{7}{2}$

57. $x^2 + 9 = 0 \quad\Leftrightarrow\quad x^2 = -9 \quad\Rightarrow\quad x = \pm 3i$

58. $9x^2 + 4 = 0 \quad\Leftrightarrow\quad 9x^2 = -4 \quad\Leftrightarrow\quad x^2 = -\dfrac{4}{9} \quad\Rightarrow\quad x = \pm\dfrac{2}{3}i$

59. $x^2 - 4x + 5 = 0 \quad\Rightarrow\quad x = \dfrac{-(-4)\pm\sqrt{(-4)^2-4(1)(5)}}{2(1)} = \dfrac{4\pm\sqrt{16-20}}{2} = \dfrac{4\pm\sqrt{-4}}{2} = \dfrac{4\pm 2i}{2} = 2\pm i$

60. $x^2 + 2x + 2 = 0 \quad\Rightarrow\quad x = \dfrac{-(2)\pm\sqrt{(2)^2-4(1)(2)}}{2(1)} = \dfrac{-2\pm\sqrt{4-8}}{2} = \dfrac{-2\pm\sqrt{-4}}{2} = \dfrac{-2\pm 2i}{2} = -1\pm i$

61. $x^2 + x + 1 = 0 \quad\Rightarrow\quad x = \dfrac{-(1)\pm\sqrt{(1)^2-4(1)(1)}}{2(1)} = \dfrac{-1\pm\sqrt{1-4}}{2} = \dfrac{-1\pm\sqrt{-3}}{2} = \dfrac{-1\pm i\sqrt{3}}{2} = -\dfrac{1}{2}\pm i\dfrac{\sqrt{3}}{2}$

62. $x^2 - 3x + 3 = 0 \quad\Rightarrow\quad x = \dfrac{-(-3)\pm\sqrt{(-3)^2-4(1)(3)}}{2(1)} = \dfrac{3\pm\sqrt{9-12}}{2} = \dfrac{3\pm\sqrt{-3}}{2} = \dfrac{3\pm\sqrt{3}i}{2} = \dfrac{3}{2}\pm i\dfrac{\sqrt{3}}{2}$

63. $2x^2 - 2x + 1 = 0 \quad\Rightarrow\quad x = \dfrac{-(-2)\pm\sqrt{(-2)^2-4(2)(1)}}{2(2)} = \dfrac{2\pm\sqrt{4-8}}{4} = \dfrac{2\pm\sqrt{-4}}{4} = \dfrac{2\pm 2i}{4} = \dfrac{1}{2}\pm\dfrac{1}{2}i$

64. $2x^2 + 3 = 2x \quad\Leftrightarrow\quad 2x^2 - 2x + 3 = 0 \quad\Rightarrow$

$x = \dfrac{-(-2)\pm\sqrt{(-2)^2-4(2)(3)}}{2(2)} = \dfrac{2\pm\sqrt{4-24}}{4} = \dfrac{2\pm\sqrt{-20}}{4} = \dfrac{2\pm 2\sqrt{5}i}{4} = \dfrac{1}{2}\pm\dfrac{\sqrt{5}}{2}i$

65. $t+3+\dfrac{3}{t} = 0 \quad\Leftrightarrow\quad t^2+3t+3 = 0 \quad\Rightarrow\quad t = \dfrac{-(3)\pm\sqrt{(3)^2-4(1)(3)}}{2(1)} = \dfrac{-3\pm\sqrt{9-12}}{2} = \dfrac{-3\pm\sqrt{-3}}{2} = \dfrac{-3\pm i\sqrt{3}}{2} = -\dfrac{3}{2}\pm i\dfrac{\sqrt{3}}{2}$

66. $z + 4 + \dfrac{12}{z} = 0 \quad\Leftrightarrow\quad z^2 + 4z + 12 = 0 \quad\Rightarrow$

$z = \dfrac{-(4)\pm\sqrt{(4)^2-4(1)(12)}}{2(1)} = \dfrac{-4\pm\sqrt{16-48}}{2} = \dfrac{-4\pm\sqrt{-32}}{2} = \dfrac{-4\pm 4\sqrt{2}i}{2} = -2\pm 2\sqrt{2}i$

67. $6x^2 + 12x + 7 = 0 \quad\Rightarrow$

$x = \dfrac{-(12)\pm\sqrt{(12)^2-4(6)(7)}}{2(6)} = \dfrac{-12\pm\sqrt{144-168}}{12} = \dfrac{-12\pm\sqrt{-24}}{12} = \dfrac{-12\pm 2i\sqrt{6}}{12} = \dfrac{-12}{12}\pm\dfrac{2i\sqrt{6}}{12} = -1\pm\dfrac{\sqrt{6}}{6}i$

68. $4x^2 - 16x + 19 = 0 \quad\Rightarrow$

$x = \dfrac{-(-16)\pm\sqrt{(-16)^2-4(4)(19)}}{2(4)} = \dfrac{16\pm\sqrt{256-304}}{8} = \dfrac{16\pm\sqrt{-48}}{8} = \dfrac{16\pm 4\sqrt{3}i}{8} = \dfrac{16}{8}\pm\dfrac{4\sqrt{3}}{8}i = 2\pm i\dfrac{\sqrt{3}}{2}$

69. $\dfrac{1}{2}x^2 - x + 5 = 0 \quad\Rightarrow\quad x = \dfrac{-(-1)\pm\sqrt{(-1)^2-4\left(\frac{1}{2}\right)(5)}}{2\left(\frac{1}{2}\right)} = \dfrac{1\pm\sqrt{1-10}}{1} = 1\pm\sqrt{-9} = 1\pm 3i$

70. $x^2 + \dfrac{1}{2}x + 1 = 0 \quad\Rightarrow$

$x = \dfrac{-\left(\frac{1}{2}\right)\pm\sqrt{\left(\frac{1}{2}\right)^2 - 4\left(1\right)\left(1\right)}}{2\left(1\right)} = \dfrac{-\frac{1}{2}\pm\sqrt{\frac{1}{4}-4}}{2} = \dfrac{-\frac{1}{2}\pm\sqrt{-\frac{15}{4}}}{2} = \dfrac{-\frac{1}{2}\pm\frac{1}{2}\sqrt{15}i}{2} = -\dfrac{1}{4}\pm\dfrac{\sqrt{15}}{4}i$

71. LHS $= \overline{z} + \overline{w} = \overline{(a+bi)} + \overline{(c+di)} = a - bi + c - di = (a+c) + (-b-d)i = (a+c) - (b+d)i$.

RHS $= \overline{z+w} = \overline{(a+bi) + (c+di)} = \overline{(a+c) + (b+d)i} = (a+c) - (b+d)i$.

Since LHS $=$ RHS, this proves the statement.

72. LHS $= \overline{zw} = \overline{(a+bi)(c+di)} = \overline{ac + adi + bci + bdi^2} = \overline{(ac-bd) + (ad+bc)i} = (ac-bd) - (ad+bc)i$.

RHS $= \overline{z}\cdot\overline{w} = \overline{a+bi}\cdot\overline{c+di} = (a-bi)(c-di) = ac - adi - bci + bdi^2 = (ac-bd) - (ad+bc)i$.

Since LHS $=$ RHS, this proves the statement.

73. LHS $= (\overline{z})^2 = \left(\overline{(a+bi)}\right)^2 = (a-bi)^2 = a^2 - 2abi + b^2i^2 = (a^2 - b^2) - 2abi$.

RHS $= \overline{z^2} = \overline{(a+bi)^2} = \overline{a^2 + 2abi + b^2i^2} = \overline{(a^2-b^2) + 2abi} = (a^2-b^2) - 2abi$.

Since LHS $=$ RHS, this proves the statement.

74. $\overline{\overline{z}} = \overline{\overline{a+bi}} = \overline{a-bi} = a+bi = z$.

75. $z + \overline{z} = (a+bi) + \overline{(a+bi)} = a + bi + a - bi = 2a$, which is a real number.

76. $z - \overline{z} = (a+bi) - \overline{(a+bi)} = a + bi - (a-bi) = a + bi - a + bi = 2bi$, which is a pure imaginary number.

77. $z \cdot \overline{z} = (a + bi) \cdot \overline{(a + bi)} = (a + bi) \cdot (a - bi) = a^2 - b^2 i^2 = a^2 + b^2$, which is a real number.

78. Suppose $z = \overline{z}$. Then we have $(a + bi) = \overline{(a + bi)} \Rightarrow a + bi = a - bi \Rightarrow 0 = -2bi \Rightarrow b = 0$, so z is real.
Now if z is real, then $z = a + 0i$ (where a is real). Since $\overline{z} = a - 0i$, we have $z = \overline{z}$.

79. Using the quadratic formula, the solutions to the equation are $x = \dfrac{-b \pm \sqrt{b^2 - 4ac}}{2a}$. Since both solutions are imaginary,

we have $b^2 - 4ac < 0 \Leftrightarrow 4ac - b^2 > 0$, so the solutions are $x = \dfrac{-b}{2a} \pm \dfrac{\sqrt{4ac - b^2}}{2a} i$, where $\sqrt{4ac - b^2}$ is a real

number. Thus the solutions are complex conjugates of each other.

80. $i = i$, $i^5 = i^4 \cdot i = i$, $i^9 = i^8 \cdot i = i$; $i^2 = -1$, $i^6 = i^4 \cdot i^2 = -1$, $i^{10} = i^8 \cdot i^2 = -1$;
$i^3 = -i$, $i^7 = i^4 \cdot i^3 = -i$, $i^{11} = i^8 \cdot i^3 = -i$; $i^4 = 1$, $i^8 = i^4 \cdot i^4 = 1$, $i^{12} = i^8 \cdot i^4 = 1$. Because $i^4 = 1$, we have
$i^n = i^r$, where r is the remainder when n is divided by 4, that is, $n = 4 \cdot k + r$, where k is an integer and $0 \le r < 4$. Since
$4446 = 4 \cdot 1111 + 2$, we must have $i^{4446} = i^2 = -1$.

81. $\left(-1 + i\sqrt{3}\right)^3 \left(-1 + i\sqrt{3}\right)^3 = \left(-1 + i\sqrt{3}\right)\left(-1 + i\sqrt{3}\right)\left(-1 + i\sqrt{3}\right) = \left(-1 + i\sqrt{3}\right)\left(1 - 2i\sqrt{3} + 3i^2\right)$

$= \left(-1 + i\sqrt{3}\right)\left[1 - 2i\sqrt{3} + 3(-1)\right] = \left(-1 + i\sqrt{3}\right)\left(-2 - 2i\sqrt{3}\right)$

$= 2 + 2i\sqrt{3} - 2i\sqrt{3} - 2i^2 \cdot 3 = 2 + 6 = 8$

$\left(-1 - i\sqrt{3}\right)^3 = \left(-1 - i\sqrt{3}\right)\left(-1 - i\sqrt{3}\right)\left(-1 - i\sqrt{3}\right) = \left(-1 - i\sqrt{3}\right)\left(1 + 2i\sqrt{3} + 3i^2\right)$

$= \left(-1 - i\sqrt{3}\right)\left(-2 + 2i\sqrt{3}\right) = 2 - 2i\sqrt{3} + 2i\sqrt{3} - 2i^2 \cdot 3 = 2 + 6 = 8$

Thus 8 has at least three cube roots (one real and two complex). Two fourth roots of 16 are ± 2. If we calculate
$(2i)^4$, we get $2^4 \cdot i^4 = 16 \cdot (-1)^2 = 16$, so $2i$ is a fourth root of 16. Also, $-2i$ is a fourth root of 16, because
$(-2i)^4 = (-1)^4 (2i)^4 = 1 \cdot 16 = 16$.

3.5 Complex Zeros and the Fundamental Theorem of Algebra

1. (a) $x^4 + 4x^2 = 0 \Leftrightarrow x^2(x^2 + 4) = 0$. So $x = 0$ or $x^2 + 4 = 0$. If $x^2 + 4 = 0$ then $x^2 = -4 \Leftrightarrow x = \pm 2i$.
Therefore, the solutions are $x = 0$ and $\pm 2i$.

(b) To get the complete factorization, we factor the remaining quadratic factor $P(x) = x^2(x + 4) = x^2(x - 2i)(x + 2i)$.

2. (a) $x^5 + 9x^3 = 0 \Leftrightarrow x^3(x^2 + 9) = 0$. So $x = 0$ or $x^2 + 9 = 0$. If $x^2 + 9 = 0$ then $x = \pm 3i$. Therefore, the zeros
of P are $x = 0, \pm 3i$.

(b) Since $-3i$ and $3i$ are the zeros from $x^2 + 9 = 0$, $x + 3i$ and $x - 3i$ are the factors of $x^2 + 9$. Thus the complete
factorization is $P(x) = x^3(x^2 + 9) = x^3(x + 3i)(x - 3i)$.

3. (a) $x^3 - 2x^2 + 2x = 0 \Leftrightarrow x(x^2 - 2x + 2) = 0$. So $x = 0$ or $x^2 - 2x + 2 = 0$. If $x^2 - 2x + 2 = 0$ then

$x = \dfrac{-(-2) \pm \sqrt{(-2)^2 - 4(1)(2)}}{2} = \dfrac{2 \pm \sqrt{-4}}{2} = \dfrac{2 \pm 2i}{2} = 1 \pm i$. Therefore, the solutions are $x = 0, 1 \pm i$.

(b) Since $1 - i$ and $1 + i$ are zeros, $x - (1 - i) = x - 1 + i$ and $x - (1 + i) = x - 1 - i$ are the factors of $x^2 - 2x + 2$.
Thus the complete factorization is $P(x) = x(x^2 - 2x + 2) = x(x - 1 + i)(x - 1 - i)$.

4. (a) $x^3 + x^2 + x = 0$ $x(x^2 + x + 1) = 0$. So $x = 0$ or $x^2 + x + 1 = 0$. If $x^2 + x + 1 = 0$ then

$x = \dfrac{-(1) \pm \sqrt{(1)^2 - 4(1)(1)}}{2(1)} = \dfrac{-1 \pm \sqrt{-3}}{2} = -\dfrac{1}{2} \pm i\dfrac{\sqrt{3}}{2}$. Therefore, the zeros of P are $x = 0, -\dfrac{1}{2} \pm i\dfrac{\sqrt{3}}{2}$.

(b) The zeros of $x^2 + x + 1 = 0$ are $-\dfrac{1}{2} - i\dfrac{\sqrt{3}}{2}$ and $-\dfrac{1}{2} + i\dfrac{\sqrt{3}}{2}$, so factoring we get $x^2 + x +$

$1 = \left[x - \left(-\dfrac{1}{2} - i\dfrac{\sqrt{3}}{2}\right)\right]\left[x - \left(-\dfrac{1}{2} + i\dfrac{\sqrt{3}}{2}\right)\right] = \left(x + \dfrac{1}{2} + i\dfrac{\sqrt{3}}{2}\right)\left(x + \dfrac{1}{2} - i\dfrac{\sqrt{3}}{2}\right)$. Thus the complete factorization

is $P(x) = x(x^2 + x + 1) = x\left(x + \dfrac{1}{2} + i\dfrac{\sqrt{3}}{2}\right)\left(x + \dfrac{1}{2} - i\dfrac{\sqrt{3}}{2}\right)$.

5. (a) $x^4 + 2x^2 + 1 = 0$ $\Leftrightarrow$ $(x^2 + 1)^2 = 0$ $\Leftrightarrow$ $x^2 + 1 = 0$ $\Leftrightarrow$ $x^2 = -1 \Leftrightarrow x = \pm i$. Therefore the zeros of P are $x = \pm i$.

(b) Since $-i$ and i are zeros, $x + i$ and $x - i$ are the factors of $x^2 + 1$. Thus the complete factorization is
$$P(x) = (x^2 + 1)^2 = [(x + i)(x - i)]^2 = (x + i)^2 (x - i)^2.$$

6. (a) $x^4 - x^2 - 2 = 0$ $\Leftrightarrow$ $(x^2 - 2)(x^2 + 1) = 0$. So $x^2 - 2 = 0$ or $x^2 + 1 = 0$. If $x^2 - 2 = 0$ then $x^2 = 2$ $\Leftrightarrow$ $x = \pm\sqrt{2}$. And if $x^2 + 1 = 0$ then $x^2 = -1$ $\Leftrightarrow$ $x = \pm i$. Therefore, the zeros of P are $x = \pm\sqrt{2}, \pm i$.

(b) To get the complete factorization, we factor the quadratic factors to get
$$P(x) = (x^2 - 2)(x^2 + 1) = (x - \sqrt{2})(x + \sqrt{2})(x - i)(x + i).$$

7. (a) $x^4 - 16 = 0$ $\Leftrightarrow$ $0 = (x^2 - 4)(x^2 + 4) = (x - 2)(x + 2)(x^2 + 4)$. So $x = \pm 2$ or $x^2 + 4 = 0$. If $x^2 + 4 = 0$ then $x^2 = -4$ $\Rightarrow$ $x = \pm 2i$. Therefore the zeros of P are $x = \pm 2, \pm 2i$.

(b) Since $-i$ and i are zeros, $x + i$ and $x - i$ are the factors of $x^2 + 1$. Thus the complete factorization is
$$P(x) = (x - 2)(x + 2)(x^2 + 4) = (x - 2)(x + 2)(x - 2i)(x + 2i).$$

8. (a) $x^4 + 6x^2 + 9 = 0$ $\Leftrightarrow$ $(x^2 + 3)^2 = 0$ $\Leftrightarrow$ $x^2 = -3$. So $x = \pm i\sqrt{3}$ are the only zeros of P (each of multiplicity 2).

(b) To get the complete factorization, we factor the quadratic factor to get
$$P(x) = (x^2 + 3)^2 = [(x - i\sqrt{3})(x + i\sqrt{3})]^2 = (x - i\sqrt{3})^2 (x + i\sqrt{3})^2.$$

9. (a) $x^3 + 8 = 0$ $\Leftrightarrow$ $(x + 2)(x^2 - 2x + 4) = 0$. So $x = -2$ or $x^2 - 2x + 4 = 0$. If $x^2 - 2x + 4 = 0$ then
$$x = \frac{-(-2) \pm \sqrt{(-2)^2 - 4(1)(4)}}{2} = \frac{2 \pm \sqrt{-12}}{2} = \frac{2 \pm 2i\sqrt{3}}{2} = 1 \pm i\sqrt{3}.$$ Therefore, the zeros of P are $x = -2, 1 \pm i\sqrt{3}$.

(b) Since $1 - i\sqrt{3}$ and $1 + i\sqrt{3}$ are the zeros from the $x^2 - 2x + 4 = 0$, $x - (1 - i\sqrt{3})$ and $x - (1 + i\sqrt{3})$ are the factors of $x^2 - 2x + 4$. Thus the complete factorization is
$$P(x) = (x + 2)(x^2 - 2x + 4) = (x + 2)[x - (1 - i\sqrt{3})][x - (1 + i\sqrt{3})]$$
$$= (x + 2)(x - 1 + i\sqrt{3})(x - 1 - i\sqrt{3})\mathrm{j}$$

10. (a) $x^3 - 8 = 0$ $\Leftrightarrow$ $(x - 2)(x^2 + 2x + 4) = 0$. So $x = 2$ or $x^2 + 2x + 4 = 0$. If $x^2 + 2x + 4 = 0$ then
$$x = \frac{-(2) \pm \sqrt{(2)^2 - 4(1)(4)}}{2} = \frac{-2 \pm \sqrt{-12}}{2} = \frac{-2 \pm 2i\sqrt{3}}{2} = -1 \pm i\sqrt{3}.$$ Therefore, the zeros of P are $x = 2, -1 \pm i\sqrt{3}$.

(b) Since $-1 - i\sqrt{3}$ and $-1 + i\sqrt{3}$ are the zeros from $x^2 + 2x + 4 = 0$, $x - (-1 - i\sqrt{3})$ and $x - (-1 + i\sqrt{3})$ are the factors of $x^2 - 2x + 4$. Thus the complete factorization is
$$P(x) = (x - 2)(x^2 + 2x + 4) = (x - 2)[x - (-1 - i\sqrt{3})][x - (-1 + i\sqrt{3})]$$
$$= (x - 2)(x + 1 + i\sqrt{3})(x + 1 - i\sqrt{3})$$

11. (a) $x^6 - 1 = 0 \Leftrightarrow 0 = (x^3 - 1)(x^3 + 1) = (x - 1)(x^2 + x + 1)(x + 1)(x^2 - x + 1)$. Clearly, $x = \pm 1$ are

solutions. If $x^2 + x + 1 = 0$, then $x = \frac{-1 \pm \sqrt{1 - 4(1)(1)}}{2} = \frac{-1 \pm \sqrt{-3}}{2} = -\frac{1}{2} \pm \frac{\sqrt{-3}}{2}$ so $x = -\frac{1}{2} \pm i \frac{\sqrt{3}}{2}$. And if

$x^2 - x + 1 = 0$, then $x = \frac{1 \pm \sqrt{1 - 4(1)(1)}}{2} = \frac{1 \pm \sqrt{-3}}{2} = \frac{1}{2} \pm \frac{\sqrt{-3}}{2} = \frac{1}{2} \pm i \frac{\sqrt{3}}{2}$. Therefore, the zeros of P are $x = \pm 1$,

$-\frac{1}{2} \pm i \frac{\sqrt{3}}{2}, \frac{1}{2} \pm i \frac{\sqrt{3}}{2}$.

(b) The zeros of $x^2 + x + 1 = 0$ are $-\frac{1}{2} - i \frac{\sqrt{3}}{2}$ and $-\frac{1}{2} + i \frac{\sqrt{3}}{2}$, so $x^2 + x + 1$ factors as

$\left[x - \left(-\frac{1}{2} - i \frac{\sqrt{3}}{2} \right) \right] \left[x - \left(-\frac{1}{2} + i \frac{\sqrt{3}}{2} \right) \right] = \left(x + \frac{1}{2} + i \frac{\sqrt{3}}{2} \right) \left(x + \frac{1}{2} - i \frac{\sqrt{3}}{2} \right)$. Similarly, since

the zeros of $x^2 - x + 1 = 0$ are $\frac{1}{2} - i \frac{\sqrt{3}}{2}$ and $\frac{1}{2} + i \frac{\sqrt{3}}{2}$, so $x^2 - x + 1$ factors as

$\left[x - \left(\frac{1}{2} - i \frac{\sqrt{3}}{2} \right) \right] \left[x - \left(\frac{1}{2} + i \frac{\sqrt{3}}{2} \right) \right] = \left(x - \frac{1}{2} + i \frac{\sqrt{3}}{2} \right) \left(x - \frac{1}{2} - i \frac{\sqrt{3}}{2} \right)$. Thus the complete

factorization is

$$P(x) = (x - 1)(x^2 + x + 1)(x + 1)(x^2 - x + 1)$$

$$= (x - 1)(x + 1) \left(x + \frac{1}{2} + i \frac{\sqrt{3}}{2} \right) \left(x + \frac{1}{2} - i \frac{\sqrt{3}}{2} \right) \left(x - \frac{1}{2} + i \frac{\sqrt{3}}{2} \right) \left(x - \frac{1}{2} - i \frac{\sqrt{3}}{2} \right)$$

12. (a) $x^6 - 7x^3 - 8 = 0 \Leftrightarrow 0 = (x^3 - 8)(x^3 + 1) = (x - 2)(x^2 + 2x + 4)(x + 1)(x^2 - x + 1)$. Clearly,

$x = -1$ and $x = 2$ are solutions. If $x^2 + 2x + 4 = 0$, then $x = \frac{-2 \pm \sqrt{4 - 4(1)(4)}}{2} = \frac{-2 \pm \sqrt{-12}}{2} = -\frac{2}{2} \pm \frac{2\sqrt{-3}}{2}$ so

$x = -1 \pm \sqrt{3}i$. If $x^2 - x + 1 = 0$, then $x = \frac{1 \pm \sqrt{1 - 4(1)(1)}}{2} = \frac{1 \pm \sqrt{-3}}{2} = \frac{1}{2} \pm \frac{\sqrt{-3}}{2} = \frac{1}{2} \pm i \frac{\sqrt{3}}{2}$. Therefore, the zeros

of P are $x = -1, 2, -1 \pm \sqrt{3}i, \frac{1}{2} \pm i \frac{\sqrt{3}}{2}$.

(b) From Exercise 10, $x^2 + 2x + 4 = (x + 1 + i\sqrt{3})(x + 1 - i\sqrt{3})$ and from Exercise 11,

$x^2 - x + 1 = \left(x - \frac{1}{2} + i \frac{\sqrt{3}}{2} \right) \left(x - \frac{1}{2} - i \frac{\sqrt{3}}{2} \right)$. Thus the complete factorization is

$$P(x) = (x - 2)(x^2 + 2x + 4)(x + 1)(x^2 - x + 1)$$

$$= (x - 2)(x + 1)(x + 1 + i\sqrt{3})(x + 1 - i\sqrt{3}) \left(x - \frac{1}{2} + i \frac{\sqrt{3}}{2} \right) \left(x - \frac{1}{2} - i \frac{\sqrt{3}}{2} \right)$$

13. $P(x) = x^2 + 25 = (x - 5i)(x + 5i)$. The zeros of P are $5i$ and $-5i$, both multiplicity 1.

14. $P(x) = 4x^2 + 9 = (2x - 3i)(2x + 3i)$. The zeros of P are $\frac{3}{2}i$ and $-\frac{3}{2}i$, both multiplicity 1.

15. $Q(x) = x^2 + 2x + 2$. Using the quadratic formula $x = \frac{-(2) \pm \sqrt{(2)^2 - 4(1)(2)}}{2(1)} = \frac{-2 \pm \sqrt{-4}}{2} = \frac{-2 \pm 2i}{2} = -1 \pm i$. So

$Q(x) = (x + 1 - i)(x + 1 + i)$. The zeros of Q are $-1 - i$ (multiplicity 1) and $-1 + i$ (multiplicity 1).

16. $Q(x) = x^2 - 8x + 17 = (x^2 - 8x + 16) + 1 = (x - 4)^2 + 1 = [(x - 4) - i][(x - 4) + i] = (x - 4 - i)(x - 4 + i)$.

The zeros of Q are $4 + i$ and $4 - i$, both multiplicity 1.

17. $P(x) = x^3 + 4x = x(x^2 + 4) = x(x - 2i)(x + 2i)$. The zeros of P are 0, $2i$, and $-2i$ (all multiplicity 1).

18. $P(x) = x^3 + x^2 + x = x(x^2 + x + 1)$. Using the quadratic formula, we have

$x = \frac{-(1) \pm \sqrt{(1)^2 - 4(1)(1)}}{2(1)} = \frac{1 \pm \sqrt{-3}}{2} = \frac{1}{2} \pm i \frac{\sqrt{3}}{2}$. The zeros of P are 0, $\frac{1}{2} + i \frac{\sqrt{3}}{2}$, and $\frac{1}{2} - i \frac{\sqrt{3}}{2}$, all of multiplicity 1. And

$P(x) = x \left(x - \frac{1}{2} - i \frac{\sqrt{3}}{2} \right) \left(x - \frac{1}{2} + i \frac{\sqrt{3}}{2} \right)$.

19. $Q(x) = x^4 - 1 = (x^2 - 1)(x^2 + 1) = (x - 1)(x + 1)(x^2 + 1) = (x - 1)(x + 1)(x - i)(x + i)$. The zeros of Q are

$1, -1, i$, and $-i$ (all of multiplicity 1).

20. $Q(x) = x^4 - 625 = (x^2 - 25)(x^2 + 25) = (x - 5)(x + 5)(x^2 + 25) = (x - 5)(x + 5)(x - 5i)(x + 5i)$. The

zeros of Q are $5, -5, 5i$, and $5i$, all multiplicity 1.

21. $P(x) = 16x^4 - 81 = (4x^2 - 9)(4x^2 + 9) = (2x - 3)(2x + 3)(2x - 3i)(2x + 3i)$. The zeros of P are $\frac{3}{2}$, $-\frac{3}{2}$, $\frac{3}{2}i$, and $-\frac{3}{2}i$ (all of multiplicity 1).

22. $P(x) = x^3 - 64 = (x - 4)(x^2 + 4x + 16)$. Using the quadratic formula, we have
$x = \frac{-4 \pm \sqrt{16 - 4(1)(16)}}{2} = \frac{-4 \pm \sqrt{-48}}{2} = \frac{-4 \pm 4\sqrt{3}i}{2} = -2 \pm 2\sqrt{3}i$. The zeros of P are 4, $-2 + 2\sqrt{3}i$, and $-2 - 2\sqrt{3}i$, all of multiplicity 1. And $P(x) = (x - 4)(x + 2 - 2\sqrt{3}i)(x + 2 + 2\sqrt{3}i)$.

23. $P(x) = x^3 + x^2 + 9x + 9 = x^2(x + 1) + 9(x + 1) = (x + 1)(x^2 + 9) = (x + 1)(x - 3i)(x + 3i)$. The zeros of P are -1, $3i$, and $-3i$ (all of multiplicity 1).

24. $P(x) = x^6 - 729 = (x^3 - 27)(x^3 + 27) = (x - 3)(x^2 + 3x + 9)(x + 3)(x^2 - 3x + 9)$. Using the quadratic formula on $x^2 + 3x + 9$ we have $x = \frac{-3 \pm \sqrt{9 - 4(1)(9)}}{2} = \frac{-3 \pm \sqrt{-27}}{2} = -\frac{3}{2} \pm \frac{\sqrt{-27}}{2}$. Using the quadratic formula on $x^2 - 3x + 9$ we have $x = \frac{3 \pm \sqrt{9 - 4(1)(9)}}{2} = \frac{3 \pm \sqrt{-27}}{2} = \frac{3}{2} \pm \frac{\sqrt{-27}}{2} = \frac{3}{2} \pm \frac{3\sqrt{3}}{2}i$. The zeros of P are 3, -3, $-\frac{3}{2} + \frac{3\sqrt{3}}{2}i$, $-\frac{3}{2} - \frac{3\sqrt{3}}{2}i$, $\frac{3}{2} + \frac{3\sqrt{3}}{2}i$, and $\frac{3}{2} - \frac{3\sqrt{3}}{2}i$, all multiplicity 1. And $P(x) = (x - 3)(x + 3)\left(x + \frac{3}{2} - \frac{3\sqrt{3}}{2}i\right)\left(x + \frac{3}{2} + \frac{3\sqrt{3}}{2}i\right)\left(x - \frac{3}{2} - \frac{3\sqrt{3}}{2}i\right)\left(x - \frac{3}{2} + \frac{3\sqrt{3}}{2}i\right)$.

25. $Q(x) = x^4 + 2x^2 + 1 = (x^2 + 1)^2 = (x - i)^2(x + i)^2$. The zeros of Q are i and $-i$ (both of multiplicity 2).

26. $Q(x) = x^4 + 10x^2 + 25 = (x^2 + 5)^2 = [(x - i\sqrt{5})(x + i\sqrt{5})]^2 = (x - i\sqrt{5})^2(x + i\sqrt{5})^2$. The zeros of Q are $i\sqrt{5}$ and $-i\sqrt{5}$, both of multiplicity 2.

27. $P(x) = x^4 + 3x^2 - 4 = (x^2 - 1)(x^2 + 4) = (x - 1)(x + 1)(x - 2i)(x + 2i)$. The zeros of P are 1, -1, $2i$, and $-2i$ (all of multiplicity 1).

28. $P(x) = x^5 + 7x^3 = x^3(x^2 + 7) = x^3(x - i\sqrt{7})(x + i\sqrt{7})$. The zeros of P are 0 (multiplicity 3), $i\sqrt{7}$ and $-i\sqrt{7}$, both of multiplicity 1.

29. $P(x) = x^5 + 6x^3 + 9x = x(x^4 + 6x^2 + 9) = x(x^2 + 3)^2 = x(x - \sqrt{3}i)^2(x + \sqrt{3}i)^2$. The zeros of P are 0 (multiplicity 1), $\sqrt{3}i$ (multiplicity 2), and $-\sqrt{3}i$ (multiplicity 2).

30. $P(x) = x^6 + 16x^3 + 64 = (x^3 + 8)^2 = (x + 2)^2(x^2 - 2x + 4)^2$. Using the quadratic formula, on $x^2 - 2x + 4$ we have $x = \frac{-(-2) \pm \sqrt{(-2)^2 - 4(1)(4)}}{2} = \frac{2 \pm \sqrt{-12}}{2} = \frac{2 \pm 2i\sqrt{3}}{2} = 1 \pm i\sqrt{3}$. The zeros of P are -2, $1 + i\sqrt{3}$, and $1 - i\sqrt{3}$, all multiplicity 2.

31. Since $1 + i$ and $1 - i$ are conjugates, the factorization of the polynomial must be
$P(x) = a(x - [1 + i])(x - [1 - i]) = a(x^2 - 2x + 2)$. If we let $a = 1$, we get $P(x) = x^2 - 2x + 2$.

32. Since $1 + i\sqrt{2}$ and $1 - i\sqrt{2}$ are conjugates, the factorization of the polynomial must be
$P(x) = c(x - [1 + i\sqrt{2}])(x - [1 - i\sqrt{2}]) = c(x^2 - 2x + 3)$. If we let $c = 1$, we get $P(x) = x^2 - 2x + 3$.

33. Since $2i$ and $-2i$ are conjugates, the factorization of the polynomial must be
$Q(x) = b(x - 3)(x - 2i)(x + 2i] = b(x - 3)(x^2 + 4) = b(x^3 - 3x^2 + 4x - 12)$. If we let $b = 1$, we get $Q(x) = x^3 - 3x^2 + 4x - 12$.

34. Since i is a zero, by the Conjugate Roots Theorem, $-i$ is also a zero. So the factorization of the polynomial must be
$Q(x) = b(x + 0)(x - i)(x + i) = bx(x^2 + 1) = b(x^3 + x)$. If we let $b = 1$, we get $Q(x) = x^3 + x$.

35. Since i is a zero, by the Conjugate Roots Theorem, $-i$ is also a zero. So the factorization of the polynomial must be
$P(x) = a(x - 2)(x - i)(x + i) = a(x^3 - 2x^2 + x - 2)$. If we let $a = 1$, we get $P(x) = x^3 - 2x^2 + x - 2$.

36. Since $1 + i$ is a zero, by the Conjugate Roots Theorem, $1 - i$ is also a zero. So the factorization of the polynomial must be

$Q(x) = a(x + 3)(x - [1 + i])(x - [1 - i]) = a(x + 3)(x^2 - 2x + 2) = a(x^3 + x^2 - 4x + 6)$. If we let $a = 1$, we

get $Q(x) = x^3 + x^2 - 4x + 6$.

37. Since the zeros are $1 - 2i$ and 1 (with multiplicity 2), by the Conjugate Roots Theorem, the other zero is $1 + 2i$. So a

factorization is

$$
\begin{aligned}
R(x) &= c(x - [1 - 2i])(x - [1 + 2i])(x - 1)^2 = c([x - 1] + 2i)([x - 1] - 2i)(x - 1)^2 \\
&= c([x - 1]^2 - [2i]^2)(x^2 - 2x + 1) = c(x^2 - 2x + 1 + 4)(x^2 - 2x + 1) = c(x^2 - 2x + 5)(x^2 - 2x + 1) \\
&= c(x^4 - 2x^3 + x^2 - 2x^3 + 4x^2 - 2x + 5x^2 - 10x + 5) = c(x^4 - 4x^3 + 10x^2 - 12x + 5)
\end{aligned}
$$

If we let $c = 1$ we get $R(x) = x^4 - 4x^3 + 10x^2 - 12x + 5$.

38. Since $S(x)$ has zeros $2i$ and $3i$, by the Conjugate Roots Theorem, the other zeros of $S(x)$ are $-2i$ and $-3i$. So a

factorization of $S(x)$ is

$$S(x) = C(x - 2i)(x + 2i)(x - 3i)(x + 3i) = C(x^2 - 4i^2)(x^2 - 9i^2) = C(x^2 + 4)(x^2 + 9) = C(x^4 + 13x^2 + 36)$$

If we let $C = 1$, we get $S(x) = x^4 + 13x^2 + 36$.

39. Since the zeros are i and $1 + i$, by the Conjugate Roots Theorem, the other zeros are $-i$ and $1 - i$. So a factorization is

$$
\begin{aligned}
T(x) &= C(x - i)(x + i)(x - [1 + i])(x - [1 - i]) \\
&= C(x^2 - i^2)([x - 1] - i)([x - 1] + i) = C(x^2 + 1)(x^2 - 2x + 1 - i^2) = C(x^2 + 1)(x^2 - 2x + 2) \\
&= C(x^4 - 2x^3 + 2x^2 + x^2 - 2x + 2) = C(x^4 - 2x^3 + 3x^2 - 2x + 2) = Cx^4 - 2Cx^3 + 3Cx^2 - 2Cx + 2C
\end{aligned}
$$

Since the constant coefficient is 12, it follows that $2C = 12 \Leftrightarrow C = 6$, and so

$T(x) = 6(x^4 - 2x^3 + 3x^2 - 2x + 2) = 6x^4 - 12x^3 + 18x^2 - 12x + 12$.

40. Since $U(x)$ has zeros $\frac{1}{2}$, -1 (with multiplicity two), and $-i$, by the Conjugate Roots Theorem, the other zero is i. So a

factorization of $U(x)$ is

$$U(x) = c\left(x - \tfrac{1}{2}\right)(x + 1)^2(x + i)(x - i) = \tfrac{1}{2}c(2x - 1)(x^2 + 2x + 1)(x^2 + 1) = \tfrac{1}{2}c(2x^5 + 3x^4 + 2x^3 + 2x^2 - 1)$$

Since the leading coefficient is 4, we have $4 = \frac{1}{2}c(2) = c$. Thus we have

$U(x) = \tfrac{1}{2}(4)(2x^5 + 3x^4 + 2x^3 + 2x^2 - 1) = 4x^5 + 6x^4 + 4x^3 + 4x^2 - 2$.

41. $P(x) = x^3 + 2x^2 + 4x + 8 = x^2(x + 2) + 4(x + 2) = (x + 2)(x^2 + 4) = (x + 2)(x - 2i)(x + 2i)$. Thus the zeros

are -2 and $\pm 2i$.

42. $P(x) = x^3 - 7x^2 + 17x - 15$. We start by trying the possible rational factors of the polynomial:

1	1	-7	17	-15
		1	-6	11
	1	-6	11	-4

3	1	-7	17	-15
		3	-12	15
	1	-4	5	0	$\Rightarrow x = 3$ is a zero.

So $P(x) = (x - 3)(x^2 - 4x + 5)$. Using the quadratic formula on the second factor, we have

$x = \frac{4 \pm \sqrt{16 - 4(1)(5)}}{2} = \frac{4 \pm \sqrt{-4}}{2} = \frac{4 \pm 2i}{2} = 2 \pm i$. Thus the zeros are 3, $2 \pm i$.

43. $P(x) = x^3 - 2x^2 + 2x - 1$. By inspection, $P(1) = 1 - 2 + 2 - 1 = 0$, and hence $x = 1$ is a zero.

$$
\begin{array}{r|rrrr}
1 & 1 & -2 & 2 & -1 \\
  &   & 1 & -1 & 1 \\
\hline
  & 1 & -1 & 1 & 0
\end{array}
$$

Thus $P(x) = (x-1)(x^2 - x + 1)$. So $x = 1$ or $x^2 - x + 1 = 0$.

Using the quadratic formula, we have $x = \frac{1 \pm \sqrt{1-4(1)(1)}}{2} = \frac{1 \pm i\sqrt{3}}{2}$. Hence, the zeros are 1 and $\frac{1 \pm i\sqrt{3}}{2}$.

44. $P(x) = x^3 + 7x^2 + 18x + 18$ has possible rational zeros $\pm 1, \pm 2, \pm 3, \pm 6, \pm 9, \pm 18$. Since all of the coefficients are positive, there are no positive real zeros.

$$
\begin{array}{r|rrrr}
-1 & 1 & 7 & 18 & 18 \\
   &   & -1 & -6 & -12 \\
\hline
   & 1 & 6 & 12 & 6
\end{array}
\qquad
\begin{array}{r|rrrr}
-2 & 1 & 7 & 18 & 18 \\
   &   & -2 & -10 & -16 \\
\hline
   & 1 & 5 & 8 & 2
\end{array}
\qquad
\begin{array}{r|rrrr}
-3 & 1 & 7 & 18 & 18 \\
   &   & -3 & -12 & -18 \\
\hline
   & 1 & 4 & 6 & 0
\end{array} \Rightarrow x = -3 \text{ is a zero.}
$$

So $P(x) = (x-3)(x^2 + 4x + 6)$. Using the quadratic formula on the second factor, we have

$x = \frac{-4 \pm \sqrt{16-4(1)(6)}}{2} = \frac{-4 \pm \sqrt{-8}}{2} = \frac{-4 \pm 2\sqrt{2}i}{2} = -2 \pm \sqrt{2}i$. Thus the zeros are $-3, -2 \pm \sqrt{2}i$.

45. $P(x) = x^3 - 3x^2 + 3x - 2$.

$$
\begin{array}{r|rrrr}
2 & 1 & -3 & 3 & -2 \\
  &   & 2 & -2 & 2 \\
\hline
  & 1 & -1 & 1 & 0
\end{array}
$$

Thus $P(x) = (x-2)(x^2 - x + 1)$. So $x = 2$ or $x^2 - x + 1 = 0$

Using the quadratic formula we have $x = \frac{1 \pm \sqrt{1-4(1)(1)}}{2} = \frac{1 \pm i\sqrt{3}}{2}$. Hence, the zeros are 2, and $\frac{1 \pm i\sqrt{3}}{2}$.

46. $P(x) = x^3 - x - 6$ has possible zeros $\pm 1, \pm 2, \pm 3$.

$$
\begin{array}{r|rrrr}
1 & 1 & 0 & -1 & -6 \\
  &   & 1 & 1 & 0 \\
\hline
  & 1 & 1 & 0 & -6
\end{array}
\qquad
\begin{array}{r|rrrr}
2 & 1 & 0 & -1 & -6 \\
  &   & 2 & 4 & 6 \\
\hline
  & 1 & 2 & 3 & 0
\end{array} \Rightarrow x = 2 \text{ is a zero.}
$$

$P(x) = (x-2)(x^2 + 2x + 3)$. Now $x^2 + 2x + 3$ has zeros $x = \frac{-2 \pm \sqrt{4-4(1)(3)}}{2} = \frac{-2 \pm 2i\sqrt{2}}{2} = -1 \pm i\sqrt{2}$. Thus the zeros are $2, -1 \pm i\sqrt{2}$.

47. $P(x) = 2x^3 + 7x^2 + 12x + 9$ has possible rational zeros $\pm 1, \pm 3, \pm 9, \pm \frac{1}{2}, \pm \frac{3}{2}, \pm \frac{9}{2}$. Since all coefficients are positive, there are no positive real zeros.

$$
\begin{array}{r|rrrr}
-1 & 2 & 7 & 12 & 9 \\
   &   & -2 & -5 & -7 \\
\hline
   & 2 & 5 & 7 & 2
\end{array}
\qquad
\begin{array}{r|rrrr}
-2 & 2 & 7 & 12 & 9 \\
   &   & -4 & -6 & -12 \\
\hline
   & 2 & 3 & 6 & -3
\end{array}
$$

There is a zero between -1 and -2.

$$
\begin{array}{r|rrrr}
-\frac{3}{2} & 2 & 7 & 12 & 9 \\
   &   & -3 & -6 & -9 \\
\hline
   & 2 & 4 & 6 & 0
\end{array} \Rightarrow x = -\frac{3}{2} \text{ is a zero.}
$$

$P(x) = \left(x + \frac{3}{2}\right)\left(2x^2 + 4x + 6\right) = 2\left(x + \frac{3}{2}\right)\left(x^2 + 2x + 3\right)$. Now $x^2 + 2x + 3$ has zeros

$x = \frac{-2 \pm \sqrt{4-4(3)(1)}}{2} = \frac{-2 \pm 2\sqrt{-2}}{2} = -1 \pm i\sqrt{2}$. Hence, the zeros are $-\frac{3}{2}$ and $-1 \pm i\sqrt{2}$.

48. Using synthetic division, we see that $(x-3)$ is a factor of the polynomial:

$$
\begin{array}{r|rrrr}
1 & 2 & -8 & 9 & -9 \\
  &   & 2 & -6 & 3 \\
\hline
  & 2 & -6 & 3 & -6
\end{array}
\qquad
\begin{array}{r|rrrr}
3 & 2 & -8 & 9 & -9 \\
  &   & 6 & -6 & 9 \\
\hline
  & 2 & -2 & 3 & 0
\end{array}
\Rightarrow x = 3 \text{ is a zero.}
$$

So $P(x) = 2x^3 - 8x^2 + 9x - 9 = (x-3)\left(2x^2 - 2x + 3\right)$. Using the quadratic formula, we find the other two solutions:

$$
x = \frac{2 \pm \sqrt{4 - 4(3)(2)}}{2(2)} = \frac{2 \pm \sqrt{-20}}{4} = \tfrac{1}{2} \pm \frac{\sqrt{5}}{2} i. \text{ Thus the zeros are } 3, \tfrac{1}{2} \pm \frac{\sqrt{5}}{2} i.
$$

49. $P(x) = x^4 + x^3 + 7x^2 + 9x - 18$. Since $P(x)$ has one change in sign, we are guaranteed a positive zero, and since $P(-x) = x^4 - x^3 + 7x^2 - 9x - 18$, there are 1 or 3 negative zeros.

$$
\begin{array}{r|rrrrr}
1 & 1 & 1 & 7 & 9 & -18 \\
  &   & 1 & 2 & 9 & 18 \\
\hline
  & 1 & 2 & 9 & 18 & 0
\end{array}
$$

Therefore, $P(x) = (x-1)\left(x^3 + 2x^2 + 9x + 18\right)$. Continuing with the quotient, we try negative zeros.

$$
\begin{array}{r|rrrr}
-1 & 1 & 2 & 9 & 18 \\
   &   & -1 & -1 & -8 \\
\hline
   & 1 & 1 & 8 & 10
\end{array}
\qquad
\begin{array}{r|rrrr}
-2 & 1 & 2 & 9 & 18 \\
   &   & -2 & 0 & -18 \\
\hline
   & 1 & 0 & 9 & 0
\end{array}
$$

$P(x) = (x-1)(x+2)\left(x^2 + 9\right) = (x-1)(x+2)(x-3i)(x+3i)$. Therefore, the zeros are $1, -2,$ and $\pm 3i$.

50. $P(x) = x^4 - 2x^3 - 2x^2 - 2x - 3$ has possible zeros $\pm 1, \pm 3$.

$$
\begin{array}{r|rrrrr}
1 & 1 & -2 & -2 & -2 & -3 \\
  &   & 1 & -1 & -3 & -5 \\
\hline
  & 1 & -1 & -3 & -5 & -8
\end{array}
\qquad
\begin{array}{r|rrrrr}
3 & 1 & -2 & -2 & -2 & -3 \\
  &   & 3 & 3 & 3 & 3 \\
\hline
  & 1 & 1 & 1 & 1 & 0
\end{array}
\Rightarrow x = 3 \text{ is a zero.}
$$

$P(x) = (x-3)\left(x^3 + x^2 + x + 1\right)$. If we factor the second factor by grouping, we get

$$
x^3 + x^2 + x + 1 = x^2(x+1) + 1(x+1) = (x+1)\left(x^2 + 1\right). \quad \text{So we have}
$$

$P(x) = (x-3)(x+1)\left(x^2 + 1\right) = (x-3)(x+1)(x-i)(x+i)$. Thus the zeros are $3, -1, i,$ and $-i$.

51. We see a pattern and use it to factor by grouping. This gives

$$
\begin{aligned}
P(x) &= x^5 - x^4 + 7x^3 - 7x^2 + 12x - 12 = x^4(x-1) + 7x^2(x-1) + 12(x-1) = (x-1)\left(x^4 + 7x^2 + 12\right) \\
&= (x-1)\left(x^2 + 3\right)\left(x^2 + 4\right) = (x-1)\left(x - i\sqrt{3}\right)\left(x + i\sqrt{3}\right)(x - 2i)(x + 2i)
\end{aligned}
$$

Therefore, the zeros are $1, \pm i\sqrt{3},$ and $\pm 2i$.

52. $P(x) = x^5 + x^3 + 8x^2 + 8 = x^3\left(x^2 + 1\right) + 8\left(x^2 + 1\right) = \left(x^2 + 1\right)\left(x^3 + 8\right) = \left(x^2 + 1\right)(x+2)\left(x^2 - 2x + 4\right)$

(factoring a sum of cubes). So $x = -2$, or $x^2 + 1 = 0$. If $x^2 + 1 = 0$, then $x^2 = -1 \Rightarrow x = \pm i$. If $x^2 - 2x + 4 = 0$,

then $x = \frac{2 \pm \sqrt{4 - 4(1)(4)}}{2} = 1 \pm \frac{\sqrt{-12}}{2} = 1 \pm \sqrt{3} i$. Thus, the zeros are $-2, \pm i, 1 \pm \sqrt{3} i$.

53. $P(x) = x^4 - 6x^3 + 13x^2 - 24x + 36$ has possible rational zeros $\pm 1, \pm 2, \pm 3, \pm 4, \pm 6, \pm 9, \pm 12, \pm 18$. $P(x)$ has 4 variations in sign and $P(-x)$ has no variation in sign.

$$
\begin{array}{r|rrrrr}
1 & 1 & -6 & 13 & -24 & 36 \\
 &   & 1 & -5 &   8 & -16 \\
\hline
 & 1 & -5 & 8 & -16 & 20
\end{array}
\qquad
\begin{array}{r|rrrrr}
2 & 1 & -6 & 13 & -24 & 36 \\
 &   & 2 & -8 & 10 & -28 \\
\hline
 & 1 & -4 & 5 & -14 & 8
\end{array}
\qquad
\begin{array}{r|rrrrr}
3 & 1 & -6 & 13 & -24 & 36 \\
 &   & 3 & -9 & 12 & -36 \\
\hline
 & 1 & -3 & 4 & -12 & 0
\end{array}
\;\Rightarrow x = 3 \text{ is a zero.}
$$

Continuing:

$$
\begin{array}{r|rrrr}
3 & 1 & -3 & 4 & -12 \\
 &   & 3 & 0 & 12 \\
\hline
 & 1 & 0 & 4 & 0
\end{array}
\;\Rightarrow x = 3 \text{ is a zero.}
$$

$P(x) = (x-3)^2 (x^2 + 4) = (x-3)^2 (x - 2i)(x + 2i)$. Therefore, the zeros are 3 (multiplicity 2) and $\pm 2i$.

54. $P(x) = x^4 - x^2 + 2x + 2$ has possible rational zeros $\pm 1, \pm 2$.

$$
\begin{array}{r|rrrrr}
1 & 1 & 0 & -1 & 2 & 2 \\
 &   & 1 & 1 & 0 & 2 \\
\hline
 & 1 & 1 & 0 & 2 & 4
\end{array}
\text{ 1 is an upper bound.}
\qquad
\begin{array}{r|rrrrr}
-1 & 1 & 0 & -1 & 2 & 2 \\
 &   & -1 & 1 & 0 & -2 \\
\hline
 & 1 & -1 & 0 & 2 & 0
\end{array}
\qquad
\begin{array}{r|rrrr}
-1 & 1 & -1 & 0 & 2 \\
 &   & -1 & 2 & -2 \\
\hline
 & 1 & -2 & 2 & 0
\end{array}
$$

$P(x) = (x+1)^2 (x^2 - 2x + 2)$. Using the quadratic formula on $x^2 - 2x + 2$, we have $x = \frac{2 \pm \sqrt{4-8}}{2} = \frac{2 \pm 2i}{2} = 1 \pm i$. Thus, the zeros of $P(x)$ are $-1, 1 \pm i$.

55. $P(x) = 4x^4 + 4x^3 + 5x^2 + 4x + 1$ has possible rational zeros $\pm 1, \pm \frac{1}{2}, \pm \frac{1}{4}$. Since there is no variation in sign, all real zeros (if there are any) are negative.

$$
\begin{array}{r|rrrrr}
-1 & 4 & 4 & 5 & 4 & 1 \\
 &   & -4 & 0 & -5 & 1 \\
\hline
 & 4 & 0 & 5 & -1 & 2
\end{array}
\qquad
\begin{array}{r|rrrrr}
-\frac{1}{2} & 4 & 4 & 5 & 4 & 1 \\
 &   & -2 & -1 & -2 & -1 \\
\hline
 & 4 & 2 & 4 & 2 & 0
\end{array}
\;\Rightarrow x = -\tfrac{1}{2} \text{ is a zero.}
$$

$P(x) = \left(x + \frac{1}{2}\right)\left(4x^3 + 2x^2 + 4x + 2\right)$. Continuing:

$$
\begin{array}{r|rrrr}
-\frac{1}{2} & 4 & 2 & 4 & 2 \\
 &   & -2 & 0 & -2 \\
\hline
 & 4 & 0 & 4 & 0
\end{array}
\;\Rightarrow x = -\tfrac{1}{2} \text{ is a zero again.}
$$

$P(x) = \left(x + \frac{1}{2}\right)^2 \left(4x^2 + 4\right)$. Thus, the zeros of $P(x)$ are $-\frac{1}{2}$ and $\pm i$.

56. $P(x) = 4x^4 + 2x^3 - 2x^2 - 3x - 1$ has possible rational zeros $\pm 1, \pm \frac{1}{2}, \pm \frac{1}{4}$. P has one variation in sign, so P has one positive real zero.

$$
\begin{array}{r|rrrrr}
1 & 4 & 2 & -2 & -3 & -1 \\
 &   & 4 & 6 & 4 & 1 \\
\hline
 & 4 & 6 & 4 & 1 & 0
\end{array}
\;\Rightarrow 1 \text{ is a zero.}
$$

$P(x) = (x - 1)\left(4x^3 + 6x^2 + 4x + 1\right)$. Continuing:

$$
\begin{array}{r|rrrr}
-1 & 4 & 6 & 4 & 1 \\
 &   & -4 & -2 & 2 \\
\hline
 & 4 & 2 & -2 & 3
\end{array}
\qquad
\begin{array}{r|rrrr}
-\frac{1}{2} & 4 & 6 & 4 & 1 \\
 &   & -2 & -2 & -1 \\
\hline
 & 4 & 4 & 2 & 0
\end{array}
\;\Rightarrow -\tfrac{1}{2} \text{ is a zero.}
$$

$P(x) = (x - 1)\left(x + \frac{1}{2}\right)\left(4x^2 + 4x + 2\right)$. Using the quadratic formula on $4x^2 + 4x + 2$, we find $x = \frac{-4 \pm \sqrt{16 - 32}}{8} = -\frac{1}{2} \pm \frac{1}{2}i$. Thus, P has zeros $1, -\frac{1}{2}, -\frac{1}{2} \pm \frac{1}{2}i$.

57. $P(x) = x^5 - 3x^4 + 12x^3 - 28x^2 + 27x - 9$ has possible rational zeros ± 1, ± 3, ± 9. $P(x)$ has 4 variations in sign and $P(-x)$ has 1 variation in sign.

$$
\begin{array}{r|rrrrrr}
1 & 1 & -3 & 12 & -28 & 27 & -9 \\
  &   & 1 & -2 & 10 & -18 & 9 \\
\hline
  & 1 & -2 & 10 & -18 & 9 & 0
\end{array}
\Rightarrow x = 1 \text{ is a zero.}
$$

$$
\begin{array}{r|rrrr}
1 & 1 & -2 & 10 & -18 & 9 \\
  &   & 1 & -1 & 9   & -9 \\
\hline
  & 1 & -1 & 9 & -9 & 0
\end{array}
\Rightarrow x = 1 \text{ is a zero.}
\qquad
\begin{array}{r|rrrr}
1 & 1 & -1 & 9 & -9 \\
  &   & 1 & 0 & 9 \\
\hline
  & 1 & 0 & 9 & 0
\end{array}
\Rightarrow x = 1 \text{ is a zero.}
$$

$P(x) = (x-1)^3 (x^2 + 9) = (x-1)^3 (x - 3i)(x + 3i)$. Therefore, the zeros are 1 (multiplicity 3) and $\pm 3i$.

58. $P(x) = x^5 - 2x^4 + 2x^3 - 4x^2 + x - 2$ has possible rational zeros ± 1, ± 2.

$$
\begin{array}{r|rrrrrr}
1 & 1 & -2 & 2 & -4 & 1 & -2 \\
  &   & 1 & -1 & 1 & -3 & -2 \\
\hline
  & 1 & -1 & 1 & -3 & -2 & -4
\end{array}
\qquad
\begin{array}{r|rrrrrr}
2 & 1 & -2 & 2 & -4 & 1 & -2 \\
  &   & 2 & 0 & 4 & 0 & 2 \\
\hline
  & 1 & 0 & 2 & 0 & 1 & 0
\end{array}
\Rightarrow x = 2 \text{ is a zero.}
$$

$P(x) = (x-2)(x^4 + 2x^2 + 1) = (x-2)(x^2+1)^2 = (x-2)(x-i)^2(x+i)^2$. Thus, the zeros of $P(x)$ are 2, $\pm i$.

59. (a) $P(x) = x^3 - 5x^2 + 4x - 20 = x^2(x-5) + 4(x-5) = (x-5)(x^2+4)$

(b) $P(x) = (x-5)(x-2i)(x+2i)$

60. (a) $P(x) = x^3 - 2x - 4$

$$
\begin{array}{r|rrrr}
1 & 1 & 0 & -2 & -4 \\
  &   & 1 & 1 & -1 \\
\hline
  & 1 & 1 & -1 & -5
\end{array}
\qquad
\begin{array}{r|rrrr}
2 & 1 & 0 & -2 & -4 \\
  &   & 2 & 4 & 4 \\
\hline
  & 1 & 2 & 2 & 0
\end{array}
$$

$P(x) = x^3 - 2x - 4 = (x-2)(x^2 + 2x + 2)$

(b) $P(x) = (x-2)(x+1-i)(x+1+i)$

61. (a) $P(x) = x^4 + 8x^2 - 9 = (x^2 - 1)(x^2 + 9) = (x-1)(x+1)(x^2+9)$

(b) $P(x) = (x-1)(x+1)(x-3i)(x+3i)$

62. (a) $P(x) = x^4 + 8x^2 + 16 = (x^2 + 4)^2$

(b) $P(x) = (x-2i)^2(x+2i)^2$

63. (a) $P(x) = x^6 - 64 = (x^3 - 8)(x^3 + 8) = (x-2)(x^2 + 2x + 4)(x+2)(x^2 - 2x + 4)$

(b) $P(x) = (x-2)(x+2)(x+1-i\sqrt{3})(x+1+i\sqrt{3})(x-1-i\sqrt{3})(x-1+i\sqrt{3})$

64. (a) $P(x) = x^5 - 16x = x(x^4 - 16) = x(x^2 - 4)(x^2 + 4) = x(x-2)(x+2)(x^2+4)$

(b) $P(x) = x(x-2)(x+2)(x-2i)(x+2i)$

65. (a) $x^4 - 2x^3 - 11x^2 + 12x = x\left(x^3 - 2x^2 - 11x + 12\right) = 0$. We first find the
bounds for our viewing rectangle.

$$
\begin{array}{r|rrrr}
 & 1 & -2 & -11 & 12 \\
\hline
5 & 1 & 3 & 4 & 32 \\
-4 & 1 & -6 & 13 & -50
\end{array}
$$

$\Rightarrow x = 5$ is an upper bound.

$\Rightarrow x = -4$ is a lower bound.

We graph $P(x) = x^4 - 2x^3 - 11x^2 + 12x$ in the viewing rectangle $[-4, 5]$ by
$[-50, 10]$ and see that it has 4 real solutions. Since this matches the degree of
$P(x)$, $P(x)$ has no imaginary solution.

(b) $x^4 - 2x^3 - 11x^2 + 12x - 5 = 0$. We use the same
bounds for our viewing rectangle, $[-4, 5]$ by $[-50, 10]$,
and see that $R(x) = x^4 - 2x^3 - 11x^2 + 12x - 5$ has
2 real solutions. Since the degree of $R(x)$ is 4, $R(x)$
must have 2 imaginary solutions.

(c) $x^4 - 2x^3 - 11x^2 + 12x + 40 = 0$. We graph
$T(x) = x^4 - 2x^3 - 11x^2 + 12x + 40$ in the viewing
rectangle $[-4, 5]$ by $[-10, 50]$, and see that T has no
real solution. Since the degree of T is 4, T must have
4 imaginary solutions.

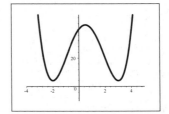

66. (a) $2x + 4i = 1 \quad \Leftrightarrow \quad 2x = 1 - 4i \quad \Leftrightarrow \quad x = \frac{1}{2} - 2i$.

(b) $x^2 - ix = 0 \quad \Leftrightarrow \quad x(x - i) = 0 \Leftrightarrow x = 0, i$.

(c) $x^2 + 2ix - 1 = 0 \quad \Leftrightarrow \quad (x + i)^2 = 0 \Leftrightarrow x = -i$.

(d) $ix^2 - 2x + i = 0$. Using the quadratic formula, we get

$$x = \frac{2 \pm \sqrt{(-2)^2 - 4(i)(i)}}{2i} = \frac{2 \pm \sqrt{8}}{2i} = \frac{2 \pm 2\sqrt{2}}{2i} = \frac{1 \pm \sqrt{2}}{i} = \left(1 \pm \sqrt{2}\right)(-i) = \left(-1 \pm \sqrt{2}\right)i.$$

67. (a) $P(x) = x^2 - (1 + i)x + (2 + 2i)$. So $P(2i) = (2i)^2 - (1 + i)(2i) + 2 + 2i = -4 - 2i + 2 + 2 + 2i = 0$,
and $P(1 - i) = (1 - i)^2 - (1 + i)(1 - i) + (2 + 2i) = 1 - 2i - 1 - 1 - 1 + 2 + 2i = 0$.
Therefore, $2i$ and $1 - i$ are solutions of the equation $x^2 - (1 + i)x + (2 + 2i) = 0$. However,
$P(-2i) = (-2i)^2 - (1 + i)(-2i) + 2 + 2i = -4 + 2i - 2 + 2 + 2i = -4 + 4i$, and
$P(1 + i) = (1 + i)^2 - (1 + i)(1 + i) + 2 + 2i = 2 + 2i$. Since, $P(-2i) \neq 0$ and $P(1 + i) \neq 0$, $-2i$ and $1 + i$ are
not solutions.

(b) This does not violate the Conjugate Roots Theorem because the coefficients of the polynomial $P(x)$ are not all real.

68. (a) Since i and $1 + i$ are zeros, $-i$ and $1 - i$ are also zeros. So

$$
\begin{aligned}
P(x) &= C(x - i)(x + i)(x - [1 + i])(x - [1 - i]) = C\left(x^2 + 1\right)\left(x^2 - 2x + 2\right) \\
&= C\left(x^4 - 2x^3 + 2x^2 + x^2 - 2x + 2\right) = C\left(x^4 - 2x^3 + 3x^2 - 2x + 2\right)
\end{aligned}
$$

Since $C = 1$, the polynomial is $P(x) = x^4 - 2x^3 + 3x^2 - 2x + 2$.

(b) Since i and $1 + i$ are zeros,

$$P(x) = C(x - i)(x - [i + 1]) = C\left(x^2 - xi - x - xi - 1 + i\right) = C\left[x^2 - (1 + 2i)x - 1 + i\right]$$

Since $C = 1$, the polynomial is $P(x) = x^2 - (1 + 2i)x - 1 + i$.

69. Since P has real coefficients, the imaginary zeros come in pairs: $a \pm bi$ (by the Conjugate Roots Theorem), where $b \neq 0$. Thus there must be an even number of imaginary zeros. Since P is of odd degree, it has an odd number of zeros (counting multiplicity). It follows that P has at least one real zero.

70. $x^4 - 1 = 0 \quad \Leftrightarrow \quad (x^2 - 1)(x^2 + 1) = 0 \quad \Leftrightarrow \quad (x - 1)(x + 1)(x + i)(x - i) = 0 \quad \Leftrightarrow \quad x = \pm 1, \pm i$. So there are four fourth roots of 1, two that are real and two that are complex. Consider $P(x) = x^n - 1$, where n is even. P has one change in sign so P has exactly one real positive zero, namely $x = 1$. Since $P(-x) = P(x)$, P also has exactly one real negative zero, namely $x = -1$. Thus P must have $n - 2$ complex roots. As a result, $x^n = 1$ has two real n th zeros and $n - 2$ complex roots.

$x^3 - 1 = 0 \quad \Leftrightarrow \quad (x - 1)(x^2 + x + 1) = 0 \Leftrightarrow x = 1, \frac{-1 \pm \sqrt{3}i}{2}$. So there is one real cube zero of unity and two complex roots. Now consider $Q(x) = x^k - 1$, where k is odd. Since Q has one change in sign, Q has exactly one real positive zero, namely $x = 1$. But $Q(-x) = -x^k - 1$ has no changes in sign, so there are no negative real zeros. As a result, $x^k = 1$ has one real k th zero and $k - 1$ complex roots.

3.6 Rational Functions

1. $r(x) = \dfrac{x}{x - 2}$

(a)

x	$r(x)$
1.5	-3
1.9	-19
1.99	-199
1.999	-1999

x	$r(x)$
2.5	5
2.1	21
2.01	201
2.001	2001

x	$r(x)$
10	1.25
50	1.042
100	1.020
1000	1.002

x	$r(x)$
-10	0.833
-50	0.962
-100	0.980
-1000	0.998

(b) $r(x) \to -\infty$ as $x \to 2^-$ and $r(x) \to \infty$ as $x \to 2^+$.

(c) r has horizontal asymptote $y = 1$.

2. $r(x) = \dfrac{4x + 1}{x - 2}$

(a)

x	$r(x)$
1.5	-14
1.9	-86
1.99	-896
1.999	-8996

x	$r(x)$
2.5	22
2.1	94
2.01	904
2.001	9004

x	$r(x)$
10	5.125
50	4.188
100	4.092
1000	4.009

x	$r(x)$
-10	3.25
-50	3.827
-100	3.912
-1000	3.991

(b) $r(x) \to -\infty$ as $x \to 2^-$ and $r(x) \to \infty$ as $x \to 2^+$.

(c) r has horizontal asymptote $y = 4$.

3. $r(x) = \dfrac{3x - 10}{(x - 2)^2}$

(a)

x	$r(x)$
1.5	-22
1.9	-430
1.99	$-40{,}300$
1.999	$-4{,}003{,}000$

x	$r(x)$
2.5	-10
2.1	-370
2.01	$-39{,}700$
2.001	$-3{,}997{,}000$

x	$r(x)$
10	0.3125
50	0.0608
100	0.0302
1000	0.0030

x	$r(x)$
-10	-0.2778
-50	-0.0592
-100	-0.0298
-1000	-0.0030

(b) $r(x) \to -\infty$ as $x \to 2$.

(c) r has horizontal asymptote $y = 0$.

4. $r(x) = \dfrac{3x^2 + 1}{(x-2)^2}$

(a)

x	$r(x)$
1.5	31
1.9	1183
1.99	128,803
1.999	12,988,003

x	$r(x)$
2.5	79
2.1	1423
2.01	131,203
2.001	13,012,003

x	$r(x)$
10	4.703
50	3.256
100	3.124
1000	3.012

x	$r(x)$
-10	2.09
-50	2.774
-100	2.884
-1000	2.988

(b) $r(x) \to \infty$ as $x \to 2$.

(c) r has horizontal asymptote $y = 3$.

5. $r(x) = \dfrac{x-1}{x+4}$. When $x = 0$, we have $r(0) = -\frac{1}{4}$, so the y-intercept is $-\frac{1}{4}$. The numerator is 0 when $x = 1$, so the x-intercept is 1.

6. $s(x) = \dfrac{3x}{x-5}$. When $x = 0$, we have $s(0) = 0$, so the y-intercept is 0. The numerator is zero when $3x = 0$ or $x = 0$, so the x-intercept is 0.

7. $t(x) = \dfrac{x^2 - x - 2}{x - 6}$. When $x = 0$, we have $t(0) = \dfrac{-2}{-6} = \frac{1}{3}$, so the y-intercept is $\frac{1}{3}$. The numerator is 0 when $x^2 - x - 2 = (x-2)(x+1) = 0$ or when $x = 2$ or $x = -1$, so the x-intercepts are 2 and -1.

8. $r(x) = \dfrac{2}{x^2 + 3x - 4}$. When $x = 0$, we have $r(0) = \dfrac{2}{-4} = -\frac{1}{2}$, so the y-intercept is $-\frac{1}{2}$. The numerator is never zero, so there is no x-intercept.

9. $r(x) = \dfrac{x^2 - 9}{x^2}$. Since 0 is not in the domain of $r(x)$, there is no y-intercept. The numerator is 0 when $x^2 - 9 = (x-3)(x+3) = 0$ or when $x = \pm 3$, so the x-intercepts are ± 3.

10. $r(x) = \dfrac{x^3 + 8}{x^2 + 4}$. When $x = 0$, we have $r(0) = \frac{8}{4} = 2$, so the y-intercept is 2. The x-intercept occurs when $x^3 + 8 = 0$ $\Leftrightarrow$ $(x+2)(x^2 - 2x + 4) = 0$ $\Leftrightarrow$ $x = -2$ or $x = 1 \pm i\sqrt{3}$, which has only one real solution, so the x-intercept is -2.

11. From the graph, the x-intercept is 3, the y-intercept is 3, the vertical asymptote is $x = 2$, and the horizontal asymptote is $y = 2$.

12. From the graph, the x-intercept is 0, the y-intercept is 0, the horizontal asymptote is $y = 0$, and the vertical asymptotes are $x = -1$ and $x = 2$.

13. From the graph, the x-intercepts are -1 and 1, the y-intercept is about $\frac{1}{4}$, the vertical asymptotes are $x = -2$ and $x = 2$, and the horizontal asymptote is $y = 1$.

14. From the graph, the x-intercepts are ± 2, the y-intercept is -6, the horizontal asymptote is $y = 2$, and there are no vertical asymptotes

15. $r(x) = \dfrac{3}{x+2}$. There is a vertical asymptote where $x + 2 = 0$ $\Leftrightarrow$ $x = -2$. We have $r(x) = \dfrac{3}{x+2} = \dfrac{3/x}{1 + (2/x)} \to 0$ as $x \to \pm\infty$, so the horizontal asymptote is $y = 0$.

16. $s(x) = \dfrac{2x+3}{x-1} = \dfrac{2 + (3/x)}{1 - (1/x)} \to 2$ as $x \to \pm\infty$. The horizontal asymptote is $y = 2$. There is a vertical asymptote when $x - 1 = 0 \Leftrightarrow x = 1$, so the vertical asymptote is $x = 1$.

17. $t(x) = \dfrac{x^2}{x^2 - x - 6} = \dfrac{x^2}{(x-3)(x+2)} = \dfrac{1}{1 - \dfrac{1}{x} - \dfrac{6}{x^2}} \to 1$ as $x \to \pm\infty$. Hence, the horizontal asymptote is $y = 1$.

The vertical asymptotes occur when $(x-3)(x+2) = 0 \quad\Leftrightarrow\quad x = 3$ or $x = -2$, and so the vertical asymptotes are $x = 3$ and $x = -2$.

18. $r(x) = \dfrac{2x - 4}{x^2 + 2x + 1} = \dfrac{\dfrac{2}{x} - \dfrac{4}{x^2}}{1 + \dfrac{2}{x} + \dfrac{1}{x^2}} \to 0$ as $x \to \pm\infty$. Thus, the horizontal asymptote is $y = 0$. Also, $y = \dfrac{2(x-2)}{(x+1)^2}$

so there is a vertical asymptote when $x + 1 = 0 \quad\Leftrightarrow\quad x = -1$, so the vertical asymptote is $x = -1$.

19. $s(x) = \dfrac{6}{x^2 + 2}$. There is no vertical asymptote since $x^2 + 2$ is never 0. Since $s(x) = \dfrac{6}{x^2 + 2} = \dfrac{\dfrac{6}{x^2}}{1 + \dfrac{2}{x^2}} \to 0$ as

$x \to \pm\infty$, the horizontal asymptote is $y = 0$.

20. $t(x) = \dfrac{(x-1)(x-2)}{(x-3)(x-4)} = \dfrac{x^2 - 3x + 2}{x^2 - 7x + 12} = \dfrac{1 - \dfrac{3}{x} + \dfrac{2}{x^2}}{1 - \dfrac{7}{x} + \dfrac{12}{x^2}} \to 1$ as $x \to \pm\infty$, so the horizontal asymptote is $y = 1$.

Also, vertical asymptotes occur when $(x-3)(x-4) = 0 \quad\Rightarrow\quad x = 3, 4$, so the two vertical asymptotes are $x = 3$ and $x = 4$.

21. $r(x) = \dfrac{6x - 2}{x^2 + 5x - 6}$. A vertical asymptote occurs when $x^2 + 5x - 6 = (x+6)(x-1) = 0 \Leftrightarrow x = 1$ or $x = -6$.

Because the degree of the denominator is greater than the degree of the numerator, the horizontal asymptote is $y = 0$.

22. $s(x) = \dfrac{3x^2}{x^2 + 2x + 5} = \dfrac{3}{1 + \dfrac{2}{x} + \dfrac{5}{x^2}} \to 3$ as $x \to \pm\infty$, so the horizontal asymptote is $y = 3$. Also, vertical asymptotes

occur when $x^2 + 2x + 5 = 0 \quad\Rightarrow\quad x = \dfrac{-2 \pm \sqrt{4 - 20}}{2} = -1 \pm 2i$. Since there is no real zero, there are no vertical asymptotes.

23. $y = \dfrac{x^2 + 2}{x - 1}$. A vertical asymptote occurs when $x - 1 = 0 \Leftrightarrow x = 1$. There are no horizontal asymptotes because the degree of the numerator is greater than the degree of the denominator.

24. $r(x) = \dfrac{x^3 + 3x^2}{x^2 - 4} = \dfrac{x^2(x+3)}{(x-2)(x+2)}$. Because the degree of the numerator is greater than the degree of the denominator, the function has no horizontal asymptotes. Two vertical asymptotes occur at $x = 2$ and $x = -2$. By using long division, we see that $r(x) = x + 3 + \dfrac{4x + 12}{x^2 - 4}$ so $y = x + 3$ is a slant asymptote.

In Exercises 25–32, let $f(x) = \dfrac{1}{x}$.

25. $r(x) = \dfrac{1}{x-1} = f(x-1)$. From this form we see that the graph of r is obtained

from the graph of f by shifting 1 unit to the right. Thus r has vertical asymptote $x = 1$ and horizontal asymptote $y = 0$.

26. $r(x) = \dfrac{1}{x+4} = f(x+4)$. From this form we see that the graph of r is obtained

from the graph of f by shifting 4 units to the left. Thus r has vertical asymptote $x = -4$ and horizontal asymptote $y = 0$.

27. $s(x) = \dfrac{3}{x+1} = 3\left(\dfrac{1}{x+1}\right) = 3f(x+1)$. From this form we see that the graph

of s is obtained from the graph of f by shifting 1 unit to the left and stretching vertically by a factor of 3. Thus s has vertical asymptote $x = -1$ and horizontal asymptote $y = 0$.

28. $s(x) = \dfrac{-2}{x-2} = -2\left(\dfrac{1}{x-2}\right) = -2f(x-2)$. From this form we see that the

graph of s is obtained from the graph of f by shifting 2 units to the right, stretching vertically by a factor of 2, and then reflecting about the x-axis. Thus r has vertical asymptote $x = 2$ and horizontal asymptote $y = 0$.

29. $t(x) = \dfrac{2x-3}{x-2} = 2 + \dfrac{1}{x-2} = f(x-2) + 2$ (see long

division below). From this form we see that the graph of t is obtained from the graph of f by shifting 2 units to the right and 2 units vertically. Thus t has vertical asymptote $x = 2$ and horizontal asymptote $y = 2$.

$$
\begin{array}{r}
2 \\
x-2 \overline{\smash{\big)}\ 2x-3} \\
2x-2 \\
\hline
1
\end{array}
$$

30. $t(x) = \dfrac{3x-3}{x+2} = 2 - \dfrac{9}{x+2} = 3 - 9\left(\dfrac{1}{x+2}\right)$

$\qquad = -9f(x+2) + 3$

From this form we see that the graph of t is obtained from the
graph of f by shifting 2 units to the left, stretching vertically
by a factor of 9, reflecting about the x-axis, and then shifting
3 units vertically. Thus t has vertical asymptote $x = -2$ and
horizontal asymptote $y = 3$.

$$
\begin{array}{r}
3 \\
x+2 \overline{\smash{\big)}\ 3x - 3} \\
\underline{3x + 6} \\
-9
\end{array}
$$

31. $r(x) = \dfrac{x+2}{x+3} = 1 - \dfrac{1}{x+3} = -f(x+3) + 1$ (see long

division below). From this form we see that the graph of r is
obtained from the graph of f by shifting 3 units to the left,
reflect about the x-axis, and then shifting vertically 1 unit.
Thus r has vertical asymptote $x = -3$ and horizontal
asymptote $y = 1$.

$$
\begin{array}{r}
1 \\
x+3 \overline{\smash{\big)}\ x + 2} \\
\underline{x + 3} \\
-1
\end{array}
$$

32. $t(x) = \dfrac{2x-9}{x-4} = 2 - \dfrac{1}{x-4} = 2 - \left(\dfrac{1}{x-4}\right)$

$\qquad = -f(x-4) + 2$

From this form we see that the graph of t is obtained from the
graph of f by shifting 4 units to the right, reflecting about the
x-axis, and then shifting 2 units vertically. Thus t has vertical
asymptote $x = 4$ and horizontal asymptote $y = 2$.

$$
\begin{array}{r}
2 \\
x-4 \overline{\smash{\big)}\ 2x - 9} \\
\underline{2x - 8} \\
-1
\end{array}
$$

33. $y = \dfrac{4x-4}{x+2}$. When $x = 0$, $y = -2$, so the y-intercept is -2. When $y = 0$,

$4x - 4 = 0 \quad\Leftrightarrow\quad x = 1$, so the x-intercept is 1. Since the degree of the
numerator and denominator are the same the horizontal asymptote is $y = \frac{4}{1} = 4$. A
vertical asymptote occurs when $x = -2$. As $x \to -2^+$, $y = \dfrac{4x-4}{x+2} \to -\infty$, and
as $x \to -2^-$, $y = \dfrac{4x-4}{x+2} \to \infty$.

34. $r(x) = \dfrac{2x+6}{-6x+3} = \dfrac{2(x+3)}{-3(2x-1)}$. When $x = 0$, we have $y = 2$, so the

y-intercept is 2. When $y = 0$, we have $x + 3 = 0 \quad\Leftrightarrow\quad x = -3$, so the
x-intercept is -3. A vertical asymptote occurs when $2x - 1 = 0 \Leftrightarrow x = \frac{1}{2}$.
Because the degree of the denominator and the numerator are the same, the
horizontal asymptote is $y = \frac{2}{-6} = -\frac{1}{3}$.

35. $s(x) = \dfrac{4 - 3x}{x + 7}$. When $x = 0$, $y = \frac{4}{7}$, so the y-intercept is $\frac{4}{7}$. The x-intercepts

occur when $y = 0$ $\Leftrightarrow$ $4 - 3x = 0$ $\Leftrightarrow$ $x = \frac{4}{3}$. A vertical asymptote

occurs when $x = -7$. Since the degree of the numerator and denominator are the

same the horizontal asymptote is $y = \dfrac{-3}{1} = -3$.

36. $s(x) = \dfrac{1 - 2x}{2x + 3}$. When $x = 0$, $y = \frac{1}{3}$, so the y-intercept is $\frac{1}{3}$. When $y = 0$, we

have $1 - 2x = 0 \Leftrightarrow x = \frac{1}{2}$, so the x-intercept is $\frac{1}{2}$. A vertical asymptote occurs

when $2x + 3 = 0$ $\Leftrightarrow$ $x = -\frac{3}{2}$, and because the degree of the denominator

and the numerator are the same, the horizontal asymptote is $y = -1$.

37. $r(x) = \dfrac{18}{(x - 3)^2}$. When $x = 0$, $y = \frac{18}{9} = 2$, and so the y-intercept is 2. Since the

numerator can never be zero, there is no x-intercept. There is a vertical asymptote

when $x - 3 = 0$ $\Leftrightarrow$ $x = 3$, and because the degree of the asymptote is $y = 0$.

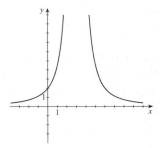

38. $r(x) = \dfrac{x - 2}{(x + 1)^2}$. When $x = 0$, we have $y = -2$, so the y-intercept is -2. When

$y = 0$, we have $x - 2 = 0$ $\Leftrightarrow$ $x = 2$, so the x-intercept is 2. A vertical

asymptote occurs when $x = -1$, and because the degree of the denominator is

greater than the degree of the numerator, the horizontal asymptote is $y = 0$.

39. $s(x) = \dfrac{4x - 8}{(x - 4)(x + 1)}$. When $x = 0$, $y = \dfrac{-8}{(-4)(1)} = 2$, so the y-intercept is 2.

When $y = 0$, $4x - 8 = 0$ $\Leftrightarrow$ $x = 2$, so the x-intercept is 2. The vertical

asymptotes are $x = -1$ and $x = 4$, and because the degree of the numerator is less

than the degree of the denominator, the horizontal asymptote is $y = 0$.

40. $s(x) = \dfrac{x+2}{(x+3)(x-1)}$. When $x = 0$, $y = \dfrac{2}{-3}$, so the y-intercept is $-\frac{2}{3}$ When

$y = 0$, we have $x + 2 = 0 \quad\Leftrightarrow\quad x = -2$, so the x-intercept is -2. A vertical

asymptote occurs when $(x+3)(x-1) = 0 \Leftrightarrow x = -3$ and $x = 1$. Because the

degree of the denominator is greater than the degree of the numerator, the

horizontal asymptote is $y = 0$.

41. $s(x) = \dfrac{6}{x^2 - 5x - 6}$. When $x = 0$, $y = \dfrac{6}{-6} = -1$, so the y-intercept is -1.

Since the numerator is never zero, there is no x-intercept. The vertical asymptotes

occur when $x^2 - 5x - 6 = (x+1)(x-6) \Leftrightarrow x = -1$ and $x = 6$, and because

the degree of the numerator is less less than the degree of the denominator, the

horizontal asymptote is $y = 0$.

42. $s(x) = \dfrac{2x-4}{x^2 + x - 2} = \dfrac{2(x-2)}{(x-1)(x+2)}$. When $x = 0$, $y = 2$, so the y-intercept

is 2. When $y = 0$, we have $2x - 4 = 0 \quad\Leftrightarrow\quad x = 2$, so the x-intercept is 2. A

vertical asymptote occurs when $(x-1)(x+2) = 0 \Leftrightarrow x = 1$ and $x = -2$.

Because the degree of the denominator is greater than the degree of the numerator,

the horizontal asymptote is $y = 0$.

43. $t(x) = \dfrac{3x+6}{x^2 + 2x - 8}$. When $x = 0$, $y = \dfrac{6}{-8} = -\dfrac{3}{4}$, so the y-intercept is $-\frac{3}{4}$.

When $y = 0$, $3x + 6 = 0 \quad\Leftrightarrow\quad x = -2$, so the x-intercept is -2. The vertical

asymptotes occur when $x^2 + 2x - 8 = (x-2)(x+4) = 0 \quad\Leftrightarrow\quad x = 2$ and

$x = -4$. Since the degree of the numerator is less than the degree of the

denominator, the horizontal asymptote is $y = 0$.

44. $t(x) = \dfrac{x-2}{x^2 - 4x} = \dfrac{x-2}{x(x-4)}$. Since $x = 0$ is not in the domain of $t(x)$, there is

no y-intercept. When $y = 0$, we have $x - 2 = 0 \Leftrightarrow x = 2$, so the x-intercept is 2.

A vertical asymptote occurs when $x(x-4) = 0 \quad\Leftrightarrow\quad x = 0$ and $x = 4$.

Because the degree of the denominator is greater than the degree of the numerator,

the horizontal asymptote is $y = 0$.

45. $r(x) = \dfrac{(x-1)(x+2)}{(x+1)(x-3)}$. When $x = 0$, $y = \frac{2}{3}$, so the y-intercept is $\frac{2}{3}$. When

$y = 0$, $(x-1)(x+2) = 0$ $\Rightarrow$ $x = -2, 1$, so the x-intercepts are -2 and 1.

The vertical asymptotes are $x = -1$ and $x = 3$, and because the degree of the

numerator and denominator are the same the horizontal asymptote is $y = \frac{1}{1} = 1$.

46. $r(x) = \dfrac{2x(x+2)}{(x-1)(x-4)}$. When $x = 0$, we have $y = 0$, so the graph passes

through the origin. Also, when $y = 0$, we have $2x(x+2) = 0 \Leftrightarrow x = 0, -2$, so

the x-intercepts are 0 and -2. There are two vertical asymptotes, $x = 1$ and

$x = 4$. Because the degree of the denominator and numerator are the same, the

horizontal asymptote is $y = \frac{2}{1} = 2$.

47. $r(x) = \dfrac{x^2 - 2x + 1}{x^2 + 2x + 1} = \dfrac{(x-1)^2}{(x+1)^2} = \left(\dfrac{x-1}{x+1}\right)^2$. When $x = 0$, $y = 1$, so the

y-intercept is 1. When $y = 0$, $x = 1$, so the x-intercept is 1 . A vertical asymptote

occurs at $x + 1 = 0 \Leftrightarrow x = -1$. Because the degree of the numerator and

denominator are the same the horizontal asymptote is $y = \frac{1}{1} = 1$.

48. $r(x) = \dfrac{4x^2}{x^2 - 2x - 3} = \dfrac{4x^2}{(x-3)(x+1)}$. When $x = 0$, we have $y = 0$, so the

graph passes through the origin. Vertical asymptotes occur at $x = -1$ and $x = 3$.

Because the degree of the denominator and numerator are the same, the horizontal

asymptote is $y = \frac{4}{1} = 4$.

49. $r(x) = \dfrac{2x^2 + 10x - 12}{x^2 + x - 6} = \dfrac{2(x-1)(x+6)}{(x-2)(x+3)}$. When $x = 0$,

$y = \dfrac{2(-1)(6)}{(-2)(3)} = 2$, so the y-intercept is 2. When $y = 0$, $2(x-1)(x+6) = 0$

$\Rightarrow$ $x = -6, 1$, so the x-intercepts are -6 and 1. Vertical asymptotes occur when

$(x-2)(x+3) = 0 \Leftrightarrow x = -3$ or $x = 2$. Because the degree of the numerator

and denominator are the same the horizontal asymptote is $y = \frac{2}{1} = 2$.

50. $r(x) = \dfrac{2x^2 + 2x - 4}{x^2 + x} = \dfrac{2(x+2)(x-1)}{x(x+1)}$. Vertical asymptotes occur at $x = 0$

and $x = -1$. Since x cannot equal zero, there is no y-intercept. When $y = 0$, we
have $x = -2$ or 1, so the x-intercepts are -2 and 1. Because the degree of the
denominator and numerator are the same, the horizontal asymptote is $y = \frac{2}{1} = 2$.

51. $y = \dfrac{x^2 - x - 6}{x^2 + 3x} = \dfrac{(x-3)(x+2)}{x(x+3)}$. The x-intercept occurs when $y = 0 \Leftrightarrow$

$(x-3)(x+2) = 0 \quad \Rightarrow \quad x = -2, 3$, so the x-intercepts are -2 and 3. There
is no y-intercept because y is undefined when $x = 0$. The vertical asymptotes are
$x = 0$ and $x = -3$. Because the degree of the numerator and denominator are the
same, the horizontal asymptotes is $y = \frac{1}{1} = 1$.

52. $r(x) = \dfrac{x^2 + 3x}{x^2 - x - 6} = \dfrac{x(x+3)}{(x-3)(x+2)}$. When $x = 0$, we have $y = 0$, so the

graph passes through the origin. When $y = 0$, we have $x = 0$ or -3, so the
x-intercepts are 0 and -3. Vertical asymptotes occur at $x = -2$ and $x = 3$.
Because the degree of the denominator and numerator are the same, the horizontal
asymptote is $y = \frac{1}{1} = 1$.

53. $r(x) = \dfrac{3x^2 + 6}{x^2 - 2x - 3} = \dfrac{3(x^2 + 2)}{(x-3)(x+1)}$. When $x = 0$, $y = -2$, so the

y-intercept is -2. Since the numerator can never equal zero, there is no
x-intercept. Vertical asymptotes occur when $x = -1, 3$. Because the degree of the
numerator and denominator are the same, the horizontal asymptote is. $y = \frac{3}{1} = 3$.

54. $r(x) = \dfrac{5x^2 + 5}{x^2 + 4x + 4} = \dfrac{5(x^2 + 1)}{(x+2)^2}$. When $x = 0$, we have $y = \frac{5}{4}$, so the

y-intercept is $\frac{5}{4}$. Since $x^2 + 1 > 0$ for all real x, y never equals zero, and there is
no x-intercept. The vertical asymptote is $x = -2$. Because the degree of the
denominator and numerator are the same, the horizontal asymptote occurs at

$y = \frac{5}{1} = 5$.

55. $s\left(x\right) = \dfrac{x^2 - 2x + 1}{x^3 - 3x^2} = \dfrac{\left(x - 1\right)^2}{x^2\left(x - 3\right)}$. Since $x = 0$ is not in the domain of $s\left(x\right)$,

there is no y-intercept. The x-intercept occurs when $y = 0 \Leftrightarrow$

$x^2 - 2x + 1 = \left(x - 1\right)^2 = 0 \quad \Rightarrow \quad x = 1$, so the x-intercept is 1. Vertical

asymptotes occur when $x = 0, 3$. Since the degree of the numerator is less than the

degree of the denominator, the horizontal asymptote is $y = 0$.

56. $r\left(x\right) = \dfrac{x^3 - x^2}{x^3 - 3x - 2} = \dfrac{x^2\left(x - 1\right)}{x^3 - 3x - 2}$. When $x = 0$, we have $y = 0$, so the

y-intercept is 0. When $y = 0$, we have $x^2\left(x - 1\right) = 0$, so the x-intercepts are 0

and 1. Vertical asymptotes occur when $x^3 - 3x - 2 = 0$. Since $x^3 - 3x - 2 = 0$

when $x = 2$, we can factor $\left(x - 2\right)\left(x + 1\right)^2 = 0$, so the vertical asymptotes occur

at $x = 2$ and $x = -1$. Because the degree of the denominator and numerator are

the same, the horizontal asymptote is $y = \frac{1}{1} = 1$.

57. $r\left(x\right) = \dfrac{x^2}{x - 2}$. When $x = 0$, $y = 0$, so the graph passes through the origin. There

is a vertical asymptote when $x - 2 = 0 \Leftrightarrow x = 2$, with $y \to \infty$ as $x \to 2^+$, and

$y \to -\infty$ as $x \to 2^-$. Because the degree of the numerator is greater than the

degree of the denominator, there is no horizontal asymptotes. By using long

division, we see that $y = x + 2 + \dfrac{4}{x - 2}$, so $y = x + 2$ is a slant asymptote.

58. $r\left(x\right) = \dfrac{x^2 + 2x}{x - 1} = \dfrac{x\left(x + 2\right)}{x - 1}$. When $x = 0$, we have $y = 0$, so the graph passes

through the origin. Also, when $y = 0$, we have $x = 0$ or -2, so the x-intercepts

are -2 and 0. The vertical asymptote is $x = 1$. There is no horizontal asymptote,

and the line $y = x + 3$ is a slant asymptote because by long division, we have

$y = x + 3 + \dfrac{2}{x - 1}$.

59. $r\left(x\right) = \dfrac{x^2 - 2x - 8}{x} = \dfrac{\left(x - 4\right)\left(x + 2\right)}{x}$. The vertical asymptote is $x = 0$, thus,

there is no y-intercept. If $y = 0$, then $\left(x - 4\right)\left(x + 2\right) = 0 \Rightarrow x = -2, 4$, so the

x-intercepts are -2 and 4. Because the degree of the numerator is greater than the

degree of the denominator, there are no horizontal asymptotes. By using long

division, we see that $y = x - 2 - \dfrac{8}{x}$, so $y = x - 2$ is a slant asymptote.

60. $r(x) = \dfrac{3x - x^2}{2x - 2} = \dfrac{x(3-x)}{2(x-1)}$. When $x = 0$, we have $y = 0$, so the graph passes

through the origin. Also, when $y = 0$, we have $x = 0$ or $x = 3$, so the x-intercepts

are 0 and 3. The vertical asymptote is $x = 1$. There is no horizontal asymptote, and

the line $y = -\frac{1}{2}x + 1$ is a slant asymptote because by long division we have

$$y = -\frac{1}{2}x + 1 + \frac{1}{x - 1}.$$

61. $r(x) = \dfrac{x^2 + 5x + 4}{x - 3} = \dfrac{(x+4)(x+1)}{x-3}$. When $x = 0$, $y = -\frac{4}{3}$, so the

y-intercept is $-\frac{4}{3}$. When $y = 0$, $(x+4)(x+1) = 0 \Leftrightarrow x = -4, -1$, so the

two x-intercepts are -4 and -1. A vertical asymptote occurs when $x = 3$, with

$y \to \infty$ as $x \to 3^+$, and $y \to -\infty$ as $x \to 3^-$. Using long division, we see that

$y = x + 8 + \dfrac{28}{x - 3}$, so $y = x + 8$ is a slant asymptote.

62. $r(x) = \dfrac{x^3 + 4}{2x^2 + x - 1} = \dfrac{x^3 + 4}{(2x-1)(x+1)}$. When $x = 0$, we have

$y = \dfrac{0 + 4}{0 + 0 - 1} = -4$, so the y-intercept is -4. Since $x^3 + 4 = 0 \Rightarrow$

$x = -\sqrt[3]{4}$, the x-intercept is $x = -\sqrt[3]{4}$. There are vertical asymptotes where

$(2x-1)(x+1) = 0 \Rightarrow x = \frac{1}{2}$ or $x = -1$. Since the degree of the numerator is

greater than the degree of the denominator, there is no horizontal asymptote. By

long division, we have $y = \frac{1}{2}x - \frac{1}{4} + \dfrac{\frac{3}{4}x + \frac{15}{4}}{2x^2 - x - 1}$, so the line $y = \frac{1}{2}x - \frac{1}{4}$ is a

slant asymptote.

63. $r(x) = \dfrac{x^3 + x^2}{x^2 - 4} = \dfrac{x^2(x+1)}{(x-2)(x+2)}$. When $x = 0$, $y = 0$, so the graph passes

through the origin. Moreover, when $y = 0$, we have $x^2(x+1) = 0 \Rightarrow$

$x = 0, -1$, so the x-intercepts are 0 and -1. Vertical asymptotes occur when

$x = \pm 2$; as $x \to \pm 2^-$, $y = -\infty$ and as $x \to \pm 2^+$, $y \to \infty$. Because the degree

of the numerator is greater than the degree of the denominator, there is no

horizontal asymptote. Using long division, we see that $y = x + 1 + \dfrac{4x + 4}{x^2 - 4}$, so

$y = x + 1$ is a slant asymptote.

64. $r(x) = \dfrac{2x^3 + 2x}{x^2 - 1} = \dfrac{2x(x^2+1)}{(x-1)(x+1)}$. When $x = 0$, we have $y = 0$, so the graph

passes through the origin. Also, note that $x^2 + 1 > 0$, for all real x, so the only

x-intercept is 0. There are two vertical asymptotes at $x = -1$ and $x = 1$. There is

no horizontal asymptote, and the line $y = 2x$ is a slant asymptote because by long

division, we have $y = 2x + \dfrac{4x}{x^2 - 1}$.

65. $f(x) = \dfrac{2x^2 + 6x + 6}{x + 3}$, $g(x) = 2x$. f has vertical asymptote $x = -3$.

66. $f(x) = \dfrac{-x^3 + 6x^2 - 5}{x^2 - 2x}$, $g(x) = -x + 4$. f has vertical asymptotes $x = 0$ and $x = 2$.

67. $f(x) = \dfrac{x^3 - 2x^2 + 16}{x - 2}$, $g(x) = x^2$. f has vertical asymptote $x = 2$.

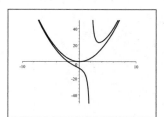

68. $f(x) = \dfrac{-x^4 + 2x^3 - 2x}{(x - 1)^2}$, $g(x) = 1 - x^2$. f has vertical asymptote $x = 1$.

69. $f(x) = \dfrac{2x^2 - 5x}{2x + 3}$ has vertical asymptote $x = -1.5$, x-intercepts 0 and 2.5, y-intercept 0, local maximum $(-3.9, -10.4)$,

and local minimum $(0.9, -0.6)$. Using long division, we get $f(x) = x - 4 + \dfrac{12}{2x + 3}$. From the graph, we see that the end

behavior of $f(x)$ is like the end behavior of $g(x) = x - 4$.

70. $f(x) = \dfrac{x^4 - 3x^3 + x^2 - 3x + 3}{x^2 - 3x}$ has vertical asymptotes are $x = 0$, $x = 3$, x-intercept 0.82, and no y-intercept. The

local minima are $(-0.80, 2.63)$ and $(3.38, 14.76)$. The local maximum is $(2.56, 4.88)$. By using long division, we see that

$f(x) = x^2 + 1 + \dfrac{3}{x^2 - 3x}$. From the second graph, we see that the end behavior of $f(x)$ is the same as the end behavior

of $g(x) = x^2 + 1$.

71. $f(x) = \dfrac{x^5}{x^3 - 1}$ has vertical asymptote $x = 1$, x-intercept 0, y-intercept 0, and local minimum $(1.4, 3.1)$.

Thus $y = x^2 + \dfrac{x^2}{x^3 - 1}$. From the graph we see that the end behavior of $f(x)$ is like the end behavior of $g(x) = x^2$.

Graph of f Graph of f and g

72. $f(x) = \dfrac{x^4}{x^2 - 2}$ has vertical asymptotes $x = \pm 1.41$, x-intercept 0, and y-intercept 0. The local maximum is $(0, 0)$. The

local minima are $(-2, 8)$ and $(2, 8)$. By using long division, we see that $f(x) = x^2 + 2 + \dfrac{4}{x^2 - 2}$. From the second graph,

we see that the end behavior of $f(x)$ is the same as the end behavior of $g(x) = x^2 + 2$.

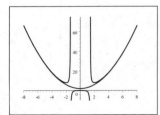

73. $f(x) = \dfrac{x^4 - 3x^3 + 6}{x - 3}$ has vertical asymptote $x = 3$, x-intercepts 1.6 and 2.7, y-intercept -2, local maxima $(-0.4, -1.8)$

and $(2.4, 3.8)$, and local minima $(0.6, -2.3)$ and $(3.4, 54.3)$. Thus $y = x^3 + \dfrac{6}{x - 3}$. From the graphs, we see that the end

behavior of $f(x)$ is like the end behavior of $g(x) = x^3$.

$$
\begin{array}{r}
x^3 \\
x - 3 \overline{\smash{\big)}\ x^4 - 3x^3 + 6} \\
\underline{x^4 - 3x^3} \\
6
\end{array}
$$

74. $r(x) = \dfrac{4 + x^2 - x^4}{x^2 - 1} = \dfrac{-x^4 + x^2 + 4}{(x - 1)(x + 1)}$ has vertical asymptotes $x \approx \pm 1.41$, x-intercepts ± 1.6, and y-intercept -1. The

local maximum is $(0, -0.4)$ and there is no local minimum.

Thus $y = -x^2 + \dfrac{6}{x^2 - 1}$. From the graphs, we see that the end behavior of $f(x)$ is like the end behavior of $g(x) = -x^2$.

$$
\begin{array}{r}
-x^2 \\
x^2 - 1 \overline{\smash{\big)}\ -x^4 + 0x^3 + x^2 + 0x + 4} \\
\underline{-x^4 \qquad\ + x^2} \\
0 \qquad\quad + 4
\end{array}
$$

75. (a)

(b) $p(t) = \dfrac{3000t}{t + 1} = 3000 - \dfrac{3000}{t + 1}$. So as $t \to \infty$, we

have $p(t) \to 3000$.

76. (a)

(b) $c(t) = \dfrac{30t}{t^2 + 2}$. Since the degree of the denominator is

larger than the degree of the numerator, $c(t) \to 0$ as

$t \to \infty$.

77. $c(t) = \dfrac{5t}{t^2 + 1}$

(a) The highest concentration of drug is 2.50 mg/L, and it is reached 1

hour after the drug is administered.

(b) The concentration of the drug in the bloodstream goes to 0.

(c) From the first viewing rectangle, we see that an approximate solution

is near $t = 15$. Thus we graph $y = \dfrac{5t}{t^2 + 1}$ and $y = 0.3$ in the

viewing rectangle $[14, 18]$ by $[0, 0.5]$. So it takes about 16.61 hours

for the concentration to drop below 0.3 mg/L.

78. Substituting for R and g, we have $h(v) = \dfrac{(6.4 \times 10^6)\, v^2}{2\,(9.8)\,(6.4 \times 10^6) - v^2}$. The vertical

asymptote is $v \approx 11{,}000$, and it represents the escape velocity from the earth's
gravitational pull: $11{,}000$ m/s ≈ 1900 mi/h.

79. $P(v) = P_0 \left(\dfrac{s_0}{s_0 - v} \right) \quad \Rightarrow \quad P(v) = 440 \left(\dfrac{332}{332 - v} \right)$

If the speed of the train approaches the speed of sound, the pitch of the whistle
becomes very loud. This would be experienced as a "sonic boom"— an effect
seldom heard with trains.

80. (a) $\dfrac{1}{x} + \dfrac{1}{y} = \dfrac{1}{F} \quad \Leftrightarrow \quad \dfrac{1}{y} = \dfrac{1}{F} - \dfrac{1}{x} \quad \Leftrightarrow \quad \dfrac{1}{y} = \dfrac{x - F}{xF} \quad \Leftrightarrow$

$y = \dfrac{xF}{x - F}$. Using $F = 55$, we get $y = \dfrac{55x}{x - 55}$. Since $y \geq 0$, we

use the viewing rectangle $[0, 1000]$ by $[0, 250]$.

(b) y approaches 55 millimeters.

(c) y approaches ∞.

81. Vertical asymptote $x = 3$: $p(x) = \dfrac{1}{x - 3}$. Vertical asymptote $x = 3$ and horizontal asymptote $y = 2$: $r(x) = \dfrac{2x}{x - 3}$.

Vertical asymptotes $x = 1$ and $x = -1$, horizontal asymptote 0, and x-intercept 4: $q(x) = \dfrac{x - 4}{(x - 1)(x + 1)}$. Of course,

other answers are possible.

82. $r(x) = \dfrac{x^6 + 10}{x^4 + 8x^2 + 15}$ has no x-intercept since the numerator has no real roots. Likewise, $r(x)$ has no vertical

asymptotes, since the denominator has no real roots. Since the degree of the numerator is two greater than the degree of the
denominator, $r(x)$ has no horizontal or slant asymptotes.

83. (a) $r(x) = \dfrac{3x^2 - 3x - 6}{x - 2} = \dfrac{3(x - 2)(x + 1)}{x - 2} = 3(x + 1)$, for $x \neq 2$. Therefore,

$r(x) = 3x + 3$, $x \neq 2$. Since $3(2) + 3 = 9$, the graph is the line $y = 3x + 3$ with

the point $(2, 9)$ removed.

(b) $s(x) = \dfrac{x^2 + x - 20}{x + 5} = \dfrac{(x-4)(x+5)}{x+5} = x - 4$, for $x \neq -5$. Therefore, $s(x) = x - 4$, $x \neq -5$. Since

$(-5) - 4 = -9$, the graph is the line $y = x - 4$ with the point $(-5, -9)$ removed.

$t(x) = \dfrac{2x^2 - x - 1}{x - 1} = \dfrac{(2x+1)(x-1)}{x-1} = 2x + 1$, for $x \neq 1$. Therefore, $t(x) = 2x + 1$, $x \neq 1$. Since

$2(1) + 1 = 3$, the graph is the line $y = 2x + 1$ with the point $(1, 3)$ removed.

$u(x) = \dfrac{x - 2}{x^2 - 2x} = \dfrac{x - 2}{x(x - 2)} = \dfrac{1}{x}$, for $x \neq 2$. Therefore, $u(x) = \dfrac{1}{x}$, $x \neq 2$. When $x = 2$, $\dfrac{1}{x} = \dfrac{1}{2}$, so the graph is

the curve $y = \dfrac{1}{x}$ with the point $\left(2, \tfrac{1}{2}\right)$ removed.

  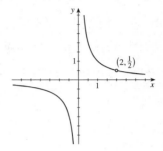

84. (a) Let $f(x) = \dfrac{1}{x^2}$. Then $r(x) = \dfrac{1}{(x-2)^2} = f(x - 2)$. From this form we see that

the graph of r is obtained from the graph of f by shifting 2 units to the right. Thus
r has vertical asymptote $x = 2$ and horizontal asymptote $y = 0$.

(b) $s(x) = \dfrac{2x^2 + 4x + 5}{x^2 + 2x + 1} = 2 + \dfrac{3}{(x+1)^2} = 3f(x+1) + 2$. From this form we see that the graph of s is obtained from

the graph of f by shifting 1 unit to the left, stretching vertically by a factor of 3, and shifting 2 units vertically. Thus r
has vertical asymptote $x = -1$ and horizontal asymptote $y = 2$.

$$
\begin{array}{r}
2 \\
x^2 + 2x + 1 \overline{\smash{\big)}\ 2x^2 + 4x + 5} \\
\underline{2x^2 + 4x + 2} \\
3
\end{array}
$$

(c) Using long division, we see that $p(x) = \dfrac{2 - 3x^2}{x^2 - 4x + 4} = -3 + \dfrac{-12x + 14}{x^2 - 4x + 4}$ which cannot be graphed by transforming

$f(x) = \dfrac{1}{x^2}$. Using long division on q we have:

$$
\begin{array}{r}
-3 \\
x^2 - 4x + 4 \overline{\smash{\big)}\ -3x^2 + 0x + 2} \\
\underline{-3x^2 + 12x - 12} \\
-12x + 14
\end{array}
\qquad
\begin{array}{r}
-3 \\
x^2 - 4x + 4 \overline{\smash{\big)}\ -3x^2 + 12x + 0} \\
\underline{-3x^2 + 12x - 12} \\
12
\end{array}
$$

So $q(x) = \dfrac{12x - 3x^2}{x^2 - 4x + 4} = -3 + \dfrac{12}{(x-2)^2} = 12f(x-2) - 3$. From this form we see that the graph of q is obtained

from the graph of f by shifting 2 units to the right, stretching vertically by a factor of 12, and then shifting 3 units

vertically down. Thus the vertical asymptote is $x = 2$ and the horizontal asymptote is $y = -3$. We show $y = p(x)$ just

to verify that we cannot obtain $p(x)$ from $y = \dfrac{1}{x^2}$.

$$y = q(x)$$

$$y = p(x)$$

Chapter 3 Review

1. $P(x) = -x^3 + 64$

2. $P(x) = 2x^3 - 16 = 2(x - 2)(x^2 + 2x + 4)$

3. $P(x) = 2(x - 1)^4 - 32$

4. $P(x) = 64 - (x - 3)^4$

5. $P(x) = 32 + (x-1)^5$

6. $P(x) = -3(x+2)^5 + 96$

7. $P(x) = x^3 - 4x + 1$. x-intercepts: $-2.1, 0.3$, and 1.9. y-intercept: 1. Local maximum is $(-1.2, 4.1)$. Local minimum is $(1.2, -2.1)$. $y \to \infty$ as $x \to \infty$; $y \to -\infty$ as $x \to -\infty$.

8. $P(x) = -2x^3 + 6x^2 - 2$. x-intercepts: $-0.5, 0.7$, and 2.9. y-intercept: -2. Local maximum is $(2, 6)$. Local minimum is $(0, -2)$. $y \to \infty$ as $x \to -\infty$ and $y \to -\infty$ as $x \to \infty$.

9. $P(x) = 3x^4 - 4x^3 - 10x - 1$. x-intercepts: -0.1 and 2.1. y-intercept: -1. Local maximum is $(1.4, -14.5)$. There is no local maximum. $y \to \infty$ as $x \to \pm\infty$.

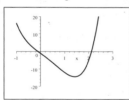

10. $P(x) = x^5 + x^4 - 7x^3 - x^2 + 6x + 3$. x-intercepts: $-3.0, 1.3$, and 1.9. y-intercept: -3. Local maxima are $(-2.4, 33.2)$ and $(0.5, 5.0)$. Local minima are $(-0.6, 0.6)$ and $(1.6, -1.6)$. $y \to -\infty$ as $x \to -\infty$ and $y \to \infty$ as $x \to \infty$.

11. (a) Use the Pythagorean Theorem and solving for y^2 we have, $x^2 + y^2 = 10^2 \quad \Leftrightarrow \quad y^2 = 100 - x^2$. Substituting we get
$$S = 13.8x\left(100 - x^2\right) = 1380x - 13.8x^3.$$
(b) Domain is $[0, 10]$.
(c)

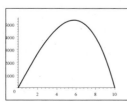

(d) The strongest beam has width 5.8 inches.

12. (a) The area of the four sides is $2x^2 + 2xy = 1200 \Leftrightarrow$
$$2xy = 1200 - 2x^2 \quad \Leftrightarrow \quad y = \frac{600 - x^2}{x}.$$
Substituting we get
$$V = x^2 y = x^2\left(\frac{600 - x^2}{x}\right) = 600x - x^3.$$
(b)

(c) V is maximized when $x \approx 14.14$, $y \approx 28.28$

13. $\dfrac{x^2 - 3x + 5}{x - 2}$

$$
\begin{array}{r|rrr}
2 & 1 & -3 & 5 \\
  &   & 2 & -2 \\
\hline
  & 1 & -1 & 3
\end{array}
$$

Using synthetic division, we see that $Q(x) = x - 1$ and $R(x) = 3$.

14. $\dfrac{x^2 + x - 12}{x - 3} = \dfrac{(x+4)(x-3)}{x-3} = x + 4$. Factoring we have $Q(x) = x + 4$ and $R(x) = 0$. This can be confirmed with synthetic division:

$$
\begin{array}{r|rrr}
3 & 1 & 1 & -12 \\
  &   & 3 & 12 \\
\hline
  & 1 & 4 & 0
\end{array}
$$

15. $\dfrac{x^3 - x^2 + 11x + 2}{x - 4}$

$$
\begin{array}{r|rrrr}
4 & 1 & -1 & 11 & 2 \\
  &   & 4 & 12 & 92 \\
\hline
  & 1 & 3 & 23 & 94
\end{array}
$$

Using synthetic division, we see that $Q(x) = x^2 + 3x + 23$ and $R(x) = 94$.

16. $\dfrac{x^3 + 2x^2 - 10}{x + 3}$

$$
\begin{array}{r|rrrr}
-3 & 1 & 2 & 0 & -10 \\
   &   & -3 & 3 & -9 \\
\hline
   & 1 & -1 & 3 & -19
\end{array}
$$

Using synthetic division, we see that $Q(x) = x^2 - x + 3$ and $R(x) = -19$.

17. $\dfrac{x^4 - 8x^2 + 2x + 7}{x + 5}$

$$
\begin{array}{r|rrrrr}
-5 & 1 & 0 & -8 & 2 & 7 \\
   &   & -5 & 25 & -85 & 415 \\
\hline
   & 1 & -5 & 17 & -83 & 422
\end{array}
$$

Using synthetic division, we see that $Q(x) = x^3 - 5x^2 + 17x - 83$ and $R(x) = 422$.

18. $\dfrac{2x^4 + 3x^3 - 12}{x + 4}$

$$
\begin{array}{r|rrrrr}
-4 & 2 & 3 & 0 & 0 & -12 \\
   &   & -8 & 20 & -80 & 320 \\
\hline
   & 2 & -5 & 20 & -80 & 308
\end{array}
$$

Using synthetic division, we see that $Q(x) = 2x^3 - 5x^2 + 20x - 80$ and $R(x) = 308$.

19. $\dfrac{2x^3 + x^2 - 8x + 15}{x^2 + 2x - 1}$

$$
\begin{array}{r}
2x - 3 \\
x^2 + 2x - 1 \overline{\smash{\big)}\ 2x^3 + x^2 - 8x + 15} \\
\underline{2x^3 + 4x^2 - 2x} \\
-3x^2 - 6x + 15 \\
\underline{-3x^2 - 6x + 3} \\
12
\end{array}
$$

Therefore, $Q(x) = 2x - 3$, and $R(x) = 12$.

20. $\dfrac{x^4 - 2x^2 + 7x}{x^2 - x + 3}$

$$
\begin{array}{r}
x^2 + x - 4 \\
x^2 - x + 3 \overline{\smash{\big)}\ x^4 + 0x^3 - 2x^2 + 7x + 0} \\
\underline{x^4 - x^3 + 3x^3} \\
x^3 - 5x^2 + 7x \\
\underline{x^3 - x^2 + 3x} \\
-4x^2 + 4x + 0 \\
\underline{-4x^2 + 4x - 12} \\
12
\end{array}
$$

Therefore, $Q(x) = x^2 + x - 4$, and $R(x) = 12$.

21. $P(x) = 2x^3 - 9x^2 - 7x + 13$; find $P(5)$.

$$
\begin{array}{r|rrrr}
5 & 2 & -9 & -7 & 13 \\
  &   & 10 & 5 & -10 \\
\hline
  & 2 & 1 & -2 & 3
\end{array}
$$

Therefore, $P(5) = 3$.

22. $Q(x) = x^4 + 4x^3 + 7x^2 + 10x + 15$; find $Q(-3)$

$$
\begin{array}{r|rrrrr}
-3 & 1 & 4 & 7 & 10 & 15 \\
   &   & -3 & -3 & -12 & 6 \\
\hline
   & 1 & 1 & 4 & -2 & 21
\end{array}
$$

By the Remainder Theorem, we have $Q(-3) = 21$.

23. $\frac{1}{2}$ is a zero of $P(x) = 2x^4 + x^3 - 5x^2 + 10x - 4$ if
$P\left(\frac{1}{2}\right) = 0$.

$$
\begin{array}{r|rrrrr}
\frac{1}{2} & 2 & 1 & -5 & 10 & -4 \\
  &   & 1 & 1 & -2 & 4 \\
\hline
  & 2 & 2 & -4 & 8 & 0
\end{array}
$$

Since $P\left(\frac{1}{2}\right) = 0$, $\frac{1}{2}$ is a zero of the polynomial.

24. $x + 4$ is a factor of
$P(x) = x^5 + 4x^4 - 7x^3 - 23x^2 + 23x + 12$ if
$P(-4) = 0$.

$$
\begin{array}{r|rrrrrr}
-4 & 1 & 4 & -7 & -23 & 23 & 12 \\
   &   & -4 & 0 & 28 & -20 & -12 \\
\hline
   & 1 & 0 & -7 & 5 & 3 & 0
\end{array}
$$

Since $P(-4) = 0$, $x + 4$ is a factor of the polynomial.

25. $P(x) = x^{500} + 6x^{201} - x^2 - 2x + 4$.   The remainder from dividing $P(x)$ by $x - 1$ is
$P(1) = (1)^{500} + 6(1)^{201} - (1)^2 - 2(1) + 4 = 8$.

26. Let $P(x) = x^{101} - x^4 + 2$. The remainder from dividing $P(x)$ by $x + 1$ is $P(-1) = (-1)^{101} - (-1)^4 + 2 = 0$.

27. (a) $P(x) = x^5 - 6x^3 - x^2 + 2x + 18$ has possible rational zeros ± 1, ± 2, ± 3, ± 6, ± 9, ± 18.

(b) Since $P(x)$ has 2 variations in sign, there are either 0 or 2 positive real zeros. Since $P(-x) = -x^5 + 6x^3 - x^2 - 2x + 18$ has 3 variations in sign, there are 1 or 3 negative real zeros.

28. (a) $P(x) = 6x^4 + 3x^3 + x^2 + 3x + 4$ has possible rational zeros ± 1, ± 2, ± 4, $\pm \frac{1}{2}$, $\pm \frac{1}{3}$, $\pm \frac{2}{3}$, $\pm \frac{4}{3}$, $\pm \frac{1}{6}$.

(b) Since $P(x)$ has no variations in sign, there are no positive real zeros. Since $P(-x) = 6x^4 - 3x^3 + x^2 - 3x + 4$ has 4 variations in sign, there are 0, 2, or 4 negative real zeros.

29. (a) $P(x) = x^3 - 16x = x\left(x^2 - 16\right)$
$\qquad = x(x - 4)(x + 4)$

has zeros -4, 0, 4 (all of multiplicity 1).

(b)

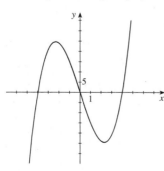

30. (a) $P(x) = 2x^3 - 16 = 2\left(x^3 - 8\right)$
$\qquad = 2(x - 2)\left(x^2 + 2x + 4\right)$

We use the quadratic formula on the remaining

quadratic: $x = \frac{-2 \pm \sqrt{4 - 16}}{2}$, which is not real. So the

only real zero is 2 (multiplicity 1).

(b)

31. (a) $P(x) = x^4 + x^3 - 2x^2 = x^2 \left(x^2 + x - 2\right)$

$= x^2 (x + 2)(x - 1)$

The zeros are 0 (multiplicity 2), -2 (multiplicity 1), and 1 (multiplicity 1)

(b)

32. (a) $P(x) = x^4 - 5x^2 + 4 = \left(x^2 - 4\right)\left(x^2 - 1\right)$

$= (x - 2)(x + 2)(x - 1)(x + 1)$

Thus, the zeros are $-1, 1, -2, 2$ (all of multiplicity 1).

(b)

33. (a) $P(x) = x^4 - 2x^3 - 7x^2 + 8x + 12$. The possible rational zeros are $\pm 1, \pm 2, \pm 3, \pm 4, \pm 6, \pm 12$. P has 2 variations in sign, so it has either 2 or 0 positive real zeros.

$$
\begin{array}{r|rrrrr}
1 & 1 & -2 & -7 & 8 & 12 \\
  &   & 1 & -1 & -8 & 0 \\
\hline
  & 1 & -1 & -8 & 0 & 12
\end{array}
\qquad
\begin{array}{r|rrrrr}
2 & 1 & -2 & -7 & 8 & 12 \\
  &   & 2 & 0 & -14 & -12 \\
\hline
  & 2 & 0 & -7 & -6 & 0
\end{array}
\Rightarrow x = 2 \text{ is a root.}
$$

$P(x) = x^4 - 2x^3 - 7x^2 + 8x + 12 = (x - 2)\left(x^3 - 7x - 6\right)$. Continuing:

$$
\begin{array}{r|rrrr}
2 & 1 & 0 & -6 & -6 \\
  &   & 2 & 4 & -4 \\
\hline
  & 1 & 2 & -2 & -10
\end{array}
\qquad
\begin{array}{r|rrrr}
3 & 1 & 0 & -7 & -6 \\
  &   & 3 & 9 & 6 \\
\hline
  & 1 & 3 & 2 & 0
\end{array}
$$

(b)

so $x = 3$ is a root and

$P(x) = (x - 2)(x - 3)\left(x^2 + 3x + 2\right)$

$= (x - 2)(x - 3)(x + 1)(x + 2)$

Therefore the real roots are $-2, -1, 2$, and 3 (all of multiplicity 1).

34. (a) $P(x) = x^4 - 2x^3 - 2x^2 + 8x - 8$

$= x^2 \left(x^2 - 2x + 2\right) - 4 \left(x^2 - 2x + 2\right)$

$= \left(x^2 - 4\right)\left(x^2 - 2x + 2\right)$

$= (x - 2)(x + 2)\left(x^2 - 2x + 2\right)$

The quadratic is irreducible, so the real roots are ± 2 (each of multiplicity 1).

(b)

35. (a) $P(x) = 2x^4 + x^3 + 2x^2 - 3x - 2$. The possible rational roots are $\pm 1, \pm 2, \pm \frac{1}{2}$. P has one variation in sign, and hence 1 positive real root. $P(-x)$ has 3 variations in sign and hence either 3 or 1 negative real roots.

$$\begin{array}{c|ccccc} 1 & 2 & 1 & 2 & -3 & -2 \\ & & 2 & 3 & 5 & 2 \\ \hline & 2 & 3 & 5 & 2 & 0 \end{array} \Rightarrow x = 1 \text{ is a zero.}$$

$P(x) = 2x^4 + x^3 + 2x^2 - 3x - 2 = (x - 1)(2x^3 + 3x^2 + 5x + 2)$. Continuing:

$$\begin{array}{c|cccc} -1 & 2 & 3 & 5 & 2 \\ & & -2 & -1 & -4 \\ \hline & 2 & 1 & 4 & -2 \end{array} \qquad \begin{array}{c|cccc} -2 & 2 & 3 & 5 & 2 \\ & & -4 & 2 & -14 \\ \hline & 2 & -1 & 7 & -12 \end{array}$$

(b)

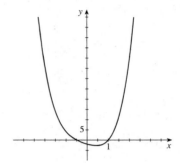

$$\begin{array}{c|cccc} -\frac{1}{2} & 2 & 3 & 5 & 2 \\ & & -1 & -1 & -2 \\ \hline & 2 & 2 & 4 & 0 \end{array} \Rightarrow x = -\frac{1}{2} \text{ is a zero.}$$

$P(x) = (x - 1)\left(x + \frac{1}{2}\right)(2x^2 + 2x + 4)$. The quadratic is irreducible, so the real zeros are 1 and $-\frac{1}{2}$ (each of multiplicity 1).

36. (a) $P(x) = 9x^5 - 21x^4 + 10x^3 + 6x^2 - 3x - 1$. The possible rational zeros are $\pm 1, \pm \frac{1}{3}, \pm \frac{1}{9}$. P has 3 variations in sign, hence 3 or 1 positive real roots. $P(-x)$ has 2 variations in sign, hence 2 or 0 real negative roots.

$$\begin{array}{c|cccccc} 1 & 9 & -21 & 10 & 6 & -3 & -1 \\ & & 9 & -12 & -2 & 4 & 1 \\ \hline & 9 & -12 & -2 & 4 & 1 & 0 \end{array} \Rightarrow x = 1 \text{ is a zero.}$$

$P(x) = (x - 1)(9x^4 - 12x^3 - 2x^2 + 4x + 1)$. Continuing:

$$\begin{array}{c|ccccc} 1 & 9 & -12 & -2 & 4 & 1 \\ & & 9 & -3 & -5 & -1 \\ \hline & 9 & -3 & -5 & -1 & 0 \end{array} \Rightarrow x = 1 \text{ is a zero again.}$$

$P(x) = (x - 1)^2 (9x^3 - 3x^2 - 5x - 1)$.
Continuing:

(b)

$$\begin{array}{c|cccc} 1 & 9 & -3 & -5 & -1 \\ & & 9 & 6 & 1 \\ \hline & 9 & 6 & 1 & 0 \end{array} \Rightarrow x = 1 \text{ is a zero yet again.}$$

$P(x) = (x - 1)^3 (9x^2 + 6x + 1)$
$\qquad = (x - 1)^3 (3x + 1)^2$

So the real zeros of P are 1 (multiplicity 3) and $-\frac{1}{3}$ (multiplicity 2).

37. $(2 - 3i) + (1 + 4i) = (2 + 1) + (-3 + 4)i = 3 + i$

38. $(3 - 6i) - (6 - 4i) = 3 - 6i - 6 + 4i = (3 - 6) + (-6 + 4)i = -3 - 2i$

39. $(2 + i)(3 - 2i) = 6 - 4i + 3i - 2i^2 = 6 - i + 2 = 8 - i$

40. $4i\left(2 - \frac{1}{2}i\right) = 8i - 2i^2 = 8i + 2 = 2 + 8i$

41. $\dfrac{4+2i}{2-i} = \dfrac{4+2i}{2-i} \cdot \dfrac{2+i}{2+i} = \dfrac{8+8i+2i^2}{4-i^2} = \dfrac{8+8i-2}{4+1} = \dfrac{6+8i}{5} = \frac{6}{5} + \frac{8}{5}i$

42. $\dfrac{8+3i}{4+3i} = \dfrac{8+3i}{4+3i} \cdot \dfrac{4-3i}{4-3i} = \dfrac{32-12i-9i^2}{16-9i^2} = \dfrac{32-12i+9}{16+9} = \dfrac{41-12i}{25} = \frac{41}{25} - \frac{12}{25}i$

43. $i^{25} = i^{24}i = \left(i^4\right)^6 i = (1)^6 i = i$

44. $(1+i)^3 = 1 + 3i + 3i^2 + i^3 = 1 + 3i - 3 - i = -2 + 2i$

45. $\left(1 - \sqrt{-1}\right)\left(1 + \sqrt{-1}\right) = (1-i)(1+i) = 1 + i - i - i^2 = 1 + 1 = 2$

46. $\sqrt{-10} \cdot \sqrt{-40} = \sqrt{10}i \cdot 2\sqrt{10}i = 20i^2 = -20$

47. Since the zeros are $-\frac{1}{2}$, 2, and 3, a factorization is

$$P(x) = C\left(x + \tfrac{1}{2}\right)(x-2)(x-3) = \tfrac{1}{2}C(2x+1)\left(x^2 - 5x + 6\right)$$
$$= \tfrac{1}{2}C\left(2x^3 - 10x^2 + 12x + x^2 - 5x + 6\right) = \tfrac{1}{2}C\left(2x^3 - 9x^2 + 7x + 6\right)$$

Since the constant coefficient is 12, $\frac{1}{2}C(6) = 12 \iff C = 4$, and so the polynomial is $P(x) = 4x^3 - 18x^2 + 14x + 12$.

48. Since the zeros are $\pm 3i$ and 4 (which is a double zero), a factorization is
$P(x) = C(x-4)^2(x-3i)(x+3i) = C\left(x^2 - 8x + 16\right)\left(x^2 + 9\right) = C\left(x^4 - 8x^3 + 25x^2 - 72x + 144\right)$. Since all of the coefficients are integers, we can choose $C = 1$, so $P(x) = x^4 - 8x^3 + 25x^2 - 72x + 144$.

49. No, there is no polynomial of degree 4 with integer coefficients that has zeros i, $2i$, $3i$ and $4i$. Since the imaginary zeros of polynomial equations with real coefficients come in complex conjugate pairs, there would have to be 8 zeros, which is impossible for a polynomial of degree 4.

50. $P(x) = 3x^4 + 5x^2 + 2 = \left(3x^2 + 2\right)\left(x^2 + 1\right)$. Since $3x^2 + 2 = 0$ and $x^2 + 1 = 0$ have no real zeros, it follows that $3x^4 + 5x^2 + 2$ has no real zeros.

51. $P(x) = x^3 - 3x^2 - 13x + 15$ has possible rational zeros ± 1, ± 3, ± 5, ± 15.

$$
\begin{array}{r|rrr}
1 & 1 & -3 & -13 & 15 \\
  &   & 1 & -2 & -15 \\
\hline
  & 1 & -2 & -15 & 0
\end{array}
\Rightarrow x = 1 \text{ is a zero.}
$$

So $P(x) = x^3 - 3x^2 - 13x + 15 = (x-1)\left(x^2 - 2x - 15\right) = (x-1)(x-5)(x+3)$. Therefore, the zeros are -3, 1, and 5.

52. $P(x) = 2x^3 + 5x^2 - 6x - 9$ has possible rational zeros ± 1, ± 3, ± 9, $\pm \frac{1}{2}$, $\pm \frac{3}{2}$, $\pm \frac{9}{2}$. Since there is one variation in sign, there is a positive real zero.

$$
\begin{array}{r|rrr}
1 & 2 & 5 & -6 & -9 \\
  &   & 2 & 7 & 1 \\
\hline
  & 2 & 7 & 1 & -8
\end{array}
\qquad
\begin{array}{r|rrr}
3 & 2 & 5 & -6 & -9 \\
  &   & 6 & 33 & 81 \\
\hline
  & 2 & 11 & 27 & 72
\end{array}
\Rightarrow x = 3 \text{ is an upper bound}
\qquad
\begin{array}{r|rrr}
\frac{3}{2} & 2 & 5 & -6 & -9 \\
  &   & 3 & 12 & 9 \\
\hline
  & 2 & 8 & 6 & 0
\end{array}
\Rightarrow x = \tfrac{3}{2} \text{ is a zero.}
$$

So $P(x) = 2x^3 + 5x^2 - 6x - 9 = (2x-3)\left(x^2 + 4x + 3\right) = (2x-3)(x+3)(x+1)$. Therefore, the zeros are -3, -1 and $\frac{3}{2}$.

53. $P(x) = x^4 + 6x^3 + 17x^2 + 28x + 20$ has possible rational zeros $\pm 1, \pm 2, \pm 4, \pm 5, \pm 10, \pm 20$. Since all of the coefficients are positive, there are no positive real zeros.

$$
\begin{array}{r|rrrrr}
-1 & 1 & 6 & 17 & 28 & 20 \\
   &   & -1 & -5 & -12 & -16 \\
\hline
   & 1 & 5 & 12 & 16 & 4
\end{array}
\qquad
\begin{array}{r|rrrrr}
-2 & 1 & 6 & 17 & 28 & 20 \\
   &   & -2 & -8 & -18 & -20 \\
\hline
   & 1 & 4 & 9 & 10 & 0
\end{array}
\Rightarrow x = -2 \text{ is a zero.}
$$

$P(x) = x^4 + 6x^3 + 17x^2 + 28x + 20 = (x+2)\left(x^3 + 4x^2 + 9x + 10\right)$. Continuing with the quotient, we have

$$
\begin{array}{r|rrrr}
-2 & 1 & 4 & 9 & 10 \\
   &   & -2 & -4 & -10 \\
\hline
   & 1 & 2 & 5 & 0
\end{array}
\Rightarrow x = -2 \text{ is a zero.}
$$

Thus $P(x) = x^4 + 6x^3 + 17x^2 + 28x + 20 = (x+2)^2\left(x^2 + 2x + 5\right)$. Now $x^2 + 2x + 5 = 0$ when $x = \frac{-2 \pm \sqrt{4 - 4(5)(1)}}{2} = \frac{-2 \pm 4i}{2} = -1 \pm 2i$. Thus, the zeros are -2 (multiplicity 2) and $-1 \pm 2i$.

54. $P(x) = x^4 + 7x^3 + 9x^2 - 17x - 20$ has possible rational zeros $\pm 1, \pm 2, \pm 4, \pm 5, \pm 10, \pm 20$.

$$
\begin{array}{r|rrrrr}
1 & 1 & 7 & 9 & -17 & -20 \\
  &   & 1 & 8 & 17 & 0 \\
\hline
  & 1 & 8 & 17 & 0 & -20
\end{array}
\quad
\begin{array}{r|rrrrr}
2 & 1 & 7 & 9 & -17 & -20 \\
  &   & 2 & 18 & 54 & 74 \\
\hline
  & 1 & 9 & 27 & 37 & 54
\end{array}
\Rightarrow x = 2 \text{ is an upper bound.}
$$

$$
\begin{array}{r|rrrrr}
-1 & 1 & 7 & 9 & -17 & -20 \\
   &   & -1 & -6 & -3 & 20 \\
\hline
   & 1 & 6 & 3 & -20 & 0
\end{array}
\Rightarrow x = -1 \text{ is a zero.}
$$

So $P(x) = x^4 + 7x^3 + 9x^2 - 17x - 20 = (x+1)\left(x^3 + 6x^2 + 3x - 20\right)$. Continuing with the quotient, we have

$$
\begin{array}{r|rrrr}
-1 & 1 & 6 & 3 & -20 \\
   &   & -1 & -5 & 2 \\
\hline
   & 1 & 5 & -2 & -18
\end{array}
\quad
\begin{array}{r|rrrr}
-2 & 1 & 6 & 3 & -20 \\
   &   & -2 & -8 & 10 \\
\hline
   & 1 & 4 & -5 & -10
\end{array}
\quad
\begin{array}{r|rrrr}
-4 & 1 & 6 & 3 & -20 \\
   &   & -4 & -8 & 20 \\
\hline
   & 1 & 2 & -5 & 0
\end{array}
\Rightarrow x = -4 \text{ is a zero.}
$$

So $P(x) = x^4 + 7x^3 + 9x^2 - 17x - 20 = (x+1)(x+4)\left(x^2 + 2x - 5\right)$. Now using the quadratic formula on $x^2 + 2x - 5$ we have: $x = \frac{-2 \pm \sqrt{4 - 4(1)(-5)}}{2} = \frac{-2 \pm 2\sqrt{6}}{2} = -1 \pm \sqrt{6}$. Thus, the zeros are $-4, -1$, and $-1 \pm \sqrt{6}$.

55. $P(x) = x^5 - 3x^4 - x^3 + 11x^2 - 12x + 4$ has possible rational zeros $\pm 1, \pm 2, \pm 4$.

$$
\begin{array}{r|rrrrrr}
1 & 1 & -3 & -1 & 11 & -12 & 4 \\
  &   & 1 & -2 & -3 & 8 & -4 \\
\hline
  & 1 & -2 & -3 & 8 & -4 & 0
\end{array}
\Rightarrow x = 1 \text{ is a zero.}
$$

$P(x) = x^5 - 3x^4 - x^3 + 11x^2 - 12x + 4 = (x-1)\left(x^4 - 2x^3 - 3x^2 + 8x - 4\right)$. Continuing with the quotient, we have

$$
\begin{array}{r|rrrrr}
1 & 1 & -2 & -3 & 8 & -4 \\
  &   & 1 & -1 & -4 & 4 \\
\hline
  & 1 & -1 & -4 & 4 & 0
\end{array}
\Rightarrow x = 1 \text{ is a zero.}
$$

$$
\begin{aligned}
x^5 - 3x^4 - x^3 + 11x^2 - 12x + 4 &= (x-1)^2\left(x^3 - x^2 - 4x + 4\right) = (x-1)^3\left(x^2 - 4\right) \\
&= (x-1)^3(x-2)(x+2)
\end{aligned}
$$

Therefore, the zeros are 1 (multiplicity 3), -2, and 2.

56. $P(x) = x^4 - 81 = \left(x^2 - 9\right)\left(x^2 + 9\right) = (x-3)(x+3)\left(x^2 + 9\right) = (x-3)(x+3)(x-3i)(x+3i)$. Thus, the zeros are $\pm 3, \pm 3i$.

57. $P(x) = x^6 - 64 = (x^3 - 8)(x^3 + 8) = (x - 2)(x^2 + 2x + 4)(x + 2)(x^2 - 2x + 4)$. Now using the quadratic formula to find the zeros of $x^2 + 2x + 4$, we have

$x = \frac{-2 \pm \sqrt{4 - 4(4)(1)}}{2} = \frac{-2 \pm 2\sqrt{3}i}{2} = -1 \pm \sqrt{3}i$, and using the quadratic formula to find the zeros of $x^2 - 2x + 4$, we have

$x = \frac{2 \pm \sqrt{4 - 4(4)(1)}}{2} = \frac{2 \pm 2\sqrt{3}i}{2} = 1 \pm \sqrt{3}i$. Therefore, the zeros are $2, -2, 1 \pm \sqrt{3}i$, and $-1 \pm \sqrt{3}i$.

58. $P(x) = 18x^3 + 3x^2 - 4x - 1$ has possible rational zeros $\pm 1, \pm \frac{1}{2}, \pm \frac{1}{3}, \pm \frac{1}{6}, \pm \frac{1}{9}, \pm \frac{1}{18}$.

$$
\begin{array}{r|rrrr}
1 & 18 & 3 & -4 & -1 \\
  &   & 18 & 21 & 17 \\
\hline
  & 18 & 21 & 17 & 16 \\
\end{array}
\Rightarrow x = 1 \text{ is an upper bound.}
$$

$$
\begin{array}{r|rrrr}
\frac{1}{2} & 18 & 3 & -4 & -1 \\
  &   & 9 & 6 & 1 \\
\hline
  & 18 & 12 & 2 & 0 \\
\end{array}
\Rightarrow x = \frac{1}{2} \text{ is a zero.}
$$

So $P(x) = 18x^3 + 3x^2 - 4x - 1 = (2x - 1)(9x^2 + 6x + 1) = (2x - 1)(3x + 1)^2$. Thus the zeros are $\frac{1}{2}$ and $-\frac{1}{3}$ (multiplicity 2).

59. $P(x) = 6x^4 - 18x^3 + 6x^2 - 30x + 36 = 6(x^4 - 3x^3 + x^2 - 5x + 6)$ has possible rational zeros $\pm 1, \pm 2, \pm 3, \pm 6$.

$$
\begin{array}{r|rrrrr}
1 & 6 & -18 & 6 & -30 & 36 \\
  &   & 6 & -12 & -6 & -36 \\
\hline
  & 6 & -12 & -6 & -36 & 0 \\
\end{array}
\Rightarrow x = 1 \text{ is a zero.}
$$

So $P(x) = 6x^4 - 18x^3 + 6x^2 - 30x + 36 = (x - 1)(6x^3 - 12x^2 - 6x - 36) = 6(x - 1)(x^3 - 2x^2 - x - 6)$. Continuing with the quotient we have

$$
\begin{array}{r|rrrr}
1 & 1 & -2 & -1 & -6 \\
  &   & 1 & -1 & -2 \\
\hline
  & 1 & -1 & -2 & -8 \\
\end{array}
\qquad
\begin{array}{r|rrrr}
2 & 1 & -2 & -1 & -6 \\
  &   & 2 & 0 & -2 \\
\hline
  & 1 & 0 & -1 & -8 \\
\end{array}
\qquad
\begin{array}{r|rrrr}
3 & 1 & -2 & -1 & -6 \\
  &   & 3 & 3 & 6 \\
\hline
  & 1 & 1 & 2 & 0 \\
\end{array}
\Rightarrow x = 3 \text{ is a zero.}
$$

So $P(x) = 6x^4 - 18x^3 + 6x^2 - 30x + 36 = 6(x - 1)(x - 3)(x^2 + x + 2)$. Now $x^2 + x + 2 = 0$ when

$x = \frac{-1 \pm \sqrt{1 - 4(1)(2)}}{2} = \frac{-1 \pm \sqrt{7}i}{2}$, and so the zeros are $1, 3$, and $\frac{-1 \pm \sqrt{7}i}{2}$.

60. $P(x) = x^4 + 15x^2 + 54 = (x^2 + 9)(x^2 + 6)$. If $x^2 = -9$, then $x = \pm 3i$. If $x^2 = -6$, then $x = \pm\sqrt{6}i$. Therefore, the zeros are $\pm 3i$ and $\pm\sqrt{6}i$.

61. $2x^2 = 5x + 3 \quad \Leftrightarrow \quad 2x^2 - 5x - 3 = 0$. The solutions are $x = -0.5, 3$.

62. Let $P(x) = x^3 + x^2 - 14x - 24$. The solutions to $P(x) = 0$ are $x = -3, -2$, and 4.

63. $x^4 - 3x^3 - 3x^2 - 9x - 2 = 0$ has solutions $x \approx -0.24$, 4.24.

64. $x^5 = x + 3 \quad \Leftrightarrow \quad x^5 - x - 3 = 0$. We graph $P(x) = x^5 - x - 3$. The only real solution is 1.34.

65. $r(x) = \dfrac{3x - 12}{x + 1}$. When $x = 0$, we have $r(0) = \dfrac{-12}{1} = -12$, so the y-intercept is -12. Since $y = 0$, when $3x - 12 = 0 \quad \Leftrightarrow \quad x = 4$, the x-intercept is 4. The vertical asymptote is $x = -1$. Because the degree of the denominator and numerator are the same, the horizontal asymptote is $y = \frac{3}{1} = 3$.

66. $r(x) = \dfrac{1}{(x + 2)^2}$. When $x = 0$, we have $r(0) = \dfrac{1}{2^2} = \frac{1}{4}$, so the y-intercept is $\frac{1}{4}$. Since the numerator is 1, y never equals zero and there is no x-intercept. There is a vertical asymptote at $x = -2$. The horizontal asymptote is $y = 0$ because the degree of the denominator is greater than the degree of the numerator.

67. $r(x) = \dfrac{x - 2}{x^2 - 2x - 8} = \dfrac{x - 2}{(x + 2)(x - 4)}$. When $x = 0$, we have $r(0) = \frac{-2}{-8} = \frac{1}{4}$, so the y-intercept is $\frac{1}{4}$. When $y = 0$, we have $x - 2 = 0 \quad \Leftrightarrow \quad x = 2$, so the x-intercept is 2. There are vertical asymptotes at $x = -2$ and $x = 4$.

68. $r(x) = \dfrac{2x^2 - 6x - 7}{x - 4}$. When $x = 0$, we have $r(0) = \dfrac{-7}{-4} = \dfrac{7}{4}$, so the y-intercept

is $y = \dfrac{7}{4}$. We use the quadratic formula to find the x-intercepts:

$x = \dfrac{-(-6) \pm \sqrt{(-6)^2 - 4(2)(-7)}}{2(2)} = \dfrac{6 \pm \sqrt{92}}{4} = \dfrac{3 \pm \sqrt{23}}{2}$. Thus the x-intercepts are

$x \approx 3.9$ and $x \approx -0.9$. The vertical asymptote is $x = 4$. Because the degree of the

numerator is greater than the degree of the denominator, there is no horizontal

asymptote. By long division, we have $r(x) = 2x + 2 + \dfrac{1}{x - 4}$, so the slant

asymptote is $r(x) = 2x + 2$.

69. $r(x) = \dfrac{x^2 - 9}{2x^2 + 1} = \dfrac{(x + 3)(x - 3)}{2x^2 + 1}$. When $x = 0$, we have $r(0) = \dfrac{-9}{1}$, so the

y-intercept is -9. When $y = 0$, we have $x^2 - 9 = 0 \quad \Leftrightarrow \quad x = \pm 3$ so the

x-intercepts are -3 and 3. Since $2x^2 + 1 > 0$, the denominator is never zero so

there are no vertical asymptotes. The horizontal asymptote is at $y = \dfrac{1}{2}$ because the

degree of the denominator and numerator are the same.

70. $r(x) = \dfrac{x^3 + 27}{x + 4}$. When $x = 0$, we have $r(0) = \dfrac{27}{4}$, so the y-intercept is $y = \dfrac{27}{4}$.

When $y = 0$, we have $x^3 + 27 = 0 \quad \Leftrightarrow \quad x^3 = -27 \Rightarrow x = -3$. Thus the

x-intercept is $x = -3$. The vertical asymptote is $x = -4$. Because the degree of

the numerator is greater than the degree of the denominator, there is no horizontal

asymptote. By long division, we have $r(x) = x^2 - 4x + 16 - \dfrac{37}{x + 4}$. So the end

behavior of y is like the end behavior of $g(x) = x^2 - 4x - 16$.

71. $r(x) = \dfrac{x - 3}{2x + 6}$. From the graph we see that the

x-intercept is 3, the y-intercept is -0.5, there is a vertical

asymptote at $x = -3$ and a horizontal asymptote at

$y = 0.5$, and there is no local extremum.

72. $r(x) = \dfrac{2x - 7}{x^2 + 9}$. From the graph we see that the

x-intercept is 3.5, the y-intercept is -0.78, there is a

horizontal asymptote at $y = 0$ and no vertical asymptote,

the local minimum is $(-1.11, -0.90)$, and the local

maximum is $(8.11, 0.12)$.

73. $r(x) = \dfrac{x^3 + 8}{x^2 - x - 2}$. From the graph we see that the x-intercept is -2, the

y-intercept is -4, there are vertical asymptotes at $x = -1$ and $x = 2$ and a

horizontal asymptote at $y = 0.5$. r has a local maximum of $(0.425, -3.599)$ and a

local minimum of $(4.216, 7.175)$. By using long division, we see that

$f(x) = x + 1 + \dfrac{10 - x}{x^2 - x - 2}$, so f has a slant asymptote of $y = x + 1$.

74. $r(x) = \dfrac{2x^3 - x^2}{x + 1}$. From the graph we see that the x-intercepts: are 0 and $\frac{1}{2}$, the

y-intercept is 0, there is a vertical asymptote at $x = -1$, the local minimum is

$(0.425, -3.599)$ and the local maxima are $(-1.57, 17.90)$ and $(0.32, -0.03)$.

Using long division, we see that $r(x) = 2x^2 - 3x + 3 - \dfrac{3}{x + 1}$. So the end

behavior of r is the same as the end behavior of $g(x) = 2x^2 - 3x + 3$.

75. The graphs of $y = x^4 + x^2 + 24x$ and $y = 6x^3 + 20$ intersect when $x^4 + x^2 + 24x = 6x^3 + 20$ $\Leftrightarrow$

$x^4 - 6x^3 + x^2 + 24x - 20 = 0$. The possible rational zeros are $\pm 1, \pm 2, \pm 4, \pm 5, \pm 10, \pm 20$.

$$
\begin{array}{r|rrrrr}
1 & 1 & -6 & 1 & 24 & -20 \\
  &   & 1 & -5 & -4 & 20 \\
\hline
  & 1 & -5 & -4 & 20 & 0 \quad \Rightarrow x = 1 \text{ is a zero.}
\end{array}
$$

So $x^4 - 6x^3 + x^2 + 24x - 20 = (x - 1)(x^3 - 5x^2 - 4x + 20) = 0$. Continuing with the quotient:

$$
\begin{array}{r|rrrr}
1 & 1 & -5 & -4 & 20 \\
  &   & 1 & -4 & -8 \\
\hline
  & 1 & -4 & -8 & 12
\end{array}
\qquad
\begin{array}{r|rrrr}
2 & 1 & -5 & -4 & 20 \\
  &   & 2 & -6 & -20 \\
\hline
  & 1 & -3 & -10 & 0 \quad \Rightarrow x = 2 \text{ is a zero.}
\end{array}
$$

So $x^4 - 6x^3 + x^2 + 24x - 20 = (x - 1)(x - 2)(x^2 - 3x - 10) = (x - 1)(x - 2)(x - 5)(x + 2) = 0$. Hence, the

points of intersection are $(1, 26)$, $(2, 68)$, $(5, 770)$, and $(-2, -28)$.

Chapter 3 Test

1. $f(x) = -(x+2)^3 + 27$ has y-intercept $y = -2^3 + 27 = 19$ and x-intercept where $-(x+2)^3 = -27 \iff x = 1$.

2. (a)

$$
\begin{array}{r|rrrrr}
2 & 1 & 0 & -4 & 2 & 5 \\
  &   & 2 & 4 & 0 & 4 \\
\hline
  & 1 & 2 & 0 & 2 & 9
\end{array}
$$

Therefore, the quotient is

$Q(x) = x^3 + 2x^2 + 2$, and the remainder is

$R(x) = 9$.

(b)

$$
\begin{array}{r}
x^3 + 2x^2 \qquad\quad + \tfrac{1}{2} \\
2x^2 - 1 \overline{\smash{\big)}\, 2x^5 + 4x^4 - x^3 - x^2 + 0x + 7} \\
\underline{2x^5 \qquad\quad - x^3} \\
4x^4 \qquad\quad - x^2 \\
\underline{4x^4 \qquad\quad - 2x^2} \\
x^2 \quad\; + 7 \\
\underline{x^2 \quad\; - \tfrac{1}{2}} \\
\tfrac{15}{2}
\end{array}
$$

Therefore, the quotient is $Q(x) = x^3 + 2x^2 + \tfrac{1}{2}$ and the remainder is $R(x) = \tfrac{15}{2}$.

3. (a) Possible rational zeros are: $\pm 1, \pm 3, \pm\tfrac{1}{2}, \pm\tfrac{3}{2}$.

(b)

$$
\begin{array}{r|rrrr}
-1 & 2 & -5 & -4 & 3 \\
   &   & -2 & 7 & -3 \\
\hline
   & 2 & -7 & 3 & 0
\end{array}
\quad \Rightarrow x = -1 \text{ is a zero.}
$$

$P(x) = (x+1)(2x^2 - 7x + 3) = (x+1)(2x-1)(x-3)$
$\qquad = 2(x+1)\left(x - \tfrac{1}{2}\right)(x-3)$

(c) The zeros of P are $x = -1, 3, \tfrac{1}{2}$.

4. (a) $(3 - 2i) + (4 + 3i) = (3 + 4) + (-2 + 3)i = 7 + i$

(b) $(3 - 2i) - (4 + 3i) = (3 - 4) + (-2 - 3)i = -1 - 5i$

(c) $(3 - 2i)(4 + 3i) = 12 + 9i - 8i - 6i^2 = 12 + i - 6(-1) = 18 + i$

(d) $\dfrac{3 - 2i}{4 + 3i} = \dfrac{(3 - 2i)(4 - 3i)}{(4 + 3i)(4 - 3i)} = \dfrac{12 - 17i - 6i^2}{16 - 9i^2} = \dfrac{6}{25} - \dfrac{17}{25}i$

(e) $i^{48} = \left(i^2\right)^{24} = (-1)^{24} = 1$

(f) $\left(\sqrt{2} - \sqrt{-2}\right)\left(\sqrt{8} + \sqrt{-2}\right) = \left(\sqrt{2} - i\sqrt{2}\right)\left(\sqrt{8} + i\sqrt{2}\right) = \sqrt{2}\sqrt{8} + i\left(\sqrt{2}\right)^2 - i\sqrt{2}\sqrt{8} - i^2\left(\sqrt{2}\right)^2$
$\qquad = \sqrt{16} + 2i - \sqrt{16}i + 2 = 6 - 2i$

5. $P(x) = x^3 - x^2 - 4x - 6$. Possible rational zeros are: $\pm 1, \pm 2, \pm 3, \pm 6$.

$$
\begin{array}{r|rrrr}
1 & 1 & -1 & -4 & -6 \\
  &   & 1 & 0 & -4 \\
\hline
  & 1 & 0 & -4 & -10
\end{array}
\qquad
\begin{array}{r|rrrr}
2 & 1 & -1 & -4 & -6 \\
  &   & 2 & 2 & -4 \\
\hline
  & 1 & 1 & -2 & -10
\end{array}
\qquad
\begin{array}{r|rrrr}
3 & 1 & -1 & -4 & -6 \\
  &   & 3 & 6 & 6 \\
\hline
  & 1 & 2 & 2 & 0
\end{array}
\Rightarrow x = 3 \text{ is a zero.}
$$

So $P(x) = (x-3)(x^2 + 2x + 2)$. Using the quadratic formula on the second factor, we have

$$x = \frac{-2 \pm \sqrt{2^2 - 4(1)(2)}}{2(1)} = \frac{-2 \pm \sqrt{-4}}{2} = \frac{-2 \pm 2\sqrt{-1}}{2} = -1 \pm i. \text{ So zeros of } P(x) \text{ are } 3, -1 - i, \text{ and } -1 + i.$$

6. $P(x) = x^4 - 2x^3 + 5x^2 - 8x + 4$. The possible rational zeros of P are: $\pm 1, \pm 2,$ and ± 4. Since there are four changes in sign, P has 4, 2, or 0 positive real zeros.

$$
\begin{array}{r|rrrrr}
1 & 1 & -2 & 5 & -8 & 4 \\
  &   & 1 & -1 & 4 & -4 \\
\hline
  & 1 & -1 & 4 & -4 & 0
\end{array}
$$

So $P(x) = (x-1)(x^3 - x^2 + 4x - 4)$. Factoring the second factor by grouping, we have
$$P(x) = (x-1)\left[x^2(x-1) + 4(x-1)\right] = (x-1)(x^2 + 4)(x-1) = (x-1)^2 (x-2i)(x+2i).$$

7. Since $3i$ is a zero of $P(x)$, $-3i$ is also a zero of $P(x)$. And since -1 is a zero of multiplicity 2,
$$P(x) = (x+1)^2(x-3i)(x+3i) = (x^2 + 2x + 1)(x^2 + 9) = x^4 + 2x^3 + 10x^2 + 18x + 9.$$

8. $P(x) = 2x^4 - 7x^3 + x^2 - 18x + 3$.

(a) Since $P(x)$ has 4 variations in sign, $P(x)$ can have 4, 2, or 0 positive real zeros. Since $P(-x) = 2x^4 + 7x^3 + x^2 + 18x + 3$ has no variations in sign, there are no negative real zeros.

(b)

$$
\begin{array}{r|rrrrr}
4 & 2 & -7 & 1 & -18 & 3 \\
  &   & 8 & 4 & 20 & 8 \\
\hline
  & 2 & 1 & 5 & 2 & 11
\end{array}
$$

Since the last row contains no negative entry, 4 is an upper bound for the real zeros of $P(x)$.

$$
\begin{array}{r|rrrrr}
-1 & 2 & -7 & 1 & -18 & 3 \\
   &   & -1 & 9 & -10 & 28 \\
\hline
   & 2 & -9 & 10 & -28 & 31
\end{array}
$$

Since the last row alternates in sign, -1 is a lower bound for the real zeros of $P(x)$.

(c) Using the upper and lower limit from part (b), we graph $P(x)$ in the viewing rectangle $[-1, 4]$ by $[-1, 1]$. The two real zeros are 0.17 and 3.93.

(d) Local minimum $(2.8, -70.3)$.

9. $r(x) = \dfrac{2x-1}{x^2-x-2}$, $s(x) = \dfrac{x^3+27}{x^2+4}$, $t(x) = \dfrac{x^3-9x}{x+2}$ and $u(x) = \dfrac{x^2+x-6}{x^2-25}$.

(a) $r(x)$ has the horizontal asymptote $y = 0$ because the degree of the denominator is greater than the degree of the numerator. $u(x)$ has the horizontal asymptote $y = \frac{1}{1} = 1$ because the degree of the numerator and the denominator are the same.

(b) The degree of the numerator of $s(x)$ is one more than the degree of the denominator, so s has a slant asymptote.

(c) The denominator of $s(x)$ is never 0, so s has no vertical asymptote.

(d) $u(x) = \dfrac{x^2+x-6}{x^2-25} = \dfrac{(x+3)(x-2)}{(x-5)(x+5)}$. When $x = 0$, we have

$u(x) = \frac{-6}{-25} = \frac{6}{25}$, so the y-intercept is $y = \frac{6}{25}$. When $y = 0$, we have $x = -3$ or $x = 2$, so the x-intercepts are -3 and 2. The vertical asymptotes are $x = -5$ and $x = 5$. The horizontal asymptote occurs at $y = \frac{1}{1} = 1$ because the degree of the denominator and numerator are the same.

(e)

$$
\begin{array}{r}
x^2 - 2x - 5 \\
x+2 \enclose{longdiv}{x^3 + 0x^2 - 9x + 0}\\
\underline{x^3 + 2x^2}\\
-2x^2 - 9x\\
\underline{-2x^2 - 4x}\\
-5x + 0\\
\underline{-5x - 10}\\
-10
\end{array}
$$

Thus $P(x) = x^2 - 2x - 5$ and $t(x) = \dfrac{x^3-9x}{x+2}$ have the same end behavior.

Focus on Modeling: Fitting Polynomial Curves to Data

1. (a) Using a graphing calculator, we obtain the quadratic polynomial

$y = -0.275428x^2 + 19.7485x - 273.5523$ (where miles are measured in thousands).

(b)

Pressure (lb/in²)

(c) Moving the cursor along the path of the polynomial, we find that 35.85 lb/in² gives the longest tire life.

2. (a) Using a graphing calculator, we obtain the quadratic polynomial

$y = -0.2783333x^2 + 18.4655x - 166.732$ (where plants/acre are measured in thousands).

(b)

Density (thousand plants/acre)

(c) Moving the cursor along the path of the polynomial, we find that yield when 37,000 plants are planted per acre is about 135 bushels/acre.

3. (a) Using a graphing calculator, we obtain the cubic polynomial

$y = 0.00203709x^3 - 0.104522x^2$
$\qquad\qquad + 1.966206x + 1.45576.$

(b)

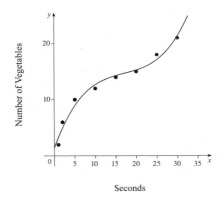

Seconds

(c) Moving the cursor along the path of the polynomial, we find that the subjects could name about 43 vegetables in 40 seconds.

(d) Moving the cursor along the path of the polynomial, we find that the subjects could name 5 vegetables in about 2.0 seconds.

4. (a) Using a graphing calculator, we obtain the quartic polynomial

$y = -0.055907634x^4 + 1.1912474x^3$
$\qquad\qquad - 8.2899063x^2 + 22.2000x + 6.0224$

(where sales are measured in thousands of dollars and January corresponds to $x = 0$, February to $x = 1$, and so forth).

(b)

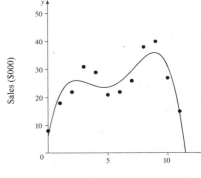

Month (January = 0)

(c) Yes since there appear to be two local maxima and one local minimum.

5. (a)

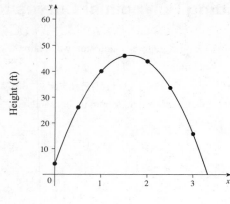

Time (s)

A quadratic model seems appropriate.

(b) Using a graphing calculator, we obtain the quadratic polynomial $y = -16.0x^2 + 51.8429x + 4.20714$.

(c) Moving the cursor along the path of the polynomial, we find that the ball is 20 ft. above the ground 0.3 seconds and 2.9 seconds after it is thrown upward.

(d) Again, moving the cursor along the path of the polynomial, we find that the maximum height is 46.2 ft.

6. (a) Using a graphing calculator, we obtain the quadratic polynomial

$$y = 0.0120536x^2 - 0.490357x + 4.96571.$$

(b)

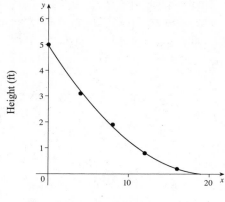

Time (min)

(c) Moving the cursor along the path of the polynomial, we find that the tank should drain is 19.0 minutes.

4 Exponential and Logarithmic Functions

4.1 Exponential Functions

1. $f(x) = 4^x$; $f(0.5) = 2$, $f\left(\sqrt{2}\right) = 7.103$, $f(\pi) = 77.880$, $f\left(\frac{1}{3}\right) = 1.587$

2. $f(x) = 3^{x+1}$; $f(-1.5) = 0.577$, $f\left(\sqrt{3}\right) = 20.115$, $f(e) = 59.439$, $f\left(-\frac{5}{4}\right) = 0.760$

3. $g(x) = \left(\frac{2}{3}\right)^{x-1}$; $g(1.3) = 0.885$, $g\left(\sqrt{5}\right) = 0.606$, $g(2\pi) = 0.117$, $g\left(-\frac{1}{2}\right) = 1.837$

4. $g(x) = \left(\frac{3}{4}\right)^{2x}$; $g(0.7) = 0.668$, $g\left(\frac{\sqrt{7}}{2}\right) = 0.467$, $g\left(\frac{1}{\pi}\right) = 0.833$, $g\left(\frac{2}{3}\right) = 0.681$

5. $f(x) = 2^x$

x	y
-4	$\frac{1}{16}$
-2	$\frac{1}{4}$
0	1
2	4
4	16

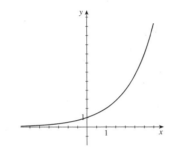

6. $g(x) = 8^x$

x	y
-2	$\frac{1}{64}$
-1	$\frac{1}{8}$
0	1
1	8
2	64

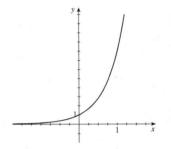

7. $f(x) = \left(\frac{1}{3}\right)^x$

x	y
-2	9
-1	3
0	1
1	$\frac{1}{3}$
2	$\frac{1}{9}$

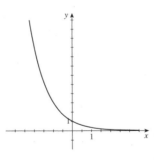

8. $h(x) = (1.1)^x$

x	y
-5	0.620921323
-1	$0.\overline{90}$
0	1
5	1.61051
10	2.59374246

9. $f(x) = 3e^x$

x	y
-2	0.406
-1	1.104
0	3
0.5	4.946
1	8.155
1.5	13.445
2	22.167

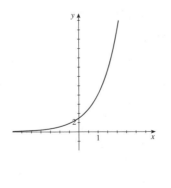

10. $g(x) = 2e^{-0.5x}$

x	y
-4	14.7761
-3	8.96338
-2	5.43656
-1	3.29744
0	2
1	1.21306
2	0.73576
3	0.44626
4	0.27067

11. $f(x) = 2^x$ and $g(x) = 2^{-x}$

12. $f(x) = 3^x$ and $g(x) = \left(\frac{1}{3}\right)^x$

13. $f(x) = 4^x$ and $g(x) = 7^x$.

14. $f(x) = \left(\frac{2}{3}\right)^x$ and $g(x) = \left(\frac{4}{3}\right)^x$.

15. From the graph, $f(2) = a^2 = 9$, so $a = 3$. Thus $f(x) = 3^x$.

16. From the graph, $f(-1) = a^{-1} = \frac{1}{5}$, so $a = 5$. Thus $f(x) = 5^x$.

17. From the graph, $f(2) = a^2 = \frac{1}{16}$, so $a = \frac{1}{4}$. Thus $f(x) = \left(\frac{1}{4}\right)^x$.

18. From the graph, $f(-3) = a^{-3} = 8$, so $a = \frac{1}{2}$. Thus $f(x) = \left(\frac{1}{2}\right)^x$.

19. III   **20.** V   **21.** I   **22.** VI   **23.** II   **24.** IV

25. The graph of $f(x) = -3^x$ is obtained by reflecting the graph of $y = 3^x$ about the x-axis. Domain: $(-\infty, \infty)$. Range: $(-\infty, 0)$. Asymptote: $y = 0$.

26. The graph of $f(x) = 10^{-x}$ is obtained by reflecting the graph of $y = 10^x$ about the y-axis. Domain: $(-\infty, \infty)$. Range: $(0, \infty)$. Asymptote: $y = 0$.

27. $g(x) = 2^x - 3$. The graph of g is obtained by shifting the graph of $y = 2^x$ downward 3 units. Domain: $(-\infty, \infty)$. Range: $(-3, \infty)$. Asymptote: $y = -3$.

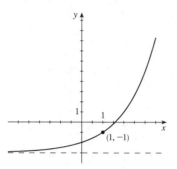

28. $g(x) = 2^{x-3}$. The graph of g is obtained by shifting the graph of $y = 2^x$ to the right 3 units. Domain: $(-\infty, \infty)$. Range: $(0, \infty)$. Asymptote: $y = 0$.

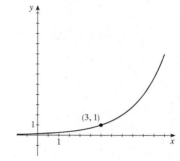

29. $h(x) = 4 + \left(\frac{1}{2}\right)^x$. The graph of h is obtained by shifting the graph of $y = \left(\frac{1}{2}\right)^x$ upward 4 units. Domain: $(-\infty, \infty)$. Range: $(4, \infty)$. Asymptote: $y = 4$.

30. $h(x) = 6 - 3^x$. The graph of h is obtained by reflecting the graph of $y = 3^x$ about the x-axis and shifting upward 6 units. Domain: $(-\infty, \infty)$. Range: $(-\infty, 6)$. Asymptote: $y = 6$.

31. $f(x) = 10^{x+3}$. The graph of f is obtained by shifting the graph of $y = 10^x$ to the left 3 units. Domain: $(-\infty, \infty)$. Range: $(0, \infty)$. Asymptote: $y = 0$.

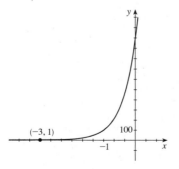

32. $f(x) = -\left(\frac{1}{5}\right)^x$. Note that $f(x) = -\left(\frac{1}{5}\right)^x = -5^{-x}$. So the graph of f is obtained by reflecting the graph of $y = 5^x$ about the y-axis and about the x-axis. Domain: $(-\infty, \infty)$. Range: $(-\infty, 0)$. Asymptote: $y = 0$.

33. $y = -e^x$. The graph of $y = -e^x$ is obtained from the graph of $y = e^x$ by reflecting it about the x-axis. Domain: $(-\infty, \infty)$. Range: $(-\infty, 0)$. Asymptote: $y = 0$.

34. $f(x) = 1 - e^x$. The graph of $f(x) = 1 - e^x$ is obtained by reflecting the graph of $y = e^x$ about the x-axis and then shifting upward 1 unit. Domain: $(-\infty, \infty)$. Range: $(-\infty, 1)$. Asymptote: $y = 1$.

35. $y = e^{-x} - 1$. The graph of $y = e^{-x} - 1$ is obtained from the graph of $y = e^x$ by reflecting it about the y-axis then shifting downward 1 unit. Domain: $(-\infty, \infty)$. Range: $(-1, \infty)$. Asymptote: $y = -1$.

36. $f(x) = -e^{-x}$. The graph of $f(x) = -e^{-x}$ is obtained by reflecting the graph of $y = e^x$ about the y-axis and then about the x-axis. Domain: $(-\infty, \infty)$. Range: $(-\infty, 0)$. Asymptote: $y = 0$.

37. $y = e^{x-2}$. The graph of $y = e^{x-2}$ is obtained from the graph of $y = e^x$ by shifting it to the right 2 units. Domain: $(-\infty, \infty)$. Range: $(0, \infty)$. Asymptote: $y = 0$.

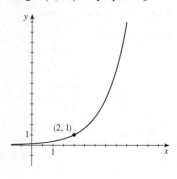

38. $f(x) = e^{x-3} + 4$. The graph of $f(x) = e^{x-3} + 4$ is obtained by shifting the graph of $y = e^x$ to the right 3 units, and then upward 4 units. Domain: $(-\infty, \infty)$. Range: $(4, \infty)$. Asymptote: $y = 4$.

39. Using the points $(0, 3)$ and $(2, 12)$, we have $f(0) = Ca^0 = 3 \iff C = 3$. We also have $f(2) = 3a^2 = 12 \iff a^2 = 4 \iff a = 2$ (recall that for an exponential function $f(x) = a^x$ we require $a > 0$). Thus $f(x) = 3 \cdot 2^x$.

40. Using the points $(-1, 15)$ and $(0, 5)$ we have $f(0) = Ca^0 = 5$ $\Leftrightarrow$ $C = 5$. Then $f(-1) = 5a^{-1} = 15$ $\Leftrightarrow$ $a^{-1} = 3$ $\Leftrightarrow$ $a = \frac{1}{3}$. Thus $f(x) = 5\left(\frac{1}{3}\right)^x$.

41. (a)

42. (a)

(b) Since $g(x) = 3(2^x) = 3f(x)$ and $f(x) > 0$, the height of the graph of $g(x)$ is always three times the height of the graph of $f(x) = 2^x$, so the graph of g is steeper than the graph of f.

(b) $f(x) = 9^{x/2} = \left(3^2\right)^{x/2} = 3^{2 \cdot x/2} = 3^x = g(x)$. So $f(x) = g(x)$, and the graphs are the same.

43. $f(x) = 10^x$, so $\dfrac{f(x+h) - f(x)}{h} = \dfrac{10^{x+h} - 10^x}{h} = \dfrac{10^x \cdot 10^h - 10^x}{h} = 10^x \dfrac{10^h - 1}{h}$.

44.

x	$f(x) = x^3$	$g(x) = 3^x$
0	0	1
1	1	3
2	8	9
3	27	27
4	64	81
5	125	243
6	216	729
7	343	2187
8	512	6561
9	729	19,683
10	1000	59,049
15	3375	14,348,907
20	8000	3,486,784,401

45.

46.

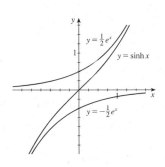

47. $\cosh(-x) = \dfrac{e^{-x} + e^{-(-x)}}{2} = \dfrac{e^{-x} + e^{x}}{2} = \dfrac{e^{x} + e^{-x}}{2} = \cosh x$

48. $\sinh(-x) = \dfrac{e^{-x} - e^{-(-x)}}{2} = \dfrac{e^{-x} - e^{x}}{2} = \dfrac{-e^{-x} + e^{x}}{2} = -\dfrac{e^{x} - e^{-x}}{2} = -\sinh x$

49. $(\cosh x)^2 - (\sinh x)^2 = \left(\dfrac{e^x + e^{-x}}{2}\right)^2 - \left(\dfrac{e^x - e^{-x}}{2}\right)^2 = \frac{1}{4}\left(e^{2x} + 2 + e^{-2x}\right) - \frac{1}{4}\left(e^{2x} - 2 + e^{-2x}\right) = \frac{2}{4} + \frac{2}{4} = 1$

50. $\sinh x \cosh y + \cosh x \sinh y = \dfrac{e^x - e^{-x}}{2} \cdot \dfrac{e^y + e^{-y}}{2} + \dfrac{e^x + e^{-x}}{2} \cdot \dfrac{e^y - e^{-y}}{2}$

$$= \dfrac{e^{x+y} + e^{x-y} - e^{y-x} - e^{-(x+y)}}{4} + \dfrac{e^{x+y} - e^{x-y} + e^{y-x} - e^{-(x+y)}}{4} = \dfrac{e^{x+y} - e^{-(x+y)}}{2} = \sinh(x+y)$$

51. (a) From the graphs below, we see that the graph of f ultimately increases much more quickly than the graph of g.

(i) $[0, 5]$ by $[0, 20]$

(ii) $[0, 25]$ by $[0, 10^7]$

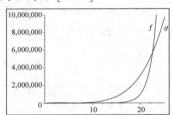

(iii) $[0, 50]$ by $[0, 10^8]$

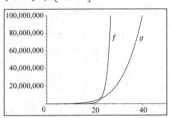

(b) From the graphs in parts (a)(i) and (a)(ii), we see that the approximate solutions are $x \approx 1.2$ and $x \approx 22.4$.

52. (a) (i) $[-4, 4]$ by $[0, 20]$

(ii) $[0, 10]$ by $[0, 5000]$

(iii) $[0, 20]$ by $[0, 10^5]$

(b) From the graphs in parts (i) and (ii), we see that the solutions of $3^x = x^4$ are $x \approx -0.80$, $x \approx 1.52$ and $x \approx 7.17$.

53.

54.

The larger the value of c, the more rapidly the graph of $f(x) = c2^x$ increases. Also notice that the graphs are just shifted horizontally 1 unit. This is because of our choice of c; each c in this exercise is of the form 2^k. So $f(x) = 2^k \cdot 2^x = 2^{x+k}$.

The larger the value of c, the more rapidly the graph of $f(x) = 2^{cx}$ increases. In general, $f(x) = 2^{cx} = (2^c)^x$; so, for example, $f(x) = 2^{2x} = (2^2)^x = 4^x$.

55.

Note from the graph that $y = [1 + (1/x)]^x$ approaches e as x get large.

56.

From the graph, we see that $f(x) = [1 - (1/x)]^x$ approaches $1/e \approx 0.368$ as x get large.

57. (a)

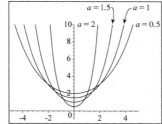

(b) As a increases the curve $y = \dfrac{a}{2}\left(e^{x/a} + e^{-x/a}\right)$

flattens out and the y intercept increases.

58. $y = 2^{1/x}$ has vertical asymptote $x = 0$ and horizontal asymptote $y = 1$.

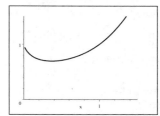

59. $y = \dfrac{e^x}{x}$ has vertical asymptote $x = 0$ and horizontal asymptote $y = 0$. As $x \to -\infty$, $y \to 0$, and as $x \to \infty$, $y \to \infty$.

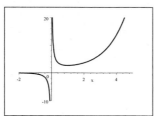

60. $g(x) = x^x$. Notice that $g(x)$ is only defined for $x \ge 0$. The graph of $g(x)$ is shown in the viewing rectangle $[0, 1.5]$ by $[0, 1.5]$. From the graph, we see that there is a local minimum of about 0.69 when $x \approx 0.37$.

61. $g(x) = e^x + e^{-3x}$. The graph of $g(x)$ is shown in the viewing rectangle $[-4, 4]$ by $[0, 20]$. From the graph, we see that there is a local minimum of approximately 1.75 when $x \approx 0.27$.

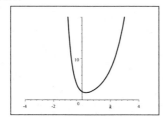

62. $y = 10^{x - x^2}$

(a) From the graph, we see that the function is increasing on $(-\infty, 0.50]$ and decreasing on $[0.50, \infty)$.

(b) From the graph, we see that the range is approximately $(0, 1.78]$.

63. $y = xe^{-x}$

(a) From the graph, we see that the function $f(x) = xe^x$ is increasing on $(-\infty, 1]$ and decreasing on $[1, \infty)$.

(b) From the graph, we see that the range is approximately $(-\infty, 0.37)$.

64. $D(t) = 50e^{-0.2t}$. So when $t = 3$ we have $D(3) = 50e^{-0.2(3)} \approx 27.4$ milligrams.

65. $m(t) = 13e^{-0.015t}$

(a) $m(0) = 13$ kg.

(b) $m(45) = 13e^{-0.015(45)} = 13e^{-0.675} = 6.619$ kg. Thus the mass of the radioactive substance after 45 days is about 6.6 kg.

66. (a) $m(0) = 6e^{-0.087(0)} \approx 6$ grams

(b) $m(20) = 6e^{-0.087(20)} \approx 6(0.1755) = 1.053$. Thus approximately 1 gram of radioactive iodine remains after 20 days.

67. $v(t) = 80\left(1 - e^{-0.2t}\right)$

(a) $v(0) = 80\left(1 - e^0\right) = 80(1 - 1) = 0$.

(b) $v(5) = 80\left(1 - e^{-0.2(5)}\right) \approx 80(0.632) = 50.57$ ft/s. So the velocity after 5 s is about 50.6 ft/s.

$v(10) = 80\left(1 - e^{-0.2(10)}\right) \approx 80(0.865) = 69.2$ ft/s. So the velocity after 10 s is about 69.2 ft/s.

(d) The terminal velocity is 80 ft/s.

(c)

68. (a) $Q(5) = 15\left(1 - e^{-0.04(5)}\right) \approx 15(0.1813) = 2.7345$. Thus approximately 2.7 lb of salt are in the barrel after 5 minutes.

(b) $Q(10) = 15\left(1 - e^{-0.04(10)}\right) \approx 15(0.3297) = 4.946$. Thus approximately 4.9 lb of salt are in the barrel after 10 minutes.

(d) The amount of salt approaches 15 lb. This is to be expected, since $50 \text{ gal} \times 0.3 \text{ lb/gal} = 15$ lb.

(c)

69. $P(t) = \dfrac{1200}{1 + 11e^{-0.2t}}$

(a) $P(0) = \dfrac{1200}{1 + 11e^{-0.2(0)}} = \dfrac{1200}{1 + 11} = 100$.

(b) $P(10) = \dfrac{1200}{1 + 11e^{-0.2(10)}} \approx 482$. $P(20) = \dfrac{1200}{1 + 11e^{-0.2(20)}} \approx 999$. $P(30) = \dfrac{1200}{1 + 11e^{-0.2(30)}} \approx 1168$.

(c) As $t \to \infty$ we have $e^{-0.2t} \to 0$, so $P(t) \to \dfrac{1200}{1 + 0} = 1200$. The graph shown confirms this.

70. $n(t) = \dfrac{5600}{0.5 + 27.5e^{-0.044t}}$

(b)

(a) $n(0) = \frac{5600}{28} = 200$

(c) From the graph, we see that $n(t)$ approaches about 11,200 as t gets large.

71. $D(t) = \dfrac{5.4}{1 + 2.9e^{-0.01t}}$. So $D(20) = \dfrac{5.4}{1 + 2.9e^{-0.01(20)}} \approx 1.600$ ft.

72. (a) Substituting $n_0 = 50$ and $t = 12$, we have

$$n(12) = \dfrac{300}{0.05 + \left(\frac{300}{50} - 0.05\right)e^{-0.55(12)}} \approx 5164.$$

(b)

(c) The population approaches 6000 rabbits.

73. Using the formula $A(t) = P(1 + i)^k$ with $P = 5000$, $i = 4\%$ per year $= \dfrac{0.04}{12}$ per month, and $k = 12 \cdot$ number of years, we fill in the table:

Time (years)	Amount
1	$5203.71
2	$5415.71
3	$5636.36
4	$5865.99
5	$6104.98
6	$6353.71

74. Using the formula $A(t) = P(1 + i)^k$ with $P = 5000$, $i = \dfrac{\text{rate per year}}{12}$ per month, and $k = 12 \cdot 5 = 60$ months, we fill in the table:

Rate per year	Amount
1%	$5256.25
2%	$5525.39
3%	$5808.08
4%	$6104.98
5%	$6416.79
6%	$6744.25

75. $P = 10,000$, $r = 0.10$, and $n = 2$. So $A(t) = 10,000\left(1 + \frac{0.10}{2}\right)^{2t} = 10,000 \cdot 1.05^{2t}$.

(a) $A(5) = 10,000 \cdot 1.05^{10} \approx 16,288.95$, and so the value of the investment is $16,288.95.

(b) $A(10) = 10,000 \cdot 1.05^{20} \approx 26,532.98$, and so the value of the investment is $26,532.98.

(c) $A(15) = 10,000 \cdot 1.05^{30} \approx 43,219.42$, and so the value of the investment is $43,219.42.

76. $P = 4,000$, $r = 0.16$, and $n = 4$. So $A(t) = 4000\left(1 + \frac{0.16}{4}\right)^{4t} = 4000 \cdot 1.04^{4t}$.

(a) $A(4) = 4000 \cdot (1.04)^{16} \approx 7491.92$, and so the amount due is $7,491.92.

(b) $A(6) = 4000 \cdot (1.04)^{24} \approx 10,253.22$, and so the amount due is $10,253.22.

(c) $A(8) = 4000 \cdot (1.04)^{32} \approx 14,032.23$, and so the amount due is $14,032.23.

77. $P = 3000$ and $r = 0.09$. Then we have $A(t) = 3000\left(1 + \dfrac{0.09}{n}\right)^{nt}$, and so $A(5) = 3000\left(1 + \dfrac{0.09}{n}\right)^{5n}$.

(a) If $n = 1$, $A(5) = 3000\left(1 + \frac{0.09}{1}\right)^{5} = 3000 \cdot 1.09^5 \approx \$4,615.87$.

(b) If $n = 2$, $A(5) = 3000\left(1 + \frac{0.09}{2}\right)^{10} = 3000 \cdot 1.045^{10} \approx \$4,658.91$.

(c) If $n = 12$, $A(5) = 3000\left(1 + \frac{0.09}{12}\right)^{60} = 3000 \cdot 1.0075^{60} \approx \$4,697.04$.

(d) If $n = 52$, $A(5) = 3000\left(1 + \frac{0.09}{52}\right)^{260} \approx \$4,703.11$.

(e) If $n = 365$, $A(5) = 3000\left(1 + \frac{0.09}{365}\right)^{1825} \approx \$4{,}704.68$.

(f) If $n = 24 \cdot 365 = 8760$, $A(5) = 3000\left(1 + \frac{0.09}{8760}\right)^{43800} \approx \$4{,}704.93$.

(g) If interest is compounded continuously, $A(5) = 3000 \cdot e^{0.45} \approx \$4{,}704.94$.

78. $P = 4000$, $n = 4$, and $t = 5$. Then $A(5) = 4000\left(1 + \frac{r}{4}\right)^{4(5)}$, and so $A(5) = 4000\left(1 + \frac{r}{4}\right)^{20}$.

(a) If $r = 0.06$, $A(5) = 4000\left(1 + \frac{0.06}{4}\right)^{20} = 4000 \cdot (1.015)^{20} \approx \$5{,}387.42$.

(b) If $r = 0.065$, $A(5) = 4000\left(1 + \frac{0.065}{4}\right)^{20} = 4000 \cdot (1.01625)^{20} \approx \$5{,}521.68$.

(c) If $r = 0.07$, $A(5) = 4000\left(1 + \frac{0.07}{4}\right)^{20} = 4000 \cdot (1.0175)^{20} \approx \$5{,}659.11$.

(d) If $r = 0.08$, $A(5) = 4000\left(1 + \frac{0.08}{4}\right)^{20} = 4000 \cdot (1.02)^{20} \approx \$5{,}943.79$.

79. We find the effective rate with $P = 1$ and $t = 1$. So $A = \left(1 + \frac{r}{n}\right)^{n}$

(i) $n = 2$, $r = 0.085$; $A(2) = \left(1 + \frac{0.085}{2}\right)^{2} = (1.0425)^{2} \approx 1.0868$.

(ii) $n = 4$, $r = 0.0825$; $A(4) = \left(1 + \frac{0.0825}{4}\right)^{4} = (1.020625)^{4} \approx 1.0851$.

(iii) Continuous compounding: $r = 0.08$; $A(1) = e^{0.08} \approx 1.0833$.

Since (i) is larger than the others, the best investment is the one at 8.5% compounded semiannually.

80. We find the effective rate for $P = 1$ and $t = 1$.

(i) If $r = 0.0925$ and $n = 2$, then $A(2) = \left(1 + \frac{0.0925}{2}\right)^{2} = (1.04625)^{2} \approx 1.0946$.

(ii) If $r = 0.09$ and interest is compounded continuously, then $A(1) = e^{0.09} \approx 1.0942$.

Since the effective rate in (i) is greater than the effective rate in (ii), we can see that the account paying $9\frac{1}{4}\%$ per year compounded semiannually is the better investment.

81. (a) We must solve for P in the equation $10000 = P\left(1 + \frac{0.09}{2}\right)^{2(3)} = P(1.045)^{6}$ ⟺ $10000 = 1.3023P$ ⟺ $P = 7678.96$. Thus the present value is $\$7{,}678.96$.

(b) We must solve for P in the equation $100000 = P\left(1 + \frac{0.08}{12}\right)^{12(5)} = P(1.00667)^{60}$ ⟺ $100000 = 1.4898P$ ⟺ $P = \$67{,}121.04$.

82. (a) $A(t) = 5000\left(1 + \frac{0.09}{2}\right)^{2t} = 5000\,(1.045)^{2t} = 5000\,(1.092025)^{t}$.   **(b)**

(c) $A(t) = 25000$ when $t \approx 18.28$ years.

83. (a) In this case the payment is $\$1$ million.

(b) In this case the total pay is $2 + 2^{2} + 2^{3} + \cdots + 2^{30} > 2^{30}$ cents $= \$10{,}737{,}418.24$. Since this is much more than method (a), method (b) is more profitable.

84. Since $f(40) = 2^{40} = 1{,}099{,}511{,}627{,}776$, it would take a sheet of paper 4 inches by $1{,}099{,}511{,}627{,}776$ inches. Since there are 12 inches in a foot and 5,280 feet in a mile, $1{,}099{,}511{,}627{,}776$ inches ≈ 1.74 million miles. So the dimensions of the sheet of paper required are 4 inches by about 1.74 million miles.

4.2 Logarithmic Functions

1.

Logarithmic form	Exponential form
$\log_8 8 = 1$	$8^1 = 8$
$\log_8 64 = 2$	$8^2 = 64$
$\log_8 4 = \frac{2}{3}$	$8^{2/3} = 4$
$\log_8 512 = 3$	$8^3 = 512$
$\log_8 \frac{1}{8} = -1$	$8^{-1} = \frac{1}{8}$
$\log_8 \frac{1}{64} = -2$	$8^{-2} = \frac{1}{64}$

2.

Logarithmic form	Exponential form
$\log_4 64 = 3$	$4^3 = 64$
$\log_4 2 = \frac{1}{2}$	$4^{1/2} = 2$
$\log_4 8 = \frac{3}{2}$	$4^{3/2} = 8$
$\log_4 \frac{1}{16} = -2$	$4^{-2} = \frac{1}{16}$
$\log_4 \frac{1}{2} = -\frac{1}{2}$	$4^{-1/2} = \frac{1}{2}$
$\log_4 \frac{1}{32} = -\frac{5}{2}$	$4^{-5/2} = \frac{1}{32}$

3. (a) $5^2 = 25$
   (b) $5^0 = 1$

4. (a) $10^{-1} = 0.1$
   (b) $8^3 = 512$

5. (a) $8^{1/3} = 2$
   (b) $2^{-3} = \frac{1}{8}$

6. (a) $3^4 = 81$
   (b) $8^{2/3} = 4$

7. (a) $e^x = 5$
   (b) $e^5 = y$

8. (a) $e^2 = x + 1$
   (b) $e^4 = x - 1$

9. (a) $\log_5 125 = 3$
   (b) $\log_{10} 0.0001 = -4$

10. (a) $\log_{10} 1000 = 3$
   (b) $\log_{81} 9 = \frac{1}{2}$

11. (a) $\log_8 \frac{1}{8} = -1$
   (b) $\log_2 \left(\frac{1}{8}\right) = -3$

12. (a) $\log_4 0.125 = -\frac{3}{2}$
   (b) $\log_7 343 = 3$

13. (a) $\ln 2 = x$
   (b) $\ln y = 3$

14. (a) $\ln 0.5 = x + 1$
   (b) $\ln t = 0.5x$

15. (a) $\log_3 3 = 1$
   (b) $\log_3 1 = \log_3 3^0 = 0$
   (c) $\log_3 3^2 = 2$

16. (a) $\log_5 5^4 = 4$
   (b) $\log_4 64 = \log_4 4^3 = 3$
   (c) $\log_9 9 = 1$

17. (a) $\log_6 36 = \log_6 6^2 = 2$
   (b) $\log_9 81 = \log_9 9^2 = 2$
   (c) $\log_7 7^{10} = 10$

18. (a) $\log_2 32 = \log_2 2^5 = 5$
   (b) $\log_8 8^{17} = 17$
   (c) $\log_6 1 = \log_6 6^0 = 0$

19. (a) $\log_3 \left(\frac{1}{27}\right) = \log_3 3^{-3} = -3$
   (b) $\log_{10} \sqrt{10} = \log_{10} 10^{1/2} = \frac{1}{2}$
   (c) $\log_5 0.2 = \log_5 \left(\frac{1}{5}\right) = \log_5 5^{-1} = -1$

20. (a) $\log_5 125 = \log_5 5^3 = 3$
   (b) $\log_{49} 7 = \log_{49} 49^{1/2} = \frac{1}{2}$
   (c) $\log_9 \sqrt{3} = \log_9 3^{1/2} = \log_9 \left(9^{1/2}\right)^{1/2} = \log_9 9^{1/4}$
   $= \frac{1}{4}$

21. (a) $2^{\log_2 37} = 37$
   (b) $3^{\log_3 8} = 8$
   (c) $e^{\ln \sqrt{5}} = \sqrt{5}$

22. (a) $e^{\ln \pi} = \pi$
   (b) $10^{\log 5} = 5$
   (c) $10^{\log 87} = 87$

23. (a) $\log_8 0.25 = \log_8 8^{-2/3} = -\frac{2}{3}$
   (b) $\ln e^4 = 4$
   (c) $\ln \left(\frac{1}{e}\right) = \ln e^{-1} = -1$

24. (a) $\log_4 \sqrt{2} = \log_4 2^{1/2} = \log_4 \left(4^{1/2}\right)^{1/2} = \log_4 4^{1/4}$
   $= \frac{1}{4}$
   (b) $\log_4 \left(\frac{1}{2}\right) = \log_4 2^{-1} = \log_4 \left(4^{1/2}\right)^{-1} = \log_4 4^{-1/2}$
   $= -\frac{1}{2}$
   (c) $\log_4 8 = \log_4 2^3 = \log_4 \left(4^{1/2}\right)^3 = \log_4 4^{3/2} = \frac{3}{2}$

25. (a) $\log_2 x = 5 \quad \Leftrightarrow \quad x = 2^5 = 32$
   (b) $x = \log_2 16 = \log_2 2^4 = 4$

26. (a) $\log_5 x = 4 \quad \Leftrightarrow \quad x = 5^4 = 625$
   (b) $x = \log_{10} (0.1) = \log_{10} 10^{-1} = -1$

27. (a) $x = \log_3 243 = \log_3 3^5 = 5$

   (b) $\log_3 x = 3 \quad\Leftrightarrow\quad x = 3^3 = 27$

28. (a) $x = \log_4 2 = \log_4 4^{1/2} = \frac{1}{2}$

   (b) $\log_4 x = 2 \quad\Leftrightarrow\quad x = 4^2 = 16$

29. (a) $\log_{10} x = 2 \quad\Leftrightarrow\quad x = 10^2 = 100$

   (b) $\log_5 x = 2 \quad\Leftrightarrow\quad x = 5^2 = 25$

30. (a) $\log_x 1000 = 3 \quad\Leftrightarrow\quad x^3 = 1000 \quad\Leftrightarrow\quad x = 10$

   (b) $\log_x 25 = 2 \quad\Leftrightarrow\quad x^2 = 25 \quad\Leftrightarrow\quad x = 5$

31. (a) $\log_x 16 = 4 \quad\Leftrightarrow\quad x^4 = 16 \quad\Leftrightarrow\quad x = 2$

   (b) $\log_x 8 = \dfrac{3}{2} \quad\Leftrightarrow\quad x^{3/2} = 8 \quad\Leftrightarrow\quad x = 8^{2/3} = 4$

32. (a) $\log_x 6 = \frac{1}{2} \quad\Leftrightarrow\quad x^{1/2} = 6 \quad\Leftrightarrow\quad x = 36$

   (b) $\log_x 3 = \frac{1}{3} \quad\Leftrightarrow\quad x^{1/3} = 3 \quad\Leftrightarrow\quad x = 27$

33. (a) $\log 2 \approx 0.3010$

   (b) $\log 35.2 \approx 1.5465$

   (c) $\log \left(\frac{2}{3}\right) \approx -0.1761$

34. (a) $\log 50 \approx 1.6990$

   (b) $\log \sqrt{2} \approx 0.1505$

   (c) $\log \left(3\sqrt{2}\right) \approx 0.6276$

35. (a) $\ln 5 \approx 1.6094$

   (b) $\ln 25.3 \approx 3.2308$

   (c) $\ln \left(1 + \sqrt{3}\right) \approx 1.0051$

36. (a) $\ln 27 \approx 3.2958$

   (b) $\ln 7.39 \approx 2.0001$

   (c) $\ln 54.6 \approx 4.0000$

37. Since the point $(5, 1)$ is on the graph, we have $1 = \log_a 5 \quad\Leftrightarrow\quad a^1 = 5$. Thus the function is $y = \log_5 x$.

38. Since the point $\left(\frac{1}{2}, -1\right)$ is on the graph, we have $-1 = \log_a \left(\frac{1}{2}\right) \quad\Leftrightarrow\quad a^{-1} = \frac{1}{2} \quad\Leftrightarrow\quad a = 2$. Thus the function is $y = \log_2 x$.

39. Since the point $\left(3, \frac{1}{2}\right)$ is on the graph, we have $\frac{1}{2} = \log_a 3 \quad\Leftrightarrow\quad a^{1/2} = 3 \quad\Leftrightarrow\quad a = 9$. Thus the function is $y = \log_9 x$.

40. Since the point $(9, 2)$ is on the graph, we have $2 = \log_a 9 \quad\Leftrightarrow\quad a^2 = 9 \quad\Leftrightarrow\quad a = 3$. Thus the function is $y = \log_3 x$.

41. II   **42.** V   **43.** III   **44.** IV   **45.** VI   **46.** I

47. The graph of $y = \log_4 x$ is obtained from the graph of $y = 4^x$ by reflecting it about the line $y = x$.

48. The graph of $y = \log_3 x$ is obtained from the graph of $y = 3^x$ by reflecting it about the line $y = x$.

49. $f(x) = \log_2(x - 4)$. The graph of f is obtained from the graph of $y = \log_2 x$ by shifting it to the right 4 units. Domain: $(4, \infty)$. Range: $(-\infty, \infty)$. Vertical asymptote: $x = 4$.

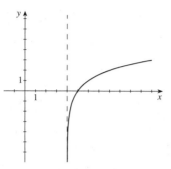

50. $f(x) = -\log_{10} x$. The graph of f is obtained from the graph of $y = \log_{10} x$ by reflecting it about the x-axis. Domain: $(0, \infty)$. Range: $(-\infty, \infty)$. Vertical asymptote: $x = 0$.

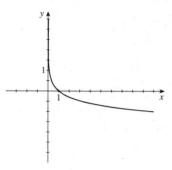

51. $g(x) = \log_5(-x)$. The graph of g is obtained from the graph of $y = \log_5 x$ by reflecting it about the y-axis. Domain: $(-\infty, 0)$. Range: $(-\infty, \infty)$. Vertical asymptote: $x = 0$.

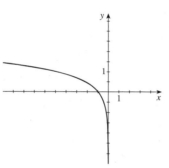

52. $g(x) = \ln(x + 2)$. The graph of g is obtained from the graph of $y = \ln x$ by shifting it to the left 2 units. Domain: $(-2, \infty)$. Range: $(-\infty, \infty)$. Vertical asymptote: $x = -2$.

53. $y = 2 + \log_3 x$. The graph of $y = 2 + \log_3 x$ is obtained from the graph of $y = \log_3 x$ by shifting it upward 2 units. Domain: $(0, \infty)$. Range: $(-\infty, \infty)$. Vertical asymptote: $x = 0$.

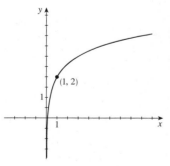

54. $y = \log_3(x - 1) - 2$. The graph of $y = \log_3(x - 1) - 2$ is obtained from the graph of $y = \log_3 x$ by shifting it to the right 1 unit and then downward 2 units. Domain: $(1, \infty)$. Range: $(-\infty, \infty)$. Vertical asymptote: $x = 1$.

55. $y = 1 - \log_{10} x$. The graph of $y = 1 - \log_{10} x$ is obtained from the graph of $y = \log_{10} x$ by reflecting it about the x-axis, and then shifting it upward 1 unit. Domain: $(0, \infty)$. Range: $(-\infty, \infty)$. Vertical asymptote: $x = 0$.

56. $y = 1 + \ln(-x)$. The graph of $y = 1 + \ln(-x)$ is obtained from the graph of $y = \ln x$ by reflecting it about the y-axis and then shifting it upward 1 unit. Domain: $(-\infty, 0)$. Range: $(-\infty, \infty)$. Vertical asymptote: $x = 0$.

57. $y = |\ln x|$. The graph of $y = |\ln x|$ is obtained from the graph of $y = \ln x$ by reflecting the part of the graph for $0 < x < 1$ about the x-axis. Domain: $(0, \infty)$. Range: $[0, \infty)$. Vertical asymptote: $x = 0$.

58. $y = \ln|x|$. Note that $y = \begin{cases} \ln x & \text{if } x > 0 \\ \ln(-x) & \text{if } x < 0 \end{cases}$ The graph of $y = \ln|x|$ is obtained by reflecting the graph of $y = \ln x$ about the x-axis. Domain: $(-\infty, 0) \cup (0, \infty)$. Range: $(-\infty, \infty)$. Vertical asymptote: $x = 0$.

59. $f(x) = \log_{10}(x + 3)$. We require that $x + 3 > 0$ $\Leftrightarrow$ $x > -3$, so the domain is $(-3, \infty)$.

60. $f(x) = \log_5(8 - 2x)$. Then we must have $8 - 2x > 0$ $\Leftrightarrow$ $8 > 2x$ $\Leftrightarrow$ $4 > x$, and so the domain is $(-\infty, 4)$.

61. $g(x) = \log_3(x^2 - 1)$. We require that $x^2 - 1 > 0$ $\Leftrightarrow$ $x^2 > 1 \Rightarrow x < -1$ or $x > 1$, so the domain is $(-\infty, -1) \cup (1, \infty)$.

62. $g(x) = \ln(x - x^2)$. Then we must have $x - x^2 > 0$ $\Leftrightarrow$ $x(1 - x) > 0$. Using the methods from Chapter 1 with the endpoints 0 and 1, we get the table at right. Thus the domain is $(0, 1)$.

Interval	$(-\infty, 0)$	$(0, 1)$	$(1, \infty)$
Sign of x	$-$	$+$	$+$
Sign of $1 - x$	$+$	$+$	$-$
Sign of $x(1 - x)$	$-$	$+$	$-$

63. $h(x) = \ln x + \ln(2 - x)$. We require that $x > 0$ and $2 - x > 0$ $\Leftrightarrow$ $x > 0$ and $x < 2$ $\Leftrightarrow$ $0 < x < 2$, so the domain is $(0, 2)$.

64. $h(x) = \sqrt{x - 2} - \log_5(10 - x)$. Then we must have $x - 2 \geq 0$ and $10 - x > 0$ $\Leftrightarrow$ $x \geq 2$ and $10 > x$ $\Leftrightarrow$ $2 \leq x < 10$. So the domain is $[2, 10)$.

65. $y = \log_{10}\left(1 - x^2\right)$ has domain $(-1, 1)$, vertical asymptotes $x = -1$ and $x = 1$, and local maximum $y = 0$ at $x = 0$.

66. $y = \ln\left(x^2 - x\right) = \ln\left(x\left(x - 1\right)\right)$ has domain $(-\infty, 0) \cup (1, \infty)$, vertical asymptotes $x = 0$ and $x = 1$, and no local maximum or minimum.

67. $y = x + \ln x$ has domain $(0, \infty)$, vertical asymptote $x = 0$, and no local maximum or minimum.

68. $y = x\left(\ln x\right)^2$ has domain $(0, \infty)$, no vertical asymptote, local minimum $y = 0$ at $x = 1$, and local maximum $y \approx 0.54$ at $x \approx 0.14$.

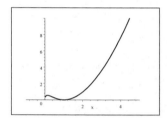

69. $y = \dfrac{\ln x}{x}$ has domain $(0, \infty)$, vertical asymptote $x = 0$, horizontal asymptote $y = 0$, and local maximum $y \approx 0.37$ at $x \approx 2.72$.

70. $y = x \log_{10}\left(x + 10\right)$ has domain $(-10, \infty)$, vertical asymptote $x = -10$, and local minimum $y \approx -3.62$ at $x \approx -5.87$.

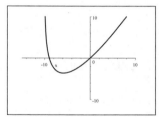

71. The graph of $g\left(x\right) = \sqrt{x}$ grows faster than the graph of $f\left(x\right) = \ln x$.

72. (a)

(b) From the graph, we see that the solution to the equation $\sqrt{x} = 1 + \ln\left(1 + x\right)$ is $x \approx 13.50$.

73. (a)

74. (a)

(b) Notice that $f(x) = \log(cx) = \log c + \log x$, so as c increases, the graph of $f(x) = \log(cx)$ is shifted upward $\log c$ units.

(b) As c increases, the graph of $f(x) = c\log(x)$ stretches vertically by a factor of c.

75. (a) $f(x) = \log_2(\log_{10} x)$. Since the domain of $\log_2 x$ is the positive real numbers, we have: $\log_{10} x > 0 \quad \Leftrightarrow \quad x > 10^0 = 1$. Thus the domain of $f(x)$ is $(1, \infty)$.

(b) $y = \log_2(\log_{10} x) \quad \Leftrightarrow \quad 2^y = \log_{10} x \quad \Leftrightarrow \quad 10^{2^y} = x$. Thus $f^{-1}(x) = 10^{2^x}$.

76. (a) $f(x) = \ln(\ln(\ln x))$. We must have $\ln(\ln x) > 0 \quad \Leftrightarrow \quad \ln x > 1 \quad \Leftrightarrow \quad x > e$. So the domain of f is (e, ∞).

(b) $y = \ln(\ln(\ln x)) \quad \Leftrightarrow \quad e^y = \ln(\ln x) \quad \Leftrightarrow \quad e^{e^y} = \ln x \quad \Leftrightarrow \quad e^{e^{e^y}} = x$. Thus the inverse function is $f^{-1}(x) = e^{e^{e^x}}$.

77. (a) $f(x) = \dfrac{2^x}{1 + 2^x}$. $y = \dfrac{2^x}{1 + 2^x} \quad \Leftrightarrow$

$y + y2^x = 2^x \quad \Leftrightarrow$

$y = 2^x - y2^x = 2^x(1 - y) \quad \Leftrightarrow$

$2^x = \dfrac{y}{1 - y} \quad \Leftrightarrow \quad x = \log_2\left(\dfrac{y}{1 - y}\right)$. Thus

$f^{-1}(x) = \log_2\left(\dfrac{x}{1 - x}\right)$.

(b) $\dfrac{x}{1 - x} > 0$. Solving this using the methods from Chapter 1, we start with the endpoints, 0 and 1.

Interval	$(-\infty, 0)$	$(0, 1)$	$(1, \infty)$
Sign of x	$-$	$+$	$+$
Sign of $1 - x$	$+$	$+$	$-$
Sign of $\dfrac{x}{1 - x}$	$-$	$+$	$-$

Thus the domain of $f^{-1}(x)$ is $(0, 1)$.

78. Using $I = 0.7I_0$ we have $C = -2500\ln\left(\dfrac{I}{I_0}\right) = -2500\ln 0.7 = 891.69$ moles/liter.

79. Using $D = 0.73D_0$ we have $A = -8267\ln\left(\dfrac{D}{D_0}\right) = -8267\ln 0.73 \approx 2601$ years.

80. Substituting $N = 1,000,000$ we get $t = 3\dfrac{\log(N/50)}{\log 2} = 3\dfrac{\log 20,000}{\log 2} \approx 42.86$ hours.

81. When $r = 6\%$ we have $t = \dfrac{\ln 2}{0.06} \approx 11.6$ years. When $r = 7\%$ we have $t = \dfrac{\ln 2}{0.07} \approx 9.9$ years. And when $r = 8\%$ we have $t = \dfrac{\ln 2}{0.08} \approx 8.7$ years.

82. Using $k = 0.25$ and substituting $C = 0.9C_0$ we have

$t = -0.25\ln\left(1 - \dfrac{C}{C_0}\right) = -0.25\ln(1 - 0.9) = -0.25\ln 0.1 \approx 0.58$ hours.

83. Using $A = 100$ and $W = 5$ we find the ID to be $\dfrac{\log(2A/W)}{\log 2} = \dfrac{\log(2 \cdot 100/5)}{\log 2} = \dfrac{\log 40}{\log 2} \approx 5.32$. Using $A = 100$

and $W = 10$ we find the ID to be $\dfrac{\log(2A/W)}{\log 2} = \dfrac{\log(2 \cdot 100/10)}{\log 2} = \dfrac{\log 20}{\log 2} \approx 4.32$. So the smaller icon is

$\dfrac{5.23}{4.32} \approx 1.23$ times harder.

84. (a) Since 2 feet= 24 inches, the height of the graph is $2^{24} = 1677216$ inches. Now, since there are 12 inches per foot and 5280 feet per mile, there are $12\,(5280) = 63{,}360$ inches per mile. So the height of the graph is $\frac{1{,}677{,}216}{63360} \approx 264.8$, or about 265 miles.

(b) Since $\log_2\left(2^{24}\right) = 24$, we must be about 2^{24} inches≈ 265 miles to the right of the origin before the height of the graph of $y = \log_2 x$ reaches 24 inches or 2 feet.

85. $\log\left(\log 10^{100}\right) = \log 100 = 2$

$\log\left(\log\left(\log 10^{\text{googol}}\right)\right) = \log\left(\log\left(\text{googol}\right)\right) = \log\left(\log 10^{100}\right) = \log\left(100\right) = 2$

86. Notice that $\log_a x$ is increasing for $a > 1$. So we have $\log_4 17 > \log_4 16 = \log_4 4^2 = 2$. Also, we have $\log_5 24 < \log_5 25 = \log_5 5^2 = 2$. Thus, $\log_5 24 < 2 < \log_4 17$.

87. The numbers between 1000 and 9999 (inclusive) each have 4 digits, while $\log 1000 = 3$ and $\log 10{,}000 = 4$. Since $[\![\log x]\!] = 3$ for all integers x where $1000 \le x < 10{,}000$, the number of digits is $[\![\log x]\!] + 1$. Likewise, if x is an integer where $10^{n-1} \le x < 10^n$, then x has n digits and $[\![\log x]\!] = n - 1$. Since $[\![\log x]\!] = n - 1 \quad \Leftrightarrow \quad n = [\![\log x]\!] + 1$, the number of digits in x is $[\![\log x]\!] + 1$.

4.3 Laws of Logarithms

1. $\log_3 \sqrt{27} = \log_3 3^{3/2} = \frac{3}{2}$

2. $\log_2 160 - \log_2 5 = \log_2 \frac{160}{5} = \log_2 32 = \log_2 2^5 = 5$

3. $\log 4 + \log 25 = \log\left(4 \cdot 25\right) = \log 100 = 2$

4. $\log \frac{1}{\sqrt{1000}} = \log 10^{-3/2} = -\frac{3}{2}$

5. $\log_4 192 - \log_4 3 = \log_4 \frac{192}{3} = \log_4 64 = \log_4 4^3 = 3$

6. $\log_{12} 9 + \log_{12} 16 = \log_{12}\left(9 \cdot 16\right) = \log_{12} 144 = \log_{12} 12^2 = 2$

7. $\log_2 6 - \log_2 15 + \log_2 20 = \log_2 \frac{6}{15} + \log_2 20 = \log_2\left(\frac{2}{5} \cdot 20\right) = \log_2 8 = \log_2 2^3 = 3$

8. $\log_3 100 - \log_3 18 - \log_3 50 = \log_3\left(\dfrac{100}{18 \cdot 50}\right) = \log_3\left(\frac{1}{9}\right) = \log_3 3^{-2} = -2$

9. $\log_4 16^{100} = \log_4\left(4^2\right)^{100} = \log_4 4^{200} = 200$

10. $\log_2 8^{33} = \log_2\left(2^3\right)^{33} = \log_2 2^{99} = 99$

11. $\log\left(\log 10^{10{,}000}\right) = \log\left(10{,}000 \log 10\right) = \log\left(10{,}000 \cdot 1\right) = \log\left(10{,}000\right) = \log 10^4 = 4 \log 10 = 4$

12. $\ln\left(\ln e^{e^{200}}\right) = \ln\left(e^{200} \ln e\right) = \ln e^{200} = 200 \ln e = 200$

13. $\log_2 2x = \log_2 2 + \log_2 x = 1 + \log_2 x$

14. $\log_3\left(5y\right) = \log_3 5 + \log_3 y$

15. $\log_2\left[x\left(x - 1\right)\right] = \log_2 x + \log_2\left(x - 1\right)$

16. $\log_5\left(\dfrac{x}{2}\right) = \log_5 x - \log_5 2$

17. $\log 6^{10} = 10 \log 6$

18. $\ln\left(\sqrt{z}\right) = \ln\left(z^{1/2}\right) = \frac{1}{2} \ln z$

19. $\log_2\left(AB^2\right) = \log_2 A + \log_2 B^2 = \log_2 A + 2 \log_2 B$

20. $\log_6 \sqrt[4]{17} = \frac{1}{4} \log_6 17$

21. $\log_3\left(x\sqrt{y}\right) = \log_3 x + \log_3 \sqrt{y} = \log_3 x + \frac{1}{2} \log_3 y$

22. $\log_2\left(xy\right)^{10} = 10 \log_2\left(xy\right) = 10\left(\log_2 x + \log_2 y\right)$

23. $\log_5 \sqrt[3]{x^2 + 1} = \frac{1}{3} \log_5\left(x^2 + 1\right)$

24. $\log_a\left(\dfrac{x^2}{yz^3}\right) = \log_a x^2 - \log_a\left(yz^3\right) = 2 \log_a x - \left(\log_a y + 3 \log_a z\right)$

25. $\ln \sqrt{ab} = \frac{1}{2} \ln ab = \frac{1}{2}\left(\ln a + \ln b\right)$

26. $\ln \sqrt[3]{3r^2 s} = \frac{1}{3} \ln\left(3r^2 s\right) = \dfrac{1}{3}\left[\ln 3 + \ln r^2 + \ln s\right] = \frac{1}{3}\left(\ln 3 + 2 \ln r + \ln s\right)$

27. $\log\left(\dfrac{x^3 y^4}{z^6}\right) = \log\left(x^3 y^4\right) - \log z^6 = 3 \log x + 4 \log y - 6 \log z$

28. $\log \dfrac{a^2}{b^4 \sqrt{c}} = \log a^2 - \log \left(b^4 \sqrt{c}\right) = 2 \log a - \left(4 \log b + \frac{1}{2} \log c\right)$

29. $\log_2 \left(\dfrac{x\left(x^2+1\right)}{\sqrt{x^2-1}}\right) = \log_2 x + \log_2 \left(x^2+1\right) - \frac{1}{2} \log_2 \left(x^2-1\right)$

30. $\log_5 \sqrt{\dfrac{x-1}{x+1}} = \frac{1}{2} \log_5 \left(\dfrac{x-1}{x+1}\right) = \frac{1}{2} \left[\log_5 (x-1) - \log_5 (x+1)\right]$

31. $\ln \left(x \sqrt{\dfrac{y}{z}}\right) = \ln x + \frac{1}{2} \ln \left(\dfrac{y}{z}\right) = \ln x + \frac{1}{2} \left(\ln y - \ln z\right)$

32. $\ln \dfrac{3x^2}{(x+1)^{10}} = \ln \left(3x^2\right) - \ln (x+1)^{10} = \ln 3 + 2 \ln x - 10 \ln (x+1)$

33. $\log \sqrt[4]{x^2+y^2} = \frac{1}{4} \log \left(x^2+y^2\right)$

34. $\log \dfrac{x}{\sqrt[3]{1-x}} = \log x - \log \sqrt[3]{1-x} = \log x - \frac{1}{3} \log (1-x)$

35. $\log \sqrt{\dfrac{x^2+4}{\left(x^2+1\right)\left(x^3-7\right)^2}} = \frac{1}{2} \log \dfrac{x^2+4}{\left(x^2+1\right)\left(x^3-7\right)^2} = \frac{1}{2} \left[\log \left(x^2+4\right) - \log \left(x^2+1\right)\left(x^3-7\right)^2\right]$

$$= \frac{1}{2} \left[\log \left(x^2+4\right) - \log \left(x^2+1\right) - 2 \log \left(x^3-7\right)\right]$$

36. $\log \sqrt{x \sqrt{y \sqrt{z}}} = \frac{1}{2} \log \left(x \sqrt{y \sqrt{z}}\right) = \frac{1}{2} \left(\log x + \log \sqrt{y \sqrt{z}}\right) = \frac{1}{2} \left[\log x + \frac{1}{2} \log (y \sqrt{z})\right]$

$$= \frac{1}{2} \left[\log x + \frac{1}{2} \left(\log y + \frac{1}{2} \log z\right)\right] = \frac{1}{2} \log x + \frac{1}{4} \log y + \frac{1}{8} \log z$$

37. $\ln \dfrac{x^3 \sqrt{x-1}}{3x+4} = \ln \left(x^3 \sqrt{x-1}\right) - \ln (3x+4) = 3 \ln x + \frac{1}{2} \ln (x-1) - \ln (3x+4)$

38. $\log \dfrac{10^x}{x\left(x^2+1\right)\left(x^4+2\right)} = \log 10^x - \log \left[x\left(x^2+1\right)\left(x^4+2\right)\right] = x - \left[\log x + \log \left(x^2+1\right) + \log \left(x^4+2\right)\right]$

39. $\log_3 5 + 5 \log_3 2 = \log_3 5 + \log_3 2^5 = \log_3 \left(5 \cdot 2^5\right) = \log_3 160$

40. $\log 12 + \frac{1}{2} \log 7 - \log 2 = \log \left(12 \sqrt{7}\right) - \log 2 = \log \dfrac{12 \sqrt{7}}{2} = \log \left(6 \sqrt{7}\right)$

41. $\log_2 A + \log_2 B - 2 \log_2 C = \log_2 (AB) - \log_2 \left(C^2\right) = \log_2 \left(\dfrac{AB}{C^2}\right)$

42. $\log_5 \left(x^2-1\right) - \log_5 (x-1) = \log_5 \dfrac{x^2-1}{x-1} = \log_5 \dfrac{(x-1)(x+1)}{x-1} = \log_5 (x+1)$

43. $4 \log x - \frac{1}{3} \log \left(x^2+1\right) + 2 \log (x-1) = \log x^4 - \log \sqrt[3]{x^2+1} + \log (x-1)^2$

$$= \log \left(\dfrac{x^4}{\sqrt[3]{x^2+1}}\right) + \log (x-1)^2 = \log \left(\dfrac{x^4 (x-1)^2}{\sqrt[3]{x^2+1}}\right)$$

44. $\ln (a+b) + \ln (a-b) - 2 \ln c = \ln [(a+b)(a-b)] - \ln \left(c^2\right) = \ln \dfrac{a^2-b^2}{c^2}$

45. $\ln 5 + 2 \ln x + 3 \ln \left(x^2+5\right) = \ln \left(5x^2\right) + \ln \left(x^2+5\right)^3 = \ln \left[5x^2 \left(x^2+5\right)^3\right]$

46. $2 \left[\log_5 x + 2 \log_5 y - 3 \log_5 z\right] = 2 \log_5 \dfrac{xy^2}{z^3} = \log_5 \left(\dfrac{xy^2}{z^3}\right)^2 = \log_5 \dfrac{x^2 y^4}{z^6}$

47. $\frac{1}{3} \log (2x+1) + \frac{1}{2} \left[\log (x-4) - \log \left(x^4-x^2-1\right)\right] = \log \sqrt[3]{2x+1} + \frac{1}{2} \log \dfrac{x-4}{x^4-x^2-1}$

$$= \log \left(\sqrt[3]{2x+1} \cdot \sqrt{\dfrac{x-4}{x^4-x^2-1}}\right)$$

48. $\log_a b + c \log_a d - r \log_a s = \log_a \left(bd^c\right) - \log_a s^r = \log_a \dfrac{bd^c}{s^r}$

49. $\log_2 5 = \dfrac{\log 5}{\log 2} \approx 2.321928$

50. $\log_5 2 = \dfrac{\log 2}{\log 5} \approx 0.430677$

51. $\log_3 16 = \dfrac{\log 16}{\log 3} \approx 2.523719$

52. $\log_6 92 = \dfrac{\log 92}{\log 6} \approx 2.523658$

53. $\log_7 2.61 = \dfrac{\log 2.61}{\log 7} \approx 0.493008$

54. $\log_6 532 = \dfrac{\log 532}{\log 6} \approx 3.503061$

55. $\log_4 125 = \dfrac{\log 125}{\log 4} \approx 3.482892$

56. $\log_{12} 2.5 = \dfrac{\log 2.5}{\log 12} \approx 0.368743$

57. $\log_3 x = \dfrac{\log_e x}{\log_e 3} = \dfrac{\ln x}{\ln 3} = \dfrac{1}{\ln 3}\ln x$. The graph of $y = \dfrac{1}{\ln 3}\ln x$ is

shown in the viewing rectangle $[-1, 4]$ by $[-3, 2]$.

58. Note that $\log_c x = \left(\dfrac{1}{\ln c}\right)\ln x$ (by the change of base formula). So

the graph of $y = \log_c x$ is obtained from the graph of $y = \ln x$ by

either shrinking or stretching vertically by a factor of $\dfrac{1}{\ln c}$ depending

on whether $\ln c > 1$ or $\ln c < 1$. All of the graphs pass through $(1, 0)$

because $\log_c 1 = 0$ for all c.

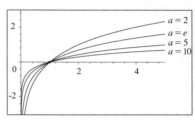

59. $\log e = \dfrac{\ln e}{\ln 10} = \dfrac{1}{\ln 10}$

60. $(\log_2 5)\,(\log_5 7) = \dfrac{\log 5}{\log 2} \cdot \dfrac{\log 7}{\log 5} = \dfrac{\log 7}{\log 2} = \log_2 7$

61. $-\ln\left(x - \sqrt{x^2-1}\right) = \ln\left(\dfrac{1}{x-\sqrt{x^2-1}}\right) = \ln\left(\dfrac{1}{x-\sqrt{x^2-1}} \cdot \dfrac{x+\sqrt{x^2-1}}{x+\sqrt{x^2-1}}\right) = \ln\left(\dfrac{x+\sqrt{x^2-1}}{x^2-(x^2-1)}\right)$

$= \ln\left(x + \sqrt{x^2-1}\right)$

62. From Example 5(a), $P = \dfrac{P_0}{(t+1)^c}$. Substituting $P_0 = 80$, $t = 24$, and $c = 0.3$ we have $P = \dfrac{80}{(24+1)^{0.3}} \approx 30.5$. So the

student should get a score of 30.

63. (a) $\log P = \log c - k\log W \quad \Leftrightarrow \quad \log P = \log c - \log W^k \quad \Leftrightarrow \quad \log P = \log\left(\dfrac{c}{W^k}\right) \quad \Leftrightarrow \quad P = \dfrac{c}{W^k}$.

(b) Using $k = 2.1$ and $c = 8000$, when $W = 2$ we have $P = \dfrac{8000}{2^{2.1}} \approx 1866$ and when $W = 10$ we have $P = \dfrac{8000}{10^{2.1}} \approx 64$.

64. (a) $\log S = \log c + k\log A \quad \Leftrightarrow \quad \log S = \log c + \log A^k \quad \Leftrightarrow \quad \log S = \log\left(cA^k\right) \quad \Leftrightarrow \quad S = cA^k$.

(b) If $A = 2A_0$ when $k = 3$ we get $S = c\,(2A_0)^3 = c \cdot 2^3 \cdot A_0^3 = 8 \cdot cA_0^3$. Thus doubling the area increases the species

eightfold.

65. (a) $M = -2.5\log\left(B/B_0\right) = -2.5\log B + 2.5\log B_0$.

(b) Suppose B_1 and B_2 are the brightness of two stars such that $B_1 < B_2$ and let M_1 and M_2 be

their respective magnitudes. Since $\log$ is an increasing function, we have $\log B_1 < \log B_2$. Then

$\log B_1 < \log B_2 \quad \Leftrightarrow \quad \log B_1 - \log B_0 < \log B_2 - \log B_0 \quad \Leftrightarrow \quad \log\left(B_1/B_0\right) < \log\left(B_2/B_0\right) \quad \Leftrightarrow$

$-2.5\log\left(B_1/B_0\right) > -2.5\log\left(B_2/B_0\right) \quad \Leftrightarrow \quad M_1 > M_2$. Thus the brighter star has less magnitudes.

(c) Let B_1 be the brightness of the star Albiero. Then $100B_1$ is the brightness of Betelgeuse, and its magnitude is

$M = -2.5\log\left(100B_1/B_0\right) = -2.5\left[\log 100 + \log\left(B_1/B_0\right)\right] = -2.5\left[2 + \log\left(B_1/B_0\right)\right] = -5 - 2.5\log\left(B_1/B_0\right)$

$= -5 + \text{magnitude of Albiero}$

66. (a) False; $\log(x/y) = \log x - \log y \neq (\log x) / (\log y)$.

(b) False; $\log_2 x - \log_2 y = \log_2 (x/y) \neq \log_2 (x - y)$.

(c) True; the equation is an identity: $\log_5 (a/b^2) = \log_5 a - \log_5 b^2 = \log_5 a - 2 \log_5 b$.

(d) True; the equation is an identity: $\log 2^z = z \log 2$.

(e) False; $\log P + \log Q = \log(PQ) \neq (\log P)(\log Q)$.

(f) False; $\log a - \log b = \log(a/b) \neq (\log a) / (\log b)$.

(g) False; $x \log_2 7 = \log_2 7^x \neq (\log_2 7)^x$.

(h) True; the equation is an identity. $\log_a a^a = a \log_a a = a \cdot 1 = a$.

(i) False; $\log(x - y) \neq (\log x) / (\log y)$. For example, $0 = \log(3 - 2) \neq (\log 3)/(\log 2)$.

(j) True; the equation is an identity: $-\ln(1/A) = -\ln A^{-1} = -1(-\ln A) = \ln A$.

67. The error is on the first line: $\log 0.1 < 0$, so $2 \log 0.1 < \log 0.1$.

68. Let $f(x) = x^2$. Then $f(2x) = (2x)^2 = 4x^2 = 4f(x)$. Now the graph of $f(2x)$ is the same as the graph of f shrunk horizontally by a factor of $\frac{1}{2}$, whereas the graph of $4f(x)$ is the same as the graph of $f(x)$ stretched vertically by a factor of 4.

Let $g(x) = e^x$. Then $g(x + 2) = e^{x+2} = e^2 e^x = e^2 g(x)$. This shows that a horizontal shift of 2 units to the right is the same as a vertical stretch by a factor of e^2.

Let $h(x) = \ln x$. Then $h(2x) = \ln 2x = \ln 2 + \ln x = \ln 2 + h(x)$. This shows that a horizontal shrinking by a factor of $\frac{1}{2}$ is the same as a vertical shift upward by $\ln 2$.

4.4   Exponential and Logarithmic Equations

1. $10^x = 25 \quad \Leftrightarrow \quad \log 10^x = \log 25 \quad \Leftrightarrow \quad x \log 10 = \log 25 \quad \Leftrightarrow \quad x \approx 1.398$

2. $10^{-x} = 4 \quad \Leftrightarrow \quad \log 10^{-x} = \log 4 \quad \Leftrightarrow \quad -x = \log 4 \quad \Leftrightarrow \quad x = -\log 4 \approx -0.6021$

3. $e^{-2x} = 7 \quad \Leftrightarrow \quad \ln e^{-2x} = \ln 7 \quad \Leftrightarrow \quad -2x \ln e = \ln 7 \quad \Leftrightarrow \quad -2x = \ln 7 \quad \Leftrightarrow \quad x = -\frac{1}{2} \ln 7 \approx -0.9730$

4. $e^{3x} = 12 \quad \Leftrightarrow \quad \ln e^{3x} = \ln 12 \quad \Leftrightarrow \quad 3x = \ln 12 \quad \Leftrightarrow \quad x = \dfrac{\ln 12}{3} \approx 0.8283$

5. $2^{1-x} = 3 \quad \Leftrightarrow \quad \log 2^{1-x} = \log 3 \quad \Leftrightarrow \quad (1 - x) \log 2 = \log 3 \quad \Leftrightarrow \quad 1 - x = \dfrac{\log 3}{\log 2} \quad \Leftrightarrow$

$x = 1 - \dfrac{\log 3}{\log 2} \approx -0.5850$

6. $3^{2x-1} = 5 \quad \Leftrightarrow \quad \log 3^{2x-1} = \log 5 \quad \Leftrightarrow \quad (2x - 1) \log 3 = \log 5 \quad \Leftrightarrow \quad 2x - 1 = \dfrac{\log 5}{\log 3} \quad \Leftrightarrow \quad 2x = 1 + \dfrac{\log 5}{\log 3}$

$\Leftrightarrow \quad x = \frac{1}{2} \left(1 + \dfrac{\log 5}{\log 3} \right) \approx 1.2325$

7. $3e^x = 10 \quad \Leftrightarrow \quad e^x = \frac{10}{3} \quad \Leftrightarrow \quad x = \ln\left(\frac{10}{3} \right) \approx 1.2040$

8. $2e^{12x} = 17 \quad \Leftrightarrow \quad e^{12x} = \frac{17}{2} \quad \Leftrightarrow \quad 12x = \ln\left(\frac{17}{2} \right) \quad \Leftrightarrow \quad x = \frac{1}{12} \left[\ln\left(\frac{17}{2} \right) \right] \approx 0.1783$

9. $e^{1-4x} = 2 \quad \Leftrightarrow \quad 1 - 4x = \ln 2 \quad \Leftrightarrow \quad -4x = -1 + \ln 2 \quad \Leftrightarrow \quad x = \dfrac{1 - \ln 2}{4} = 0.0767$

10. $4(1 + 10^{5x}) = 9 \quad \Leftrightarrow \quad 1 + 10^{5x} = \frac{9}{4} \quad \Leftrightarrow \quad 10^{5x} = \frac{5}{4} \quad \Leftrightarrow \quad 5x = \log\left(\frac{5}{4} \right) \quad \Leftrightarrow$

$x = \frac{1}{5} [\log 5 - \log 4] \approx 0.0194$

11. $4 + 3^{5x} = 8 \quad \Leftrightarrow \quad 3^{5x} = 4 \quad \Leftrightarrow \quad \log 3^{5x} = \log 4 \quad \Leftrightarrow \quad 5x \log 3 = \log 4 \quad \Leftrightarrow \quad 5x = \dfrac{\log 4}{\log 3} \quad \Leftrightarrow$

$x = \dfrac{\log 4}{5 \log 3} \approx 0.2524$

12. $2^{3x} = 34 \quad \Leftrightarrow \quad \log 2^{3x} = \log 34 \quad \Leftrightarrow \quad 3x \log 2 = \log 34 \quad \Leftrightarrow \quad x = \dfrac{\log 34}{3 \log 2} \approx 1.6958$

13. $8^{0.4x} = 5 \quad \Leftrightarrow \quad \log 8^{0.4x} = \log 5 \quad \Leftrightarrow \quad 0.4x \log 8 = \log 5 \quad \Leftrightarrow \quad 0.4x = \dfrac{\log 5}{\log 8} \quad \Leftrightarrow \quad x = \dfrac{\log 5}{0.4 \log 8} \approx 1.9349$

14. $3^{x/14} = 0.1 \quad \Leftrightarrow \quad \log 3^{x/14} = \log 0.1 \quad \Leftrightarrow \quad \left(\dfrac{x}{14}\right) \log 3 = \log 0.1 \quad \Leftrightarrow \quad x = \dfrac{14 \log 0.1}{\log 3} \approx -29.3426$

15. $5^{-x/100} = 2 \quad \Leftrightarrow \quad \log 5^{-x/100} = \log 2 \quad \Leftrightarrow \quad -\dfrac{x}{100} \log 5 = \log 2 \quad \Leftrightarrow \quad x = -\dfrac{100 \log 2}{\log 5} \approx -43.0677$

16. $e^{3-5x} = 16 \quad \Leftrightarrow \quad 3 - 5x = \ln 16 \quad \Leftrightarrow \quad -5x = \ln 16 - 3 \quad \Leftrightarrow \quad x = -\dfrac{1}{5}\left(\ln 16 - 3\right) \approx 0.0455$

17. $e^{2x+1} = 200 \quad \Leftrightarrow \quad 2x + 1 = \ln 200 \quad \Leftrightarrow \quad 2x = -1 + \ln 200 \quad \Leftrightarrow \quad x = \dfrac{-1 + \ln 200}{2} \approx 2.1492$

18. $\left(\frac{1}{4}\right)^x = 75 \quad \Leftrightarrow \quad 4^{-x} = 75 \quad \Leftrightarrow \quad \log 4^{-x} = \log 75 \quad \Leftrightarrow \quad (-x)(\log 4) = \log 75 \quad \Leftrightarrow \quad -x = \dfrac{\log 75}{\log 4} \quad \Leftrightarrow$

$x = -\dfrac{\log 75}{\log 4} \approx -3.1144$

19. $5^x = 4^{x+1} \quad \Leftrightarrow \quad \log 5^x = \log 4^{x+1} \quad \Leftrightarrow \quad x \log 5 = (x+1) \log 4 = x \log 4 + \log 4 \quad \Leftrightarrow \quad x \log 5 - x \log 4 = \log 4$

$\Leftrightarrow \quad x(\log 5 - \log 4) = \log 4 \quad \Leftrightarrow \quad x = \dfrac{\log 4}{\log 5 - \log 4} \approx 6.2126$

20. $10^{1-x} = 6^x \quad \Leftrightarrow \quad \log 10^{1-x} = \log 6^x \quad \Leftrightarrow \quad 1 - x = x(\log 6) \quad \Leftrightarrow \quad 1 = x(\log 6) + x \quad \Leftrightarrow \quad 1 = x(\log 6 + 1)$

$\Leftrightarrow \quad x = \dfrac{1}{\log 6 + 1} \approx 0.5624$

21. $2^{3x+1} = 3^{x-2} \quad \Leftrightarrow \quad \log 2^{3x+1} = \log 3^{x-2} \quad \Leftrightarrow \quad (3x+1) \log 2 = (x-2) \log 3 \quad \Leftrightarrow \quad 3x \log 2 +$

$\log 2 = x \log 3 - 2 \log 3 \quad \Leftrightarrow \quad 3x \log 2 - x \log 3 = -\log 2 - 2 \log 3 \quad \Leftrightarrow \quad x(3 \log 2 - \log 3) = -(\log 2 + 2 \log 3)$

$\Leftrightarrow \quad s = -\dfrac{\log 2 + 2 \log 3}{3 \log 2 - \log 3} \approx -2.9469$

22. $7^{x/2} = 5^{1-x} \quad \Leftrightarrow \quad \log 7^{x/2} = \log 5^{1-x} \quad \Leftrightarrow \quad \left(\dfrac{x}{2}\right) \log 7 = (1-x) \log 5 \quad \Leftrightarrow \quad \left(\dfrac{x}{2}\right) \log 7 = \log 5 - x \log 5$

$\Leftrightarrow \quad \left(\dfrac{x}{2}\right) \log 7 + x \log 5 = \log 5 \quad \Leftrightarrow \quad x\left(\frac{1}{2} \log 7 + \log 5\right) = \log 5 \quad \Leftrightarrow \quad x = \dfrac{\log 5}{\frac{1}{2} \log 7 + \log 5} \approx 0.6232$

23. $\dfrac{50}{1 + e^{-x}} = 4 \quad \Leftrightarrow \quad 50 = 4 + 4e^{-x} \quad \Leftrightarrow \quad 46 = 4e^{-x} \quad \Leftrightarrow \quad 11.5 = e^{-x} \quad \Leftrightarrow \quad \ln 11.5 = -x \quad \Leftrightarrow$

$x = -\ln 11.5 \approx -2.4423$

24. $\dfrac{10}{1 + e^{-x}} = 2 \quad \Leftrightarrow \quad 10 = 2 + 2e^{-x} \quad \Leftrightarrow \quad 8 = 2e^{-x} \quad \Leftrightarrow \quad 4 = e^{-x} \quad \Leftrightarrow \quad \ln 4 = -x \quad \Leftrightarrow$

$x = -\ln 4 \approx -1.3863$

25. $100(1.04)^{2t} = 300 \quad \Leftrightarrow \quad 1.04^{2t} = 3 \quad \Leftrightarrow \quad \log 1.04^{2t} = \log 3 \quad \Leftrightarrow \quad 2t \log 1.04 = \log 3 \quad \Leftrightarrow$

$t = \dfrac{\log 3}{2 \log 1.04} \approx 14.0055$

26. $(1.00625)^{12t} = 2 \quad \Leftrightarrow \quad \log 1.00625^{12t} = \log 2 \quad \Leftrightarrow \quad 12t \log 1.00625 = \log 2 \quad \Leftrightarrow$

$t = \dfrac{\log 2}{12 \log 1.00625} \approx 9.2708$

27. $x^2 2^x - 2^x = 0 \quad \Leftrightarrow \quad 2^x\left(x^2 - 1\right) = 0 \Rightarrow 2^x = 0$ (never) or $x^2 - 1 = 0$. If $x^2 - 1 = 0$, then $x^2 = 1 \Rightarrow x = \pm 1$. So the only solutions are $x = \pm 1$.

28. $x^2 10^x - x 10^x = 2(10^x) \quad \Leftrightarrow \quad x^2 10^x - x 10^x - 2(10^x) = 0 \quad \Leftrightarrow \quad 10^x\left(x^2 - x - 2\right) = 0 \Rightarrow 10^x = 0$ (never) or $x^2 - x - 2 = 0$. If $x^2 - x - 2 = 0$, then $(x-2)(x+1) = 0 \Rightarrow x = 2, -1$. So the only solutions are $x = 2, -1$.

29. $4x^3 e^{-3x} - 3x^4 e^{-3x} = 0 \quad \Leftrightarrow \quad x^3 e^{-3x}(4 - 3x) = 0 \Rightarrow x = 0$ or $e^{-3x} = 0$ (never) or $4 - 3x = 0$. If $4 - 3x = 0$, then $3x = 4 \quad \Leftrightarrow \quad x = \frac{4}{3}$. So the solutions are $x = 0$ and $x = \frac{4}{3}$.

30. $x^2 e^x + xe^x - e^x = 0$ $\Leftrightarrow$ $e^x(x^2 + x - 1) = 0 \Rightarrow e^x = 0$ (impossible) or $x^2 + x - 1 = 0$. If $x^2 + x - 1 = 0$, then $x = \dfrac{-1 \pm \sqrt{5}}{2}$. So the solutions are $x = \dfrac{-1 \pm \sqrt{5}}{2}$.

31. $e^{2x} - 3e^x + 2 = 0$ $\Leftrightarrow$ $(e^x - 1)(e^x - 2) = 0 \Rightarrow e^x - 1 = 0$ or $e^x - 2 = 0$. If $e^x - 1 = 0$, then $e^x = 1$ $\Leftrightarrow$ $x = \ln 1 = 0$. If $e^x - 2 = 0$, then $e^x = 2$ $\Leftrightarrow$ $x = \ln 2 \approx 0.6931$. So the solutions are $x = 0$ and $x \approx 0.6931$.

32. $e^{2x} - e^x - 6 = 0$ $\Leftrightarrow$ $(e^x - 3)(e^x + 2) = 0 \Rightarrow e^x + 2 = 0$ (impossible) or $e^x - 3 = 0$. If $e^x - 3 = 0$, then $e^x = 3$ $\Leftrightarrow$ $x = \ln 3 \approx 1.0986$. So the only solution is $x \approx 1.0986$.

33. $e^{4x} + 4e^{2x} - 21 = 0$ $\Leftrightarrow$ $(e^{2x} + 7)(e^{2x} - 3) = 0 \Rightarrow e^{2x} = -7$ or $e^{2x} = 3$. Now $e^{2x} = -7$ has no solution, since $e^{2x} > 0$ for all x. But we can solve $e^{2x} = 3$ $\Leftrightarrow$ $2x = \ln 3$ $\Leftrightarrow$ $x = \frac{1}{2}\ln 3 \approx 0.5493$. So the only solution is $x \approx 0.5493$.

34. $e^x - 12e^{-x} - 1 = 0$ $\Leftrightarrow$ $e^x - 1 - 12e^{-x} = 0$ $\Leftrightarrow$ $e^x(e^x - 1 - 12e^{-x}) = 0 \cdot e^x$ $\Leftrightarrow$ $e^{2x} - e^x - 12 = 0$ $\Leftrightarrow$ $(e^x - 4)(e^x + 3) = 0 \Rightarrow e^x + 3 = 0$ (impossible) or $e^x - 4 = 0$. If $e^x - 4 = 0$, then $e^x = 4$ $\Leftrightarrow$ $x = \ln 4 \approx 1.3863$. So the only solution is $x \approx 1.3863$.

35. $\ln x = 10$ $\Leftrightarrow$ $x = e^{10} \approx 22026$

36. $\ln(2 + x) = 1$ $\Leftrightarrow$ $2 + x = e^1$ $\Leftrightarrow$ $x = e - 2 \approx 0.7183$

37. $\log x = -2$ $\Leftrightarrow$ $x = 10^{-2} = 0.01$

38. $\log(x - 4) = 3$ $\Leftrightarrow$ $x - 4 = 10^3 = 1000$ $\Leftrightarrow$ $x = 1004$

39. $\log(3x + 5) = 2$ $\Leftrightarrow$ $3x + 5 = 10^2 = 100$ $\Leftrightarrow$ $3x = 95$ $\Leftrightarrow$ $x = \frac{95}{3} \approx 31.6667$

40. $\log_3(2 - x) = 3$ $\Leftrightarrow$ $2 - x = 3^3 = 27$ $\Leftrightarrow$ $-x = 25$ $\Leftrightarrow$ $x = -25$

41. $2 - \ln(3 - x) = 0$ $\Leftrightarrow$ $2 = \ln(3 - x)$ $\Leftrightarrow$ $e^2 = 3 - x$ $\Leftrightarrow$ $x = 3 - e^2 \approx -4.3891$

42. $\log_2(x^2 - x - 2) = 2$ $\Leftrightarrow$ $x^2 - x - 2 = 2^2 = 4$ $\Leftrightarrow$ $x^2 - x - 6 = 0$ $\Leftrightarrow$ $(x - 3)(x + 2) = 0$ $\Leftrightarrow$ $x = 3$ or $x = -2$. Thus the solutions are $x = 3$ and $x = -2$.

43. $\log_2 3 + \log_2 x = \log_2 5 + \log_2(x - 2)$ $\Leftrightarrow$ $\log_2(3x) = \log_2(5x - 10)$ $\Leftrightarrow$ $3x = 5x - 10$ $\Leftrightarrow$ $2x = 10$ $\Leftrightarrow$ $x = 5$

44. $2\log x = \log 2 + \log(3x - 4)$ $\Leftrightarrow$ $\log(x^2) = \log(6x - 8)$ $\Leftrightarrow$ $x^2 = 6x - 8$ $\Leftrightarrow$ $x^2 - 6x + 8 = 0$ $\Leftrightarrow$ $(x - 4)(x - 2) = 0$ $\Leftrightarrow$ $x = 4$ or $x = 2$. Thus the solutions are $x = 4$ and $x = 2$.

45. $\log x + \log(x - 1) = \log(4x)$ $\Leftrightarrow$ $\log[x(x - 1)] = \log(4x)$ $\Leftrightarrow$ $x^2 - x = 4x$ $\Leftrightarrow$ $x^2 - 5x = 0$ $\Leftrightarrow$ $x(x - 5) = 0 \Rightarrow x = 0$ or $x = 5$. So the possible solutions are $x = 0$ and $x = 5$. However, when $x = 0$, $\log x$ is undefined. Thus the only solution is $x = 5$.

46. $\log_5 x + \log_5(x + 1) = \log_5 20$ $\Leftrightarrow$ $\log_5(x^2 + x) = \log_5 20$ $\Leftrightarrow$ $x^2 + x = 20$ $\Leftrightarrow$ $x^2 + x - 20 = 0$ $\Leftrightarrow$ $(x + 5)(x - 4) = 0$ $\Leftrightarrow$ $x = -5$ or $x = 4$. Since $\log_5(-5)$ is undefined, the only solution is $x = 4$.

47. $\log_5(x + 1) - \log_5(x - 1) = 2$ $\Leftrightarrow$ $\log_5\left(\dfrac{x + 1}{x - 1}\right) = 2$ $\Leftrightarrow$ $\dfrac{x + 1}{x - 1} = 5^2$ $\Leftrightarrow$ $x + 1 = 25x - 25$ $\Leftrightarrow$ $24x = 26$ $\Leftrightarrow$ $x = \frac{13}{12}$

48. $\log x + \log(x - 3) = 1$ $\Leftrightarrow$ $\log[x(x - 3)] = 1$ $\Leftrightarrow$ $x^2 - 3x = 10$ $\Leftrightarrow$ $x^2 - 3x - 10 = 0$ $\Leftrightarrow$ $(x + 2)(x - 5) = 0$ $\Leftrightarrow$ $x = -2$ or $x = 5$. Since $\log(-2)$ is undefined, the only solution is $x = 5$.

49. $\log_9(x - 5) + \log_9(x + 3) = 1$ $\Leftrightarrow$ $\log_9[(x - 5)(x + 3)] = 1$ $\Leftrightarrow$ $(x - 5)(x + 3) = 9^1$ $\Leftrightarrow$ $x^2 - 2x - 24 = 0$ $\Leftrightarrow$ $(x - 6)(x + 4) = 0 \Rightarrow x = 6$ or -4. However, $x = -4$ is inadmissible, so $x = 6$ is the only solution.

50. $\ln(x - 1) + \ln(x + 2) = 1$ $\Leftrightarrow$ $\ln[(x - 1)(x + 2)] = 1$ $\Leftrightarrow$ $x^2 + x - 2 = e$ $\Leftrightarrow$ $x^2 + x - (2 + e) = 0 \Rightarrow$ $x = \dfrac{-1 \pm \sqrt{1 + 4(2 + e)}}{2} = \dfrac{-1 \pm \sqrt{9 + 4e}}{2}$. Since $x - 1 < 0$ when $x = \dfrac{-1 - \sqrt{9 + 4e}}{2}$, the only solution is $x = \dfrac{-1 + \sqrt{9 + 4e}}{2} \approx 1.7290$

51. $\log(x + 3) = \log x + \log 3$ $\Leftrightarrow$ $\log(x + 3) = \log(3x)$ $\Leftrightarrow$ $x + 3 = 3x$ $\Leftrightarrow$ $2x = 3$ $\Leftrightarrow$ $x = \frac{3}{2}$

52. $(\log x)^3 = 3\log x$ $\Leftrightarrow$ $(\log x)^3 - 3\log x = 0$ $\Leftrightarrow$ $(\log x)\left((\log x)^2 - 3\right)$ $\Leftrightarrow$ $(\log x) = 0$ or $(\log x)^2 - 3 = 0$.

Now $\log x = 0$ $\Leftrightarrow$ $x = 1$. Also $(\log x)^2 - 3 = 0$ $\Leftrightarrow$ $(\log x)^2 = 3$ $\Leftrightarrow$ $\log x = \pm\sqrt{3}$ $\Leftrightarrow$ $x = 10^{\pm\sqrt{3}}$,

so $x = 10^{\sqrt{3}} \approx 53.9574$ or $x = 10^{-\sqrt{3}} \approx 0.0185$. Thus the solutions to the equation are $x = 1$, $x = 10^{\sqrt{3}} \approx 53.9574$ and

$x = 10^{-\sqrt{3}} \approx 0.0185$.

53. $2^{2/\log_5 x} = \frac{1}{16}$ $\Leftrightarrow$ $\log_2 2^{2/\log_5 x} = \log_2\left(\frac{1}{16}\right)$ $\Leftrightarrow$ $\dfrac{2}{\log_5 x} = -4$ $\Leftrightarrow$ $\log_5 x = -\frac{1}{2}$ $\Leftrightarrow$

$x = 5^{-1/2} = \frac{1}{\sqrt{5}} \approx 0.4472$

54. $\log_2\left(\log_3 x\right) = 4$ $\Leftrightarrow$ $\log_3 x = 2^4 = 16$ $\Leftrightarrow$ $x = 3^{16} = 43{,}046{,}721$

55. $\ln x = 3 - x$ $\Leftrightarrow$ $\ln x + x - 3 = 0$. Let
$f(x) = \ln x + x - 3$. We need to solve the equation
$f(x) = 0$. From the graph of f, we get $x \approx 2.21$.

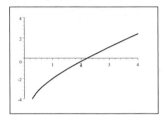

56. $\log x = x^2 - 2$ $\Leftrightarrow$ $\log x - x^2 + 2 = 0$. Let
$f(x) = \log x - x^2 + 2$. We need to solve the equation
$f(x) = 0$. From the graph of f, we get $x \approx 0.01$ or
$x \approx 1.47$.

57. $x^3 - x = \log_{10}(x + 1)$ $\Leftrightarrow$
$x^3 - x - \log_{10}(x + 1) = 0$. Let
$f(x) = x^3 - x - \log_{10}(x + 1)$. We need to solve the
equation $f(x) = 0$. From the graph of f, we get $x = 0$ or
$x \approx 1.14$.

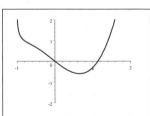

58. $x = \ln\left(4 - x^2\right)$ $\Leftrightarrow$ $x - \ln\left(4 - x^2\right) = 0$. Let
$f(x) = x - \ln\left(4 - x^2\right)$. We need to solve the equation
$f(x) = 0$. From the graph of f, we get $xx \approx -1.96$ or
$x \approx 1.06$.

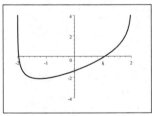

59. $e^x = -x$ $\Leftrightarrow$ $e^x + x = 0$. Let $f(x) = e^x + x$. We
need to solve the equation $f(x) = 0$. From the graph of f,
we get $x \approx -0.57$.

60. $2^{-x} = x - 1$ $\Leftrightarrow$ $2^{-x} - x + 1 = 0$. Let
$f(x) = 2^{-x} - x + 1$. We need to solve the equation
$f(x) = 0$. From the graph of f, we get $x \approx 1.38$.

61. $4^{-x} = \sqrt{x}$ $\Leftrightarrow$ $4^{-x} - \sqrt{x} = 0$. Let $f(x) = 4^{-x} - \sqrt{x}$. We need to solve the equation $f(x) = 0$. From the graph of f, we get $x \approx 0.36$.

62. $e^{x^2} - 2 = x^3 - x$ $\Leftrightarrow$ $e^{x^2} - 2 - x^3 + x = 0$. Let $f(x) = e^{x^2} - 2 - x^3 + x$. We need to solve the equation $f(x) = 0$. From the graph of f, we get $x \approx -0.89$ or $x \approx 0.71$.

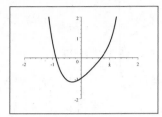

63. $\log(x-2) + \log(9-x) < 1$ $\Leftrightarrow$ $\log[(x-2)(9-x)] < 1$ $\Leftrightarrow$ $\log(-x^2 + 11x - 18) < 1 \Rightarrow$ $-x^2 + 11x - 18 < 10^1$ $\Leftrightarrow$ $0 < x^2 - 11x + 28$ $\Leftrightarrow$ $0 < (x-7)(x-4)$. Also, since the domain of a logarithm is positive we must have $0 < -x^2 + 11x - 18$ $\Leftrightarrow$ $0 < (x-2)(9-x)$. Using the methods from Chapter 1 with the endpoints 2, 4, 7, 9 for the intervals, we make the following table:

Interval	$(-\infty, 2)$	$(2, 4)$	$(4, 7)$	$(7, 9)$	$(9, \infty)$
Sign of $x - 7$	$-$	$-$	$-$	$+$	$+$
Sign of $x - 4$	$-$	$-$	$+$	$+$	$+$
Sign of $x - 2$	$-$	$+$	$+$	$+$	$+$
Sign of $9 - x$	$+$	$+$	$+$	$+$	$-$
Sign of $(x-7)(x-4)$	$+$	$+$	$-$	$+$	$+$
Sign of $(x-2)(9-x)$	$-$	$+$	$+$	$+$	$-$

Thus the solution is $(2, 4) \cup (7, 9)$.

64. $3 \le \log_2 x \le 4$ $\Leftrightarrow$ $2^3 \le x \le 2^4$ $\Leftrightarrow$ $8 \le x \le 16$.

65. $2 < 10^x < 5$ $\Leftrightarrow$ $\log 2 < x < \log 5$ $\Leftrightarrow$ $0.3010 < x < 0.6990$. Hence the solution to the inequality is approximately the interval $(0.3010, 0.6990)$.

66. $x^2 e^x - 2e^x < 0$ $\Leftrightarrow$ $e^x(x^2 - 2) < 0$ $\Leftrightarrow$ $e^x(x - \sqrt{2})(x + \sqrt{2}) < 0$. We use the methods of Chapter 1 with the endpoints $-\sqrt{2}$ and $\sqrt{2}$, noting that $e^x > 0$ for all x. We make a table:

Interval	$(-\infty, -\sqrt{2})$	$(-\sqrt{2}, \sqrt{2})$	$(\sqrt{2}, \infty)$
Sign of e^x	$+$	$+$	$+$
Sign of $(x - \sqrt{2})$	$-$	$-$	$+$
Sign of $(x + \sqrt{2})$	$-$	$+$	$+$
Sign of $e^x(x - \sqrt{2})(x + \sqrt{2})$	$+$	$-$	$+$

Thus $-\sqrt{2} < x < \sqrt{2}$.

67. (a) $A(3) = 5000\left(1 + \dfrac{0.085}{4}\right)^{4(3)} = 5000\left(1.02125^{12}\right) = 6435.09$. Thus the amount after 3 years is $\$6{,}435.09$.

(b) $10000 = 5000\left(1 + \dfrac{0.085}{4}\right)^{4t} = 5000\left(1.02125^{4t}\right)$ $\Leftrightarrow$ $2 = 1.02125^{4t}$ $\Leftrightarrow$ $\log 2 = 4t \log 1.02125$ $\Leftrightarrow$

$t = \dfrac{\log 2}{4 \log 1.02125} \approx 8.24$ years. Thus the investment will double in about 8.24 years.

68. (a) $A(2) = 6500e^{0.06(2)} \approx \$7328.73$

(b) $8000 = 6500e^{0.06t}$ $\Leftrightarrow$ $\frac{16}{13} = e^{0.06t}$ $\Leftrightarrow$ $\ln\left(\frac{16}{13}\right) = 0.06t$ $\Leftrightarrow$ $t = \frac{1}{0.06}\ln\left(\frac{16}{13}\right) \approx 3.46$. So the

investment doubles in about $3\frac{1}{2}$ years.

69. $8000 = 5000\left(1 + \frac{0.075}{4}\right)^{4t} = 5000\left(1.01875^{4t}\right)$ $\Leftrightarrow$ $1.6 = 1.01875^{4t}$ $\Leftrightarrow$ $\log 1.6 = 4t\log 1.01875$ $\Leftrightarrow$

$t = \frac{\log 1.6}{4\log 1.01875} \approx 6.33$ years. The investment will increase to \$8000 in approximately 6 years and 4 months.

70. $5000 = 4000\left(1 + \frac{0.0975}{2}\right)^{2t}$ $\Leftrightarrow$ $1.25 = (1.04875)^{2t}$ $\Leftrightarrow$ $\log 1.25 = 2t\log 1.04875$ $\Leftrightarrow$

$t = \frac{\log 1.25}{2\log 1.04875} \approx 2.344$. So it takes about $2\frac{1}{3}$ years to save \$5000.

71. $2 = e^{0.085t}$ $\Leftrightarrow$ $\ln 2 = 0.085t$ $\Leftrightarrow$ $t = \frac{\ln 2}{0.085} \approx 8.15$ years. Thus the investment will double in about 8.15 years.

72. $1435.77 = 1000\left(1 + \frac{r}{2}\right)^{2(4)}$ $\Leftrightarrow$ $1.43577 = \left(1 + \frac{r}{2}\right)^8$ $\Leftrightarrow$ $1 + \frac{r}{2} = \sqrt[8]{1.43577}$ $\Leftrightarrow$ $\frac{r}{2} = \sqrt[8]{1.43577} - 1$

$\Leftrightarrow$ $r = 2\left(\sqrt[8]{1.43577} - 1\right) \approx 0.0925$. Thus the rate was about 9.25%.

73. $r_{\text{eff}} = \left(1 + \frac{r}{n}\right)^n - 1$. Here $r = 0.08$ and $n = 12$, so $r_{\text{eff}} = \left(1 + \frac{0.08}{12}\right)^{12} - 1 = (1.0066667)^{12} - 1 = 8.30\%$.

74. $r_{\text{APY}} = e^r - 1$. Here $r = 0.05.5$ so $r_{\text{APY}} = e^{0.055} - 1 \approx 1.0565 - 1 = 0.565$. So the annual percentage yield is about 5.65%.

75. $15e^{-0.087t} = 5$ $\Leftrightarrow$ $e^{-0.087t} = \frac{1}{3}$ $\Leftrightarrow$ $-0.087t = \ln\left(\frac{1}{3}\right) = -\ln 3$ $\Leftrightarrow$ $t = \frac{\ln 3}{0.087} \approx 12.6277$. So only 5 grams remain after approximately 13 days.

76. We want to solve for t in the equation $80\left(e^{-0.2t} - 1\right) = -70$ (when motion is downwards, the velocity is negative). Then $80\left(e^{-0.2t} - 1\right) = -70$ $\Leftrightarrow$ $e^{-0.2t} - 1 = -\frac{7}{8}$ $\Leftrightarrow$ $e^{-0.2t} = \frac{1}{8}$ $\Leftrightarrow$ $-0.2t = \ln\left(\frac{1}{8}\right)$ $\Leftrightarrow$ $t = \frac{\ln\left(\frac{1}{8}\right)}{-0.2} \approx 10.4$ seconds. Thus the velocity is 70 ft/sec after about 10 seconds.

77. (a) $P(3) = \frac{10}{1 + 4e^{-0.8(3)}} = 7.337$, so there are approximately 7337 fish after 3 years.

(b) We solve for t. $\frac{10}{1 + 4e^{-0.8t}} = 5$ $\Leftrightarrow$ $1 + 4e^{-0.8t} = \frac{10}{5} = 2$ $\Leftrightarrow$ $4e^{-0.8t} = 1$ $\Leftrightarrow$ $e^{-0.8t} = 0.25$ $\Leftrightarrow$

$-0.8t = \ln 0.25$ $\Leftrightarrow$ $t = \frac{\ln 0.25}{-0.8} = 1.73$. So the population will reach 5000 fish in about 1 year and 9 months.

78. (a) $I = 10e^{-0.008(30)} = 10e^{-0.24} = 7.87$. So at 30 ft the intensity is 7.87 lumens.

(b) $5 = 10e^{-0.008x}$ $\Leftrightarrow$ $e^{-0.008x} = \frac{1}{2}$ $\Leftrightarrow$ $-0.008x = \ln\left(\frac{1}{2}\right)$ $\Leftrightarrow$ $x = \frac{\ln(1/2)}{-0.008} \approx 86.6$. So the intensity drops to 25 lumens at 86.6 ft.

79. (a) $\ln\left(\frac{P}{P_0}\right) = -\frac{h}{k}$ $\Leftrightarrow$ $\frac{P}{P_0} = e^{-h/k}$ $\Leftrightarrow$ $P = P_0 e^{-h/k}$. Substituting $k = 7$ and $P_0 = 100$ we get

$P = 100e^{-h/7}$.

(b) When $h = 4$ we have $P = 100e^{-4/7} \approx 56.47$ kPa.

80. (a) $\ln\left(\frac{T - 20}{200}\right) = -0.11t$ $\Leftrightarrow$ $\frac{T - 20}{200} = e^{-0.11t}$ $\Leftrightarrow$ $T - 20 = 200e^{-0.11t}$ $\Leftrightarrow$ $T = 20 + 200e^{-0.11t}$.

(b) When $t = 20$ we have $T = 20 + 200e^{-0.11(20)} = 20 + 200e^{-2.2} \approx 42.2°$ F.

81. (a) $I = \frac{60}{13}\left(1 - e^{-13t/5}\right)$ $\Leftrightarrow$ $\frac{13}{60}I = 1 - e^{-13t/5}$ $\Leftrightarrow$ $e^{-13t/5} = 1 - \frac{13}{60}I$ $\Leftrightarrow$ $-\frac{13}{5}t = \ln\left(1 - \frac{13}{60}I\right)$ $\Leftrightarrow$
$t = -\frac{5}{13}\ln\left(1 - \frac{13}{60}I\right)$.

(b) Substituting $I = 2$, we have $t = -\frac{5}{13}\ln\left[1 - \frac{13}{60}(2)\right] \approx 0.218$ seconds.

82. (a) $P = M - Ce^{-kt}$ $\Leftrightarrow$ $Ce^{-kt} = M - P$ $\Leftrightarrow$ **(c)**

$e^{-kt} = \frac{M - P}{C}$ $\Leftrightarrow$ $-kt = \ln\left(\frac{M - P}{C}\right)$ $\Leftrightarrow$ $t = -\frac{1}{k}$

$\ln\left(\frac{M - P}{C}\right)$

(b) $P(t) = 20 - 14e^{-0.024t}$. Substituting $M = 20$, $C = 14$, $k = 0.024$,

and $P = 12$ into $t = -\frac{1}{k}\ln\left(\frac{M - P}{C}\right)$, we have

$t = -\frac{1}{0.024}\ln\left(\frac{20 - 12}{14}\right) \approx 23.32$. So it takes about 23 months.

83. Since $9^1 = 9$, $9^2 = 81$, and $9^3 = 729$, the solution of $9^x = 20$ must be between 1 and 2 (because 20 is between 9 and 81), whereas the solution to $9^x = 100$ must be between 2 and 3 (because 100 is between 81 and 729).

84. Notice that $\log\left(x^{1/\log x}\right) = \frac{1}{\log x}\log x = 1$, so $x^{1/\log x} = 10^1$ for all $x > 0$. So

$x^{1/\log x} = 5$ has no solution, and $x^{1/\log x} = k$ has a solution only when $k = 10$.

This is verified by the graph of $f(x) = x^{1/\log x}$.

85. (a) $(x-1)^{\log(x-1)} = 100(x-1)$ $\Leftrightarrow$ $\log\left((x-1)^{\log(x-1)}\right) = \log(100(x-1))$ $\Leftrightarrow$

$[\log(x-1)]\log(x-1) = \log 100 + \log(x-1)$ $\Leftrightarrow$ $[\log(x-1)]^2 - \log(x-1) - 2 = 0$ $\Leftrightarrow$

$[\log(x-1) - 2][\log(x-1) + 1] = 0$. Thus either $\log(x-1) = 2$ $\Leftrightarrow$ $x = 101$ or $\log(x-1) = -1$ $\Leftrightarrow$

$x = \frac{11}{10}$.

(b) $\log_2 x + \log_4 x + \log_8 x = 11$ $\Leftrightarrow$ $\log_2 x + \log_2 \sqrt{x} + \log_2 \sqrt[3]{x} = 11$ $\Leftrightarrow$ $\log_2\left(x\sqrt{x}\sqrt[3]{x}\right) = 11$ $\Leftrightarrow$

$\log_2\left(x^{11/6}\right) = 11$ $\Leftrightarrow$ $\frac{11}{6}\log_2 x = 11$ $\Leftrightarrow$ $\log_2 x = 6$ $\Leftrightarrow$ $x = 2^6 = 64$

(c) $4^x - 2^{x+1} = 3$ $\Leftrightarrow$ $(2^x)^2 - 2(2^x) - 3 = 0$ $\Leftrightarrow$ $(2^x - 3)(2^x + 1) = 0$ $\Leftrightarrow$ either $2^x = 3$ $\Leftrightarrow$

$x = \frac{\ln 3}{\ln 2}$ or $2^x = -1$, which has no real solution. So $x = \frac{\ln 3}{\ln 2}$ is the only real solution.

4.5 Modeling with Exponential and Logarithmic Functions

1. (a) $n(0) = 500$.

(b) The relative growth rate is $0.45 = 45\%$.

(c) $n(3) = 500e^{0.45(3)} \approx 1929$.

(d) $10{,}000 = 500e^{0.45t}$ $\Leftrightarrow$ $20 = e^{0.45t}$ $\Leftrightarrow$ $0.45t = \ln 20$ $\Leftrightarrow$ $t = \frac{\ln 20}{0.45} \approx 6.66$ hours, or 6 hours 40 minutes.

2. (a) The relative growth rate is $0.012 = 1.2\%$.

(b) $n(5) = 12e^{0.012(5)} = 12e^{0.06} \approx 12.74$ million fish.

(c) $30 = 12e^{0.012t}$ $\Leftrightarrow$ $2.5 = e^{0.012t}$ $\Leftrightarrow$ $0.012t = \ln 2.5$ $\Leftrightarrow$

$t = \dfrac{\ln 2.5}{0.012} \approx 76.36$. Thus the fish population reaches 30 million after

about 76 years.

(d)

3. (a) $r = 0.08$ and $n(0) = 18000$. Thus the population is given by the

formula $n(t) = 18{,}000e^{0.08t}$.

(b) $t = 2008 - 2000 = 8$. Then we have

$n(8) = 18000e^{0.08(8)} = 18000e^{0.64} \approx 34{,}137$. Thus there should

be 34,137 foxes in the region by the year 2008.

(c)

4. $n(t) = n_0 e^{rt}$; $n_0 = 110$ million, $t = 2020 - 1995 = 25$

(a) $r = 0.03$; $n(25) = 110{,}000{,}000e^{0.03(25)} = 110{,}000{,}000e^{0.75} \approx 232{,}870{,}000$. Thus at a 3% growth rate, the

projected population will be approximately 233 million people by the year 2020.

(b) $r = 0.02$; $n(25) = 110{,}000{,}000e^{0.02(25)} = 110{,}000{,}000e^{0.50} \approx 181{,}359{,}340$. Thus at a 2% growth rate, the

projected population will be approximately 181 million people by the year 2020.

5. (a) $n(t) = 112{,}000e^{0.04t}$.

(b) $t = 2000 - 1994 = 6$ and $n(6) = 112{,}000e^{0.04(6)} \approx 142380$. The projected population is about 142,000.

(c) $200{,}000 = 112{,}000e^{0.04t}$ $\Leftrightarrow$ $\frac{25}{14} = e^{0.04t}$ $\Leftrightarrow$ $0.04t = \ln\left(\frac{25}{14}\right)$ $\Leftrightarrow$ $t = 25\ln\left(\frac{25}{14}\right) \approx 14.5$. Since

$1994 + 14.5 = 2008.5$, the population will reach 200,000 during the year 2008.

6. (a) $n(t) = n_0 e^{rt}$ with $n_0 = 85$ and $r = 0.18$. Thus $n(t) = 85e^{0.18t}$.

(b) $n(3) = 85e^{0.18(3)} \approx 146$ frogs.

(c) $600 = 85e^{0.18t}$ $\Leftrightarrow$ $\frac{120}{17} = e^{0.18t}$ $\Leftrightarrow$ $0.18t = \ln\left(\frac{120}{17}\right)$ $\Leftrightarrow$ $t = \frac{1}{0.18}\ln\left(\frac{120}{17}\right) \approx 10.86$. So the

population will reach 600 frogs in about 11 years.

7. (a) The deer population in 1996 was 20,000.

(b) Using the model $n(t) = 20{,}000e^{rt}$ and the point $(4, 31000)$, we have $31{,}000 = 20{,}000e^{4r}$ $\Leftrightarrow$ $1.55 = e^{4r}$ $\Leftrightarrow$

$4r = \ln 1.55$ $\Leftrightarrow$ $r = \frac{1}{4}\ln 1.55 \approx 0.1096$. Thus $n(t) = 20{,}000e^{0.1096t}$

(c) $n(8) = 20{,}000e^{0.1096(8)} \approx 48{,}218$, so the projected deer population in 2004 is about 48,000.

(d) $100{,}000 = 20{,}000e^{0.1096t}$ $\Leftrightarrow$ $5 = e^{0.1096t}$ $\Leftrightarrow$ $0.1096t = \ln 5$ $\Leftrightarrow$ $t = \dfrac{\ln 5}{0.1096} \approx 14.63$. Since

$1996 + 14.63 = 2010.63$, the deer population will reach 100,000 during the year 2010.

8. (a) Since the population grows exponentially, the population is represented by $n(t) = n_0 e^{rt}$, with $n_0 = 1500$

and $n(30) = 3000$. Solving for r, we have $3000 = 1500e^{30r}$ $\Leftrightarrow$ $2 = e^{30r}$ $\Leftrightarrow$ $30r = \ln 2$ $\Leftrightarrow$

$r = (\ln 2)/30 \approx 0.023$. Thus $n(t) = 1500e^{0.023t}$.

(b) Since 2 hours is 120 minutes, the number of bacteria in 2 hours is $n(120) = 1500e^{0.023(120)} \approx 24{,}000$.

(c) We need to solve $4000 = 1500e^{0.023t}$ for t. So $4000 = 1500e^{0.023t}$ $\Leftrightarrow$ $\frac{8}{3} = e^{0.023t}$ $\Leftrightarrow$ $0.023t = \ln\frac{8}{3}$ $\Leftrightarrow$

$t = \dfrac{\ln(8/3)}{0.023} \approx 42.6$. Thus the bacteria population will reach 4000 in about 43 minutes.

9. (a) Using the formula $n(t) = n_0 e^{rt}$ with $n_0 = 8600$ and $n(1) = 10000$, we solve for r, giving $10000 = n(1) = 8600e^r$ $\Leftrightarrow$ $\frac{50}{43} = e^r$ $\Leftrightarrow$ $r = \ln\left(\frac{50}{43}\right) \approx 0.1508$. Thus $n(t) = 8600e^{0.1508t}$.

(b) $n(2) = 8600e^{0.1508(2)} \approx 11627$. Thus the number of bacteria after two hours is about 11,600.

(c) $17200 = 8600e^{0.1508t}$ $\Leftrightarrow$ $2 = e^{0.1508t}$ $\Leftrightarrow$ $0.1508t = \ln 2$ $\Leftrightarrow$ $t = \dfrac{\ln 2}{0.1508} \approx 4.596$. Thus the number of bacteria will double in about 4.6 hours.

10. (a) Using $n(t) = n_0 e^{rt}$ with $n(2) = 400$ and $n(6) = 25{,}600$, we have $n_0 e^{2r} = 400$ and $n_0 e^{6r} = 25{,}600$. Dividing the second equation by the first gives $\dfrac{n_0 e^{6r}}{n_0 e^{2r}} = \dfrac{25{,}600}{400} = 64$ $\Leftrightarrow$ $e^{4r} = 64$ $\Leftrightarrow$ $4r = \ln 64$ $\Leftrightarrow$ $r = \frac{1}{4}\ln 64 \approx 1.04$. Thus the relative rate of growth is about 104%.

(b) Since $r = \frac{1}{4}\ln 64 = \frac{1}{2}\ln 8$, we have from part (a) $n(t) = n_0 e^{\left(\frac{1}{2}\ln 8\right)t}$. Since $n(2) = 400$, we have $400 = n_0 e^{\ln 8}$ $\Leftrightarrow$ $n_0 = \dfrac{400}{e^{\ln 8}} = \frac{400}{8} = 50$. So the initial size of the culture was 50.

(c) Substituting $n_0 = 50$ and $r = 1.04$, we have $n(t) = n_0 e^{rt} = 50e^{1.04t}$.

(d) $n(4.5) = 50e^{1.04(4.5)} = 50e^{4.68} \approx 5388.5$, so the size after 4.5 hours is approximately 5400.

(e) $n(t) = 50{,}000 = 50e^{1.04t}$ $\Leftrightarrow$ $e^{1.04t} = 1000$ $\Leftrightarrow$ $1.04t = \ln 1000$ $\Leftrightarrow$ $t = \dfrac{\ln 1000}{1.04} \approx 6.64$. Hence the population will reach 50,000 after roughly $6\frac{2}{3}$ hours.

11. (a) $2n_0 = n_0 e^{0.02t}$ $\Leftrightarrow$ $2 = e^{0.02t}$ $\Leftrightarrow$ $0.02t = \ln 2$ $\Leftrightarrow$ $t = 50\ln 2 \approx 34.65$. So we have $t = 1995 + 34.65 = 2029.65$, and hence at the current growth rate the population will double by the year 2029.

(b) $3n_0 = n_0 e^{0.02t}$ $\Leftrightarrow$ $3 = e^{0.02t}$ $\Leftrightarrow$ $0.02t = \ln 3$ $\Leftrightarrow$ $t = 50\ln 3 \approx 54.93$. So we have $t = 1995 + 54.93 = 2049.93$, and hence at the current growth rate the population will triple by the year 2050.

12. (a) Calculating dates relative to 1950 gives $n_0 = 10{,}586{,}223$ and $n(30) = 23{,}668{,}562$. Then $n(30) = 10{,}586{,}223e^{30r} = 23{,}668{,}562$ $\Leftrightarrow$ $e^{30r} = \frac{23{,}668{,}562}{10{,}586{,}223} \approx 2.2358$ $\Leftrightarrow$ $30r = \ln 2.2358$ $\Leftrightarrow$ $r = \frac{1}{30}\ln 2.2358 \approx 0.0268$. Thus $n(t) = 10{,}586{,}223e^{0.0268t}$.

(b) $2(10{,}586{,}223) = 10{,}586{,}223e^{0.0268t}$ $\Leftrightarrow$ $2 = e^{0.0268t}$ $\Leftrightarrow$ $\ln 2 = 0.0268t$ $\Leftrightarrow$ $t = \dfrac{\ln 2}{0.0268} \approx 25.86$. So the population doubles in about 26 years.

(c) $t = 2000 - 1950 = 50$; $n(50) \approx 10586223e^{0.0268(50)} \approx 40{,}429{,}246$ and so the population in the year 2000 will be approximately 40,429,000.

13. $n(t) = n_0 e^{2t}$. When $n_0 = 1$, the critical level is $n(24) = e^{2(24)} = e^{48}$. We solve the equation $e^{48} = n_0 e^{2t}$, where $n_0 = 10$. This gives $e^{48} = 10e^{2t}$ $\Leftrightarrow$ $48 = \ln 10 + 2t$ $\Leftrightarrow$ $2t = 48 - \ln 10$ $\Leftrightarrow$ $t = \frac{1}{2}(48 - \ln 10) \approx 22.85$ hours.

14. From the formula for radioactive decay, we have $m(t) = m_0 e^{-rt}$, where $r = \dfrac{\ln 2}{h}$.

(a) We have $m_0 = 22$ and $h = 1600$, so $r = \dfrac{\ln 2}{1600} \approx 0.000433$ and the amount after t years is given by $m(t) = 22e^{-0.000433t}$.

(b) $m(4000) = 22e^{-0.000433(4000)} \approx 3.89$, so the amount after 4000 years is about 4 mg.

(c) We have to solve for t in the equation $18 = 22\,e^{-0.000433t}$. This gives $18 = 22e^{-0.000433t}$ $\Leftrightarrow$ $\frac{9}{11} = e^{-0.000433t}$ $\Leftrightarrow$ $-0.000433t = \ln\left(\frac{9}{11}\right)$ $\Leftrightarrow$ $t = \dfrac{\ln\left(\frac{9}{11}\right)}{-0.000433} \approx 463.4$, so it takes about 463 years.

15. (a) Using $m(t) = m_0 e^{-rt}$ with $m_0 = 10$ and $h = 30$, we have $r = \dfrac{\ln 2}{h} = \dfrac{\ln 2}{30} \approx 0.0231$. Thus $m(t) = 10e^{-0.0231t}$.

(b) $m(80) = 10e^{-0.0231(80)} \approx 1.6$ grams.

(c) $2 = 10e^{-0.0231t} \quad\Leftrightarrow\quad \frac{1}{5} = e^{-0.0231t} \quad\Leftrightarrow\quad \ln\left(\frac{1}{5}\right) = -0.0231t \quad\Leftrightarrow\quad t = \dfrac{-\ln 5}{-0.0231} \approx 70$ years.

16. (a) $m(60) = 40e^{-0.0277(60)} \approx 7.59$, so the mass remaining after 60 days is about 8 g.

(b) $10 = 40e^{-0.0277t} \quad\Leftrightarrow\quad 0.25 = e^{-0.0277t} \quad\Leftrightarrow\quad \ln 0.25 = -0.0277t \quad\Leftrightarrow\quad t = -\dfrac{\ln 0.25}{0.0277} \approx 50.05$, so it takes about 50 days.

(c) We need to solve for t in the equation $20 = 40e^{-0.0277t}$. We have $20 = 40e^{-0.0277t} \quad\Leftrightarrow\quad e^{-0.277t} = \frac{1}{2} \quad\Leftrightarrow$

$-0.0277t = \ln\frac{1}{2} \quad\Leftrightarrow\quad t = \dfrac{\ln\frac{1}{2}}{-0.0277} \approx 25.02$. Thus the half-life of thorium-234 is about 25 days.

17. By the formula in the text, $m(t) = m_0 e^{-rt}$ where $r = \dfrac{\ln 2}{h}$, so $m(t) = 50e^{-[(\ln 2)/28]t}$. We need to solve

for t in the equation $32 = 50e^{-[(\ln 2)/28]t}$. This gives $e^{-[(\ln 2)/28]t} = \frac{32}{50} \quad\Leftrightarrow\quad -\dfrac{\ln 2}{28}t = \ln\left(\frac{32}{50}\right) \quad\Leftrightarrow$

$t = -\dfrac{28}{\ln 2} \cdot \ln\left(\frac{32}{50}\right) \approx 18.03$, so it takes about 18 years.

18. From the formula for radioactive decay, we have $m(t) = m_0 e^{-rt}$, where $r = \dfrac{\ln 2}{h}$. Since $h = 30$, we have

$r = \dfrac{\ln 2}{30} \approx 0.0231$ and $m(t) = m_0 e^{-0.0231t}$. In this exercise we have to solve for t in the equation $0.05m_0 = m_0 e^{-0.0231t}$

$\Leftrightarrow\quad e^{-0.0231t} = 0.05 \quad\Leftrightarrow\quad -0.0231t = \ln 0.05 \quad\Leftrightarrow\quad t = \dfrac{\ln 0.05}{-0.0231} \approx 129.7$. So it will take about 130 s.

19. By the formula for radioactive decay, we have $m(t) = m_0 e^{-rt}$, where $r = \dfrac{\ln 2}{h}$, in other words $m(t) = m_0 e^{-[(\ln 2)/h]t}$.

In this exercise we have to solve for h in the equation $200 = 250e^{-[(\ln 2)/h]\cdot 48} \quad\Leftrightarrow\quad 0.8 = e^{-[(\ln 2)/h]\cdot 48} \quad\Leftrightarrow$

$\ln(0.8) = -\dfrac{\ln 2}{h} \cdot 48 \quad\Leftrightarrow\quad h = -\dfrac{\ln 2}{\ln 0.8} \cdot 48 \approx 149.1$ hours. So the half-life is approximately 149 hours.

20. From the formula for radioactive decay, we have $m(t) = m_0 e^{-rt}$, where $r = \dfrac{\ln 2}{h}$. In other words, $m(t) = m_0 e^{-[(\ln 2)/h]t}$.

(a) Using $m(3) = 0.58m_0$, we have to solve for h in the equation $0.58m_0 = m(3) = m_0 e^{-[(3\ln 2)/h]3}$.

Then $0.58m_0 = m_0 e^{-[(3\ln 2)/h]} \quad\Leftrightarrow\quad e^{-[(3\ln 2)/h]} = 0.58 \quad\Leftrightarrow\quad -\dfrac{3\ln 2}{h} = \ln 0.58 \quad\Leftrightarrow$

$h = -\dfrac{3\ln 2}{\ln 0.58} \approx 3.82$ days. Thus the half-life of Radon-222 is about 3.82 days.

(b) Here we have to solve for t in the equation $0.2m_0 = m_0 e^{-[(\ln 2)/3.82]t}$. So we have $0.2m_0 = m_0 e^{-[(\ln 2)/3.82]t} \quad\Leftrightarrow$

$0.2 = e^{-[(\ln 2)/3.82]t} \quad\Leftrightarrow\quad -\dfrac{\ln 2}{3.82}t = \ln 0.2 \quad\Leftrightarrow\quad t = -\dfrac{3.82\ln 0.2}{\ln 2} \approx 8.87$. So it takes roughly 9 days for a sample of Radon-222 to decay to 20% of its original mass.

21. By the formula in the text, $m(t) = m_0 e^{-[(\ln 2)/h]\cdot t}$, so we have $0.65 = 1 \cdot e^{-[(\ln 2)/5730]\cdot t} \quad\Leftrightarrow\quad \ln(0.65) = -\dfrac{\ln 2}{5730}t$

$\Leftrightarrow\quad t = -\dfrac{5730\ln 0.65}{\ln 2} \approx 3561$. Thus the artifact is about 3560 years old.

22. From the formula for radioactive decay, we have $m(t) = m_0 e^{-rt}$ where $r = \dfrac{\ln 2}{h}$. Since $h = 5730$, $r = \dfrac{\ln 2}{5730} \approx 0.000121$

and $m(t) = m_0 e^{-0.000121t}$. We need to solve for t in the equation $0.59m_0 = m_0 e^{-0.000121t} \quad\Leftrightarrow\quad e^{-0.000121t} = 0.59$

$\Leftrightarrow\quad -0.000121t = \ln 0.59 \quad\Leftrightarrow\quad t = \dfrac{\ln 0.59}{-0.000121} \approx 4360.6$. So it will take about 4360 years.

23. (a) $T(0) = 65 + 145e^{-0.05(0)} = 65 + 145 = 210°$ F.

(b) $T(10) = 65 + 145e^{-0.05(10)} \approx 152.9$. Thus the temperature after 10 minutes is about $153°$ F.

(c) $100 = 65 + 145e^{-0.05t}$ $\Leftrightarrow$ $35 = 145e^{-0.05t}$ $\Leftrightarrow$ $0.2414 = e^{-0.05t}$ $\Leftrightarrow$ $\ln 0.2414 = -0.05t$ $\Leftrightarrow$
$t = -\dfrac{\ln 0.2414}{0.05} \approx 28.4$. Thus the temperature will be $100°$ F in about 28 minutes.

24. (a) We use Newton's Law of Cooling: $T(t) = T_s + D_0 e^{-kt}$ with $k = 0.1947$, $T_s = 60$, and $D_0 = 98.6 - 60 = 38.6$.
So $T(t) = 60 + 38.6e^{-0.1947t}$.

(b) Solve $T(t) = 72$. So $72 = 60 + 38.6e^{-0.1947t}$ $\Leftrightarrow$ $38.6e^{-0.1947t} = 12$ $\Leftrightarrow$ $e^{-0.1947t} = \dfrac{12}{38.6}$ $\Leftrightarrow$
$-0.1947t = \ln\left(\dfrac{12}{38.6}\right)$ $\Leftrightarrow$ $t = -\dfrac{1}{0.1947}\ln\left(\dfrac{12}{38.6}\right) \approx 6.00$, and the time of death was about 6 hours ago.

25. Using Newton's Law of Cooling, $T(t) = T_s + D_0 e^{-kt}$ with $T_s = 75$ and $D_0 = 185 - 75 = 110$. So $T(t) = 75 + 110e^{-kt}$.

(a) Since $T(30) = 150$, we have $T(30) = 75 + 110e^{-30k} = 150$ $\Leftrightarrow$ $110e^{-30k} = 75$ $\Leftrightarrow$ $e^{-30k} = \dfrac{15}{22}$ $\Leftrightarrow$
$-30k = \ln\left(\frac{15}{22}\right)$ $\Leftrightarrow$ $k = -\frac{1}{30}\ln\left(\frac{15}{22}\right)$. Thus we have $T(45) = 75 + 110e^{(45/30)\ln(15/22)} \approx 136.9$, and so the
temperature of the turkey after 45 minutes is about $137°$ F.

(b) The temperature will be $100°$F when $75 + 110e^{(t/30)\ln(15/22)} = 100$ $\Leftrightarrow$ $e^{(t/30)\ln(15/22)} = \dfrac{25}{110} = \dfrac{5}{22}$ $\Leftrightarrow$
$\left(\dfrac{t}{30}\right)\ln\left(\frac{15}{22}\right) = \ln\left(\frac{5}{22}\right)$ $\Leftrightarrow$ $t = 30\dfrac{\ln\left(\frac{5}{22}\right)}{\ln\left(\frac{15}{22}\right)} \approx 116.1$. So the temperature will be $100°$ F after 116 minutes.

26. We use Newton's Law of Cooling: $T(t) = T_s + D_0 e^{-kt}$, with $T_s = 20$ and
$D_0 = 100 - 20 = 80$. So $T(t) = 20 + 80e^{-kt}$. Since $T(15) = 75$, we have
$20 + 80e^{-15k} = 75$ $\Leftrightarrow$ $80e^{-15k} = 55$ $\Leftrightarrow$ $e^{-15k} = \dfrac{11}{16}$ $\Leftrightarrow$
$-15k = \ln\left(\frac{11}{16}\right)$ $\Leftrightarrow$ $k = -\frac{1}{15}\ln\left(\frac{11}{16}\right)$. Thus
$T(25) = 20 + 80e^{(25/15)\cdot\ln(11/16)} \approx 62.8$, and so the temperature after another
10 min is $63°$ C. The function $T(t) = 20 + 80e^{(1/15)\cdot\ln(11/16)t}$ is shown in the
viewing rectangle $[0, 30]$ by $[50, 100]$.

27. (a) $\text{pH} = -\log\left[\text{H}^+\right] = -\log\left(5.0 \times 10^{-3}\right) \approx 2.3$

(b) $\text{pH} = -\log\left[\text{H}^+\right] = -\log\left(3.2 \times 10^{-4}\right) \approx 3.5$

(c) $\text{pH} = -\log\left[\text{H}^+\right] = -\log\left(5.0 \times 10^{-9}\right) \approx 8.3$

28. $\text{pH} = -\log\left[\text{H}^+\right] = -\log\left(3.1 \times 10^{-8}\right) \approx 7.5$ and the substance is basic.

29. (a) $\text{pH} = -\log\left[\text{H}^+\right] = 3.0$ $\Leftrightarrow$ $\left[\text{H}^+\right] = 10^{-3}$ M

(b) $\text{pH} = -\log\left[\text{H}^+\right] = 6.5$ $\Leftrightarrow$ $\left[\text{H}^+\right] = 10^{-6.5} \approx 3.2 \times 10^{-7}$ M

30. (a) $\text{pH} = -\log\left[\text{H}^+\right] = 4.6$ $\Leftrightarrow$ $\left[\text{H}^+\right] = 10^{-4.6}$ M $\approx 2.5 \times 10^{-5}$ M

(b) $\text{pH} = -\log\left[\text{H}^+\right] = 7.3$ $\Leftrightarrow$ $\left[\text{H}^+\right] = 10^{-7.3}$ M $\approx 5.0 \times 10^{-8}$ M

31. $4.0 \times 10^{-7} \leq \left[\text{H}^+\right] \leq 1.6 \times 10^{-5}$ $\Leftrightarrow$ $\log\left(4.0 \times 10^{-7}\right) \leq \log\left[\text{H}^+\right] \leq \log\left(1.6 \times 10^{-5}\right)$ $\Leftrightarrow$
$-\log\left(4.0 \times 10^{-7}\right) \geq \text{pH} \geq -\log\left(1.6 \times 10^{-5}\right)$ $\Leftrightarrow$ $6.4 \geq \text{pH} \geq 4.8$. Therefore the range of pH readings for cheese
is approximately 4.8 to 6.4.

32. $2.8 \leq \text{pH} \leq 3.8$ $\Leftrightarrow$ $-2.8 \geq -\text{pH} \geq -3.8$ $\Leftrightarrow$ $10^{-2.8} \geq 10^{-\text{pH}} \geq 10^{-3.8}$ $\Leftrightarrow$
$1.58 \times 10^{-3} \geq \left[\text{H}^+\right] \geq 1.58 \times 10^{-4}$. The range of $\left[\text{H}^+\right]$ is 1.58×10^{-4} to 1.58×10^{-3}.

33. Let I_0 be the intensity of the smaller earthquake and I_1 the intensity of the larger earthquake. Then $I_1 = 20I_0$. Notice that $M_0 = \log\left(\dfrac{I_0}{S}\right) = \log I_0 - \log S$ and $M_1 = \log\left(\dfrac{I_1}{S}\right) = \log\left(\dfrac{20I_0}{S}\right) = \log 20 + \log I_0 - \log S$. Then

$M_1 - M_0 = \log 20 + \log I_0 - \log S - \log I_0 + \log S = \log 20 \approx 1.3$. Therefore the magnitude is 1.3 times larger.

34. Let the subscript S represent the San Francisco earthquake and J the Japan earthquake. Then we have

$$M_S = \log\left(\frac{I_S}{S}\right) = 8.3 \quad \Leftrightarrow \quad I_S = S \cdot 10^{8.3} \text{ and } M_J = \log\left(\frac{I_J}{S}\right) = 4.9 \quad \Leftrightarrow \quad I_J = S \cdot 10^{4.9}. \text{ So}$$

$\dfrac{I_S}{I_J} = \dfrac{10^{8.3}}{10^{4.9}} = 10^{3.4} \approx 2511.9$, and so the San Francisco earthquake was 2500 times more intense than the Japan earthquake.

35. Let the subscript A represent the Alaska earthquake and S represent the San Francisco earthquake. Then

$$M_A = \log\left(\frac{I_A}{S}\right) = 8.6 \quad \Leftrightarrow \quad I_A = S \cdot 10^{8.6} \text{ ; also, } M_S = \log\left(\frac{I_S}{S}\right) = 8.3 \quad \Leftrightarrow \quad I_S = S \cdot 10^{8.6}. \text{So}$$

$\dfrac{I_A}{I_S} = \dfrac{S \cdot 10^{8.6}}{S \cdot 10^{8.3}} = 10^{0.3} \approx 1.995$, and hence the Alaskan earthquake was roughly twice as intense as the San Francisco earthquake.

36. Let the subscript N represent the Northridge, California earthquake and K the Kobe, Japan earthquake. Then

$$M_N = \log\left(\frac{I_N}{S}\right) = 6.8 \quad \Leftrightarrow \quad I_N = S \cdot 10^{6.8} \text{ and } M_K = \log\left(\frac{I_K}{S}\right) = 7.2 \quad \Leftrightarrow \quad I_K = S \cdot 10^{7.2}. \text{ So}$$

$\dfrac{I_K}{I_N} = \dfrac{10^{7.2}}{10^{6.8}} = 10^{0.4} \approx 2.51$, and so the Kobe, Japan earthquake was 2.5 times more intense than the Northridge, California earthquake.

37. Let the subscript M represent the Mexico City earthquake, and T represent the Tangshan earthquake. We have

$$\frac{I_T}{I_M} = 1.26 \quad \Leftrightarrow \quad \log 1.26 = \log\frac{I_T}{I_M} = \log\frac{I_T/S}{I_M/S} = \log\frac{I_T}{S} - \log\frac{I_M}{S} = M_T - M_M. \text{ Therefore}$$

$M_T = M_M + \log 1.26 \approx 8.1 + 0.1 = 8.2$. Thus the magnitude of the Tangshan earthquake was roughly 8.2.

38. $\beta = 10\log\left(\dfrac{I}{I_0}\right) = 10\log\left(\dfrac{2.0 \times 10^{-5}}{1.0 \times 10^{-12}}\right) = 10\log\left(2 \times 10^7\right) = 10\left(\log 2 + \log 10^7\right) = 10\left(\log 2 + 7\right) \approx 73.$

Therefore the intensity level was 73 dB.

39. $98 = 10\log\left(\dfrac{I}{10^{-12}}\right) \quad \Leftrightarrow \quad \log\left(I \cdot 10^{12}\right) = 9.8 \quad \Leftrightarrow \quad \log I = 9.8 - \log 10^{12} = -2.2 \quad \Leftrightarrow$

$I = 10^{-2.2} \approx 6.3 \times 10^{-3}$. So the intensity was 6.3×10^{-3} watts/m^2.

40. Let the subscript M represent the power mower and C the rock concert. Then $106 = 10\log\left(\dfrac{I_M}{10^{-12}}\right) \quad \Leftrightarrow$

$\log\left(I_M \cdot 10^{12}\right) = 10.6 \quad \Leftrightarrow \quad I_M \cdot 10^{12} = 10^{10.6}$. Also $120 = 10\log\left(\dfrac{I_C}{10^{-12}}\right) \quad \Leftrightarrow \quad \log\left(I_C \cdot 10^{12}\right) = 12.0 \quad \Leftrightarrow$

$I_C \cdot 10^{12} = 10^{12.0}$. So $\dfrac{I_C}{I_M} = \dfrac{10^{12}}{10^{10.6}} = 10^{1.4} \approx 25.12$, and so the ratio of intensity is roughly 25.

41. (a) $\beta_1 = 10\log\left(\dfrac{I_1}{I_0}\right)$ and $I_1 = \dfrac{k}{d_1^2} \Leftrightarrow \beta_1 = 10\log\left(\dfrac{k}{d_1^2 I_0}\right) = 10\left[\log\left(\dfrac{k}{I_0}\right) - 2\log d_1\right] = 10\log\left(\dfrac{k}{I_0}\right) - 20\log d_1.$

Similarly, $\beta_2 = 10\log\left(\dfrac{k}{I_0}\right) - 20\log d_2$. Substituting the expression for β_1 gives

$\beta_2 = 10\log\left(\dfrac{k}{I_0}\right) - 20\log d_1 + 20\log d_1 - 20\log d_2 = \beta_1 + 20\log d_1 - 20\log d_2 = \beta_1 + 20\log\left(\dfrac{d_1}{d_2}\right).$

(b) $\beta_1 = 120$, $d_1 = 2$, and $d_2 = 10$. Then $\beta_2 = \beta_1 + 20\log\left(\dfrac{d_1}{d_2}\right) = 120 + 20\log\left(\frac{2}{10}\right) = 120 + 20\log 0.2 \approx 106$, and so the intensity level at 10 m is approximately 106 dB.

Chapter 4 Review

1. $f(x) = 2^{-x+1}$. Domain $(-\infty, \infty)$, range $(0, \infty)$, asymptote $y = 0$.

2. $f(x) = 3^{x-2}$. domain $(-\infty, \infty)$, range $(0, \infty)$, asymptote $y = 0$.

3. $g(x) = 3 + 2^x$. Domain $(-\infty, \infty)$, range $(3, \infty)$, asymptote $y = 3$.

4. $g(x) = 5^{-x} - 5$. Domain $(-\infty, \infty)$, range $(-5, \infty)$, asymptote $y = -5$.

5. $f(x) = \log_3(x - 1)$. Domain $(1, \infty)$, range $(-\infty, \infty)$, asymptote $x = 1$.

6. $g(x) = \log(-x)$. Domain $(-\infty, 0)$, range $(-\infty, \infty)$, asymptote $x = 0$.

7. $f(x) = 2 - \log_2 x$. Domain $(0, \infty)$, range $(-\infty, \infty)$, asymptote $x = 0$.

8. $f(x) = 3 + \log_5(x + 4)$. Domain $(-4, \infty)$, range $(-\infty, \infty)$, asymptote $x = -4$.

9. $F(x) = e^x - 1$. Domain $(-\infty, \infty)$, range $(-1, \infty)$, asymptote $y = -1$.

10. $G(x) = \frac{1}{2}e^{x-1}$. Domain $(-\infty, \infty)$, range $(0, \infty)$, asymptote $y = 0$.

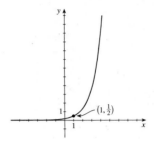

11. $g(x) = 2\ln x$. Domain $(0, \infty)$, range $(-\infty, \infty)$, asymptote $x = 0$.

12. $g(x) = \ln(x^2)$. Domain
$\{x \mid x \neq 0\} = (-\infty, 0) \cup (0, \infty)$, range $(-\infty, \infty)$, asymptote $x = 0$.

13. $f(x) = 10^{x^2} + \log(1 - 2x)$. Since $\log u$ is defined only for $u > 0$, we require $1 - 2x > 0$ $\Leftrightarrow$ $-2x > -1$ $\Leftrightarrow$ $x < \frac{1}{2}$, and so the domain is $\left(-\infty, \frac{1}{2}\right)$.

14. $g(x) = \ln(2 + x - x^2)$. We must have $2 + x - x^2 > 0$ (since $\ln y$ is defined only for $y > 0$) $\Leftrightarrow$ $x^2 - x - 2 < 0$ $\Leftrightarrow$ $(x - 2)(x + 1) < 0$. The endpoints of the intervals are 2 and -1.

Interval	$(-\infty, -1)$	$(-1, 2)$	$(2, \infty)$
Sign of $x - 2$	$-$	$-$	$+$
Sign of $x + 1$	$-$	$+$	$+$
Sign of $(x - 2)(x + 1)$	$+$	$-$	$+$

Thus the domain is $(-1, 2)$.

15. $h(x) = \ln(x^2 - 4)$. We must have $x^2 - 4 > 0$ (since $\ln y$ is defined only for $y > 0$) $\Leftrightarrow$ $x^2 - 4 > 0$ $\Leftrightarrow$ $(x - 2)(x + 2) > 0$. The endpoints of the intervals are -2 and 2.

Interval	$(-\infty, -2)$	$(-2, 2)$	$(2, \infty)$
Sign of $x - 2$	$-$	$-$	$+$
Sign of $x + 2$	$-$	$+$	$+$
Sign of $(x - 2)(x + 2)$	$+$	$-$	$+$

Thus the domain is $(-\infty, -2) \cup (2, \infty)$.

16. $k(x) = \ln|x|$. We must have $|x| > 0$. So $|x| > 0$ $\Leftrightarrow$ $-x > 0$ or $x > 0$. Since $-x > 0$ $\Leftrightarrow$ $x < 0$, the domain is $x < 0$ or $x > 0$ which is equivalent to $x \neq 0$. In interval notation, $(-\infty, 0) \cup (0, \infty)$.

17. $\log_2 1024 = 10 \quad \Leftrightarrow \quad 2^{10} = 1024$

18. $\log_6 37 = x \quad \Leftrightarrow \quad 6^x = 37$

19. $\log x = y \quad \Leftrightarrow \quad 10^y = x$

20. $\ln c = 17 \quad \Leftrightarrow \quad e^{17} = c$

21. $2^6 = 64 \quad \Leftrightarrow \quad \log_2 64 = 6$

22. $49^{-1/2} = \frac{1}{7} \quad \Leftrightarrow \quad \log_{49} \frac{1}{7} = -\frac{1}{2}$

23. $10^x = 74 \quad \Leftrightarrow \quad \log_{10} 74 = x \quad \Leftrightarrow \quad \log 74 = x$

24. $e^k = m \quad \Leftrightarrow \quad \ln m = k$

25. $\log_2 128 = \log_2 (2^7) = 7$

26. $\log_8 1 = \log_8 (8^0) = 0$

27. $10^{\log 45} = 45$

28. $\log 0.000001 = \log 10^{-6} = -6$

29. $\ln (e^6) = 6$

30. $\log_4 8 = \log_4 \left(4^{3/2}\right) = \frac{3}{2}$

31. $\log_3 \frac{1}{27} = \log_3 3^{-3} = -3$

32. $2^{\log_2 13} = 13$

33. $\log_5 \sqrt{5} = \log_5 5^{1/2} = \frac{1}{2}$

34. $e^{2\ln 7} = \left(e^{\ln 7}\right)^2 = 7^2 = 49$

35. $\log 25 + \log 4 = \log (25 \cdot 4) = \log 10^2 = 2$

36. $\log_3 \sqrt{243} = \log_3 \left(3^{5/2}\right) = \frac{5}{2}$

37. $\log_2 \left(16^{23}\right) = \log_2 \left(2^4\right)^{23} = \log_2 2^{92} = 92$

38. $\log_5 250 - \log_5 2 = \log_5 \frac{250}{2} = \log_5 125 = \log_5 5^3 = 3$

39. $\log_8 6 - \log_8 3 + \log_8 2 = \log_8 \left(\frac{6}{3} \cdot 2\right) = \log_8 4 = \log_8 8^{2/3} = \frac{2}{3}$

40. $\log_{10} \left(\log_{10} 10^{100}\right) = \log_{10} 100 = \log_{10} 10^2 = 2$

41. $\log \left(AB^2 C^3\right) = \log A + 2\log B + 3\log C$

42. $\log_2 \left(x\sqrt{x^2 + 1}\right) = \log_2 x + \log_2 \sqrt{x^2 + 1} = \log_2 x + \frac{1}{2} \log_2 \left(x^2 + 1\right)$

43. $\ln \sqrt{\dfrac{x^2 - 1}{x^2 + 1}} = \frac{1}{2} \ln \left(\dfrac{x^2 - 1}{x^2 + 1}\right) = \frac{1}{2} \left[\ln \left(x^2 - 1\right) - \ln \left(x^2 + 1\right)\right]$

44. $\log \left(\dfrac{4x^3}{y^2 (x - 1)^5}\right) = \log \left(4x^3\right) - \log \left[y^2 (x - 1)^5\right] = \log 4 + 3\log x - [2\log y + 5\log (x - 1)]$

45. $\log_5 \left(\dfrac{x^2 (1 - 5x)^{3/2}}{\sqrt{x^3 - x}}\right) = \log_5 x^2 (1 - 5x)^{3/2} - \log_5 \sqrt{x (x^2 - 1)} = 2\log_5 x + \frac{3}{2} \log_5 (1 - 5x) - \frac{1}{2} \log_5 \left(x^3 - x\right)$

46. $\ln \left(\dfrac{\sqrt[3]{x^4 + 12}}{(x + 16) \sqrt{x - 3}}\right) = \frac{1}{3} \ln \left(x^4 + 12\right) - \left[\ln (x + 16) + \frac{1}{2} \ln (x - 3)\right]$

47. $\log 6 + 4\log 2 = \log 6 + \log 2^4 = \log \left(6 \cdot 2^4\right) = \log 96$

48. $\log x + \log \left(x^2 y\right) + 3\log y = \log \left(x \cdot x^2 y \cdot y^3\right) = \log \left(x^3 y^4\right)$

49. $\frac{3}{2} \log_2 (x - y) - 2\log_2 \left(x^2 + y^2\right) = \log_2 (x - y)^{3/2} - \log_2 \left(x^2 + y^2\right)^2 = \log_2 \left(\dfrac{(x - y)^{3/2}}{(x^2 + y^2)^2}\right)$

50. $\log_5 2 + \log_5 (x + 1) - \frac{1}{3} \log_5 (3x + 7) = \log_5 [2 (x + 1)] - \log_5 (3x + 7)^{1/3} = \log_5 \left(\dfrac{2 (x + 1)}{\sqrt[3]{3x + 7}}\right)$

51. $\log (x - 2) + \log (x + 2) - \frac{1}{2} \log \left(x^2 + 4\right) = \log [(x - 2) (x + 2)] - \log \sqrt{x^2 + 4} = \log \left(\dfrac{x^2 - 4}{\sqrt{x^2 + 4}}\right)$

52. $\frac{1}{2} \left[\ln (x - 4) + 5\ln \left(x^2 + 4x\right)\right] = \frac{1}{2} \ln \left[(x - 4) \left(x^2 + 4x\right)^5\right] = \ln \sqrt{(x - 4) (x^2 + 4x)^5}$

53. $\log_2 (1 - x) = 4 \quad \Leftrightarrow \quad 1 - x = 2^4 \quad \Leftrightarrow \quad x = 1 - 2^4 = -15$

54. $2^{3x-5} = 7 \quad \Leftrightarrow \quad \log 2^{3x-5} = \log 7 \quad \Leftrightarrow \quad 3x - 5 = \dfrac{\log 7}{\log 2} \quad \Leftrightarrow \quad x = \frac{1}{3} \left(5 + \dfrac{\log 7}{\log 2}\right) \approx 2.60$

55. $5^{5-3x} = 26 \quad \Leftrightarrow \quad \log_5 26 = 5 - 3x \quad \Leftrightarrow \quad 3x = 5 - \log_5 26 \quad \Leftrightarrow \quad x = \frac{1}{3} (5 - \log_5 26) \approx 0.99$

56. $\ln(2x - 3) = 14$ $\Leftrightarrow$ $e^{\ln(2x-3)} = e^{14}$ $\Leftrightarrow$ $2x - 3 = e^{14}$ $\Leftrightarrow$ $x = \frac{1}{2}\left(3 + e^{14}\right) \approx 601303.64$

57. $e^{3x/4} = 10$ $\Leftrightarrow$ $\ln e^{3x/4} = \ln 10$ $\Leftrightarrow$ $\frac{3x}{4} = \ln 10$ $\Leftrightarrow$ $x = \frac{4}{3}\ln 10 \approx 3.07$

58. $2^{1-x} = 3^{2x+5}$ $\Leftrightarrow$ $\log 2^{1-x} = \log 3^{2x+5}$ $\Leftrightarrow$ $(1 - x)\log 2 = (2x + 5)\log 3$ $\Leftrightarrow$

$x(2\log 3 + \log 2) = \log 2 - 5\log 3$ $\Leftrightarrow$ $x = \dfrac{\log 2 - 5\log 3}{\log 2 + 2\log 3} = \dfrac{\log \dfrac{2}{3^5}}{\log(2 \cdot 9)} \approx -1.66$

59. $\log x + \log(x + 1) = \log 12$ $\Leftrightarrow$ $\log[x(x + 1)] = \log 12$ $\Leftrightarrow$ $x(x + 1) = 12$ $\Leftrightarrow$ $x^2 + x - 12 = 0$ $\Leftrightarrow$
$(x + 4)(x - 3) = 0 \Rightarrow x = 3$ or -4. Because $\log x$ and $\log(x + 1)$ are undefined at $x = -4$, it follows that $x = 3$ is the
only solution.

60. $\log_8(x + 5) - \log_8(x - 2) = 1$ $\Leftrightarrow$ $\log_8\left(\dfrac{x + 5}{x - 2}\right) = 1$ $\Leftrightarrow$ $\dfrac{x + 5}{x - 2} = 8^1 = 8$ $\Leftrightarrow$ $x + 5 = 8x - 16$ $\Leftrightarrow$

$7x = 21$ $\Leftrightarrow$ $x = 3$

61. $x^2 e^{2x} + 2x e^{2x} = 8e^{2x}$ $\Leftrightarrow$ $e^{2x}\left(x^2 + 2x - 8\right) = 0$ $\Leftrightarrow$ $x^2 + 2x - 8 = 0$ (since $e^{2x} > 0$ for all x) $\Leftrightarrow$
$(x + 4)(x - 2) = 0$ $\Leftrightarrow$ $x = 2, -4$

62. $2^{3^x} = 5$ $\Leftrightarrow$ $\log 2^{3^x} = \log 5$ $\Leftrightarrow$ $3^x \log 2 = \log 5$ $\Leftrightarrow$ $3^x = \dfrac{\log 5}{\log 2}$ $\Leftrightarrow$ $\log 3^x = \log\left(\dfrac{\log 5}{\log 2}\right)$ $\Leftrightarrow$

$x\log 3 = \log\left(\dfrac{\log 5}{\log 2}\right)$ $\Leftrightarrow$ $x = \dfrac{1}{\log 3} \cdot \log\left(\dfrac{\log 5}{\log 2}\right) \approx 0.77$

63. $5^{-2x/3} = 0.63$ $\Leftrightarrow$ $\dfrac{-2x}{3}\log 5 = \log 0.63$ $\Leftrightarrow$ $x = -\dfrac{3\log 0.63}{2\log 5} \approx 0.430618$

64. $2^{3x-5} = 7$ $\Leftrightarrow$ $(3x - 5)\log 2 = \log 7$ $\Leftrightarrow$ $x = \frac{1}{3}\left(5 + \dfrac{\log 7}{\log 2}\right) \approx 2.602452$

65. $5^{2x+1} = 3^{4x-1}$ $\Leftrightarrow$ $(2x + 1)\log 5 = (4x - 1)\log 3$ $\Leftrightarrow$ $2x\log 5 + \log 5 = 4x\log 3 - \log 3$ $\Leftrightarrow$

$x(2\log 5 - 4\log 3) = -\log 3 - \log 5$ $\Leftrightarrow$ $x = \dfrac{\log 3 + \log 5}{4\log 3 - 2\log 5} \approx 2.303600$

66. $e^{-15k} = 10000$ $\Leftrightarrow$ $-15k = \ln 10000$ $\Leftrightarrow$ $k = -\frac{1}{15}\ln 10000 \approx -0.614023$

67. $y = e^{x/(x+2)}$. Vertical asymptote $x = -2$, horizontal
asymptote $y = 2.72$, no maximum or minimum.

68. $y = 2x^2 - \ln x$. Vertical asymptote $x = 0$, no horizontal
asymptote, local minimum of about 1.19 at $x \approx 0.5$.

69. $y = \log\left(x^3 - x\right)$. Vertical asymptotes $x = -1$, $x = 0$,
$x = 1$, no horizontal asymptote, local maximum of about
-0.41 when $x \approx -0.58$.

70. $y = 10^x - 5^x$. No vertical asymptote, horizontal
asymptote $y = 0$, local minimum of about -0.13 at
$x \approx -0.5$.

71. $3 \log x = 6 - 2x$. We graph $y = 3 \log x$ and $y = 6 - 2x$ in the same viewing rectangle. The solution occurs where the two graphs intersect. From the graphs, we see that the solution is $x \approx 2.42$.

72. $4 - x^2 = e^{-2x}$. From the graphs, we see that the solutions are $x \approx -0.64$ and $x \approx 2$.

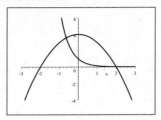

73. $\ln x > x - 2$. We graph the function $f(x) = \ln x - x + 2$, and we see that the graph lies above the x-axis for $0.16 < x < 3.15$. So the approximate solution of the given inequality is $0.16 < x < 3.15$.

74. $e^x < 4x^2 \quad \Leftrightarrow \quad e^x - 4x^2 < 0$. We graph the function $f(x) = e^x - 4x^2$, and we see that the graph lies below the x-axis for $(-\infty, -0.41) \cup (0.71, 4.31)$.

75. $f(x) = e^x - 3e^{-x} - 4x$. We graph the function $f(x)$, and we see that the function is increasing on $(-\infty, 0]$ and $[1.10, \infty)$ and that it is decreasing on $[0, 1.10]$.

76. The line has x-intercept at $x = e^0 = 1$. When $x = e^a$, $y = \ln e^a = a$. Therefore, using the point-slope equation, we have $y - 0 = \dfrac{a - 0}{e^a - 1}(x - 1) \quad \Leftrightarrow$

$$y = \frac{a}{e^a - 1}(x - 1).$$

77. $\log_4 15 = \dfrac{\log 15}{\log 4} = 1.953445$

78. $0.2 \le \log x < 2 \quad \Leftrightarrow \quad 10^{0.2} \le x < 10^2 \quad \Leftrightarrow \quad \sqrt[5]{10} \le x < 100$.

79. Notice that $\log_4 258 > \log_4 256 = \log_4 4^4 = 4$ and so $\log_4 258 > 4$. Also $\log_5 620 < \log_5 625 = \log_5 5^4 = 4$ and so $\log_5 620 < 4$. Then $\log_4 258 > 4 > \log_5 620$ and so $\log_4 258$ is larger.

80. $f(x) = 2^{3^x}$. Then $y = 2^{3^x} \quad \Leftrightarrow \quad \log_2 y = 3^x \quad \Leftrightarrow \quad \log_3(\log_2 y) = x$, and so the inverse function is $f^{-1}(x) = \log_3(\log_2 x)$. Since $\log_3 y$ is defined only when $y > 0$, we have $\log_2 x > 0 \quad \Leftrightarrow \quad x > 1$. Therefore the domain is $(1, \infty)$, and the range is $(-\infty, \infty)$.

81. $P = 12{,}000$, $r = 0.10$, and $t = 3$. Then $A = P\left(1 + \dfrac{r}{n}\right)^{nt}$.

   (a) For $n = 2$, $A = 12{,}000\left(1 + \frac{0.10}{2}\right)^{2(3)} = 12{,}000\left(1.05^6\right) \approx \$16{,}081.15$.

   (b) For $n = 12$, $A = 12{,}000\left(1 + \frac{0.10}{12}\right)^{12(3)} \approx \$16{,}178.18$.

   (c) For $n = 365$, $A = 12{,}000\left(1 + \frac{0.10}{365}\right)^{365(3)} \approx \$16{,}197.64$.

   (d) For $n = \infty$, $A = Pe^{rt} = 12{,}000e^{0.10(3)} \approx \$16{,}198.31$.

82. $P = 5000$, $r = 0.085$, and $n = 2$.

   (a) For $t = 1.5$, $A = 5000\left(1 + \frac{0.085}{2}\right)^{2(1.5)} = 5000 \cdot 1.0425^3 \approx \$5664.98$.

   (b) We want to find t such that $A = 7000$. Then $A = 5000 \cdot 1.0425^{2t} = 7000 \quad \Leftrightarrow \quad 1.0425^{2t} = \frac{7000}{5000} = \frac{7}{5} \quad \Leftrightarrow$

   $2t = \dfrac{\log\left(\frac{7}{5}\right)}{\log 1.0425} \quad \Leftrightarrow \quad t = \dfrac{\log\left(\frac{7}{5}\right)}{2\log 1.0425} \approx 4.04$, and so the investment will amount to \$7000 after approximately 4 years.

83. (a) Using the model $n(t) = n_0 e^{rt}$, with $n_0 = 30$ and $r = 0.15$, we have the formula $n(t) = 30e^{0.15t}$.

   (b) $n(4) = 30e^{0.15(4)} \approx 55$.

   (c) $500 = 30e^{0.15t} \quad \Leftrightarrow \quad \frac{50}{3} = e^{0.15t} \quad \Leftrightarrow \quad 0.15t = \ln\left(\frac{50}{3}\right) \quad \Leftrightarrow \quad t = \dfrac{1}{0.15}\ln\left(\frac{50}{3}\right) \approx 18.76$. So the stray cat population will reach 500 in about 19 years.

84. Using the model $n(t) = n_0 e^{rt}$, with $n_0 = 10000$ and $n(1) = 25000$, we have $25000 = n(1) = 10000e^{r \cdot 1} \quad \Leftrightarrow$

   $e^r = \frac{5}{2} \quad \Leftrightarrow \quad r = \ln\frac{5}{2} \approx 0.916$. So $n(t) = 10000e^{0.916t}$.

   (a) Here we must solve the equation $n(t) = 20000$ for t. So $n(t) = 10000e^{0.916t} = 20000 \quad \Leftrightarrow \quad e^{0.916t} = 2 \quad \Leftrightarrow$

   $0.916t = \ln 2 \quad \Leftrightarrow \quad t = \dfrac{\ln 2}{0.916} \approx 0.756$. Thus the doubling period is about 45 minutes.

   (b) $n(3) = 10000e^{0.916 \cdot 3} \approx 156250$, so the population after 3 hours is about 156,250.

85. (a) From the formula for radioactive decay, we have $m(t) = 10e^{-rt}$, where $r = -\dfrac{\ln 2}{2.7 \times 10^5}$. So after 1000 years the amount remaining is $m(1000) = 10 \cdot e^{\left[-\ln 2/\left(2.7 \times 10^5\right)\right] \cdot 1000} = 10e^{-(\ln 2)/\left(2.7 \times 10^2\right)} = 10e^{-(\ln 2)/270} \approx 9.97$. Therefore the amount remaining is about 9.97 mg.

   (b) We solve for t in the equation $7 = 10e^{-\left[\ln 2/\left(2.7 \times 10^5\right)\right] \cdot t}$. We have $7 = 10e^{-\left[\ln 2/\left(2.7 \times 10^5\right)\right] \cdot t} \quad \Leftrightarrow$

   $0.7 = e^{-\left[\ln 2/\left(2.7 \times 10^5\right)\right] \cdot t} \quad \Leftrightarrow \quad \ln 0.7 = -\dfrac{\ln 2}{2.7 \times 10^5} \cdot t \quad \Leftrightarrow \quad t = -\dfrac{\ln 0.7}{\ln 2} \cdot 2.7 \times 10^5 \approx 138{,}934.75$. Thus it takes about 139,000 years.

86. From the formula for radioactive decay, we have $m(t) = m_0 e^{-rt}$, where $r = \dfrac{\ln 2}{h}$. So $m(t) = m_0 e^{-[(\ln 2)/h]t}$.

   (a) Using $m(8) = 0.33m_0$, we solve for h. We have $0.33m_0 = m(8) = m_0 e^{-(\ln 2)/h} \quad \Leftrightarrow \quad 0.33 = e^{-(8\ln 2)/h} \quad \Leftrightarrow$

   $-\dfrac{8\ln 2}{h} = \ln 0.33 \quad \Leftrightarrow \quad h = -\dfrac{8\ln 2}{\ln 0.33} \approx 5.002$. So the half-life of this element is roughly 5 days.

   (b) $m(12) = m_0 e^{-[(\ln 2)/5] \cdot 12} \approx 0.19m_0$, so about 19% of the original mass remains.

87. (a) From the formula for radioactive decay, $r = \dfrac{\ln 2}{1590} \approx 0.0004359$ and $n(t) = 150 \cdot e^{-0.0004359t}$.

   (b) $n(1000) = 150 \cdot e^{-0.0004359 \cdot 1000} \approx 97.00$, and so the amount remaining is about 97.00 mg.

   (c) Find t so that $50 = 150 \cdot e^{-0.0004359t}$. We have $50 = 150 \cdot e^{-0.0004359t} \quad \Leftrightarrow \quad \frac{1}{3} = e^{-0.0004359t} \quad \Leftrightarrow$

   $t = -\dfrac{1}{0.0004359}\ln\left(\frac{1}{3}\right) \approx 2520$. Thus only 50 mg remain after about 2520 years.

88. From the formula for radioactive decay, we have $m(t) = m_0 e^{-rt}$, where $r = \dfrac{\ln 2}{h}$. Since $h = 4$, we have

$r = \dfrac{\ln 2}{4} \approx 0.173$ and $m(t) = m_0 e^{-0.173t}$.

(a) Using $m(20) = 0.375$, we solve for m_0. We have $0.375 = m(20) = m_0 e^{-0.173 \cdot 20}$ $\Leftrightarrow$ $0.03125 m_0 = 0.375$

$\Leftrightarrow$ $m_0 = \dfrac{0.375}{0.03125} \approx 12$. So the initial mass of the sample was about 12 g.

(b) $m(t) = 12 e^{-0.173t}$.

(c) $m(3) = 12 e^{-0.173 \cdot 3} \approx 7.135$. So there are about 7.1 g remaining after 3 days.

(d) Here we solve $m(t) = 0.15$ for t: $0.15 = 12 e^{-0.173t}$ $\Leftrightarrow$ $0.0125 = e^{-0.173t}$ $\Leftrightarrow$ $-0.173t = \ln 0.0125$ $\Leftrightarrow$

$t = \dfrac{\ln 0.0125}{-0.173} \approx 25.3$. So it will take about 25 days until only 15% of the substance remains.

89. (a) Using $n_0 = 1500$ and $n(5) = 3200$ in the formula $n(t) = n_0 e^{rt}$, we have $3200 = n(5) = 1500 e^{5r}$ $\Leftrightarrow$

$e^{5r} = \frac{32}{15}$ $\Leftrightarrow$ $5r = \ln\left(\frac{32}{15}\right)$ $\Leftrightarrow$ $r = \frac{1}{5}\ln\left(\frac{32}{15}\right) \approx 0.1515$. Thus $n(t) = 1500 \cdot e^{0.1515t}$.

(b) We have $t = 1999 - 1988 = 11$ so $n(11) = 1500 e^{0.1515 \cdot 11} \approx 7940$. Thus in 1999 the bird population should be about 7940.

90. We use Newton's Law of Cooling: $T(t) = T_s + D_0 e^{-kt}$ with $k = 0.0341$, $T_s = 60$ and $D_0 = 190 - 60 = 130$. So

$90 = T(t) = 60 + 130 e^{-0.0341t}$ $\Leftrightarrow$ $90 = 60 + 130 e^{-0.0341t}$ $\Leftrightarrow$ $130 e^{-0.0341t} = 30$ $\Leftrightarrow$ $e^{-0.0341t} = \frac{3}{13}$

$\Leftrightarrow$ $-0.0341t = \ln\left(\frac{3}{13}\right)$ $\Leftrightarrow$ $t = \dfrac{-\ln(3/13)}{0.0341} \approx 43.0$, so the engine cools to $90°$ F in about 43 minutes.

91. $[\text{H}^+] = 1.3 \times 10^{-8}$ M. Then $\text{pH} = -\log[\text{H}^+] = -\log(1.3 \times 10^{-8}) \approx 7.9$, and so fresh egg whites are basic.

92. $\text{pH} = 1.9 = -\log[\text{H}^+]$. Then $[\text{H}^+] = 10^{-1.9} \approx 1.26 \times 10^{-2}$ M.

93. Let I_0 be the intensity of the smaller earthquake and I_1 be the intensity of the larger earthquake. Then $I_1 = 35 I_0$. Since

$M = \log\left(\dfrac{I}{S}\right)$, we have $M_0 = \log\left(\dfrac{I_0}{S}\right) = 6.5$ and $M_1 = \log\left(\dfrac{I_1}{S}\right) = \log\left(\dfrac{35 I_0}{S}\right) = \log 35 + \log\left(\dfrac{I_0}{S}\right) = \log 35 +$

$M_0 = \log 35 + 6.5 \approx 8.04$. So the magnitude on the Richter scale of the larger earthquake is approximately 8.0.

94. Let the subscript J represent the jackhammer and W the whispering: $\beta_J = 132 = 10\log\left(\dfrac{I_J}{I_0}\right)$ $\Leftrightarrow$

$\log\left(\dfrac{I_J}{I_0}\right) = 13.2$ $\Leftrightarrow$ $\dfrac{I_J}{I_0} = 10^{13.2}$. Similarly $\dfrac{I_W}{I_0} = 10^{2.8}$. So $\dfrac{I_J}{I_W} = \dfrac{10^{13.2}}{10^{2.8}} = 10^{10.4} \approx 2.51 \times 10^{10}$, and so the ratio of intensities is 2.51×10^{10}.

Chapter 4 Test

1. $y = 2^x$ and $y = \log_2 x$.

2. $f(x) = \log(x+1)$ has domain $(-2, \infty)$, range $(-\infty, \infty)$, and vertical asymptote $x = -1$.

3. (a) $\log_3 \sqrt{27} = \log_3 \left(3^3\right)^{1/2} = \log_3 3^{3/2} = \frac{3}{2}$

(b) $\log_2 80 - \log_2 10 = \log_2 \left(\frac{80}{10}\right) = \log_2 8 = \log_2 2^3 = 3$

(c) $\log_8 4 = \log_8 8^{2/3} = \frac{2}{3}$

(d) $\log_6 4 + \log_6 9 = \log_6 (4 \cdot 9) = \log_6 6^2 = 2$

4. $\log \sqrt[3]{\dfrac{x+2}{x^4\left(x^2+4\right)}} = \frac{1}{3} \log \left(\dfrac{x+2}{x^4\left(x^2+4\right)}\right) = \frac{1}{3}\left[\log\left(x+2\right) - \left(4\log x + \log\left(x^2+4\right)\right)\right]$

$$= \frac{1}{3}\log\left(x+2\right) - \frac{4}{3}\log x - \frac{1}{3}\log\left(x^2+4\right)$$

5. $\ln x - 2\ln\left(x^2+1\right) + \frac{1}{2}\ln\left(3-x^4\right) = \ln\left(x\sqrt{3-x^4}\right) - \ln\left(x^2+1\right)^2 = \ln\left(\dfrac{x\sqrt{3-x^4}}{\left(x^2+1\right)^2}\right)$

6. (a) $2^{x-1} = 10 \quad\Leftrightarrow\quad \log 2^{x-1} = \log 10 = 1 \quad\Leftrightarrow\quad (x-1)\log 2 = 1 \quad\Leftrightarrow\quad x - 1 = \dfrac{1}{\log 2} \quad\Leftrightarrow$

$x = 1 + \dfrac{1}{\log 2} \approx 4.32$

(b) $5\ln\left(3-x\right) = 4 \quad\Leftrightarrow\quad \ln\left(3-x\right) = \frac{4}{5} \quad\Leftrightarrow\quad e^{\ln(3-x)} = e^{4/5} \quad\Leftrightarrow\quad 3 - x = e^{4/5} \quad\Leftrightarrow$

$x = 3 - e^{4/5} \approx 0.77$

(c) $10^{x+3} = 6^{2x} \quad\Leftrightarrow\quad \log 10^{x+3} = \log 6^{2x} \quad\Leftrightarrow\quad x + 3 = 2x\log 6 \quad\Leftrightarrow\quad 2x\log 6 - x = 3 \quad\Leftrightarrow$

$x\left(2\log 6 - 1\right) = 3 \quad\Leftrightarrow\quad x = \dfrac{3}{2\log 6 - 1} \approx 5.39$

(d) $\log_2\left(x+2\right) + \log_2\left(x-1\right) = 2 \quad\Leftrightarrow\quad \log_2\left(\left(x+2\right)\left(x-1\right)\right) = 2 \quad\Leftrightarrow\quad x^2 + x - 2 = 2^2 \quad\Leftrightarrow$

$x^2 + x - 6 = 0 \quad\Leftrightarrow\quad \left(x+3\right)\left(x-2\right) = 0 \Rightarrow x = -3$ or $x = 2$. However, both logarithms are undefined at $x = -3$, so the only solution is $x = 2$.

7. (a) From the formula for population growth, we have $8000 = 1000e^{r\cdot 1}$

$\Leftrightarrow\quad 8 = e^r \quad\Leftrightarrow\quad r = \ln 8 \approx 2.07944$. Thus

$n\left(t\right) = 1000e^{2.07944t}$.

(b) $n\left(1.5\right) = 1000e^{2.07944(1.5)} \approx 22{,}627$

(c) $15000 = 1000e^{2.07944t} \quad\Leftrightarrow\quad 15 = e^{2.07944t} \quad\Leftrightarrow$

$\ln 15 = 2.07944t \quad\Leftrightarrow\quad t = \dfrac{\ln 15}{2.07944} \approx 1.3$. Thus the population

will reach 15,000 after approximately 1.3 hours.

(d)

8. (a) $A\left(t\right) = 12{,}000\left(1 + \frac{0.056}{12}\right)^{12t}$, where t is in years.

(b) $A\left(t\right) = 12{,}000\left(1 + \frac{0.056}{365}\right)^{365t}$. So $A\left(3\right) = 12{,}000\left(1 + \dfrac{0.056}{365}\right)^{365(3)} = \$14{,}195.06$.

(c) $A\left(t\right) = 12{,}000\left(1 + \frac{0.056}{2}\right)^{2t} = 12{,}000\left(1.028\right)^{2t}$. So $20{,}000 = 12{,}000\left(1.028\right)^{2t} \quad\Leftrightarrow\quad 1.6667 = 1.028^{2t} \quad\Leftrightarrow$

$\ln 1.6667 = \ln 1.028^{2t} \quad\Leftrightarrow\quad \ln 1.6667 = 2t\ln 1.028 \quad\Leftrightarrow\quad t = \frac{\ln 1.6667}{2\ln 1.028} \approx 9.25$ years.

9. $f(x) = \dfrac{e^x}{x^3}$

(a)

(b) f has vertical asymptote $x = 0$ and horizontal asymptote $y = 0$.

(c) f has a local minimum of about 0.74 when $x \approx 3.00$.

(d) The range of f is approximately $(-\infty, 0) \cup [0.74, \infty)$.

(e) $\dfrac{e^x}{x^3} = 2x + 1$.

We see that the graphs intersect at $x \approx -0.85$, 0.96, and 9.92.

Focus on Modeling: Fitting Exponential and Power Curves to Data

1. (a)

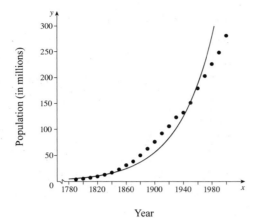

Year

(b) Using a graphing calculator, we obtain the model $y = ab^t$, where $a = 1.1806094 \times 10^{-15}$ and $b = 1.0204139$, and y is the population (in millions) in the year t.

(c) Substituting $t = 2010$ into the model of part (b), we get $y = ab^{2010} \approx 515.9$ million.

(d) According to the model, the population in 1965 should have been about $y = ab^{1965} \approx 207.8$ million.

(e) The values given by the model are clearly much too large. This means that an exponential model is *not* appropriate for these data.

2. (a)

Time (s)

(b) We let t represent the time (in seconds) and y the distance fallen (in meters). Using a calculator, we obtain the power model: $y = 4.9622t^{2.0027}$.

(c) When $t = 3$ the model predicts that $y = 44.792$ m.

3. (a) Yes.

(b)

Year t	Health Expenditures E ($bn)	ln E
1970	74.3	4.30811
1980	251.1	5.52585
1985	434.5	6.07420
1987	506.2	6.22693
1990	696.6	6.54621
1992	820.3	6.70967
1994	937.2	6.84290
1996	1039.4	6.94640
1998	1150.0	7.04752
2000	1310.0	7.17778
2001	1424.5	7.26158

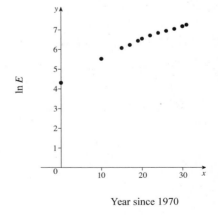

Year since 1970

Yes, the scatter plot appears to be roughly linear.

(c) Let t be the number of years elapsed since 1970. Then $\ln E = 4.551437 + 0.09238268t$, where E is expenditure in billions of dollars.

(d) $E = e^{4.551437+0.09238268t} = 94.76849e^{0.09238268t}$

(e) In 2009 we have $t = 2009 - 1970 = 39$, so the estimated 2009 health-care expenditures are $94.76849e^{0.09238268(39)} \approx 3478.5$ billion dollars.

4. (a)

Time (h)

(b) Let t be the time (in hours) and y be amount of iodine-131 (in grams). Using a calculator, we obtain the exponential model $y = ab^t$, where $a = 4.79246$ and $b = 0.99642$.

(c) To find the half-life of iodine-131, we must find the time when the sample has decayed to half its original mass. Setting $y = 2.40$ g, we get

$2.40 = 4.79246 \cdot (0.99642)^t \quad \Leftrightarrow$

$\ln 2.40 = \ln 4.79246 + t \ln 0.99642 \quad \Leftrightarrow$

$t = \dfrac{\ln 2.40 - \ln 4.79246}{\ln 0.99642} \approx 192.8$ h.

5. (a) Using a graphing calculator, we find that $I_0 = 22.7586444$ and $k = 0.1062398$.

(c) We solve $0.15 = 22.7586444e^{-0.1062398x}$ for x:

$0.15 = 22.7586444e^{-0.1062398x} \quad \Leftrightarrow$

$0.006590902 = e^{-0.1062398x} \quad \Leftrightarrow$

$-5.022065 = -0.1062398x \quad \Leftrightarrow \quad x \approx 47.27$. So light intensity drops below 0.15 lumens below around 47.27 feet.

(b)

Depth (ft)

6. (a) Using a graphing calculator, we find the power function model $y = 49.70030t^{-0.15437}$ and the exponential model $y = 44.82418 \cdot (0.99317^t)$.

(c) The power function, $y = 49.70030t^{-0.15437}$, seems to provide a better model.

(b)

Time (hours)

7. (a) Let t be the number of years elapsed since 1970, and let y be the number of millions of tons of lead emissions in year t. Using a graphing calculator, we obtain the exponential model $y = ab^t$, where $a = 301.813054$ and $b = 0.819745$.

(b) Using a graphing calculator, we obtain the fourth-degree polynomial model

$y = at^4 + bt^3 + ct^2 + dt + f$, where $a = -0.002430$, $b = 0.135159$, $c = -2.014322$, $d = -4.055294$, and $f = 199.092227$.

(d) Using the exponential model, we estimate emissions in 1972 to be $y(2) \approx 202.8$ million metric tons and emissions in 1982 to be $y(12) \approx 27.8$ million metric tons.

Using the polynomial model, we estimate emissions in 1972 to be $y(2) \approx 184.0$ million metric tons and emissions in 1982 to be $y(12) \approx 43.5$ million metric tons.

(c) The exponential and polynomial models are shown. From the graph, the polynomial model appears to fit the data better.

Year since 1970

8. Let x be the reduction in emissions (in percent), and y be the cost (in dollars). First we make a scatter plot of the data. A linear model does not appear appropriate, so we try an exponential model. Using a calculator, we get the model $y = ab^x$, where $a = 2.414$ and $b = 1.05452$. This model is graphed on the scatter plot.

Reduction in emissions (%)

9. (a)

(b)

x	y	$\ln x$	$\ln y$
2	0.08	0.69315	-2.52573
4	0.12	1.38629	-2.12026
6	0.18	1.79176	-1.71480
8	0.25	2.07944	-1.38629
10	0.36	2.30259	-1.02165
12	0.52	2.48491	-0.65393
14	0.73	2.63906	-0.31471
16	1.06	2.77259	0.05827

(b)

(c) The exponential function.

(d) $y = a \cdot b^x$ where $a = 0.057697$ and $b = 1.200236$.

10. (a)

(b)

x	y	$\ln x$	$\ln y$
10	29	2.30259	3.36730
20	82	2.99573	4.40672
30	151	3.40120	5.01728
40	235	3.68888	5.45959
50	330	3.91202	5.79909
60	430	4.09434	6.06379
70	546	4.24850	6.30262
80	669	4.38203	6.50578
90	797	4.49981	6.68085

(b)

(c) The power function is more appropriate.

(d) $y = ax^n$ where $a = 0.893421326$ and $n = 1.50983$.

11. (a) Using the `Logistic` command on a TI-83 we get $y = \dfrac{c}{1 + ae^{-bx}}$ where $a = 49.10976596$, $b = 0.4981144989$, and $c = 500.855793$.

(b) Using the model $N = \dfrac{c}{1 + ae^{-bt}}$ we solve for t. So $N = \dfrac{c}{1 + ae^{-bt}}$ $\Leftrightarrow$ $1 + ae^{-bt} = \dfrac{c}{N}$

$\Leftrightarrow$ $ae^{-bt} = \left(\dfrac{c}{N}\right) - 1 = \dfrac{c - N}{N}$ $\Leftrightarrow$ $e^{-bt} = \dfrac{c - N}{aN}$ $\Leftrightarrow$ $-bt = \ln(c - N) - \ln aN$

$\Leftrightarrow$ $t = \dfrac{1}{b}[\ln aN - \ln(c - N)]$. Substituting the values for a, b, and c, with $N = 400$ we have

$t = \dfrac{1}{0.4981144989}(\ln 19643.90638 - \ln 100.855793) \approx 10.58$ days.

12. (a) Using the `LnReg` command on a TI-83, we get $y = a + b \ln x$ where $a = -7154.888128$ and $b = 1061.006551$.

(b) Using the model $C = -7154.888128 + (1061.006551) \ln 2005 \approx 912$ metric tons.

5 Trigonometric Functions of Real Numbers

5.1 The Unit Circle

1. Since $\left(\frac{4}{5}\right)^2 + \left(-\frac{3}{5}\right)^2 = \frac{16}{25} + \frac{9}{25} = 1$, $P\left(\frac{4}{5}, -\frac{3}{5}\right)$ lies on the unit circle.

2. Since $\left(-\frac{5}{13}\right)^2 + \left(\frac{12}{13}\right)^2 = \frac{144}{169} + \frac{25}{169} = 1$, $P\left(-\frac{5}{13}, \frac{12}{13}\right)$ lies on the unit circle.

3. Since $\left(\frac{7}{25}\right)^2 + \left(\frac{24}{25}\right)^2 = \frac{49}{625} + \frac{576}{625} = 1$, $P\left(\frac{7}{25}, \frac{24}{25}\right)$ lies on the unit circle.

4. Since $\left(-\frac{5}{7}\right)^2 + \left(-\frac{2\sqrt{6}}{7}\right)^2 = \frac{25}{49} + \frac{24}{49} = 1$, $P\left(-\frac{5}{7}, -\frac{2\sqrt{6}}{7}\right)$ lies on the unit circle.

5. Since $\left(-\frac{\sqrt{5}}{3}\right)^2 + \left(\frac{2}{3}\right)^2 = \frac{5}{9} + \frac{4}{9} = 1$, $P\left(-\frac{\sqrt{5}}{3}, \frac{2}{3}\right)$ lies on the unit circle.

6. Since $\left(\frac{\sqrt{11}}{6}\right)^2 + \left(\frac{5}{6}\right)^2 = \frac{11}{36} + \frac{25}{36} = 1$, $P\left(\frac{\sqrt{11}}{6}, \frac{5}{6}\right)$ lies on the unit circle.

7. $\left(-\frac{3}{5}\right)^2 + y^2 = 1 \Leftrightarrow y^2 = 1 - \frac{9}{25} \Leftrightarrow y^2 = \frac{16}{25} \Leftrightarrow y = \pm\frac{4}{5}$. Since $P(x, y)$ is in quadrant III, y is negative, so the point is $P\left(-\frac{3}{5}, -\frac{4}{5}\right)$.

8. $x^2 + \left(-\frac{7}{25}\right)^2 = 1 \Leftrightarrow x^2 = 1 - \frac{49}{625} \Leftrightarrow x^2 = \frac{576}{625} \Leftrightarrow x = \pm\frac{24}{25}$. Since P is in quadrant IV, x is positive, so the point is $P\left(\frac{24}{25}, -\frac{7}{25}\right)$.

9. $x^2 + \left(\frac{1}{3}\right)^2 = 1 \Leftrightarrow x^2 = 1 - \frac{1}{9} \Leftrightarrow x^2 = \frac{8}{9} \Leftrightarrow x = \pm\frac{2\sqrt{2}}{3}$. Since P is in quadrant II, x is negative, so the point is $P\left(-\frac{2\sqrt{2}}{3}, \frac{1}{3}\right)$.

10. $\left(\frac{2}{5}\right)^2 + y^2 = 1 \Leftrightarrow y^2 = 1 - \frac{4}{25} \Leftrightarrow y^2 = \frac{21}{25} \Leftrightarrow y = \pm\frac{\sqrt{21}}{5}$. Since P is in quadrant I, y is positive, so the point is $P\left(\frac{2}{5}, \frac{\sqrt{21}}{5}\right)$.

11. $x^2 + \left(-\frac{2}{7}\right)^2 = 1 \Leftrightarrow x^2 = 1 - \frac{4}{49} \Leftrightarrow x^2 = 5 \Leftrightarrow x = \pm\sqrt{5}$. Since $P(x, y)$ is in quadrant IV, x is positive, so the point is $P\left(\sqrt{5}, -\frac{2}{7}\right)$.

12. $\left(-\frac{2}{3}\right)^2 + y^2 = 1 \Leftrightarrow y^2 = 1 - \frac{4}{9} \Leftrightarrow y^2 = \frac{5}{9} \Leftrightarrow y = \pm\frac{\sqrt{5}}{9}$. Since P is in quadrant II, y is positive, so the point is $P\left(-\frac{2}{3}, \frac{\sqrt{5}}{9}\right)$.

13. $\left(\frac{4}{5}\right)^2 + y^2 = 1 \Leftrightarrow y^2 = 1 - \frac{16}{25} \Leftrightarrow y^2 = \frac{9}{25} \Leftrightarrow y = \pm\frac{3}{5}$. Since its y-coordinate is positive, the point is $P\left(\frac{4}{5}, \frac{3}{5}\right)$.

14. $x^2 + \left(-\frac{1}{3}\right)^2 = 1 \Leftrightarrow x^2 = 1 - \frac{1}{9} \Leftrightarrow x^2 = \frac{8}{9} \Leftrightarrow x = \pm\frac{2\sqrt{2}}{3}$. Since its x-coordinate is positive, the point is $P\left(\frac{2\sqrt{2}}{3}, -\frac{1}{3}\right)$.

15. $x^2 + \left(\frac{2}{3}\right)^2 = 1 \Leftrightarrow x^2 = 1 - \frac{4}{9} \Leftrightarrow x^2 = \frac{5}{9} \Leftrightarrow x = \pm\frac{\sqrt{5}}{3}$. Since its x-coordinate is negative, the point is $P\left(-\frac{\sqrt{5}}{3}, \frac{2}{3}\right)$.

16. $x^2 + \left(-\frac{\sqrt{5}}{5}\right)^2 = 1 \Leftrightarrow x^2 = 1 - \frac{5}{25} \Leftrightarrow x^2 = \frac{20}{25} \Leftrightarrow x = \pm\frac{2\sqrt{5}}{5}$. Since its x-coordinate is positive, the point is $P\left(\frac{2\sqrt{5}}{5}, -\frac{\sqrt{5}}{5}\right)$.

17. $\left(-\frac{\sqrt{2}}{3}\right)^2 + y^2 = 1 \Leftrightarrow y^2 = 1 - \frac{2}{9} \Leftrightarrow y^2 = \frac{7}{9} \Leftrightarrow y = \pm\frac{\sqrt{7}}{3}$. Since P lies below the x-axis, its y-coordinate is negative, so the point is $P\left(-\frac{\sqrt{2}}{3}, -\frac{\sqrt{7}}{3}\right)$.

18. $\left(-\frac{2}{5}\right)^2 + y^2 = 1 \Leftrightarrow y^2 = 1 - \frac{4}{25} \Leftrightarrow y^2 = \frac{21}{25} \Leftrightarrow y = \pm\frac{\sqrt{21}}{5}$. Since P lies above the x-axis, its y-coordinate is positive, so the point is $P\left(-\frac{2}{5}, \frac{\sqrt{21}}{5}\right)$.

19.

t	Terminal Point
0	$(1, 0)$
$\frac{\pi}{4}$	$\left(\frac{\sqrt{2}}{2}, \frac{\sqrt{2}}{2}\right)$
$\frac{\pi}{2}$	$(0, 1)$
$\frac{3\pi}{4}$	$\left(-\frac{\sqrt{2}}{2}, \frac{\sqrt{2}}{2}\right)$
π	$(-1, 0)$

t	Terminal Point
π	$(-1, 0)$
$\frac{5\pi}{4}$	$\left(-\frac{\sqrt{2}}{2}, -\frac{\sqrt{2}}{2}\right)$
$\frac{3\pi}{2}$	$(0, -1)$
$\frac{7\pi}{4}$	$\left(\frac{\sqrt{2}}{2}, -\frac{\sqrt{2}}{2}\right)$
2π	$(1, 0)$

20.

t	Terminal Point
0	$(1, 0)$
$\frac{\pi}{6}$	$\left(\frac{\sqrt{3}}{2}, \frac{1}{2}\right)$
$\frac{\pi}{3}$	$\left(\frac{1}{2}, \frac{\sqrt{3}}{2}\right)$
$\frac{\pi}{2}$	$(0, 1)$
$\frac{2\pi}{3}$	$\left(-\frac{1}{2}, \frac{\sqrt{3}}{2}\right)$
$\frac{5\pi}{6}$	$\left(-\frac{\sqrt{3}}{2}, \frac{1}{2}\right)$
π	$(-1, 0)$

t	Terminal Point
π	$(-1, 0)$
$\frac{7\pi}{6}$	$\left(-\frac{\sqrt{3}}{2}, -\frac{1}{2}\right)$
$\frac{4\pi}{3}$	$\left(-\frac{1}{2}, -\frac{\sqrt{3}}{2}\right)$
$\frac{3\pi}{2}$	$(0, -1)$
$\frac{5\pi}{3}$	$\left(\frac{1}{2}, -\frac{\sqrt{3}}{2}\right)$
$\frac{11\pi}{6}$	$\left(\frac{\sqrt{3}}{2}, -\frac{1}{2}\right)$
2π	$(1, 0)$

21. $P(x, y) = (0, 1)$

22. $P(x, y) = (0, -1)$

23. $P(x, y) = \left(-\frac{\sqrt{3}}{2}, \frac{1}{2}\right)$

24. $P(x, y) = \left(-\frac{\sqrt{3}}{2}, -\frac{1}{2}\right)$

25. $P(x, y) = \left(\frac{1}{2}, -\frac{\sqrt{3}}{2}\right)$

26. $P(x, y) = \left(\frac{1}{2}, -\frac{\sqrt{3}}{2}\right)$

27. $P(x, y) = \left(-\frac{1}{2}, \frac{\sqrt{3}}{2}\right)$

28. $P(x, y) = (0, -1)$

29. $P(x, y) = \left(-\frac{\sqrt{2}}{2}, -\frac{\sqrt{2}}{2}\right)$

30. $P(x, y) = \left(\frac{\sqrt{3}}{2}, -\frac{1}{2}\right)$

31. Let $Q(x, y) = \left(\frac{3}{5}, \frac{4}{5}\right)$ be the terminal point determined by t.

    (a) $\pi - t$ determines the point $P(-x, y) = \left(-\frac{3}{5}, \frac{4}{5}\right)$.

    (b) $-t$ determines the point $P(x, -y) = \left(\frac{3}{5}, -\frac{4}{5}\right)$.

    (c) $\pi + t$ determines the point $P(-x, -y) = \left(-\frac{3}{5}, -\frac{4}{5}\right)$.

    (d) $2\pi + t$ determines the point $P(x, y) = \left(\frac{3}{5}, \frac{4}{5}\right)$.

32. Let $Q(x, y) = \left(\frac{3}{4}, \frac{\sqrt{7}}{4}\right)$ be the terminal point determined by t.

    (a) $-t$ determines the point $P(x, -y) = \left(\frac{3}{4}, -\frac{\sqrt{7}}{4}\right)$.

    (b) $4\pi + t$ determines the point $P(x, y) = \left(\frac{3}{4}, \frac{\sqrt{7}}{4}\right)$.

    (c) $\pi - t$ determines the point $P(-x, y) = \left(-\frac{3}{4}, \frac{\sqrt{7}}{4}\right)$.

    (d) $t - \pi$ determines the point $P(-x, -y) = \left(-\frac{3}{4}, -\frac{\sqrt{7}}{4}\right)$.

33. **(a)** $\bar{t} = \frac{5\pi}{4} - \pi = \frac{\pi}{4}$

    (b) $\bar{t} = \frac{7\pi}{3} - 2\pi = \frac{\pi}{3}$

    (c) $\bar{t} = \frac{4\pi}{3} - \pi = \frac{\pi}{3}$

    (d) $\bar{t} = \frac{\pi}{6}$

34. **(a)** $\bar{t} = \pi - \frac{5\pi}{6} = \frac{\pi}{6}$

    (b) $\bar{t} = \frac{7\pi}{6} - \pi = \frac{\pi}{6}$

    (c) $\bar{t} = 4\pi - \frac{11\pi}{3} = \frac{\pi}{3}$

    (d) $\bar{t} = 2\pi - \frac{7\pi}{4} = \frac{\pi}{4}$

35. **(a)** $\bar{t} = \pi - \frac{5\pi}{7} = \frac{2\pi}{7}$

    (b) $\bar{t} = \pi - \frac{7\pi}{9} = \frac{2\pi}{9}$

    (c) $\bar{t} = \pi - 3 \approx 0.142$

    (d) $\bar{t} = 2\pi - 5 \approx 1.283$

34. **(a)** $\bar{t} = \frac{11\pi}{5} - 2\pi = \frac{\pi}{5}$

    (b) $\bar{t} = \frac{9\pi}{7} - \pi = \frac{2\pi}{7}$

    (c) $\bar{t} = 2\pi - 6 \approx 0.283$

    (d) $\bar{t} = 7 - 2\pi \approx 0.717$

37. **(a)** $\bar{t} = \pi - \frac{2\pi}{3} = \frac{\pi}{3}$

    (b) $P\left(-\frac{1}{2}, \frac{\sqrt{3}}{2}\right)$

38. **(a)** $\bar{t} = \frac{4\pi}{3} - \pi = \frac{\pi}{3}$

    (b) $P\left(-\frac{1}{2}, -\frac{\sqrt{3}}{2}\right)$

39. **(a)** $\bar{t} = \pi - \frac{3\pi}{4} = \frac{\pi}{4}$

    (b) $P\left(-\frac{\sqrt{2}}{2}, \frac{\sqrt{2}}{2}\right)$

40. **(a)** $\bar{t} = \frac{7\pi}{3} - 2\pi = \frac{\pi}{3}$

    (b) $P\left(\frac{1}{2}, \frac{\sqrt{3}}{2}\right)$

41. (a) $\bar{t} = \pi - \frac{2\pi}{3} = \frac{\pi}{3}$
   (b) $P\left(-\frac{1}{2}, -\frac{\sqrt{3}}{2}\right)$

42. (a) $\bar{t} = \frac{7\pi}{6} - \pi = \frac{\pi}{6}$
   (b) $P\left(-\frac{\sqrt{3}}{2}, \frac{1}{2}\right)$

43. (a) $\bar{t} = \frac{13\pi}{4} - 3\pi = \frac{\pi}{4}$
   (b) $P\left(-\frac{\sqrt{2}}{2}, -\frac{\sqrt{2}}{2}\right)$

44. (a) $\bar{t} = \frac{13\pi}{6} - 2\pi = \frac{\pi}{6}$
   (b) $P\left(\frac{\sqrt{3}}{2}, \frac{1}{2}\right)$

45. (a) $\bar{t} = \frac{7\pi}{6} - \pi = \frac{\pi}{6}$
   (b) $P\left(-\frac{\sqrt{3}}{2}, -\frac{1}{2}\right)$

46. (a) $\bar{t} = \frac{17\pi}{4} - 4\pi = \frac{\pi}{4}$
   (b) $P\left(\frac{\sqrt{2}}{2}, \frac{\sqrt{2}}{2}\right)$

47. (a) $\bar{t} = 4\pi - \frac{11\pi}{3} = \frac{\pi}{3}$
   (b) $P\left(\frac{1}{2}, \frac{\sqrt{3}}{2}\right)$

48. (a) $\bar{t} = \frac{31\pi}{6} - 5\pi = \frac{\pi}{6}$
   (b) $P\left(-\frac{\sqrt{3}}{2}, -\frac{1}{2}\right)$

49. (a) $\bar{t} = \frac{16\pi}{3} - 5\pi = \frac{\pi}{3}$
   (b) $P\left(-\frac{1}{2}, -\frac{\sqrt{3}}{2}\right)$

50. (a) $\bar{t} = -10\pi - \left(-\frac{41\pi}{4}\right) = \frac{\pi}{4}$
   (b) $P\left(\frac{\sqrt{2}}{2}, -\frac{\sqrt{2}}{2}\right)$

51. $t = 1 \quad \Rightarrow \quad (0.5, 0.8)$

52. $t = 2.5 \quad \Rightarrow \quad P(-0.8, 0.6)$

53. $t = -1.1 \quad \Rightarrow \quad (0.5, -0.9)$

54. $t = 4.2 \quad \Rightarrow \quad P(-0.6, -0.9)$

55. The distances PQ and PR are equal because they both subtend arcs of length $\frac{\pi}{3}$. Since $P(x, y)$ is a point on the unit circle, $x^2 + y^2 = 1$. Now $d(P, Q) = \sqrt{(x-x)^2 + (y-(-y))^2} = 2y$ and $d(R, S) = \sqrt{(x-0)^2 + (y-1)^2} = \sqrt{x^2 + y^2 - 2y + 1} = \sqrt{2 - 2y}$ (using the fact that $x^2 + y^2 = 1$). Setting these equal gives $2y = \sqrt{2 - 2y} \quad \Rightarrow \quad 4y^2 = 2 - 2y \Leftrightarrow 4y^2 + 2y - 2 = 0 \quad \Leftrightarrow 2(2y-1)(y+1) = 0$. So $y = -1$ or $y = \frac{1}{2}$. Since P is in quadrant I, $y = \frac{1}{2}$ is the only viable solution. Again using $x^2 + y^2 = 1$ we have $x^2 + \left(\frac{1}{2}\right)^2 = 1 \Leftrightarrow x^2 = \frac{3}{4}$ $\Rightarrow \quad x = \pm\frac{\sqrt{3}}{2}$. Again, since P is in quadrant I the coordinates must be $\left(\frac{\sqrt{3}}{2}, \frac{1}{2}\right)$.

56. P is the reflection of Q about the line $y = x$. Since Q is the point $Q\left(\frac{\sqrt{3}}{2}, \frac{1}{2}\right)$ it follows that P is the point $P\left(\frac{1}{2}, \frac{\sqrt{3}}{2}\right)$.

5.2   Trigonometric Functions of Real Numbers

1.

t	$\sin t$	$\cos t$
0	0	1
$\frac{\pi}{4}$	$\frac{\sqrt{2}}{2}$	$\frac{\sqrt{2}}{2}$
$\frac{\pi}{2}$	1	0
$\frac{3\pi}{4}$	$\frac{\sqrt{2}}{2}$	$-\frac{\sqrt{2}}{2}$
π	0	-1
$\frac{5\pi}{4}$	$-\frac{\sqrt{2}}{2}$	$-\frac{\sqrt{2}}{2}$
$\frac{3\pi}{2}$	-1	0
$\frac{7\pi}{4}$	$-\frac{\sqrt{2}}{2}$	$\frac{\sqrt{2}}{2}$
2π	0	1

2.

t	$\sin t$	$\cos t$	t	$\sin t$	$\cos t$
0	0	1	π	0	-1
$\frac{\pi}{6}$	$\frac{1}{2}$	$\frac{\sqrt{3}}{2}$	$\frac{7\pi}{6}$	$-\frac{1}{2}$	$-\frac{\sqrt{3}}{2}$
$\frac{\pi}{3}$	$\frac{\sqrt{3}}{2}$	$\frac{1}{2}$	$\frac{4\pi}{3}$	$-\frac{\sqrt{3}}{2}$	$-\frac{1}{2}$
$\frac{\pi}{2}$	1	0	$\frac{3\pi}{2}$	-1	0
$\frac{2\pi}{3}$	$\frac{\sqrt{3}}{2}$	$-\frac{1}{2}$	$\frac{5\pi}{3}$	$-\frac{\sqrt{3}}{2}$	$\frac{1}{2}$
$\frac{5\pi}{6}$	$\frac{1}{2}$	$-\frac{\sqrt{3}}{2}$	$\frac{11\pi}{6}$	$-\frac{1}{2}$	$\frac{\sqrt{3}}{2}$
π	0	-1	2π	0	1

3. (a) $\sin \frac{2\pi}{3} = \frac{\sqrt{3}}{2}$

   (b) $\cos \frac{2\pi}{3} = -\frac{1}{2}$

   (c) $\tan \frac{2\pi}{3} = -\sqrt{3}$

4. (a) $\sin \frac{5\pi}{6} = \frac{1}{2}$

   (b) $\cos \frac{5\pi}{6} = -\frac{\sqrt{3}}{2}$

   (c) $\tan \frac{5\pi}{6} = -\frac{\sqrt{3}}{3}$

5. (a) $\sin \frac{7\pi}{6} = -\frac{1}{2}$

   (b) $\sin \left(-\frac{\pi}{6}\right) = -\frac{1}{2}$

   (c) $\sin \frac{11\pi}{6} = -\frac{1}{2}$

6. (a) $\cos \frac{5\pi}{3} = \frac{1}{2}$

   (b) $\cos \left(-\frac{5\pi}{3}\right) = \frac{1}{2}$

   (c) $\cos \frac{7\pi}{3} = \frac{1}{2}$

7. (a) $\cos \frac{3\pi}{4} = -\frac{\sqrt{2}}{2}$

   (b) $\cos \frac{5\pi}{4} = -\frac{\sqrt{2}}{2}$

   (c) $\cos \frac{7\pi}{4} = \frac{\sqrt{2}}{2}$

8. (a) $\sin \frac{3\pi}{4} = \frac{\sqrt{2}}{2}$

   (b) $\sin \frac{5\pi}{4} = -\frac{\sqrt{2}}{2}$

   (c) $\sin \frac{7\pi}{4} = -\frac{\sqrt{2}}{2}$

9. (a) $\sin \frac{7\pi}{3} = \frac{\sqrt{3}}{2}$

   (b) $\csc \frac{7\pi}{3} = \frac{2\sqrt{3}}{3}$

   (c) $\cot \frac{7\pi}{3} = \frac{\sqrt{3}}{3}$

10. (a) $\cos \left(-\frac{\pi}{3}\right) = \frac{1}{2}$

   (b) $\sec \left(-\frac{\pi}{3}\right) = 2$

   (c) $\tan \left(-\frac{\pi}{3}\right) = -\sqrt{3}$

11. (a) $\sin \left(-\frac{\pi}{2}\right) = -1$

   (b) $\cos \left(-\frac{\pi}{2}\right) = 0$

   (c) $\cot \left(-\frac{\pi}{2}\right) = 0$

12. (a) $\sin \left(-\frac{3\pi}{2}\right) = 1$

   (b) $\cos \left(-\frac{3\pi}{2}\right) = 0$

   (c) $\cot \left(-\frac{3\pi}{2}\right) = 0$

13. (a) $\sec \frac{11\pi}{3} = 2$

   (b) $\csc \frac{11\pi}{3} = -\frac{2\sqrt{3}}{3}$

   (c) $\sec \left(-\frac{\pi}{3}\right) = 2$

14. (a) $\cos \frac{7\pi}{6} = -\frac{\sqrt{3}}{2}$

   (b) $\sec \frac{7\pi}{6} = -\frac{2\sqrt{3}}{3}$

   (c) $\csc \frac{7\pi}{6} = -2$

15. (a) $\tan \frac{5\pi}{6} = -\frac{\sqrt{3}}{3}$

   (b) $\tan \frac{7\pi}{6} = \frac{\sqrt{3}}{3}$

   (c) $\tan \frac{11\pi}{6} = -\frac{\sqrt{3}}{3}$

16. (a) $\cot \left(-\frac{\pi}{3}\right) = -\frac{\sqrt{3}}{3}$

   (b) $\cot \frac{2\pi}{3} = -\frac{\sqrt{3}}{3}$

   (c) $\cot \frac{5\pi}{3} = -\frac{\sqrt{3}}{3}$

17. (a) $\cos \left(-\frac{\pi}{4}\right) = \frac{\sqrt{2}}{2}$

   (b) $\csc \left(-\frac{\pi}{4}\right) = -\sqrt{2}$

   (c) $\cot \left(-\frac{\pi}{4}\right) = -1$

18. (a) $\sin \frac{5\pi}{4} = -\frac{\sqrt{2}}{2}$

   (b) $\sec \frac{5\pi}{4} = -\sqrt{2}$

   (c) $\tan \frac{5\pi}{4} = 1$

19. (a) $\csc \left(-\frac{\pi}{2}\right) = -1$

   (b) $\csc \frac{\pi}{2} = 1$

   (c) $\csc \frac{3\pi}{2} = -1$

20. (a) $\sec (-\pi) = -1$

   (b) $\sec \pi = -1$

   (c) $\sec 4\pi = 1$

21. (a) $\sin 13\pi = 0$

   (b) $\cos 14\pi = 1$

   (c) $\tan 15\pi = 0$

22. (a) $\sin \frac{25\pi}{2} = 1$

   (b) $\cos \frac{25\pi}{2} = 0$

   (c) $\tan \frac{25\pi}{2}$ is undefined

23. $t = 0 \quad \Rightarrow \quad \sin t = 0, \cos t = 1, \tan t = 0, \sec t = 1, \csc t$ and $\cot t$ are undefined.

24. $t = \frac{\pi}{2} \quad \Rightarrow \quad \sin t = 1, \cos t = 0, \csc t = 1, \cot t = 0, \tan t$ and $\sec t$ are undefined.

25. $t = \pi \quad \Rightarrow \quad \sin t = 0, \cos t = -1, \tan t = 0, \sec t = -1, \csc t$ and $\cot t$ are undefined.

26. $t = \frac{3\pi}{2} \quad \Rightarrow \quad \sin t = -1, \cos t = 0, \csc t = -1, \cot t = 0, \tan t$ and $\sec t$ are undefined.

27. $\left(\frac{3}{5}\right)^2 + \left(\frac{4}{5}\right)^2 = \frac{9}{25} + \frac{1}{2} = 1$. So $\sin t = \frac{4}{5}$, $\cos t = \frac{3}{5}$, and $\tan t = \frac{\frac{4}{5}}{\frac{3}{5}} = \frac{4}{3}$.

28. $\left(-\frac{3}{5}\right)^2 + \left(\frac{4}{5}\right)^2 = \frac{9}{25} + \frac{1}{2} = 1$. So $\sin t = \frac{4}{5}$, $\cos t = -\frac{3}{5}$, and $\tan t = \frac{\frac{4}{5}}{-\frac{3}{5}} = -\frac{4}{3}$.

29. $\left(\frac{\sqrt{5}}{4}\right)^2 + \left(-\frac{\sqrt{11}}{4}\right)^2 = \frac{5}{16} + \frac{11}{16} = 1$. So $\sin t = -\frac{\sqrt{11}}{4}$, $\cos t = \frac{\sqrt{5}}{4}$, and $\tan t = \dfrac{-\frac{\sqrt{11}}{4}}{\frac{\sqrt{5}}{4}} = -\frac{\sqrt{11}}{\sqrt{5}} = -\frac{\sqrt{55}}{5}$.

30. $\left(-\frac{1}{3}\right)^2 + \left(-\frac{2\sqrt{2}}{3}\right)^2 = \frac{1}{9} + \frac{8}{9} = 1$. So $\sin t = -\frac{2\sqrt{2}}{3}$, $\cos t = -\frac{1}{3}$, and $\tan t = \dfrac{-\frac{2\sqrt{2}}{3}}{-\frac{1}{3}} = 2\sqrt{2}$.

31. $\left(-\frac{6}{7}\right)^2 + \left(\frac{\sqrt{13}}{7}\right)^2 = \frac{36}{49} + \frac{13}{49} = 1$. So $\sin t = \frac{\sqrt{13}}{7}$, $\cos t = -\frac{6}{7}$, and $\tan t = \dfrac{\frac{\sqrt{13}}{7}}{-\frac{6}{7}} = -\frac{\sqrt{13}}{6}$.

32. $\left(\frac{40}{41}\right)^2 + \left(\frac{9}{41}\right)^2 = \frac{1600}{1681} + \frac{81}{1681} = 1$. So $\sin t = \frac{9}{41}$, $\cos t = \frac{40}{41}$, and $\tan t = \dfrac{\frac{9}{41}}{\frac{40}{41}} = \frac{9}{40}$.

33. $\left(-\frac{5}{13}\right)^2 + \left(-\frac{12}{13}\right)^2 = \frac{25}{169} + \frac{144}{169} = 1$. So $\sin t = -\frac{12}{13}$, $\cos t = -\frac{5}{13}$, and $\tan t \dfrac{-\frac{12}{13}}{-\frac{5}{13}} = \frac{12}{5}$.

34. $\left(\frac{\sqrt{5}}{5}\right)^2 + \left(\frac{2\sqrt{5}}{5}\right)^2 = \frac{5}{25} + \frac{20}{25} = 1$. So $\sin t = \frac{2\sqrt{5}}{5}$, $\cos t = \frac{\sqrt{5}}{5}$, and $\tan t = \dfrac{\frac{2\sqrt{5}}{5}}{\frac{\sqrt{5}}{5}} = 2$.

35. $\left(-\frac{20}{29}\right)^2 + \left(\frac{21}{29}\right)^2 = \frac{400}{841} + \frac{441}{841} = 1$. So $\sin t = \frac{21}{29}$, $\cos t = -\frac{20}{29}$, and $\tan t = \dfrac{\frac{21}{29}}{-\frac{20}{29}} = -\frac{21}{20}$.

36. $\left(\frac{24}{25}\right)^2 + \left(-\frac{7}{25}\right)^2 = \frac{576}{625} + \frac{49}{625} = 1$. So $\sin t = -\frac{7}{25}$, $\cos t = \frac{24}{25}$, and $\tan t = \dfrac{-\frac{7}{25}}{\frac{24}{25}} = -\frac{7}{24}$.

37. (a) 0.8   **38. (a)** 0.7   **39. (a)** 0.9   **40. (a)** 0.3

   (b) 0.84147   **(b)** 0.69671   **(b)** 0.93204   **(b)** 0.28366

41. (a) 1.0   **42. (a)** -3.6 **43. (a)** -0.6 **44. (a)** 0.9

   (b) 1.02964   **(b)** -3.60210 **(b)** -0.57482 **(b)** 0.88345

45. $\sin t \cdot \cos t$. Since $\sin t$ is positive in quadrant II and $\cos t$ is negative in quadrant II, their product is negative.

46. $\tan t \cdot \sec t$ is negative in quadrant IV because $\tan t$ is negative and $\cos t$ is positive in quadrant IV.

47. $\dfrac{\tan t \cdot \sin t}{\cot t} = \tan t \cdot \dfrac{1}{\cot t} \cdot \sin t = \tan t \cdot \tan t \cdot \sin t = \tan^2 t \cdot \sin t$. Since $\tan^2 t$ is always positive and $\sin t$ is negative in quadrant III, the expression is negative in quadrant III.

48. $\cos t \cdot \sec t$ is positive in any quadrant, since $\cos t \cdot \sec t = \cos t \cdot \dfrac{1}{\cos t} = 1$, provided $\cos t \neq 0$.

49. Quadrant II   **50.** Quadrant III   **51.** Quadrant II   **52.** Quadrant II

53. $\sin t = \sqrt{1 - \cos^2 t}$ **54.** $\cos t = \sqrt{1 - \sin^2 t}$

55. $\tan t = \dfrac{\sin t}{\cos t} = \dfrac{\sin t}{\sqrt{1 - \sin^2 t}}$ **56.** $\tan t = -\dfrac{\sqrt{1 - \cos^2 t}}{\cos t}$

57. $\sec t = -\sqrt{1 + \tan^2 t}$ **58.** $\csc t = -\sqrt{1 + \cot^2 t}$

59. $\tan t = \sqrt{\sec^2 t - 1}$ **60.** $\sin t = -\sqrt{1 - \cos^2 t} = -\sqrt{1 - \dfrac{1}{\sec^2 t}}$

61. $\tan^2 t = \dfrac{\sin^2 t}{\cos^2 t} = \dfrac{\sin^2 t}{1 - \sin^2 t}$ **62.** $\sec^2 t \cdot \sin^2 t = \dfrac{1}{\cos^2 t} \cdot (1 - \cos^2 t) = \dfrac{1}{\cos^2 t} - 1$

63. $\sin t = \frac{3}{5}$ and t is in quadrant II, so the terminal point determined by t is $P\left(x, \frac{3}{5}\right)$. Since P is on the unit circle $x^2 + \left(\frac{3}{5}\right)^2 = 1$. Solving for x gives $x = \pm\sqrt{1 - \frac{9}{25}} = \pm\sqrt{\frac{1}{2}} = \pm\frac{4}{5}$. Since t is in quadrant III, $x = -\frac{4}{5}$. Thus the terminal point is $P\left(-\frac{4}{5}, \frac{3}{5}\right)$. Thus, $\cos t = -\dfrac{4}{5}$, $\tan t = -\frac{3}{4}$, $\csc t = \frac{5}{3}$, $\sec t = -\frac{5}{4}$, $\cot t = -\frac{4}{3}$.

64. $\cos t = -\frac{4}{5}$ and t lies in quadrant III, so the terminal point determined by t is $P\left(-\frac{4}{5}, y\right)$. Since P is on the unit circle $\left(-\frac{4}{5}\right)^2 + y^2 = 1$. Solving for y gives $x = \pm\sqrt{1 - \frac{1}{2}} = \pm\sqrt{\frac{9}{25}} = \pm\frac{3}{5}$. Since t is in quadrant III, $y = -\frac{3}{5}$. Thus the terminal point is $P\left(-\frac{4}{5}, -\frac{3}{5}\right)$. Thus, $\sin t = -\frac{3}{5}$, $\tan t = \frac{3}{4}$, $\csc t = -\frac{5}{3}$, $\sec t = -\frac{5}{4}$, $\cot t = \frac{4}{3}$.

65. $\sec t = 3$ and t lies in quadrant IV. Thus, $\cos t = \frac{1}{3}$ and the terminal point determined by t is $P\left(\frac{1}{3}, y\right)$. Since P is on the unit circle $\left(\frac{1}{3}\right)^2 + y^2 = 1$. Solving for y gives $y = \pm\sqrt{1 - \frac{1}{9}} = \pm\sqrt{\frac{8}{9}} = \pm\frac{2\sqrt{2}}{3}$. Since t is in quadrant IV, $y = -\frac{2\sqrt{2}}{3}$. Thus the terminal point is $P\left(\frac{1}{3}, -\frac{2\sqrt{2}}{3}\right)$. Therefore, $\sin t = -\frac{2\sqrt{2}}{3}$, $\cos t = \frac{1}{3}$, $\tan t = -2\sqrt{2}$, $\csc t = -\frac{3}{2\sqrt{2}} = -\frac{3\sqrt{2}}{4}$, $\cot t = -\frac{1}{2\sqrt{2}} = -\frac{\sqrt{2}}{4}$.

66. $\tan t = \frac{1}{4}$ and t lies in quadrant III. Since $\sec^2 t = \tan^2 t + 1$ we have $\sec^2 t = \left(\frac{1}{4}\right)^2 + 1 = \frac{1}{16} + 1 = \frac{17}{16}$. Thus $\sec t = \pm\sqrt{\frac{17}{16}} = \pm\frac{\sqrt{17}}{4}$. Since $\sec t < 0$ in quadrant III we have $\sec t = -\frac{\sqrt{17}}{4}$, so $\cos t = \frac{1}{\sec t} = \frac{1}{-\frac{\sqrt{17}}{4}} = -\frac{4}{\sqrt{17}} = -\frac{4\sqrt{17}}{17}$. Since $\tan t \cdot \cos t = \sin t$ we have $\sin t = \left(\frac{1}{4}\right)\left(-\frac{4}{\sqrt{17}}\right) = -\frac{1}{\sqrt{17}} = -\frac{\sqrt{17}}{17}$. Thus, the terminal point determined by t is $P\left(-\frac{4\sqrt{17}}{17}, -\frac{\sqrt{17}}{17}\right)$. Therefore, $\sin t = -\frac{\sqrt{17}}{17}$, $\cos t = -\frac{4\sqrt{17}}{17}$, $\csc t = -\sqrt{17}$, $\sec t = -\frac{\sqrt{17}}{4}$, $\cot t = 4$.

67. $\tan t = -\frac{3}{4}$ and $\cos t > 0$, so t is in quadrant IV. Since $\sec^2 t = \tan^2 t + 1$ we have $\sec^2 t = \left(-\frac{3}{4}\right)^2 + 1 = \frac{9}{16} + 1 = \frac{25}{16}$. Thus $\sec t = \pm\sqrt{\frac{25}{16}} = \pm\frac{5}{4}$. Since $\cos t > 0$, we have $\cos t = \frac{1}{\sec t} = \frac{1}{\frac{5}{4}} = \frac{4}{5}$. Let $P\left(\frac{4}{5}, y\right)$. Since $\tan t \cdot \cos t = \sin t$ we have $\sin t = \left(-\frac{3}{4}\right)\left(\frac{4}{5}\right) = -\frac{3}{5}$. Thus, the terminal point determined by t is $P\left(\frac{4}{5}, -\frac{3}{5}\right)$, and so $\sin t = -\frac{3}{5}$, $\cos t = \frac{4}{5}$, $\csc t = -\frac{5}{3}$, $\sec t = \frac{5}{4}$, $\cot t = -\frac{4}{3}$.

68. $\sec t = 2$ and $\sin t < 0$, so t is in quadrant IV. Thus, $\cos t = \frac{1}{2}$ and the terminal point determined by t is $P\left(\frac{1}{2}, y\right)$. Since P is on the unit circle $\left(\frac{1}{2}\right)^2 + y^2 = 1$. Solving for y gives $y = \pm\sqrt{1 - \frac{1}{4}} = \pm\sqrt{\frac{3}{4}} = \pm\frac{\sqrt{3}}{2}$. Since t is in quadrant IV, $y = -\frac{\sqrt{3}}{2}$. Thus the terminal point is $P\left(\frac{1}{2}, -\frac{\sqrt{3}}{2}\right)$, and so $\sin t = -\frac{\sqrt{3}}{2}$, $\cos t = \frac{1}{2}$, $\tan t = -\sqrt{3}$, $\csc t = -\frac{2}{\sqrt{3}} = -\frac{2\sqrt{3}}{3}$, $\cot t = -\frac{1}{\sqrt{3}} = -\frac{\sqrt{3}}{3}$.

69. $\sin t = -\frac{1}{4}$, $\sec t < 0$, so t is in quadrant III. So the terminal point determined by t is $P\left(x, -\frac{1}{4}\right)$. Since P is on the unit circle $x^2 + \left(-\frac{1}{4}\right)^2 = 1$. Solving for x gives $x = \pm\sqrt{1 - \frac{1}{16}} = \pm\sqrt{\frac{15}{16}} = \pm\frac{\sqrt{15}}{4}$. Since t is in quadrant III, $x = -\frac{\sqrt{15}}{4}$. Thus, the terminal point determined by t is $P\left(-\frac{\sqrt{15}}{4}, -\frac{1}{4}\right)$, and so $\cos t = -\frac{\sqrt{15}}{4}$, $\tan t = \frac{1}{\sqrt{15}} = \frac{\sqrt{15}}{15}$, $\csc t = -4$, $\sec t = -\frac{4}{\sqrt{15}} = -\frac{4\sqrt{15}}{15}$, $\cot t = \sqrt{15}$.

70. $\tan t = -4$ and t lies in quadrant II. Since $\sec^2 t = \tan^2 t + 1$ we have $\sec^2 t = (-4)^2 + 1 = 16 + 1 = 17$. Thus $\sec t = \pm\sqrt{17}$. Since $\sec t < 0$, we have $\sec t = -\sqrt{17}$ and $\cos t = \frac{1}{\sec t} = \frac{1}{-\sqrt{17}} = -\frac{\sqrt{17}}{17}$. Since $\tan t \cdot \cos t = \sin t$ we have $\sin t = (-4)\left(-\frac{\sqrt{17}}{17}\right) = \frac{4\sqrt{17}}{17}$. Thus, the terminal point determined by t is $P\left(-\frac{\sqrt{17}}{17}, \frac{4\sqrt{17}}{17}\right)$. Thus, $\sin t = \frac{4\sqrt{17}}{17}$, $\cos t = -\frac{\sqrt{17}}{17}$, $\csc t = \frac{\sqrt{17}}{4}$, $\sec t = -\sqrt{17}$, $\cot t = -\frac{1}{4}$.

71. $f(-x) = (-x)^2 \sin(-x) = -x^2 \sin x = -f(x)$, so f is odd.

72. $f(-x) = (-x)^2 \cos 2(-x) = x^2 \cos 2x = f(x)$, so f is even.

73. $f(-x) = \sin(-x)\cos(-x) = -\sin x \cos x = -f(x)$, so f is odd.

74. $f(-x) = e^{(-x)} \sin(-x) = -e^{-x}\sin x$ which is neither $f(x)$ nor $-f(x)$, so f is neither even nor odd.

75. $f(-x) = |-x| \cos(-x) = |x| \cos x = f(x)$, so f is even.

76. $f(-x) = -x \sin^3(-x) = -x [\sin(-x)]^3 = -x(-\sin x)^3 = x \sin^3 x = f(x)$, so f is even.

77. $f(-x) = (-x)^3 + \cos(-x) = -x^3 + \cos x$ which is neither $f(x)$ nor $-f(x)$, so f is neither even nor odd.

78. $f(-x) = \cos(\sin(-x)) = \cos(-\sin x) = \cos(\sin x) = f(x)$, so f is even.

79.

t	$y(t)$
0	4
0.25	-2.83
0.50	0
0.75	2.83
1.00	-4
1.25	2.83

80. (a) $B(6) = 80 + 7 \sin \frac{\pi}{2} = 87$

(b) $B(10.5) = 80 + 7 \sin \frac{10.5\pi}{12} \approx 82.7$

(c) $B(12) = 80 + 7 \sin \pi = 80$

(d) $B(20) = 80 + 7 \sin \frac{20\pi}{12} = 80 - \frac{7\sqrt{3}}{2} \approx 73.9$

81. (a) $I(0.1) = 0.8e^{-0.3} \sin 1 \approx 0.499$ A

(b) $I(0.5) = 0.8e^{-1.5} \sin 5 \approx -0.171$ A

82.

t	$H(t)$
0	175
1	150.4
2	100
4	38.6
6	100
8	150.3
12	58.8

83. Notice that if $P(t) = (x, y)$, then $P(t + \pi) = (-x, -y)$. Thus,

(a) $\sin(t + \pi) = -y$ and $\sin t = y$. Therefore, $\sin(t + \pi) = -\sin t$.

(b) $\cos(t + \pi) = -x$ and $\cos t = x$. Therefore, $\cos(t + \pi) = -\cos t$.

(c) $\tan(t + \pi) = \dfrac{\sin(t + \pi)}{\cos(t + \pi)} = \dfrac{-y}{-x} = \dfrac{y}{x} = \dfrac{\sin t}{\cos t} = \tan t$.

84. To prove that $\triangle AOB = \triangle CDO$, first note that $OB = OD = 1$ and $\angle OAB = \angle OCD = \frac{\pi}{2}$. Now $\angle COD + \angle AOB + \frac{\pi}{2} = \pi \quad \Leftrightarrow \quad \angle COD = \frac{\pi}{2} - \angle AOB = \angle ABO$. Since we know two angles and one side to be equal, the triangles are (SAA) congruent. Thus $AB = OC$ and $OA = CD$, so if B has coordinates (x, y), then D has coordinates $(-y, x)$. Therefore,

(a) $\sin\left(t + \frac{\pi}{2}\right) = x = \cos t$

(b) $\cos\left(t + \frac{\pi}{2}\right) = -y$, and $\sin t = y$. Therefore, $\cos\left(t + \frac{\pi}{2}\right) = -\sin t$.

(c) $\tan\left(t + \frac{\pi}{2}\right) = \dfrac{x}{-y} = -\dfrac{x}{y} = -\dfrac{\cos t}{\sin t} = -\cot t$

5.3   **Trigonometric Graphs**

1. $f(x) = 1 + \cos x$

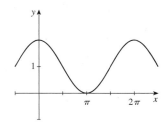

2. $f(x) = 3 + \sin x$

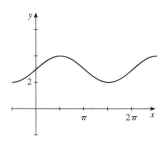

3. $f(x) = -\sin x$

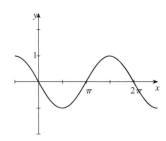

4. $f(x) = 2 - \cos x$

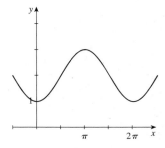

5. $f(x) = -2 + \sin x$

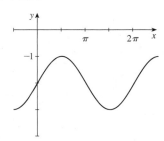

6. $f(x) = -1 + \cos x$

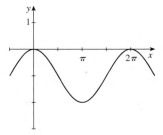

7. $g(x) = 3\cos x$

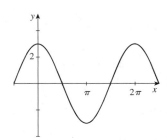

8. $g(x) = 2\sin x$

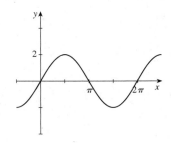

9. $g(x) = -\frac{1}{2}\sin x$

10. $g(x) = -\frac{2}{3}\cos x$

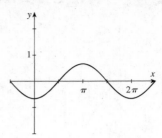

11. $g(x) = 3 + 3\cos x$

12. $g(x) = 4 - 2\sin x$

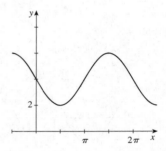

13. $h(x) = |\cos x|$

14. $h(x) = |\sin x|$

15. $y = \cos 2x$ has amplitude 1 and period π.

16. $y = -\sin 2x$ has amplitude 1 and period π.

17. $y = -3\sin 3x$ has amplitude 3 and period $\frac{2\pi}{3}$.

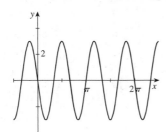

18. $y = \frac{1}{2}\cos 4x$ has amplitude $\frac{1}{2}$ and period $\frac{\pi}{2}$.

19. $y = 10\sin\frac{1}{2}x$ has amplitude 10 and period 4π.

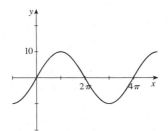

20. $y = 5\cos\frac{1}{4}x$ has amplitude 5 and period 8π.

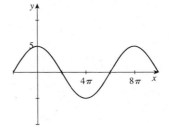

21. $y = -\frac{1}{3}\cos\frac{1}{3}x$ has amplitude $\frac{1}{3}$ and period 6π.

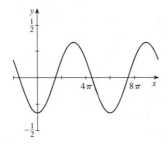

22. $y = 4\sin(-2x)$ has amplitude 4 and period π.

23. $y = -2\sin 2\pi x$ has amplitude 2 and period 1.

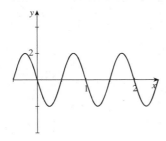

24. $y = -3\sin \pi x$ has amplitude 3 and period 2.

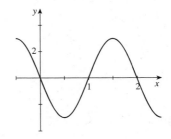

25. $y = 1 + \frac{1}{2} \cos \pi x$ has amplitude $\frac{1}{2}$ and period 2.

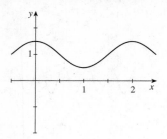

26. $y = -2 + \cos 4\pi x$ has amplitude 1 and period $\frac{1}{2}$.

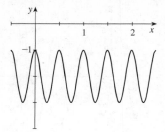

27. $y = \cos\left(x - \frac{\pi}{2}\right)$ has amplitude 1, period 2π, and phase shift $\frac{\pi}{2}$.

28. $y = 2 \sin\left(x - \frac{\pi}{3}\right)$ has amplitude 2, period 2π, and phase shift $\frac{\pi}{3}$.

29. $y = -2 \sin\left(x - \frac{\pi}{6}\right)$ has amplitude 2, period 2π, and phase shift $\frac{\pi}{6}$.

30. $y = 3 \cos\left(x + \frac{\pi}{4}\right)$ has amplitude 3, period 2π, and phase shift $\frac{\pi}{4}$.

31. $y = -4 \sin 2\left(x + \frac{\pi}{2}\right)$ has amplitude 4, period π, and phase shift $-\frac{\pi}{2}$.

32. $y = \sin \frac{1}{2}\left(x + \frac{\pi}{4}\right)$ has amplitude 1, period 4π, and phase shift $-\frac{\pi}{4}$.

33. $y = 5\cos\left(3x - \frac{\pi}{4}\right) = 5\cos 3\left(x - \frac{\pi}{12}\right)$ has amplitude 5, period $\frac{2\pi}{3}$, and phase shift $\frac{\pi}{12}$.

34. $y = 2\sin\left(\frac{2}{3}x - \frac{\pi}{6}\right) = 2\sin\frac{2}{3}\left(x - \frac{\pi}{4}\right)$ has amplitude 2, period 3π, and phase shift $\frac{\pi}{4}$.

35. $y = -\frac{1}{2}\cos\left(2x - \frac{\pi}{3}\right) = -\frac{1}{2}\cos 2\left(x - \frac{\pi}{6}\right)$ has amplitude $\frac{1}{2}$, period π, and phase shift $\frac{\pi}{6}$.

36. $y = 1 + \cos\left(3x + \frac{\pi}{2}\right) = 1 + \cos 3\left(x + \frac{\pi}{6}\right)$ has amplitude 1, period $\frac{2\pi}{3}$, and phase shift $-\frac{\pi}{6}$.

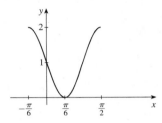

37. $y = 3\cos\pi\left(x + \frac{1}{2}\right)$ has amplitude 3, period 2, and phase shift $-\frac{1}{2}$.

38. $y = 3 + 2\sin 3\left(x + 1\right)$ has amplitude 2, period $\frac{2\pi}{3}$, and phase shift -1.

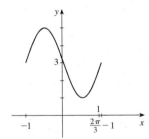

39. $y = \sin\left(3x + \pi\right) = \sin 3\left(x + \frac{\pi}{3}\right)$ has amplitude 1, period $\frac{2\pi}{3}$, and phase shift $-\frac{\pi}{3}$

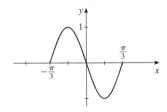

40. $y = \cos\left(\frac{\pi}{2} - x\right) = \cos\left(x - \frac{\pi}{2}\right)$ has amplitude 1, period 2π, and phase shift $\frac{\pi}{2}$.

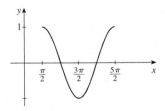

41. (a) This function has amplitude $a = 4$, period $\frac{2\pi}{k} = 2\pi$, and phase shift $b = 0$ as a sine curve.

   (b) $y = a\sin k\left(x - b\right) = 4\sin x$

42. (a) This curve has amplitude $a = 2$, period $\frac{2\pi}{k} = \pi$, and phase shift $b = 0$ as a cosine curve.

   (b) $y = a\cos k\left(x - b\right) = 2\cos 2x$

43. (a) This curve has amplitude $a = \frac{3}{2}$, period $\frac{2\pi}{k} = \frac{2\pi}{3}$, and phase shift $b = 0$ as a cosine curve.

   (b) $y = a \cos k \,(x - b) = \frac{3}{2} \cos 3x$

44. (a) This curve has amplitude $a = 3$, period $\frac{2\pi}{k} = 4\pi$, and phase shift $b = 0$ as a sine curve.

   (b) $y = 3 \sin \frac{1}{2}x$

45. (a) This curve has amplitude $a = \frac{1}{2}$, period $\frac{2\pi}{k} = \pi$, and phase shift $b = -\frac{\pi}{3}$ as a cosine curve.

   (b) $y = -\frac{1}{2} \cos 2 \left(x + \frac{\pi}{3}\right)$

46. (a) This curve has amplitude $a = \frac{1}{10}$, period $\frac{2\pi}{k} = \pi$, and phase shift $b = -\frac{\pi}{2}$ as a sine curve.

   (b) $y = \frac{1}{10} \sin 2 \left(x + \frac{\pi}{2}\right)$

47. (a) This curve has amplitude $a = 4$, period $\frac{2\pi}{k} = \frac{3}{2}$, and phase shift $b = -\frac{1}{2}$ as a sine curve.

   (b) $y = 4 \sin \frac{4\pi}{3} \left(x + \frac{1}{2}\right)$

48. (a) This curve has amplitude $a = 5$, period $\frac{2\pi}{k} = 1$, and phase shift $b = 0$ as a cosine curve.

   (b) $y = 5 \cos 2\pi x$

49. $f(x) = \cos 100x$, $[-0.1, 0.1]$ by $[-1.5, 1.5]$

50. $f(x) = 3 \sin 120x$, $[-0.1, 0.1]$ by $[-4, 4]$

51. $f(x) = \sin \dfrac{x}{40}$, $[-250, 250]$ by $[-1.5, 1.5]$

52. $f(x) = \cos \dfrac{x}{80}$, $[0, 500]$ by $[-1, 1]$

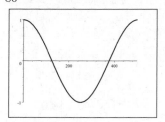

53. $y = \tan 25x$, $[-0.2, 0.2]$ by $[-3, 3]$

54. $y = \csc 40x$, $[-0.1, 0.1]$ by $[-10, 10]$

55. $y = e^{\sin 20x}$, $[-0.5, 0.5]$ by $[0, 3]$

56. $y = \sqrt{\tan 10\pi x}$, $[-0.2, 0.2]$ by $[-1, 4]$

57. $f(x) = x$, $g(x) = \sin x$

58. $f(x) = \sin x$, $g(x) = \sin 2x$

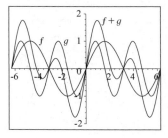

59. $y = x^2 \sin x$ is a sine curve that lies between the graphs of $y = x^2$ and $y = -x^2$.

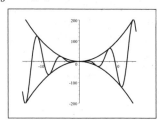

60. $y = x \cos x$ is a cosine curve that lies between the graphs of $y = x$ and $y = -x$.

61. $y = e^x \sin 5\pi x$ is a sine curve that lies between the graphs of $y = e^x$ and $y = -e^x$.

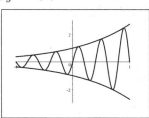

62. $y = \dfrac{\cos 2\pi x}{1 + x^2}$ is a cosine curve that lies between the graphs of $y = \dfrac{1}{1 + x^2}$ and $y = -\dfrac{1}{1 + x^2}$.

63. $y = \cos 3\pi x \cos 21\pi x$ is a cosine curve that lies between the graphs of $y = \cos 3\pi x$ and $y = -\cos 3\pi x$.

64. $y = \sin 2\pi x \sin 10\pi x$ is a sine curve that lies between the graphs of $y = \sin 2\pi x$ and $y = -\sin 2\pi x$.

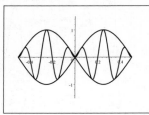

65. $y = \sin x + \sin 2x$. The period is 2π, so we graph the function over one period, $(-\pi, \pi)$. Maximum value 1.76 when $x \approx 0.94 + 2n\pi$, minimum value -1.76 when $x \approx -0.94 + 2n\pi$, n any integer.

66. $y = x - 2\sin x$, $0 \le x \le 2\pi$. Maximum value 6.97 when $x \approx 5.24$, minimum value -0.68 when $x \approx 1.05$.

67. $y = 2\sin x + \sin^2 x$. The period is 2π, so we graph the function over one period, $(-\pi, \pi)$. Maximum value 3.00 when $x \approx 1.57 + 2n\pi$, minimum value -1.00 when $x \approx -1.57 + 2n\pi$, n any integer.

68. $y = \dfrac{\cos x}{2 + \sin x}$. The period is 2π, so we graph the function over one period. Maximum value 0.58 when $x \approx 5.76 + 2n\pi$ (exact value $x = \frac{11\pi}{6} + 2n\pi$); Minimum value -0.58 when $x \approx 3.67 + 2n\pi$ (exact value $x = \frac{7\pi}{6} + 2n\pi$) for any integer n.

69. $\cos x = 0.4$, $x \in [0, \pi]$. The solution is $x \approx 1.16$.

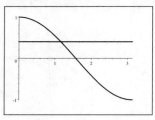

70. $\tan x = 2$, $x \in [0, \pi]$. The solution is $x \approx 1.11$.

71. $\csc x = 3$, $x \in [0, \pi]$. The solutions are $x \approx 0.34$, 2.80.

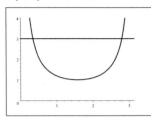

72. $\cos x = x$, $x \in [0, \pi]$. The solution is $x \approx 0.74$.

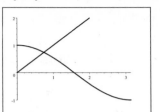

73. $f(x) = \dfrac{1 - \cos x}{x}$

(a) Since $f(-x) = \dfrac{1 - \cos(-x)}{-x} = \dfrac{1 - \cos x}{-x} = -f(x)$, the function

is odd.

(b) The x-intercepts occur when $1 - \cos x = 0 \quad \Leftrightarrow \quad \cos x = 1 \quad \Leftrightarrow$

$x = 0, \pm 2\pi, \pm 4\pi, \pm 6\pi, \ldots$

(d) As $x \to \pm\infty$, $f(x) \to 0$.

(e) As $x \to 0$, $f(x) \to 0$.

(c)

74. $f(x) = \dfrac{\sin 4x}{2x}$

(a) $f(-x) = \dfrac{\sin(-4x)}{2(-x)} = \dfrac{-\sin 4x}{-2x} = f(x)$, so the function is even.

(b) The x-intercepts occur when $\sin 4x = 0$, $x \neq 0 \Leftrightarrow 4x = n\pi \quad \Leftrightarrow$

$x = \frac{1}{4} n\pi$, n any nonzero integer.

(d) As $x \to \pm\infty$, $f(x) \to 0$.

(e) As $x \to 0$, $f(x) \to 2$.

(c)

75. (a) The period of the wave is $\dfrac{2\pi}{\pi/10} = 20$ seconds.

(b) Since $h(0) = 3$ and $h(10) = -3$, the wave height is $3 - (-3) = 6$ feet.

76. (a) The period of the vibration is $\dfrac{2\pi}{880\pi} = \dfrac{1}{440}$ second.

(b) Since each vibration takes $\dfrac{1}{440}$ of a second, there are 440 vibrations

per second.

(c)

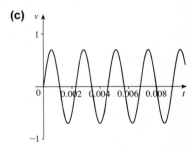

77. (a) The period of p is $\dfrac{2\pi}{160\pi} = \dfrac{1}{80}$ minute.

(b) Since each period represents a heart beat, there are 80 heart beats per

minute.

(d) The maximum (or systolic) is $115 + 25 = 140$ and the minimum (or

diastolic) is $115 - 25 = 90$. The read would be $140/90$ which higher

than normal.

(c)

78. (a) The period of R Leonis is $\dfrac{2\pi}{\pi/156} = 312$ days.

(c)

(b) The maximum brightness is $7.9 + 2.1 = 10$; the minimum brightness is $7.9 - 2.1 = 5.8$.

79. (a) $y = \sin\left(\sqrt{x}\right)$. This graph looks like a sine function which has been stretched horizontally (stretched more for larger values of x). It is defined only for $x \geq 0$, so it is neither even nor odd.

(b) $y = \sin\left(x^2\right)$. This graph looks like a graph of $\sin|x|$ which has been shrunk for $|x| > 1$ (shrunk more for larger values of x) and stretched for $|x| < 1$. It is an even function, whereas $\sin x$ is odd.

80. (a) This function is periodic with period 2.

(b) This function is not periodic. $f(2.5) \neq f(4.5)$.

(c) This function is not periodic; its graph on the interval $[-2, 0]$ is different from its graph on the interval $[0, 2]$.

(d) This function is periodic with period 3.

81. (a) The graph of $y = |\sin x|$ is shown in the viewing rectangle $[-6.28, 6.28]$ by $[-0.5, 1.5]$. This function is periodic with period π.

(b) The graph of $y = \sin|x|$ is shown in the viewing rectangle $[-10, 10]$ by $[-1.5, 1.5]$. The function is not periodic. Note that while $\sin|x + 2\pi| = \sin|x|$ for many values of x, it is false for $x \in (-2\pi, 0)$. For example $\sin\left|-\frac{\pi}{2}\right| = \sin\frac{\pi}{2} = 1$ while $\sin\left|-\frac{\pi}{2} + 2\pi\right| = \sin\frac{3\pi}{2} = -1$.

(c) The graph of $y = 2^{\cos x}$ is shown in the viewing rectangle $[-10, 10]$ by $[-1, 3]$. This function is periodic with period $= 2\pi$.

(d) The graph of $y = x - [\![x]\!]$ is shown in the viewing rectangle $[-7.5, 7.5]$ by $[-0.5, 1.5]$. This function is periodic with period 1. Be sure to turn off "connected" mode when graphing functions with gaps in their graph.

82. From the graph we see that the amplitude is 5 and the period is 2π. In Exercises 25 and 26 in Section 7.2, we will prove the reduction formulas $\sin(x - \pi) = -\sin x$ and $\cos(x - \pi) = -\cos x$. So starting with $y = -5 \sin x$ we may also represent the curve by $y = -5 \sin(x - b)$ where $b = 2n\pi$, where n is an integer; $y = 5 \sin(x - b)$ where $b = (2n + 1)\pi$, where n is an integer. Then starting with $y = -5 \cos\left(x - \frac{\pi}{2}\right)$ we may also represent the curve by $y = -5 \cos(x - b)$ where $b = \frac{\pi}{2} + 2n\pi$, where n is an integer; $y = 5 \cos(x - b)$ where $b = \frac{\pi}{2} + (2n + 1)\pi$, where n is an integer.

5.4   More Trigonometric Graphs

1. $f(x) = \tan\left(x + \frac{\pi}{4}\right)$ corresponds to Graph II. f is undefined at $x = \frac{\pi}{4}$ and $x = \frac{3\pi}{4}$, and Graph II has the shape of a graph of a tangent function.

2. $f(x) = \sec 2x$ corresponds to Graph III. f is undefined at $x = \frac{\pi}{4}$ and $x = \frac{3\pi}{4}$, and Graph III has the shape of a graph of a secant function.

3. $f(x) = \cot 2x$ corresponds to Graph VI.

4. $f(x) = -\tan x$ corresponds to Graph I.

5. $f(x) = 2 \sec x$ corresponds to Graph IV.

6. $f(x) = 1 + \csc x$ corresponds to Graph V.

7. $y = 4 \tan x$ has period π.

8. $y = -4 \tan x$ has period π.

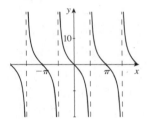

9. $y = -\frac{1}{2} \tan x$ has period π.

10. $y = \frac{1}{2} \tan x$ has period π.

11. $y = -\cot x$ has period π.

12. $y = 2 \cot x$ has period π.

13. $y = 2 \csc x$ has period 2π.

14. $y = \frac{1}{2} \csc x$ has period 2π.

15. $y = 3 \sec x$ has period 2π.

16. $y = -3 \sec x$ has period 2π.

17. $y = \tan\left(x + \frac{\pi}{2}\right)$ has period π.

18. $y = \tan\left(x - \frac{\pi}{4}\right)$ has period π.

19. $y = \csc\left(x - \frac{\pi}{2}\right)$ has period 2π.

20. $y = \sec\left(x + \frac{\pi}{4}\right)$ has period 2π.

21. $y = \cot\left(x + \frac{\pi}{4}\right)$ has period π.

22. $y = 2 \csc\left(x - \frac{\pi}{3}\right)$ has period 2π.

23. $y = \frac{1}{2} \sec \left(x - \frac{\pi}{6}\right)$ has period 2π.

24. $y = 3 \csc \left(x + \frac{\pi}{2}\right)$ has period 2π.

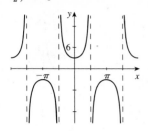

25. $y = \tan 2x$ has period $\frac{\pi}{2}$.

26. $y = \tan \left(\frac{1}{2}x\right)$ has period $\dfrac{\pi}{\left(\frac{1}{2}\right)} = 2\pi$.

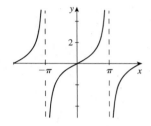

27. $y = \tan \left(\frac{\pi}{4}x\right)$ has period $\dfrac{\pi}{\frac{\pi}{4}} = 4$.

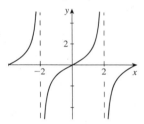

28. $y = \cot \left(\frac{\pi}{2}x\right)$ has period $\dfrac{\pi}{\left(\frac{\pi}{2}\right)} = 2$.

29. $y = \sec 2x$ has period $\dfrac{2\pi}{2} = \pi$.

30. $y = 5 \csc \left(3x\right)$ has period $\frac{2\pi}{3}$.

31. $y = \csc 2x$ has period $\dfrac{2\pi}{2} = \pi$.

32. $y = \csc \left(\frac{1}{2}x\right)$ has period $\dfrac{2\pi}{\left(\frac{1}{2}\right)} = 4\pi$.

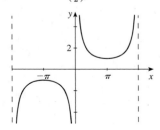

33. $y = 2 \tan 3\pi x$ has period $\frac{1}{3}$.

34. $y = 2 \tan \left(\frac{\pi}{2} x\right)$ has period $\frac{\pi}{\left(\frac{\pi}{2}\right)} = 2.$

35. $y = 5 \csc \frac{3\pi}{2} x$ has period $\frac{2\pi}{\frac{3\pi}{2}} = \frac{4}{3}.$

36. $y = 5 \sec (2\pi x)$ has period $\frac{2\pi}{2\pi} = 1.$

37. $y = \tan 2 \left(x + \frac{\pi}{2}\right)$ has period $\frac{\pi}{2}.$

38. $y = \csc 2 \left(x + \frac{\pi}{2}\right)$ has period $\frac{2\pi}{2} = \pi.$

39. $y = \tan 2 (x - \pi) = \tan 2x$ has period $\frac{\pi}{2}.$

40. $y = \sec 2 \left(x - \frac{\pi}{2}\right)$ has period $\frac{2\pi}{2} = \pi.$

41. $y = \cot \left(2x - \frac{\pi}{2}\right) = \cot 2 \left(x - \frac{\pi}{4}\right)$ has period $\frac{\pi}{2}.$

42. $y = \frac{1}{2} \tan (\pi x - \pi) = \frac{1}{2} \tan \pi (x - 1)$ has period $\frac{\pi}{\pi} = 1.$

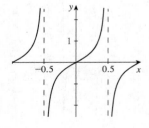

43. $y = 2\csc\left(\pi x - \frac{\pi}{3}\right) = 2\csc\pi\left(x - \frac{1}{3}\right)$ has period $\frac{2\pi}{\pi} = 2$.

44. $y = 2\sec\left(\frac{1}{2}x - \frac{\pi}{3}\right) = 2\sec\frac{1}{2}\left(x - \frac{2\pi}{3}\right)$ has period $2\pi/\left(\frac{1}{2}\right) = 4\pi$.

45. $y = 5\sec\left(3x - \frac{\pi}{2}\right) = 5\sec 3\left(x - \frac{\pi}{6}\right)$ has period $\frac{2\pi}{3}$.

46. $y = \frac{1}{2}\sec\left(2\pi x - \pi\right) = \frac{1}{2}\sec 2\pi\left(x - \frac{1}{2}\right)$ has period $\frac{2\pi}{2\pi} = 1$.

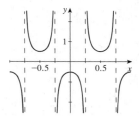

47. $y = \tan\left(\frac{2}{3}x - \frac{\pi}{6}\right) = \tan\frac{2}{3}\left(x - \frac{\pi}{4}\right)$ has period $\pi/\left(\frac{2}{3}\right) = \frac{3\pi}{2}$.

48. $y = \tan\frac{1}{2}\left(x + \frac{\pi}{4}\right)$ has period $\frac{\pi}{\left(\frac{1}{2}\right)} = 2\pi$.

49. $y = 3\sec\pi\left(x + \frac{1}{2}\right)$ has period $\frac{2\pi}{\pi} = 2$.

50. $y = \sec\left(3x + \frac{\pi}{2}\right) = \sec 3\left(x + \frac{\pi}{6}\right)$ has period $\frac{2\pi}{3}$.

51. $y = -2\tan\left(2x - \frac{\pi}{3}\right) = -2\tan 2\left(x - \frac{\pi}{6}\right)$ has period $\frac{\pi}{2}$.

52. $y = 2\csc\left(3x + 3\right) = 2\csc 3\left(x + 1\right)$ has period $\frac{2\pi}{3}$.

53. (a) If f is periodic with period p, then by the definition of a period, $f(x+p) = f(x)$ for all x in the domain of f.

Therefore, $\dfrac{1}{f(x+p)} = \dfrac{1}{f(x)}$ for all $f(x) \neq 0$. Thus, $\dfrac{1}{f}$ is also periodic with period p.

(b) Since $\sin x$ has period 2π, it follows from part (a) that $\csc x = \dfrac{1}{\sin x}$ also has period 2π. Similarly, since $\cos x$ has

period 2π, we conclude $\sec x = \dfrac{1}{\cos x}$ also has period 2π.

54. If f and g are periodic with period p, then $f(x+p) = f(x)$ for all x and $g(x+p) = g(x)$ for all x. Thus

$\dfrac{f(x+p)}{g(x+p)} = \dfrac{f(x)}{g(x)}$ for all x [unless $g(x)$ is undefined, in which case both are undefined.] But consider $f(x) = \sin x$

(period 2π) and $g(x) = \cos x$ (period 2π). Their quotient is $\dfrac{f(x)}{g(x)} = \dfrac{\sin x}{\cos x} = \tan x$, whose period is π.

55. (a) $d(t) = 3\tan \pi t$, so $d(0.15) \approx 1.53$, $d(0.25) \approx 3.00$,
and $d(0.45) \approx 18.94$.

(b)

(c) $d \to \infty$ as $t \to \frac{1}{2}$.

56. (a) $S(t) = 6\left|\cot \frac{\pi}{12}t\right|$, so $S(2) \approx 10.39$, $S(6) = 0$,
$S(8) \approx 3.46$, $S(11.75) \approx 91.54$, and $S(12)$ is
undefined.

(b)

(c) From the graph, it appears that $S(t) = 6$ at
approximately $t = 3$ and $t = 9$, corresponding to
9 A.M. and 3 P.M.

(d) As $t \to 12^{-}$, the sun approaches the horizon and the
man's shadow grows longer and longer.

57. The graph of $y = -\cot x$ is the same as the graph of $y = \tan x$ shifted $\frac{\pi}{2}$ units to the right, and the graph of $y = \csc x$ is
the same as the graph of $y = \sec x$ shifted $\frac{\pi}{2}$ units to the right.

5.5   Modeling Harmonic Motion

1. $y = 2\sin 3t$

(a) Amplitude 2, period $\frac{2\pi}{3}$, frequency $\dfrac{1}{\text{period}} = \dfrac{3}{2\pi}$.

(b)

2. $y = 3\cos \frac{1}{2}t$

(a) Amplitude 3, period $\dfrac{2\pi}{\left(\frac{1}{2}\right)} = 4\pi$, frequency

$\dfrac{1}{\text{period}} = \dfrac{1}{4\pi}$.

(b)

3. $y = -\cos 0.3t$

(a) Amplitude 1, period $\frac{2\pi}{0.3} = \frac{20\pi}{3}$, frequency $\frac{3}{20\pi}$.

(b)

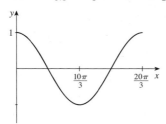

4. $y = 2.4 \sin 3.6t$

(a) Amplitude 2.4, period $\frac{2\pi}{3.6} = \frac{5\pi}{9}$, frequency $\frac{9}{5\pi}$.

(b)

5. $y = -0.25 \cos \left(1.5t - \frac{\pi}{3}\right) = -0.25 \cos \left(\frac{3}{2}t - \frac{\pi}{3}\right)$
$= -0.25 \cos \frac{3}{2}\left(t - \frac{2\pi}{9}\right)$

(a) Amplitude 0.25, period $\frac{2\pi}{\frac{3}{2}} = \frac{4\pi}{3}$, frequency $\frac{3}{4\pi}$.

(b)

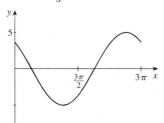

6. $y = -\frac{3}{2} \sin (0.2t + 1.4) = -\frac{3}{2} \sin 0.2 (t + 7)$

(a) Amplitude $\frac{3}{2}$, period $\frac{2\pi}{0.2} = 10\pi$, frequency $\frac{1}{10\pi}$.

(b)

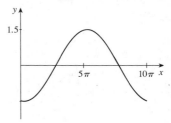

7. $y = 5 \cos \left(\frac{2}{3}t + \frac{3}{4}\right) = 5 \cos \frac{2}{3}\left(t + \frac{9}{8}\right)$

(a) Amplitude 5, period $\frac{2\pi}{\frac{2}{3}} = 3\pi$, frequency $\frac{1}{3\pi}$.

(b)

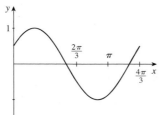

8. $y = 1.6 \sin (t - 1.8)$

(a) Amplitude 1.6, period 2π, frequency $\frac{1}{2\pi}$.

(b)

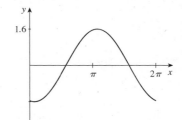

9. The amplitude is $a = 10$ cm, the period is $\frac{2\pi}{k} = 3$ s, and $f(0) = 0$, so $f(x) = 10 \sin \frac{2\pi}{3}t$.

10. The amplitude is 24 ft, the period is $\frac{2\pi}{k} = 2$ min, and $f(0) = 0$, so $f(x) = 24 \sin \pi t$.

11. The amplitude is 6 in., the frequency is $\frac{k}{2\pi} = \frac{5}{\pi}$ Hz, and $f(0) = 0$, so $f(x) = 6 \sin 10t$.

12. The amplitude is 1.2 m, the frequency is $\frac{k}{2\pi} = 0.5$ Hz, and $f(0) = 0$, so $f(x) = 1.2 \sin \pi t$.

13. The amplitude is 60 ft, the period is $\frac{2\pi}{k} = 0.5$ min, and $f(0) = 60$, so $f(x) = 60 \cos 4\pi t$.

14. The amplitude is 35 cm, the period is $\frac{2\pi}{k} = 8$ s, and $f(0) = 35$, so $f(x) = 35 \cos \frac{\pi}{4}t$.

15. The amplitude is 2.4 m, the frequency is $\frac{k}{2\pi} = 750$ Hz, and $f(0) = 2.4$, so $f(x) = 2.4 \cos 1500\pi t$.

16. The amplitude is 6.25 in., the frequency is $\frac{k}{2\pi} = 60$ Hz, and $f(0) = 6.25$, so $f(x) = 6.25 \cos 120\pi t$.

17. (a) $k = 2$, $c = 1.5$, and $f = 3 \Rightarrow \omega = 6\pi$, so we have
$y = 2e^{-1.5t} \cos 6\pi t$.

(b)

18. (a) $k = 15$, $c = 0.25$, and $f = 0.6 \Rightarrow \omega = 1.2\pi$, so we have $y = 15e^{-0.25t} \cos 1.2\pi t$.

(b)

19. (a) $k = 100$, $c = 0.05$, and $p = 4 \Rightarrow \omega = \frac{\pi}{2}$, so we have
$y = 100e^{-0.05t} \cos \frac{\pi}{2}t$.

(b)

20. (a) $k = 0.75$, $c = 3$, and $p = 3\pi \Rightarrow \omega = \frac{2}{3}$, so we have
$y = 0.75e^{-3t} \cos \frac{2}{3}t$.

(b)

21. (a) $k = 7$, $c = 10$, and $p = \frac{\pi}{6} \Rightarrow \omega = 12$, so we have
$y = 7e^{-10t} \sin 12t$.

(b)

22. (a) $k = 1$, $c = 1$, and $p = 1 \Rightarrow \omega = 2\pi$, so we have
$y = e^{-t} \sin 2\pi t$.

(b)

23. (a) $k = 0.3$, $c = 0.2$, and $f = 20 \Rightarrow \omega = 40\pi$, so we have $y = 0.3e^{-0.2t} \sin 40\pi t$.

(b)

24. (a) $k = 12$, $c = 0.01$, and $f = 8 \Rightarrow \omega = 16\pi$, so we have
$y = 12e^{-0.01t} \sin 16\pi t$.

(b)

25. $y = 0.2 \cos 20\pi t + 8$

(a) The frequency is $\frac{20\pi}{2\pi} = 10$ cycles/min.

(b)

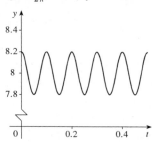

(c) Since $y = 0.2 \cos 20\pi t + 8 \leq 0.2\,(1) + 8 = 8.2$ and when $t = 0$, $y = 8.2$, the maximum displacement is 8.2 ft.

26. $y = a \sin\left(2\pi\,(9.15 \times 10^7)\, t\right)$. The period is

$$\frac{2\pi}{2\pi\,(9.15 \times 10^7)} = \frac{1}{9.15} \times 10^{-7} = 1.09 \times 10^{-8} \text{ and the}$$

frequency is $\dfrac{2\pi\,(9.15 \times 10^7)}{2\pi} = 9.15 \times 10^7$.

27. (a) When $t = 0, \pi, 2\pi, \ldots$ we have $\cos 2t = 1$ so y is maximized at $y = 8900$.

(b) The length of time between successive periods of maximum population is the length of a period which is $\frac{2\pi}{2} = \pi \approx 3.14$ years.

28. $p\,(t) = 115 + 25 \sin\,(160\pi t)$

(a) Amplitude 25, period $\frac{2\pi}{160\pi} = \frac{1}{80} = 0.0125$, frequency $\dfrac{1}{\text{period}} = 80$.

(c) The period decreases and the frequency increases.

(b)

29. The graph resembles a sine wave with an amplitude of 5, a period of $\frac{2}{5}$, and no phase shift. Therefore, $a = 5$, $\dfrac{2\pi}{\omega} = \frac{2}{5}$ $\Leftrightarrow$ $\omega = 5\pi$, and a formula is $d\,(t) = 5 \sin 5\pi t$.

30. From the graph we see that the amplitude is 6 feet and the period is 12 hours. Also, the sine curve is shifted 6 hours (exactly half its period) to the right, which is equivalent to reflecting the curve about the x-axis. Thus, the equation is $y = -\,(6) \sin\left(\frac{2\pi}{12}\right) x = -6 \sin \frac{\pi}{6} x$.

31. $a = 21$, $f = \frac{1}{12}$ cycle/hour $\Rightarrow$ $\dfrac{\omega}{2\pi} = \frac{1}{12}$ $\Leftrightarrow$ $\omega = \frac{\pi}{6}$. So,

$y = 21 \sin\left(\frac{\pi}{6} t\right)$ (assuming the tide is at mean level and rising when $t = 0$).

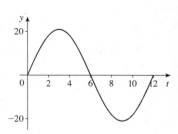

32. $a = 2$, $\dfrac{2\pi}{\omega} = 1$ $\Leftrightarrow$ $\omega = 2\pi$. So $y = -2 \cos 2\pi t$.

33. Since the mass travels from its highest point (compressed spring) to its lowest point in $\frac{1}{2}$ s, it completes half a period in $\frac{1}{2}$ s.

So, $\frac{1}{2}$ (one period) $= \frac{1}{2}$ s $\Rightarrow$ $\frac{1}{2} \cdot \dfrac{2\pi}{\omega} = \frac{1}{2}$ $\Leftrightarrow$ $\omega = 2\pi$. Also, $a = 5$. So $y = 5 \cos 2\pi t$.

34. (a) $m = 10$ g, $k = 3$, $a = 5$ cm. Then $f(t) = 5\cos\left(\sqrt{\frac{3}{10}}t\right)$.

(b) The function $f(t) = a\cos\sqrt{k/m}\,t$ describes an object oscillating in simple harmonic motion, so by comparing it with the general equation $y = a\cos\omega t$ we see that $\omega = \sqrt{k/m}$. This means the frequency is

$$f = \frac{\omega}{2\pi} = \frac{\sqrt{k/m}}{2\pi} = \frac{1}{2}\cdot\sqrt{\frac{k}{m}}.$$

(c) If the mass is increased, then the denominator of $\sqrt{\dfrac{k}{m}}$ increases, so overall the frequency decreases. If the frequency has decreased, then by definition the oscillations are slower.

(d) If a stiffer spring is used, k is larger and so the numerator of $\sqrt{\dfrac{k}{m}}$ increases. Thus, overall the frequency increases. If the frequency has increased, then by definition the oscillations are faster.

35. Since the Ferris wheel has a radius of 10 m and the bottom of the wheel is 1 m above the ground, the minimum height is 1 m and the maximum height is 21 m. Then $a = 10$ and $\dfrac{2\pi}{\omega} = 20$ s $\Leftrightarrow$ $\omega = \frac{\pi}{10}$, and so $y = 11 + 10\sin\left(\frac{\pi}{10}t\right)$, where t is in seconds.

36. Let $f(t)$ represent the measure of the angle θ at time t. The amplitude of this motion is 10. Since the period is 2s, we have $\dfrac{2\pi}{\omega} = 2$ $\Leftrightarrow$ $\omega = \pi$. Thus $f(t) = 10\sin\pi t$.

37. $a = 0.2$, $\dfrac{2\pi}{\omega} = 10$ $\Leftrightarrow$ $\omega = \frac{\pi}{5}$. Then $y = 3.8 + 0.2\sin\left(\frac{\pi}{5}t\right)$.

38. $a = 1.5$, $\dfrac{\omega}{2\pi} = \dfrac{1}{5.4}$ $\Leftrightarrow$ $\omega = \dfrac{2\pi}{5.4}$. So $R(t) = 20 + 1.5\sin\left(\dfrac{2\pi}{5.4}t\right)$, where R is in millions of miles and t is in days.

39. $E_0 = 310$, frequency is 100 $\Rightarrow$ $\dfrac{\omega}{2\pi} = 100$ $\Leftrightarrow$ $\omega = 200\pi$. Then, $E(t) = 310\cos 200\pi t$. The maximum voltage produced occurs when $\cos 2\pi t = 1$, and hence is $E_{\max} = 310$ V. The rms voltage is $\dfrac{310}{\sqrt{2}} \approx 219$ V.

40. The amplitude is $\frac{1}{2}(100 - 80) = 10$ mmHG, the period is 24 hours, and the phase shift is 8 hours, so $f(t) = 10\sin\left(\frac{\pi}{12}(t - 8)\right) + 90$.

41. (a) The maximum voltage is the amplitude, that is, $V_{\max} = a = 45$ V.

(b) From the graph we see that 4 cycles are completed every 0.1 seconds, or equivalently, 40 cycles are completed every second, so $f = 40$.

(c) The number of revolutions per second of the armature is the frequency, that is, $\dfrac{\omega}{2\pi} = f = 40$.

(d) $a = 45$, $f = \dfrac{\omega}{2\pi} = 40$ $\Leftrightarrow$ $\omega = 80\pi$. Then $V(t) = 45\cos 80\pi t$.

42. (a) As the car approaches, the perceived frequency is $f = 500\left(\frac{1130}{1130-110}\right) \approx 553.9$ Hz. As it moves away, the perceived frequency is $f = 500\left(\frac{1130}{1130+110}\right) \approx 455.6$ Hz.

(b) The frequency is $\dfrac{\omega}{2\pi} = 500\left(\frac{1130}{1130\pm110}\right)$, so $\omega = 1000\pi\left(\frac{1130}{1130\pm110}\right) \approx 3480.4$ (approaching) or 2862.9 (receding). Thus, models are $y = A\sin 3480.4t$ and $A\sin 2862.9t$.

43. $k = 1$, $c = 0.9$, and $\dfrac{\omega}{2\pi} = \frac{1}{2}$ $\Leftrightarrow$ $\omega = \pi$. Since $f(0) = 0$, $f(t) = e^{-0.9t}\sin\pi t$.

44. $k = 6$, $c = 2.8$, and $\dfrac{\omega}{2\pi} = 2$ $\Leftrightarrow$ $\omega = 4\pi$.

(a) Since $f(0) = 6$, $f(t) = 6e^{-2.8t}\cos 4\pi t$.

(b) The amplitude of the vibration is 0.5 when $6e^{-2.8t} = 0.5$ $\Rightarrow$ $e^{-2.8t} = \frac{1}{12}$ $\Rightarrow$ $-2.8t = \ln\frac{1}{12}$ $\Rightarrow$ $t = -\frac{1}{2}\ln\frac{1}{12} = \frac{\ln 12}{2.8} \approx 0.88$ s.

45. $\dfrac{ke^{-ct}}{ke^{-c(t+3)}} = 4 \Leftrightarrow e^{-ct+c(t+3)} = 4 \quad \Leftrightarrow \quad e^{3c} = 4 \quad \Leftrightarrow \quad 3c = \ln 4 \quad \Leftrightarrow \quad c = \tfrac{1}{3}\ln 4 \approx 0.46.$

46. (a) $\dfrac{ke^{-c\cdot 0}}{ke^{-c\cdot 2}} = \dfrac{3}{0.6} = 5 \quad \Leftrightarrow \quad e^{2c} = 5 \quad \Leftrightarrow \quad 2c = \ln 5 \quad \Leftrightarrow \quad c = \tfrac{1}{2}\ln 5 \approx 0.80.$

(b) $f(t) = 3e^{-0.8t}\cos \omega t.$ If the frequency is 165 cycles per second, then $\dfrac{\omega}{2\pi} = 165 \quad \Leftrightarrow \quad \omega = 330\pi.$ Thus,
$f(t) = 3e^{-0.8t}\cos 330\pi t.$

Chapter 5 Review

1. (a) Since $\left(-\frac{\sqrt{3}}{2}\right)^2 + \left(\frac{1}{2}\right)^2 = \frac{3}{4} + \frac{1}{4} = 1$, the point $P\left(-\frac{\sqrt{3}}{2}, \frac{1}{2}\right)$ lies on the unit circle.

(b) $\sin t = \frac{1}{2}$, $\cos t = -\frac{\sqrt{3}}{2}$, $\tan t = \dfrac{\frac{1}{2}}{-\frac{\sqrt{3}}{2}} = -\frac{\sqrt{3}}{3}.$

2. (a) Since $\left(\frac{3}{5}\right)^2 + \left(-\frac{4}{5}\right)^2 = \frac{9}{25} + \frac{1}{2} = 1$, the point $P\left(\frac{3}{5}, -\frac{4}{5}\right)$ lies on the unit circle.

(b) $\sin t = -\frac{4}{5}$, $\cos t = \frac{3}{5}$, $\tan t = \dfrac{-\frac{4}{5}}{\frac{3}{5}} = -\frac{4}{3}.$

3. $t = \frac{2\pi}{3}$

(a) $\bar{t} = \pi - \frac{2\pi}{3} = \frac{\pi}{3}$
(b) $P\left(-\frac{1}{2}, \frac{\sqrt{3}}{2}\right)$
(c) $\sin t = \frac{\sqrt{3}}{2}$, $\cos t = -\frac{1}{2}$, $\tan t = -\sqrt{3}$, $\csc t = \frac{2\sqrt{3}}{3}$,
$\sec t = -2$, and $\cot t = -\frac{\sqrt{3}}{3}.$

4. $t = \frac{5\pi}{3}$

(a) $\bar{t} = 2\pi - \frac{5\pi}{3} = \frac{\pi}{3}$
(b) $P\left(\frac{1}{2}, -\frac{\sqrt{3}}{2}\right)$
(c) $\sin t = -\frac{\sqrt{3}}{2}$, $\cos t = \frac{1}{2}$, $\tan t = -\sqrt{3}$,
$\csc t = -\frac{2\sqrt{3}}{3}$, $\sec t = 2$, and $\cot t = -\frac{\sqrt{3}}{3}.$

5. $t = -\frac{11\pi}{4}$

(a) $\bar{t} = 3\pi + \left(-\frac{11\pi}{4}\right) = \frac{\pi}{4}$
(b) $P\left(-\frac{\sqrt{2}}{2}, -\frac{\sqrt{2}}{2}\right)$
(c) $\sin t = -\frac{\sqrt{2}}{2}$, $\cos t = -\frac{\sqrt{2}}{2}$, $\tan t = 1$, $\csc t = -\sqrt{2}$,
$\sec t = -\sqrt{2}$, and $\cot t = 1.$

6. $t = -\frac{7\pi}{6}$

(a) $\bar{t} = \frac{7\pi}{6} - \pi = \frac{\pi}{6}$
(b) $P\left(-\frac{\sqrt{3}}{2}, \frac{1}{2}\right)$
(c) $\sin t = \frac{1}{2}$, $\cos t = -\frac{\sqrt{3}}{2}$, $\tan t = -\frac{\sqrt{3}}{3}$, $\csc t = 2$,
$\sec t = -\frac{2\sqrt{3}}{3}$, and $\cot t = -\sqrt{3}.$

7. (a) $\sin \frac{3\pi}{4} = \sin \frac{\pi}{4} = \frac{\sqrt{2}}{2}$
(b) $\cos \frac{3\pi}{4} = -\cos \frac{\pi}{4} = -\frac{\sqrt{2}}{2}$

8. (a) $\tan \frac{\pi}{3} = \sqrt{3}$
(b) $\tan \left(-\frac{\pi}{3}\right) = -\sqrt{3}$

9. (a) $\sin 1.1 \approx 0.89121$
(b) $\cos 1.1 \approx 0.45360$

10. (a) $\cos \frac{\pi}{5} \approx 0.80902$
(b) $\cos \left(-\frac{\pi}{5}\right) \approx 0.80902$

11. (a) $\cos \frac{9\pi}{2} = \cos \frac{\pi}{2} = 0$
(b) $\sec \frac{9\pi}{2}$ is undefined

12. (a) $\sin \frac{\pi}{7} \approx 0.43388$
(b) $\csc \frac{\pi}{7} \approx 2.30476$

13. (a) $\tan \frac{5\pi}{2}$ is undefined
(b) $\cot \frac{5\pi}{2} = \cot \frac{\pi}{2} = 0$

14. (a) $\sin 2\pi = 0$
(b) $\csc 2\pi$ is undefined

15. (a) $\tan \frac{5\pi}{6} = -\frac{\sqrt{3}}{3}$
(b) $\cot \frac{5\pi}{6} = -\sqrt{3}$

16. (a) $\cos \frac{\pi}{3} = \frac{1}{2}$
(b) $\sin \frac{\pi}{6} = \frac{1}{2}$

17. $\dfrac{\tan t}{\cos t} = \dfrac{\frac{\sin t}{\cos t}}{\cos t} = \dfrac{\sin t}{\cos^2 t} = \dfrac{\sin t}{1 - \sin^2 t}$

18. $\tan^2 t \cdot \sec t = \tan^2 t \cdot \dfrac{1}{\cos t} = \dfrac{\sin^2 t}{\cos^2 t} \cdot \dfrac{1}{\cos t} = \dfrac{1 - \cos^2 t}{\cos^3 t}$

19. $\tan t = \dfrac{\sin t}{\cos t} = \dfrac{\sin t}{\pm\sqrt{1 - \sin^2 t}} = \dfrac{\sin t}{\sqrt{1 - \sin^2 t}}$ (since t is in quadrant IV, $\cos t$ is positive)

20. $\sec t = \dfrac{1}{\cos t} = \dfrac{1}{\pm\sqrt{1 - \sin^2 t}} = \dfrac{1}{-\sqrt{1 - \sin^2 t}}$ (since t is in quadrant II $\Rightarrow$ $\cos t$ is negative)

21. $\sin t = \frac{5}{13}$, $\cos t = -\frac{12}{13}$. Then $\tan t = \dfrac{\frac{5}{13}}{-\frac{12}{13}} = -\frac{5}{12}$, $\csc t = \frac{13}{5}$, $\sec t = -\frac{13}{12}$, and $\cot t = -\frac{12}{5}$.

22. $\sin t = -\frac{1}{2}$, $\cos t > 0$. Since $\sin t$ is negative and $\cos t$ is positive, t is in quadrant IV. Thus, t determines the terminal point

$P\left(\frac{\sqrt 3}{2}, -\frac{1}{2}\right)$, and $\cos t = \dfrac{\sqrt 3}{2}$, $\tan t = -\dfrac{\sqrt 3}{3}$, $\csc t = -2$, $\sec t = \dfrac{2\sqrt 3}{3}$, $\cot t = -\sqrt 3$.

23. $\cot t = -\frac{1}{2}$, $\csc t = \frac{\sqrt 5}{2}$. Since $\csc t = \dfrac{1}{\sin t}$, we know $\sin t = \dfrac{2}{\sqrt 5} = \dfrac{2\sqrt 5}{5}$. Now $\cot t = \dfrac{\cos t}{\sin t}$, so

$\cos t = \sin t \cdot \cot t = \frac{2\sqrt 5}{5} \cdot \left(-\frac{1}{2}\right) = -\frac{\sqrt 5}{5}$, and $\tan t = \dfrac{1}{\left(-\frac{1}{2}\right)} = -2$ while $\sec t = \dfrac{1}{\cos t} = \dfrac{1}{\left(-\frac{\sqrt 5}{5}\right)} = -\dfrac{5}{\sqrt 5} = -\sqrt 5$.

24. $\cos t = -\frac{3}{5}$, $\tan t < 0$. Since $\cos t$ and $\tan t$ are both negative, t is in quadrant II. Thus, t determines the terminal point

$P\left(-\frac{3}{5}, \frac{4}{5}\right)$, and $\sin t = \frac{4}{5}$, $\tan t = -\frac{4}{3}$, $\csc t = \frac{5}{4}$, $\sec t = -\dfrac{5}{3}$, $\cot t = -\frac{3}{4}$.

25. $\tan t = \frac{1}{4}$, t is in quadrant III $\Rightarrow$

$\sec t + \cot t = -\sqrt{\tan^2 t + 1} + \dfrac{1}{\tan t} = -\sqrt{\left(\frac{1}{4}\right)^2 + 1} + 4 = -\sqrt{\frac{17}{16}} + 4 = 4 - \dfrac{\sqrt{17}}{4} = \dfrac{16 - \sqrt{17}}{4}$

26. $\sin t = -\frac{8}{17}$, t is in quadrant IV $\Rightarrow$

$\csc t + \sec t = \dfrac{1}{\sin t} + \dfrac{1}{\cos t} = \dfrac{\cos t + \sin t}{\sin t \cos t} = \dfrac{\sqrt{1 - \sin^2 t} + \sin t}{\sin t \sqrt{1 - \sin^2 t}} = \dfrac{\frac{15}{17} + \left(-\frac{8}{17}\right)}{\left(-\frac{8}{17}\right) \cdot \frac{15}{17}}$

$= \dfrac{7}{17} \cdot \dfrac{17^2}{-8 \cdot 15} = -\dfrac{7 \cdot 17}{8 \cdot 15} = \dfrac{119}{120} \approx -0.99167$ (since $\cos t$ is positive in quadrant IV)

27. $\cos t = \frac{3}{5}$, t is in quadrant I $\Rightarrow$

$\tan t + \sec t = \dfrac{\sin t}{\cos t} + \dfrac{1}{\cos t} = \dfrac{\sqrt{1 - \cos^2 t}}{\cos t} + \dfrac{1}{\cos t} = \dfrac{\sqrt{1 - \left(\frac{3}{5}\right)^2}}{\frac{3}{5}} + \dfrac{5}{3} = \dfrac{\sqrt{\frac{1}{2}}}{\frac{3}{5}} + \dfrac{5}{3} = \dfrac{4}{5} \cdot \dfrac{5}{3} + \dfrac{5}{3} = \dfrac{9}{3} = 3$

28. The value of $\sec t$ is irrelevant, since $\sin^2 t + \cos^2 t = 1$ for all t.

29. $y = 10\cos\frac{1}{2}x$

(a) This function has amplitude 10, period $\dfrac{2\pi}{\frac{1}{2}} = 4\pi$, and phase shift 0.

(b)

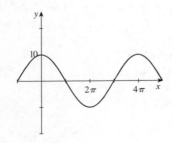

30. $y = 4\sin 2\pi x$

(a) This function has amplitude 4, period $\frac{2\pi}{2\pi} = 1$, and phase shift 0.

(b)

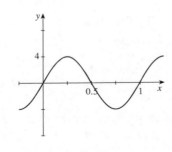

31. $y = -\sin \frac{1}{2}x$

(a) This function has amplitude 1, period $\dfrac{2\pi}{\left(\frac{1}{2}\right)} = 4\pi$, and phase shift 0.

(b)

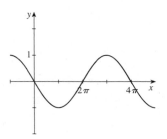

32. $y = 2\sin\left(x - \frac{\pi}{4}\right)$

(a) This function has amplitude 2, period 2π, and phase shift $\frac{\pi}{4}$.

(b)

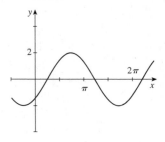

33. $y = 3\sin(2x - 2) = 3\sin 2(x - 1)$

(a) This function has amplitude 3, period $\frac{2\pi}{2} = \pi$, and phase shift 1.

(b)

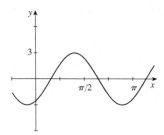

34. $y = \cos 2\left(x - \frac{\pi}{2}\right)$

(a) This function has amplitude 1, period $\frac{2\pi}{2} = \pi$, and phase shift $\frac{\pi}{2}$.

(b)

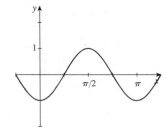

35. $y = -\cos\left(\frac{\pi}{2}x + \frac{\pi}{6}\right) = -\cos\frac{\pi}{2}\left(x + \frac{1}{3}\right)$

(a) This function has amplitude 1, period $\dfrac{2\pi}{\left(\frac{\pi}{2}\right)} = 4$, and phase shift $-\frac{1}{3}$.

(b)

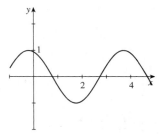

36. $y = 10\sin\left(2x - \frac{\pi}{2}\right) = 10\sin 2\left(x - \frac{\pi}{4}\right)$

(a) This function has amplitude 10, period $\frac{2\pi}{2} = \pi$, and phase shift $\frac{\pi}{4}$.

(b)

37. From the graph we see that the amplitude is 5, the period is $\frac{\pi}{2}$, and there is no phase shift. Therefore, the function is $y = 5\sin 4x$.

38. From the graph we see that the amplitude is 2, the period is 4 since $\frac{1}{4}$ of the period has been completed at $(1, 2)$, and there is no phase shift. Thus, $\dfrac{2\pi}{k} = 4 \Leftrightarrow k = \frac{\pi}{2}$. Therefore, the function is $y = 2\sin\frac{\pi}{2}x$.

39. From the graph we see that the amplitude is $\frac{1}{2}$, the period is 1, and there is a phase shift of $-\frac{1}{3}$. Therefore, the function is $y = \frac{1}{2}\sin 2\pi\left(x + \frac{1}{3}\right)$.

40. From the graph we see that the amplitude is 4, the period is $\frac{4\pi}{3}$. Thus, $\frac{2\pi}{k} = \frac{4\pi}{3} \Leftrightarrow k = \frac{3}{2}$. The phase shift is $-\frac{\pi}{3}$.
Therefore, the function is $y = 4 \sin \frac{3}{2} \left(x + \frac{\pi}{3} \right)$.

41. $y = 3 \tan x$ has period π.

42. $y = \tan \pi x$ has period $\frac{\pi}{\pi} = 1$.

43. $y = 2 \cot \left(x - \frac{\pi}{2} \right)$ has period π.

44. $y = \sec \left(\frac{1}{2} x - \frac{\pi}{2} \right) = \sec \frac{1}{2} \left(x - \pi \right)$ has period
$$\frac{2\pi}{\left(\frac{1}{2} \right)} = 4\pi.$$

45. $y = 4 \csc \left(2x + \pi \right) = 4 \csc 2 \left(x + \frac{\pi}{2} \right)$ has period
$\frac{2\pi}{2} = \pi$.

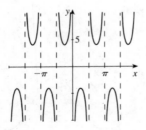

46. $y = \tan \left(x + \frac{\pi}{6} \right)$ has period π.

47. $y = \tan \left(\frac{1}{2} x - \frac{\pi}{8} \right) = \tan \frac{1}{2} \left(x - \frac{\pi}{4} \right)$ has period $\frac{\pi}{\frac{1}{2}} = 2\pi$.   **48.** $y = -4 \sec \left(4 \pi x \right)$ has period $\frac{2\pi}{4\pi} = \frac{1}{2}$.

49. (a) $y = |\cos x|$

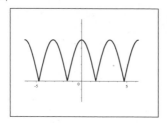

(b) This function has period π.

(c) This function is even.

50. (a) $y = \sin(\cos x)$

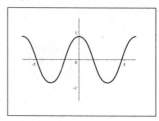

(b) This function has period 2π.

(c) This function is even.

51. (a) $y = \cos\left(2^{0.1x}\right)$

(b) This function is not periodic.

(c) This function is neither even nor odd.

52. (a) $y = 1 + 2^{\cos x}$

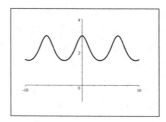

(b) This function has period 2π.

(c) This function is even.

53. (a) $y = e^{-|x|} \cos 3x$

(b) This function is not periodic.

(c) This function is even.

54. (a) $y = \ln x \sin x \ (x > 0)$

(b) This function is not periodic.

(c) This function is neither even nor odd.

55. $y = x \sin x$ is a sine function whose graph lies between those of $y = x$ and $y = -x$.

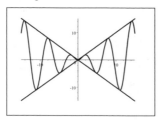

56. $y = 2^{-x} \cos 4\pi x$ is a cosine function whose graph lies between the graphs of $y = 2^{-x}$ and $y = -2^{-x}$.

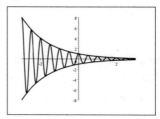

57. $y = x + \sin 4x$ is the sum of the two functions $y = x$ and $y = \sin 4x$.

58. $y = \sin^2 x + \cos^2 x$ is the sum of the two functions $y = \sin^2 x$ and $y = \cos^2 x$. Note that $\sin^2 x + \cos^2 x = 1$ for all x.

59. $y = \cos x + \sin 2x$. Since the period is 2π, we graph over the interval $[-\pi, \pi]$. The maximum value is 1.76 when $x \approx 0.63 \pm 2n\pi$, the minimum value is -1.76 when $x \approx 2.51 \pm 2n\pi$, n an integer.

60. $y = \cos x + \sin^2 x$. Since the period of this function is 2π, we graph this function over the interval $-\pi$ to π. The maximum value is 1.25 when $x \approx 1.05 \pm 2n\pi$, the minimum value is -1 when $x = \frac{\pi}{2} \pm 2n\pi \approx 1.57 \pm 2n\pi$, n an integer.

61. We want to find solutions to $\sin x = 0.3$ in the interval $[0, 2\pi]$, so we plot the functions $y = \sin x$ and $y = 0.3$ and look for their intersection. We see that $x \approx 0.305$ or $x \approx 2.837$.

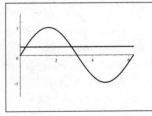

62. We want to find solutions to $\cos 3x = x$ in the interval $[0, \pi]$, so we plot the functions $y = \cos 3x$ and $y = x$ and look for their intersection. We see that $x \approx 0.390$.

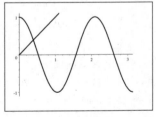

63. $f(x) = \dfrac{\sin^2 x}{x}$

(a) The function is odd.

(b) The graph intersects the x-axis at $x = 0, \pm\pi, \pm2\pi, \pm3\pi, \ldots$

(d) As $x \to \pm\infty$, $f(x) \to 0$.

(e) As $x \to 0$, $f(x) \to 0$.

(c)

64. $y_1 = \cos(\sin x)$, $y_2 = \sin(\cos x)$

(a)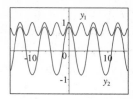

    (b) y_1 has period π, while y_2 has period 2π.

    (c) $\sin(\cos x) < \cos(\sin x)$ for all x.

65. The amplitude is $a = 50$ cm, the frequency is 8 Hz, and the point is at its maximum displacement when $t = 0$, so a function describing the motion of P is $f(t) = 50\cos 16\pi t$.

66. The amplitude is $\frac{1}{2}(100) = 50$ cm, the frequency is 4 Hz, and the mass is at its lowest point when $t = 0$, so a function describing the distance of the mass from its rest position is $f(t) = -50\cos 8\pi t$.

67. From the graph, we see that the amplitude is 4 ft, the period is 12 hours, and there is no phase shift. Thus, the variation in water level is described by $y = 4\cos\frac{\pi}{6}t$.

68. **(a)** The initial amplitude is 16 cm and the frequency is 1.4 Hz, so

      a function describing the motion is $y = 16e^{-0.72t}\cos 2.8\pi t$.

    (c) When $t = 10$ s, $y \approx 16e^{-7.2}\cos 28\pi \approx 0.019$ cm.

(b)

Chapter 5 Test

1. Since $P(x, y)$ lies on the unit circle, $x^2 + y^2 = 1 \Rightarrow y = \pm\sqrt{1 - \left(\frac{\sqrt{11}}{6}\right)^2} = \pm\sqrt{\frac{25}{36}} = \pm\frac{5}{6}$. But $P(x, y)$ lies in the

    fourth quadrant. Therefore y is negative $\Rightarrow$ $y = -\frac{5}{6}$.

2. Since P is on the unit circle, $x^2 + y^2 = 1 \Leftrightarrow x^2 = 1 - y^2$. Thus, $x^2 = 1 - \left(\frac{4}{5}\right)^2 = \frac{9}{25}$, and so $x = \pm\frac{3}{5}$. From the diagram,

    x is clearly negative, so $x = -\frac{3}{5}$. Therefore, P is the point $\left(-\frac{3}{5}, \frac{4}{5}\right)$.

    (a) $\sin t = \frac{4}{5}$ **(b)** $\cos t = -\frac{3}{5}$

    (c) $\tan t = \dfrac{\frac{4}{5}}{-\frac{3}{5}} = -\frac{4}{3}$ **(d)** $\sec(t) = -\frac{5}{3}$

3. **(a)** $\sin\frac{7\pi}{6} = -0.5$ **(b)** $\cos\dfrac{13\pi}{4} = -\dfrac{\sqrt{2}}{2}$

    (c) $\tan\left(-\frac{5\pi}{3}\right) = \sqrt{3}$ **(d)** $\csc\left(\frac{3\pi}{2}\right) = -1$

4. $\tan t = \dfrac{\sin t}{\cos t} = \dfrac{\sin t}{\pm\sqrt{1 - \sin^2 t}}$. But t is in quadrant II $\Rightarrow$ $\cos t$ is negative, so we choose the negative square root.

    Thus, $\tan t = \dfrac{\sin t}{-\sqrt{1 - \sin^2 t}}$.

5. $\cos t = -\frac{8}{17}$, t in quadrant III $\Rightarrow$ $\tan t \cdot \cot t + \csc t = 1 + \dfrac{1}{-\sqrt{1 - \cos^2 t}}$ (since t is in

    quadrant III)$= 1 - \dfrac{1}{-\sqrt{1 - \frac{64}{289}}} = 1 - \dfrac{1}{\frac{15}{17}} = -\frac{2}{15}$.

6. $y = -5\cos 4x$

(a) This function has amplitude 5, period $\frac{2\pi}{4} = \frac{\pi}{2}$, and phase shift 0.

(b)

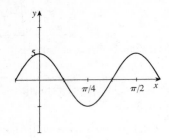

7. $y = 2\sin\left(\frac{1}{2}x - \frac{\pi}{6}\right) = \sin\frac{1}{2}\left(x - \frac{\pi}{3}\right)$

(a) This function has amplitude 2, period $\dfrac{2\pi}{\frac{1}{2}} = 4\pi$, and phase shift $\frac{\pi}{3}$.

(b)

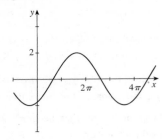

8. $y = -\csc 2x$ has period $\frac{2\pi}{2} = \pi$.

9. $y = \tan 2\left(x - \frac{\pi}{4}\right)$ has period $\frac{\pi}{2}$.

10. From the graph, we see that the amplitude is 2 and the phase shift is $-\frac{\pi}{3}$. Also, the period is π, so $\frac{2\pi}{k} = \pi \;\Rightarrow\; k = \frac{2\pi}{\pi} = 2$. Thus, the function is $y = 2\sin 2\left(x + \frac{\pi}{3}\right)$.

11. $y = \dfrac{\cos x}{1 + x^2}$

(b) The function is even.

(c) The function has a minimum value of approximately -0.11 when $x \approx \pm 2.54$ and a maximum value of 1 when $x = 0$.

(a)

12. The amplitude is $\frac{1}{2}(10) = 5$ cm and the frequency is 2 Hz. Assuming that the mass is at its rest position and moving upward when $t = 0$, a function describing the distance of the mass from its rest position is $f(t) = 5\sin 4\pi t$.

13. (a) The initial amplitude is 16 in and the frequency is 12 Hz, so a function describing the motion is
$$y = 16e^{-0.1t}\cos 24\pi t.$$

(b)

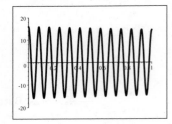

Focus on Modeling: Fitting Sinusoidal Curves to Data

1. (a) See the graph in part (c).

(b) Using the method of Example 1, we find the vertical shift

$b = \frac{1}{2}$ (maximum value + minimum value) $= \frac{1}{2}(2.1 - 2.1) = 0$, the amplitude

$a = \frac{1}{2}$ (maximum value − minimum value) $= \frac{1}{2}(2.1 - (-2.1)) = 2.1$, the period $\dfrac{2\pi}{\omega} = 2(6 - 0) = 12$ (so

$\omega \approx 0.5236$), and the phase shift $c = 0$. Thus, our model is $y = 2.1\cos\frac{\pi}{6}t$.

(c)

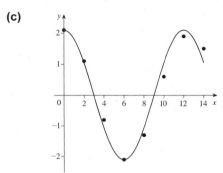

The curve fits the data quite well.

(d) Using the SinReg command on the TI-83, we find

$$y = 2.048714222\sin(0.5030795477t + 1.551856108)$$
$$- 0.0089616507.$$

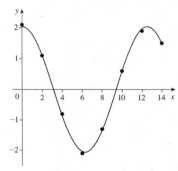

(e) Our model from part (b) is equivalent to $y = 2.1\sin(0.5236t + 1.5708)$, which is close to the model in part (d).

2. (a) See the graph in part (c).

(b) Using the method of Example 1, we find the vertical shift

$b = \frac{1}{2}$ (maximum value + minimum value) $= \frac{1}{2}(200 + 95) = 147.5$, the amplitude

$a = \frac{1}{2}$ (maximum value − minimum value) $= \frac{1}{2}(200 - 95) = 52.5$, the period $\dfrac{2\pi}{\omega} = 2(275 - 125) = 300$ (so

$\omega \approx 0.02094$), and the phase shift $c = 275$. Thus, our model is $y = 52.5\cos(0.02094(t - 275)) + 147.5$.

(c)

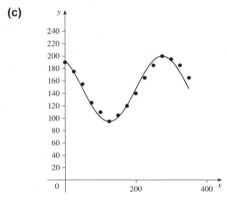

The curve fits the data quite well.

(d) Using the SinReg command on the TI-83, we find

$$y = 49.70329025\sin(0.0200800412x + 2.093611012)$$
$$+ 149.1294508.$$

(e) Our model from part (b) is equivalent to $y = 52.5\sin(0.02094t + 2.094) + 147.5$, which is close to the model in part (d).

3. (a) See the graph in part (c).

(b) Using the method of Example 1, we find the vertical shift
$b = \frac{1}{2}$ (maximum value + minimum value) $= \frac{1}{2}(25.1 + 1.0) = 13.05$, the amplitude
$a = \frac{1}{2}$ (maximum value − minimum value) $= \frac{1}{2}(25.1 - 1.0) = 12.05$, the period $\dfrac{2\pi}{\omega} = 2(1.5 - 0.9) = 1.2$ (so
$\omega \approx 5.236$), and the phase shift $c = 0.3$. Thus, our model is $y = 12.05 \cos(5.236(t - 0.3)) + 13.05$.

(c)

The curve fits the data fairly well.

(d) Using the `SinReg` command on the TI-83, we find
$$y = 11.71905062 \sin(5.048853286t + 0.2388957877)$$
$$+ 12.96070536.$$

(e) Our model from part (b) is equivalent to $y = 12.05 \sin 5.236t + 13.05$, which is close to the model in part (d).

4. (a) See the graph in part (c).

(b) Using the method of Example 1, we find the vertical shift
$b = \frac{1}{2}$ (maximum value + minimum value) $= \frac{1}{2}(0.63 - 0.10) = 0.265$, the amplitude
$a = \frac{1}{2}$ (maximum value − minimum value) $= \frac{1}{2}(0.63 - (-0.10)) = 0.365$, the period $\dfrac{2\pi}{\omega} = 2(5.5 - 2.5) = 6$ (so
$\omega \approx 1.047$), and the phase shift $c = 5.5$. Thus, our model is $y = 0.365 \cos(1.047(t - 5.5)) + 0.265$.

(c)

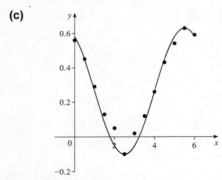

The curve fits the data reasonably well.

(d) Using the `SinReg` command on the TI-83, we find
$$y = 0.327038879 \sin(1.021164911t + 2.118186963)$$
$$+ 0.2896017397.$$

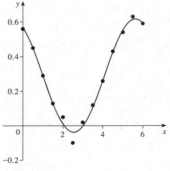

(e) Our model from part (b) is equivalent to $y = 0.365 \cos(1.047t + 2.094) + 0.265$, which is close to the model in part (d). Our model in part (b) gives undue weight to the minimum value of -0.10.

5. (a) See the graph in part (c).

(b) Let t be the time (in months) from January. We find a function of the form $y = a \cos \omega (t - c) + b$, where y is temperature in °F.

$a = \frac{1}{2} (85.8 - 40) = 22.9$. The period is $2 (\text{Jul} - \text{Jan}) = 2 (6 - 0) = 12$ and so $\omega = \frac{2\pi}{12} \approx 0.52$.

$b = \frac{1}{2} (85.8 + 40) = 62.9$. Since the maximum value occurs in July, $c = 6$. Thus the function is $y = 22.9 \cos 0.52 (t - 6) + 62.9$.

(c)

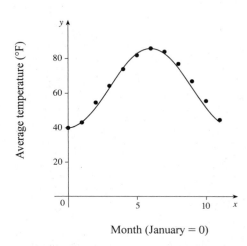

Month (January = 0)

(d) Using the `SinReg` command on the TI-83 we find that for the function $y = a \sin (bt + c) + d$, where $a = 23.4$, $b = 0.48$, $c = -1.36$, and $d = 62.2$. Thus we get the model $y = 23.4 \sin (0.48t - 1.36) + 62.2$.

6. (a) See the graph in part (c).

(b) Let t be the time since midnight. We find a function of the form $y = a \sin \omega (t - c) + b$. $a = \frac{1}{2} (37.4 - 36.6) = 0.4$. The period is 24 and so $\omega = \frac{2\pi}{24} \approx 0.26$. $b = \frac{1}{2} (37.4 + 36.6) = 37$. Since the average value occurs at $t = 10$, we get $c = 10$. Thus the function is $y = 0.4 \sin 0.26 (t - 10) + 37$.

(c)

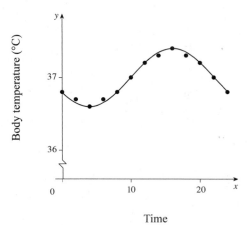

Time

(d) Using the `SinReg` command on the TI-83 we obtain the function $y = a \sin (bt + c) + d$, where $a = 0.4$, $b = 0.26$, $c = -2.64$, and $d = 37.0$. Thus we get the model $y = 0.4 \sin (0.26t - 2.64) + 37.0$.

7. (a) See the graph in part (c).

(b) Let t be the time years. We find a function of the form $y = a \sin \omega (t - c) + b$, where y is the owl population. $a = \frac{1}{2} (80 - 20) = 30$. The period is $2 (9 - 3) = 12$ and so $\omega = \frac{2\pi}{12} \approx 0.52$. $b = \frac{1}{2} (80 + 20) = 50$. Since the values start at the middle we have $c = 0$. Thus the function is $y = 30 \sin 0.52t + 50$.

(c)

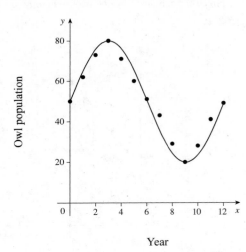

Year

(d) Using the `SinReg` command on the TI–83 we find that for the function $y = a \sin (bt + c) + d$, where $a = 25.8$, $b = 0.52$, $c = -0.02$, and $d = 50.6$. Thus we get the model $y = 25.8 \sin (0.52t - 0.02) + 50.6$.

8. (a) See the graph in part (c).

(b) Let t be the time since 1985. We find a function of the form $y = a \cos \omega (t - c) + b$. $a = \frac{1}{2} (63 - 22) = 20.5$. The periodis $2 (15 - 9) = 12$ and so $\omega = \frac{2\pi}{20} \approx 0.52$. $b = \frac{1}{2} (63 + 22) = 42.5$. The maximum value occurs in the ninth year, so $c = 9$. Thus, our model is $y = 20.5 \cos 0.52 (t - 9) + 42.5$.

(c)

Year since 1985

(d) Using the `SinReg` command on the TI–83, we find that for the function $y = a \sin (bt + c) + d$, where $a = 17.8$, $b = 0.52$, $c = 3.11$, and $d = 42.4$. Thus we get the model $y = 17.8 \sin (0.52t - 3.11) + 42.4$.

9. (a) See the graph in part (c).

(b) Let t be the time since 1975. We find a function of the form $y = a \cos \omega (t - c) + b$. $a = \frac{1}{2} (158 - 9) = 74.5$. The first period seems to stretch from 1980 to 1989 (maximum to maximum) and the second period from 1989 to 2000, so the period is about 10 years and so $\omega = \frac{2\pi}{10} \approx 0.628$. $b = \frac{1}{2} (158 + 9) = 83.5$. The first maximum value occurs in the fifth year, so $c = 5$. Thus, our model is $y = 74.5 \cos 0.628 (t - 5) + 83.5$.

(c)

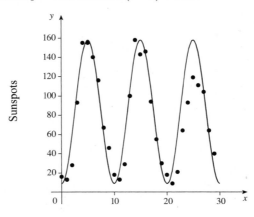

Year since 1975

(d) Using the `SinReg` command on the TI-83, we find that for the function $y = a \sin (bt + c) + d$, where $a = 67.65094323$, $b = 0.6205550572$, $c = -1.654463632$, and $d = 74.50460325$. Thus we get the model $y = 67.65 \sin (0.62t - 1.65) + 74.5$. This model is more accurate for more recent years than the one we found in part (b).

6 Trigonometric Functions of Angles

6.1 Angle Measure

1. $72° = 72° \cdot \frac{\pi}{180°}$ rad $= \frac{2\pi}{5}$ rad ≈ 1.257 rad

2. $54° = 54° \cdot \frac{\pi}{180°}$ rad $= \frac{3\pi}{10}$ rad ≈ 0.942 rad

3. $-45° = -45° \cdot \frac{\pi}{180°}$ rad $= -\frac{\pi}{4}$ rad ≈ -0.785 rad

4. $-60° = -60° \cdot \frac{\pi}{180°}$ rad $= -\frac{\pi}{3}$ rad ≈ -1.047 rad

5. $-75° = -75° \cdot \frac{\pi}{180°}$ rad $= -\frac{5\pi}{12}$ rad ≈ -1.309 rad

6. $-300° = -300° \cdot \frac{\pi}{180°}$ rad $= -\frac{5\pi}{3}$ rad ≈ -5.236 rad

7. $1080° = 1080° \cdot \frac{\pi}{180°}$ rad $= 6\pi$ rad ≈ 18.850 rad

8. $3960° = 3960° \cdot \frac{\pi}{180°}$ rad $= 22\pi$ rad ≈ 69.115 rad

9. $96° = 96° \cdot \frac{\pi}{180°}$ rad $= \frac{8\pi}{15}$ rad ≈ 1.676 rad

10. $15° = 15° \cdot \frac{\pi}{180°}$ rad $= \frac{\pi}{12}$ rad ≈ 0.262 rad

11. $7.5° = 7.5° \cdot \frac{\pi}{180°}$ rad $= \frac{\pi}{2}$ rad ≈ 0.131 rad

12. $202.5° = 202.5° \cdot \frac{\pi}{180°}$ rad $= \frac{9\pi}{8}$ rad ≈ 3.534 rad

13. $\frac{7\pi}{6} = \frac{7\pi}{6} \cdot \frac{180°}{\pi} = 210°$

14. $\frac{11\pi}{3} = \frac{11\pi}{3} \cdot \frac{180°}{\pi} = 660°$

15. $-\frac{5\pi}{4} = -\frac{5\pi}{4} \cdot \frac{180°}{\pi} = -225°$

16. $-\frac{3\pi}{2} = -\frac{3\pi}{2} \cdot \frac{180°}{\pi} = -270°$

17. $3 = 3 \cdot \frac{180°}{\pi} = \frac{540°}{\pi} \approx 171.9°$

18. $-2 = -2 \cdot \frac{180°}{\pi} = -\frac{360°}{\pi} \approx -114.6°$

19. $-1.2 = -1.2 \cdot \frac{180°}{\pi} = -\frac{216°}{\pi} = -68.8°$

20. $3.4 = 3.4 \cdot \frac{180°}{\pi} = \frac{612°}{\pi} \approx 194.8°$

21. $\frac{\pi}{10} = \frac{\pi}{10} \cdot \frac{180°}{\pi} = 18°$

22. $\frac{5\pi}{18} = \frac{5\pi}{18} \cdot \frac{180°}{\pi} = 50°$

23. $50°$ is coterminal with $50° + 360° = 410°$, $50° + 720° = 770°$, $50° - 360° = -310°$, and $50° - 720° = -670°$. (Other answers are possible.)

24. $135°$ is coterminal with $135° + 360° = 495°$, $135° + 720° = 855°$, $135° - 360° = -225°$, and $135° - 720° = -585°$. (Other answers are possible.)

25. $\frac{3\pi}{4}$ is coterminal with $\frac{3\pi}{4} + 2\pi = \frac{11\pi}{4}$, $\frac{3\pi}{4} + 4\pi = \frac{19\pi}{4}$, $\frac{3\pi}{4} - 2\pi = -\frac{5\pi}{4}$, and $\frac{3\pi}{4} - 4\pi = -\frac{13\pi}{4}$. (Other answers are possible.)

26. $\frac{11\pi}{6}$ is coterminal with $\frac{11\pi}{6} + 2\pi = \frac{23\pi}{6}$, $\frac{11\pi}{6} + 4\pi = \frac{35\pi}{6}$, $\frac{11\pi}{6} - 2\pi = -\frac{\pi}{6}$, and $\frac{11\pi}{6} - 4\pi = -\frac{13\pi}{6}$. (Other answers are possible.)

27. $-\frac{\pi}{4}$ is coterminal with $-\frac{\pi}{4} + 2\pi = \frac{7\pi}{4}$, $-\frac{\pi}{4} + 4\pi = \frac{15\pi}{4}$, $-\frac{\pi}{4} - 2\pi = -\frac{9\pi}{4}$, and $-\frac{\pi}{4} - 4\pi = -\frac{17\pi}{4}$. (Other answers are possible.)

28. $-45°$ is coterminal with $-45° + 360° = 315°$, $-45° + 720° = 675°$, $-45° - 360° = -405°$, and $-45° - 720° = -765°$. (Other answers are possible.)

29. $-\frac{2\pi}{15}$ is coterminal with $-\frac{2\pi}{15} + 2\pi = \frac{28\pi}{15}$, $-\frac{2\pi}{15} + 4\pi = \frac{58\pi}{15}$, $-\frac{2\pi}{15} - 2\pi = -\frac{32\pi}{15}$, and $-\frac{2\pi}{15} - 4\pi = -\frac{62\pi}{15}$. (Other answers are possible.)

30. $-\frac{13\pi}{12}$ is coterminal with $-\frac{13\pi}{12} + 2\pi = \frac{11\pi}{12}$, $-\frac{13\pi}{12} + 4\pi = \frac{35\pi}{12}$, $-\frac{13\pi}{12} - 2\pi = -\frac{37\pi}{12}$, and $-\frac{13\pi}{12} - 4\pi = -\frac{61\pi}{12}$. (Other answers are possible.)

31. Since $430° - 70° = 360°$, the angles are coterminal.

32. Since $330° - (-30°) = 360°$, the angles are coterminal.

33. Since $\frac{17\pi}{6} - \frac{5\pi}{6} = \frac{12\pi}{6} = 2\pi$; the angles are coterminal.

34. Since $\frac{32\pi}{3} - \frac{11\pi}{3} = \frac{21\pi}{3} = 7\pi$ is not a multiple of 2π, the angles are not coterminal.

35. Since $875° - 155° = 720° = 2 \cdot 360°$, the angles are coterminal.

36. Since $340° - 50° = 290°$ is not a multiple of $360°$, the angles are not coterminal.

37. Since $733° - 2 \cdot 360° = 13°$, the angles $733°$ and $13°$ are coterminal.

38. Since $361° - 1° = 360°$, the angles $361°$ and $1°$ are coterminal.

39. Since $1110° - 3 \cdot 360° = 30°$, the angles $1110°$ and $30°$ are coterminal.

40. Since $-100° - 260° = -360°$ is a multiple of $360°$, the angles $-100°$ and $260°$ are coterminal.

41. Since $-800° + 3 \cdot 360° = 280°$, the angles $-800°$ and $280°$ are coterminal.

42. Since $1270° - 190° = 1080° = 3 \cdot 360°$ is a multiple of $360°$, the angles $1270°$ and $190°$ are coterminal.

43. Since $\frac{17\pi}{6} - 2\pi = \frac{5\pi}{6}$, the angles $\frac{17\pi}{6}$ and $\frac{5\pi}{6}$ are coterminal.

44. Since $-\frac{7\pi}{3} - \frac{5\pi}{3} = 4\pi$ is a multiple of 2π, the angles $-\frac{7\pi}{3}$ and $\frac{5\pi}{3}$ are coterminal.

45. Since $87\pi - 43 \cdot 2\pi = \pi$, the angles 87π and π are coterminal.

46. Since $10 - 2\pi \approx 3.717$, the angles 10 and $10 - 2\pi$ are coterminal.

47. Since $\frac{17\pi}{4} - 2 \cdot 2\pi = \frac{\pi}{4}$, the angles $\frac{17\pi}{4}$ and $\frac{\pi}{4}$ are coterminal.

48. Since $\frac{51\pi}{2} - \frac{3\pi}{2} = 24\pi = 12 \cdot 2\pi$, the angles $\frac{51\pi}{2}$ and $\frac{3\pi}{2}$ are coterminal.

49. Using the formula $s = \theta r$, the length of the arc is $s = \left(220° \cdot \frac{\pi}{180°}\right) \cdot 5 = \frac{55\pi}{9} \approx 19.2$.

50. $\theta = \frac{s}{r} = \frac{10}{5} = 2 \text{ rad} = 2 \cdot \frac{180°}{\pi} \approx 114.6°$

51. Solving for r we have $r = \frac{s}{\theta}$, so the radius of the circle is $r = \frac{8}{2} = 4$.

52. Using the formula $s = \theta r$, the length of the arc is $s = 45° \cdot \frac{\pi}{180°} \cdot 10 = \frac{5\pi}{2} \approx 7.85$ m

53. Using the formula $s = \theta r$, the length of the arc is $s = 2 \cdot 2 = 4$ mi.

54. Solving for θ, we have $\theta = \frac{s}{r}$, the measure of the central angle is $\theta = \frac{6}{5} = 1.2 \text{ rad} = 1.2 \cdot \frac{180°}{\pi} \approx 68.8°$.

55. Solving for θ, we have $\theta = \frac{s}{r}$, so the measure of the central angle is $\theta = \frac{100}{50} = 2 \text{ rad}$. Converting to degrees we have
$\theta = 2 \cdot \frac{180°}{\pi} \approx 114.6°$

56. Solving for r, we have $r = \frac{s}{\theta}$, so the radius of the circle is $r = \dfrac{3}{25° \cdot \frac{\pi}{180°}} = 3 \cdot \frac{36}{5\pi} \approx 6.88$ ft.

57. Solving for r, we have $r = \frac{s}{\theta}$, so the radius of the circle is $r = \frac{6}{\pi/6} = \frac{36}{\pi} \approx 11.46$ m.

58. Solving for r, we have $r = \frac{s}{\theta}$, so the radius of the circle is $r = \dfrac{4}{135° \cdot \frac{\pi}{180°}} = \frac{16}{3\pi} \approx 1.70$ ft.

59. **(a)** $A = \frac{1}{2}r^2\theta = \frac{1}{2} \cdot 8^2 \cdot 80° \cdot \frac{\pi}{180°} = 32 \cdot \frac{4\pi}{9} = \frac{128\pi}{9} \approx 35.45$

   (b) $A = \frac{1}{2}r^2\theta = \frac{1}{2} \cdot 10^2 \cdot 0.5 = 25$

60. **(a)** $A = \frac{1}{2}r^2\theta \Rightarrow r = \sqrt{\dfrac{2A}{\theta}}$, so the radius is $\sqrt{\dfrac{2 \cdot 12}{0.7}} \approx 5.86$.

   (b) $r = \sqrt{\dfrac{2A}{\theta}} = \sqrt{\dfrac{2 \cdot 12}{150° \cdot \frac{\pi}{180°}}} \approx 3.03$

61. $A = \frac{1}{2}r^2\theta = \frac{1}{2} \cdot 10^2 \cdot 1 = 50$ m^2

62. $\theta = 60° = 60° \cdot \frac{\pi}{180°} = \frac{\pi}{3}$ rad. Then $A = \frac{1}{2}r^2\theta = \frac{1}{2} \cdot 3^2 \cdot \frac{\pi}{3} = \frac{3\pi}{2} \approx 4.7$ mi^2

63. $\theta = 2$ rad, $A = 16$ m^2. Since $A = \frac{1}{2}r^2\theta$, we have $r = \sqrt{2A/\theta} = \sqrt{2 \cdot 16/2} = \sqrt{16} = 4$ m.

64. $r = 24$ mi, $A = 288$ mi^2. Then $\theta = \dfrac{2A}{r^2} = \dfrac{2 \cdot 288}{24^2} = 1 \text{ rad} \approx 57.3°$.

65. Since the area of the circle is 72 cm^2, the radius of the circle is $r = \sqrt{A/\pi} = \sqrt{72/\pi}$. Then the area of the sector is
$A = \frac{1}{2}r^2\theta = \frac{1}{2} \cdot \frac{72}{\pi} \cdot \frac{\pi}{6} = 6$ cm^2.

66. Referring to the figure, we have $AC = 3 + 1 = 4$, $BC = 1 + 2 = 3$, and $AB = 2 + 3 = 5$. Since $AB^2 = AC^2 + BC^2$, then by the Pythagorean Theorem, the triangle is a right triangle. Therefore, $\theta = \frac{\pi}{2}$ and $A = \frac{1}{2}r^2\theta = \frac{1}{2} \cdot 1^2 \cdot \frac{\pi}{2} = \frac{\pi}{4}$ ft^2.

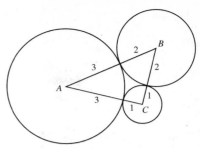

67. The circumference of each wheel is $\pi d = 28\pi$ in. If the wheels revolve 10,000 times, the distance traveled is $10{,}000 \cdot 28\pi$ in. $\cdot \dfrac{1 \text{ ft}}{12 \text{ in.}} \cdot \dfrac{1 \text{ mi}}{5280 \text{ ft}} \approx 13.88$ mi.

68. Since the diameter is 30 in., we have $r = 15$ in. In one revolution, the arc length (distance traveled) is $s = \theta r = 2\pi \cdot 15 = 30\pi$ in. The total distance traveled is 1 mi $\cdot$ 5280 ft/mi $\cdot$ 12 in/ft $= 63{,}360$ in. $= 63{,}360$ in. $\cdot \dfrac{1 \text{ rev}}{30\pi \text{ in}} \approx 672.27$ rev. Therefore the car wheel will make approximately 672 revolutions.

69. We find the measure of the angle in degrees and then convert to radians. $\theta = 40.5° - 25.5° = 15°$ and $15 \cdot \frac{\pi}{180°}$ rad $= \frac{\pi}{12}$ rad. Then using the formula $s = \theta r$, we have $s = \frac{\pi}{12} \cdot 3960 = 330\pi \approx 1036.725$ and so the distance between the two cities is roughly 1037 mi.

70. $\theta = 35° - 30° = 5° = 5° \cdot \frac{\pi}{180°}$ rad $= \frac{\pi}{3}$ rad. Then using the formula $s = \theta r$, the length of the arc is $s = \frac{\pi}{3} \cdot 3960 = 110\pi \approx 345.575$. So the distance between the two cities is roughly 346 mi.

71. In one day, the earth travels $\frac{1}{365}$ of its orbit which is $\frac{2\pi}{365}$ rad. Then $s = \theta r = \frac{2\pi}{365} \cdot 93{,}000{,}000 \approx 1{,}600{,}911.3$, so the distance traveled is approximately 1.6 million miles.

72. Since the sun is so far away, we can assume that the rays of the sun are parallel when striking the earth. Thus, the angle formed at the center of the earth is also $\theta = 7.2°$. So $r = \dfrac{s}{\theta} = \dfrac{500}{7.2° \cdot \frac{\pi}{180°}} = \dfrac{180 \cdot 500}{7.2\pi} \approx 3980$ mi, and the circumference is $c = 2\pi r = \dfrac{2\pi \cdot 180 \cdot 500}{7.2\pi} = 25{,}000$ mi.

73. The central angle is 1 minute $= \left(\frac{1}{60}\right)° = \frac{1}{60} \cdot \frac{\pi}{180°}$ rad $= \frac{\pi}{10{,}800}$ rad. Then $s = \theta r = \frac{\pi}{10{,}800} \cdot 3960 \approx 1.152$, and so a nautical mile is approximately 1.152 mi.

74. The area is $A = \frac{1}{2}r^2\theta = \frac{1}{2} \cdot 300^2 \cdot \left(280° \cdot \frac{\pi}{180°}\right) \approx 219{,}900$ ft^2.

75. The area is equal to the area of the large sector (with radius 34 in.) minus the area of the small sector (with radius 14 in.). Thus, $A = \frac{1}{2}r_1^2\theta - \frac{1}{2}r_2^2\theta = \frac{1}{2}\left(34^2 - 14^2\right)\left(135° \cdot \frac{\pi}{180°}\right) \approx 1131$ in.^{2}.

76. The area available to the cow is shown in the diagram. Its area is the sum of four quarter-circles:

$$
\begin{aligned}
A &= \tfrac{1}{4}\pi\left(100^2 + 50^2 + 40^2 + 30^2\right) \\
&= 3750\pi \\
&\approx 11{,}781 \text{ ft}^2
\end{aligned}
$$

77. $v = \dfrac{8 \cdot 2\pi \cdot 2}{15} = \dfrac{32\pi}{15} \approx 6.702$ ft/s.

78. (a) The angular speed is $\omega = \dfrac{45 \cdot 2\pi \text{ rad}}{1 \text{ min}} = 90\pi$ rad/min.

(b) The linear speed is $v = \dfrac{45 \cdot 2\pi \cdot 16}{1} = 1440\pi$ in./min ≈ 4523.9 in./min.

79. (a) The angular speed is $\omega = \dfrac{1000 \cdot 2\pi \text{ rad}}{1 \text{ min}} = 2000\pi$ rad/min.

(b) The linear speed is $v = \dfrac{1000 \cdot 2\pi \cdot \frac{6}{12}}{60} = \dfrac{50\pi}{3}$ ft/s ≈ 52.4 ft/s.

80. 23 h 56 min 4 s = 23.9344 hr. So the linear speed is $\dfrac{1 \cdot 2\pi \cdot (3960)}{1 \text{ day}} \cdot \dfrac{1 \text{ day}}{23.9344 \text{ hr}} \approx 1039.57$ mi/h.

81. $v = \dfrac{600 \cdot 2\pi \cdot \frac{11}{12} \text{ ft}}{1 \text{ min}} \cdot \dfrac{1 \text{ mi}}{5280 \text{ ft}} \cdot \dfrac{60 \text{ min}}{1 \text{ hr}} = 12.5\pi$ mi/h ≈ 39.3 mi/h.

82. (a) The angular speed is $\omega = \dfrac{\text{linear speed}}{\text{radius}} = \dfrac{50 \text{ mi/h}}{4 \text{ ft}} \cdot \dfrac{1 \text{ h}}{60 \text{ min}} \cdot \dfrac{5280 \text{ ft}}{1 \text{ mi}} = 1100$ rad/min.

(b) The rate of revolution is $\dfrac{\text{angular speed}}{2\pi} = \dfrac{1100 \text{ rad/min}}{2\pi} \approx 175$ revolutions/min.

83. $v = \dfrac{100 \cdot 2\pi \cdot 0.20 \text{ m}}{60 \text{ s}} = \dfrac{2\pi}{3} \approx 2.09$ m/s.

84. (a) The angular speed is $\omega = \dfrac{\text{linear speed of pedal}}{\text{radius of wheel sprocket}} = \dfrac{40 \cdot 2\pi \cdot 4}{2} = 160\pi$ rad/min.

(b) The linear speed of the bicycle is $v = $ angular speed $\cdot$ radius $= (160\pi \text{ rad/min}) \cdot (13 \text{ in}) = 2080\pi$ in/min ≈ 6.2 mi/h.

85. (a) The circumference of the opening is the length of the arc subtended by the angle θ on the flat piece of paper, that is, $C = s = r\theta = 6 \cdot \frac{5\pi}{3} = 10\pi \approx 31.4$ cm.

(b) Solving for r, we find $r = \dfrac{C}{2\pi} = \dfrac{10\pi}{2\pi} = 5$ cm.

(c) By the Pythagorean Theorem, $h^2 = 6^2 - 5^2 = 11$, so $h = \sqrt{11} \approx 3.3$ cm.

(d) The volume of a cone is $V = \frac{1}{3}\pi r^2 h$. In this case $V = \frac{1}{3}\pi \cdot 5^2 \cdot \sqrt{11} \approx 86.8$ cm^3.

86. (a) With an arbitrary angle θ, the circumference of the opening is

$C = 6\theta$, $r = \dfrac{C}{2\pi} = \dfrac{3\theta}{\pi}$, $h = \sqrt{6^2 - r^2} = \sqrt{36 - \dfrac{9\theta^2}{\pi^2}}$, and

$V = \frac{1}{3}\pi r^2 h = \dfrac{\pi}{3} \cdot \dfrac{9\theta^2}{\pi^2} \sqrt{36 - \dfrac{9\theta^2}{\pi^2}} = \dfrac{9}{\pi^2}\theta^2 \sqrt{4\pi^2 - \theta^2}$.

(b)

(c) The volume seems to be maximized for $\theta \approx 5.13$ rad or about $293°$.

87. Answers will vary, although of course everyone prefers radians.

88. There are 5 hours 45 minutes between 1:00 P.M. and 6:45 P.M.. Since 45 minutes is 0.75 hour, the minute hand moves through $5.75 \cdot 2\pi = 11.5\pi \approx 36.128$ rad. The hour hand moves through $5.75 \cdot \frac{1}{12} \cdot 2\pi = \frac{23}{24}\pi \approx 3.011$ rad.

6.2   Trigonometry of Right Triangles

1. $\sin\theta = \frac{4}{5}$, $\cos\theta = \frac{3}{5}$, $\tan\theta = \frac{4}{3}$, $\csc\theta = \frac{5}{4}$, $\sec\theta = \frac{5}{3}$, $\cot\theta = \frac{3}{4}$

2. $\sin\theta = \frac{7}{25}$, $\cos\theta = \frac{24}{25}$, $\tan\theta = \frac{7}{24}$, $\csc\theta = \frac{25}{7}$, $\sec\theta = \frac{25}{24}$, $\cot\theta = \frac{24}{7}$

3. The remaining side is obtained by the Pythagorean Theorem: $\sqrt{41^2 - 40^2} = \sqrt{81} = 9$. Then $\sin\theta = \frac{40}{41}$, $\cos\theta = \frac{9}{41}$, $\tan\theta = \frac{40}{9}$, $\csc\theta = \frac{41}{40}$, $\sec\theta = \frac{41}{9}$, $\cot\theta = \frac{9}{40}$

4. The hypotenuse is obtained by the Pythagorean Theorem: $\sqrt{8^2 + 15^2} = \sqrt{289} = 17$. Then $\sin\theta = \frac{15}{17}$, $\cos\theta = \frac{8}{17}$, $\tan\theta = \frac{15}{8}$, $\csc\theta = \frac{17}{15}$, $\sec\theta = \frac{17}{8}$, $\cot\theta = \frac{8}{15}$

5. The remaining side is obtained by the Pythagorean Theorem: $\sqrt{3^2 + 2^2} = \sqrt{13}$. Then $\sin\theta = \frac{2}{\sqrt{13}} = \frac{2\sqrt{13}}{13}$, $\cos\theta = \frac{3}{\sqrt{13}} = \frac{3\sqrt{13}}{13}$, $\tan\theta = \frac{2}{3}$, $\csc\theta = \frac{\sqrt{13}}{2}$, $\sec\theta = \frac{\sqrt{13}}{3}$, $\cot\theta = \frac{3}{2}$

6. The remaining side is obtained by the Pythagorean Theorem: $\sqrt{8^2 - 7^2} = \sqrt{15}$. Then $\sin\theta = \frac{7}{8}$, $\cos\theta = \frac{\sqrt{15}}{8}$, $\tan\theta = \frac{7}{\sqrt{15}} = \frac{7\sqrt{15}}{15}$, $\csc\theta = \frac{8}{7}$, $\sec\theta = \frac{8}{\sqrt{15}} = \frac{8\sqrt{15}}{15}$, $\cot\theta = \frac{\sqrt{15}}{7}$

7. $c = \sqrt{5^2 + 3^2} = \sqrt{34}$

    (a) $\sin\alpha = \cos\beta = \frac{3}{\sqrt{34}} = \frac{3\sqrt{34}}{34}$

    (b) $\tan\alpha = \cot\beta = \frac{3}{5}$

    (c) $\sec\alpha = \csc\beta = \frac{\sqrt{34}}{5}$

8. $b = \sqrt{7^2 - 4^2} = \sqrt{33}$

    (a) $\sin\alpha = \cos\beta = \frac{4}{7}$

    (b) $\tan\alpha = \cot\beta = \frac{4}{\sqrt{33}}$

    (c) $\sec\alpha = \csc\beta = \frac{7}{\sqrt{33}}$

9. Since $\sin 30° = \frac{x}{25}$, we have $x = 25\sin 30° = 25 \cdot \frac{1}{2} = \frac{25}{2}$.

10. Since $\sin 45° = \frac{12}{x}$, we have $x = \frac{12}{\sin 45°} = \frac{12}{\frac{1}{\sqrt{2}}} = 12\sqrt{2}$.

11. Since $\sin 60° = \frac{x}{13}$, we have $x = 13\sin 60° = 13 \cdot \frac{\sqrt{3}}{2} = \frac{13\sqrt{3}}{2}$.

12. Since $\tan 30° = \frac{4}{x}$, we have $x = \frac{4}{\tan 30°} = \frac{4}{\frac{1}{\sqrt{3}}} = 4\sqrt{3}$.

13. Since $\tan 36° = \frac{12}{x}$, we have $x = \frac{12}{\tan 36°} \approx 16.51658$.

14. Since $\sin 53° = \frac{25}{x}$, we have $x = \frac{25}{\sin 53°} \approx 31.30339$.

15. $\frac{x}{28} = \cos\theta \quad\Leftrightarrow\quad x = 28\cos\theta$, and $\frac{y}{28} = \sin\theta \quad\Leftrightarrow\quad y = 28\sin\theta$.

16. $\frac{x}{4} = \tan\theta \quad\Leftrightarrow\quad x = 4\tan\theta$, and $\frac{4}{y} = \cos\theta \quad\Leftrightarrow\quad y = \frac{4}{\cos\theta} = 4\sec\theta$.

17. $\sin\theta = \frac{3}{5}$. Then the third side is $x = \sqrt{5^2 - 3^2} = 4$. The other five ratios are $\cos\theta = \frac{4}{5}$, $\tan\theta = \frac{3}{4}$, $\csc\theta = \frac{5}{3}$, $\sec\theta = \frac{5}{4}$, and $\cot\theta = \frac{4}{3}$.

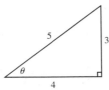

18. $\cos\theta = \frac{9}{40}$. The third side is $y = \sqrt{40^2 - 9^2} = \sqrt{1519} = 7\sqrt{31}$. The other five ratios are $\sin\theta = \frac{7\sqrt{31}}{40}$, $\tan\theta = \frac{7\sqrt{31}}{9}$, $\csc\theta = \frac{40}{7\sqrt{31}} = \frac{40\sqrt{31}}{217}$, $\sec\theta = \frac{40}{9}$, and $\cot\theta = \frac{9}{7\sqrt{31}} = \frac{9\sqrt{31}}{217}$.

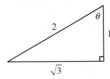

19. $\cot\theta = 1$. Then the third side is $r = \sqrt{1^2 + 1^2} = \sqrt{2}$. The other five ratios are $\sin\theta = \frac{1}{\sqrt{2}} = \frac{\sqrt{2}}{2}$, $\cos\theta = \frac{1}{\sqrt{2}} = \frac{\sqrt{2}}{2}$, $\tan\theta = 1$, $\csc\theta = \sqrt{2}$, and $\sec\theta = \sqrt{2}$.

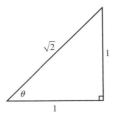

20. $\tan\theta = \sqrt{3}$. The third side is $r = \sqrt{1^2 + 3} = 2$. The other five ratios are $\sin\theta = \frac{\sqrt{3}}{2}$, $\cos\theta = \frac{1}{2}$, $\csc\theta = \frac{2}{\sqrt{3}}$, $\sec\theta = 2$, and $\cot\theta = \frac{1}{\sqrt{3}}$.

21. $\sec\theta = 7$. The third side is
$y = \sqrt{7^2 - 2^2} = \sqrt{45} = 3\sqrt{5}$ The other five ratios are
$\sin\theta = \frac{3\sqrt{5}}{7}$, $\cos\theta = \frac{2}{7}$, $\tan\theta = \frac{3\sqrt{5}}{2}$,
$\csc\theta = \frac{7}{3\sqrt{5}} = \frac{7\sqrt{5}}{15}$, and $\cot\theta = \frac{2}{3\sqrt{5}} = \frac{2\sqrt{5}}{15}$.

22. $\csc\theta = \frac{13}{12}$. The third side is $x = \sqrt{13^2 - 12^2} = 5$. The
other five ratios are $\sin\theta = \frac{12}{13}$, $\cos\theta = \frac{5}{13}$, $\tan\theta = \frac{12}{5}$,
$\sec\theta = \frac{13}{5}$, and $\cot\theta = \frac{5}{12}$.

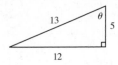

23. $\sin\frac{\pi}{6} + \cos\frac{\pi}{6} = \frac{1}{2} + \frac{\sqrt{3}}{2} = \frac{1+\sqrt{3}}{2}$

24. $\sin 30° \csc 30° = \sin 30° \cdot \dfrac{1}{\sin 30°} = 1$

25. $\sin 30° \cos 60° + \sin 60° \cos 30° = \frac{1}{2} \cdot \frac{1}{2} + \frac{\sqrt{3}}{2} \cdot \frac{\sqrt{3}}{2} = \frac{1}{4} + \frac{3}{4} = 1$

26. $(\sin 60°)^2 + (\cos 60°)^2 = \left(\frac{\sqrt{3}}{2}\right)^2 + \left(\frac{1}{2}\right)^2 = \frac{3}{4} + \frac{1}{4} = 1$

27. $(\cos 30°)^2 - (\sin 30°)^2 = \left(\frac{\sqrt{3}}{2}\right)^2 - \left(\frac{1}{2}\right)^2 = \frac{3}{4} - \frac{1}{4} = \frac{1}{2}$

28. $\left(\sin\frac{\pi}{3}\cos\frac{\pi}{4} - \sin\frac{\pi}{4}\cos\frac{\pi}{3}\right)^2 = \left(\frac{\sqrt{3}}{2}\cdot\frac{1}{\sqrt{2}} - \frac{1}{\sqrt{2}}\cdot\frac{1}{2}\right)^2 = \left[\frac{1}{2\sqrt{2}}\left(\sqrt{3}-1\right)\right]^2 = \frac{1}{8}\left(\sqrt{3}-1\right)^2 = \frac{1}{8}\left(3 - 2\sqrt{3} + 1\right)$
$= \frac{1}{8}\left(4 - 2\sqrt{3}\right) = \frac{1}{4}\left(2 - \sqrt{3}\right)$

29. This is an isosceles right triangle, so the other leg has length $16\tan 45° = 16$, the hypotenuse has length
$\dfrac{16}{\sin 45°} = 16\sqrt{2} \approx 22.63$, and the other angle is $90° - 45° = 45°$.

30. The other leg has length $100\tan 75° \approx 26.79$, the hypotenuse has length $\dfrac{100}{\sin 75°} \approx 103.52$, and the other angle is
$90° - 75° = 15°$.

31. The other leg has length $35\tan 52° \approx 44.79$, the hypotenuse has length $\dfrac{35}{\cos 52°} \approx 56.85$, and the other angle is
$90° - 52° = 52°$.

32. The adjacent leg has length $1000\cos 68° \approx 374.61$, the opposite leg has length $1000\sin 68° \approx 927.18$, and the other angle
is $90° - 68° = 22°$.

33. The adjacent leg has length $33.5\cos\frac{\pi}{8} \approx 30.95$, the opposite leg has length $33.5\sin\frac{\pi}{8} \approx 12.82$, and the other angle is
$\frac{\pi}{2} - \frac{\pi}{8} = \frac{3\pi}{8}$.

34. The opposite leg has length $72.3\tan\frac{\pi}{6} \approx 41.74$, the hypotenuse has length $\dfrac{72.3}{\cos\frac{\pi}{6}} \approx 83.48$, and the other angle is

$\frac{\pi}{2} - \frac{\pi}{6} = \frac{\pi}{3}$.

35. The adjacent leg has length $\dfrac{106}{\tan\frac{\pi}{5}} \approx 145.90$, the hypotenuse has length $\dfrac{106}{\sin\frac{\pi}{5}} \approx 180.34$, and the other angle is

$\frac{\pi}{2} - \frac{\pi}{5} = \frac{3\pi}{10}$.

36. The adjacent leg has length $425\cos\frac{3\pi}{8} \approx 162.64$, the opposite leg has length $425\sin\frac{3\pi}{8} \approx 392.65$, and the other angle is
$\frac{\pi}{2} - \frac{3\pi}{8} = \frac{\pi}{8}$.

37. $\sin\theta \approx \frac{1}{2.24} \approx 0.45$. $\cos\theta \approx \frac{2}{2.24} \approx 0.89$, $\tan\theta = \frac{1}{2}$, $\csc\theta \approx 2.24$, $\sec\theta \approx \frac{2.24}{2} \approx 1.12$, $\cot\theta \approx 2.00$.

38.

$\sin 40° \approx 0.64$, $\cos 40° \approx 0.77$, $\tan 40° \approx \dfrac{0.64}{0.77} \approx 0.83$, $\csc 40° \approx 1.56$,
$\sec 40° \approx 1.39$, $\cot 40° \approx 1.20$.

39. $x = \dfrac{100}{\tan 60°} + \dfrac{100}{\tan 30°} \approx 230.9$

40. Let d be the length of the base of the 60° triangle. Then $\tan 60° = \dfrac{85}{d} \;\Leftrightarrow\; d = \dfrac{85}{\tan 60°} \approx 49.075$, and so

$\tan 30° = \dfrac{85}{d+x} \Leftrightarrow d+x = \dfrac{85}{\tan 30°} \;\Leftrightarrow\; x = \dfrac{85}{\tan 30°} - d \approx 98.1$.

41. Let h be the length of the shared side. Then $\sin 60° = \dfrac{50}{h} \;\Leftrightarrow\; h = \dfrac{50}{\sin 60°} \approx 57.735 \;\Leftrightarrow\; \sin 65° = \dfrac{h}{x} \Leftrightarrow$

$x = \dfrac{h}{\sin 65°} \approx 63.7$

42. Let h be the hypotenuse of the top triangle. Then $\sin 30° = \dfrac{5}{h} \;\Leftrightarrow\; h = \dfrac{5}{\sin 30°} = 10$, and so $\tan 60° = \dfrac{h}{x} \Leftrightarrow$

$x = \dfrac{h}{\tan 60°} = \dfrac{10}{\tan 60°} \approx 5.8$.

43.

From the diagram, $\sin \theta = \dfrac{x}{y}$ and $\tan \theta = \dfrac{y}{10}$, so $x = y \sin \theta = 10 \sin \theta \tan \theta$.

44. $\sin \theta = \dfrac{1}{a} \;\Leftrightarrow\; a = \sin \theta,\ \tan \theta = \dfrac{b}{1} \;\Leftrightarrow\; b = \tan \theta,\ \cos \theta = \dfrac{1}{c} \;\Leftrightarrow\; c = \sec \theta,\ \cos \theta = \dfrac{d}{1} \;\Leftrightarrow\; d = \cos \theta$

45. Let h be the height, in feet, of the Empire State Building. Then $\tan 11° = \dfrac{h}{5280} \;\Leftrightarrow\; h = 5280 \cdot \tan 11° \approx 1026$ ft.

46. (a) Let r be the distance, in feet, between the plane and the Gateway Arch. Therefore, $\sin 22° = \dfrac{35,000}{r} \Leftrightarrow$

$r = \dfrac{35,000}{\sin 22°} \approx 93,431$ ft.

(b) Let x be the distance, also in feet, between a point on the ground directly below the plane and the Gateway Arch. Then

$\tan 22° = \dfrac{35,000}{x} \;\Leftrightarrow\; x = \dfrac{35,000}{\tan 22°} \approx 86,628$ ft.

47. (a) Let h be the distance, in miles, that the beam has diverged. Then $\tan 0.5° = \dfrac{h}{240,000} \Leftrightarrow$

$h = 240,000 \cdot \tan 0.5° \approx 2100$ mi.

(b) Since the deflection is about 2100 mi whereas the radius of the moon is about 1000 mi, the beam will not strike the moon.

48. Let x be the distance, in feet, of the ship from the base of the lighthouse. Then $\tan 23° = \dfrac{200}{x} \Leftrightarrow$

$x = \dfrac{200}{\tan 23°} \approx 471$ ft.

49. Let h represent the height, in feet, that the ladder reaches on the building. Then $\sin 72° = \dfrac{h}{20} \Leftrightarrow$

$h = 20 \sin 72° \approx 19$ ft.

50. Let θ represent the angle of elevation of the ladder. Let h represent the height, in feet, that the ladder reaches on the building. Then $\cos \theta = \frac{6}{20} = 0.3 \;\Leftrightarrow\; \theta = \cos^{-1} 0.3 \approx 1.266$ rad $\approx 72.5°$. By the Pythagorean Theorem $h^2 + 6^2 = 20^2 \Leftrightarrow$

$h = \sqrt{400 - 36} = \sqrt{364} \approx 19$ ft.

51. Let θ be the angle of elevation of the sun. Then $\tan \theta = \frac{96}{120} = 0.8 \;\Leftrightarrow\; \theta = \tan^{-1} 0.8 \approx 0.675 \approx 38.7°$.

52. Let h be the height, in feet, of the communication tower. Then $\sin 65° = \dfrac{h}{600} \;\Leftrightarrow\; h = 600 \sin 65° \approx 544$ ft.

53. Let h be the height, in feet, of the kite above the ground. Then $\sin 50° = \dfrac{h}{450} \;\Leftrightarrow\; h = 450 \sin 50° \approx 345$ ft.

54.

Let h_1 be the height of the flagpole above elevation and let h_2 be the height below, as shown in the figure. So $\tan 18° = \dfrac{h_1}{x} \Leftrightarrow h_1 = x \tan 18°$. Similarly, $h_2 = x \tan 14°$. Since the flagpole is 60 feet tall, we have $h_1 + h_2 = 60$, so

$$x\left(\tan 18° + \tan 14°\right) = 60 \Leftrightarrow x = \frac{60}{\tan 18° + \tan 14°} \approx 104.5 \text{ ft.}$$

55. Let h_1 be the height of the window in feet and h_2 be the height from the window to the top of the tower. Then

$\tan 25° = \dfrac{h_1}{325} \Leftrightarrow h_1 = 325 \cdot \tan 25° \approx 152$ ft. Also, $\tan 39° = \dfrac{h_2}{325} \Leftrightarrow h_2 = 325 \cdot \tan 39° \approx 263$ ft. Therefore, the height of the window is approximately 152 ft and the height of the tower is approximately $152 + 263 = 415$ ft.

56.

Let d_1 be the distance, in feet, between a point directly below the plane and one car, and d_2 be the distance, in feet, between the same point and the other car. Then $\tan 52° = \dfrac{5150}{d_1} \Leftrightarrow d_1 = \dfrac{5150}{\tan 52°} \approx 4023.62$ ft, and $\tan 35° = \dfrac{5150}{d_2} \Leftrightarrow$

$d_2 = \dfrac{5150}{\tan 35°} \approx 7354.96$ ft. So the distance between the two cars is about $d_1 + d_2 \approx 4023.62 + 7354.96 \approx 11{,}379$ ft.

57. Let d_1 be the distance, in feet, between a point directly below the plane and one car, and d_2 be the distance, in feet, between the same point and the other car. Then $\tan 52° = \dfrac{d_1}{5150} \Leftrightarrow d_1 = 5150 \cdot \tan 52° \approx 6591.7$ ft. Also, $\tan 38° = \dfrac{d_2}{5150} \Leftrightarrow$ $d_2 = 5150 \cdot \tan 38° \approx 4023.6$ ft. So in this case, the distance between the two cars is about 2570 ft.

58. Let x be the distance, in feet, between a point directly below the balloon and the first mile post. Let h be the height, in feet, of the balloon. Then $\tan 22° = \dfrac{h}{x}$ and $\tan 20° = \dfrac{h}{x + 5280}$. So $h = x \tan 22° = (x + 5280) \tan 20°$

$\Leftrightarrow x = \dfrac{5280 \cdot \tan 20°}{\tan 22° - \tan 20°} \approx 47{,}977$ mi. Therefore $h \approx 47{,}976.9 \cdot \tan 22° \approx 19.384 \approx 3.7$ mi.

59. Let x be the horizontal distance, in feet, between a point on the ground directly below the top of the mountain and the point on the plain closest to the mountain. Let h be the height, in feet, of the mountain. Then $\tan 35° = \dfrac{h}{x}$ and

$\tan 32° = \dfrac{h}{x + 1000}$. So $h = x \tan 35° = (x + 1000) \tan 32° \Leftrightarrow x = \dfrac{1000 \cdot \tan 32°}{\tan 35° - \tan 32°} \approx 8294.2$. Thus $h \approx 8294.2 \cdot \tan 35° \approx 5808$ ft.

60.

Since the angle of elevation from the observer is $45°$, the distance from the observer is h, as shown in the figure. Thus, the length of the leg in the smaller right triangle is $600 - h$. Then $\tan 75° = \dfrac{h}{600 - h} \Leftrightarrow (600 - h) \tan 75° = h \Leftrightarrow$

$600 \tan 75° = h\left(1 + \tan 75°\right) \Leftrightarrow h = \dfrac{600 \tan 75°}{1 + \tan 75°} \approx 473$ ft.

61. Let d be the distance, in miles, from the earth to the sun. Then $\tan 89.95° = \dfrac{d}{240{,}000} \Leftrightarrow$

$d = 240{,}000 \cdot \tan 89.95° \approx 91.7$ million miles.

62. (a) $s = r\theta \Leftrightarrow \theta = \dfrac{s}{r} = \dfrac{6155}{3960} \approx 1.5543$ rad $\approx 89.05°$

(b) Let d represent the distance, in miles, from the center of the earth to the moon. Since $\cos \theta = \dfrac{3960}{d}$, we have

$d = \dfrac{3960}{\cos \theta} \approx \dfrac{3960}{\cos 89.05°} \approx 239{,}961.5$. So the distance AC is $239{,}961.5 - 3960 \approx 236{,}000$ mi.

63. Let r represent the radius, in miles, of the earth. Then $\sin 60.276° = \frac{r}{r+600}$ $\Leftrightarrow$ $(r+600)\sin 60.276° = r$ $\Leftrightarrow$

$600\sin 60.276° = r\left(1 - \sin 60.276°\right)$ $\Leftrightarrow$ $r = \frac{600\sin 60.276°}{1-\sin 60.276°} \approx 3960.099$. So the radius of the earth is approximately

3960 mi.

64. Let d represent the distance, in miles, from the earth to Alpha Centauri. Since $\sin 0.000211° = \frac{93,000,000}{d}$, we have

$d = \frac{93,000,000}{\sin 0.000211°} \approx 25,253,590,022,410$. So the distance from the earth to Alpha Centauri is about 2.53×10^{13} mi.

65. If two triangles are similar, then their corresponding angles are equal and their corresponding sides are proportional. That is, if triangle ABC is similar to triangle $A'B'C'$ then $|AB| = r\,|A'B'|$, $|AC| = r\,|A'C'|$, and $|BC| = r\,|B'C'|$. Thus when we express any trigonometric ratio of these lengths as a fraction, the factor r cancels out.

6.3 Trigonometric Functions of Angles

1. (a) The reference angle for $150°$ is $180° - 150° = 30°$.

  (b) The reference angle for $330°$ is $360° - 330° = 30°$.

  (c) The reference angle for $-30°$ is $-(-30°) = 30°$.

2. (a) The reference angle for $120°$ is $180° - 120° = 60°$.

  (b) The reference angle for $-210°$ is $210° - 180° = 30°$.

  (c) The reference angle for $780°$ is $780° - 720° = 60°$.

3. (a) The reference angle for $225°$ is $225° - 180° = 45°$.

  (b) The reference angle for $810°$ is $810° - 720° = 90°$.

  (c) The reference angle for $-105°$ is $180° - 105° = 75°$.

4. (a) The reference angle for $99°$ is $180° - 99° = 81°$.

  (b) The reference angle for $-199°$ is $199° - 180° = 19°$.

  (c) The reference angle for $359°$ is $360° - 359° = 1°$.

5. (a) The reference angle for $\frac{11\pi}{4}$ is $3\pi - \frac{11\pi}{4} = \frac{\pi}{4}$.

  (b) The reference angle for $-\frac{11\pi}{6}$ is $2\pi - \frac{11\pi}{6} = \frac{\pi}{6}$.

  (c) The reference angle for $\frac{11\pi}{3}$ is $4\pi - \frac{11\pi}{3} = \frac{\pi}{3}$.

6. (a) The reference angle for $\frac{4\pi}{3}$ is $\frac{4\pi}{3} - \pi = \frac{\pi}{3}$.

  (b) The reference angle for $\frac{33\pi}{4}$ is $\frac{33\pi}{4} - 8\pi = \frac{\pi}{4}$.

  (c) The reference angle for $-\frac{23\pi}{6}$ is $4\pi - \frac{23\pi}{6} = \frac{\pi}{6}$.

7. (a) The reference angle for $\frac{5\pi}{7}$ is $\pi - \frac{5\pi}{7} = \frac{2\pi}{7}$.

  (b) The reference angle for -1.4π is $1.4\pi - \pi = 0.4\pi$.

  (c) The reference angle for 1.4 is 1.4 because $1.4 < \frac{\pi}{2}$.

8. (a) The reference angle for 2.3π is $2.3\pi - 2\pi = 0.3\pi$.

  (b) The reference angle for 2.3 is $\pi - 2.3 \approx 0.84$.

  (c) The reference angle for -10π is $10\pi - 10\pi = 0$.

9. $\sin 150° = \sin 30° = \frac{1}{2}$

10. $\sin 225° = -\sin 45° = -\frac{1}{\sqrt{2}} = -\frac{\sqrt{2}}{2}$

11. $\cos 135° = -\cos 45° = -\frac{1}{\sqrt{2}} = -\frac{\sqrt{2}}{2}$

12. $\cos(-60°) = \cos 60° = \frac{1}{2}$

13. $\tan(-60°) = -\tan 60° = -\sqrt{3}$

14. $\sec 300° = \sec 60° = \dfrac{1}{\cos 60°} = 2$

15. $\csc(-630°) = \csc 90° = \dfrac{1}{\sin 90°} = 1$

16. $\cot 210° = \cot 30° = \dfrac{1}{\tan 30°} = \sqrt{3}$

17. $\cos 570° = -\cos 30° = -\frac{\sqrt{3}}{2}$

18. $\sec 120° = -\sec 60° = -\dfrac{1}{\cos 60°} = -2$

19. $\tan 750° = \tan 30° = \frac{1}{\sqrt{3}} = \frac{\sqrt{3}}{3}$

20. $\cos 660° = \cos 60° = \frac{1}{2}$

21. $\sin \frac{2\pi}{3} = \sin \frac{\pi}{3} = \frac{\sqrt{3}}{2}$

22. $\sin \frac{5\pi}{3} = -\sin \frac{\pi}{3} = -\frac{\sqrt{3}}{2}$

23. $\sin \frac{3\pi}{2} = -\sin \frac{\pi}{2} = -1$

24. $\cos \frac{7\pi}{3} = \cos \frac{\pi}{3} = \frac{1}{2}$

25. $\cos\left(-\frac{7\pi}{3}\right) = \cos \frac{\pi}{3} = \frac{1}{2}$

26. $\tan \frac{5\pi}{6} = -\tan \frac{\pi}{6} = -\frac{1}{\sqrt{3}} = -\frac{\sqrt{3}}{3}$

27. $\sec \frac{17\pi}{3} = \sec \frac{\pi}{3} = \dfrac{1}{\cos \frac{\pi}{3}} = 2$

28. $\csc \frac{5\pi}{4} = -\csc \frac{\pi}{4} = -\dfrac{1}{\sin \frac{\pi}{4}} = -\sqrt{2}$

29. $\cot\left(-\frac{\pi}{4}\right) = -\cot \frac{\pi}{4} = \dfrac{-1}{\tan \frac{\pi}{4}} = -1$

30. $\cos \frac{7\pi}{4} = \cos \frac{\pi}{4} = \frac{1}{\sqrt{2}} = \frac{\sqrt{2}}{2}$

31. $\tan \frac{5\pi}{2} = \tan \frac{\pi}{2}$ which is undefined.

32. $\sin \frac{11\pi}{6} = -\sin \frac{\pi}{6} = -\frac{1}{2}$

33. Since $\sin\theta < 0$ and $\cos\theta < 0$, θ is in quadrant III.

34. Since both $\tan\theta$ and $\sin\theta$ are negative, θ is in quadrant IV.

35. $\sec\theta > 0 \Rightarrow \cos\theta > 0$. Also $\tan\theta < 0 \Rightarrow \dfrac{\sin\theta}{\cos\theta} < 0 \Leftrightarrow \sin\theta < 0$ (since $\cos\theta > 0$). Since $\sin\theta < 0$ and $\cos\theta > 0$, θ is in quadrant IV.

36. Since $\csc\theta > 0 \Rightarrow \sin\theta > 0$ and $\cos\theta < 0$, θ is in quadrant II.

37. $\sec^2\theta = 1 + \tan^2\theta \Leftrightarrow \tan^2\theta = \dfrac{1}{\cos^2\theta} - 1 \Leftrightarrow$

$\tan\theta = \sqrt{\dfrac{1}{\cos^2\theta} - 1} = \sqrt{\dfrac{1 - \cos^2\theta}{\cos^2\theta}} = \dfrac{\sqrt{1 - \cos^2\theta}}{|\cos\theta|} = \dfrac{\sqrt{1 - \cos^2\theta}}{-\cos\theta}$ (since $\cos\theta < 0$ in quadrant III,

$|\cos\theta| = -\cos\theta$). Thus $\tan\theta = -\dfrac{\sqrt{1 - \cos^2\theta}}{\cos\theta}$.

38. $\cot\theta = \dfrac{\cos\theta}{\sin\theta} = \dfrac{-\sqrt{1 - \sin^2\theta}}{\sin\theta}$ because $\cos\theta < 0$ in quadrant II.

39. $\cos^2\theta + \sin^2\theta = 1 \Leftrightarrow \cos\theta = \sqrt{1 - \sin^2\theta}$ because $\cos\theta > 0$ in quadrant IV.

40. $\sec\theta = \dfrac{1}{\cos\theta} = \dfrac{1}{\sqrt{1 - \sin^2\theta}}$ because all trigonometric functions are positive in quadrant I.

41. $\sec^2\theta = 1 + \tan^2\theta \Leftrightarrow \sec\theta = -\sqrt{1 + \tan^2\theta}$ because $\sec\theta < 0$ in quadrant II.

42. $\csc^2\theta = 1 + \cot^2\theta \Leftrightarrow \csc\theta = -\sqrt{1 + \cot^2\theta}$ because $\csc\theta < 0$ in quadrant III.

43. $\sin\theta = \frac{3}{5}$. Then $x = -\sqrt{5^2 - 3^2} = -\sqrt{16} = -4$, since θ is in quadrant II. Thus, $\cos\theta = -\frac{4}{5}$, $\tan\theta = -\frac{3}{4}$, $\csc\theta = \frac{5}{3}$, $\sec\theta = -\frac{5}{4}$, and $\cot\theta = -\frac{4}{3}$.

44. $\cos\theta = -\frac{7}{12}$. Since θ is in quadrant III, $y = -\sqrt{12^2 - 7^2} = -\sqrt{95}$, and so $\sin\theta = -\frac{\sqrt{95}}{12}$, $\tan\theta = \frac{\sqrt{95}}{7}$, $\csc\theta = -\frac{12}{\sqrt{95}}$, $\sec\theta = -\frac{12}{7}$, and $\cot\theta = \frac{7}{\sqrt{95}}$.

45. $\tan\theta = -\frac{3}{4}$. Then $r = \sqrt{3^2 + 4^2} = 5$, and so $\sin\theta = -\frac{3}{5}$, $\cos\theta = \frac{4}{5}$, $\csc\theta = -\frac{5}{3}$, $\sec\theta = \frac{5}{4}$, and $\cot\theta = -\frac{4}{3}$.

46. $\sec\theta = 5$. Then $\cos\theta = \frac{1}{5}$ and $y = -\sqrt{5^2 - 1^2} = -2\sqrt{6}$. So $\sin\theta = -\frac{2\sqrt{6}}{5}$, $\cos\theta = \frac{1}{5}$, $\tan\theta = -2\sqrt{6}$, $\csc\theta = -\frac{5}{2\sqrt{6}}$, and $\cot\theta = -\frac{1}{2\sqrt{6}}$.

47. $\csc\theta = 2$. Then $\sin\theta = \frac{1}{2}$ and $x = \sqrt{2^2 - 1^2} = \sqrt{3}$. So $\sin\theta = \frac{1}{2}$, $\cos\theta = \frac{\sqrt{3}}{2}$, $\tan\theta = \frac{1}{\sqrt{3}} = \frac{\sqrt{3}}{3}$, $\sec\theta = \frac{2}{\sqrt{3}} = \frac{2\sqrt{3}}{3}$, and $\cot\theta = \sqrt{3}$.

48. $\cot\theta = \frac{1}{4}$. Then $\tan\theta = 4$ and $r = \sqrt{4^2 + 1^2} = \sqrt{17}$. So $\sin\theta = -\frac{4}{\sqrt{17}}$, $\cos\theta = -\frac{1}{\sqrt{17}}$, $\tan\theta = 4$, $\csc\theta = -\frac{\sqrt{17}}{4}$, and $\sec\theta = -\sqrt{17}$.

49. $\cos\theta = -\frac{2}{7}$. Then $y = \sqrt{7^2 - 2^2} = \sqrt{45} = 3\sqrt{5}$, and so $\sin\theta = \frac{3\sqrt{5}}{7}$, $\tan\theta = -\frac{3\sqrt{5}}{2}$, $\csc\theta = \frac{7}{3\sqrt{5}} = \frac{7\sqrt{5}}{15}$, $\sec\theta = -\frac{7}{2}$, and $\cot\theta = -\frac{2}{3\sqrt{5}} = -\frac{2\sqrt{5}}{15}$.

50. $\tan\theta = -4$. Then $r = \sqrt{4^2 + 1^2} = \sqrt{17}$, and so $\sin\theta = \frac{4}{\sqrt{17}}$, $\cos\theta = -\frac{1}{\sqrt{17}}$, $\csc\theta = \frac{\sqrt{17}}{4}$, $\sec\theta = -\sqrt{17}$, and $\cot\theta = -\frac{1}{4}$.

51. **(a)** $\sin 2\theta = \sin\left(2\cdot\frac{\pi}{3}\right) = \sin\frac{2\pi}{3} = \sin\frac{\pi}{3} = \frac{\sqrt{3}}{2}$, while $2\sin\theta = 2\sin\frac{\pi}{3} = 2\cdot\frac{\sqrt{3}}{2} = \sqrt{3}$.

    (b) $\sin\frac{1}{2}\theta = \sin\left(\frac{1}{2}\cdot\frac{\pi}{3}\right) = \sin\frac{\pi}{6} = \frac{1}{2}$, while $\frac{1}{2}\sin\theta = \frac{1}{2}\sin\frac{\pi}{3} = \frac{1}{2}\cdot\frac{\sqrt{3}}{2} = \frac{\sqrt{3}}{4}$.

    (c) $\sin^2\theta = \left(\sin\frac{\pi}{3}\right)^2 = \left(\frac{\sqrt{3}}{2}\right)^2 = \frac{3}{4}$, while $\sin\left(\theta^2\right) = \sin\left(\frac{\pi}{3}\right)^2 = \sin\frac{\pi^2}{9} \approx 0.88967$.

52. $a = 7$, $b = 9$, and $\theta = 72°$. Thus, $A = \frac{1}{2}(7)(9)\sin 72° = \frac{63}{2}\sin 72° \approx 30.0$.

53. $a = 10$, $b = 22$, and $\theta = 10°$. Thus, the area of the triangle is $A = \frac{1}{2}(10)(22)\sin 10° = 110\sin 10° \approx 19.1$.

54. Since the triangle is equilateral, $\theta = 60°$ and $a = b = 10$. Thus, $A = \frac{1}{2}(10)^2\sin 60° = 25\sqrt{3} \approx 43.3$.

55. $A = 16$, $a = 5$, and $b = 7$. So $\sin\theta = \dfrac{2A}{ab} = \dfrac{2\cdot 16}{5\cdot 7} = \dfrac{32}{35}$ $\Leftrightarrow$ $\theta = \sin^{-1}\frac{32}{35} \approx 66.1°$.

56. Let the length of each of the equal sides be x. Then $A = \frac{1}{2}x^2\sin\theta \Rightarrow x = \sqrt{\dfrac{2A}{\sin\theta}}$. Substituting, we find

$$x = \sqrt{\dfrac{48}{\sin\frac{5\pi}{6}}} = 4\sqrt{6} \approx 9.8 \text{ cm}.$$

57. For the sector defined by the two sides, $A_1 = \frac{1}{2}r^2\theta = \frac{1}{2}\cdot 2^2\cdot 120°\cdot\frac{\pi}{180°} = \frac{4\pi}{3}$. For the triangle defined by the two sides, $A_2 = \frac{1}{2}ab\sin\theta = \frac{1}{2}\cdot 2\cdot 2\cdot\sin 120° = 2\sin 60° = \sqrt{3}$. Thus the area of the region is $A_1 - A_2 = \frac{4\pi}{3} - \sqrt{3} \approx 2.46$.

58. The area of the entire circle is $\pi r^2 = \pi\cdot 12^2 = 144\pi$, the area of the sector is $\frac{1}{2}r^2\theta = \frac{1}{2}\cdot 12^2\cdot\frac{\pi}{3} = 24\pi$, and the area of the triangle is $\frac{1}{2}ab\sin\theta = \frac{1}{2}\cdot 12^2\cdot\sin\frac{\pi}{3} = 36\sqrt{3}$, so the area of the shaded region is

$$A_1 - A_2 + A_3 = 144\pi - 24\pi + 36\sqrt{3} = 120\pi + 36\sqrt{3} \approx 439.3.$$

59. $\sin^2\theta + \cos^2\theta = 1$ $\Leftrightarrow$ $\left(\sin^2\theta + \cos^2\theta\right)\cdot\dfrac{1}{\cos^2\theta} = 1\cdot\dfrac{1}{\cos^2\theta}$ $\Leftrightarrow$ $\tan^2\theta + 1 = \sec^2\theta$

60. $\sin^2\theta + \cos^2\theta = 1$ $\Leftrightarrow$ $\left(\sin^2\theta + \cos^2\theta\right)\cdot\dfrac{1}{\sin^2\theta} = 1\cdot\dfrac{1}{\sin^2\theta}$ $\Leftrightarrow$ $1 + \cot^2\theta = \csc^2\theta$

61. **(a)** $\tan\theta = \dfrac{h}{1\text{ mile}}$, so $h = \tan\theta\cdot 1\text{ mile}\cdot\dfrac{5280\text{ ft}}{1\text{ mile}} = 5280\tan\theta$ ft.

(b)

θ	$20°$	$60°$	$80°$	$85°$
h	1922	9145	29,944	60,351

62. **(a)** Let the depth of the water be h. Then the cross-sectional area of the gutter is a trapezoid whose height is $h = 10\sin\theta$. The bases are 10 and $10 + 2\,(10\cos\theta) = 10 + 20\cos\theta$. Thus, the area is

$$A(\theta) = \dfrac{b_1 + b_2}{2}\cdot h = \dfrac{10 + 10 + 20\cos\theta}{2}\cdot 10\sin\theta = 100\sin\theta + 100\sin\theta\cos\theta.$$

(b)

(c)

From the graph, the largest area is achieved when $\theta \approx 1.047$ rad $\approx 60°$.

63. **(a)** From the figure in the text, we express depth and width in terms of θ.

Since $\sin\theta = \dfrac{\text{depth}}{20}$ and $\cos\theta = \dfrac{\text{width}}{20}$, we have depth $= 20\sin\theta$ and width $= 20\cos\theta$. Thus, the cross-section area of the beam is

$A(\theta) = (\text{depth})(\text{width}) = (20\cos\theta)(20\sin\theta) = 400\cos\theta\sin\theta$.

(b)
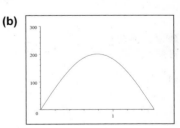

(c) The beam with the largest cross-sectional area is the square beam, $10\sqrt{2}$ by $10\sqrt{2}$ (about 14.14 by 14.14).

64. Using depth $= 20\sin\theta$ and width $= 20\cos\theta$, from Exercise 63, we have strength $= k\,(\text{width})(\text{depth})^2$. Thus $S(\theta) = k\,(20\cos\theta)(20\sin\theta)^2 = 8000k\cos\theta\sin^2\theta$.

65. (a) On Earth, the range is $R = \dfrac{v_0^2 \sin(2\theta)}{g} = \dfrac{12^2 \sin \frac{\pi}{3}}{32} = \dfrac{9\sqrt{3}}{4} \approx 3.897$ ft and the height is

$$H = \dfrac{v_0^2 \sin^2 \theta}{2g} = \dfrac{12^2 \sin^2 \frac{\pi}{6}}{2 \cdot 32} = \dfrac{9}{16} = 0.5625 \text{ ft.}$$

(b) On the moon, $R = \dfrac{12^2 \sin \frac{\pi}{3}}{5.2} \approx 23.982$ ft and $H = \dfrac{12^2 \sin^2 \frac{\pi}{6}}{2 \cdot 5.2} \approx 3.462$ ft

66. Substituting, $t = \sqrt{\dfrac{2000}{16 \sin 30°}} = 5\sqrt{10} \approx 15.8$ s.

67. (a) $W = 3.02 - 0.38 \cot \theta + 0.65 \csc \theta$

(b) From the graph, it appears that W has its minimum value at about
$\theta = 0.946 \approx 54.2°$.

68. (a) We label the lengths L_1 and L_2 as shown in the

figure. Since $\sin \theta = \dfrac{9}{L_1}$ and $\cos \theta = \dfrac{6}{L_2}$, we

have $L_1 = 9 \csc \theta$ and $L_2 = 6 \sec \theta$. Thus
$L(\theta) = L_1 + L_2 = 9 \csc \theta + 6 \sec \theta$.

(c) The minimum value of $L(\theta)$ is 21.07.

(d) The minimum value of $L(\theta)$ is the shortest
distance the pipe must pass through.

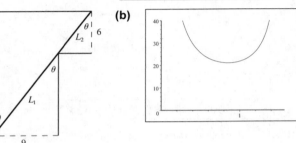

(b)

69. We have $\sin \alpha = k \sin \beta$, where $\alpha = 59.4°$ and $k = 1.33$. Substituting, $\sin 59.4° = 1.33 \sin \beta$

$\Rightarrow \sin \beta = \dfrac{\sin 59.4°}{1.33} \approx 0.6472$. Using a calculator, we find that $\beta \approx \sin^{-1} 0.6472 \approx 40.3°$, so

$\theta = 4\beta - 2\alpha \approx 4(40.3°) - 2(59.4°) = 42.4°$.

70. $\sin 4° = 0.0697564737$ but $\sin 4 = -0.7568024953$. Your partner has found $\sin 4°$ instead of $\sin 4$ radians.

71. $\cos \theta = \dfrac{\text{adj}}{\text{hyp}} = \dfrac{|OP|}{|OR|} = \dfrac{|OP|}{1} = |OP|$. Since QS is tangent to the circle at R, $\triangle ORQ$ is a right triangle. Then

$\tan \theta = \dfrac{\text{opp}}{\text{adj}} = \dfrac{|RQ|}{|OR|} = |RQ|$ and $\sec \theta = \dfrac{\text{hyp}}{\text{adj}} = \dfrac{|OQ|}{|OR|} = |OQ|$. Since $\angle SOQ$ is a right angle $\triangle SOQ$ is a right

triangle and $\angle OSR = \theta$. Then $\csc \theta = \dfrac{\text{hyp}}{\text{opp}} = \dfrac{|OS|}{|OR|} = |OS|$ and $\cot \theta = \dfrac{\text{adj}}{\text{opp}} = \dfrac{|SR|}{|OR|} = |SR|$. Summarizing, we have

$\sin \theta = |PR|$, $\cos \theta = |OP|$, $\tan \theta = |RQ|$, $\sec \theta = |OQ|$, $\csc \theta = |OS|$, and $\cot \theta = |SR|$.

6.4   The Law of Sines

1. $\angle C = 180° - 98.4° - 24.6° = 57°$. $x = \dfrac{376 \sin 57°}{\sin 98.4°} \approx 318.75$.

2. $\angle C = 180° - 37.5° - 28.1° = 114.4°$. $x = \dfrac{17 \sin 114.4°}{\sin 37.5°} \approx 25.4$.

3. $\angle C = 180° - 52° - 70° = 58°$. $x = \dfrac{26.7 \sin 52°}{\sin 58°} \approx 24.8$.

4. $\sin \theta = \dfrac{56.3 \sin 67°}{80.2} \approx 0.646$. Then $\theta \approx \sin^{-1} 0.646 \approx 40.3°$.

5. $\sin C = \dfrac{36\sin 120°}{45} \approx 0.693 \Leftrightarrow \angle C \approx \sin^{-1} 0.693 \approx 44°.$

6. $\angle C = 180° - 102° - 28° = 50°.$ $x = \dfrac{185\sin 50°}{\sin 102°} \approx 144.9.$

7. $\angle C = 180° - 46° - 20° = 114°.$ Then $a = \dfrac{65\sin 46°}{\sin 114°} \approx 51$ and $b = \dfrac{65\sin 20°}{\sin 114°} \approx 24.$

8. $\angle B = 180° - 30° - 100° = 50°.$ Then $c = \dfrac{2\sin 100°}{\sin 50°} \approx 2.57$ and $a = \dfrac{2\sin 30°}{\sin 50°} \approx 1.31.$

9. $\angle B = 68°,$ so $\angle A = 180° - 68° - 68° = 44°$ and $a = \dfrac{12\sin 44°}{\sin 68°} \approx 8.99.$

10. $\sin B = \dfrac{3.4\sin 80°}{6.5} \approx 0.515,$ so $\angle B = \sin^{-1} 0.515 \approx 31°.$ Then $\angle C = 180° - 80° - 31° = 69°$ and
$c = \dfrac{6.5\sin 69°}{\sin 80°} \approx 6.2.$

11. $\angle C = 180° - 50° - 68° = 62°.$ Then
$a = \dfrac{230\sin 50°}{\sin 62°} \approx 200$ and $b = \dfrac{230\sin 68°}{\sin 62°} \approx 242.$

12. $\angle C = 180° - 110° - 23° = 47°.$ Then
$a = \dfrac{50\sin 23°}{\sin 47°} \approx 26.7$ and $b = \dfrac{50\sin 110°}{\sin 47°} \approx 64.2.$

13. $\angle B = 180° - 30° - 65° = 85°.$ Then
$a = \dfrac{10\sin 30°}{\sin 85°} \approx 5.0$ and $c = \dfrac{10\sin 65°}{\sin 85°} \approx 9.$

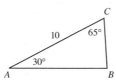

14. $\angle C = 180° - 95° - 22° = 63°.$ Then
$b = \dfrac{420\sin 95°}{\sin 22°} \approx 1116.9$ and
$c = \dfrac{420\sin 63°}{\sin 22°} \approx 999.0.$

15. $\angle A = 180° - 51° - 29° = 100°.$ Then
$a = \dfrac{44\sin 100°}{\sin 29°} \approx 89$ and $c = \dfrac{44\sin 51°}{\sin 29°} \approx 71.$

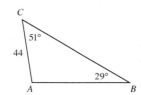

16. $\angle A = 180° - 100° - 10° = 70°.$ Then
$a = \dfrac{115\sin 70°}{\sin 100°} \approx 109.7$ and $b = \dfrac{115\sin 10°}{\sin 100°} \approx 20.3.$

17. Since $\angle A > 90°$ there is only one triangle. $\sin B = \dfrac{15\sin 110°}{28} \approx 0.503 \quad \Leftrightarrow \quad \angle B \approx \sin^{-1} 0.503 \approx 30°.$ Then
$\angle C \approx 180° - 110° - 30° = 40°,$ and so $c = \dfrac{28\sin 40°}{\sin 110°} \approx 19.$ Thus $\angle B \approx 30°,$ $\angle C \approx 40°,$ and $c \approx 19.$

18. $\sin C = \dfrac{40 \sin 37°}{30} \approx 0.802 \Leftrightarrow \angle C_1 \approx \sin^{-1} 0.822 \approx 53.4°$ or $\angle C_2 \approx 180° - 53.4° \approx 126.6°$.

If $\angle C_1 \approx 53.4°$, then $\angle B_1 \approx 180° - 37° - 53.4° = 89.6°$ and $b_1 = \dfrac{30 \sin 89.6°}{\sin 37°} \approx 49.8$.

If $\angle C_2 \approx 126.6°$, then $\angle B_2 \approx 180° - 37° - 126.6° = 16.4°$ and $b_2 = \dfrac{30 \sin 16.4°}{\sin 37°} \approx 14.1$.

Thus, one triangle has $\angle B_1 \approx 89.6°$, $\angle C_1 \approx 53.4°$, and $b_1 \approx 49.8$; the other has $\angle B_2 \approx 16.4°$, $\angle C_2 \approx 126.6°$, and $b_2 \approx 14.1$.

19. $\angle A = 125°$ is the largest angle, but since side a is not the longest side, there can be no such triangle.

20. $\sin B = \dfrac{45 \sin 38°}{42} \approx 0.660 \Leftrightarrow \angle B_1 \approx \sin^{-1} 0.660 \approx 41.3°$ or $\angle B_2 \approx 180° - 41.3° \approx 138.7°$.

If $\angle B_1 \approx 41.3°$, then $\angle A_1 \approx 180° - 38° - 41.3° = 100.7°$ and $a_1 = \dfrac{42 \sin 100.7°}{\sin 38°} \approx 67$.

If $\angle B_2 \approx 138.7°$, then $\angle A_2 \approx 180° - 38° - 138.7° = 3.3°$ and $a_2 = \dfrac{42 \sin 3.3°}{\sin 38°} \approx 3.9$.

Thus, one triangle has $\angle A_1 \approx 100.7°$, $\angle B_1 \approx 41.3°$, and $a_1 \approx 67$; the other has $\angle A_2 \approx 3.3°$, $\angle B_2 \approx 138.7°$, and $a_2 \approx 3.9$.

21. $\sin C = \dfrac{30 \sin 25°}{25} \approx 0.507 \Leftrightarrow \angle C_1 \approx \sin^{-1} 0.507 \approx 30.47°$ or $\angle C_2 \approx 180° - 39.47° = 149.53°$.

If $\angle C_1 = 30.47°$, then $\angle A_1 \approx 180° - 25° - 30.47° = 124.53°$ and $a_1 = \dfrac{25 \sin 124.53°}{\sin 25°} \approx 48.73$.

If $\angle C_2 = 149.53°$, then $\angle A_2 \approx 180° - 25° - 149.53° = 5.47°$ and $a_2 = \dfrac{25 \sin 5.47°}{\sin 25°} \approx 5.64$.

Thus, one triangle has $\angle A_1 \approx 125°$, $\angle C_1 \approx 30°$, and $a_1 \approx 49$; the other has $\angle A_2 \approx 5°$, $\angle C_2 \approx 150°$, and $a_2 \approx 5.6$.

22. $\sin B = \dfrac{100 \sin 30°}{75} = \dfrac{2}{3} \Leftrightarrow \angle B_1 \approx \sin^{-1} \dfrac{2}{3} \approx 41.8°$ or $\angle B_2 \approx 180° - 41.8° = 138.2°$.

If $\angle B_1 \approx 41.8°$, then $\angle C_1 \approx 180° - 30° - 41.8° = 108.2°$ and $c_1 \approx \dfrac{75 \sin 108.2°}{\sin 30°} \approx 142.5$.

If $\angle B_2 \approx 138.2°$, then $\angle A_2 \approx 180° - 30° - 138.2° = 11.8°$ and $c_2 \approx \dfrac{75 \sin 11.8°}{\sin 30°} \approx 30.7$.

Thus, one triangle has $\angle B_1 \approx 41.8°$, $\angle C_1 \approx 108.2°$, and $c_1 \approx 142.5$; the other has $\angle B_2 \approx 138.2°$, $\angle C_2 \approx 11.8°$, and $c_2 \approx 30.7$.

23. $\sin B = \dfrac{100 \sin 50°}{50} \approx 1.532$. Since $|\sin \theta| \leq 1$ for all θ, there can be no such angle B, and thus no such triangle.

24. $\sin B = \dfrac{80 \sin 135°}{100} \approx 0.566 \Leftrightarrow \angle B_1 \approx \sin^{-1} 0.566 \approx 34.4°$ or $\angle B_2 \approx 180° - 34.4° = 145.6°$.

If $\angle B_1 \approx 34.4°$, then $\angle C \approx 180° - 135° - 34.4° = 10.6°$ and $c \approx \dfrac{100 \sin 10.6°}{\sin 135°} \approx 25.9$.

If $\angle B_2 \approx 180° - 34.4° = 145.6°$, then $\angle A + \angle B_2 = 135° + 145.6° > 180°$, so there is no such triangle.

Thus, the only possible triangle is $\angle B \approx 34.4°$, $\angle C \approx 10.6°$, and $c \approx 25.9$.

25. $\sin A = \dfrac{26 \sin 29°}{15} \approx 0.840 \Leftrightarrow \angle A_1 \approx \sin^{-1} 0.840 \approx 57.2°$ or $\angle A_2 \approx 180° - 57.2° = 122.8°$.

If $\angle A_1 \approx 57.2°$, then $\angle B_1 = 180° - 29° - 57.2° = 93.8°$ and $b_1 \approx \dfrac{15 \sin 93.8°}{\sin 29°} \approx 30.9$.

If $\angle A_2 \approx 122.8°$, then $\angle B_2 = 180 - 29° - 122.8° = 28.2°$ and $b_2 \approx \dfrac{15 \sin 28.1°}{\sin 29°} \approx 14.6$.

Thus, one triangle has $\angle A_1 \approx 57.2°$, $\angle B_1 \approx 93.8°$, and $b_1 \approx 30.9$; the other has $\angle A_2 \approx 122.8°$, $\angle B_2 \approx 28.2°$, and $b_2 \approx 14.6$.

26. $\sin C = \dfrac{82 \sin 58°}{73} \approx 0.953$, so $\angle C_1 \approx \sin^{-1} 0.953 \approx 72.4°$ or $\angle C_2 \approx 180 - 72.4° = 107.6°$.

If $\angle C_1 \approx 72.4°$, then $\angle A_1 \approx 180° - 58° - 72.4° = 49.6°$ and $a_1 \approx \dfrac{73 \sin 49.6°}{\sin 58°} \approx 65.6$.

If $\angle C_2 \approx 107.6°$, then $\angle A_2 \approx 180° - 58° - 107.6° = 14.4°$ and $a_2 \approx \dfrac{73 \sin 14.4°}{\sin 58°} \approx 21.4$.

Thus, one triangle has $\angle A_1 \approx 49.6°$, $\angle C_1 \approx 72.4°$, and $a_1 \approx 65.6$; the other has $\angle A_2 \approx 14.4°$, $\angle C_2 \approx 107.6°$, and $a_2 \approx 21.4$.

27. (a) From $\triangle ABC$ and the Law of Sines we get $\dfrac{\sin 30°}{20} = \dfrac{\sin B}{28} \Leftrightarrow \sin B = \dfrac{28 \sin 30°}{20} = 0.7$,

so $\angle B \approx \sin^{-1} 0.7 \approx 44.427°$. Since $\triangle BCD$ is isosceles, $\angle B = \angle BDC \approx 44.427°$. Thus, $\angle BCD = 180° - 2\angle B \approx 91.146° \approx 91.1°$.

(b) From $\triangle ABC$ we get $\angle BCA = 180° - \angle A - \angle B \approx 180° - 30° - 44.427° = 105.573°$. Hence $\angle DCA = \angle BCA - \angle BCD \approx 105.573° - 91.146° = 14.4°$.

28. By symmetry, $\angle DCB = 25°$, so $\angle A = 180° - 25° - 50° = 105°$. Then by the Law of Sines, $|AD| = \dfrac{12 \sin 25°}{\sin 105°} \approx 5.25$.

29. (a) $\sin B = \dfrac{20 \sin 40°}{15} \approx 0.857 \Leftrightarrow \angle B_1 \approx \sin^{-1} 0.857 \approx 58.99°$ or $\angle B_2 \approx 180° - 58.99° \approx 121.01°$.

If $\angle B_1 = 30.47°$, then $\angle C_1 \approx 180° - 15° - 58.99° = 106.01°$ and $c_1 = \dfrac{15 \sin 106.01°}{\sin 40°} \approx 22.43$.

If $\angle B_2 = 121.01°$, then $\angle C_2 \approx 180° - 15° - 121.01° = 43.99°$ and $c_2 = \dfrac{15 \sin 43.99}{\sin 40°} \approx 16.21$. Thus there are two triangles.

(b) By the area formula given in Section 6.3, $\dfrac{\text{Area of } \triangle ABC}{\text{Area of } \triangle A'B'C'} = \dfrac{\frac{1}{2} ab \sin C}{\frac{1}{2} ab \sin C'} = \dfrac{\sin C}{\sin C'}$, since a and b are the same in both triangles.

30. By the formula of Section 6.3, the area of $\triangle ABC$ is $A = \frac{1}{2} ab \sin C$. Since we are given a and the three angles, we need to find b in terms of these. By the Law of Sines, $\dfrac{\sin B}{b} = \dfrac{\sin A}{a} \Leftrightarrow b = \dfrac{a \sin B}{\sin A}$. Thus,

$A = \frac{1}{2} ab \sin C = \frac{1}{2} a \left(\dfrac{a \sin B}{\sin A} \right) \sin C = \dfrac{a^2 \sin B \sin C}{2 \sin A}$.

31. (a) Let a be the distance from satellite to the tracking station A in miles. Then the subtended angle at the satellite is $\angle C = 180° - 93° - 84.2° = 2.8°$, and so $a = \dfrac{50 \sin 84.2°}{\sin 2.8°} \approx 1018$ mi.

(b) Let d be the distance above the ground in miles. Then $d = 1018.3 \sin 87° \approx 1017$ mi.

32. (a) Let x be the distance from the plane to point A. Then $\dfrac{x}{AB} = \dfrac{\sin 48°}{\sin(180° - 32° - 48°)} = \dfrac{\sin 48°}{\sin 100°} \Leftrightarrow$

$x = 5 \cdot \dfrac{\sin 48°}{\sin 100°} \approx 3.77$ mi.

(b) Let h be the height of the plane. Then $\sin 32° = \dfrac{h}{x} \Rightarrow h = 3.77 \sin 32° \approx 2.00$ mi.

33. $\angle C = 180° - 82° - 52° = 46°$, so by the Law of Sines, $\dfrac{|AC|}{\sin 52°} = \dfrac{|AB|}{\sin 46°} \Leftrightarrow |AC| = \dfrac{|AB| \sin 52°}{\sin 46°}$, so substituting we have $|AC| = \dfrac{200 \sin 52°}{\sin 46°} \approx 219$ ft.

34. $\sin \angle ABC = \dfrac{312 \sin 48.6°}{527} \approx 0.444 \Leftrightarrow \angle ABC \approx \sin^{-1} 0.444 \approx 26.4°$, and so

$\angle BCA \approx 180° - 48.6° - 26.4° = 105°$. Then the distance between A and B is $|AB| = \dfrac{527 \sin 105°}{\sin 48.6°} \approx 678.5$ ft.

35.

We draw a diagram. A is the position of the tourist and C is the top of the tower. $\angle B = 90° - 5.6° = 84.4°$ and so $\angle C = 180° - 29.2° - 84.4° = 66.4°$. Thus, by the Law of Sines, the length of the tower is $|BC| = \dfrac{105 \sin 29.2°}{\sin 66.4°} \approx 55.9$ m.

36.

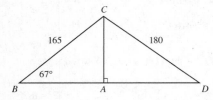

The situation is illustrated in the diagram. $|AC| = 165 \sin 67° \approx 151.9$ ft, so using the Pythagorean Theorem we can calculate $|BA| = \sqrt{165^2 - 151.9^2} \approx 64.4$ ft and $|AD| = \sqrt{180^2 - 151.9^2} \approx 96.6$ ft. Thus the anchor points are $|BA| + |AD| \approx 64.4 + 96.6 = 161$ ft apart.

37. The angle subtended by the top of the tree and the sun's rays is $\angle A = 180° - 90° - 52° = 38°$. Thus the height of the tree is $h = \dfrac{215 \sin 30°}{\sin 38°} \approx 175$ ft.

38.

Let x be the length of the wire, as shown in the figure. Since $\alpha = 12°$, other angles in $\triangle ABC$ are $\beta = 90° + 58° = 148°$, and $\gamma = 180° - (12° + 148°) = 20°$.

Thus, $\dfrac{x}{\sin 148°} = \dfrac{100}{\sin 20°} \quad \Leftrightarrow \quad x = 100 \cdot \dfrac{\sin 148°}{\sin 20°} \approx 155$ ft.

39. Call the balloon's position R. Then in $\triangle PQR$, we see that $\angle P = 62° - 32° = 30°$, and $\angle Q = 180° - 71° + 32° = 141°$. Therefore, $\angle R = 180° - 30° - 141° = 9°$. So by the Law of Sines, $\dfrac{QR}{\sin 30°} = \dfrac{PQ}{\sin 9°} \Leftrightarrow QR = 60 \cdot \dfrac{\sin 30°}{\sin 9°} \approx 192$ m.

40.

Label the diagram as shown, and let the hill's angle of elevation be α. Then applying the Law of Sines to $\triangle ABC$, $\dfrac{\sin \beta}{120} = \dfrac{\sin 8°}{30} \quad \Leftrightarrow$

$\sin \beta = 4 \sin 8° \approx 0.55669 \Rightarrow \beta \approx \sin^{-1} 0.55669 \approx 33.8°$. But from $\triangle ABD$, $\angle BAD + \angle B = (\alpha + 8°) + \beta = 90°$, so $\alpha \approx 90° - 8° - 33.8° = 48.2°$.

41.

$b > a > b \sin A$: Two solutions $a = b \sin A$: One solution $a < b \sin A$: No solution

$a \geq b$: One solution

$\angle A = 30°$, $b = 100$, $\sin A = \frac{1}{2}$. If $a \geq b = 100$ then there is one triangle. If $100 > a > 100 \sin 30° = 50$, then there are two possible triangles. If $a = 50$, then there is one (right) triangle. And if $a < 50$, then no triangle is possible.

6.5   The Law of Cosines

1. $x^2 = 21^2 + 42^2 - 2 \cdot 21 \cdot 42 \cdot \cos 39° = 441 + 1764 - 1764 \cos 39° \approx 834.115$ and so $x \approx \sqrt{834.115} \approx 28.9$.

2. $x^2 = 15^2 + 18^2 - 2 \cdot 15 \cdot 18 \cdot \cos 108° = 225 + 324 - 540 \cos 108° \approx 715.869$ and so $x \approx \sqrt{715.869} \approx 26.8$.

3. $x^2 = 25^2 + 25^2 - 2 \cdot 25 \cdot 25 \cdot \cos 140° = 625 + 625 - 1250 \cos 140° \approx 2207.556$ and so $x \approx \sqrt{2207.556} \approx 47$.

4. $x^2 = 2^2 + 8^2 - 2 \cdot 2 \cdot 8 \cdot \cos 88° = 4 + 64 - 32 \cos 88° \approx 66.883$ and so $x \approx \sqrt{66.883} \approx 8.2$.

5. $37.83^2 = 68.01^2 + 42.15^2 - 2 \cdot 68.01 \cdot 42.15 \cdot \cos \theta$. Then $\cos \theta = \dfrac{37.83^2 - 68.01^2 - 42.15^2}{-2 \cdot 68.01 \cdot 42.15} \approx 0.867$ ⇔

$\theta \approx \cos^{-1} 0.867 \approx 29.89°$.

6. $154.6^2 = 60.1^2 + 122.5^2 - 2 \cdot 60.1 \cdot 122.5 \cdot \cos \theta$. Then $\cos \theta = \dfrac{154.6^2 - 60.1^2 - 122.5^2}{-2 \cdot 60.1 \cdot 122.5} \approx -0.359$ ⇔

$\theta \approx \cos^{-1} (-0.359) \approx 111°$.

7. $x^2 = 24^2 + 30^2 - 2 \cdot 24 \cdot 30 \cdot \cos 30° = 576 + 900 - 1440 \cos 30° \approx 228.923$ and so $x \approx \sqrt{228.923} \approx 15$.

8. $20^2 = 10^2 + 12^2 - 2 \cdot 10 \cdot 12 \cdot \cos \theta$. Then $\cos \theta = \dfrac{20^2 - 10^2 - 12^2}{-2 \cdot 10 \cdot 12} = \dfrac{156}{-240} = -0.65$ ⇔

$\theta \approx \cos^{-1} (-0.65) \approx 130.54°$.

9. $c^2 = 10^2 + 18^2 - 2 \cdot 10 \cdot 18 \cdot \cos 120° = 100 + 324 - 360 \cos 120° = 604$ and so $c \approx \sqrt{604} \approx 24.576$. Then

$\sin A \approx \dfrac{18 \sin 120°}{24.576} \approx 0.634295$ ⇔ $\angle A \approx \sin^{-1} 0.634295 \approx 39.4°$, and $\angle B \approx 180° - 120° - 39.4° = 20.6°$.

10. $12^2 = 40^2 + 44^2 - 2 \cdot 40 \cdot 44 \cdot \cos B$ ⇔ $\cos B = \dfrac{12^2 - 40^2 - 44^2}{-2 \cdot 40 \cdot 44} \approx 0.964$ ⇔ $\angle B \approx \cos^{-1} 0.964 \approx 15°$. Then

$\sin A = \dfrac{40 \sin 15.5°}{12} \approx 0.891$ ⇔ $\angle A \approx \sin^{-1} 0.891 \approx 63°$, and so $\angle C \approx 180° - 15° - 63° = 102°$.

11. $c^2 = 3^2 + 4^2 - 2 \cdot 3 \cdot 4 \cdot \cos 53° = 9 + 16 - 24 \cos 53° \approx 10.556$ ⇔ $c \approx \sqrt{10.556} \approx 3.2$. Then

$\sin B = \dfrac{4 \sin 53°}{3.25} \approx 0.983$ ⇔ $\angle B \approx \sin^{-1} 0.983 \approx 79°$ and $\angle A \approx 180° - 53° - 79° = 48°$.

12. $a^2 = 60^2 + 30^2 - 2 \cdot 60 \cdot 30 \cdot \cos 70° = 3600 + 900 - 3600 \cos 70° \approx 3268.73$

⇔ $a = \sqrt{3268.73} \approx 57.2$. Then $\sin C \approx \dfrac{30 \sin 70°}{57.2} \approx 0.493$ ⇔

$\angle C \approx \sin^{-1} 0.493 \approx 29.5°$, and $\angle B \approx 180° - 70° - 29.5° = 80.5°$.

13. $20^2 = 25^2 + 22^2 - 2 \cdot 25 \cdot 22 \cdot \cos A$ ⇔ $\cos A = \dfrac{20^2 - 25^2 - 22^2}{-2 \cdot 25 \cdot 22} \approx 0.644$ ⇔ $\angle A \approx \cos^{-1} 0.644 \approx 50°$. Then

$\sin B \approx \dfrac{25 \sin 49.9°}{20} \approx 0.956$ ⇔ $\angle B \approx \sin^{-1} 0.956 \approx 73°$, and so $\angle C \approx 180° - 50° - 73° = 57°$.

14. $10^2 = 12^2 + 16^2 - 2 \cdot 12 \cdot 16 \cdot \cos A$ ⇔ $\cos A = \dfrac{10^2 - 12^2 - 16^2}{-2 \cdot 12 \cdot 16} = 0.78125$ ⇔

$\angle A \approx \cos^{-1} 0.78125 \approx 38.6°$. Then $\sin B \approx \dfrac{12 \sin 38.6°}{10} \approx 0.749$ ⇔

$\angle B \approx \sin^{-1} 0.749 \approx 48.5°$, and so $\angle C \approx 180° - 38.6° - 48.5° = 92.9°$.

15. $\sin C = \dfrac{162 \sin 40°}{125} \approx 0.833 \Leftrightarrow \angle C_1 \approx \sin^{-1} 0.833 \approx 56.4°$ or $\angle C_2 \approx 180° - 56.4° \approx 123.6°$.

If $\angle C_1 \approx 56.4°$, then $\angle A_1 \approx 180° - 40° - 56.4° = 83.6°$ and $a_1 = \dfrac{125 \sin 83.6°}{\sin 40°} \approx 193$.

If $\angle C_2 \approx 123.6°$, then $\angle A_2 \approx 180° - 40° - 123.6° = 16.4°$ and $a_2 = \dfrac{125 \sin 16.4°}{\sin 40°} \approx 54.9$.

Thus, one possible triangle has $\angle A \approx 83.6°$, $\angle C \approx 56.4°$, and $a \approx 193$; the other has $\angle A \approx 16.4°$, $\angle C \approx 123.6°$, and $a \approx 54.9$.

16. $\sin A = \dfrac{65 \sin 52°}{50} \approx 1.024$. Since $|\sin \theta| \leq 1$ for all θ, there is no such $\angle A$, and hence there is no such triangle.

17. $\sin B = \dfrac{65 \sin 55°}{50} \approx 1.065$. Since $|\sin \theta| \leq 1$ for all θ, there is no such $\angle B$, and hence there is no such triangle.

18. $\angle A = 180° - 61° - 83° = 36°$. Then $b = \dfrac{73.5 \sin 61°}{\sin 36°} \approx 109.4$ and $c = \dfrac{73.5 \sin 83°}{\sin 36°} \approx 124.1$.

19. $\angle B = 180° - 35° - 85° = 60°$. Then $x = \dfrac{3 \sin 35°}{\sin 60°} \approx 2$.

20. $x^2 = 10° + 18° - 2 \cdot 10 \cdot 18 \cdot \cos 40° = 100 + 324 - 360 \cos 40° \approx 148.224$ and so $x \approx \sqrt{148.224} \approx 12.2$.

21. $x = \dfrac{50 \sin 30°}{\sin 100°} \approx 25.4$

22. $4^2 = 10^2 + 11^2 - 2 \cdot 10 \cdot 11 \cdot \cos \theta$. Then $\cos \theta = \dfrac{4^2 - 10^2 - 11^2}{-2 \cdot 10 \cdot 11} = \dfrac{-205}{-220} \approx 0.932 \quad \Leftrightarrow \quad \theta \approx \cos^{-1} 0.932 \approx 21.3°$.

23. $b^2 = 110^2 + 138^2 - 2(110)(138) \cdot \cos 38° = 12{,}100 + 19{,}044 - 30{,}360 \cos 38° \approx 7220.0$ and so $b \approx 85.0$. Therefore $\sin \theta \approx \dfrac{138 \sin 38°}{80.4} \approx 0.999544 \quad \Leftrightarrow \quad \theta \approx 88.3°$.

24. $\sin \theta = \dfrac{10 \sin 40°}{8} \approx 0.803 \Leftrightarrow \theta \approx \sin^{-1} 0.803 \approx 53.5°$ or $\theta \approx 180° - 53.5° \approx 126.5°$.

25. $x^2 = 38^2 + 48^2 - 2 \cdot 38 \cdot 48 \cdot \cos 30° = 1444 + 2304 - 3648 \cos 30° \approx 588.739$ and so $x \approx 24.3$.

26. $\angle A = 180° - 98° - 25° = 57°$. Then $x = \dfrac{1000 \sin 98°}{\sin 57°} \approx 1180.8$.

27. The semiperimeter is $s = \dfrac{9 + 12 + 15}{2} = 18$, so by Heron's Formula the area is
$A = \sqrt{18(18 - 9)(18 - 12)(18 - 15)} = \sqrt{2916} = 54$.

28. The semiperimeter is $s = \dfrac{1 + 2 + 2}{2} = \dfrac{5}{2}$, so by Heron's Formula the area is
$A = \sqrt{\frac{5}{2}\left(\frac{5}{2} - 1\right)\left(\frac{5}{2} - 2\right)\left(\frac{5}{2} - 2\right)} = \sqrt{\frac{15}{16}} = \frac{\sqrt{15}}{4} \approx 0.968$.

29. The semiperimeter is $s = \dfrac{7 + 8 + 9}{2} = 12$, so by Heron's Formula the area is
$A = \sqrt{12(12 - 7)(12 - 8)(12 - 9)} = \sqrt{720} = 12\sqrt{5} \approx 26.8$.

30. The semiperimeter is $s = \dfrac{11 + 100 + 101}{2} = 106$, so by Heron's Formula the area is
$A = \sqrt{106(106 - 11)(106 - 100)(106 - 101)} = \sqrt{302{,}100} = 10\sqrt{3021} \approx 550$.

31. The semiperimeter is $s = \dfrac{3 + 4 + 6}{2} = \dfrac{13}{2}$, so by Heron's Formula the area is
$A = \sqrt{\frac{13}{2}\left(\frac{13}{2} - 3\right)\left(\frac{13}{2} - 4\right)\left(\frac{13}{2} - 6\right)} = \sqrt{\frac{455}{16}} = \frac{\sqrt{455}}{4} \approx 5.33$.

32. Both of the smaller triangles have the same area. The semiperimeter of each is $s = \dfrac{2 + 5 + 5}{2} = 6$, so by Heron's Formula the area of each is $A = \sqrt{6(6 - 2)(6 - 5)(6 - 5)} = \sqrt{24} = 2\sqrt{6}$, so the shaded area is $4\sqrt{6} \approx 9.80$.

33. We draw a diagonal connecting the vertices adjacent to the $100°$ angle. This forms two triangles. Consider the triangle with sides of length 5 and 6 containing the $100°$ angle. The area of this triangle is $A_1 = \frac{1}{2}(5)(6)\sin 100° \approx 14.77$. To use Heron's Formula to find the area of the second triangle, we need to find the length of the diagonal using the Law of Cosines: $c^2 = a^2 + b^2 - 2ab\cos C = 5^2 + 6^2 - 2\cdot5\cdot6\cos100° \approx 71.419 \Rightarrow c \approx 8.45$. Thus the second triangle has semiperimeter $s = \dfrac{8+7+8.45}{2} \approx 11.7255$ and area $A_2 = \sqrt{11.7255\,(11.7255-8)\,(11.7255-7)\,(11.7255-8.45)} \approx 26.00$. The area of the quadrilateral is the sum of the areas of the two triangles: $A = A_1 + A_2 \approx 14.77 + 26.00 = 40.77$.

34. We draw a line segment with length x bisecting the $60°$ angle to create two triangles. By the Law of Cosines, $3^2 = 4^2 + x^2 - 2\cdot4x\cos30° \quad\Leftrightarrow\quad x^2 - 4\sqrt{3}x + 7 = 0$. Using the quadratic formula, we find $x = 2\sqrt{3} \pm \sqrt{5}$. The minus sign provides the correct length of about 1.23 (the other solution is about 5.7, which corresponds to a convex quadrilateral with the same side lengths), so the semiperimeter of each triangle is $s = \dfrac{3+4+2\sqrt{3}-\sqrt{5}}{2}$ and the total area of the figure is $A = 2\sqrt{s\,(s-3)\,(s-4)\,(s-2\sqrt{3}+\sqrt{5})} \approx 2.46$.

35.

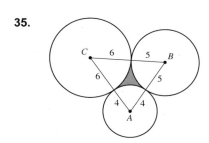

Label the centers of the circles A, B, and C, as in the figure. By the Law of Cosines, $\cos A = \dfrac{AB^2 + AC^2 - BC^2}{2\,(AB)\,(AC)} = \dfrac{9^2 + 10^2 - 11^2}{2\,(9)\,(10)} = \frac{1}{3} \Rightarrow$ $\angle A \approx 70.53°$. Now, by the Law of Sines, $\dfrac{\sin 70.53°}{11} = \dfrac{\sin B}{AC} = \dfrac{\sin C}{AB}$. So $\sin B = \frac{10}{11}\sin 70.53° \approx 0.85710 \Rightarrow B \approx \sin^{-1} 0.85710 \approx 58.99°$ and $\sin C = \frac{9}{11}\sin 70.53° \approx 0.77139 \Rightarrow C \approx \sin^{-1} 0.77139 \approx 50.48°$. The area of $\triangle ABC$ is $\frac{1}{2}(AB)(AC)\sin A = \frac{1}{2}(9)(10)(\sin 70.53°) \approx 42.426$.

The area of sector A is given by $S_A = \pi R^2 \cdot \dfrac{\theta}{360°} = \pi(4)^2 \cdot \dfrac{70.53°}{360°} \approx 9.848$. Similarly, the areas of sectors B and C are $S_B \approx 12.870$ and $S_C \approx 15.859$. Thus, the area enclosed between the circles is $A = \triangle ABC - S_A - S_B - S_C \Rightarrow A \approx 42.426 - 9.848 - 12.870 - 15.859 \approx 3.85 \text{ cm}^2$.

36. In any $\triangle ABC$, the Law of Cosines gives $a^2 = b^2 + c^2 - 2bc\cdot\cos A$, $b^2 = a^2 + c^2 - 2ac\cdot\cos B$, and $c^2 = a^2 + b^2 - 2ab\cdot\cos C$. Adding the second and third equations gives

$$
\begin{aligned}
b^2 &= a^2 + c^2 - 2ac\cdot\cos B \\
c^2 &= a^2 + b^2 - 2ab\cdot\cos C \\
b^2 + c^2 &= 2a^2 + b^2 + c^2 - 2a\,(c\cos B + b\cos C)
\end{aligned}
$$

Thus

$$
\begin{aligned}
2a^2 - 2a\,(c\cos B + b\cos C) &= 0 \\
2a\,(a - c\cos B + b\cos C) &= 0
\end{aligned}
$$

Since $a \neq 0$ we must have $a - (c\cos B + b\cos C) = 0 \Leftrightarrow a = b\cos C + c\cos B$. The other laws follow from the symmetry of a, b, and c.

37. Let c be the distance across the lake, in miles. Then $c^2 = 2.82^2 + 3.56^2 - 2\,(2.82)\,(3.56)\cdot\cos 40.3° \approx 5.313 \quad\Leftrightarrow\quad c \approx 2.30$ mi.

38. Suppose $ABCD$ is a parallelogram with $AB = DC = 5$, $AD = BC = 3$, and $\angle A = 50°$ (see the figure). Since opposite angles are equal in a parallelogram, it follows that $\angle C = 50°$, and

$$\angle B + \angle D = 360° - 100° = 260°. \text{ Thus, } \angle B = \angle D = \frac{260°}{2} = 130°.$$

By the Law of Cosines, $AC^2 = 3^2 + 5^2 - 2(3)(5) \cdot \cos 130° \Rightarrow AC = \sqrt{9 + 25 - 30 \cdot \cos 130°} \approx 7.3$. Similarly, $BD = \sqrt{3^2 + 5^2 - 2(3)(5) \cdot \cos 50°} \approx 3.8$.

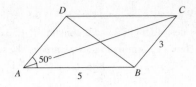

39. In half an hour, the faster car travels 25 miles while the slower car travels 15 miles. The distance between them is given by the Law of Cosines: $d^2 = 25^2 + 15^2 - 2(25)(15) \cdot \cos 65° \Rightarrow d = \sqrt{25^2 + 15^2 - 2(25)(15) \cdot \cos 65°} = 5\sqrt{25 + 9 - 30 \cdot \cos 65°} \approx 23.1$ mi.

40. Let x be the car's distance from its original position. Since the car travels at a constant speed of 40 miles per hour, it must have traveled 40 miles east, and then 20 miles northeast (which is $45°$ east of "due north"). From the diagram, we see that $\angle \beta = 135°$, so

$$x = \sqrt{20^2 + 40^2 - 2(20)(40) \cdot \cos 135°} = 10\sqrt{4 + 16 - 16 \cdot \cos 135°} \approx 56.0 \text{ mi.}$$

41. The pilot travels a distance of $625 \cdot 1.5 = 937.5$ miles in her original direction and $625 \cdot 2 = 1250$ miles in the new direction. Since she makes a course correction of $10°$ to the right, the included angle is $180° - 10° = 170°$. From the figure, we use the Law of Cosines to get

the expression $d^2 = 937.5^2 + 1250^2 - 2(937.5)(1250) \cdot \cos 170° \approx 4,749,549.42$, so $d \approx 2179$ miles. Thus, the pilot's distance from her original position is approximately 2179 miles.

42. Let d be the distance between the two boats in miles. After one hour, the boats have traveled distances of 30 miles and 26 miles. Also, the angle subtended by their directions is $180° - 50° - 70° = 60°$. Then $d^2 = 30^2 + 26^2 - 2 \cdot 30 \cdot 26 \cdot \cos 60° = 796 \Leftrightarrow d \approx \sqrt{796} \approx 28.2$. Thus the distance between the two boats is about 28 miles.

43. (a) The angle subtended at Egg Island is $100°$. Thus using the Law of Cosines, the distance from Forrest Island to the fisherman's home port is

$$x^2 = 30^2 + 50^2 - 2 \cdot 30 \cdot 50 \cdot \cos 100°$$
$$= 900 + 2500 - 3000 \cos 100° \approx 3920.945$$

and so $x \approx \sqrt{3920.945} \approx 62.62$ miles.

(b) Let θ be the angle shown in the figure. Using the Law of Sines,

$$\sin \theta = \frac{50 \sin 100°}{62.62} \approx 0.7863 \Leftrightarrow \theta \approx \sin^{-1} 0.7863 \approx 51.8°. \text{ Then}$$

$\gamma = 90° - 20° - 51.8° = 18.2°$. Thus the bearing to his home port is S 18.2° E.

44. (a) In the 30 minutes the pilot flies 100 miles due east. So using the Law of Cosines, $x^2 = 100^2 + 300^2 - 2 \cdot 100 \cdot 300 \cdot \cos 40° = 100^2 (1 + 9 - 6 \cos 40°) \approx 100^2 (5.404)$ and so $x \approx \sqrt{100^2 (5.404)} \approx 232.5$. Thus the pilot is 232.5 miles from his destination.

(b) Using the Law of Sines, $\sin \theta = \dfrac{300 \sin 40°}{232.5} \approx 0.829 \quad \Leftrightarrow$

$\theta \approx \sin^{-1} 0.829 \approx 56°$. However, since $\theta > 90°$, the angle we seek is $180° - 56° = 124°$. Hence the bearing is $124° - 90° = 34°$, N 50° E.

45. The largest angle is the one opposite the longest side; call this angle θ. Then by the Law of Cosines,

$44^2 = 36^2 + 22^2 - 2 (36) (22) \cdot \cos \theta \quad \Leftrightarrow \quad \cos \theta = \dfrac{36^2 + 22^2 - 44^2}{2 (36) (22)} = -0.09848 \Rightarrow \theta \approx \cos^{-1} (-0.09848) \approx 96°$.

46. Let θ be the angle formed by the cables. The two tugboats and the barge form a triangle: the side opposite θ has a length of 120 ft and the other two sides have lengths of 212 and 230 ft. Therefore, $120^2 = 212^2 + 230^2 - 2 (212) (230) \cdot \cos \theta$

$\Leftrightarrow \quad \cos \theta = \dfrac{212^2 + 230^2 - 120^2}{2 (212) (230)} \Rightarrow \cos \theta = 0.8557 \Rightarrow \theta \approx \cos^{-1} 0.8557 \approx 31°$.

47. Let d be the distance between the kites; then $d^2 \approx 380^2 + 420^2 - 2 (380) (420) \cdot \cos 30° \Rightarrow d \approx \sqrt{380^2 + 420^2 - 2 (380) (420) \cdot \cos 30°} \approx 211$ ft.

48. Let x be the length of the wire and let θ be the angle opposite x, as shown in the figure. Since the mountain is inclined 32°, we must have $\theta = 180° - (90° - 32°) = 122°$. Thus,

$x = \sqrt{55^2 + 125^2 - 2 (55) (125) \cdot \cos 122°} \approx 161$ ft.

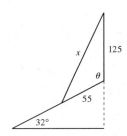

49. *Solution 1:* From the figure, we see that $\gamma = 106°$ and $\sin 74° = \dfrac{3400}{b} \quad \Leftrightarrow$

$b = \dfrac{3400}{\sin 74°} \approx 3537$. Thus, $x^2 = 800^2 + 3537^2 - 2 (800) (3537) \cos 106° \quad \Rightarrow$

$x = \sqrt{800^2 + 3537^2 - 2 (800) (3537) \cos 106°} \quad \Rightarrow \quad x \approx 3835$ ft.

Solution 2: Notice that $\tan 74° = \dfrac{3400}{a} \quad \Leftrightarrow \quad a = \dfrac{3400}{\tan 74°} \approx 974.9$. By the

Pythagorean theorem, $x^2 = (a + 800)^2 + 3400^2$. So

$x = \sqrt{(974.9 + 800)^2 + 3400^2} \approx 3835$ ft.

50. Let the woman be at point A, the first landmark (at 62°) be at point B, and the other landmark be at point C. We want to find the length BC. Now, $\cos 62° = \dfrac{1150}{AB} \Leftrightarrow AB = \dfrac{1150}{\cos 62°} \approx 2450$. Similarly, $\cos 54° = \dfrac{1150}{AC} \quad \Leftrightarrow$

$AC = \dfrac{1150}{\cos 54°} \approx 1956$. Therefore, by the Law of Cosines, $BC^2 = AB^2 + AC^2 - 2 (AB) (AC) \cdot \cos 43° \quad \Rightarrow$

$BC = \sqrt{2450^2 + 1956^2 - 2 (2450) (1956) \cdot \cos 43°} \Rightarrow BC \approx 1679$. Thus, the two landmarks are roughly 1679 feet apart.

51. By Heron's formula, $A = \sqrt{s(s-a)(s-b)(s-c)}$, where $s = \dfrac{a+b+c}{2} = \dfrac{112+148+190}{2} = 225$. Thus,

$A = \sqrt{225(225-112)(225-148)(225-190)} \approx 8277.7 \text{ ft}^2$. Since the land value is \$20 per square foot, the value of the lot is approximately $8277.7 \cdot 20 = \$165,554$.

52. Having found $a \approx 13.2$ using the Law of Cosines, we use the Law of Sines to find $\angle B$: $\dfrac{\sin B}{10.5} = \dfrac{\sin 46.5°}{13.2} \quad \Leftrightarrow$

$\sin B = \dfrac{10.5 \sin 46.5°}{13.2} \approx 0.577$. Now there are two angles $\angle B$ between $0°$ and $180°$ which have $\sin B = 0.577$, namely $\angle B_1 \approx 35.2°$ and $\angle B_2 \approx 144.8°$. But we must choose $\angle B_1$, since otherwise $\angle A + \angle B > 180°$.

Using the Law of Sines again, $\dfrac{\sin C}{18.0} = \dfrac{\sin 46.5°}{13.2} \quad \Leftrightarrow \quad \sin C = \dfrac{18.0 \sin 46.5°}{13.2} \approx 0.989$, so either $\angle C \approx 81.5°$ or $\angle C \approx 98.5°$. In this case we must choose $\angle C \approx 98.5°$ so that the sum of the angles in the triangle is $\angle A + \angle B + \angle C \approx 46.5° + 35.2° + 98.5° \approx 180°$. (The fact that the angles do not sum to exactly $180°$, and the discrepancies between these results and those of Example 3, are due to roundoff error.)

The method in this exercise is slightly easier computationally, but the method in Example 3 is more foolproof.

Chapter 6 Review

1. (a) $60° = 60 \cdot \frac{\pi}{180} = \frac{\pi}{3} \approx 1.05$ rad

    (b) $330° = 330 \cdot \frac{\pi}{180} = \frac{11\pi}{6} \approx 5.76$ rad

    (c) $-135° = -135 \cdot \frac{\pi}{180} = -\frac{3\pi}{4} \approx -3.36$ rad

    (d) $-90° = -90 \cdot \frac{\pi}{180} = -\frac{\pi}{2} \approx -1.57$ rad

2. (a) $24° = 24 \cdot \frac{\pi}{180} = \frac{2\pi}{15} \approx 0.42$ rad

    (b) $-330° = -330 \cdot \frac{\pi}{180} = -\frac{11\pi}{6} \approx -5.76$ rad

    (c) $750° = 750 \cdot \frac{\pi}{180} = \frac{25\pi}{6} \approx 13.09$ rad

    (d) $5° = 5 \cdot \frac{\pi}{180} = \frac{\pi}{3} \approx 0.87$ rad

3. (a) $\frac{5\pi}{2}$ rad $= \frac{5\pi}{2} \cdot \frac{180}{\pi} = 450°$

    (b) $-\frac{\pi}{6}$ rad $= -\frac{\pi}{6} \cdot \frac{180}{\pi} = -30°$

    (c) $\frac{9\pi}{4}$ rad $= \frac{9\pi}{4} \cdot \frac{180}{\pi} = 405°$

    (d) 3.1 rad $= 3.1 \cdot \frac{180}{\pi} = \frac{558}{\pi} \approx 177.6°$

2. (a) 8 rad $= 8 \cdot \frac{180}{\pi} = \frac{1440}{\pi} \approx 458.37°$

    (b) $-\frac{5}{2}$ rad $= -\frac{5}{2} \cdot \frac{180}{\pi} = \frac{450}{\pi} \approx 143.24°$

    (c) $\frac{11\pi}{6}$ rad $= \frac{11\pi}{6} \cdot \frac{180}{\pi} = 330°$

    (d) $\frac{3\pi}{5}$ rad $= \frac{3\pi}{5} \cdot \frac{180}{\pi} = 108°$

5. $r = 8$ m, $\theta = 1$ rad. Then $s = r\theta = 8 \cdot 1 = 8$ m.

6. $s = 7$ ft, $r = 5$ ft. Then $\theta = \dfrac{s}{r} = \frac{7}{5} = 1.4$ rad $\approx 80.2°$

7. $s = 100$ ft, $\theta = 70° = 70 \cdot \frac{\pi}{180} = \frac{7\pi}{18}$ rad. Then $r = \frac{s}{\theta} = 100 \cdot \frac{18}{7\pi} = \frac{1800}{7\pi} \approx 82$ ft.

8. Since the diameter is 28 in, $r = 14$ in. In one revolution, the arc length (distance traveled) is $s = \theta r = 2\pi \cdot 14 = 28\pi$ in. The total distance traveled is 60 mi/h $\cdot$ 0.5 h $= 30$ mi $= 30$ mi $\cdot$ 5280 ft/mi $\cdot$ 12 in./ft $= 1{,}900{,}800$ in. The number of revolution is $1{,}900{,}800$ in $\cdot \dfrac{1 \text{ rev}}{28\pi \text{ in.}} \approx 21608.7$ rev. Therefore the car wheel will make approximately 21,609 revolutions.

9. $r = 3960$ miles, $s = 2450$ miles. Then $\theta = \dfrac{s}{r} = \dfrac{2450}{3960} \approx 0.619$ rad $= 0.619 \cdot \frac{\pi}{180} \approx 35.448°$ and so the angle is approximately $35.4°$.

10. $r = 5$ m, $\theta = 2$ rad. Then $A = \frac{1}{2}r^2\theta = \frac{1}{2} \cdot 5^2 \cdot 2 = 25 \text{ m}^2$.

11. $A = \frac{1}{2}r^2\theta = \frac{1}{2}(200)^2 \left(52° \cdot \frac{\pi}{180°}\right) \approx 18{,}151 \text{ ft}^2$

12. $A = 125 \text{ ft}^2$, $r = 25$ ft. Then $\theta = \dfrac{2A}{r^2} = \dfrac{2 \cdot 125}{25^2} = \frac{250}{625} = 0.4$ rad $\approx 22.9°$

13. The angular speed is $\omega = \dfrac{150 \cdot 2\pi \text{ rad}}{1 \text{ min}} = 300\pi$ rad/min ≈ 942.5 rad/min. The linear speed is

$v = \dfrac{150 \cdot 2\pi \cdot 8}{1} = 2400\pi$ in./min ≈ 7539.8 in./min.

14. (a) The angular speed of the engine is $\omega_e = \frac{3500 \cdot 2\pi \text{ rad}}{1 \text{ min}} = 7000\pi$ rad/min.

(b) To find the angular speed of the wheels, we calculate $g = \frac{\text{angular speed of the engine}}{\omega_w} = \frac{7000\pi \text{ rad/min}}{\omega_w} = 0.9 \quad \Leftrightarrow$
$\omega_w = 7777.8$ rad/min.

(c) The speed of the car is the angular speed of the wheels times their radius:
$\frac{7777.8 \text{ rad}}{\text{min}} \cdot (11 \text{ in}) \cdot \frac{60 \text{ min}}{1 \text{ hr}} \cdot \frac{1 \text{ mile}}{63,360 \text{ in.}} = 81$ mi/h.

15. $r = \sqrt{5^2 + 7^2} = \sqrt{74}$. Then $\sin\theta = \frac{5}{\sqrt{74}}$, $\cos\theta = \frac{7}{\sqrt{74}}$, $\tan\theta = \frac{5}{7}$, $\csc\theta = \frac{\sqrt{74}}{5}$, $\sec\theta = \frac{\sqrt{74}}{7}$, and $\cot\theta = \frac{7}{5}$.

16. $x = \sqrt{10^2 - 3^2} = \sqrt{91}$. Then $\sin\theta = \frac{3}{10}$, $\cos\theta = \frac{\sqrt{91}}{10}$, $\tan\theta = \frac{3}{\sqrt{91}}$, $\csc\theta = \frac{10}{3}$, $\sec\theta = \frac{10}{\sqrt{91}}$, and $\cot\theta = \frac{\sqrt{91}}{3}$.

17. $\frac{x}{5} = \cos 40° \quad \Leftrightarrow \quad x = 5\cos 40° \approx 3.83$, and $\frac{y}{5} = \sin 40° \quad \Leftrightarrow \quad y = 5\sin 40° \approx 3.21$.

18. $\cos 35° = \frac{2}{x} \quad \Leftrightarrow \quad x = \frac{2}{\cos 35°} \approx 2.44$, and $\tan 35° = \frac{y}{2} \Leftrightarrow y = 2\tan 35° \approx 1.40$.

19. $\frac{1}{x} = \sin 20° \quad \Leftrightarrow \quad x = \frac{1}{\sin 20°} \approx 2.92$, and $\frac{x}{y} = \cos 20° \quad \Leftrightarrow \quad y = \frac{x}{\cos 20°} \approx \frac{2.924}{0.9397} \approx 3.11$.

20. $\cos 30° = \frac{x}{4} \quad \Leftrightarrow \quad x = 4\cos 30° \approx 3.46$, and $\sin 30° = \frac{y}{x} \Leftrightarrow y = x\sin 30° = 3.46 \cdot 0.5 \approx 1.73$.

21. $w = 3\sin 20° \approx 1.026$,
$v = 3\cos 20° \approx 2.819$.

22. The other angle is $90° - 60° = 30°$,
$\tan 60° = l/20 \Leftrightarrow l = 20\tan 60° \approx 34.64$,
and $\cos 60° = 20/h \Leftrightarrow$
$h = 20/(\cos 60°) = 40$.

23. $\tan\theta = \frac{1}{a} \quad \Leftrightarrow \quad a = \frac{1}{\tan\theta} = \cot\theta$, $\sin\theta = \frac{1}{b} \quad \Leftrightarrow \quad b = \frac{1}{\sin\theta} = \csc\theta$

24. Let h be the height of the tower in meters. Then $\tan 28.81° = \frac{h}{1000} \quad \Leftrightarrow \quad h = 1000\tan 28.81° \approx 550$ m.

25.

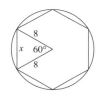

One side of the hexagon together with radial line segments through its endpoints forms a triangle with two sides of length 8 m and subtended angle $60°$. Let x be the length of one such side (in meters). By the Law of Cosines,
$$x^2 = 8^2 + 8^2 - 2 \cdot 8 \cdot 8 \cdot \cos 60° = 64 \quad \Leftrightarrow \quad x = 8.$$ Thus the perimeter of the hexagon is $6x = 6 \cdot 8 = 48$ m.

26. As the crankshaft moves in its circular pattern, point Q is determined by the angle θ, namely it has coordinates $Q(2\cos\theta, 2\sin\theta)$. We split the triangle into two right triangles $\triangle OQR$ and $\triangle PQR$, as shown in the figure. Let h be the height of the piston. We consider two cases, $0° \le \theta < 180°$ and $180° \le \theta < 360°$.

If $0° \le \theta < 180°$, then h is the sum of OR and RP. Using the Pythagorean Theorem, we find

$RP = \sqrt{8^2 - (2\cos\theta)^2}$, while OR is the y-coordinate of the point Q, $2\sin\theta$. Thus $h = \sqrt{64 - 4\cos^2\theta} + 2\sin\theta$.

If $180° \le \theta < 360°$, then h is the difference between RP and RO. Again, $RP = \sqrt{64 - 4\cos^2\theta}$ and OR is the y-coordinate of the point Q, $2\sin\theta$. Thus $h = \sqrt{64 - 4\cos^2\theta} - 2|\sin\theta|$. Since $\sin\theta < 0$ for $180° < \theta < 360°$, this also reduces to $h = \sqrt{64 - 4\cos^2\theta} + 2\sin\theta$.

Since we get the same result in both cases, the height of the piston in terms of θ is $h = \sqrt{64 - 4\cos^2\theta} + 2\sin\theta$.

27. Let r represent the radius, in miles, of the moon. Then $\tan \dfrac{\theta}{2} = \dfrac{r}{r + |AB|}$, $\theta = 0.518°$

$\Leftrightarrow \quad r = (r + 236{,}900) \cdot \tan 0.259° \quad \Leftrightarrow \quad r(1 - \tan 0.259°) = 236{,}900 \cdot \tan 0.259° \Leftrightarrow$

$r = \dfrac{236{,}900 \cdot \tan 0.259°}{1 - \tan 0.259°} \approx 1076$ and so the radius of the moon is roughly 1076 miles.

28. Let d_1 represent the horizontal distance from a point directly below the plane to the closer ship in feet, and d_2 represent the horizontal distance to the other ship in feet. Then $\tan 52° = \dfrac{35{,}000}{d_1} \quad \Leftrightarrow \quad d_1 = \dfrac{35{,}000}{\tan 52°}$,

and similarly $\tan 40° = \dfrac{35{,}000}{d_2} \quad \Leftrightarrow \quad d_2 = \dfrac{35{,}000}{\tan 40°}$. So the distance between the two ships is

$d_2 - d_1 = \dfrac{35{,}000}{\tan 40°} - \dfrac{35{,}000}{\tan 52°} \approx 14{,}400$ ft.

29. $\sin 315° = -\sin 45° = -\dfrac{1}{\sqrt{2}} = -\dfrac{\sqrt{2}}{2}$

30. $\csc \dfrac{9\pi}{4} = \csc \dfrac{\pi}{4} = \sqrt{2}$

31. $\tan(-135°) = \tan 45° = 1$

32. $\cos \dfrac{5\pi}{6} = -\cos \dfrac{\pi}{6} = -\dfrac{\sqrt{3}}{2}$

33. $\cot\left(-\dfrac{22\pi}{3}\right) = \cot \dfrac{2\pi}{3} = \cot \dfrac{\pi}{3} = -\dfrac{1}{\sqrt{3}} = -\dfrac{\sqrt{3}}{3}$

34. $\sin 405° = \sin 45° = \dfrac{1}{\sqrt{2}} = \dfrac{\sqrt{2}}{2}$

35. $\cos 585° = \cos 225° = -\cos 45° = -\dfrac{1}{\sqrt{2}} = -\dfrac{\sqrt{2}}{2}$

36. $\sec \dfrac{22\pi}{3} = \sec \dfrac{4\pi}{3} = -\sec \dfrac{\pi}{3} = -2$

37. $\csc \dfrac{8\pi}{3} = \csc \dfrac{2\pi}{3} = \csc \dfrac{\pi}{3} = \dfrac{2}{\sqrt{3}} = \dfrac{2\sqrt{3}}{3}$

38. $\sec \dfrac{13\pi}{6} = \sec \dfrac{\pi}{6} = \dfrac{2\sqrt{3}}{3}$

39. $\cot(-390°) = \cot(-30°) = -\cot 30° = -\sqrt{3}$

40. $\tan \dfrac{23\pi}{4} = \tan \dfrac{3\pi}{4} = -\tan \dfrac{\pi}{4} = -1$

41. $r = \sqrt{(-5)^2 + 12^2} = \sqrt{169} = 13$. Then $\sin\theta = \dfrac{12}{13}$, $\cos\theta = -\dfrac{5}{13}$, $\tan\theta = -\dfrac{12}{5}$, $\csc\theta = \dfrac{13}{12}$, $\sec\theta = -\dfrac{13}{5}$, and $\cot\theta = -\dfrac{5}{12}$.

42. If θ is in standard position, then the terminal point of θ on the unit circle is simply $(\cos\theta, \sin\theta)$. Since the terminal point is given as $\left(-\dfrac{\sqrt{3}}{2}, \dfrac{1}{2}\right)$, $\sin\theta = \dfrac{1}{2}$.

43. $y - \sqrt{3}x + 1 = 0 \Leftrightarrow y = \sqrt{3}x - 1$, so the slope of the line is $m = \sqrt{3}$. Then $\tan\theta = m = \sqrt{3} \Leftrightarrow \theta = 60°$.

44. $4y - 2x - 1 = 0 \Leftrightarrow y = \dfrac{1}{2}x + \dfrac{1}{4}$. The slope of the line is $m = \dfrac{1}{2}$. Then $\tan\theta = m = \dfrac{1}{2}$ and $r = \sqrt{1^2 + 2^2} = \sqrt{5}$. So $\sin\theta = -\dfrac{1}{\sqrt{5}}$, $\cos\theta = -\dfrac{2}{\sqrt{5}}$, $\tan\theta = \dfrac{1}{2}$, $\csc\theta = -\sqrt{5}$, $\sec\theta = -\dfrac{\sqrt{5}}{2}$, and $\cot\theta = 2$.

45. $\sec^2\theta = 1 + \tan^2\theta \quad \Leftrightarrow \quad \tan^2\theta = \dfrac{1}{\cos^2\theta} - 1 \quad \Leftrightarrow$

$\tan\theta = \sqrt{\dfrac{1}{\cos^2\theta} - 1} = \sqrt{\dfrac{1 - \cos^2\theta}{\cos^2\theta}} = \dfrac{\sqrt{1 - \cos^2\theta}}{|\cos\theta|} = \dfrac{\sqrt{1 - \cos^2\theta}}{-\cos\theta}$ (since $\cos\theta < 0$ in quadrant III,

$|\cos\theta| = -\cos\theta$). Thus $\tan\theta = -\dfrac{\sqrt{1 - \cos^2\theta}}{\cos\theta}$.

46. $\sec\theta = \dfrac{1}{\cos\theta} = \dfrac{1}{-\sqrt{1 - \sin^2\theta}}$ (since $\cos\theta < 0$ in quadrant III).

47. $\tan^2\theta = \dfrac{\sin^2\theta}{\cos^2\theta} = \dfrac{\sin^2\theta}{1 - \sin^2\theta}$

48. $\csc^2\theta \cos^2\theta = \dfrac{1}{\sin^2\theta} \cdot \cos^2\theta = \dfrac{1 - \sin^2\theta}{\sin^2\theta} = \dfrac{1}{\sin^2\theta} - 1$

49. $\tan\theta = \dfrac{\sqrt{7}}{3}$, $\sec\theta = \dfrac{4}{3}$. Then $\cos\theta = \dfrac{3}{4}$ and $\sin\theta = \tan\theta \cdot \cos\theta = \dfrac{\sqrt{7}}{4}$, $\csc\theta = \dfrac{4}{\sqrt{7}} = \dfrac{4\sqrt{7}}{7}$, and $\cot\theta = \dfrac{3}{\sqrt{7}} = \dfrac{3\sqrt{7}}{7}$.

50. $\sec\theta = \dfrac{41}{40}$, $\csc\theta = -\dfrac{41}{9}$. Then $\sin\theta = -\dfrac{9}{41}$, $\cos\theta = \dfrac{40}{41}$, $\tan\theta = \dfrac{\sin\theta}{\cos\theta} = \dfrac{-\frac{9}{41}}{\frac{40}{41}} = -\dfrac{9}{40}$, and $\cot\theta = -\dfrac{40}{9}$.

51. $\sin\theta = \dfrac{3}{5}$. Since $\cos\theta < 0$, θ is in quadrant II. Thus, $x = -\sqrt{5^2 - 3^2} = -\sqrt{16} = -4$ and so $\cos\theta = -\dfrac{4}{5}$, $\tan\theta = -\dfrac{3}{4}$, $\csc\theta = \dfrac{5}{3}$, $\sec\theta = -\dfrac{5}{4}$, $\cot\theta = -\dfrac{4}{3}$.

52. $\sec\theta = -\frac{13}{5}$ and $\tan\theta > 0$. Then $\cos\theta = -\frac{5}{13}$, and θ must be in quadrant III $\Rightarrow \sin\theta < 0$. Therefore,

$\sin\theta = -\sqrt{1 - \cos^2\theta} = -\sqrt{1 - \frac{25}{169}} = -\frac{12}{13}$, $\csc\theta = -\frac{13}{12}$, $\tan\theta = \frac{\sin\theta}{\cos\theta} = \frac{12}{5}$, and $\cot\theta = \frac{5}{12}$.

53. $\tan\theta = -\frac{1}{2}$. $\sec^2\theta = 1 + \tan^2\theta = 1 + \frac{1}{4} = \frac{5}{4}$ $\Leftrightarrow$ $\cos^2\theta = \frac{4}{5}$ $\Rightarrow$ $\cos\theta = -\sqrt{\frac{4}{5}} = -\frac{2}{\sqrt{5}}$ since

$\cos\theta < 0$ in quadrant II. But $\tan\theta = \frac{\sin\theta}{\cos\theta} = -\frac{1}{2}$ $\Leftrightarrow$ $\sin\theta = -\frac{1}{2}\cos\theta = -\frac{1}{2}\left(-\frac{2}{\sqrt{5}}\right) = \frac{1}{\sqrt{5}}$. Therefore,

$\sin\theta + \cos\theta = \frac{1}{\sqrt{5}} + \left(-\frac{2}{\sqrt{5}}\right) = -\frac{1}{\sqrt{5}} = -\frac{\sqrt{5}}{5}$.

54. $\sin\theta = \frac{1}{2}$ for θ in quadrant I. Then $\tan\theta + \sec\theta = \frac{\sin\theta}{\cos\theta} + \frac{1}{\cos\theta} = \frac{\sin\theta + 1}{\cos\theta} = \frac{\sin\theta + 1}{\sqrt{1 - \sin^2\theta}} = \frac{\frac{1}{2} + 1}{\sqrt{1 - \frac{1}{2}}} = \frac{2\sqrt{3}}{2} = \sqrt{3}$.

55. By the Pythagorean Theorem, $\sin^2\theta + \cos^2\theta = 1$ for any angle θ.

56. $\cos\theta = -\frac{\sqrt{3}}{2}$ and $\frac{\pi}{2} < \theta < \pi$. Then $\theta = \frac{5\pi}{6}$ $\Rightarrow$ $2\theta = \frac{10\pi}{6} = \frac{5\pi}{3}$. So $\sin 2\theta = \sin\frac{5\pi}{3} = -\sin\frac{\pi}{3} = -\frac{\sqrt{3}}{2}$.

57. $\angle B = 180° - 30° - 80° = 70°$, and so by the Law of Sines, $x = \frac{10\sin 30°}{\sin 70°} \approx 5.32$.

58. $x = \frac{2\sin 45°}{\sin 105°} \approx 1.46$

59. $x^2 = 100^2 + 210^2 - 2 \cdot 100 \cdot 210 \cdot \cos 40° \approx 21{,}926.133$ $\Leftrightarrow$ $x \approx 148.07$

60. $x^2 = 2^2 + 8^2 - 2\,(2)\,(8)\cos 120° = 84$ $\Leftrightarrow$ $x \approx \sqrt{84} \approx 9.17$

61. $\sin B = \frac{20\sin 60°}{70} \approx 0.247 \Leftrightarrow \angle B \approx \sin^{-1}0.247 \approx 14.33°$. Then $\angle C \approx 180° - 60° - 14.33° = 105.67°$, and so

$x \approx \frac{70\sin 105.67°}{\sin 60°} \approx 77.82$.

62. $\sin B = \frac{4\sin 110°}{6} \approx 0.626 \Leftrightarrow \angle B \approx 38.79°$. Then $\angle C \approx 180° - 110° - 38.79° = 31.21°$, and so

$x \approx \frac{6\sin 31.21°}{\sin 110°} \approx 3.3$.

63. After 2 hours the ships have traveled distances $d_1 = 40$ mi and $d_2 = 56$ mi. The subtended angle is $180° - 32° - 42° = 106°$. Let d be the distance between the two ships in miles. Then by the Law of Cosines, $d^2 = 40^2 + 56^2 - 2\,(40)\,(56)\cos 106° \approx 5970.855$ $\Leftrightarrow$ $d \approx 77.3$ miles.

64. Let h represent the height of the building in feet, and x the horizontal distance from the building to point B. Then $\tan 24.1° = \frac{h}{x + 600}$ and $\tan 30.2° = \frac{h}{x}$ $\Leftrightarrow$ $x = h\cot 30.2°$. Substituting

for x gives $\tan 24.1° = \frac{h}{h\cot 30.2° + 600}$ $\Leftrightarrow$ $h = \tan 24.1°\,(h\cot 30.2° + 600)$ $\Leftrightarrow$

$h = \frac{600 \cdot \tan 24.1°}{1 - \tan 24.1°\cot 30.2°} \approx 1160$ ft.

65. Let d be the distance, in miles, between the points A and B. Then by the Law of Cosines, $d^2 = 3.2^2 + 5.6^2 - 2\,(3.2)\,(5.6)\cos 42° \approx 14.966$ $\Leftrightarrow$ $d \approx 3.9$ mi.

66. $\angle C = 180° - 42.3° - 68.9° = 68.8°$. Then $b = \frac{120\sin 68.9°}{\sin 68.8°} \approx 120.08$ miles. Let d be the shortest distance, in miles, to the shore. Then $d = b\sin A \approx 120.08\sin 42.3° \approx 80.8$ miles.

67. $A = \frac{1}{2}ab\sin\theta = \frac{1}{2}\,(8)\,(14)\sin 35° \approx 32.12$

68. By Heron's Formula, $A = \sqrt{s\,(s - a)\,(s - b)\,(s - c)}$, where $s = \frac{a + b + c}{2} = \frac{5 + 6 + 8}{2} = 9.5$. Thus,

$A = \sqrt{9.5\,(9.5 - 5)\,(9.5 - 6)\,(9.5 - 8)} \approx 14.98$.

Chapter 6 Test

1. $330° = 330 \cdot \frac{\pi}{180} = \frac{11\pi}{6}$ rad. $-135° = -135 \cdot \frac{\pi}{180} = -\frac{3\pi}{4}$ rad.

2. $\frac{4\pi}{3}$ rad $= \frac{4\pi}{3} \cdot \frac{180}{\pi} = 240°$. -1.3 rad $= -1.3 \cdot \frac{180}{\pi} = -\frac{234}{\pi} \approx -74.5°$

3. (a) The angular speed is $\omega = \frac{120 \cdot 2\pi \text{ rad}}{1 \text{ min}} = 240\pi$ rad/min.

    (b) The linear speed is

$$v = \frac{120 \cdot 2\pi \cdot 16}{1} = 3840\pi \text{ ft/min}$$

$$\approx 12{,}063.7 \text{ ft/min}$$

$$\approx 2.28 \text{ miles/min}.$$

4. (a) $\sin 405° = \sin 45° = \frac{1}{\sqrt{2}} = \frac{\sqrt{2}}{2}$

    (b) $\tan(-150°) = \tan 30° = \frac{1}{\sqrt{3}} = \frac{\sqrt{3}}{3}$

    (c) $\sec \frac{5\pi}{3} = \sec \frac{\pi}{3} = 2$

    (d) $\csc \frac{5\pi}{2} = \csc \frac{\pi}{2} = 1$

5. $r = \sqrt{3^2 + 2^2} = \sqrt{13}$. Then $\tan\theta + \sin\theta = \frac{2}{3} + \frac{2}{\sqrt{13}} = \frac{2(\sqrt{13}+3)}{3\sqrt{13}} = \frac{26+6\sqrt{13}}{39}$.

6. $\sin\theta = \frac{a}{24} \iff a = 24\sin\theta$. Also, $\cos\theta = \frac{b}{24} \iff b = 24\cos\theta$.

7. $\cos\theta = -\frac{1}{3}$ and θ is in quadrant III, so $r = 3$, $x = -1$, and $y = -\sqrt{3^2 - 1^2} = -2\sqrt{2}$. Then

$$\tan\theta\cot\theta + \csc\theta = \tan\theta \cdot \frac{1}{\tan\theta} + \csc\theta = 1 - \frac{3}{2\sqrt{2}} = \frac{2\sqrt{2}-3}{2\sqrt{2}} = \frac{4-3\sqrt{2}}{4}.$$

8. $\sin\theta = \frac{5}{13}$, $\tan\theta = -\frac{5}{12}$. Then $\sec\theta = \frac{1}{\cos\theta} = \frac{1}{\cos\theta} \cdot \frac{\sin\theta}{\sin\theta} = \tan\theta \cdot \frac{1}{\sin\theta} = -\frac{5}{12} \cdot \frac{13}{5} = -\frac{13}{12}$.

9. $\sec^2\theta = 1 + \tan^2\theta \iff \tan\theta = \pm\sqrt{\sec^2\theta - 1}$. Thus, $\tan\theta = -\sqrt{\sec^2\theta - 1}$ since $\tan\theta < 0$ in quadrant II.

10. $\tan 73° = \frac{h}{6} \implies h = 6\tan 73° \approx 19.6$ ft.

11. By the Law of Cosines, $x^2 = 10^2 + 12^2 - 2(10)(12) \cdot \cos 48° \approx 8.409 \iff x \approx 9.1$.

12. $\angle C = 180° - 52° - 69° = 59°$. Then by the Law of Sines, $x = \frac{230\sin 69°}{\sin 59°} \approx 250.5$.

13. Let h be the height of the shorter altitude. Then $\tan 20° = \frac{h}{50} \iff h = 50\tan 20°$ and $\tan 28° = \frac{x+h}{50} \iff$

$x + h = 50\tan 28° \iff x = 50\tan 28° - h = 50\tan 28° - 50\tan 20° \approx 8.4$.

14. Let $\angle A$ and $\angle X$ be the other angles in the triangle. Then $\sin A = \frac{15\sin 108°}{28} \approx 0.509 \iff \angle A \approx 30.63°$. Then

$\angle X \approx 180° - 108° - 30.63° \approx 41.37°$, and so $x \approx \frac{28\sin 41.37°}{\sin 108°} \approx 19.5$.

15. (a) $A(\text{sector}) = \frac{1}{2}r^2\theta = \frac{1}{2} \cdot 10^2 \cdot 72 \cdot \frac{\pi}{180} = 50 \cdot \frac{72\pi}{180}$. $A(\text{triangle}) = \frac{1}{2}r \cdot r\sin\theta = \frac{1}{2} \cdot 10^2\sin 72°$. Thus, the area of the

    shaded region is $A(\text{shaded}) = A(\text{sector}) - A(\text{triangle}) = 50\left(\frac{72\pi}{180} - \sin 72°\right) \approx 15.3 \text{ m}^2$.

    (b) The shaded region is bounded by two pieces: one piece is part of the triangle, the other is part of the circle. The

    first part has length $l = \sqrt{10^2 + 10^2 - 2(10)(10) \cdot \cos 72°} = 10\sqrt{2 - 2 \cdot \cos 72°}$. The second has length

    $s = 10 \cdot 72 \cdot \frac{\pi}{180} = 4\pi$. Thus, the perimeter of the shaded region is $p = l + s = 10\sqrt{2 - 2\cos 72°} + 4\pi \approx 24.3$ m.

16. (a) If θ is the angle opposite the longest side, then by the Law of Cosines $\cos\theta = \frac{9^2+13^2-20^2}{2(9)(20)} = -0.6410$. Therefore,

    $\theta = \cos^{-1}(-0.6410) \approx 129.9°$.

    (b) From part (a), $\theta \approx 129.9°$, so the area of the triangle is $A = \frac{1}{2}(9)(13)\sin 129.9° \approx 44.9 \text{ units}^2$. Another way to find

    the area is to use Heron's Formula: $A = \sqrt{s(s-a)(s-b)(s-c)}$, where $s = \frac{a+b+c}{2} = \frac{9+13+20}{2} = 21$. Thus,

    $A = \sqrt{21(21-20)(21-13)(21-9)} = \sqrt{2016} \approx 44.9 \text{ units}^2$.

17. Label the figure as shown. Now $\angle\beta = 85° - 75° = 10°$, so by the Law of Sines,

$$\frac{x}{\sin 75°} = \frac{100}{\sin 10°} \iff x = 100 \cdot \frac{\sin 75°}{\sin 10°}. \text{ Now } \sin 85° = \frac{h}{x} \iff$$

$$h = x\sin 85° = 100 \cdot \frac{\sin 75°}{\sin 10°}\sin 85° \approx 554.$$

Focus on Modeling: Surveying

1. Let x be the distance between the church and City Hall. To apply the Law of Sines to the triangle with vertices at City Hall, the church, and the first bridge, we first need the measure of the angle at the first bridge, which is $180° - 25° - 30° = 125°$. Then $\dfrac{x}{\sin 125°} = \dfrac{0.86}{\sin 30°} \Leftrightarrow x = \dfrac{0.86 \sin 125°}{\sin 30°} \approx 1.4089$. So the distance between the church and City Hall is about 1.41 miles.

2. To find the distance z between the fire hall and the school, we use the distance found in the text between the bank and the cliff. To find z we first need to find the length of the edges labeled x and y. In the bank-second bridge-cliff triangle, the third angle is

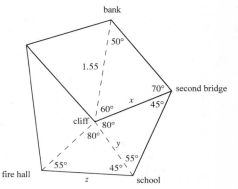

$180° - 50° - 60° = 70°$, so $x = \dfrac{1.55 \sin 50°}{\sin 70°} \approx 1.26$. In the

second bridge-school-cliff triangle, the third angle is

$180° - 80° - 55° = 45°$, so $y = \dfrac{1.26 \sin 45°}{\sin 55°} \approx 1.09$. Finally, in

the school-fire hall-cliff triangle, the third angle is

$180° - 45° - 80° = 55°$, so $z = \dfrac{1.09 \sin 80°}{\sin 55°} \approx 1.31$. Thus, the

fire hall and the school are about 1.31 miles apart.

3. First notice that $\angle DBC = 180° - 20° - 95° - 65°$ and $\angle DAC = 180° - 60° - 45° = 75°$. From $\triangle ACD$ we get $\dfrac{|AC|}{\sin 45°} = \dfrac{20}{\sin 75°} \Leftrightarrow |AC| = \dfrac{20 \sin 45°}{\sin 75°} \approx 14.6°$. From $\triangle BCD$ we get $\dfrac{|BC|}{\sin 95°} = \dfrac{20}{\sin 65°} \Leftrightarrow |BC| = \dfrac{20 \sin 95°}{\sin 65°} \approx 22.0$. By applying the Law of Cosines to $\triangle ABC$ we get $|AB|^2 = |AC|^2 + |BC|^2 - 2|AC||BC| \cos 40° \approx 14.6^2 + 22.0^2 - 2 \cdot 14.6 \cdot 22.0 \cdot \cos 40° \approx 205$, so $|AB| \approx \sqrt{205} \approx 14.3$ m. Therefore, the distance between A and B is approximately 14.3 m.

4. Let h represent the height in meters of the cliff, and d the horizontal distance to the cliff. The third horizontal angle is $180° - 69.4° - 51.6° = 59°$ and so $d = \dfrac{200 \sin 51.6°}{\sin 59°} \approx 182.857$. Then $\tan 33.1° = \dfrac{h}{d} \Leftrightarrow h = d \tan 33.1° \approx 182.857 \tan 33.1° \approx 119.2$ m.

5. (a) In $\triangle ABC$, $\angle B = 180° - \beta$, so $\angle C = 180° - \alpha - (180° - \beta) = \beta - \alpha$. By the Law of Sines, $\dfrac{|BC|}{\sin \alpha} = \dfrac{|AB|}{\sin (\beta - \alpha)}$

$\Rightarrow |BC| = |AB| \dfrac{\sin \alpha}{\sin (\beta - \alpha)} = \dfrac{d \sin \alpha}{\sin (\beta - \alpha)}$.

(b) From part (a) we know that $|BC| = \dfrac{d \sin \alpha}{\sin (\beta - \alpha)}$. But $\sin \beta = \dfrac{h}{|BC|} \Leftrightarrow |BC| = \dfrac{h}{\sin \beta}$. Therefore,

$|BC| = \dfrac{d \sin \alpha}{\sin (\beta - \alpha)} = \dfrac{h}{\sin \beta} \Rightarrow h = \dfrac{d \sin \alpha \sin \beta}{\sin (\beta - \alpha)}$.

(c) $h = \dfrac{d \sin \alpha \sin \beta}{\sin (\beta - \alpha)} = \dfrac{800 \sin 25° \sin 29°}{\sin 4°} \approx 2350$ ft

6. Let the surveyor be at point A, the first landmark (with angle of depression $42°$) be at point B, and the other landmark be at point C. We want to find $|BC|$. Now $\sin 42° = \dfrac{2430}{|AB|} \Leftrightarrow |AB| = \dfrac{2430}{\sin 42°} \approx 3631.6$. Similarly, $\sin 39° = \dfrac{2430}{|AC|}$

$\Leftrightarrow |AC| = \dfrac{2430}{\sin 39°} \approx 3861.3$. Therefore, by the Law of Cosines, $|BC|^2 = |AB|^2 + |AC|^2 - 2|AB||AC| \cos 68° \Rightarrow$

$BC = \sqrt{3631.6^2 + 3861.3^2 - 2(3631.6)(3861.3) \cos 68°} \approx 4194$. Thus, the two landmarks are approximately 4194 ft apart.

7. We start by labeling the edges and calculating the remaining angles, as shown in the first figure. Using the Law of Sines, we find the following: $\dfrac{a}{\sin 29°} = \dfrac{150}{\sin 60°} \Leftrightarrow a = \dfrac{150 \sin 29°}{\sin 60°} \approx 83.97$, $\dfrac{b}{\sin 91°} = \dfrac{150}{\sin 60°} \Leftrightarrow b = \dfrac{150 \sin 91°}{\sin 60°} \approx 173.18$,

$\dfrac{c}{\sin 32°} = \dfrac{173.18}{\sin 87°} \Leftrightarrow c = \dfrac{173.18 \sin 32°}{\sin 87°} \approx 91.90$, $\dfrac{d}{\sin 61°} = \dfrac{173.18}{\sin 87°} \Leftrightarrow e = \dfrac{173.18 \sin 61°}{\sin 87°} \approx 151.67$,

$\dfrac{e}{\sin 41°} = \dfrac{151.67}{\sin 51°} \Leftrightarrow e = \dfrac{151.67 \sin 41°}{\sin 51°} \approx 128.04$, $\dfrac{f}{\sin 88°} = \dfrac{151.67}{\sin 51°} \Leftrightarrow f = \dfrac{151.67 \sin 88°}{\sin 51°} \approx 195.04$,

$\dfrac{g}{\sin 50°} = \dfrac{195.04}{\sin 92°} \Leftrightarrow g = \dfrac{195.04 \sin 50°}{\sin 92°} \approx 149.50$, and $\dfrac{h}{\sin 38°} = \dfrac{195.04}{\sin 92°} \Leftrightarrow h = \dfrac{195.04 \sin 38°}{\sin 92°} \approx 120.15$. Note that we used two decimal places throughout our calculations. Our results are shown (to one decimal place) in the second figure.

8. Answers will vary. Mount Everest was measured to be exactly 29,000 ft high, but the surveyors published the height as 29,002 ft to make it clear that they considered their measurement accurate to within a foot. The accepted figure today is 29,028 ft.

7 Analytic Trigonometry

7.1 Trigonometric Functions

1. $\cos t \tan t = \cos t \cdot \dfrac{\sin t}{\cos t} = \sin t$

2. $\cos t \csc t = \cos t \cdot \dfrac{1}{\sin t} = \cot t$

3. $\sin \theta \sec \theta = \sin \theta \cdot \dfrac{1}{\cos \theta} = \tan t$

4. $\tan \theta \csc \theta = \dfrac{\sin \theta}{\cos \theta} \cdot \dfrac{1}{\sin \theta} = \dfrac{1}{\cos \theta} = \sec \theta$

5. $\tan^2 x - \sec^2 x = \dfrac{\sin^2 x}{\cos^2 x} - \dfrac{1}{\cos^2 x} = \dfrac{\sin^2 x - 1}{\cos^2 x} = \dfrac{-\cos^2 x}{\cos^2 x} = -1$

6. $\dfrac{\sec x}{\csc x} = \dfrac{\dfrac{1}{\cos x}}{\dfrac{1}{\sin x}} = \dfrac{\sin x}{\cos x} = \tan x$

7. $\sin u + \cot u \cos u = \sin u + \dfrac{\cos u}{\sin u} \cdot \cos u = \dfrac{\sin^2 u + \cos^2 u}{\sin u} = \dfrac{1}{\sin u} = \csc u$

8. $\cos^2 \theta \left(1 + \tan^2 \theta\right) = \cos^2 \theta \left(1 + \dfrac{\sin^2 \theta}{\cos^2 \theta}\right) = \cos^2 \theta + \sin^2 \theta = 1$

9. $\dfrac{\sec \theta - \cos \theta}{\sin \theta} = \dfrac{\dfrac{1}{\cos \theta} - \cos \theta}{\sin \theta} = \dfrac{1 - \cos^2 \theta}{\sin \theta \cos \theta} = \dfrac{\sin^2 \theta}{\sin \theta \cos \theta} = \dfrac{\sin \theta}{\cos \theta} = \tan \theta$

10. $\dfrac{\cot \theta}{\csc \theta - \sin \theta} = \dfrac{\dfrac{\cos \theta}{\sin \theta}}{\dfrac{1}{\sin \theta} - \sin \theta} = \dfrac{\cos \theta}{1 - \sin^2 \theta} = \dfrac{\cos \theta}{\cos^2 \theta} = \sec \theta$

11. $\dfrac{\sin x \sec x}{\tan x} = \dfrac{\sin x \cdot \dfrac{1}{\cos x}}{\dfrac{\cos x}{\sin x}} = 1$

12. $\cos^3 x + \sin^2 x \cos x = \cos x \left(\cos^2 x + \sin^2 x\right) = \cos x$

13. $\dfrac{1 + \cos y}{1 + \sec y} = \dfrac{1 + \cos y}{1 + \dfrac{1}{\cos y}} = \dfrac{1 + \cos y}{\dfrac{\cos y + 1}{\cos y}} = \dfrac{1 + \cos y}{1} \cdot \dfrac{\cos y}{\cos y + 1} = \cos y$

14. $\dfrac{\tan x}{\sec (-x)} = \dfrac{\tan x}{\sec x} = \dfrac{\sin x}{\cos x} \cdot \cos x = \sin x$

15. $\dfrac{\sec^2 x - 1}{\sec^2 x} = \dfrac{\tan^2 x}{\sec^2 x} = \dfrac{\sin^2 x}{\cos^2 x} \cdot \cos^2 x = \sin^2 x.$ *Another method:* $\dfrac{\sec^2 x - 1}{\sec^2 x} = 1 - \dfrac{1}{\sec^2 x} = 1 - \cos^2 x = \sin^2 x$

16. $\dfrac{\sec x - \cos x}{\tan x} = \dfrac{\dfrac{1}{\cos x} - \dfrac{\cos^2 x}{\cos x}}{\dfrac{\sin x}{\cos x}} = \dfrac{1 - \cos^2 x}{\sin x} = \dfrac{\sin^2 x}{\sin x} = \sin x$

17. $\dfrac{1 + \csc x}{\cos x + \cot x} = \dfrac{1 + \dfrac{1}{\sin x}}{\cos x + \dfrac{\cos x}{\sin x}} = \dfrac{1 + \dfrac{1}{\sin x}}{\cos x + \dfrac{\cos x}{\sin x}} \cdot \dfrac{\sin x}{\sin x} = \dfrac{\sin x + 1}{\cos x (\sin x + 1)} = \dfrac{1}{\cos x} = \sec x$

18. $\dfrac{\sin x}{\csc x} + \dfrac{\cos x}{\sec x} = \sin x \sin x + \cos x \cos x = \sin^2 x + \cos^2 x = 1$

19. $\dfrac{1 + \sin u}{\cos u} + \dfrac{\cos u}{1 + \sin u} = \dfrac{(1 + \sin u)^2 + \cos^2 u}{\cos u \,(1 + \sin u)} = \dfrac{1 + 2\sin u + \sin^2 u + \cos^2 u}{\cos u \,(1 + \sin u)} = \dfrac{1 + 2\sin u + 1}{\cos u \,(1 + \sin u)}$

$$= \dfrac{2 + 2\sin u}{\cos u \,(1 + \sin u)} = \dfrac{2\,(1 + \sin u)}{\cos u \,(1 + \sin u)} = \dfrac{2}{\cos u} = 2\sec u$$

20. $\tan x \cos x \csc x = \dfrac{\sin x}{\cos x} \cdot \cos x \cdot \dfrac{1}{\sin x} = 1$

21. $\dfrac{2 + \tan^2 x}{\sec^2 x} - 1 = \dfrac{1 + 1 + \tan^2 x}{\sec^2 x} - 1 = \dfrac{1}{\sec^2 x} + \dfrac{1 + \tan^2 x}{\sec^2 x} - 1 = \dfrac{1}{\sec^2 x} + \dfrac{\sec^2 x}{\sec^2 x} - 1$

$$= \dfrac{1}{\sec^2 x} + 1 - 1 = \dfrac{1}{\sec^2 x} = \cos^2 x$$

22. $\dfrac{1 + \cot A}{\csc A} = (1 + \cot A)\sin A = \sin A + \sin A \cot A = \sin A + \sin A \dfrac{\cos A}{\sin A} = \sin A + \cos A$

23. $\tan \theta + \cos(-\theta) + \tan(-\theta) = \tan \theta + \cos \theta - \tan \theta = \cos \theta$

24. $\dfrac{\cos x}{\sec x + \tan x} = \dfrac{\cos x}{\dfrac{1}{\cos x} + \dfrac{\sin x}{\cos x}} = \dfrac{\cos^2 x}{1 + \sin x} = \dfrac{1 - \sin^2 x}{1 + \sin x} = \dfrac{(1 + \sin x)(1 - \sin x)}{1 + \sin x} = 1 - \sin x$

25. $\dfrac{\sin \theta}{\tan \theta} = \dfrac{\sin \theta}{\dfrac{\sin \theta}{\cos \theta}} = \sin \theta \cdot \dfrac{\cos \theta}{\sin \theta} = \cos \theta$

26. $\dfrac{\tan x}{\sec x} = \dfrac{\sin x}{\cos x} \cdot \cos x = \sin x$

27. $\dfrac{\cos u \sec u}{\tan u} = \cos u \dfrac{1}{\cos u} \cot u = \cot u$

28. $\dfrac{\cot x \sec x}{\csc x} = \dfrac{\cos x}{\sin x} \cdot \dfrac{1}{\cos x} \cdot \sin x = 1$

29. $\dfrac{\tan y}{\csc y} = \dfrac{\sin y}{\cos y} \sin y = \dfrac{\sin^2 y}{\cos y} = \dfrac{1 - \cos^2 y}{\cos y} = \sec y - \cos y$

30. $\dfrac{\cos v}{\sec v \sin v} = \cos v \cdot \dfrac{\cos v}{\sin v} = \dfrac{1 - \sin^2 v}{\sin v} = \csc v - \sin v$

31. $\sin B + \cos B \cot B = \sin B + \cos B \dfrac{\cos B}{\sin B} = \dfrac{\sin^2 B + \cos^2 B}{\sin B} = \dfrac{1}{\sin B} = \csc B$

32. $\cos(-x) - \sin(-x) = \cos x - (-\sin x) = \cos x + \sin x$

33. $\cot(-\alpha)\cos(-\alpha) + \sin(-\alpha) = -\dfrac{\cos \alpha}{\sin \alpha}\cos \alpha - \sin \alpha = \dfrac{-\cos^2 \alpha - \sin^2 \alpha}{\sin \alpha} = \dfrac{-1}{\sin \alpha} = -\csc \alpha$

34. $\csc x\,[\csc x + \sin(-x)] = \csc^2 x - \sin x \csc x = \csc^2 x - 1 = \cot^2 x$

35. $\tan \theta + \cot \theta = \dfrac{\sin \theta}{\cos \theta} + \dfrac{\cos \theta}{\sin \theta} = \dfrac{\sin^2 \theta + \cos^2 \theta}{\cos \theta \sin \theta} = \dfrac{1}{\cos \theta \sin \theta} = \sec \theta \csc \theta$

36. $(\sin x + \cos x)^2 = \sin^2 x + 2\sin x \cos x + \cos^2 x = 1 + 2\sin x \cos x$

37. $(1 - \cos \beta)(1 + \cos \beta) = 1 - \cos^2 \beta = \sin^2 \beta = \dfrac{1}{\csc^2 \beta}$

38. $\dfrac{\cos x}{\sec x} + \dfrac{\sin x}{\csc x} = \cos^2 x + \sin^2 x = 1$

39. $\dfrac{(\sin x + \cos x)^2}{\sin^2 x - \cos^2 x} = \dfrac{(\sin x + \cos x)^2}{(\sin x + \cos x)(\sin x - \cos x)} = \dfrac{\sin x + \cos x}{\sin x - \cos x} = \dfrac{(\sin x + \cos x)(\sin x - \cos x)}{(\sin x - \cos x)(\sin x - \cos x)}$

$$= \dfrac{\sin^2 x - \cos^2 x}{(\sin x - \cos x)^2}$$

40. $(\sin x + \cos x)^4 = \left[(\sin x + \cos x)^2\right]^2 = \left(\sin^2 x + 2\sin x \cos x + \cos^2 x\right)^2 = (1 + 2\sin x \cos x)^2$

41. $\dfrac{\sec t - \cos t}{\sec t} = \dfrac{\dfrac{1}{\cos t} - \cos t}{\dfrac{1}{\cos t}} = \dfrac{\dfrac{1}{\cos t} - \cos t}{\dfrac{1}{\cos t}} \cdot \dfrac{\cos t}{\cos t} = \dfrac{1 - \cos^2 t}{1} = \sin^2 t$

42. $\dfrac{1 - \sin x}{1 + \sin x} = \dfrac{1 - \sin x}{1 + \sin x} \cdot \dfrac{1 - \sin x}{1 - \sin x} = \dfrac{1 - 2\sin x + \sin^2 x}{1 - \sin^2 x} = \dfrac{1 - 2\sin x + \sin^2 x}{\cos^2 x} = \dfrac{1}{\cos^2 x} - \dfrac{2\sin x}{\cos^2 x} + \dfrac{\sin^2 x}{\cos^2 x}$

$$= \sec^2 x - 2\sec x \tan x + \tan^2 x = (\sec x - \tan x)^2$$

43. $\dfrac{1}{1 - \sin^2 y} = \dfrac{1}{\cos^2 y} = \sec^2 y = 1 + \tan^2 y$

44. $\csc x - \sin x = \dfrac{1}{\sin x} - \sin x = \dfrac{1 - \sin^2 x}{\sin x} = \dfrac{\cos^2 x}{\sin x} = \cos x \cot x$

45. $(\cot x - \csc x)(\cos x + 1) = \cot x \cos x + \cot x - \csc x \cos x - \csc x = \dfrac{\cos^2 x}{\sin x} + \dfrac{\cos x}{\sin x} - \dfrac{\cos x}{\sin x} - \dfrac{1}{\sin x}$

$$= \dfrac{\cos^2 x - 1}{\sin x} = \dfrac{-\sin^2 x}{\sin x} = -\sin x$$

46. $\sin^4 \theta - \cos^4 \theta = (\sin^2 \theta)^2 - (\cos^2 \theta)^2 = (\sin^2 \theta - \cos^2 \theta)(\sin^2 \theta + \cos^2 \theta) = \sin^2 \theta - \cos^2 \theta$

47. $(1 - \cos^2 x)(1 + \cot^2 x) = \sin^2 x \left(1 + \dfrac{\cos^2 x}{\sin^2 x}\right) = \sin^2 x + \cos^2 x = 1$

48. $\cos^2 x - \sin^2 x = \cos^2 x - (1 - \cos^2 x) = 2\cos^2 x - 1$

49. $2\cos^2 x - 1 = 2(1 - \sin^2 x) - 1 = 2 - 2\sin^2 x - 1 = 1 - 2\sin^2 x$

50. $\tan y + \cot y = \dfrac{\sin y}{\cos y} + \dfrac{\cos y}{\sin y} = \dfrac{\sin^2 y + \cos^2 y}{\sin y \cos y} = \dfrac{1}{\sin y \cos y} = \sec y \csc y$

51. $\dfrac{1 - \cos \alpha}{\sin \alpha} = \dfrac{1 - \cos \alpha}{\sin \alpha} \cdot \dfrac{1 + \cos \alpha}{1 + \cos \alpha} = \dfrac{1 - \cos^2 \alpha}{\sin \alpha (1 + \cos \alpha)} = \dfrac{\sin^2 \alpha}{\sin \alpha (1 + \cos \alpha)} = \dfrac{\sin \alpha}{1 + \cos \alpha}$

52. $\sin^2 \alpha + \cos^2 \alpha + \tan^2 \alpha = 1 + \tan^2 \alpha = \sec^2 \alpha$

53. $\tan^2 \theta \sin^2 \theta = \tan^2 \theta (1 - \cos^2 \theta) = \tan^2 \theta - \dfrac{\sin^2 \theta}{\cos^2 \theta} \cos^2 \theta = \tan^2 \theta - \sin^2 \theta$

54. $\cot^2 \theta \cos^2 \theta = \cot^2 \theta (1 - \sin^2 \theta) = \cot^2 \theta - \dfrac{\cos^2 \theta}{\sin^2 \theta} \sin^2 \theta = \cot^2 \theta - \cos^2 \theta$

55. $\dfrac{\sin x - 1}{\sin x + 1} = \dfrac{\sin x - 1}{\sin x + 1} \cdot \dfrac{\sin x + 1}{\sin x + 1} = \dfrac{\sin^2 x - 1}{(\sin x + 1)^2} = \dfrac{-\cos^2 x}{(\sin x + 1)^2}$

56. $\dfrac{\sin w}{\sin w + \cos w} = \dfrac{\sin w}{\sin w + \cos w} \cdot \dfrac{\dfrac{1}{\cos w}}{\dfrac{1}{\cos w}} = \dfrac{\tan w}{1 + \tan w}$

57. $\dfrac{(\sin t + \cos t)^2}{\sin t \cos t} = \dfrac{\sin^2 t + 2\sin t \cos t + \cos^2 t}{\sin t \cos t} = \dfrac{\sin^2 t + \cos^2 t}{\sin t \cos t} + \dfrac{2\sin t \cos t}{\sin t \cos t} = \dfrac{1}{\sin t \cos t} + 2 = 2 + \sec t \cos t$

58. $\sec t \csc t (\tan t + \cot t) = \dfrac{1}{\cos t} \dfrac{1}{\sin t} \left(\dfrac{\sin t}{\cos t} + \dfrac{\cos t}{\sin t}\right) = \dfrac{1}{\cos^2 t} + \dfrac{1}{\sin^2 t} = \sec^2 t + \csc^2 t$

59. $\dfrac{1 + \tan^2 u}{1 - \tan^2 u} = \dfrac{1 + \dfrac{\sin^2 u}{\cos^2 u}}{1 - \dfrac{\sin^2 u}{\cos^2 u}} = \dfrac{1 + \dfrac{\sin^2 u}{\cos^2 u}}{1 - \dfrac{\sin^2 u}{\cos^2 u}} \cdot \dfrac{\cos^2 u}{\cos^2 u} = \dfrac{\cos^2 u + \sin^2 u}{\cos^2 u - \sin^2 u} = \dfrac{1}{\cos^2 u - \sin^2 u}$

60. $\dfrac{1 + \sec^2 x}{1 + \tan^2 x} = \dfrac{1 + \sec^2 x}{\sec^2 x} = \dfrac{1}{\sec^2 x} + 1 = \cos^2 x + 1$

61. $\dfrac{\sec x}{\sec x - \tan x} = \dfrac{\sec x}{\sec x - \tan x} \cdot \dfrac{\sec x + \tan x}{\sec x + \tan x} = \dfrac{\sec x (\sec x + \tan x)}{\sec^2 x - \tan^2 x} = \dfrac{\sec x (\sec x + \tan x)}{1}$

$$= \sec x (\sec x + \tan x)$$

62. $\dfrac{\sec x + \csc x}{\tan x + \cot x} = \dfrac{\dfrac{1}{\cos x} + \dfrac{1}{\sin x}}{\dfrac{\sin x}{\cos x} + \dfrac{\cos x}{\sin x}} = \dfrac{\dfrac{1}{\cos x} + \dfrac{1}{\sin x}}{\dfrac{\sin x}{\cos x} + \dfrac{\cos x}{\sin x}} \cdot \dfrac{\sin x \cos x}{\sin x \cos x} = \dfrac{\sin x + \cos x}{\sin^2 x + \cos^2 x} = \sin x + \cos x$

63. $\sec v - \tan v = (\sec v - \tan v) \cdot \dfrac{\sec v + \tan v}{\sec v + \tan v} = \dfrac{\sec^2 v - \tan^2 v}{\sec v + \tan v} = \dfrac{1}{\sec v + \tan v}$

64. $\dfrac{\sin A}{1 - \cos A} - \cot A = \dfrac{\sin A}{1 - \cos A} \cdot \dfrac{1 + \cos A}{1 + \cos A} - \cot A = \dfrac{\sin A (1 + \cos A)}{1 - \cos^2 A} - \cot A = \dfrac{\sin A (1 + \cos A)}{\sin^2 A} - \dfrac{\cos A}{\sin A}$

$\qquad\qquad = \dfrac{1}{\sin A} + \dfrac{\cos A}{\sin A} - \dfrac{\cos A}{\sin A} = \dfrac{1}{\sin A} = \csc A$

65. $\dfrac{\sin x + \cos x}{\sec x + \csc x} = \dfrac{\sin x + \cos x}{\dfrac{1}{\cos x} + \dfrac{1}{\sin x}} = \dfrac{\sin x + \cos x}{\dfrac{\sin x + \cos x}{\cos x \sin x}} = (\sin x + \cos x) \dfrac{\cos x \sin x}{\sin x + \cos x} = \cos x \sin x$

66. $\dfrac{1 - \cos x}{\sin x} + \dfrac{\sin x}{1 - \cos x} = \dfrac{1 - \cos x}{\sin x} \cdot \dfrac{1 - \cos x}{1 - \cos x} + \dfrac{\sin x}{1 - \cos x} \cdot \dfrac{\sin x}{\sin x} = \dfrac{1 - 2\cos x + \cos^2 x + \sin^2 x}{\sin x (1 - \cos x)}$

$\qquad\qquad = \dfrac{2 - 2\cos x}{\sin x (1 - \cos x)} = \dfrac{2(1 - \cos x)}{\sin x (1 - \cos x)} = 2\csc x$

67. $\dfrac{\csc x - \cot x}{\sec x - 1} = \dfrac{\dfrac{1}{\sin x} - \dfrac{\cos x}{\sin x}}{\dfrac{1}{\cos x} - 1} = \dfrac{\dfrac{1}{\sin x} - \dfrac{\cos x}{\sin x}}{\dfrac{1}{\cos x} - 1} \cdot \dfrac{\sin x \cos x}{\sin x \cos x} = \dfrac{\cos x (1 - \cos x)}{\sin x (1 - \cos x)} = \dfrac{\cos x}{\sin x} = \cot x$

68. $\dfrac{\csc^2 x - \cot^2 x}{\sec^2 x} = \dfrac{1}{\sec^2 x} = \cos^2 x$

69. $\tan^2 u - \sin^2 u = \dfrac{\sin^2 u}{\cos^2 u} - \dfrac{\sin^2 u \cos^2 u}{\cos^2 u} = \dfrac{\sin^2 u}{\cos^2 u}\left(1 - \cos^2 u\right) = \tan^2 u \sin^2 u$

70. $\dfrac{\tan v \sin v}{\tan v + \sin v} = \dfrac{\tan v \sin v}{\tan v + \sin v} \cdot \dfrac{\tan v - \sin v}{\tan v - \sin v} = \dfrac{\tan v \sin v (\tan v - \sin v)}{\tan^2 v - \sin^2 v} = \dfrac{\tan v \sin v (\tan v - \sin v)}{\sin^2 v (\sec^2 v - 1)}$

$\qquad\qquad = \dfrac{\tan v \sin v (\tan v - \sin v)}{\tan^2 v \sin^2 v} = \dfrac{\tan v - \sin v}{\tan v \sin v}$

71. $\sec^4 x - \tan^4 x = \left(\sec^2 x - \tan^2 x\right)\left(\sec^2 x + \tan^2 x\right) = 1\left(\sec^2 x + \tan^2 x\right) = \sec^2 x + \tan^2 x$

72. $\dfrac{\cos\theta}{1 - \sin\theta} = \dfrac{\cos\theta}{1 - \sin\theta} \cdot \dfrac{1 + \sin\theta}{1 + \sin\theta} = \dfrac{\cos\theta (1 + \sin\theta)}{1 - \sin^2\theta} = \dfrac{\cos\theta (1 + \sin\theta)}{\cos^2\theta} = \dfrac{1}{\cos\theta} + \dfrac{\sin\theta}{\cos\theta} = \sec\theta + \tan\theta$

73. $\dfrac{\sin\theta - \csc\theta}{\cos\theta - \cot\theta} = \dfrac{\sin\theta - \dfrac{1}{\sin\theta}}{\cos\theta - \dfrac{\cos\theta}{\sin\theta}} = \dfrac{\dfrac{\sin^2\theta - 1}{\sin\theta}}{\dfrac{\cos\theta \sin\theta - \cos\theta}{\sin\theta}} = \dfrac{\cos^2\theta}{\cos\theta (\sin\theta - 1)} = \dfrac{\cos\theta}{\sin\theta - 1}$

74. $\dfrac{1 + \tan x}{1 - \tan x} = \dfrac{1 + \dfrac{\sin x}{\cos x}}{1 - \dfrac{\sin x}{\cos x}} \cdot \dfrac{\cos x}{\cos x} = \dfrac{\cos x + \sin x}{\cos x - \sin x}$

75. $\dfrac{\cos^2 t + \tan^2 t - 1}{\sin^2 t} = \dfrac{-\sin^2 t + \tan^2 t}{\sin^2 t} = -1 + \dfrac{\sin^2 t}{\cos^2 t} \cdot \dfrac{1}{\sin^2 t} = -1 + \sec^2 t = \tan^2 t$

76. $\dfrac{1}{1 - \sin x} - \dfrac{1}{1 + \sin x} = \dfrac{(1 + \sin x) - (1 - \sin x)}{(1 - \sin x)(1 + \sin x)} = \dfrac{2\sin x}{1 - \sin^2 x} = \dfrac{2\sin x}{\cos^2 x} = 2\dfrac{\sin x}{\cos x} \cdot \dfrac{1}{\cos x} = 2\tan x \sec x$

77. $\dfrac{1}{\sec x + \tan x} + \dfrac{1}{\sec x - \tan x} = \dfrac{\sec x - \tan x + \sec x + \tan x}{(\sec x + \tan x)(\sec x - \tan x)} = \dfrac{2\sec x}{\sec^2 x - \tan^2 x} = \dfrac{2\sec x}{1} = 2\sec x$

78. $\dfrac{1 + \sin x}{1 - \sin x} - \dfrac{1 - \sin x}{1 + \sin x} = \dfrac{(1 + \sin x)^2 - (1 - \sin x)^2}{(1 - \sin x)(1 + \sin x)} = \dfrac{1 + 2\sin x + \sin^2 x - 1 + 2\sin x - \sin^2 x}{1 - \sin^2 x}$

$\qquad\qquad = \dfrac{4\sin x}{\cos^2 x} = 4\dfrac{\sin x}{\cos x} \cdot \dfrac{1}{\cos x} = 4\tan x \sec x$

79. $(\tan x + \cot x)^2 = \tan^2 x + 2\tan x \cot x + \cot^2 x = \tan^2 x + 2 + \cot^2 x = \left(\tan^2 x + 1\right) + \left(\cot^2 x + 1\right) = \sec^2 x + \csc^2 x$

80. $\tan^2 x - \cot^2 x = \left(\sec^2 x - 1\right) - \left(\csc^2 x - 1\right) = \sec^2 x - \csc^2 x$

81. $\dfrac{\sec u - 1}{\sec u + 1} = \dfrac{\dfrac{1}{\cos u} - 1}{\dfrac{1}{\cos u} + 1} \cdot \dfrac{\cos u}{\cos u} = \dfrac{1 - \cos u}{1 + \cos u}$

82. $\dfrac{\cot x + 1}{\cot x - 1} = \dfrac{\cot x + 1}{\cot x - 1} \cdot \dfrac{\tan x}{\tan x} = \dfrac{\tan x \cot x + \tan x}{\tan x \cot x - \tan x} = \dfrac{1 + \tan x}{1 - \tan x}$

83. $\dfrac{\sin^3 x + \cos^3 x}{\sin x + \cos x} = \dfrac{\left(\sin x + \cos x\right)\left(\sin^2 x - \sin x \cos x + \cos^2 x\right)}{\sin x + \cos x} = \sin^2 - \sin x \cos x + \cos^2 x = 1 - \sin x \cos x$

84. $\dfrac{\tan v - \cot v}{\tan^2 v - \cot^2 v} = \dfrac{\tan v - \cot v}{\left(\tan v - \cot v\right)\left(\tan v + \cot v\right)} = \dfrac{1}{\tan v + \cot v} = \dfrac{1}{\dfrac{\sin v}{\cos v} + \dfrac{\cos v}{\sin v}} \cdot \dfrac{\sin v \cos v}{\sin v \cos v}$

$$= \dfrac{\sin v \cos v}{\sin^2 v + \cos^2 v} = \sin v \cos v$$

85. $\dfrac{1 + \sin x}{1 - \sin x} = \dfrac{1 + \sin x}{1 - \sin x} \cdot \dfrac{1 + \sin x}{1 + \sin x} = \dfrac{\left(1 + \sin x\right)^2}{1 - \sin^2 x} = \dfrac{\left(1 + \sin x\right)^2}{\cos^2 x} = \left(\dfrac{1 + \sin x}{\cos x}\right)^2 = \left(\tan x + \sec x\right)^2$

86. $\dfrac{\tan x + \tan y}{\cot x + \cot y} = \dfrac{\dfrac{\sin x}{\cos x} + \dfrac{\sin y}{\cos y}}{\dfrac{\cos x}{\sin x} + \dfrac{\cos y}{\sin y}} = \dfrac{\dfrac{\sin x \cos y + \cos x \sin y}{\cos x \cos y}}{\dfrac{\cos x \sin y + \sin x \cos y}{\sin x \sin y}}$

$$= \left(\dfrac{\sin x \cos y + \cos x \sin y}{\cos x \cos y}\right)\left(\dfrac{\sin x \sin y}{\cos x \sin y + \sin x \cos y}\right) = \dfrac{\sin x \sin y}{\cos x \cos y} = \tan x \tan y$$

87. $\left(\tan x + \cot x\right)^4 = \left(\dfrac{\sin x}{\cos x} + \dfrac{\cos x}{\sin x}\right)^4 = \left(\dfrac{\sin^2 x + \cos^2 x}{\sin x \cos x}\right)^4 = \left(\dfrac{1}{\sin x \cos x}\right)^4 = \sec^4 x \csc^4 x$

88. $\left(\sin \alpha - \tan \alpha\right)\left(\cos \alpha - \cot \alpha\right) = \left(\sin \alpha - \dfrac{\sin \alpha}{\cos \alpha}\right)\left(\cos \alpha - \dfrac{\cos \alpha}{\sin \alpha}\right) = \sin \alpha \left(1 - \dfrac{1}{\cos \alpha}\right) \cdot \cos \alpha \left(1 - \dfrac{1}{\sin \alpha}\right)$

$$= \cos \alpha \left(1 - \dfrac{1}{\cos \alpha}\right) \sin \alpha \left(1 - \dfrac{1}{\sin \alpha}\right) = \left(\cos \alpha - 1\right)\left(\sin \alpha - 1\right)$$

89. $x = \sin \theta$; then $\dfrac{x}{\sqrt{1 - x^2}} = \dfrac{\sin \theta}{\sqrt{1 - \sin^2 \theta}} = \dfrac{\sin \theta}{\sqrt{\cos^2 \theta}} = \dfrac{\sin \theta}{\cos \theta} = \tan \theta$ (since $\cos \theta \geq 0$ for $0 \leq \theta \leq \frac{\pi}{2}$).

90. $x = \tan \theta$; then $\sqrt{1 + x^2} = \sqrt{1 + \tan^2 \theta} = \sqrt{1 + \left(\sec^2 \theta - 1\right)} = \sqrt{\sec^2 \theta} = \sec \theta$ (since $\sec \theta \geq 0$ for $0 \leq \theta \leq \frac{\pi}{2}$).

91. $x = \sec \theta$; then $\sqrt{x^2 - 1} = \sqrt{\sec^2 \theta - 1} = \sqrt{\left(\tan^2 \theta + 1\right) - 1} = \sqrt{\tan^2 \theta} = \tan \theta$ (since $\tan \theta \geq 0$ for $0 \leq \theta < \frac{\pi}{2}$)

92. $x = 2 \tan \theta$; then

$$\dfrac{1}{x^2 \sqrt{4 + x^2}} = \dfrac{1}{\left(2 \tan \theta\right)^2 \sqrt{4 + \left(2 \tan \theta\right)^2}} = \dfrac{1}{4 \tan^2 \theta \cdot \sqrt{4 \left(1 + \tan^2 \theta\right)}} = \dfrac{1}{4 \tan^2 \theta \cdot 2\sqrt{\sec^2 \theta}}$$

$$= \dfrac{1}{8 \tan^2 \theta \cdot \sec \theta} = \tfrac{1}{8} \cdot \dfrac{\cos^3 \theta}{\sin^2 \theta} \text{ (since } \sec \theta > 0 \text{ for } 0 \leq \theta < \frac{\pi}{2}\text{).}$$

93. $x = 3 \sin \theta$; then $\sqrt{9 - x^2} = \sqrt{9 - \left(3 \sin \theta\right)^2} = \sqrt{9 - 9 \sin^2 \theta} = \sqrt{9 \left(1 - \sin^2 \theta\right)} = 3\sqrt{\cos^2 \theta} = 3 \cos \theta$ (since $\cos \theta \geq 0$ for $0 \leq \theta < \frac{\pi}{2}$).

94. $x = 5 \sec \theta$; then $\dfrac{\sqrt{x^2 - 25}}{x} = \dfrac{\sqrt{\left(5 \sec \theta\right)^2 - 25}}{5 \sec \theta} = \dfrac{\sqrt{25 \left(\sec^2 \theta - 1\right)}}{5 \sec \theta} = \dfrac{5\sqrt{\tan^2 \theta}}{5 \sec \theta} = \dfrac{\tan \theta}{\sec \theta} = \dfrac{\dfrac{\sin \theta}{\cos \theta}}{\dfrac{1}{\cos \theta}} = \sin \theta$ (since

$\tan \theta > 0$ for $0 \leq \theta < \frac{\pi}{2}$).

95. $f(x) = \cos^2 x - \sin^2 x$, $g(x) = 1 - 2\sin^2 x$. From the graph, $f(x) = g(x)$ this appears to be an identity. *Proof:*

$$f(x) = \cos^2 x - \sin^2 x = \cos^2 x + \sin^2 x - 2\sin^2 x = 1 - 2\sin^2 x = g(x).$$

Since $f(x) = g(x)$ for all x, this is an identity.

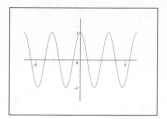

96. $f(x) = \tan x\,(1 + \sin x)$, $g(x) = \dfrac{\sin x \cos x}{1 + \sin x}$. From the graph, $f(x) = g(x)$ does not appear to be an identity. In order to show this, let $x = \frac{\pi}{4}$. Then,

$$f\left(\tfrac{\pi}{4}\right) = (1) \cdot \left[1 + \left(\tfrac{1}{\sqrt{2}}\right)\right] = \tfrac{\sqrt{2}+1}{\sqrt{2}}. \text{ However,}$$

$$g\left(\tfrac{\pi}{4}\right) = \frac{\tfrac{1}{\sqrt{2}} \cdot \tfrac{1}{\sqrt{2}}}{\left[1 + \left(\tfrac{1}{\sqrt{2}}\right)\right]} = \frac{1}{2} \cdot \frac{1}{\tfrac{\sqrt{2}+1}{\sqrt{2}}} = \tfrac{\sqrt{2}}{2}. \text{ Since } f\left(\tfrac{\pi}{4}\right) \neq g\left(\tfrac{\pi}{4}\right), \text{ this is not an}$$

identity.

97. $f(x) = (\sin x + \cos x)^2$, $g(x) = 1$. From the graph, $f(x) = g(x)$ does not appear to be an identity. In order to show this, we can set $x = \frac{\pi}{4}$. Then we have

$$f\left(\tfrac{\pi}{4}\right) = \left(\tfrac{1}{\sqrt{2}} + \tfrac{1}{\sqrt{2}}\right)^2 = \left(\tfrac{2}{\sqrt{2}}\right)^2 = \left(\sqrt{2}\right)^2 = 2 \neq 1 = g\left(\tfrac{\pi}{4}\right). \text{ Since}$$

$f\left(\tfrac{\pi}{4}\right) \neq g\left(\tfrac{\pi}{4}\right)$, this is not an identity.

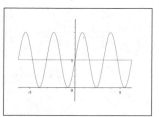

98. $f(x) = \cos^4 x - \sin^4 x$, $g(x) = 2\cos^2 x - 1$. From the graph, $f(x) = g(x)$ appears to be an identity. In order to prove this, simplify the expression $f(x)$:

$$\begin{aligned}
f(x) &= \cos^4 x - \sin^4 x = \left(\cos^2 x - \sin^2 x\right)\left(\cos^2 x + \sin^2 x\right) \\
&= \left(\cos^2 x - \sin^2 x\right)(1) = \left(2\cos^2 x - \cos^2 x\right) - \sin^2 x \\
&= 2\cos^2 x - \left(\cos^2 x + \sin^2 x\right) = 2\cos^2 x - 1 = g(x)
\end{aligned}$$

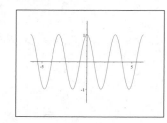

Since $f(x) = g(x)$ for all x, this is an identity.

99. (a) Choose $x = \frac{\pi}{2}$. Then $\sin 2x = \sin \pi = 0$ whereas $2 \sin x = 2 \sin \frac{\pi}{2} = 2$.

(b) Choose $x = \frac{\pi}{4}$ and $y = \frac{\pi}{4}$. Then $\sin(x + y) = \sin \frac{\pi}{2} = 1$ whereas $\sin x + \sin y = \sin \frac{\pi}{4} + \sin \frac{\pi}{4} = \frac{1}{\sqrt{2}} + \frac{1}{\sqrt{2}} = \frac{2}{\sqrt{2}}$. Since these are not equal, the equation is not an identity.

(c) Choose $\theta = \frac{\pi}{4}$. Then $\sec^2 \theta + \csc^2 \theta = \left(\sqrt{2}\right)^2 + \left(\sqrt{2}\right)^2 = 4 \neq 1$.

(d) Choose $x = \frac{\pi}{4}$. Then $\dfrac{1}{\sin x + \cos x} = \dfrac{1}{\sin \frac{\pi}{4} + \cos \frac{\pi}{4}} = \dfrac{1}{\frac{1}{\sqrt{2}} + \frac{1}{\sqrt{2}}} = \frac{1}{\sqrt{2}}$ whereas

$\csc x + \sec x = \csc \frac{\pi}{4} + \sec \frac{\pi}{4} = \sqrt{2} + \sqrt{2}$. Since these are not equal, the equation is not an identity.

100. Label a the side opposite v, b the side opposite u, and c the hypotenuse. Since $u + v + \frac{\pi}{2} = \pi$, we must have

$u + v = \frac{\pi}{2} \Leftrightarrow v = \frac{\pi}{2} - u$. Next we express all six trigonometric function for each angle: $\cos u = \frac{a}{c} = \sin v$

$\Rightarrow \cos u = \sin\left(\frac{\pi}{2} - u\right)$, $\sin u = \frac{b}{c} = \cos v \Rightarrow \sin u = \cos\left(\frac{\pi}{2} - u\right)$, $\tan u = \frac{b}{a} = \cot v \Rightarrow \tan u = \cot\left(\frac{\pi}{2} - u\right)$,

$\cot u = \frac{a}{b} = \tan v \Rightarrow \cot u = \tan\left(\frac{\pi}{2} - u\right)$, $\sec u = \frac{c}{a} = \csc v \Rightarrow \sec u = \csc\left(\frac{\pi}{2} - u\right)$, and $\csc u = \frac{c}{b} = \sec v \Rightarrow$

$\csc u = \sec\left(\frac{\pi}{2} - u\right)$.

101. No. All this proves is that $f(x) = g(x)$ for x in the range of the viewing rectangle. It does not prove that these functions

are equal for all values of x. For example, let $f(x) = 1 - \dfrac{x^2}{2} + \dfrac{x^4}{24} - \dfrac{x^6}{720}$ and $g(x) = \cos x$. In the first viewing rectangle

the graphs of these two functions appear identical. However, when the domain is expanded in the second viewing rectangle,

you can see that these two functions are not identical.

 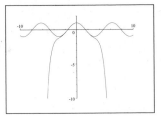

102. Answers will vary.

7.2 Addition and Subtraction Formulas

1. $\sin 75° = \sin(45° + 30°) = \sin 45° \cos 30° + \cos 45° \sin 30° = \dfrac{\sqrt{2}}{2} \cdot \dfrac{\sqrt{3}}{2} + \dfrac{\sqrt{2}}{2} \cdot \dfrac{1}{2} = \dfrac{\sqrt{6}+\sqrt{2}}{4}$

2. $\sin 15° = \sin(45° - 30°) = \sin 45° \cos 30° - \cos 45° \sin 30° = \dfrac{\sqrt{2}}{2} \cdot \dfrac{\sqrt{3}}{2} - \dfrac{\sqrt{2}}{2} \cdot \dfrac{1}{2} = \dfrac{\sqrt{6}-\sqrt{2}}{4}$

3. $\cos 105° = \cos(60° + 45°) = \cos 60° \cos 45° - \sin 60° \sin 45° = \dfrac{1}{2} \cdot \dfrac{\sqrt{2}}{2} - \dfrac{\sqrt{3}}{2} \cdot \dfrac{\sqrt{2}}{2} = \dfrac{\sqrt{2}-\sqrt{6}}{4}$

4. $\cos 195° = -\cos 15° = -\cos(45° - 30°) = -(\cos 45° \cos 30° + \sin 45° \sin 30°) = -\left(\dfrac{\sqrt{2}}{2} \cdot \dfrac{\sqrt{3}}{2} + \dfrac{\sqrt{2}}{2} \cdot \dfrac{1}{2} \right)$

  $= -\dfrac{\sqrt{6}+\sqrt{2}}{4}$

5. $\tan 15° = \tan(45° - 30°) = \dfrac{\tan 45° - \tan 30°}{1 + \tan 45° \tan 30°} = \dfrac{1 - \frac{\sqrt{3}}{3}}{1 + 1 \cdot \frac{\sqrt{3}}{3}} = \dfrac{3 - \sqrt{3}}{3 + \sqrt{3}} = 2 - \sqrt{3}$

6. $\tan 165° = -\tan 15° = -\tan(45° - 30°) = -\dfrac{\tan 45° - \tan 30°}{1 + \tan 45° \tan 30°} = \dfrac{\frac{\sqrt{3}}{3} - 1}{1 + 1 \cdot \frac{\sqrt{3}}{3}} = \dfrac{\sqrt{3} - 3}{3 + \sqrt{3}} = \sqrt{3} - 2$

7. $\sin \dfrac{19\pi}{12} = -\sin \dfrac{7\pi}{12} = -\sin\left(\dfrac{\pi}{4} + \dfrac{\pi}{3} \right) = -\sin \dfrac{\pi}{4} \cos \dfrac{\pi}{3} + \cos \dfrac{\pi}{4} \sin \dfrac{\pi}{3} = -\dfrac{\sqrt{2}}{2} \cdot \dfrac{1}{2} + \dfrac{\sqrt{2}}{2} \cdot \dfrac{\sqrt{3}}{2} = \dfrac{\sqrt{6}-\sqrt{2}}{4}$

8. $\cos \dfrac{17\pi}{12} = -\cos \dfrac{5\pi}{12} = -\sin\left(\dfrac{\pi}{4} + \dfrac{\pi}{6} \right) = -\sin \dfrac{\pi}{4} \cos \dfrac{\pi}{6} + \cos \dfrac{\pi}{4} \sin \dfrac{\pi}{6} = -\dfrac{\sqrt{2}}{2} \cdot \dfrac{\sqrt{3}}{2} + \dfrac{\sqrt{2}}{2} \cdot \dfrac{1}{2} = \dfrac{\sqrt{2}-\sqrt{6}}{4}$

9. $\tan\left(-\dfrac{\pi}{12} \right) = -\tan \dfrac{\pi}{12} = -\tan\left(\dfrac{\pi}{3} - \dfrac{\pi}{4} \right) = -\dfrac{\tan \frac{\pi}{3} - \tan \frac{\pi}{4}}{1 + \tan \frac{\pi}{3} \tan \frac{\pi}{4}} = \dfrac{1 - \sqrt{3}}{1 + \sqrt{3}} = \sqrt{3} - 2$

10. $\sin\left(-\dfrac{5\pi}{12} \right) = -\sin \dfrac{5\pi}{12} = -\sin\left(\dfrac{\pi}{4} + \dfrac{\pi}{6} \right) = \sin \dfrac{\pi}{4} \cos \dfrac{\pi}{6} + \cos \dfrac{\pi}{4} \sin \dfrac{\pi}{6} = \dfrac{\sqrt{2}}{2} \cdot \dfrac{\sqrt{3}}{2} + \dfrac{\sqrt{2}}{2} \cdot \dfrac{1}{2} = \dfrac{\sqrt{6}+\sqrt{2}}{4}$

11. $\cos \dfrac{11\pi}{12} = -\cos \dfrac{\pi}{12} = -\cos\left(\dfrac{\pi}{3} - \dfrac{\pi}{4} \right) = -\cos \dfrac{\pi}{3} \cos \dfrac{\pi}{4} - \sin \dfrac{\pi}{3} \sin \dfrac{\pi}{4} = -\dfrac{\sqrt{3}}{2} \cdot \dfrac{\sqrt{2}}{2} - \dfrac{1}{2} \cdot \dfrac{\sqrt{2}}{2} = -\dfrac{\sqrt{6}+\sqrt{2}}{4}$

12. $\tan \dfrac{7\pi}{12} = -\tan \dfrac{5\pi}{12} = -\tan\left(\dfrac{\pi}{4} + \dfrac{\pi}{6} \right) = -\dfrac{\tan \frac{\pi}{4} + \tan \frac{\pi}{6}}{1 - \tan \frac{\pi}{4} \tan \frac{\pi}{6}} = \dfrac{1 + \frac{\sqrt{3}}{3}}{1 - 1 \cdot \frac{\sqrt{3}}{3}} = \dfrac{3 + \sqrt{3}}{3 - \sqrt{3}} = 2 + \sqrt{3}$

13. $\sin 18° \cos 27° + \cos 18° \sin 27° = \sin(18° + 27°) = \sin 45° = \dfrac{1}{\sqrt{2}} = \dfrac{\sqrt{2}}{2}$

14. $\cos 10° \cos 80° - \sin 10° \sin 80° = \cos(10° + 80°) = \cos 90° = 0$

15. $\cos \dfrac{3\pi}{7} \cos \dfrac{2\pi}{21} + \sin \dfrac{3\pi}{7} \sin \dfrac{2\pi}{21} = \cos\left(\dfrac{3\pi}{7} - \dfrac{2\pi}{21} \right) = \cos \dfrac{9\pi}{21} = \cos \dfrac{\pi}{3} = \dfrac{1}{2}$

16. $\dfrac{\tan \frac{\pi}{18} + \tan \frac{\pi}{9}}{1 - \tan \frac{\pi}{18} \tan \frac{\pi}{9}} = \tan\left(\dfrac{\pi}{18} + \dfrac{\pi}{9} \right) = \tan \dfrac{3\pi}{18} = \tan \dfrac{\pi}{6} = \dfrac{\sqrt{3}}{3}$

17. $\dfrac{\tan 73° - \tan 13°}{1 + \tan 73° \tan 13°} = \tan(73° - 13°) = \tan 60° = \sqrt{3}$

18. $\cos \dfrac{13\pi}{15} \cos\left(-\dfrac{\pi}{5} \right) - \sin \dfrac{13\pi}{15} \sin\left(-\dfrac{\pi}{5} \right) = \cos\left(\dfrac{13\pi}{15} + \left(-\dfrac{\pi}{5} \right) \right) = \cos \dfrac{10\pi}{15} = \cos \dfrac{2\pi}{3} = -\dfrac{1}{2}$

19. $\tan\left(\frac{\pi}{2} - u\right) = \dfrac{\sin\left(\frac{\pi}{2} - u\right)}{\cos\left(\frac{\pi}{2} - u\right)} = \dfrac{\sin\frac{\pi}{2}\cos u - \cos\frac{\pi}{2}\sin u}{\cos\frac{\pi}{2}\cos u + \sin\frac{\pi}{2}\sin u} = \dfrac{1\cdot\cos u - 0\cdot\sin u}{0\cdot\cos u + 1\cdot\sin u} = \dfrac{\cos u}{\sin u} = \cot u$

20. $\cot\left(\frac{\pi}{2} - u\right) = \dfrac{\cos\left(\frac{\pi}{2} - u\right)}{\sin\left(\frac{\pi}{2} - u\right)} = \dfrac{\cos\frac{\pi}{2}\cos u + \sin\frac{\pi}{2}\sin u}{\sin\frac{\pi}{2}\cos u - \cos\frac{\pi}{2}\sin u} = \dfrac{0\cdot\cos u + 1\cdot\sin u}{1\cdot\cos u - 0\cdot\sin u} = \dfrac{\sin u}{\cos u} = \tan u$

21. $\sec\left(\frac{\pi}{2} - u\right) = \dfrac{1}{\cos\left(\frac{\pi}{2} - u\right)} = \dfrac{1}{\cos\frac{\pi}{2}\cos u + \sin\frac{\pi}{2}\sin u} = \dfrac{1}{0\cdot\cos u + 1\cdot\sin u} = \dfrac{1}{\sin u} = \csc u$

22. $\csc\left(\frac{\pi}{2} - u\right) = \dfrac{1}{\sin\left(\frac{\pi}{2} - u\right)} = \dfrac{1}{\sin\frac{\pi}{2}\cos u - \cos\frac{\pi}{2}\sin u} = \dfrac{1}{1\cdot\cos u - 0\cdot\sin u} = \dfrac{1}{\cos u} = \sec u$

23. $\sin\left(x - \frac{\pi}{2}\right) = \sin x\cos\frac{\pi}{2} - \cos x\sin\frac{\pi}{2} = 0\cdot\sin x - 1\cdot\cos x = -\cos x$

24. $\cos\left(x - \frac{\pi}{2}\right) = \cos x\cos\frac{\pi}{2} + \sin x\sin\frac{\pi}{2} = 0\cdot\cos x + 1\cdot\sin x = \sin x$

25. $\sin(x - \pi) = \sin x\cos\pi - \cos x\sin\pi = -1\cdot\sin x - 0\cdot\cos x = -\sin x$

26. $\cos(x - \pi) = \cos x\cos\pi + \sin x\sin\pi = -1\cdot\cos x + 0\cdot\sin x = -\cos x$

27. $\tan(x - \pi) = \dfrac{\tan x - \tan\pi}{1 + \tan x\tan\pi} = \dfrac{\tan x - 0}{1 + \tan x\cdot 0} = \tan x$

28. $\text{LHS} = \sin\left(\frac{\pi}{2} - x\right) = \sin\frac{\pi}{2}\cos x - \cos\frac{\pi}{2}\sin x = 1\cdot\cos x - 0\cdot\sin x = \cos x$ and

$\text{RHS} = \sin\left(\frac{\pi}{2} + x\right) = \sin\frac{\pi}{2}\cos x + \cos\frac{\pi}{2}\sin x = 1\cdot\cos x + 0\cdot\sin x = \cos x$. Therefore, LHS = RHS.

29. $\cos\left(x + \frac{\pi}{6}\right) + \sin\left(x - \frac{\pi}{3}\right) = \cos x\cos\frac{\pi}{6} - \sin x\sin\frac{\pi}{6} + \sin x\cos\frac{\pi}{3} - \cos x\sin\frac{\pi}{3}$

30. $\tan\left(x - \frac{\pi}{4}\right) = \dfrac{\tan x - \tan\frac{\pi}{4}}{1 + \tan x\tan\frac{\pi}{4}} = \dfrac{\tan x - 1}{1 + \tan x\cdot 1} = \dfrac{\tan x - 1}{\tan x + 1}$

31. $\sin(x + y) - \sin(x - y) = \sin x\cos y + \cos x\sin y - (\sin x\cos y - \cos x\sin y) = 2\cos x\sin y$

32. $\cos(x + y) + \cos(x - y) = \cos x\cos y - \sin x\sin y + \cos x\cos y + \sin x\sin y = 2\cos x\cos y$

33. $\cot(x - y) = \dfrac{1}{\tan(x - y)} = \dfrac{1 + \tan x\tan y}{\tan x - \tan y} = \dfrac{1 + \dfrac{1}{\cot x}\dfrac{1}{\cot y}}{\dfrac{1}{\cot x} - \dfrac{1}{\cot y}}\cdot\dfrac{\cot x\cot y}{\cot x\cot y} = \dfrac{\cot x\cot y + 1}{\cot y - \cot x}$

34. $\cot(x + y) = \dfrac{1}{\tan(x + y)} = \dfrac{1 - \tan x\tan y}{\tan x + \tan y} = \dfrac{1 - \dfrac{1}{\cot x}\dfrac{1}{\cot y}}{\dfrac{1}{\cot x} + \dfrac{1}{\cot y}}\cdot\dfrac{\cot x\cot y}{\cot x\cot y} = \dfrac{\cot x\cot y - 1}{\cot x + \cot y}$

35. $\tan x - \tan y = \dfrac{\sin x}{\cos x} - \dfrac{\sin y}{\cos y} = \dfrac{\sin x\cos y - \cos x\sin y}{\cos x\cos y} = \dfrac{\sin(x - y)}{\cos x\cos y}$

36. $1 - \tan x\tan y = 1 - \dfrac{\sin x\sin y}{\cos x\cos y} = \dfrac{\cos x\cos y - \sin x\sin y}{\cos x\cos y} = \dfrac{\cos(x + y)}{\cos x\cos y}$

37. $\dfrac{\sin(x + y) - \sin(x - y)}{\cos(x + y) + \cos(x - y)} = \dfrac{\sin x\cos y + \cos x\sin y - (\sin x\cos y - \cos x\sin y)}{\cos x\cos y - \sin x\sin y + \cos x\cos y + \sin x\sin y} = \dfrac{2\cos x\sin y}{2\cos x\cos y} = \tan y$

38. $\cos(x + y)\cos(x - y) = (\cos x\cos y - \sin x\sin y)(\cos x\cos y + \sin x\sin y) = \cos^2 x\cos^2 y - \sin^2 x\sin^2 y$

$= \cos^2 x\left(1 - \sin^2 y\right) - \left(1 - \cos^2 x\right)\sin^2 y = \cos^2 x - \sin^2 y\cos^2 x + \sin^2 y\cos^2 x - \sin^2 y$

$= \cos^2 x - \sin^2 y$

39. $\sin(x + y + z) = \sin((x + y) + z) = \sin(x + y)\cos z + \cos(x + y)\sin z$

$= \cos z(\sin x\cos y + \cos x\sin y) + \sin z(\cos x\cos y - \sin x\sin y)$

$= \sin x\cos y\cos z + \cos x\sin y\cos z + \cos x\cos y\sin z - \sin x\sin y\sin z$

40. The addition formula for the tangent function can be written as $\tan A + \tan B = \tan(A + B)(1 - \tan A \tan B)$. Also note that $\tan(-A) = -\tan A$. Using these facts, we get

$$
\begin{aligned}
\tan(x - y) + \tan(y - z) + \tan(z - x) &= \tan(x - y + y - z)\left[1 - \tan(x - y)\tan(y - z)\right] + \tan(z - x) \\
&= \tan(x - z)\left[1 - \tan(x - y)\tan(y - z)\right] + \tan(z - x) \\
&= \tan(x - z) + \tan(z - x) - \tan(x - y)\tan(y - z)\tan(x - z) \\
&= \tan(x - z) - \tan(x - z) - \tan(x - y)\tan(y - z)\tan(x - z) \\
&= 0 - \tan(x - y)\tan(y - z)\tan(x - z) \\
&= \tan(x - y)\tan(y - z)\tan(z - x)
\end{aligned}
$$

41. $k = \sqrt{A^2 + B^2} = \sqrt{\left(-\sqrt{3}\right)^2 + 1^2} = \sqrt{4} = 2$. $\sin\phi = \frac{1}{2}$ and $\cos\phi = \dfrac{-\sqrt{3}}{2} \Rightarrow \phi = \frac{5\pi}{6}$. Therefore, $-\sqrt{3}$ $\sin x + \cos x = k\sin(x + \phi) = 2\sin\left(x + \frac{5\pi}{6}\right)$.

42. $k = \sqrt{A^2 + B^2} = \sqrt{1^2 + 1^2} = \sqrt{2}$ and ϕ satisfies $\sin\phi = \frac{1}{\sqrt{2}}$, $\cos\phi = \frac{1}{\sqrt{2}} \Leftrightarrow \phi = \frac{\pi}{4}$. Thus, $\sin x + \cos x = k\sin(x + \phi) = \sqrt{2}\sin\left(x + \frac{\pi}{4}\right) = \frac{\sqrt{3}}{2}\cos x - \frac{1}{2}\sin x + \frac{1}{2}\sin x - \frac{\sqrt{3}}{2}\cos x = 0$

43. $k = \sqrt{A^2 + B^2} = \sqrt{5^2 + (-5)^2} = \sqrt{50} = 5\sqrt{2}$. $\sin\phi = -\frac{5}{5\sqrt{2}} = -\frac{1}{\sqrt{2}}$ and $\cos\phi = \frac{5}{5\sqrt{2}} = \frac{1}{\sqrt{2}} \Rightarrow \phi = \frac{7\pi}{4}$. Therefore, $5(\sin 2x - \cos 2x) = k\sin(2x + \phi) = 5\sqrt{2}\sin\left(2x + \frac{7\pi}{4}\right)$.

44. $k = \sqrt{A^2 + B^2} = \sqrt{3^2 + \left(3\sqrt{3}\right)^2} = \sqrt{36} = 6$ and ϕ satisfies $\sin\phi = \frac{3\sqrt{3}}{6} = \frac{\sqrt{3}}{2}$, $\cos\phi = \frac{3}{6} = \frac{1}{2} \Leftrightarrow \phi = \frac{\pi}{3}$. Thus, $3\sin\pi x + 3\sqrt{3}\cos\pi x = k\sin(\pi x + \phi) = 6\sin\left(\pi x + \frac{\pi}{3}\right) = 6\sin\pi\left(x + \frac{1}{3}\right)$.

45. (a) $f(x) = \sin x + \cos x \Rightarrow k = \sqrt{1^2 + 1^2} = \sqrt{2}$, and ϕ satisfies $\sin\phi = \cos\phi = \frac{1}{\sqrt{2}} \Rightarrow \phi = \frac{\pi}{4}$.

Thus, we can write

$f(x) = k\sin(x + \phi) = \sqrt{2}\sin\left(x + \frac{\pi}{4}\right)$.

(b) This is a sine curve with amplitude $\sqrt{2}$, period 2π, and phase shift $-\frac{\pi}{4}$.

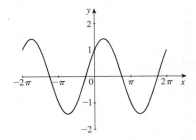

46. (a) $g(x) = \cos 2x + \sqrt{3}\sin 2x \Rightarrow$

$k = \sqrt{1^2 + \left(\sqrt{3}\right)^2} = \sqrt{4} = 2$, and ϕ satisfies

$\sin\phi = \frac{1}{2}$, $\cos\phi = \frac{\sqrt{3}}{2} \Rightarrow \phi = \frac{\pi}{6}$. Thus, we can

write

$g(x) = k\sin(2x + \phi) = 2\sin\left(2x + \frac{\pi}{6}\right) = 2\sin 2\left(x + \frac{\pi}{12}\right)$.

(b) This is a sine curve with amplitude 2, period π, and phase shift $-\frac{\pi}{12}$.

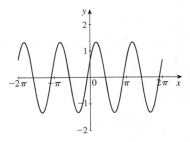

47. If $\beta - \alpha = \frac{\pi}{2}$, then $\beta = \alpha + \frac{\pi}{2}$. Now if we let $y = x + \alpha$, then $\sin(x + \alpha) + \cos\left(x + \alpha + \frac{\pi}{2}\right) = \sin y + \cos\left(y + \frac{\pi}{2}\right) = \sin y + (-\sin y) = 0$. Therefore, $\sin(x + \alpha) + \cos(x + \beta) = 0$.

48. $g(x) = \cos x$. Now

$$\frac{g(x+h) - g(x)}{h} = \frac{\cos(x+h) - \cos x}{h} = \frac{\cos x \cos h - \sin x \sin h - \cos x}{h}$$

$$= \frac{-\cos x(1 - \cos h) - \sin h(\sin x)}{h} = -\cos x\left(\frac{1 - \cos h}{h}\right) - \left(\frac{\sin h}{h}\right)\sin x$$

49. Let $\angle A$ and $\angle B$ be the two angles shown in the diagram. Then

$180° = \gamma + A + B$, $90° = \alpha + A$, and $90° = \beta + B$.

Subtracting the second and third equation from the first, we get

$180° - 90° - 90° = \gamma + A + B - (\alpha + A) - (\beta + B)$ ⟺

$\alpha + \beta = \gamma$. Then

$$\tan\gamma = \tan(\alpha + \beta) = \frac{\tan\alpha + \tan\beta}{1 - \tan\alpha\tan\beta} = \frac{\frac{4}{6} + \frac{3}{4}}{1 - \frac{4}{6}\cdot\frac{3}{4}} = \frac{\frac{8}{12} + \frac{9}{12}}{1 - \frac{1}{2}} = 2\cdot\frac{17}{12} = \frac{17}{6}.$$

50. (a) By definition, $m = \dfrac{\Delta y}{\Delta x}$ and $\tan\theta = \dfrac{\Delta y}{\Delta x}$. Thus, $m = \tan\theta$.

(b) $\tan\psi = \tan(\theta_2 - \theta_1) = \dfrac{\tan\theta_2 - \tan\theta_1}{1 + \tan\theta_2\tan\theta_1}$. From part (a), we have $m_1 = \tan\theta_1$ and $m_2 = \tan\theta_2$. Then by substitution, $\tan\psi = \dfrac{m_2 - m_1}{1 + m_1 m_2}$.

(c) Let ψ be the unknown angle as in part (b). Since $m_1 = \frac{1}{3}$ and $m_2 = -\frac{1}{2}$, $\tan\psi = \dfrac{m_2 - m_1}{1 + m_1 m_2} = \dfrac{-\frac{1}{2} - \frac{1}{3}}{1 + \frac{1}{3}\left(-\frac{1}{2}\right)} = \dfrac{-\frac{5}{6}}{\frac{5}{6}} = -1$

⟺ $\psi = \frac{3\pi}{4}$.

(d) From part (b), we have $\cot\psi = \dfrac{1 + m_1 m_2}{m_2 - m_1}$. If the two lines are perpendicular then $\psi = 90°$ and so $\cot\psi = 0$. Thus we have $0 = \dfrac{1 + m_1 m_2}{m_2 - m_1} \Leftrightarrow 0 = 1 + m_1 m_2 \quad \Leftrightarrow \quad m_1 m_2 = -1 \Leftrightarrow m_2 = -1/m_1$. Thus m_2 is the negative reciprocal of m_1.

51. (a) $y = \sin^2\left(x + \frac{\pi}{4}\right) + \sin^2\left(x - \frac{\pi}{4}\right)$. From the graph we see that the value of y seems to always be equal to 1.

(b) $y = \sin^2\left(x + \frac{\pi}{4}\right) + \sin^2\left(x - \frac{\pi}{4}\right) = \left(\sin x\cos\frac{\pi}{4} + \cos x\sin\frac{\pi}{4}\right)^2 + \left(\sin x\cos\frac{\pi}{4} - \cos x\sin\frac{\pi}{4}\right)^2$

$= \left[\frac{1}{\sqrt{2}}(\sin x + \cos x)\right]^2 + \left[\frac{1}{\sqrt{2}}(\sin x - \cos x)\right]^2 = \frac{1}{2}\left[(\sin x + \cos x)^2 + (\sin x - \cos x)^2\right]$

$= \frac{1}{2}\left[(\sin^2 x + 2\sin x\cos x + \cos^2 x) + (\sin^2 x - 2\sin x\cos x + \cos^2 x)\right]$

$= \frac{1}{2}\left[(1 + 2\sin x\cos x) + (1 - 2\sin x\cos x)\right] = \frac{1}{2}\cdot 2 = 1$

52. (a) $y = -\frac{1}{2}\left[\cos\left(x+\pi\right)+\cos\left(x-\pi\right)\right]$. The graph of y appears to be the same as that of $\cos x$.

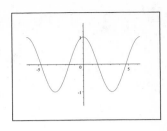

(b) $y = -\frac{1}{2}\left[\cos\left(x+\pi\right)+\cos\left(x-\pi\right)\right]$
$\qquad = -\frac{1}{2}\left[\left(\cos x \cos\pi - \sin x \sin\pi\right)+\left(\cos x \cos\pi + \sin x \sin\pi\right)\right]$
$\qquad = -\frac{1}{2}\left[\left(-\cos x - 0\right)+\left(-\cos x + 0\right)\right] = -\frac{1}{2}\left(-2\cos x\right) = \cos x$

53. Clearly $C = \frac{\pi}{4}$. Now $\tan\left(A+B\right) = \dfrac{\tan A + \tan B}{1 - \tan A \tan B} = \dfrac{\frac{1}{3}+\frac{1}{2}}{1 - \frac{1}{3}\cdot\frac{1}{2}} = 1$. Thus $A + B = \frac{\pi}{4}$, so $A + B + C = \frac{\pi}{4}+\frac{\pi}{4} = \frac{\pi}{2}$.

54. (a) $y = f_1\left(t\right)+f_2\left(t\right) = 5\sin t + 5\cos t = 5\left(\sin t + \cos t\right)$

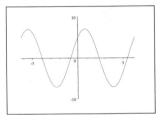

(b) $k = \sqrt{A^2 + B^2} = \sqrt{5^2 + 5^2} = 5\sqrt{2}$.

Therefore, $\sin\phi = \dfrac{B}{\sqrt{A^2+B^2}} = \dfrac{5}{5\sqrt{2}} = \dfrac{1}{\sqrt{2}}$

and $\cos\phi = \dfrac{A}{\sqrt{A^2+B^2}} = \dfrac{1}{\sqrt{2}}$. Thus, $\phi = \frac{\pi}{4}$.

55. (a) $f\left(t\right) = C\sin\omega t + C\sin\left(\omega t + \alpha\right) = C\sin\omega t + C\left(\sin\omega t \cos\alpha + \cos\omega t \sin\alpha\right)$
$\qquad = C\left(1 + \cos\alpha\right)\sin\omega t + C\sin\alpha\cos\omega t = A\sin\omega t + B\cos\omega t$

where $A = C\left(1 + \cos\alpha\right)$ and $B = C\sin\alpha$.

(b) In this case, $f\left(t\right) = 10\left(1 + \cos\frac{\pi}{3}\right)\sin\omega t + 10\sin\frac{\pi}{3}\cos\omega t = 15\sin\omega t + 5\sqrt{3}\cos\omega t$. Thus

$k = \sqrt{15^2 + \left(5\sqrt{3}\right)^2} = 10\sqrt{3}$ and ϕ has $\cos\phi = \frac{15}{10\sqrt{3}} = \frac{\sqrt{3}}{2}$ and $\sin\phi = \frac{5\sqrt{3}}{10\sqrt{3}} = \frac{1}{2}$, so $\phi = \frac{\pi}{6}$. Therefore,

$f\left(t\right) = 10\sqrt{3}\sin\left(\omega t + \frac{\pi}{6}\right)$.

56. $\sin\left(s+t\right) = \cos\left[\frac{\pi}{2} - \left(s+t\right)\right] = \cos\left[\left(\frac{\pi}{2}-s\right)-t\right] = \cos\left(\frac{\pi}{2}-s\right)\cos t + \sin\left(\frac{\pi}{2}-s\right)\sin t = \sin s \cos t + \cos s \sin t$. The last equality comes from again applying the cofunction identities.

57. $\tan\left(s+t\right) = \dfrac{\sin\left(s+t\right)}{\cos\left(s+t\right)} = \dfrac{\sin s \cos t + \cos s \sin t}{\cos s \cos t + \sin s \sin t}$

$\qquad = \dfrac{\sin s \cos t + \cos s \sin t}{\cos s \cos t - \sin s \sin t}\cdot\dfrac{\dfrac{1}{\cos s \cos t}}{\dfrac{1}{\cos s \cos t}} = \dfrac{\dfrac{\sin s}{\cos s}+\dfrac{\sin t}{\cos t}}{1 - \dfrac{\sin s}{\cos s}\cdot\dfrac{\sin t}{\cos t}} = \dfrac{\tan s + \tan t}{1 - \tan s \tan t}$

7.3 Double-Angle, Half-Angle, and Product-Sum Formulas

1. $\sin x = \frac{5}{13}$, x in quadrant I $\Rightarrow \cos x = \frac{12}{13}$ and $\tan x = \frac{5}{12}$. Thus, $\sin 2x = 2\sin x \cos x = 2\left(\frac{5}{13}\right)\left(\frac{12}{13}\right) = \frac{120}{169}$,

$\cos 2x = \cos^2 x - \sin^2 x = \left(\frac{12}{13}\right)^2 - \left(\frac{5}{13}\right)^2 = \frac{144-25}{169} = \frac{119}{169}$, and $\tan 2x = \frac{\sin 2x}{\cos 2x} = \frac{\frac{120}{169}}{\frac{119}{169}} = \frac{120}{169} \cdot \frac{169}{119} = \frac{120}{119}$.

2. $\tan x = -\frac{4}{3}$. Then $\sin x = \frac{4}{5}$ and $\cos x = -\frac{3}{5}$ (x is in quadrant II). Thus, $\sin 2x = 2\sin x \cos x = 2 \cdot \frac{4}{5}\left(-\frac{3}{5}\right) = -\frac{24}{25}$,

$\cos 2x = \cos^2 x - \sin^2 x = \left(-\frac{3}{5}\right)^2 - \left(\frac{4}{5}\right)^2 = \frac{9-16}{25} = -\frac{7}{25}$, and $\tan 2x = \frac{\sin 2x}{\cos 2x} = \frac{-\frac{24}{25}}{-\frac{7}{25}} = \frac{24}{25} \cdot \frac{25}{7} = \frac{24}{7}$.

3. $\cos x = \frac{4}{5}$. Then $\sin x = -\frac{3}{5}$ ($\csc x < 0$) and $\tan x = -\frac{3}{4}$. Thus, $\sin 2x = 2\sin x \cos x = 2\left(-\frac{3}{5}\right) \cdot \frac{4}{5} = -\frac{24}{25}$,

$\cos 2x = \cos^2 x - \sin^2 x = \left(\frac{4}{5}\right)^2 - \left(-\frac{3}{5}\right)^2 = \frac{16-9}{25} = \frac{7}{25}$, and $\tan 2x = \frac{\sin 2x}{\cos 2x} = \frac{-\frac{24}{25}}{\frac{7}{25}} = -\frac{24}{25} \cdot \frac{25}{7} = -\frac{24}{7}$.

4. $\csc x = 4$. Then $\sin x = \frac{1}{4}$, $\cos x = -\frac{\sqrt{15}}{4}$, and $\tan x = -\frac{1}{\sqrt{15}}$ ($\tan x < 0$). Thus,

$\sin 2x = 2\sin x \cos x = 2 \cdot \frac{1}{4}\left(-\frac{\sqrt{15}}{4}\right) = -\frac{\sqrt{15}}{8}$, $\cos 2x = \cos^2 x - \sin^2 x = \left(-\frac{\sqrt{15}}{4}\right)^2 - \left(\frac{1}{4}\right)^2 = \frac{15-1}{16} = \frac{7}{8}$, and

$\tan 2x = \frac{\sin 2x}{\cos 2x} = \frac{-\frac{\sqrt{15}}{8}}{\frac{7}{8}} = -\frac{\sqrt{15}}{8} \cdot \frac{8}{7} = -\frac{\sqrt{15}}{7}$.

5. $\sin x = -\frac{3}{5}$. Then, $\cos x = -\frac{4}{5}$ and $\tan x = \frac{3}{4}$ (x is in quadrant III). Thus, $\sin 2x = 2\sin x \cos x = 2\left(-\frac{3}{5}\right)\left(-\frac{4}{5}\right) = \frac{24}{25}$,

$\cos 2x = \cos^2 x - \sin^2 x = \left(-\frac{4}{5}\right)^2 - \left(-\frac{3}{5}\right)^2 = \frac{16-9}{25} = \frac{7}{25}$, and $\tan 2x = \frac{\sin 2x}{\cos 2x} = \frac{\frac{24}{25}}{\frac{7}{25}} = \frac{24}{25} \cdot \frac{25}{7} = \frac{24}{7}$.

6. $\sec x = 2$. Then $\cos x = \frac{1}{2}$, $\sin x = -\frac{\sqrt{3}}{2}$, and $\tan x = -\sqrt{3}$ (x is in quadrant IV). Thus,

$\sin 2x = 2\sin x \cos x = 2\left(-\frac{\sqrt{3}}{2}\right)\left(\frac{1}{2}\right) = -\frac{\sqrt{3}}{2}$, $\cos 2x = \cos^2 x - \sin^2 x = \left(\frac{1}{2}\right)^2 - \left(-\frac{\sqrt{3}}{2}\right)^2 = -\frac{1}{2}$, and

$\tan 2x = \frac{\sin 2x}{\cos 2x} = \frac{-\frac{\sqrt{3}}{2}}{-\frac{1}{2}} = \sqrt{3}$.

7. $\tan x = -\frac{1}{3}$ and $\cos x > 0$, so $\sin x < 0$. Thus, $\sin x = -\frac{1}{\sqrt{10}}$ and $\cos x = \frac{3}{\sqrt{10}}$. Thus,

$\sin 2x = 2\sin x \cos x = 2\left(-\frac{1}{\sqrt{10}}\right)\left(\frac{3}{\sqrt{10}}\right) = -\frac{6}{10} = -\frac{3}{5}$, $\cos 2x = \cos^2 x - \sin^2 x = \left(\frac{3}{\sqrt{10}}\right)^2 - \left(-\frac{1}{\sqrt{10}}\right)^2 = \frac{8}{10} = \frac{4}{5}$,

and $\tan 2x = \frac{\sin 2x}{\cos 2x} = \frac{-\frac{3}{5}}{\frac{4}{5}} = -\frac{3}{5} \cdot \frac{5}{4} = -\frac{3}{4}$.

8. $\cot x = \frac{2}{3}$. Then $\tan x = \frac{3}{2}$, $\sin x = \frac{3}{\sqrt{13}}$ ($\sin x > 0$), and $\cos x = \frac{2}{\sqrt{13}}$. Thus,

$\sin 2x = 2\sin x \cos x = 2\left(\frac{3}{\sqrt{13}}\right)\left(\frac{2}{\sqrt{13}}\right) = \frac{12}{13}$, $\cos 2x = \cos^2 x - \sin^2 x = \left(\frac{2}{\sqrt{13}}\right)^2 - \left(\frac{3}{\sqrt{13}}\right)^2 = \frac{4-9}{13} = -\frac{5}{13}$, and

$\tan 2x = \frac{\sin 2x}{\cos 2x} = \frac{\frac{12}{13}}{-\frac{5}{13}} = \frac{12}{13} \cdot \left(-\frac{13}{5}\right) = -\frac{12}{5}$.

9. $\sin^4 x = \left(\sin^2 x\right)^2 = \left(\frac{1-\cos 2x}{2}\right)^2 = \frac{1}{4} - \frac{1}{2}\cos 2x + \frac{1}{4}\cos^2 2x$

$= \frac{1}{4} - \frac{1}{2}\cos 2x + \frac{1}{4} \cdot \frac{1+\cos 4x}{2} = \frac{1}{4} - \frac{1}{2}\cos 2x + \frac{1}{8} + \frac{1}{8}\cos 4x = \frac{3}{8} - \frac{1}{2}\cos 2x + \frac{1}{8}\cos 4x$

$= \frac{1}{2}\left(\frac{3}{4} - \cos 2x + \frac{1}{4}\cos 4x\right)$

10. $\cos^4 x = \left(\cos^2 x\right)^2 = \left(\frac{1+\cos 2x}{2}\right)^2 = \frac{1}{4} + \frac{1}{2}\cos 2x + \frac{1}{4}\cos^2 2x$

$= \frac{1}{4} + \frac{1}{2}\cos 2x + \frac{1}{4} \cdot \frac{1+\cos 4x}{2} = \frac{1}{4} + \frac{1}{2}\cos 2x + \frac{1}{8} + \frac{1}{8}\cos 4x = \frac{3}{8} + \frac{1}{2}\cos 2x + \frac{1}{8}\cos 4x$

$= \frac{1}{2}\left(\frac{3}{4} + \cos 2x + \frac{1}{4}\cos 4x\right)$

11. We use the result of Example 4 to get $\cos^2 x \sin^4 x = \left(\sin^2 x \cos^2 x\right)\sin^2 x = \left(\frac{1}{8} - \frac{1}{8}\cos 4x\right) \cdot \left(\frac{1}{2} - \frac{1}{2}\cos 2x\right) = \frac{1}{16} - \frac{1}{16}\cos 2x - \frac{1}{16}\cos 4x + \frac{1}{16}\cos 2x \cos 4x$.

12. Using Example 4, we have $\cos^4 x \sin^2 x = \cos^2 x \left(\cos^2 x \sin^2 x\right) = \frac{1}{2}\left(1 + \cos 2x\right) \cdot \frac{1}{8}\left(1 - \cos 4x\right) = \frac{1}{16}\left(1 - \cos 4x + \cos 2x - \cos 2x \cos 4x\right)$.

13. Since $\sin^4 x \cos^4 x = \left(\sin^2 x \cos^2 x\right)^2$ we can use the result of Example 4 to get

$$
\begin{aligned}
\sin^4 x \cos^4 x &= \left(\frac{1}{8} - \frac{1}{8}\cos 4x\right)^2 = \frac{1}{64} - \frac{1}{32}\cos 4x + \frac{1}{64}\cos^2 4x \\
&= \frac{1}{64} - \frac{1}{32}\cos 4x + \frac{1}{64} \cdot \frac{1}{2}\left(1 + \cos 8x\right) = \frac{1}{64} - \frac{1}{32}\cos 4x + \frac{1}{128} + \frac{1}{128}\cos 8x \\
&= \frac{3}{128} - \frac{1}{32}\cos 4x + \frac{1}{128}\cos 8x = \frac{1}{32}\left(\frac{3}{4} - \cos 4x + \frac{1}{4}\cos 8x\right)
\end{aligned}
$$

14. Using the result of Exercise 10, we have

$$
\begin{aligned}
\cos^6 x &= \left(\cos^2 x\right)^2 \cdot \cos^2 x = \left(\frac{3}{8} + \frac{1}{2}\cos 2x + \frac{1}{8}\cos 4x\right)\left(\frac{1}{2} + \frac{1}{2}\cos 2x\right) \\
&= \frac{3}{16} + \frac{1}{4}\cos 2x + \frac{1}{16}\cos 4x + \frac{3}{16}\cos 2x + \frac{1}{16}\cos 2x \cos 4x \\
&= \frac{3}{16} + \frac{7}{16}\cos 2x + \frac{1}{16}\cos 4x + \frac{1}{16}\cos 2x \cos 4x = \frac{1}{16}\left(3 + 7\cos 2x + \cos 4x + \cos 2x \cos 4x\right)
\end{aligned}
$$

15. $\sin 15° = \sqrt{\frac{1}{2}\left(1 - \cos 30°\right)} = \sqrt{\frac{1}{2}\left(1 - \frac{\sqrt{3}}{2}\right)} = \sqrt{\frac{1}{4}\left(2 - \sqrt{3}\right)} = \frac{1}{2}\sqrt{2 - \sqrt{3}}$

16. $\tan 15° = \dfrac{1 - \cos 30°}{\sin 30°} = \dfrac{1 - \frac{\sqrt{3}}{2}}{\frac{1}{2}} = 2 - \sqrt{3}$

17. $\tan 22.5° = \dfrac{1 - \cos 45°}{\sin 45°} = \dfrac{1 - \frac{\sqrt{2}}{2}}{\frac{\sqrt{2}}{2}} = \sqrt{2} - 1$

18. $\sin 75° = \sqrt{\frac{1}{2}\left(1 - \cos 150°\right)} = \sqrt{\frac{1}{2}\left(1 - \left[-\frac{\sqrt{3}}{2}\right]\right)} = \sqrt{\frac{1}{4}\left(2 + \sqrt{3}\right)} = \frac{1}{2}\sqrt{2 + \sqrt{3}}$

19. $\cos 165° = -\sqrt{\frac{1}{2}\left(1 + \cos 330°\right)} = -\sqrt{\frac{1}{2}\left(1 + \cos 30°\right)} = -\sqrt{\frac{1}{2}\left(1 + \frac{\sqrt{3}}{2}\right)} = -\frac{1}{4}\left(\sqrt{6} + \sqrt{2}\right)$

20. $\cos 112.5° = -\sqrt{\frac{1}{2}\left(1 + \cos 225°\right)} = -\sqrt{\frac{1}{2}\left(1 - \cos 45°\right)} = -\sqrt{\frac{1}{2}\left(1 - \frac{\sqrt{2}}{2}\right)} = -\frac{1}{2}\sqrt{2 - \sqrt{2}}$

21. $\tan \frac{\pi}{8} = \dfrac{1 - \cos \frac{\pi}{4}}{\sin \frac{\pi}{4}} = \dfrac{1 - \frac{\sqrt{2}}{2}}{\frac{\sqrt{2}}{2}} = \sqrt{2} - 1$

22. $\cos \frac{3\pi}{8} = \cos\left(\frac{1}{2} \cdot \frac{3\pi}{4}\right) = \sqrt{\dfrac{1 + \cos \frac{3\pi}{4}}{2}} = -\sqrt{\dfrac{1 - \frac{\sqrt{2}}{2}}{2}} = -\sqrt{\dfrac{2 - \sqrt{2}}{4}} = -\frac{\sqrt{2}}{2}$. Note that we have chosen the positive root because $\frac{3\pi}{8}$ is in quadrant I, so $\cos \frac{3\pi}{8} > 0$.

23. $\cos \frac{\pi}{12} = \sqrt{\frac{1}{2}\left(1 + \cos \frac{\pi}{6}\right)} = \sqrt{\frac{1}{2}\left(1 + \frac{\sqrt{3}}{2}\right)} = \frac{1}{4}\left(\sqrt{6} + \sqrt{2}\right)$

24. $\tan \frac{5\pi}{12} = \dfrac{1 - \cos \frac{5\pi}{6}}{\sin \frac{5\pi}{6}} = \dfrac{1 + \frac{\sqrt{3}}{2}}{\frac{1}{2}} = 2 + \sqrt{3}$

25. $\sin \frac{9\pi}{8} = -\sqrt{\frac{1}{2}\left(1 - \cos \frac{9\pi}{4}\right)} = -\sqrt{\frac{1}{2}\left(1 - \frac{\sqrt{2}}{2}\right)} = -\frac{1}{2}\sqrt{2 - \sqrt{2}}$. We have chosen the negative root because $\frac{9\pi}{8}$ is in quadrant III, so $\sin \frac{9\pi}{8} < 0$.

26. $\sin \frac{11\pi}{12} = \sqrt{\frac{1}{2}\left(1 - \cos \frac{11\pi}{6}\right)} = \sqrt{\frac{1}{2}\left(1 - \frac{\sqrt{3}}{2}\right)} = \frac{1}{4}\left(\sqrt{6} - \sqrt{2}\right)$. We have chosen the positive root because $\frac{11\pi}{12}$ is in quadrant II, so $\sin \frac{11\pi}{12} > 0$.

27. (a) $2\sin 18° \cos 18° = \sin 36°$

(b) $2\sin 3\theta \cos 3\theta = \sin 6\theta$

28. (a) $\dfrac{2\tan 7°}{1 - \tan^2 7°} = \tan 14°$

(b) $\dfrac{2\tan 7\theta}{1 - \tan^2 7\theta} = \tan 14\theta$

29. (a) $\cos^2 34° - \sin^2 34° = \cos 68°$

(b) $\cos^2 5\theta - \sin^2 5\theta = \cos 10\theta$

30. (a) $\cos^2 \dfrac{\theta}{2} - \sin^2 \dfrac{\theta}{2} = \cos\theta$

(b) $2\sin \dfrac{\theta}{2} \cos \dfrac{\theta}{2} = \sin\theta$

31. (a) $\dfrac{\sin 8°}{1 + \cos 8°} = \tan \dfrac{8°}{2} = \tan 4°$

(b) $\dfrac{1 - \cos 4\theta}{\sin 4\theta} = \tan \dfrac{4\theta}{2} = \tan 2\theta$

32. (a) $\sqrt{\dfrac{1 - \cos 30°}{2}} = \sin 15°$

(b) $\sqrt{\dfrac{1 - \cos 8\theta}{2}} = \sin 4\theta$

33. $\sin(x + x) = \sin x \cos x + \cos x \sin x = 2\sin x \cos x$

34. $\tan(x + x) = \dfrac{\tan x + \tan x}{1 - \tan x \tan x} = \dfrac{2\tan x}{1 - \tan^2 x}$

35. $\sin x = \frac{3}{5}$. Since x is in quadrant I, $\cos x = \frac{4}{5}$ and $\frac{x}{2}$ is also in quadrant I. Thus,

$\sin \frac{x}{2} = \sqrt{\frac{1}{2}(1 - \cos x)} = \sqrt{\frac{1}{2}\left(1 - \frac{4}{5}\right)} = \frac{1}{\sqrt{10}} = \frac{\sqrt{10}}{10}$, $\cos \frac{x}{2} = \sqrt{\frac{1}{2}(1 + \cos x)} = \sqrt{\frac{1}{2}\left(1 + \frac{4}{5}\right)} = \frac{3}{\sqrt{10}} = \frac{3\sqrt{10}}{10}$, and

$\tan \frac{x}{2} = \dfrac{\sin \frac{x}{2}}{\cos \frac{x}{2}} = \frac{1}{\sqrt{10}} \cdot \frac{\sqrt{10}}{3} = \frac{1}{3}$.

36. $\cos x = -\frac{4}{5}$. Since x is in quadrant III, $\sin x = -\frac{3}{5}$ and $\tan x = \frac{3}{4}$. Also, since $180° \leq x \leq 270°$,

$90° \leq \frac{x}{2} \leq 135°$ and so $\frac{x}{2}$ is in quadrant II. Thus, $\sin \frac{x}{2} = \sqrt{\frac{1}{2}(1 - \cos x)} = \sqrt{\frac{1}{2}\left(1 + \frac{4}{5}\right)} = \frac{3}{\sqrt{10}} = \frac{3\sqrt{10}}{10}$,

$\cos \frac{x}{2} = -\sqrt{\frac{1}{2}(1 + \cos x)} = -\sqrt{\frac{1}{2}\left(1 - \frac{4}{5}\right)} = -\frac{1}{\sqrt{10}} = -\frac{\sqrt{10}}{10}$, and $\tan \frac{x}{2} = \dfrac{\sin \frac{x}{2}}{\cos \frac{x}{2}} = \frac{3}{\sqrt{10}} \cdot \frac{\sqrt{10}}{-1} = -3$.

37. $\csc x = 3$. Then, $\sin x = \frac{1}{3}$ and since x is in quadrant II, $\cos x = -\dfrac{2\sqrt{2}}{3}$. Since $90° \leq x \leq 180°$, we have

$45° \leq \frac{x}{2} \leq 90°$ and so $\frac{x}{2}$ is in quadrant I. Thus, $\sin \frac{x}{2} = \sqrt{\frac{1}{2}(1 - \cos x)} = \sqrt{\frac{1}{2}\left(1 + \frac{2\sqrt{2}}{3}\right)} = \sqrt{\frac{1}{6}(3 + 2\sqrt{2})}$,

$\cos \frac{x}{2} = \sqrt{\frac{1}{2}(1 + \cos x)} = \sqrt{\frac{1}{2}\left(1 - \frac{2\sqrt{2}}{3}\right)} = \sqrt{\frac{1}{6}(3 - 2\sqrt{2})}$, and $\tan \frac{x}{2} = \dfrac{\sin \frac{x}{2}}{\cos \frac{x}{2}} = \sqrt{\frac{3 + 2\sqrt{2}}{3 - 2\sqrt{2}}} = 3 + 2\sqrt{2}$.

38. $\tan x = 1$. Then $\sin x = \frac{\sqrt{2}}{2}$ and $\cos x = \frac{\sqrt{2}}{2}$, since x is in quadrant I. Also, since $0° \leq x \leq 90°$,

$0° \leq \frac{x}{2} \leq 45°$ and so $\frac{x}{2}$ is also in quadrant I. Thus, $\sin \frac{x}{2} = \sqrt{\frac{1}{2}(1 - \cos x)} = \sqrt{\frac{1}{2}\left(1 - \frac{\sqrt{2}}{2}\right)} = \frac{1}{2}\sqrt{2 - \sqrt{2}}$,

$\cos \frac{x}{2} = \sqrt{\frac{1}{2}(1 + \cos x)} = \sqrt{\frac{1}{2}\left(1 + \frac{\sqrt{2}}{2}\right)} = \frac{1}{2}\sqrt{2 + \sqrt{2}}$, and $\tan \frac{x}{2} = \dfrac{1 - \cos x}{\sin x} = \dfrac{1 - \frac{\sqrt{2}}{2}}{\frac{\sqrt{2}}{2}} = \sqrt{2} - 1$.

39. $\sec x = \frac{3}{2}$. Then $\cos x = \frac{2}{3}$ and since x is in quadrant IV, $\sin x = -\dfrac{\sqrt{5}}{3}$. Since $270° \leq x \leq 360°$, we have

$135° \leq \frac{x}{2} \leq 180°$ and so $\frac{x}{2}$ is in quadrant II. Thus, $\sin \frac{x}{2} = \sqrt{\frac{1}{2}(1 - \cos x)} = \sqrt{\frac{1}{2}\left(1 - \frac{2}{3}\right)} = \frac{1}{\sqrt{6}} = \frac{\sqrt{6}}{6}$,

$\cos \frac{x}{2} = -\sqrt{\frac{1}{2}(1 + \cos x)} = -\sqrt{\frac{1}{2}\left(1 + \frac{2}{3}\right)} = -\frac{\sqrt{5}}{\sqrt{6}} = -\dfrac{\sqrt{30}}{6}$, and $\tan \frac{x}{2} = \dfrac{\sin \frac{x}{2}}{\cos \frac{x}{2}} = \frac{1}{\sqrt{6}} \cdot \frac{\sqrt{6}}{-\sqrt{5}} = -\frac{1}{\sqrt{5}} = -\dfrac{\sqrt{5}}{5}$.

40. $\cot x = 5$. Then, $\cos x = -\dfrac{5}{\sqrt{26}}$ and $\sin x = -\dfrac{1}{\sqrt{2}}$ ($\csc x < 0$). Since $\cot x > 0$ and

$\csc x < 0$, it follows that x is in quadrant III. Thus $180° \leq x \leq 270°$ and so $90° \leq \frac{x}{2} \leq 135°$.

Thus $\frac{x}{2}$ is in quadrant II. $\sin \frac{x}{2} = \sqrt{\frac{1}{2}(1 - \cos x)} = \sqrt{\frac{1}{2}\left(1 + \frac{5}{\sqrt{26}}\right)} = \frac{1}{2}\sqrt{\dfrac{26 + 5\sqrt{26}}{13}}$,

$\cos \frac{x}{2} = -\sqrt{\frac{1}{2}(1 + \cos x)} = -\sqrt{\frac{1}{2}\left(1 - \frac{5}{\sqrt{26}}\right)} = -\frac{1}{2}\sqrt{\dfrac{26 - 5\sqrt{26}}{13}}$, and $\tan \frac{x}{2} = \dfrac{1 - \cos x}{\sin x} = \dfrac{1 + \frac{5}{\sqrt{26}}}{-\frac{1}{\sqrt{2}}} = -5 - \sqrt{26}$.

41. $\sin 2x \cos 3x = \frac{1}{2}\left[\sin\left(2x+3x\right)+\sin\left(2x-3x\right)\right] = \frac{1}{2}\left(\sin 5x - \sin x\right)$

42. $\sin x \sin 5x = \frac{1}{2}\left[\cos\left(x-5x\right)-\cos\left(x+5x\right)\right] = \frac{1}{2}\left(\cos 4x - \cos 6x\right)$

43. $\cos x \sin 4x = \frac{1}{2}\left[\sin\left(4x+x\right)+\sin\left(4x-x\right)\right] = \frac{1}{2}\left(\sin 5x + \sin 3x\right)$

44. $\cos 5x \cos 3x = \frac{1}{2}\left[\cos\left(5x+3x\right)+\cos\left(5x-3x\right)\right] = \frac{1}{2}\left(\cos 8x + \cos 2x\right)$

45. $3\cos 4x \cos 7x = 3 \cdot \frac{1}{2}\left[\cos\left(4x+7x\right)+\cos\left(4x-7x\right)\right] = \frac{3}{2}\left(\cos 11x + \cos 3x\right)$

46. $11\sin\frac{x}{2}\cos\frac{x}{4} = 11 \cdot \frac{1}{2}\left[\sin\left(\frac{x}{2}+\frac{x}{4}\right)+\sin\left(\frac{x}{2}-\frac{x}{4}\right)\right] = \frac{11}{2}\left(\sin\frac{3x}{4}+\sin\frac{x}{4}\right)$

47. $\sin 5x + \sin 3x = 2\sin\left(\dfrac{5x+3x}{2}\right)\cos\left(\dfrac{5x-3x}{2}\right) = 2\sin 4x \cos x$

48. $\sin x - \sin 4x = 2\cos\left(\dfrac{x+4x}{2}\right)\sin\left(\dfrac{x-4x}{2}\right) = 2\cos\frac{5x}{2}\sin\left(-\frac{3x}{2}\right) = -2\cos\frac{5x}{2}\sin\frac{3x}{2}$

49. $\cos 4x - \cos 6x = -2\sin\left(\dfrac{4x+6x}{2}\right)\sin\left(\dfrac{4x-6x}{2}\right) = -2\sin 5x \sin\left(-x\right) = 2\sin 5x \sin x$

50. $\cos 9x + \cos 2x = 2\cos\left(\dfrac{9x+2x}{2}\right)\cos\left(\dfrac{9x-2x}{2}\right) = 2\cos\frac{11x}{2}\cos\frac{7x}{2}$

51. $\sin 2x - \sin 7x = 2\cos\left(\dfrac{2x+7x}{2}\right)\sin\left(\dfrac{2x-7x}{2}\right) = 2\cos\frac{9x}{2}\sin\left(-\frac{5x}{2}\right) = -2\cos\frac{9x}{2}\sin\frac{5x}{2}$

52. $\sin 3x + \sin 4x = 2\sin\left(\dfrac{3x+4x}{2}\right)\cos\left(\dfrac{3x-4x}{2}\right) = 2\sin\frac{7x}{2}\cos\left(-\frac{x}{2}\right) = 2\sin\frac{7x}{2}\cos\frac{x}{2}$

53. $2\sin 52.5° \sin 97.5° = 2 \cdot \frac{1}{2}\left[\cos\left(52.5° - 97.5°\right)-\cos\left(52.5° + 97.5°\right)\right] = \cos\left(-45°\right) - \cos 150°$
$= \cos 45° - \cos 150° = \frac{\sqrt{2}}{2} + \frac{\sqrt{3}}{2} = \frac{1}{2}\left(\sqrt{2}+\sqrt{3}\right)$

54. $3\cos 37.5° \cos 7.5° = \frac{3}{2}\left(\cos 45° + \cos 30°\right) = \frac{3}{2}\left(\frac{\sqrt{2}}{2}+\frac{\sqrt{3}}{2}\right) = \frac{3}{4}\left(\sqrt{2}+\sqrt{3}\right)$

55. $\cos 37.5° \sin 7.5° = \frac{1}{2}\left(\sin 45° - \sin 30°\right) = \frac{1}{2}\left(\frac{\sqrt{2}}{2}-\frac{1}{2}\right) = \frac{1}{4}\left(\sqrt{2}-1\right)$

56. $\sin 75° + \sin 15° = 2\sin\left(\dfrac{75°+15°}{2}\right)\cos\left(\dfrac{75°-15°}{2}\right) = 2\sin 45° \cos 30° = 2 \cdot \frac{\sqrt{2}}{2} \cdot \frac{\sqrt{3}}{2} = \frac{\sqrt{6}}{2}$

57. $\cos 255° - \cos 195° = -2\sin\left(\dfrac{255°+195°}{2}\right)\sin\left(\dfrac{255°-195°}{2}\right) = -2\sin 225° \sin 30° = -2\left(-\frac{\sqrt{2}}{2}\right)\frac{1}{2} = \frac{\sqrt{2}}{2}$

58. $\cos\frac{\pi}{12} + \cos\frac{5\pi}{12} = 2\cos\left[\frac{1}{2}\left(\frac{\pi}{12}+\frac{5\pi}{12}\right)\right]\cos\left[\frac{1}{2}\left(\frac{\pi}{12}-\frac{5\pi}{12}\right)\right] = 2\cos\frac{\pi}{4}\cos\frac{\pi}{6} = 2 \cdot \frac{\sqrt{2}}{2} \cdot \frac{\sqrt{3}}{2} = \frac{\sqrt{6}}{2}$

59. $\cos^2 5x - \sin^2 5x = \cos\left(2 \cdot 5x\right) = \cos 10x$

60. $\sin 8x = \sin\left(2 \cdot 4x\right) = 2\sin 4x \cos 4x$

61. $\left(\sin x + \cos x\right)^2 = \sin^2 x + 2\sin x \cos x + \cos^2 x = 1 + 2\sin x \cos x = 1 + \sin 2x$

62. $\dfrac{2\tan x}{1+\tan^2 x} = \dfrac{2\tan x}{\sec^2 x} = 2 \cdot \dfrac{\sin x}{\cos x}\cos^2 x = 2\sin x \cos x = \sin 2x$

63. $\dfrac{\sin 4x}{\sin x} = \dfrac{2\sin 2x \cos 2x}{\sin x} = \dfrac{2\left(2\sin x \cos x\right)\left(\cos 2x\right)}{\sin x} = 4\cos x \cos 2x$

64. $\dfrac{1+\sin 2x}{\sin 2x} = \dfrac{1+2\sin x \cos x}{2\sin x \cos x} = 1 + \dfrac{1}{2\sin x \cos x} = 1 + \frac{1}{2}\csc x \sec x$

65. $\dfrac{2\left(\tan x - \cot x\right)}{\tan^2 x - \cot^2 x} = \dfrac{2\left(\tan x - \cot x\right)}{\left(\tan x + \cot x\right)\left(\tan x - \cot x\right)} = \dfrac{2}{\tan x + \cot x} = \dfrac{2}{\dfrac{\sin x}{\cos x}+\dfrac{\cos x}{\sin x}}$

$= \dfrac{2}{\dfrac{\sin x}{\cos x}+\dfrac{\cos x}{\sin x}} \cdot \dfrac{\sin x \cos x}{\sin x \cos x} = \dfrac{2\sin x \cos x}{\sin^2 x + \cos^2 x} = 2\sin x \cos x = \sin 2x$

66. $\cot 2x = \dfrac{1}{\tan 2x} = \dfrac{1}{\dfrac{2\tan x}{1-\tan^2 x}} = \dfrac{1-\tan^2 x}{2\tan x}$

67. $\tan 3x = \tan(2x + x) = \dfrac{\tan 2x + \tan x}{1 - \tan 2x \tan x} = \dfrac{\dfrac{2\tan x}{1 - \tan^2 x} + \tan x}{1 - \dfrac{2\tan x}{1 - \tan^2 x}\tan x} = \dfrac{2\tan x + \tan x\left(1 - \tan^2 x\right)}{1 - \tan^2 x - 2\tan x \tan x}$

$= \dfrac{3\tan x - \tan^3 x}{1 - 3\tan^2 x}$

68. $4\left(\sin^6 x + \cos^6 x\right) = 4\left[\left(\sin^2 x + \cos^2 x\right)^3 - 3\left(\sin^4 x \cos^2 x + \sin^2 x \cos^4 x\right)\right]$

$= 4\left[1 - 3\sin^2 x \cos^2 x\left(\sin^2 x + \cos^2 x\right)\right] = 4 - 12\sin^2 x \cos^2 x$

$= 4 - 3\left(2\sin x \cos x\right)^2 = 4 - 3\sin^2 2x$

69. $\cos^4 x - \sin^4 x = \left(\cos^2 x + \sin^2 x\right)\left(\cos^2 x - \sin^2 x\right) = \cos^2 x - \sin^2 x = \cos 2x$

70. Let $y = \dfrac{x}{2} + \dfrac{\pi}{4} \Leftrightarrow 2y = x + \dfrac{\pi}{2}.$ Then

$\tan^2\left(\dfrac{x}{2} + \dfrac{\pi}{4}\right) = \tan^2 y = \dfrac{1 - \cos 2y}{1 + \cos 2y} = \dfrac{1 - \cos\left(x + \frac{\pi}{2}\right)}{1 + \cos\left(x + \frac{\pi}{2}\right)} = \dfrac{1 - (-\sin x)}{1 + (-\sin x)} = \dfrac{1 + \sin x}{1 - \sin x}$

71. $\dfrac{\sin x + \sin 5x}{\cos x + \cos 5x} = \dfrac{2\sin 3x \cos 2x}{2\cos 3x \cos 2x} = \dfrac{\sin 3x}{\cos 3x} = \tan 3x$

72. $\dfrac{\sin 3x + \sin 7x}{\cos 3x - \cos 7x} = \dfrac{2\sin 5x \cos 2x}{-2\sin 5x \sin(-2x)} = \dfrac{\cos 2x}{\sin 2x} = \cot 2x$

73. $\dfrac{\sin 10x}{\sin 9x + \sin x} = \dfrac{2\sin 5x \cos 5x}{2\sin 5x \cos 4x} = \dfrac{\cos 5x}{\cos 4x}$

74. $\dfrac{\sin x + \sin 3x + \sin 5x}{\cos x + \cos 3x + \cos 5x} = \dfrac{\sin x + \sin 5x + \sin 3x}{\cos x + \cos 5x + \cos 3x} = \dfrac{2\sin 3x \cos 2x + \sin 3x}{2\cos 3x \cos 2x + \cos 3x} = \dfrac{\sin 3x\left(2\cos 2x + 1\right)}{\cos 3x\left(2\cos 2x + 1\right)} = \tan 3x$

75. $\dfrac{\sin x + \sin y}{\cos x + \cos y} = \dfrac{2\sin\left(\frac{x+y}{2}\right)\cos\left(\frac{x-y}{2}\right)}{2\cos\left(\frac{x+y}{2}\right)\cos\left(\frac{x-y}{2}\right)} = \dfrac{\sin\left(\frac{x+y}{2}\right)}{\cos\left(\frac{x+y}{2}\right)} = \tan\left(\dfrac{x+y}{2}\right)$

76. $\dfrac{\sin(x+y) - \sin(x-y)}{\cos(x+y) + \cos(x-y)} = \dfrac{2\sin\left(\frac{x+y+x-y}{2}\right)\cos\left(\frac{x+y-x+y}{2}\right)}{2\cos\left(\frac{x+y+x-y}{2}\right)\cos\left(\frac{x+y-x+y}{2}\right)} = \dfrac{\sin x}{\cos x} = \tan x$

77. $\sin 130° - \sin 110° = 2\cos\dfrac{130° + 110°}{2}\sin\dfrac{130° - 110°}{2} = 2\cos 120° \sin 10° = 2\left(-\frac{1}{2}\right)\sin 10° = -\sin 10°$

78. $\cos 100° - \cos 200° = -2\sin\dfrac{100° + 200°}{2}\sin\dfrac{100° - 200°}{2} = -2\sin 150° \sin(-50°)$

$= -2\left(\frac{1}{2}\right)(-\sin 50°) = \sin 50°$

79. $\sin 45° + \sin 15° = 2\sin\left(\dfrac{45° + 15°}{2}\right)\cos\left(\dfrac{45° - 15°}{2}\right) = 2\sin 30° \cos 15° = 2 \cdot \frac{1}{2} \cdot \cos 15°$

$= \cos 15° = \sin(90° - 15°) = \sin 75°$ (applying the cofunction identity)

80. $\cos 87° + \cos 33° = 2\cos\dfrac{87° + 33°}{2}\cos\dfrac{87° - 33°}{2} = 2\cos 60° \cos 27°$

$= 2 \cdot \frac{1}{2}\cos 27° = \cos 27° = \sin(90° - 27°) = \sin 63°$

81. $\dfrac{\sin x + \sin 2x + \sin 3x + \sin 4x + \sin 5x}{\cos x + \cos 2x + \cos 3x + \cos 4x + \cos 5x} = \dfrac{(\sin x + \sin 5x) + (\sin 2x + \sin 4x) + \sin 3x}{(\cos x + \cos 5x) + (\cos 2x + \cos 4x) + \cos 3x}$

$= \dfrac{2\sin 3x \cos 2x + 2\sin 3x \cos x + \sin 3x}{2\cos 3x \cos 2x + 2\cos 3x \cos x + \cos 3x} = \dfrac{\sin 3x\left(2\cos 2x + 2\cos x + 1\right)}{\cos 3x\left(2\cos 2x + 2\cos x + 1\right)} = \tan 3x$

82. $n = 1$: $\sin\left(2^1 x\right) = 2\sin x \cos x = 2^1 \sin x \cos\left(2^0 x\right)$

$n = 2$: $\sin\left(2^2 x\right) = \sin 4x = 2\sin 2x \cos 2x = 2\left(2\sin x \cos x\right)\cos 2x = 4\sin x \cos x \cos 2x = 2^2 \sin x \cos x \cos\left(2^1 x\right)$

$n = 3$: $\sin\left(2^3 x\right) = \sin 8x = 2\sin 4x \cos 4x = 2\left(4\sin x \cos x \cos 2x\right)\cos 4x = 8\sin x \cos x \cos 2x \cos 4x$

$\qquad = 2^3 \sin x \cos x \cos 2x \cos\left(2^2 x\right)$

In general, for $n > 0$ we have

$$\begin{aligned}
\sin\left(2^n x\right) &= \sin 2\left(2^{n-1} x\right) = 2\sin\left(2^{n-1} x\right)\cos\left(2^{n-1} x\right) \\
&= 2\left[2^{n-1}\sin x \cos x \cos 2x \cos 4x \cos 8x \cdots \cos\left(2^{n-2} x\right)\right]\cos\left(2^{n-1} x\right) \\
&= 2^n \sin x \cos x \cos 2x \cos 4x \cos 8x \cdots \cos\left(2^{n-2} x\right)\cos\left(2^{n-1} x\right)
\end{aligned}$$

83. (a) $f\left(x\right) = \dfrac{\sin 3x}{\sin x} - \dfrac{\cos 3x}{\cos x}$

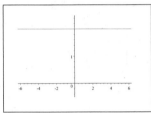

The function appears to have a constant value of 2 wherever it is defined.

(b) $f\left(x\right) = \dfrac{\sin 3x}{\sin x} - \dfrac{\cos 3x}{\cos x}$

$= \dfrac{\sin 3x \cos x - \cos 3x \sin x}{\sin x \cos x} = \dfrac{\sin\left(3x - x\right)}{\sin x \cos x}$

$= \dfrac{\sin 2x}{\sin x \cos x} = \dfrac{2\sin x \cos x}{\sin x \cos x} = 2$

for all x for which the function is defined.

84. (a) $f\left(x\right) = \cos 2x + 2\sin^2 x$

The function appears to have a constant value of 1.

(b) $f\left(x\right) = \cos 2x + 2\sin^2 x$

$= \left(\cos^2 x - \sin^2 x\right) + 2\sin^2 x$

$= \cos^2 x + \sin^2 x = 1$

85. (a) $y = \sin 6x + \sin 7x$

(b) By a sum-to-product formula,

$y = \sin 6x + \sin 7x$

$= 2\sin\left(\dfrac{6x + 7x}{2}\right)\cos\left(\dfrac{6x - 7x}{2}\right)$

$= 2\sin\left(\tfrac{13}{2}x\right)\cos\left(-\tfrac{1}{2}x\right)$

$= 2\sin\tfrac{13}{2}x \cos\tfrac{1}{2}x$

(c) We graph $y = \sin 6x + \sin 7x$, $y = 2\cos\left(\tfrac{1}{2}x\right)$, and $y = -2\cos\left(\tfrac{1}{2}x\right)$.

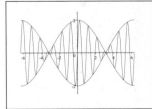

The graph of $y = f\left(x\right)$ lies between the other two graphs.

86. From Example 2, we have $\cos 3x = 4\cos^3 x - 3\cos x$. If $3x = \frac{\pi}{3}$, then $\cos\frac{\pi}{3} = \frac{1}{2} = 4\cos^3 x - 3\cos x \Leftrightarrow$
$1 = 8\cos^3 x - 6\cos x \quad \Leftrightarrow \quad 8\cos^3 x - 6\cos x - 1 = 0$. Substituting $y = \cos x$ gives $8y^3 - 6y - 1 = 0$.

87. (a) $\cos 4x = \cos(2x + 2x) = 2\cos^2 2x - 1 = 2(2\cos^2 x - 1)^2 - 1 = 8\cos^4 x - 8\cos^2 x + 1$. Thus the desired polynomial is $P(t) = 8t^4 - 8t^2 + 1$.

(b) $\cos 5x = \cos(4x + x) = \cos 4x \cos x - \sin 4x \sin x = \cos x (8\cos^4 x - 8\cos^2 x + 1) - 2\sin 2x \cos 2x \sin x$

$$= 8\cos^5 x - 8\cos^3 x + \cos x - 4\sin x \cos x (2\cos^2 x - 1)\sin x \quad \text{[from part (a)]}$$

$$= 8\cos^5 x - 8\cos^3 x + \cos x - 4\cos x (2\cos^2 x - 1)\sin^2 x$$

$$= 8\cos^5 x - 8\cos^3 x + \cos x - 4\cos x (2\cos^2 x - 1)(1 - \cos^2 x)$$

$$= 8\cos^5 x - 8\cos^3 x + \cos x + 8\cos^5 x - 12\cos^3 x + 4\cos x = 16\cos^5 x - 20\cos^3 x + 5\cos x$$

Thus, the desired polynomial is $P(t) = 16t^5 - 20t^3 + 5t$.

88. Let c_1 and c_2 be the lengths of the segments shown in the figure. By the Law of

Sines applied to $\triangle ABC$, we have $\dfrac{c}{\sin 2x} = \dfrac{b}{\sin B}$ or $c = \dfrac{b \sin 2x}{\sin B}$. Also by the

Law of Sines applied to $\triangle BCD$ and $\triangle ACD$ we have $\dfrac{s}{\sin B} = \dfrac{c_1}{\sin x}$ and

$\dfrac{s}{\sin A} = \dfrac{c_2}{\sin x}$. So $c_1 = \dfrac{s \sin x}{\sin B}$ and $c_2 = \dfrac{s \sin x}{\sin A}$. Since $c = c_1 + c_2$, we have

$\dfrac{b \sin 2x}{\sin B} = \dfrac{s \sin x}{\sin B} + \dfrac{s \sin x}{\sin A} = s \sin x \left(\dfrac{1}{\sin B} + \dfrac{1}{\sin A} \right)$. By applying the Law of Sines to $\triangle ABC$, $\dfrac{b}{\sin B} = \dfrac{a}{\sin A}$

$\Leftrightarrow \quad \dfrac{1}{\sin A} = \dfrac{b}{a \sin B}$. Substituting we have $\dfrac{b \sin 2x}{\sin B} = s \sin x \left(\dfrac{1}{\sin B} + \dfrac{b}{a \sin B} \right) = s \dfrac{\sin x}{\sin B} \left(1 + \dfrac{b}{a} \right) \quad \Leftrightarrow$

$b \sin 2x = s \sin x \left(1 + \dfrac{b}{a} \right) \quad \Leftrightarrow \quad 2b \sin x \cos x = \sin x \left(1 + \dfrac{b}{a} \right) \quad \Leftrightarrow \quad 2b \cos x = s \left(1 + \dfrac{b}{a} \right) = s \left(\dfrac{a + b}{a} \right)$

$\Leftrightarrow \quad s = \dfrac{2ab \cos x}{a + b}$.

89. Using a product-to-sum formula,
$\text{RHS} = 4 \sin A \sin B \sin C = 4 \sin A \left\{ \frac{1}{2} [\cos(B - C) - \cos(B + C)] \right\} = 2 \sin A \cos(B - C) - 2 \sin A \cos(B + C)$.
Using another product-to-sum formula, this is equal to

$2 \left\{ \frac{1}{2} [\sin(A + B - C) + \sin(A - B + C)] \right\} - 2 \left\{ \frac{1}{2} [\sin(A + B + C) + \sin(A - B - C)] \right\}$

$$= \sin(A + B - C) + \sin(A - B + C) - \sin(A + B + C) - \sin(A - B - C)$$

Now $A + B + C = \pi$, so $A + B - C = \pi - 2C$, $A - B + C = \pi - 2B$, and $A - B - C = 2A - \pi$. Thus our expression simplifies to

$\sin(A + B - C) + \sin(A - B + C) - \sin(A + B + C) - \sin(A - B - C)$

$$= \sin(\pi - 2C) + \sin(\pi - 2B) + 0 - \sin(2A - \pi) = \sin 2C + \sin 2B + \sin 2A = \text{LHS}$$

90. (a) The length of the base of the inscribed rectangle twice the length of the adjacent side which is $2(5 \cos \theta)$ and the length of the opposite side is $5 \sin \theta$. Thus the area of the rectangle is modeled by $A(\theta) = 2(5 \cos \theta)(5 \sin \theta) = 25(2 \sin \theta \cos \theta) = 25 \sin 2\theta$.

(b) The function $y = \sin u$ is maximized when $u = \frac{\pi}{2}$. So $2\theta = \frac{\pi}{2} \quad \Leftrightarrow \quad \theta = \frac{\pi}{4}$. Thus the maximum cross-sectional area is $A\left(\frac{\pi}{4}\right) = 25 \sin 2\left(\frac{\pi}{4}\right) = 25$ cm^2.

(c) The length of the base is $2\left(5 \cos \frac{\pi}{4}\right) = 5\sqrt{2} \approx 7.07$ cm and the width of the rectangle is $5 \sin \frac{\pi}{4} = \frac{5\sqrt{2}}{2} = 3.54$ cm.

91. (a) In both logs the length of the adjacent side is $20 \cos \theta$ and the length of the opposite side is $20 \sin \theta$. Thus the cross-sectional area of the beam is modeled by

$A(\theta) = (20 \cos \theta)(20 \sin \theta) = 400 \sin \theta \cos \theta = 200(2 \sin \theta \cos \theta) = 200 \sin 2\theta$.

(b) The function $y = \sin u$ is maximized when $u = \frac{\pi}{2}$. So $2\theta = \frac{\pi}{2} \quad \Leftrightarrow \quad \theta = \frac{\pi}{4}$. Thus the maximum cross-sectional area is $A\left(\frac{\pi}{4}\right) = 200 \sin 2\left(\frac{\pi}{4}\right) = 200$.

92. We first label the figure as shown. Because the sheet of paper is folded over,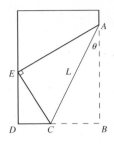
$\angle EAC = \angle CAB = \theta$. Thus $\angle BCA = \angle ACE = 90° - \theta$. It follows that
$\angle ECD = 180° - \angle BCA - \angle ACE = 180° - (90° - \theta) - (90° - \theta) = 2\theta$.
Also, from the figure we see that $BC = L \sin \theta$ and $CE = L \sin \theta$, so
$DC = EC \cos 2\theta = L \sin \theta \cos 2\theta$. Thus $6 = DB = DC +$
$CB = L \sin \theta \cos 2\theta + L \sin \theta = L \sin \theta \, (1 + \cos 2\theta) = L \sin \theta \cdot 2 \cos^2 \theta$. So
$$L = \frac{6}{2 \sin \theta \cos^2 \theta} = \frac{3}{\sin \theta \cos^2 \theta}.$$

93. (a) $y = f_1 (t) + f_2 (t) = \cos 11t + \cos 13t$

(b) Using the identity
$$\cos \alpha + \cos y = 2 \cdot \cos \left(\frac{\alpha + y}{2} \right) \cos \left(\frac{\alpha - y}{2} \right), \text{ we have}$$
$$f (t) = \cos 11t + \cos 13t = 2 \cdot \cos \left(\frac{11t + 13t}{2} \right) \cos \left(\frac{11t - 13t}{2} \right)$$
$$= 2 \cdot \cos 12t \cdot \cos (-t) = 2 \cos 12t \cos t$$

(c) We graph $y = \cos 11t + \cos 13t$,
$y = 2 \cos t$, and $y = -2 \cos t$.

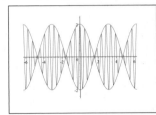

The graph of f lies between the graphs of
$y = 2 \cos t$ and $y = -2 \cos t$. Thus, the
loudness of the sound varies between
$y = \pm 2 \cos t$.

94. (a) $f_1 = 770$ Hz and $f_2 = 1209$ Hz, so
$$y = \sin (2\pi \cdot 770t) + \sin (2\pi \cdot 1209t)$$
$$= \sin 1540\pi t + \sin 2418\pi t$$

(b) Using a sum-to-product formula, we have
$$y = 2 \sin \frac{1540\pi t + 2418\pi t}{2} \cos \frac{1540\pi t - 2418\pi t}{2}$$
$$= 2 \sin 1979\pi t \cos 439\pi t$$

(c)

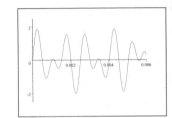

95. We find the area of $\triangle ABC$ in two different ways. First, let AB be the base and
CD be the height. Since $\angle BOC = 2\theta$ we see that $CD = \sin 2\theta$. So the area is
$\frac{1}{2} (\text{base}) (\text{height}) = \frac{1}{2} \cdot 2 \cdot \sin 2\theta = \sin 2\theta$. On the other hand, in $\triangle ABC$ we see
that $\angle C$ is a right angle. So $BC = 2 \sin \theta$ and $AC = 2 \cos \theta$, and the area is
$\frac{1}{2} (\text{base}) (\text{height}) = \frac{1}{2} \cdot (2 \sin \theta) (2 \cos \theta) = 2 \sin \theta \cos \theta$. Equating the two
expressions for the area of $\triangle ABC$, we get $\sin 2\theta = 2 \sin \theta \cos \theta$.

7.4 Inverse Trigonometric Functions

1. (a) $\sin^{-1} \frac{1}{2} = \frac{\pi}{6}$

   (b) $\cos^{-1} \frac{1}{2} = \frac{\pi}{3}$

   (c) $\cos^{-1} 2$ is not defined.

2. (a) $\sin^{-1} \frac{\sqrt{3}}{2} = \frac{\pi}{3}$

   (b) $\cos^{-1} \frac{\sqrt{3}}{2} = \frac{\pi}{6}$

   (c) $\cos^{-1} \left(-\frac{\sqrt{3}}{2}\right) = \frac{5\pi}{6}$

3. (a) $\sin^{-1} \frac{\sqrt{2}}{2} = \frac{\pi}{4}$

   (b) $\cos^{-1} \frac{\sqrt{2}}{2} = \frac{\pi}{4}$

   (c) $\sin^{-1} \left(-\frac{\sqrt{2}}{2}\right) = -\frac{\pi}{4}$

4. (a) $\tan^{-1} \sqrt{3} = \frac{\pi}{3}$

   (b) $\tan^{-1} \left(-\sqrt{3}\right) = -\frac{\pi}{3}$

   (c) $\sin^{-1} \sqrt{3}$ is not defined.

5. (a) $\sin^{-1} 1 = \frac{\pi}{2}$

   (b) $\cos^{-1} 1 = 0$

   (c) $\cos^{-1} (-1) = \pi$

6. (a) $\tan^{-1} 1 = \frac{\pi}{4}$

   (b) $\tan^{-1} (-1) = -\frac{\pi}{4}$

   (c) $\tan^{-1} 0 = 0$

7. (a) $\tan^{-1} \frac{\sqrt{3}}{3} = \frac{\pi}{6}$

   (b) $\tan^{-1} \left(-\frac{\sqrt{3}}{3}\right) = -\frac{\pi}{6}$

   (c) $\sin^{-1} (-2)$ is not defined.

8. (a) $\sin^{-1} 0 = 0$

   (b) $\cos^{-1} 0 = \frac{\pi}{2}$

   (c) $\cos^{-1} \left(-\frac{1}{2}\right) = \frac{2\pi}{3}$

9. (a) $\sin^{-1} (0.13844) \approx 0.13889$

   (b) $\cos^{-1} (-0.92761) \approx 2.75876$

10. (a) $\cos^{-1} (0.31187) \approx 1.25364$

   (b) $\tan^{-1} (26.23110) \approx 1.53269$

11. (a) $\tan^{-1} (1.23456) \approx 0.88998$

   (b) $\sin^{-1} (1.23456)$ is not defined.

12. (a) $\cos^{-1} (-0.25713) \approx 1.83085$

   (b) $\tan^{-1} (-0.25713) \approx -0.25168$

13. $\sin \left(\sin^{-1} \frac{1}{4}\right) = \frac{1}{4}$

14. $\cos \left(\cos^{-1} \frac{3}{2}\right) = \frac{3}{2}$

15. $\tan \left(\tan^{-1} 5\right) = 5$

16. $\sin \left(\sin^{-1} 5\right)$ does not exist because 5 is not in the domain of the function $\sin^{-1}$.

17. $\cos^{-1} \left(\cos \frac{\pi}{3}\right) = \frac{\pi}{3}$

18. $\tan^{-1} \left(\tan \frac{\pi}{6}\right) = \frac{\pi}{6}$

19. $\sin^{-1} \left(\sin \left(-\frac{\pi}{6}\right)\right) = -\frac{\pi}{6}$

20. Since $\sin \frac{5\pi}{6} = \sin \frac{\pi}{6}$, $\sin^{-1} \left(\sin \frac{5\pi}{6}\right) = \frac{\pi}{6}$

21. $\tan^{-1} \left(\tan \frac{2\pi}{3}\right) = \tan^{-1} \left(\tan \left(\frac{2\pi}{3} - \pi\right)\right)$
         $= \tan^{-1} \left(\tan \left(-\frac{\pi}{3}\right)\right) = -\frac{\pi}{3}$ since $\frac{2\pi}{3} > \frac{\pi}{2}$.

22. Since $\cos \left(-\frac{\pi}{4}\right) = \cos \frac{\pi}{4}$, $\cos^{-1} \left(\cos \left(-\frac{\pi}{4}\right)\right) = \frac{\pi}{4}$.

23. $\tan \left(\sin^{-1} \frac{1}{2}\right) = \tan \frac{\pi}{6} = \frac{\sqrt{3}}{3}$

24. $\sin \left(\sin^{-1} 0\right) = 0$

25. $\cos \left(\sin^{-1} \frac{\sqrt{3}}{2}\right) = \cos \frac{\pi}{3} = \frac{1}{2}$

26. $\tan \left(\sin^{-1} \frac{\sqrt{2}}{2}\right) = \tan \frac{\pi}{4} = 1$

27. $\tan^{-1} \left(2 \sin \frac{\pi}{3}\right) = \tan^{-1} \left(2 \cdot \frac{\sqrt{3}}{2}\right) = \tan^{-1} \sqrt{3} = \frac{\pi}{3}$

28. $\cos^{-1} \left(\sqrt{3} \sin \frac{\pi}{6}\right) = \cos^{-1} \left(\sqrt{3} \cdot \frac{1}{2}\right) = \frac{\pi}{6}$

29. Let $u = \cos^{-1} \frac{3}{5}$, so $\cos u = \frac{3}{5}$. Then from the triangle, $\sin \left(\cos^{-1} \frac{3}{5}\right) = \sin u = \frac{4}{5}$.

30. Let $u = \sin^{-1} \frac{4}{5}$, so $\sin u = \frac{4}{5}$. Then from the triangle, $\tan \left(\sin^{-1} \frac{4}{5}\right) = \tan u = \frac{4}{3}$.

31. Let $u = \tan^{-1} \frac{12}{5}$, so $\tan u = \frac{12}{5}$. Then from the triangle,
$\sin\left(\tan^{-1} \frac{12}{5}\right) = \sin u = \frac{12}{13}$.

32. Let $u = \tan^{-1} 5$, so $\tan u = 5$. Then from the triangle,
$\cos\left(\tan^{-1} 5\right) = \cos u = \frac{1}{\sqrt{2}}$.

33. Let $\theta = \sin^{-1} \frac{12}{13}$, so $\sin\theta = \frac{12}{13}$. Then from the triangle,
$\sec\left(\sin^{-1} \frac{12}{13}\right) = \sec\theta = \frac{13}{5}$.

34. Let $\alpha = \cos^{-1} \frac{7}{25}$, so $\cos\alpha = \frac{7}{25}$. Then from the triangle,
$\csc\left(\cos^{-1} \frac{7}{25}\right) = \csc\alpha = \frac{25}{24}$.

35. Let $u = \tan^{-1} 2$, so $\tan u = 2$. Then from the triangle,
$\cos\left(\tan^{-1} 2\right) = \cos u = \frac{1}{\sqrt{5}} = \frac{\sqrt{5}}{5}$.

36. Let $u = \sin^{-1} \frac{2}{3}$, so $\sin u = \frac{2}{3}$. Then from the triangle,
$\cot\left(\sin^{-1} \frac{2}{3}\right) = \cot u = \frac{\sqrt{5}}{2}$.

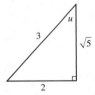

37. Let $u = \cos^{-1} \frac{3}{5}$, so $\cos u = \frac{3}{5}$. From the triangle,
$\sin u = \frac{4}{5}$, so
$$\sin\left(2\cos^{-1} \frac{3}{5}\right) = \sin\left(2u\right) = 2\sin u\cos u$$
$$= 2 \cdot \frac{4}{5} \cdot \frac{3}{5} = \frac{24}{25}$$

38. Let $u = \tan^{-1} \frac{5}{13}$, so $\tan u = \frac{5}{13}$. Then from the triangle,
$$\tan\left(2\tan^{-1} \frac{5}{13}\right) = \tan 2u = \frac{2\tan u}{1 - \tan^2 u} = \frac{2 \cdot \frac{5}{13}}{1 - \frac{25}{169}}$$
$$= \frac{10}{13} \cdot \frac{169}{144} = \frac{65}{72}$$

39. Let $u = \cos^{-1}\frac{1}{2}$ and $v = \sin^{-1}\frac{1}{2}$, so $\cos u = \frac{1}{2}$ and $\sin v = \frac{1}{2}$. From the triangle,

$$\sin\left(\sin^{-1}\frac{1}{2} + \cos^{-1}\frac{1}{2}\right) = \sin(v + u)$$
$$= \sin v \cos u + \cos v \sin u = \frac{1}{2} \cdot \frac{1}{2} + \frac{\sqrt{3}}{2} \cdot \frac{\sqrt{3}}{2} = 1$$

Another method:

$$\sin\left(\sin^{-1}\frac{1}{2} + \cos^{-1}\frac{1}{2}\right) = \sin\left(\frac{\pi}{6} + \frac{\pi}{3}\right) = \sin\frac{\pi}{2} = 1$$

40. Let $\theta = \sin^{-1}\frac{3}{5}$ and $\gamma = \cos^{-1}\frac{3}{5}$, so $\sin\theta = \frac{3}{5}$ and $\cos\gamma = \frac{3}{5}$. From the triangle,

$$\cos\left(\sin^{-1}\frac{3}{5} - \cos^{-1}\frac{3}{5}\right)$$
$$= \cos\left(\sin^{-1}\frac{3}{5}\right)\cos\left(\cos^{-1}\frac{3}{5}\right)$$
$$+ \sin\left(\sin^{-1}\frac{3}{5}\right)\sin\left(\cos^{-1}\frac{3}{5}\right)$$
$$= \cos\theta\cos\gamma + \sin\theta\sin\gamma = \frac{4}{5} \cdot \frac{3}{5} + \frac{3}{5} \cdot \frac{4}{5} = \frac{24}{25}$$

41. Let $u = \sin^{-1}x$, so $\sin u = x$. From the triangle,

$$\cos\left(\sin^{-1}x\right) = \cos u = \sqrt{1 - x^2}.$$

42. Let $u = \tan^{-1}x$, so $\tan u = x$. Then from the triangle,

$$\sin\left(\tan^{-1}x\right) = \sin u = \frac{x}{\sqrt{1 + x^2}}.$$

43. Let $u = \sin^{-1}x$, so $\sin u = x$. From the triangle,

$$\tan\left(\sin^{-1}x\right) = \tan u = \frac{x}{\sqrt{1 - x^2}}.$$

44. Let $u = \tan^{-1}x$, so $\tan u = x$. Then from the triangle,

$$\cos\left(\tan^{-1}x\right) = \cos u = \frac{1}{\sqrt{1 + x^2}}.$$

45. Let $u = \tan^{-1}x$, so $\tan u = x$. From the triangle,

$$\cos\left(2\tan^{-1}x\right) = \cos 2u - 1 = 2\cos^2 u - 1$$
$$= \frac{2}{1 + x^2} - 1 = \frac{1 - x^2}{1 + x^2}$$

46. Let $u = \sin^{-1}x$, so $\sin u = x$. From the triangle,

$$\sin\left(2\sin^{-1}x\right) = \sin 2u = 2\sin u \cos u = 2x\sqrt{1 - x^2}.$$

47. Let $u = \cos^{-1} x$ and $v = \sin^{-1} x$, so $\cos u = x$ and $\sin v = x$. From the triangle,

$$\cos\left(\cos^{-1} x + \sin^{-1} x\right) = \cos\left(\cos^{-1} x\right)\cos\left(\sin^{-1} x\right) - \sin\left(\cos^{-1} x\right)\sin\left(\sin^{-1} x\right)$$

$$= \cos u \cos v - \sin u \sin v = x\sqrt{1 - x^2} - x\sqrt{1 - x^2} = 0$$

48. Let $u = \tan^{-1} x$ and $v = \sin^{-1} x$, so $\tan u = x$ and $\sin v = x$. From the triangles we have

$$\sin\left(\tan^{-1} x - \sin^{-1} x\right) = \sin(u - v) = \sin u \cos v - \cos u \sin v$$

$$= \frac{x}{\sqrt{1 + x^2}} \cdot \sqrt{1 - x^2} - \frac{1}{\sqrt{1 + x^2}} \cdot x$$

$$= \frac{x\sqrt{1 - x^2} - 1}{\sqrt{1 + x^2}}$$

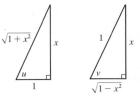

49. (a) $y = \sin^{-1} x + \cos^{-1} x$. Note the domain of both $\sin^{-1} x$ and $\cos^{-1} x$ is $[-1, 1]$.

Conjecture: $y = \frac{\pi}{2}$ for $-1 \le x \le 1$.

(b) To prove this conjecture, let $\sin^{-1} x = u \quad\Leftrightarrow\quad \sin u = x$, $-\frac{\pi}{2} \le u \le \frac{\pi}{2}$. Using the cofunction identity

$$\sin u = \cos\left(\frac{\pi}{2} - u\right) = x, \cos^{-1} x = \frac{\pi}{2} - u. \text{ Therefore,}$$

$$\sin^{-1} x + \cos^{-1} x = u + \left(\frac{\pi}{2} - u\right) = \frac{\pi}{2}.$$

50. (a) $y = \tan^{-1} x + \tan^{-1}\left(\dfrac{1}{x}\right)$

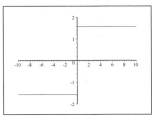

Conjecture: $y = \begin{cases} \frac{\pi}{2} & \text{if } x > 0 \\ -\frac{\pi}{2} & \text{if } x < 0 \end{cases}$

(b) To prove this conjecture, let $\tan^{-1} x = u \quad\Leftrightarrow\quad \tan u = x$, for $-\frac{\pi}{2} < u < \frac{\pi}{2}$. Then, $\dfrac{1}{x} = \dfrac{1}{\tan u} = \cot u = \tan\left(\frac{\pi}{2} - u\right)$ by the cofunction identity. So

$$\tan^{-1} x + \tan^{-1}\left(\frac{1}{x}\right) = u + \tan^{-1}\left(\tan\left(\frac{\pi}{2} - u\right)\right).$$

If $x > 0$, then $\frac{\pi}{2} > u > 0$, so $0 < \frac{\pi}{2} - u < \frac{\pi}{2} \Rightarrow \frac{\pi}{2} - u$ is in quadrant I. Therefore, $\tan^{-1}\left(\tan\left(\frac{\pi}{2} - u\right)\right) = \frac{\pi}{2} - u$, so

$$\tan^{-1} x + \tan^{-1}\left(\frac{1}{x}\right) = u + \left(\frac{\pi}{2} - u\right) = \frac{\pi}{2}.$$

If $x < 0$, then $-\frac{\pi}{2} < u < 0$, so $\pi > \frac{\pi}{2} - u > \frac{\pi}{2} \Rightarrow \frac{\pi}{2} - u$ is in quadrant II. Thus, $\tan^{-1}\left(\tan\left(\frac{\pi}{2} - u\right)\right) = \left(\frac{\pi}{2} - u\right) - \pi = -\frac{\pi}{2} - u$, and hence $\tan^{-1} x + \tan^{-1}\left(\dfrac{1}{x}\right) = u + \left(-\frac{\pi}{2} - u\right) = -\frac{\pi}{2}.$

51. (a) $\tan^{-1} x + \tan^{-1} 2x = \frac{\pi}{4}$

From the graph, the solution is $x \approx 0.28$.

(b) To solve the equation exactly, we set $\tan^{-1} x + \tan^{-1} 2x = \frac{\pi}{4}$ $\Leftrightarrow$

$\tan^{-1} x = \frac{\pi}{4} - \tan^{-1} 2x \Rightarrow \tan\left(\tan^{-1} x\right) = \tan\left(\frac{\pi}{4} - \tan^{-1} 2x\right)$

$\Rightarrow x = \dfrac{\tan\frac{\pi}{4} - \tan\left(\tan^{-1} 2x\right)}{1 + \tan\frac{\pi}{4} \cdot \tan\left(\tan^{-1} 2x\right)} = \dfrac{1 - 2x}{1 + (1)\, 2x} \Rightarrow$

$x\left(1 + 2x\right) = 1 - 2x$ $\Leftrightarrow$ $x + 2x^2 = 1 - 2x$. Thus,

$2x^2 + 3x - 1 = 0$. We use the quadratic formula to solve for x:

$x = \dfrac{-3 \pm \sqrt{3^2 - 4(2)(-1)}}{2(2)} = \dfrac{-3 \pm \sqrt{17}}{4}$. Substituting into the original

equation, we see that $x = \frac{-3-\sqrt{17}}{4}$ is not a solution, and so

$x = \frac{-3+\sqrt{17}}{4} \approx 0.28$ is the only root.

52. (a) $y = \sin^{-1} x - \cos^{-1} x$

From the graph, we see that $y = 0$ when $x \approx 0.71$.

(b) To solve the equation exactly, we set $\tan^{-1} x + \tan^{-1} 2x = \frac{\pi}{4}$ $\Leftrightarrow$

$\tan^{-1} x = \frac{\pi}{4} - \tan^{-1} 2x \Rightarrow \tan\left(\tan^{-1} x\right) = \tan\left(\frac{\pi}{4} - \tan^{-1} 2x\right)$

$\Rightarrow x = \dfrac{\tan\frac{\pi}{4} - \tan\left(\tan^{-1} 2x\right)}{1 + \tan\frac{\pi}{4} \cdot \tan\left(\tan^{-1} 2x\right)} = \dfrac{1 - 2x}{1 + (1)\, 2x} \Rightarrow$

$x\left(1 + 2x\right) = 1 - 2x$ $\Leftrightarrow$ $x + 2x^2 = 1 - 2x$. Thus,

$2x^2 + 3x - 1 = 0$. We use the quadratic formula to solve for x:

$x = \dfrac{-3 \pm \sqrt{3^2 - 4(2)(-1)}}{2(2)} = \dfrac{-3 \pm \sqrt{17}}{4}$. Substituting into the original

equation, we see that $x = \frac{-3-\sqrt{17}}{4}$ is not a solution, and so

$x = \frac{-3+\sqrt{17}}{4} \approx 0.28$ is the only root. To find the exact solution, we

set $\sin^{-1} x - \cos^{-1} x = 0 \Leftrightarrow \sin^{-1} x = \cos^{-1} x \Rightarrow$

$\sin\left(\sin^{-1} x\right) = \sin\left(\cos^{-1} x\right) \Rightarrow x = \sqrt{1 - x^2} \Rightarrow x^2 = 1 - x^2$

$\Leftrightarrow \quad 2x^2 = 1 \Rightarrow x = \pm\frac{1}{\sqrt{2}}$. But $x = \sqrt{1 - x^2} \geq 0$, so $x = \frac{1}{\sqrt{2}}$.

53. (a) Solving $\tan\theta = h/2$ for h we have $h = 2\tan\theta$.

(b) Solving $\tan\theta = h/2$ for θ we have $\theta = \tan^{-1}(h/2)$.

54. (a) Solving $\tan\theta = 50/s$ for s we have $s = 50/(\tan\theta)$.

(b) Set $s = 20$ ft to get $\tan\theta = \frac{50}{20}$ for θ we have $\theta = \tan^{-1}\left(\frac{5}{2}\right) = 1.1903$ rad.

55. (a) Solving $\sin\theta = h/680$ for θ we have $\theta = \sin^{-1}(h/680)$.

(b) Set $h = 500$ to get $\theta = \sin^{-1}\left(\frac{500}{680}\right) = 0.82610$ rad.

56. (a) Since the radius of the earth is 3960 miles, we have the relationship $\cos\theta = \frac{3960}{h+3960}$. Solving for θ, we get

$\theta = \cos^{-1}\left(\frac{3960}{h+3960}\right)$.

(b) The arc length is $s = (\text{radius})(\text{included angle}) = (3960)(2\theta) = 7920\theta$.

(c) $s = 7920 \cos^{-1}\left(\frac{3960}{h+3960}\right)$.

(d) When $h = 100$ we have $s = 7920 \cos^{-1}\left(\frac{3960}{100+3960}\right) = 7920\cos^{-1}\left(\frac{3960}{4060}\right) \approx 1761.5$ miles.

(e) When $s = 2450$ we have $2450 = 7920\cos^{-1}\left(\frac{3960}{h+3960}\right)$ $\Leftrightarrow$ $\frac{2450}{7920} = \cos^{-1}\left(\frac{3960}{h+3960}\right)$ $\Leftrightarrow$

$\frac{3960}{h+3960} = \cos\left(\frac{2450}{7920}\right)$ $\Leftrightarrow$ $h + 3960 = 3960\sec\left(\frac{2450}{7920}\right)$ $\Leftrightarrow$ $h = 3960\sec\left(\frac{2450}{7920}\right) - 3960$.

57. (a) $\theta = \sin^{-1}\left(\dfrac{1}{(2\cdot 3 + 1)\tan 10°}\right) = \sin^{-1}\left(\dfrac{1}{7\tan 10°}\right) \approx \sin^{-1} 0.8102 \approx 54.1°$

(b) For $n = 2$, $\theta = \sin^{-1}\left(\dfrac{1}{5\tan 15°}\right) \approx 48.3°$. For $n = 3$, $\theta = \sin^{-1}\left(\dfrac{1}{7\tan 15°}\right) \approx 32.2°$. For $n = 4$,

$\theta = \sin^{-1}\left(\dfrac{1}{9\tan 15°}\right) \approx 24.5°$. $n = 0$ and $n = 1$ are outside of the domain for $\beta = 15°$, because $\dfrac{1}{\tan 15°} \approx 3.732$

and $\dfrac{1}{3\tan 15°} \approx 1.244$, neither of which is in the domain of $\sin^{-1}$.

58. $f(x) = \sin\left(\sin^{-1} x\right) = x$ has domain $[-1, 1]$ and range $[-1, 1]$.

$g(x) = \sin^{-1}(\sin x)$ has domain $(-\infty, \infty)$ and range $\left[-\frac{\pi}{2}, \frac{\pi}{2}\right]$. Note that $g(x) = x$ only for $x \in \left[-\frac{\pi}{2}, \frac{\pi}{2}\right]$.

59. (a) Let $\theta = \sec^{-1} x$. Then $\sec\theta = x$, as shown in the figure. Then $\cos\theta = \dfrac{1}{x}$, so

$\theta = \cos^{-1}\left(\dfrac{1}{x}\right)$. Thus $\sec^{-1} x = \cos^{-1}\left(\dfrac{1}{x}\right)$, $x \geq 1$.

(b) Let $\gamma = \csc^{-1} x$. Then $\csc\gamma = x$, as shown in the figure. Then $\sin\gamma = \dfrac{1}{x}$, so

$\gamma = \sin^{-1}\left(\dfrac{1}{x}\right)$. Thus $\csc^{-1} x = \sin^{-1}\left(\dfrac{1}{x}\right)$, $x \geq 1$.

(c) Let $\beta = \cot^{-1} x$. Then $\cot\beta = x$, as shown in the figure. Then $\tan\beta = \dfrac{1}{x}$, so

$\beta = \tan^{-1}\left(\dfrac{1}{x}\right)$. Thus $\cot^{-1} x = \tan^{-1}\left(\dfrac{1}{x}\right)$, $x \geq 1$.

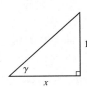

7.5   Trigonometric Equations

1. $\cos x + 1 = 0 \iff \cos x = -1$. In the interval $[0, 2\pi)$ the only solution is $x = \pi$. Thus the solutions are $x = (2k + 1)\pi$ for any integer k.

2. $\sin x + 1 = 0 \iff \sin x = -1$. In the interval $[0, 2\pi)$ the only solution is $x = \frac{3\pi}{2}$. Therefore, the solutions are $x = \frac{3\pi}{2} + 2k\pi$ for any integer k.

3. $2\sin x - 1 = 0 \iff 2\sin x = 1 \iff \sin x = \frac{1}{2}$. In the interval $[0, 2\pi)$ the solutions are $x = \frac{\pi}{6}, \frac{5\pi}{6}$. Therefore, the solutions are $x = \frac{\pi}{6} + 2k\pi$, $\frac{5\pi}{6} + 2k\pi$, $k = 0, \pm1, \pm2, \dots$.

4. $\sqrt{2}\cos x - 1 = 0 \iff \sqrt{2}\cos x = 1 \iff \cos x = \frac{1}{\sqrt{2}}$. The solutions in the interval $[0, 2\pi)$ are $x = \frac{\pi}{4}, \frac{7\pi}{4}$. Thus the solutions are $x = \frac{\pi}{4} + 2k\pi$, $\frac{7\pi}{4} + 2k\pi$ for any integer k.

5. $\sqrt{3}\tan x + 1 = 0$ $\Leftrightarrow$ $\sqrt{3}\tan x = -1 \Leftrightarrow \tan x = -\frac{\sqrt{3}}{3}$. In the interval $[0, \pi)$ the only solution is $x = \frac{5\pi}{6}$. Therefore, the solutions are $x = \frac{5\pi}{6} + k\pi$, $k = 0, \pm1, \pm2, \dots$.

6. $\cot x + 1 = 0$ $\Leftrightarrow$ $\cot x = -1$. The solution in the interval $(0, \pi)$ is $x = \frac{3\pi}{4}$. Thus, the solutions are $x = -\frac{\pi}{4} + k\pi$ for any integer k.

7. $4\cos^2 x - 1 = 0$ $\Leftrightarrow$ $4\cos^2 x = 1 \Leftrightarrow 4\cos^2 x = 1$ $\Leftrightarrow$ $\cos^2 x = \frac{1}{4} \Leftrightarrow \cos x = \pm\frac{1}{2}$. In the interval $[0, 2\pi)$ the solutions are $x = \frac{\pi}{3}, \frac{2\pi}{3}, \frac{4\pi}{3}, \frac{5\pi}{3}$. So the solutions are $x = \frac{\pi}{3} + 2k\pi, \frac{2\pi}{3} + 2k\pi, \frac{4\pi}{3} + 2k\pi, \frac{5\pi}{3} + 2k\pi$, which can be expressed more simply as $x = \frac{\pi}{3} + k\pi, \frac{2\pi}{3} + k\pi$ for any integer k.

8. $2\cos^2 x - 1 = 0$ $\Leftrightarrow$ $\cos^2 x = \frac{1}{2} \Leftrightarrow \cos x = \pm\frac{1}{\sqrt{2}}$ $\Leftrightarrow$ $x = \frac{\pi}{4}, \frac{3\pi}{4}, \frac{5\pi}{4}, \frac{7\pi}{4}$ in $[0, 2\pi)$. Thus, the solutions are $x = \frac{\pi}{4} + k\frac{\pi}{2}$ for any integer k.

9. $\sec^2 x - 2 = 0$ $\Leftrightarrow$ $\sec^2 x = 2 \Leftrightarrow \sec x = \pm\sqrt{2}$. In the interval $[0, 2\pi)$ the solutions are $x = \frac{\pi}{4}, \frac{3\pi}{4}, \frac{5\pi}{4}, \frac{7\pi}{4}$. Thus, the solutions are $x = \frac{\pi}{4} + k\frac{\pi}{2}$ for any integer k.

10. $\csc^2 x - 4 = 0$ $\Leftrightarrow$ $\csc^2 x = 4 \Leftrightarrow \csc x = \pm2$. In the interval $[0, 2\pi)$ the solutions are $x = \frac{\pi}{6}, \frac{5\pi}{6}, \frac{7\pi}{6}, \frac{11\pi}{6}$. So the solutions are $x = \frac{\pi}{6} + k\pi, \frac{5\pi}{6} + k\pi$ for any integer k.

11. $3\csc^2 x - 4 = 0$ $\Leftrightarrow$ $\csc^2 x = \frac{4}{3} \Leftrightarrow \csc x = \pm\frac{2}{\sqrt{3}}$ $\Leftrightarrow$ $\sin x = \pm\frac{\sqrt{3}}{2}$ $\Leftrightarrow$ $x = \frac{\pi}{3}, \frac{2\pi}{3}, \frac{4\pi}{3}, \frac{5\pi}{3}$ for x in $[0, 2\pi)$. Thus, the solutions are $x = \frac{\pi}{3} + k\pi, \frac{2\pi}{3} + k\pi$ for any integer k.

12. $1 - \tan^2 x = 0$ $\Leftrightarrow$ $\tan^2 x = 1 \Leftrightarrow \tan x = \pm1$ $\Leftrightarrow$ $x = -\frac{\pi}{4}, \frac{\pi}{4}$ in $\left(-\frac{\pi}{2}, \frac{\pi}{2}\right)$. Thus, the solutions are $\frac{\pi}{4} + k\frac{\pi}{2}$ for any integer k.

13. $\cos x(2\sin x + 1) = 0$ $\Leftrightarrow$ $\cos x = 0$ or $2\sin x + 1 = 0$ $\Leftrightarrow$ $\sin x = -\frac{1}{2}$. On $[0, 2\pi)$, $\cos x = 0$ $\Leftrightarrow$ $x = \frac{\pi}{2}$, $\frac{3\pi}{2}$ and $\sin x = -\frac{1}{2}$ $\Leftrightarrow$ $x = \frac{7\pi}{6}, \frac{11\pi}{6}$. Thus the solutions are $x = \frac{\pi}{2} + k\pi$, $x = \frac{7\pi}{6} + 2k\pi$, $x = \frac{11\pi}{6} + 2k\pi$, $k = 0, \pm1, \pm2, \dots$.

14. $\sec x(2\cos x - \sqrt{2}) = 0$ $\Leftrightarrow$ $\sec x = 0$ or $2\cos x - \sqrt{2} = 0$. Since $|\sec x| \geq 1$, $\sec x = 0$ has no solution. Thus $2\cos x - \sqrt{2} = 0 \Leftrightarrow 2\cos x = \sqrt{2}$ $\Leftrightarrow$ $\cos x = \frac{\sqrt{2}}{2} \Leftrightarrow x = \frac{\pi}{4}, \frac{7\pi}{4}$ in $[0, 2\pi)$. Thus $x = \frac{\pi}{4} + 2k\pi, \frac{7\pi}{4} + 2k\pi$ for any integer k.

15. $\left(\tan x + \sqrt{3}\right)(\cos x + 2) = 0 \Leftrightarrow \tan x + \sqrt{3} = 0$ or $\cos x + 2 = 0$. Since $|\cos x| \leq 1$ for all x, there is no solution for $\cos x + 2 = 0$. Hence, $\tan x + \sqrt{3} = 0$ $\Leftrightarrow$ $\tan x = -\sqrt{3} \Leftrightarrow x = -\frac{\pi}{3}$ on $\left(-\frac{\pi}{2}, \frac{\pi}{2}\right)$. Thus the solutions are $x = -\frac{\pi}{3} + k\pi$, $k = 0, \pm1, \pm2, \dots$.

16. $\left(2\cos x + \sqrt{3}\right)(2\sin x - 1) = 0 \Leftrightarrow 2\cos x + \sqrt{3} = 0$ or $2\sin x - 1 = 0$ $\Leftrightarrow$ $\cos x = -\frac{\sqrt{3}}{2}$ or $\sin x = \frac{1}{2}$ $\Leftrightarrow$ $x = \frac{\pi}{6}, \frac{5\pi}{6}, \frac{7\pi}{6}$ in $[0, 2\pi)$. Thus, $x = \frac{\pi}{6} + k\pi, \frac{5\pi}{6} + 2k\pi$ for any integer k.

17. $\cos x\sin x - 2\cos x = 0$ $\Leftrightarrow$ $\cos x(\sin x - 2) = 0$ $\Leftrightarrow$ $\cos x = 0$ or $\sin x - 2 = 0$. Since $|\sin x| \leq 1$ for all x, there is no solution for $\sin x - 2 = 0$. Hence, $\cos x = 0$ $\Leftrightarrow$ $x = \frac{\pi}{2} + 2k\pi, \frac{3\pi}{2} + 2k\pi$ $\Leftrightarrow$ $x = \frac{\pi}{2} + k\pi$, $k = 0, \pm1, \pm2, \dots$.

18. $\tan x\sin x + \sin x = 0$ $\Leftrightarrow$ $\sin x(\tan x + 1) = 0$ $\Leftrightarrow$ $\sin x = 0$ or $\tan x + 1 = 0$. Now $\sin x = 0$ when $x = k\pi$ and $\tan x + 1 = 0$ $\Leftrightarrow$ $\tan x = -1 \Rightarrow x = \frac{3\pi}{4} + k\pi$. Thus, the solutions are $x = k\pi, \frac{3\pi}{4} + k\pi$ for any integer k.

19. $4\cos^2 x - 4\cos x + 1 = 0$ $\Leftrightarrow$ $(2\cos x - 1)^2 = 0$ $\Leftrightarrow$ $2\cos x - 1 = 0$ $\Leftrightarrow$ $\cos x = \frac{1}{2}$ $\Leftrightarrow$ $x = \frac{\pi}{3} + 2k\pi$, $\frac{5\pi}{3} + 2k\pi$, $k = 0, \pm1, \pm2, \dots$.

20. $2\sin^2 x - \sin x - 1 = 0$ $\Leftrightarrow$ $(2\sin x + 1)(\sin x - 1) = 0$ $\Leftrightarrow$ $2\sin x + 1 = 0$ or $\sin x - 1 = 0$. Since $2\sin x + 1 = 0$ $\Leftrightarrow$ $2\sin x = -\frac{1}{2} \Leftrightarrow x = \frac{7\pi}{6}, \frac{11\pi}{6}$ in $[0, 2\pi)$ and $\sin x = 1$ $\Leftrightarrow$ $x = \frac{\pi}{2}$ in $[0, 2\pi)$. Thus the solutions are $x = \frac{7\pi}{6} + 2k\pi, \frac{11\pi}{6} + 2k\pi, \frac{\pi}{2} + 2k\pi$ for any integer k.

21. $\sin^2 x = 2\sin x + 3$ $\Leftrightarrow$ $\sin^2 x - 2\sin x - 3 = 0 \Leftrightarrow (\sin x - 3)(\sin x + 1) = 0 \Leftrightarrow \sin x - 3 = 0$ or $\sin x + 1 = 0$. Since $|\sin x| \leq 1$ for all x, there is no solution for $\sin x - 3 = 0$. Hence $\sin x + 1 = 0$ $\Leftrightarrow$ $\sin x = -1$ $\Leftrightarrow$ $x = \frac{3\pi}{2} + 2k\pi$, $k = 0, \pm1, \pm2, \dots$.

22. $3\tan^3 x = \tan x \quad \Leftrightarrow \quad 3\tan^3 x - \tan x = 0 \Leftrightarrow \tan x \left(3\tan^2 x - 1\right) = 0 \quad \Leftrightarrow \quad \tan x = 0$ or $3\tan^2 x - 1 = 0$.
Now $\tan x = 0 \Rightarrow x = k\pi$ and $3\tan^2 x - 1 = 0 \quad \Leftrightarrow \quad \tan^2 x = \frac{1}{3} \Rightarrow \tan x = \pm\frac{1}{\sqrt{3}} \Rightarrow x = \frac{\pi}{6} + k\pi, \frac{5\pi}{6} + k\pi$. Thus
the solutions are $x = k\pi, \frac{\pi}{6} + k\pi, \frac{5\pi}{6} + k\pi$ for any integer k.

23. $\sin^2 x = 4 - 2\cos^2 x \quad \Leftrightarrow \quad \sin^2 x + \cos^2 x + \cos^2 x = 4 \quad \Leftrightarrow \quad 1 + \cos^2 x = 4 \quad \Leftrightarrow \quad \cos^2 x = 3$ Since $|\cos x| \le 1$
for all x, it follows that $\cos^2 x \le 1$ and so there is no solution for $\cos^2 x = 3$.

24. $2\cos^2 x + \sin x = 1 \quad \Leftrightarrow \quad 2\left(1 - \sin^2 x\right) + \sin x - 1 = 0 \quad \Leftrightarrow \quad -2\sin^2 x + \sin x + 1 = 0 \Leftrightarrow 2\sin^2 x - \sin x - 1 = 0$
which we solved in Exercise 20. Thus $x = \frac{7\pi}{6} + 2k\pi, \frac{11\pi}{6} + 2k\pi, \frac{\pi}{2} + 2k\pi$ for any integer k.

25. $2\sin 3x + 1 = 0 \quad \Leftrightarrow \quad 2\sin 3x = -1 \Leftrightarrow \sin 3x = -\frac{1}{2}$. In the interval $[0, 6\pi)$ the solution are $3x = \frac{7\pi}{6}, \frac{11\pi}{6}, \frac{19\pi}{6}, \frac{23\pi}{6},$
$\frac{31\pi}{6}, \frac{35\pi}{6} \Leftrightarrow x = \frac{7\pi}{18}, \frac{11\pi}{18}, \frac{19\pi}{18}, \frac{23\pi}{18}, \frac{25\pi}{18}, \frac{29\pi}{18}$. So $x = \frac{7\pi}{18} + 2k\frac{\pi}{3}, \frac{11\pi}{18} + 2k\frac{\pi}{3}$ for any integer k.

26. $2\cos 2x + 1 = 0 \quad \Leftrightarrow \quad \cos 2x = -\frac{1}{2} \Leftrightarrow 2x = \frac{2\pi}{3} + 2k\pi, \frac{4\pi}{3} + 2k\pi \Leftrightarrow x = \frac{\pi}{3} + k\pi, \frac{2\pi}{3} + k\pi$ for any integer k.

27. $\sec 4x - 2 = 0 \quad \Leftrightarrow \quad \sec 4x = 2 \quad \Leftrightarrow \quad 4x = \frac{\pi}{3} + 2k\pi, \frac{5\pi}{3} + 2k\pi \quad \Leftrightarrow \quad x = \frac{\pi}{12} + \frac{1}{2}k\pi, \frac{5\pi}{12} + \frac{1}{2}k\pi$ for any integer k.

28. $\sqrt{3}\tan 3x + 1 = 0 \quad \Leftrightarrow \quad \tan 3x = -\frac{1}{\sqrt{3}} \quad \Leftrightarrow \quad 3x = \frac{5\pi}{6} + k\pi \quad \Leftrightarrow \quad x = \frac{5\pi}{18} + \frac{1}{3}k\pi$ for any integer k.

29. $\sqrt{3}\sin 2x = \cos 2x \quad \Leftrightarrow \quad \tan 2x = \frac{1}{\sqrt{3}}$ (if $\cos 2x \neq 0$) $\quad \Leftrightarrow \quad 2x = \frac{\pi}{6} + k\pi \quad \Leftrightarrow \quad x = \frac{\pi}{12} + \frac{1}{2}k\pi$ for any integer k.

30. $\csc 3x = \sin 3x \quad \Leftrightarrow \quad \dfrac{1}{\sin 3x} = \sin 3x \quad \Leftrightarrow \quad \sin^2 3x = 1 \quad \Leftrightarrow \quad \sin 3x = \pm 1 \Leftrightarrow 3x = \frac{\pi}{2} + k\pi \quad \Leftrightarrow$
$x = \frac{\pi}{6} + k\frac{\pi}{3}$ for any integer k. Notice that multiplying by $\sin 3x$ in the first step did not introduce extraneous roots.

31. $\cos\frac{x}{2} - 1 = 0 \quad \Leftrightarrow \quad \cos\frac{x}{2} = 1 \Leftrightarrow \frac{x}{2} = 2k\pi \quad \Leftrightarrow \quad x = 4k\pi$ for any integer k.

32. $2\sin\frac{x}{3} + \sqrt{3} = 0 \quad \Leftrightarrow \quad 2\sin\frac{x}{3} = -\sqrt{3} \quad \Leftrightarrow \quad \sin\frac{x}{3} = -\frac{\sqrt{3}}{2} \Leftrightarrow \frac{x}{3} = \frac{4\pi}{3} + 2k\pi, \frac{5\pi}{3} + 2k\pi \quad \Leftrightarrow \quad x = 4\pi + 6k\pi,$
$5\pi + 6k\pi$ for any integer k.

33. $\tan\frac{x}{4} + \sqrt{3} = 0 \quad \Leftrightarrow \quad \tan\frac{x}{4} = -\sqrt{3} \quad \Leftrightarrow \quad \frac{x}{4} = \frac{2\pi}{3} + k\pi \Leftrightarrow x = \frac{8\pi}{3} + 4k\pi$ for any integer k.

34. $\sec\frac{x}{2} = \cos\frac{x}{2} \quad \Leftrightarrow \quad \cos^2\frac{x}{2} = 1 \Rightarrow \cos\frac{x}{2} = \pm 1 \Leftrightarrow \frac{x}{2} = k\pi \quad \Leftrightarrow \quad x = 2k\pi$ for any integer k.

35. $\tan^5 x - 9\tan x = 0 \quad \Leftrightarrow \quad \tan x \left(\tan^4 x - 9\right) = 0 \quad \Leftrightarrow \quad \tan x = 0$ or $\tan^4 x = 9 \Leftrightarrow \tan x = 0$ or $\tan x = \pm\sqrt{3}$
$\Leftrightarrow \quad x = 0, \pi, \frac{\pi}{3}, \frac{2\pi}{3}, \frac{4\pi}{3}, \frac{5\pi}{3}$ in $[0, 2\pi)$. Thus, $x = \frac{k\pi}{3}$ for any integer k.

36. $3\tan^3 x - 3\tan^2 x - \tan x + 1 = 0 \quad \Leftrightarrow \quad (\tan x - 1)\left(3\tan^2 x - 1\right) = 0 \quad \Leftrightarrow \quad \tan x = 1$ or $3\tan^2 x = 1 \quad \Leftrightarrow$
$\tan x = 1$ or $\tan x = \pm\frac{1}{\sqrt{3}} \quad \Leftrightarrow \quad x = \frac{\pi}{6}, \frac{\pi}{4}, \frac{5\pi}{6},$ for $x \in [0, \pi)$. Thus $x = \frac{\pi}{6} + k\pi, \frac{\pi}{4} + k\pi, \frac{5\pi}{6} + k\pi$ for any integer k.

37. $4\sin x \cos x + 2\sin x - 2\cos x - 1 = 0 \quad \Leftrightarrow \quad (2\sin x - 1)(2\cos x + 1) = 0 \quad \Leftrightarrow \quad 2\sin x - 1 = 0$ or $2\cos x + 1 = 0$
$\Leftrightarrow \quad \sin x = \frac{1}{2}$ or $\cos x = -\frac{1}{2} \quad \Leftrightarrow \quad x = \frac{\pi}{6}, \frac{5\pi}{6}, \frac{2\pi}{3}, \frac{4\pi}{3}$ in $[0, 2\pi)$. Thus $x = \frac{\pi}{6} + 2k\pi, \frac{5\pi}{6} + 2k\pi, \frac{2\pi}{3} + 2k\pi,$
$\frac{4\pi}{3} + 2k\pi$ for any integer k.

38. $\sin 2x = 2\tan 2x \quad \Leftrightarrow \quad \sin 2x = \dfrac{2\sin 2x}{\cos 2x} \quad \Leftrightarrow \quad \sin 2x \cos 2x - 2\sin 2x = 0 \quad \Leftrightarrow \quad \sin 2x \left(\cos 2x - 2\right) = 0$
$\Leftrightarrow \quad \cos 2x = 2$ (which is impossible since $|\cos u| \le 1$) or $\sin 2x = 0 \Leftrightarrow 2x = k\pi \quad \Leftrightarrow \quad x = \frac{1}{2}k\pi$ for any integer k.

39. $\cos^2 2x - \sin^2 2x = 0 \quad \Leftrightarrow \quad (\cos 2x - \sin 2x)(\cos 2x + \sin 2x) = 0 \quad \Leftrightarrow \quad \cos 2x = \pm\sin 2x \quad \Leftrightarrow \quad \tan 2x = \pm 1$
$\Leftrightarrow \quad 2x = \frac{\pi}{4}, \frac{3\pi}{4}, \frac{5\pi}{4}, \frac{7\pi}{4}, \frac{9\pi}{4}, \frac{11\pi}{4}, \frac{13\pi}{4}, \frac{15\pi}{4}$ in $[0, 4\pi) \quad \Leftrightarrow \quad x = \frac{\pi}{8}, \frac{3\pi}{8}, \frac{5\pi}{8}, \frac{7\pi}{8}, \frac{9\pi}{8}, \frac{11\pi}{8}, \frac{13\pi}{8}, \frac{15\pi}{8}$ in $[0, 2\pi)$. So the
solution can be expressed as the odd multiples of $\frac{\pi}{8}$ which are $x = \frac{\pi}{8} + \frac{k\pi}{4}$ for any integer k.

40. $\sec x - \tan x = \cos x \quad \Leftrightarrow \quad \cos x \left(\sec x - \tan x\right) = \cos x \left(\cos x\right) \quad \Leftrightarrow \quad 1 - \sin x = \cos^2 x \quad \Leftrightarrow$
$1 - \sin x = 1 - \sin^2 x \quad \Leftrightarrow \quad \sin x = \sin^2 x \quad \Leftrightarrow \quad \sin^2 x - \sin x = 0 \Leftrightarrow \sin x \left(\sin x - 1\right) = 0 \quad \Leftrightarrow \quad \sin x = 0$
or $\sin x = 1 \quad \Leftrightarrow \quad x = 0, \pi$ or $x = \frac{\pi}{2}, \frac{3\pi}{2}$ in $[0, 2\pi)$. However, since the equation is undefined when $x = \frac{\pi}{2}, \frac{3\pi}{2}$, the
solutions are $x = k\pi$ for any integer k.

41. $2\cos 3x = 1 \quad \Leftrightarrow \quad \cos 3x = \frac{1}{2} \Rightarrow 3x = \frac{\pi}{3}, \frac{5\pi}{3}, \frac{7\pi}{3}, \frac{11\pi}{3}, \frac{13\pi}{3}, \frac{17\pi}{3}$ on $[0, 6\pi) \quad \Leftrightarrow \quad x = \frac{\pi}{9}, \frac{5\pi}{9}, \frac{7\pi}{9}, \frac{11\pi}{9}, \frac{13\pi}{9}, \frac{17\pi}{9}$ on
$[0, 2\pi)$.

42. $3\csc^2 x = 4 \quad \Leftrightarrow \quad \csc^2 x = \frac{4}{3} \Rightarrow \csc x = \pm\frac{2}{\sqrt{3}} \quad \Leftrightarrow \quad \sin x = \pm\frac{\sqrt{3}}{2} \Rightarrow x = \frac{\pi}{3}, \frac{2\pi}{3}$ in $[0, 2\pi)$.

43. $2\sin x \tan x - \tan x = 1 - 2\sin x \quad \Leftrightarrow \quad 2\sin x \tan x - \tan x + 2\sin x - 1 = 0 \quad \Leftrightarrow \quad (2\sin x - 1)(\tan x + 1) = 0$
$\Leftrightarrow \quad 2\sin x - 1 = 0 \text{ or } \tan x + 1 = 0 \Leftrightarrow \sin x = \frac{1}{2} \text{ or } \tan x = -1 \quad \Leftrightarrow \quad x = \frac{\pi}{6}, \frac{5\pi}{6} \text{ or } x = \frac{3\pi}{4}, \frac{7\pi}{4}$. Thus, the
solutions in $[0, 2\pi)$ are $\frac{\pi}{6}, \frac{3\pi}{4}, \frac{5\pi}{6}, \frac{7\pi}{4}$.

44. $\sec x \tan x - \cos x \cot x = \sin x \quad \Leftrightarrow \quad \dfrac{1}{\cos x} \dfrac{\sin x}{\cos x} - \cos x \cdot \dfrac{\cos x}{\sin x} = \sin x \Leftrightarrow \dfrac{\sin x}{\cos^2 x} - \dfrac{\cos^2 x}{\sin x} = \sin x.$
Multiplying both sides by the common denominator $\cos^2 x \sin x$ gives $\sin^2 x - \cos^4 x = \sin^2 x \cos^2 x \quad \Leftrightarrow$
$\sin^2 x - \cos^4 x = (1 - \cos^2 x) \cos^2 x \quad \Leftrightarrow \quad \sin^2 x - \cos^4 x = \cos^2 x - \cos^4 x \quad \Leftrightarrow \quad \sin^2 x = \cos^2 x \quad \Leftrightarrow$
$\sin^2 x = 1 - \sin^2 x \Leftrightarrow 2\sin^2 x = 1 \quad \Leftrightarrow \quad \sin x = \pm\frac{1}{\sqrt{2}} \quad \Leftrightarrow \quad x = \frac{\pi}{4}, \frac{3\pi}{4}, \frac{5\pi}{4}, \frac{7\pi}{4}$. Since we multiplied the above
equation by $\cos^2 x \sin x$ (which could be zero) we must check to see if we have introduced extraneous solutions. However,
each of the values of x satisfies the original equation and so the solutions on $[0, 2\pi)$ are $x = \frac{\pi}{4}, \frac{3\pi}{4}, \frac{5\pi}{4}, \frac{7\pi}{4}$.

45. $\tan x - 3\cot x = 0 \quad \Leftrightarrow \quad \dfrac{\sin x}{\cos x} - \dfrac{3\cos x}{\sin x} = 0 \quad \Leftrightarrow \quad \dfrac{\sin^2 x - 3\cos^2 x}{\cos x \sin x} = 0 \quad \Leftrightarrow \quad \dfrac{\sin^2 x + \cos^2 x - 4\cos^2 x}{\cos x \sin x} = 0$
$\Leftrightarrow \quad \dfrac{1 - 4\cos^2 x}{\cos x \sin x} = 0 \quad \Leftrightarrow \quad 1 - 4\cos^2 x = 0 \quad \Leftrightarrow \quad 4\cos^2 x = 1 \Leftrightarrow \cos x = \pm\frac{1}{2} \quad \Leftrightarrow \quad x = \frac{\pi}{3}, \frac{2\pi}{3}, \frac{4\pi}{3}, \frac{5\pi}{3}$ in
$[0, 2\pi)$.

46. $2\sin^2 x - \cos x = 1 \quad \Leftrightarrow \quad 2(1 - \cos^2 x) - \cos x - 1 = 0 \quad \Leftrightarrow \quad -2\cos^2 x - \cos x + 1 = 0 \Leftrightarrow$
$(2\cos x - 1)(\cos x + 1) = 0 \Leftrightarrow 2\cos x - 1 = 0 \text{ or } \cos x + 1 = 0 \quad \Leftrightarrow \quad \cos x = \frac{1}{2} \text{ or } \cos x = -1 \quad \Leftrightarrow \quad x = \frac{\pi}{3}, \frac{5\pi}{3},$
π in $[0, 2\pi)$.

47. $\tan 3x + 1 = \sec 3x \Rightarrow (\tan 3x + 1)^2 = \sec^2 3x \quad \Leftrightarrow \quad \tan^2 3x + 2\tan 3x + 1 = \sec^2 3x \Leftrightarrow$
$\sec^2 3x + 2\tan 3x = \sec^2 3x \quad \Leftrightarrow \quad 2\tan 3x = 0 \quad \Leftrightarrow \quad 3x = 0, \pi, 2\pi, 3\pi, 4\pi, 5\pi \text{ in } [0, 6\pi) \quad \Leftrightarrow \quad x = 0, \frac{\pi}{3}, \frac{2\pi}{3},$
$\pi, \frac{4\pi}{3}, \frac{5\pi}{3}$ in $[0, 2\pi)$. Since squaring both sides is an operation that can introduce extraneous solutions, we must check each
of the possible solution in the original equation. We see that $x = \frac{\pi}{3}, \pi, \frac{5\pi}{3}$ are not solutions. Hence the only solutions are
$x = 0, \frac{2\pi}{3}, \frac{4\pi}{3}$.

48. $3\sec^2 x + 8\cos^2 x = 7 \quad \Leftrightarrow \quad \dfrac{3}{\cos^2 x} + 4\cos^2 x - 7 = 0 \text{ (for } \cos x \neq 0) \quad \Leftrightarrow \quad 3 + 4\cos^4 x - 7\cos^2 x = 0$
$\Leftrightarrow \quad 4\cos^4 x - 7\cos^2 x + 3 = 0 \Leftrightarrow (4\cos^2 x - 3)(\cos^2 x - 1) = 0 \Leftrightarrow 4\cos^2 x - 3 = 0 \text{ or } \cos^2 x - 1 = 0 \quad \Leftrightarrow$
$\cos x = \pm\frac{\sqrt{3}}{2} \text{ or } \cos x = \pm 1 \quad \Leftrightarrow \quad x = \frac{\pi}{6}, \frac{5\pi}{6}, \frac{7\pi}{6}, \frac{11\pi}{6} \text{ or } x = 0, \pi \text{ in } [0, 2\pi)$. So the solutions are $x = 0, \frac{\pi}{6}, \frac{5\pi}{6}, \pi,$
$\frac{7\pi}{6}, \frac{11\pi}{6}$.

49. (a) Since the period of cosine is 2π the solutions are $x \approx 1.15928 + 2k\pi$ and $x \approx 5.12391 + 2k\pi$ for any integer k.

(b) $\cos x = 0.4 \Rightarrow x = \cos^{-1} 0.4 \approx 1.15928$. The other solution is $2\pi - \cos^{-1} 0.4 \approx 5.12391$.

50. (a) Since the period is π, the solutions are of the form $x \approx 1.41815 + k\pi$ for any integer k.

(b) $2\tan x = 13 \quad \Leftrightarrow \quad \tan x = \frac{13}{2} \Rightarrow x \approx 1.41815$. Since the period for tangent is π, the other solution in $[0, 2\pi]$ is
$x \approx 1.41815 + \pi \approx 4.55974$.

51. (a) Since the period of secant is 2π the solutions are $x \approx 1.36943 \pm 2k\pi$ and $\approx 4.91375 \pm 2k\pi$ for any integer k.

(b) $\sec x = 5 \quad \Leftrightarrow \quad \cos x = \frac{1}{5} \Rightarrow x = \cos^{-1} \frac{1}{5} \approx 1.36944$. The other solution is $2\pi - \cos^{-1} \frac{1}{5} \approx 4.91375$.

52. (a) Since the period is π, the solutions are of the form $x \approx 1.16590 + k\pi$ for any integer k.

(b) Since $\cos x = 0$ is not a solution, we divide both sides by $\cos x$. $3\sin x = 7\cos x \quad \Leftrightarrow \quad \tan x = \frac{7}{3} \Rightarrow x \approx 1.16590$.
Since the period for tangent is π, the other solution in $[0, 2\pi]$ is $x \approx 1.16590 + \pi \approx 4.30750$.

53. (a) Since $\sin(\pi + x) = -\sin x$, we can express the general solutions as $x \approx 0.46365 + k\pi$ and $x \approx 2.67795 + k\pi$ for
any integer k.

(b) $5\sin^2 x - 1 = 0 \Rightarrow \sin^2 x = \dfrac{1}{5} \Rightarrow \sin x = \pm\frac{1}{\sqrt{5}}$. Now $\sin x = \frac{1}{\sqrt{5}} \Rightarrow x = \sin^{-1}\left(\frac{1}{\sqrt{5}}\right) \approx 0.46365$, and
$x \approx \pi - 0.46365 \approx 2.67795$. Also, $\sin x = -\frac{1}{\sqrt{5}} \Rightarrow x = \sin^{-1}\left(-\frac{1}{\sqrt{5}}\right) \approx -0.46365$, so in the interval $[0, 2\pi)$,
$x \approx \pi - (-0.46365) \approx 3.60524$ and $x \approx 2\pi - 0.46365 \approx 5.81954$.

54. (a) Since the period is 2π, the solutions are of the form $x \approx 1.57080 + k\pi, x \approx 0.25268 + 2k\pi, x \approx 2.88891 + 2k\pi$ for any integer k.

(b) $2\sin 2x - \cos x = 0 \quad \Leftrightarrow \quad 2(2\sin x \cos x) - \cos x = 0 \quad \Leftrightarrow \quad 4\sin x \cos x - \cos x = 0 \Leftrightarrow$
$\cos x(4\sin x - 1) = 0 \quad \Leftrightarrow \quad \cos x = 0$ or $4\sin x - 1 = 0$. Now $\cos x = 0 \quad \Leftrightarrow \quad x = \frac{\pi}{2}, \frac{3\pi}{2}$ and $4\sin x - 1 = 0$
$\Leftrightarrow \quad \sin x = \frac{1}{4} \Rightarrow x \approx 0.25268$ or $x \approx \pi - 0.25268 \approx 2.88891$. Thus the solutions in $[0, 2\pi)$ are $x \approx 0.25268$, $1.57080, 2.88891, 4.71239$.

55. (a) Since the period for sine is 2π, the general solution is of the form $x \approx 0.33984 + 2k\pi$ and $x \approx 2.80176 + 2k\pi$ for any integer k.

(b) $3\sin^2 x - 7\sin x + 2 = 0 \Rightarrow (3\sin x - 1)(\sin x - 2) = 0 \Rightarrow 3\sin x - 1 = 0$ or $\sin x - 2 = 0$. Since $|\sin x| \leq 1$, $\sin x - 2 = 0$ has no solution. Thus $3\sin x - 1 = 0 \Rightarrow \sin x = \frac{1}{3} \Rightarrow x \approx 0.33984$ and $x \approx \pi - 0.33984 \approx 2.80176$.

56. (a) Since the period is π, the solutions are of the form $x \approx 1.10715 + k\pi, x \approx 2.03444 + k\pi, x \approx 1.24905 + k\pi, x \approx 1.89255 + k\pi$ for any integer k.

(b) $\tan^4 x - 13\tan^2 x + 36 = 0 \quad \Leftrightarrow \quad (\tan^2 x - 4)(\tan^2 x - 9) = 0 \quad \Leftrightarrow \quad \tan x = \pm 2$ or $\tan x = \pm 3 \Rightarrow$
$x \approx 1.10715, -1.10715, 1.24905, -1.24905$ in $\left(-\frac{\pi}{2}, \frac{\pi}{2}\right)$. Since the period for tangent is π, the solutions in $[0, 2\pi)$
are $x \approx 1.10715, 1.24905, 1.89255, 2.03444, 4.24874, 4.39064, 5.03414, 5.17604$.

57. $f(x) = 3\cos x + 1; g(x) = \cos x - 1. f(x) = g(x)$ when
$3\cos x + 1 = \cos x - 1 \Leftrightarrow 2\cos x = -2 \quad \Leftrightarrow \quad \cos x = -1 \Leftrightarrow$
$x = \pi + 2k\pi = (2k + 1)\pi$. The points of intersection are $((2k + 1)\pi, -2)$ for
any integer k.

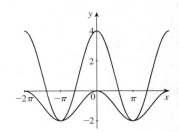

58. $f(x) = \sin 2x; g(x) = 2\sin 2x + 1. f(x) = g(x)$ when $\sin 2x = 2\sin 2x + 1$
$\Leftrightarrow \sin 2x = -1 \quad \Leftrightarrow \quad 2x = \frac{3\pi}{2} + 2k\pi \quad \Leftrightarrow \quad x = \frac{3\pi}{4} + k\pi$ for any integer k.

59. $f(x) = \tan x; g(x) = \sqrt{3}. f(x) = g(x)$ when $\tan x = \sqrt{3} \Leftrightarrow$
$x = \frac{\pi}{3} + k\pi$. The intersection points are $\left(\frac{\pi}{3} + k\pi, \sqrt{3}\right)$ for any integer k.

60. $f(x) = \sin x - 1$; $g(x) = \cos x$. $f(x) = g(x)$ when $\sin x - 1 = \cos x \Rightarrow$

$(\sin x - 1)^2 = \cos^2 x \quad \Leftrightarrow \quad \sin^2 x - 2\sin x + 1 = \cos^2 x \quad \Leftrightarrow$

$\sin^2 x - 2\sin x + 1 - \cos^2 x = 0 \Leftrightarrow 2\sin^2 x - 2\sin x = 0 \quad \Leftrightarrow$

$2\sin x (\sin x - 1) = 0 \quad \Leftrightarrow \quad \sin x = 0$ or $\sin x = 1 \Leftrightarrow x = k\pi, \frac{\pi}{2} + 2k\pi$.

However, $x = k\pi$ is not a solution when k is even. (The extraneous solutions were

introduced by squaring both sides.) So the solutions are $x = (2k+1)\pi, \frac{\pi}{2} + 2k\pi$,

and the intersection points are $(\pi + 2k\pi, -1)$, $\left(\frac{\pi}{2} + 2k\pi, 0\right)$ for any integer k.

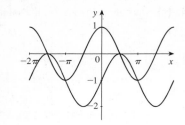

Another method: $\sin x - 1 = \cos x \quad \Leftrightarrow \quad \sin x - \cos x = 1 \quad \Leftrightarrow \quad \sqrt{2}\left(\frac{1}{\sqrt{2}}\sin x - \frac{1}{\sqrt{2}}\cos x\right) = 1 \quad \Leftrightarrow \quad \frac{\sqrt{2}}{2}\sin x -$

$\frac{\sqrt{2}}{2}\cos x = \frac{\sqrt{2}}{2}$. Since $\sin\frac{\pi}{4} = \cos\frac{\pi}{4} = \frac{\sqrt{2}}{2}$, we may write $\frac{\sqrt{2}}{2}\sin x - \frac{\sqrt{2}}{2}\cos x = \cos\frac{\pi}{4}\sin x - \sin\frac{\pi}{4}\cos x = \frac{\sqrt{2}}{2} \quad \Leftrightarrow$

$\sin\left(x - \frac{\pi}{4}\right) = \frac{\sqrt{2}}{2} \quad \Leftrightarrow \quad x - \frac{\pi}{4} = \frac{\pi}{4}, \frac{3\pi}{4} \quad \Leftrightarrow \quad x = \frac{\pi}{2}, \pi$ in $[0, 2\pi)$. So the solutions are $x = (2k+1)\pi, \frac{\pi}{2} + 2k\pi$,

and the intersection points are $(\pi + 2k\pi, -1)$, $\left(\frac{\pi}{2} + 2k\pi, 0\right)$ for any integer k.

61. $\cos x \cos 3x - \sin x \sin 3x = 0 \quad \Leftrightarrow \quad \cos(x + 3x) = 0 \quad \Leftrightarrow \quad \cos 4x = 0 \quad \Leftrightarrow \quad 4x = \frac{\pi}{2}, \frac{3\pi}{2}, \frac{5\pi}{2}, \frac{7\pi}{2}, \frac{9\pi}{2}, \frac{11\pi}{2},$

$\frac{13\pi}{2}, \frac{15\pi}{2}$ in $[0, 8\pi) \quad \Leftrightarrow \quad x = \frac{\pi}{8}, \frac{3\pi}{8}, \frac{5\pi}{8}, \frac{7\pi}{8}, \frac{9\pi}{8}, \frac{11\pi}{8}, \frac{13\pi}{8}, \frac{15\pi}{8}$ in $[0, 2\pi)$.

62. $\cos x \cos 2x + \sin x \sin 2x = \frac{1}{2} \quad \Leftrightarrow \quad \cos(x - 2x) = \frac{1}{2} \quad \Leftrightarrow \quad \cos(-x) = \frac{1}{2} \quad \Leftrightarrow \quad \cos x = \frac{1}{2} \Leftrightarrow x = \frac{\pi}{3}, \frac{5\pi}{3}$ in

$[0, 2\pi)$.

63. $\sin 2x \cos x + \cos 2x \sin x = \frac{\sqrt{3}}{2} \Leftrightarrow \sin(2x + x) = \frac{\sqrt{3}}{2} \Leftrightarrow \sin 3x = \frac{\sqrt{3}}{2} \quad \Leftrightarrow \quad 3x = \frac{\pi}{3}, \frac{2\pi}{3}, \frac{7\pi}{3}, \frac{8\pi}{3}, \frac{13\pi}{3}, \frac{14\pi}{3}$ in

$[0, 6\pi) \Leftrightarrow x = \frac{\pi}{9}, \frac{2\pi}{9}, \frac{7\pi}{9}, \frac{8\pi}{9}, \frac{13\pi}{9}, \frac{14\pi}{9}$ in $[0, 2\pi)$.

64. $\sin 3x \cos x - \cos 3x \sin x = 0 \quad \Leftrightarrow \quad \sin(3x - x) = 0 \quad \Leftrightarrow \quad \sin 2x = 0 \quad \Leftrightarrow \quad 2x = 0, \pi, 2\pi, 3\pi, 4\pi$ in $[0, 4\pi)$

$\Leftrightarrow x = 0, \frac{\pi}{2}, \pi, \frac{3\pi}{2}$ in $[0, 2\pi)$.

65. $\sin 2x + \cos x = 0 \quad \Leftrightarrow \quad 2\sin x \cos x + \cos x = 0 \Leftrightarrow \cos x (2\sin x + 1) = 0 \quad \Leftrightarrow \quad \cos x = 0$ or $\sin x = -\frac{1}{2} \quad \Leftrightarrow$

$x = \frac{\pi}{2}, \frac{7\pi}{6}, \frac{3\pi}{2}, \frac{11\pi}{6}$.

66. $\tan\frac{x}{2} - \sin x = 0 \quad \Leftrightarrow \quad \frac{\sin x}{1 + \cos x} - \sin x = 0 \quad \Leftrightarrow \quad \sin x - \sin x (1 + \cos x) = 0$ (and $\cos x \neq -1 \quad \Leftrightarrow \quad x \neq \pi$)

$\Leftrightarrow \quad \sin x (-\cos x) = 0 \quad \Leftrightarrow \quad \sin x = 0$ or $\cos x = 0 \quad \Leftrightarrow \quad x = 0, \frac{\pi}{2}, \frac{3\pi}{2}$ in $[0, 2\pi)$ ($x = \pi$ is inadmissible).

67. $\cos 2x + \cos x = 2 \quad \Leftrightarrow \quad 2\cos^2 x - 1 + \cos x - 2 = 0 \Leftrightarrow 2\cos^2 x + \cos x - 3 = 0 \quad \Leftrightarrow \quad (2\cos x + 3)(\cos x - 1) = 0$

$\Leftrightarrow \quad 2\cos x + 3 = 0$ or $\cos x - 1 = 0 \quad \Leftrightarrow \quad \cos x = -\frac{3}{2}$ (which is impossible) or $\cos x = 1 \quad \Leftrightarrow \quad x = 0$ in $[0, 2\pi)$.

68. $\tan x + \cot x = 4\sin 2x \quad \Leftrightarrow \quad \frac{\sin x}{\cos x} + \frac{\cos x}{\sin x} = 8\sin x \cos x \quad \Leftrightarrow \quad \left(\frac{\sin x}{\cos x} + \frac{\cos x}{\sin x}\right) \cdot \sin x \cos x = (8\sin x \cos x) \cdot$

$\sin x \cos x \quad \Leftrightarrow \quad \sin^2 x + \cos^2 x = 8\sin^2 x \cos^2 x \quad \Leftrightarrow \quad 1 = 2(2\sin x \cos x)^2 \quad \Leftrightarrow \quad (\sin 2x)^2 = \frac{1}{2} \Leftrightarrow$

$\sin 2x = \pm\frac{1}{\sqrt{2}}$. Therefore, $2x = \frac{\pi}{4} + k\pi$ or $2x = \frac{3\pi}{4} + k\pi \quad \Leftrightarrow \quad x = \frac{\pi}{8} + \frac{k\pi}{2}$ or $x = \frac{3\pi}{8} + \frac{k\pi}{2}$. Thus on the interval

$[0, 2\pi)$ the solutions are $x = \frac{\pi}{8}, \frac{5\pi}{8}, \frac{9\pi}{8}, \frac{13\pi}{8}$ and $\frac{3\pi}{8}, \frac{7\pi}{8}, \frac{11\pi}{8}, \frac{15\pi}{8}$. Together we write the solutions as $x = \frac{\pi}{8}, \frac{3\pi}{8}, \frac{5\pi}{8}, \frac{7\pi}{8}$,

$\frac{9\pi}{8}, \frac{11\pi}{8}, \frac{13\pi}{8}, \frac{15\pi}{8}$, which are odd multiples of $\frac{\pi}{8}$. So we can express the general solution as $x = \frac{\pi}{8} + k\frac{\pi}{4}$ where k is any

integer.

69. $\sin x + \sin 3x = 0 \quad \Leftrightarrow \quad 2\sin 2x \cos(-x) = 0 \quad \Leftrightarrow \quad 2\sin 2x \cos x = 0 \quad \Leftrightarrow \quad \sin 2x = 0$ or $\cos x = 0 \quad \Leftrightarrow$

$2x = k\pi$ or $x = k\frac{\pi}{2} \Leftrightarrow x = k\frac{\pi}{2}$ for any integer k.

70. $\cos 5x - \cos 7x = 0 \quad \Leftrightarrow \quad -2\sin 6x \sin(-x) = 0 \quad \Leftrightarrow \quad \sin 6x \sin x = 0 \quad \Leftrightarrow \quad \sin 6x = 0$ or $\sin x = 0 \quad \Leftrightarrow$

$6x = k\pi$ or $x = k\pi \Leftrightarrow x = k\frac{\pi}{6}$ for any integer k.

71. $\cos 4x + \cos 2x = \cos x \quad \Leftrightarrow \quad 2\cos 3x \cos x = \cos x \quad \Leftrightarrow \quad \cos x (2\cos 3x - 1) = 0 \Leftrightarrow \cos x = 0$ or $\cos 3x = \frac{1}{2}$

$\Leftrightarrow \quad x = \frac{\pi}{2}$ or $3x = \frac{\pi}{3} + 2k\pi, \frac{5\pi}{3} + 2k\pi, \frac{7\pi}{3} + 2k\pi, \frac{11\pi}{3} + 2k\pi, \frac{13\pi}{3} + 2k\pi, \frac{17\pi}{3} + 2k\pi \quad \Leftrightarrow \quad x = \frac{\pi}{2}, \frac{\pi}{9} + 2k\frac{\pi}{3},$

$\frac{5\pi}{9} + 2k\frac{\pi}{3}$.

72. $\sin 5x - \sin 3x = \cos 4x \quad \Leftrightarrow \quad 2 \cos 4x \sin x = \cos 4x \quad \Leftrightarrow \quad \cos 4x (2 \sin x - 1) = 0 \Leftrightarrow \cos 4x = 0$ or $\sin x = \frac{1}{2}$
$\Leftrightarrow \quad 4x = \frac{\pi}{2} + k\pi$ or $x = \frac{\pi}{6} + 2k\pi, \frac{5\pi}{6} + 2k\pi \Leftrightarrow x = \frac{\pi}{8} + k\frac{\pi}{4}, \frac{\pi}{6} + 2k\pi, \frac{5\pi}{6} + 2k\pi$.

73. $\sin 2x = x$

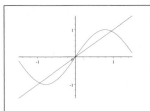

The three solutions are $x = 0$ and $x \approx \pm 0.95$.

74. $\cos x = \frac{x}{3}$

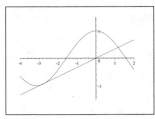

The three solutions are $x \approx 1.17, -2.66$, and -2.94.

75. $2^{\sin x} = x$

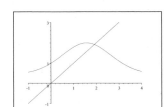

The only solution is $x \approx 1.92$.

76. $\sin x = x^3$

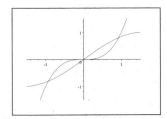

The three solutions are $x = 0$ and $x \approx \pm 0.93$.

77. $\frac{\cos x}{1 + x^2} = x^2$

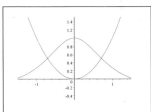

The two solutions are $x \approx \pm 0.71$.

78. $\sin x = \frac{1}{2} \left(e^x + e^{-x} \right)$

This equation has no solution.

79. We substitute $v_0 = 2200$ and $R(\theta) = 5000$ and solve for θ. So $5000 = \dfrac{(2200)^2 \sin 2\theta}{32} \quad \Leftrightarrow \quad 5000 = 151250 \sin 2\theta$
$\Leftrightarrow \quad \sin 2\theta = 0.03308 \Rightarrow 2\theta = 1.89442°$ or $2\theta = 180° - 1.89442° = 178.10558°$. If $2\theta = 1.89442°$, then $\theta = 0.94721°$, and if $2\theta = 178.10558°$, then $\theta = 89.05279°$.

80. Since $4e^{-3t} > 0$, we have $0 = 4e^{-3t} \sin 2\pi t \Leftrightarrow 0 = \sin 2\pi t \quad \Leftrightarrow \quad 2\pi t = 0, \pi, 2\pi, \ldots \quad \Leftrightarrow \quad t = 0, \frac{1}{2}, 1, \frac{3}{2}, \ldots$.

81. We substitute $\theta_1 = 70°$ and $\dfrac{v_1}{v_2} = 1.33$ into Snell's Law to get $\dfrac{\sin 70°}{\sin \theta_2} = 1.33 \quad \Leftrightarrow \quad \sin \theta_2 = \dfrac{\sin 70°}{1.33} = 0.7065 \Rightarrow$
$\theta_2 \approx 44.95°$.

82. The index of refraction from glass to air is $\dfrac{1}{1.52} \approx 0.658$, so we substitute $\theta_2 = 90°$ into Snell's Law to get
$\dfrac{\sin \theta_1}{\sin 90°} = 0.658 \Rightarrow \sin \theta_1 \approx 0.658 \Rightarrow \theta_1 \approx 41.1°$.

83. (a) $10 = 12 + 2.83 \sin\left(\frac{2\pi}{3}(t-80)\right)$ $\Leftrightarrow$ $2.83 \sin\left(\frac{2\pi}{3}(t-80)\right) = -2$ $\Leftrightarrow$ $\sin\left(\frac{2\pi}{3}(t-80)\right) = -0.70671$.

Now $\sin\theta = -0.70671$ and $\theta = -0.78484$. If $\frac{2\pi}{3}(t-80) = -0.78484 \Leftrightarrow t - 80 = 45.6$ $\Leftrightarrow$ $t = 34.4$.

Now in the interval $[0, 2\pi)$, we have $\theta = \pi + 0.78484 \approx 3.92644$ and $\theta = 2\pi - 0.78484 \approx 5.49834$. If

$\frac{2\pi}{3}(t-80) = 3.92644$ $\Leftrightarrow$ $t - 80 = 228.1 \Leftrightarrow t = 308.1$. And if $\frac{2\pi}{3}(t-80) = 5.49834$ $\Leftrightarrow$ $t - 80 = 319.4$

$\Leftrightarrow$ $t = 399.4$ $(399.4 - 365 = 34.4)$. So according to this model, there should be 10 hours of sunshine on the

34th day (February 3) and on the 308th day (November 4).

(b) Since $L(t) = 12 + 2.83 \sin\left(\frac{2\pi}{3}(t-80)\right) \geq 10$ for $t \in [34, 308]$, the number of days with more than 10 hours of daylight is $308 - 34 + 1 = 275$ days.

84. (a) $F = \frac{1}{2}(1 - \cos\theta) = 0 \Rightarrow \cos\theta = 1 \Rightarrow \theta = 0$

(b) $F = \frac{1}{2}(1 - \cos\theta) = 0.25 \Rightarrow 1 - \cos\theta = 0.5 \Rightarrow \cos\theta = 0.5 \Rightarrow \theta = 60°$ or $120°$

(c) $F = \frac{1}{2}(1 - \cos\theta) = 0.5 \Rightarrow 1 - \cos\theta = 1 \Rightarrow \cos\theta = 0 \Rightarrow \theta = 90°$ or $270°$

(d) $F = \frac{1}{2}(1 - \cos\theta) = 1 \Rightarrow 1 - \cos\theta = 2 \Rightarrow \cos\theta = -1 \Rightarrow \theta = 180°$

85. (a) First note that $\alpha = \frac{\pi}{2} - \frac{\theta}{2}$. The part of the belt touching the larger

pulley has length $2(\pi - \alpha)R = (\theta + \pi)R$ and similarly the part

touching the smaller belt has length $(\theta + \pi)r$. To calculate a and

b, we write $\cot\frac{\theta}{2} = \frac{a}{R} = \frac{b}{r} \Rightarrow a = R\cot\frac{\theta}{2}$ and $b = r\cot\frac{\theta}{2}$, so

the length of the straight parts of the belt is $2a + 2b = 2(R + r)\cot\frac{\theta}{2}$. Thus, the total length of the belt is

$L = (\theta + \pi)R + (\theta + \pi)r + 2(R + r)\cot\frac{\theta}{2} = (R + r)\left(\theta + \pi + 2\cot\frac{\theta}{2}\right)$ and so $\theta + \pi + 2\cot\frac{\theta}{2} = \frac{L}{R + r}$ $\Leftrightarrow$

$\theta + 2\cot\frac{\theta}{2} = \frac{L}{R + r} - \pi$.

(b) We plot $\theta + 2\cot\frac{\theta}{2}$ and $\frac{L}{R + r} - \pi = \frac{27.78}{2.42 + 1.21} - \pi \approx 4.5113$ in the same

viewing rectangle. The solution is $\theta \approx 1.047$ rad $\approx 60°$.

86. Statement A is true: every identity is an equation. However, Statement B is false: not every equation is an identity. The difference between an identity and an equation is that an identity is true for all values in the domain, whereas an equation may only be true for certain values in the domain and false for others. For example, $x = 0$ is an equation but not an identity, because it is true for only one value of x.

87. $\sin(\cos x)$ is a function of a function, that is, a composition of trigonometric functions (see Section 2.7). Most of the other equations involve sums, products, differences, or quotients of trigonometric functions.

$\sin(\cos x) = 0$ $\Leftrightarrow$ $\cos x = 0$ or $\cos x = \pi$. However, since $|\cos x| \leq 1$, the only solution is $\cos x = 0 \Rightarrow x = \frac{\pi}{2} + k\pi$. The graph of $f(x) = \sin(\cos x)$ is shown.

Chapter 7 Review

1. $\sin\theta\left(\cot\theta+\tan\theta\right)=\sin\theta\left(\dfrac{\cos\theta}{\sin\theta}+\dfrac{\sin\theta}{\cos\theta}\right)=\cos\theta+\dfrac{\sin^2\theta}{\cos\theta}=\dfrac{\cos^2\theta+\sin^2\theta}{\cos\theta}=\dfrac{1}{\cos\theta}=\sec\theta$

2. $\left(\sec\theta-1\right)\left(\sec\theta+1\right)=\sec^2\theta-1=\tan^2\theta$

3. $\cos^2 x\csc x-\csc x=\left(1-\sin^2 x\right)\csc x-\csc x=\csc x-\sin^2 x\csc x-\csc x=-\sin^2 x\cdot\dfrac{1}{\sin x}=-\sin x$

4. $\dfrac{1}{1-\sin^2 x}=\dfrac{1}{\cos^2 x}=\sec^2 x=1+\tan^2 x$

5. $\dfrac{\cos^2 x-\tan^2 x}{\sin^2 x}=\dfrac{\cos^2 x}{\sin^2 x}-\dfrac{\tan^2 x}{\sin^2 x}=\cot^2 x-\dfrac{1}{\cos^2 x}=\cot^2 x-\sec^2 x$

6. $\dfrac{1+\sec x}{\sec x}=\dfrac{1}{\sec x}+1=1+\cos x=\left(1+\cos x\right)\cdot\dfrac{1-\cos x}{1-\cos x}=\dfrac{1-\cos^2 x}{1-\cos x}=\dfrac{\sin^2 x}{1-\cos x}$

7. $\dfrac{\cos^2 x}{1-\sin x}=\dfrac{\cos x}{\dfrac{1}{\cos x}\left(1-\sin x\right)}=\dfrac{\cos x}{\dfrac{1}{\cos x}-\dfrac{\sin x}{\cos x}}=\dfrac{\cos x}{\sec x-\tan x}$

8. $\left(1-\tan x\right)\left(1-\cot x\right)=1-\cot x-\tan x+\tan x\cot x=2-\left(\cot x+\tan x\right)=2-\left(\dfrac{\cos x}{\sin x}+\dfrac{\sin x}{\cos x}\right)$

$$=2-\dfrac{\cos^2 x+\sin^2 x}{\cos x\sin x}=2-\dfrac{1}{\cos x\sin x}=2-\sec x\csc x$$

9. $\sin^2 x\cot^2 x+\cos^2 x\tan^2 x=\sin^2 x\cdot\dfrac{\cos^2 x}{\sin^2 x}+\cos^2 x\cdot\dfrac{\sin^2 x}{\cos^2 x}=\cos^2 x+\sin^2 x=1$

10. $\left(\tan x+\cot x\right)^2=\left(\dfrac{\sin x}{\cos x}+\dfrac{\cos x}{\sin x}\right)^2=\left(\dfrac{\sin^2 x+\cos^2 x}{\cos x\sin x}\right)^2=\left(\dfrac{1}{\cos x\sin x}\right)^2=\left(\sec x\csc x\right)^2=\csc^2 x\sec^2 x$

11. $\dfrac{\sin 2x}{1+\cos 2x}=\dfrac{2\sin x\cos x}{1+2\cos^2 x-1}=\dfrac{2\sin x\cos x}{2\cos^2 x}=\dfrac{2\sin x}{2\cos x}=\tan x$

12. $\dfrac{\cos\left(x+y\right)}{\cos x\sin y}=\dfrac{\cos x\cos y-\sin x\sin y}{\cos x\sin y}=\dfrac{\cos x\cos y}{\cos x\sin y}-\dfrac{\sin x\sin y}{\cos x\sin y}=\dfrac{\cos y}{\sin y}-\dfrac{\sin x}{\cos x}=\cot y-\tan x$

13. $\tan\dfrac{x}{2}=\dfrac{1-\cos x}{\sin x}=\dfrac{1}{\sin x}-\dfrac{\cos x}{\sin x}=\csc x-\cot x$

14. $\dfrac{\sin\left(x+y\right)+\sin\left(x-y\right)}{\cos\left(x+y\right)+\cos\left(x-y\right)}=\dfrac{2\sin\left(\dfrac{(x+y)+(x-y)}{2}\right)\cos\left(\dfrac{(x+y)-(x-y)}{2}\right)}{2\cos\left(\dfrac{(x+y)+(x-y)}{2}\right)\cos\left(\dfrac{(x+y)-(x-y)}{2}\right)}=\dfrac{2\sin x\cos y}{2\cos x\cos y}=\dfrac{\sin x}{\cos x}=\tan x$

15. $\sin\left(x+y\right)\sin\left(x-y\right)=\tfrac{1}{2}\left[\cos\left((x+y)-(x-y)\right)-\cos\left((x+y)+(x-y)\right)\right]=\tfrac{1}{2}\left(\cos 2y-\cos 2x\right)$

$$=\tfrac{1}{2}\left[1-2\sin^2 y-\left(1-2\sin^2 x\right)\right]=\tfrac{1}{2}\left(2\sin^2 x-2\sin^2 y\right)=\sin^2 x-\sin^2 y$$

16. $\csc x-\tan\dfrac{x}{2}=\csc x-\dfrac{1-\cos x}{\sin x}=\csc x-\left(\csc x-\cot x\right)=\cot x$

17. $1+\tan x\tan\dfrac{x}{2}=1+\dfrac{\sin x}{\cos x}\cdot\dfrac{1-\cos x}{\sin x}=1+\dfrac{1-\cos x}{\cos x}=1+\dfrac{1}{\cos x}-1=\dfrac{1}{\cos x}=\sec x$

18. $\dfrac{\sin 3x+\cos 3x}{\cos x-\sin x}=\dfrac{\sin\left(x+2x\right)+\cos\left(x+2x\right)}{\cos x-\sin x}=\dfrac{\sin x\cos 2x+\cos x\sin 2x+\cos x\cos 2x-\sin x\sin 2x}{\cos x-\sin x}$

$$=\dfrac{\cos 2x\left(\sin x+\cos x\right)+\sin 2x\left(\cos x-\sin x\right)}{\cos x-\sin x}=\dfrac{\cos 2x\left(\sin x+\cos x\right)}{\cos x-\sin x}+\sin 2x$$

$$=\dfrac{\left(\cos^2 x-\sin^2 x\right)\left(\sin x+\cos x\right)}{\cos x-\sin x}+\sin 2x=\left(\cos x+\sin x\right)\left(\sin x+\cos x\right)+\sin 2x$$

$$=\sin^2 x+\cos^2 x+2\sin x\cos x+\sin 2x=1+\sin 2x+\sin 2x=1+2\sin 2x$$

19. $\left(\cos\dfrac{x}{2}-\sin\dfrac{x}{2}\right)^2=\cos^2\dfrac{x}{2}-2\sin\dfrac{x}{2}\cos\dfrac{x}{2}+\sin^2\dfrac{x}{2}=\sin^2\dfrac{x}{2}+\cos^2\dfrac{x}{2}-2\sin\dfrac{x}{2}\cos\dfrac{x}{2}=1-\sin\left(2\cdot\dfrac{x}{2}\right)=1-\sin x$

20. $\dfrac{\cos 3x - \cos 7x}{\sin 3x + \sin 7x} = \dfrac{-2\sin\left(\dfrac{3x+7x}{2}\right)\sin\left(\dfrac{3x-7x}{2}\right)}{2\sin\left(\dfrac{3x+7x}{2}\right)\cos\left(\dfrac{3x-7x}{2}\right)} = \dfrac{-2\sin 5x \sin(-2x)}{2\sin 5x \cos(-2x)} = \dfrac{2\sin 5x \sin 2x}{2\sin 5x \cos 2x} = \dfrac{\sin 2x}{\cos 2x} = \tan 2x$

21. $\dfrac{\sin 2x}{\sin x} - \dfrac{\cos 2x}{\cos x} = \dfrac{2\sin x \cos x}{\sin x} - \dfrac{2\cos^2 x - 1}{\cos x} = 2\cos x - 2\cos x + \dfrac{1}{\cos x} = \sec x$

22. $(\cos x + \cos y)^2 + (\sin x - \sin y)^2 = \cos^2 x + 2\cos x \cos y + \cos^2 y + \sin^2 x - 2\sin x \sin y + \sin^2 y = (\cos^2 x + \sin^2 x) +$
$(\sin^2 y + \cos^2 y) + 2(\cos x \cos y - \sin x \sin y) = 2 + 2\cos(x+y)$

23. $\tan\left(x + \dfrac{\pi}{4}\right) = \dfrac{\tan x + \tan\frac{\pi}{4}}{1 - \tan x \tan\frac{\pi}{4}} = \dfrac{1 + \tan x}{1 - \tan x}$

24. $\dfrac{\sec x - 1}{\sin x \sec x} = \dfrac{\dfrac{1}{\cos x} - 1}{\sin x \dfrac{1}{\cos x}} = \dfrac{\dfrac{1}{\cos x} - 1}{\sin x \dfrac{1}{\cos x}} \cdot \dfrac{\cos x}{\cos x} = \dfrac{1 - \cos x}{\sin x} = \tan\dfrac{x}{2}$

25. (a) $f(x) = 1 - \left(\cos\frac{x}{2} - \sin\frac{x}{2}\right)^2$, $g(x) = \sin x$

(b) The graphs suggest that $f(x) = g(x)$ is an identity. To prove this, expand $f(x)$ and simplify, using the double-angle formula for sine:

$$\begin{aligned} f(x) &= 1 - \left(\cos\tfrac{x}{2} - \sin\tfrac{x}{2}\right)^2 \\ &= 1 - \left(\cos^2\tfrac{x}{2} - 2\cos\tfrac{x}{2}\sin\tfrac{x}{2} + \sin^2\tfrac{x}{2}\right) \\ &= 1 + 2\cos\tfrac{x}{2}\sin\tfrac{x}{2} - \left(\cos^2\tfrac{x}{2} + \sin^2\tfrac{x}{2}\right) \\ &= 1 + \sin x - (1) = \sin x = g(x) \end{aligned}$$

26. (a) $f(x) = \sin x + \cos x$,

$g(x) = \sqrt{\sin^2 x + \cos^2 x}$

(b) The graphs suggest that $f(x) \neq g(x)$ in general. For example, choose $x = \frac{\pi}{6}$ and evaluate the functions:

$f\left(\frac{\pi}{6}\right) = \frac{1}{2} + \frac{\sqrt{3}}{2} = \frac{1+\sqrt{3}}{2}$, whereas

$g\left(\frac{\pi}{6}\right) = \sqrt{\frac{1}{4} + \frac{3}{4}} = \sqrt{1} = 1$, so $f(x) \neq g(x)$.

27. (a) $f(x) = \tan x \tan\frac{x}{2}$, $g(x) = \dfrac{1}{\cos x}$

(b) The graphs suggest that $f(x) \neq g(x)$ in general. For example, choose $x = \frac{\pi}{3}$ and evaluate: $f\left(\frac{\pi}{3}\right) = \tan\frac{\pi}{3}$

$\tan\frac{\pi}{6} = \sqrt{3} \cdot \frac{1}{\sqrt{3}} = 1$, whereas $g\left(\frac{\pi}{3}\right) = \dfrac{1}{\frac{1}{2}} = 2$, so

$f(x) \neq g(x)$.

28. (a) $f(x) = 1 - 8\sin^2 x + 8\sin^4 x$, $g(x) = \cos 4x$

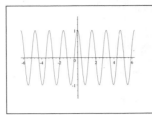

(b) The graphs suggest that $f(x) = g(x)$ is an identity. To show this, expand $g(x)$ by using double-angle identities:

$$
\begin{aligned}
g(x) &= \cos 4x = \cos(2(2x)) = 1 - 2\sin^2 2x \\
&= 1 - 2(2\sin x \cos x)^2 = 1 - 2(4\sin^2 x \cos^2 x) \\
&= 1 - 8\sin^2 x \cdot (1 - \sin^2 x) \\
&= 1 - 8\sin^2 x + 8\sin^4 x = f(x)
\end{aligned}
$$

29. (a) $f(x) = 2\sin^2 3x + \cos 6x$

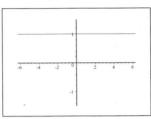

(b) The graph suggests that $f(x) = 1$ for all x. To prove this, we use the double angle formula to note that $\cos 6x = \cos(2(3x)) = 1 - 2\sin^2 3x$, so $f(x) = 2\sin^2 3x + (1 - 2\sin^2 3x) = 1$.

30. (a) $f(x) = \sin x \cot \dfrac{x}{2}$, $g(x) = \cos x$

Conjecture: $f(x) = g(x) + 1$

(b) *Proof:*

$$
\begin{aligned}
f(x) &= \sin x \cot \tfrac{x}{2} = \sin x \cdot \left(\frac{\cos \tfrac{x}{2}}{\sin \tfrac{x}{2}}\right) \\
&= \left(2\sin \tfrac{x}{2} \cos \tfrac{x}{2}\right) \cdot \left(\frac{\cos \tfrac{x}{2}}{\sin \tfrac{x}{2}}\right) = 2\cos^2 \tfrac{x}{2}
\end{aligned}
$$

Now subtract and add 1, so $f(x) = 2$

$$
\cos^2 \frac{x}{2} - 1 + 1 = \cos x + 1 = g(x) + 1.
$$

31. $\cos x \sin x - \sin x = 0 \;\Leftrightarrow\; \sin x (\cos x - 1) = 0 \;\Leftrightarrow\; \sin x = 0$ or $\cos x = 1 \Leftrightarrow x = 0, \pi$ or $x = 0$. Therefore, the solutions are $x = 0$ and π.

32. $\sin x - 2\sin^2 x = 0 \;\Leftrightarrow\; \sin x (1 - 2\sin x) = 0 \;\Leftrightarrow\; \sin x = 0$ or $\sin x = \tfrac{1}{2} \Leftrightarrow x = 0, \pi$ or $x = \tfrac{\pi}{6}, \tfrac{5\pi}{6}$. Therefore, the solutions in $[0, 2\pi)$ are $x = 0, \tfrac{\pi}{6}, \tfrac{5\pi}{6}, \pi$.

33. $2\sin^2 x - 5\sin x + 2 = 0 \;\Leftrightarrow\; (2\sin x - 1)(\sin x - 2) = 0 \;\Leftrightarrow\; \sin x = \tfrac{1}{2}$ or $\sin x = 2$ (which is inadmissible) $\;\Leftrightarrow\; x = \tfrac{\pi}{6}, \tfrac{5\pi}{6}$. Thus, the solutions in $[0, 2\pi)$ are $x = \tfrac{\pi}{6}$ and $\tfrac{5\pi}{6}$.

34. $\sin x - \cos x - \tan x = -1 \;\Leftrightarrow\; \sin x \cos x - \cos^2 x - \sin x = -\cos x \;\Leftrightarrow\; \sin x \cos x - \sin x - \cos^2 x + \cos x = 0$ $\;\Leftrightarrow\; \sin x (\cos x - 1) - \cos x (\cos x - 1) = 0 \;\Leftrightarrow\; (\sin x - \cos x)(\cos x - 1) = 0 \;\Leftrightarrow\; \sin x = \cos x$ or $\cos x = 1 \Leftrightarrow \tan x = 1$ or $\cos x = 1 \;\Leftrightarrow\; x = \tfrac{\pi}{4}, \tfrac{5\pi}{4}$ or $x = 0$. Therefore, the solutions in $[0, 2\pi)$ are $x = 0, \tfrac{\pi}{4}, \tfrac{5\pi}{4}$.

35. $2\cos^2 x - 7\cos x + 3 = 0 \;\Leftrightarrow\; (2\cos x - 1)(\cos x - 3) = 0 \;\Leftrightarrow\; \cos x = \tfrac{1}{2}$ or $\cos x = 3$ (which is inadmissible) $\;\Leftrightarrow\; x = \tfrac{\pi}{3}, \tfrac{5\pi}{3}$. Therefore, the solutions in $[0, 2\pi)$ are $x = \tfrac{\pi}{3}, \tfrac{5\pi}{3}$.

36. $4\sin^2 x + 2\cos^2 x = 3 \;\Leftrightarrow\; 2\sin^2 x + 2(\sin^2 x + \cos^2 x) - 3 = 0 \;\Leftrightarrow\; 2\sin^2 x + 2 - 3 = 0 \;\Leftrightarrow\; 2\sin^2 x = 1$ $\;\Leftrightarrow\; \sin x = \pm\tfrac{1}{\sqrt{2}}$. So the solutions in $[0, 2\pi)$ are $x = \tfrac{\pi}{4}, \tfrac{3\pi}{4}, \tfrac{5\pi}{4}, \tfrac{7\pi}{4}$.

37. Note that $x = \pi$ is not a solution because the denominator is zero. $\dfrac{1 - \cos x}{1 + \cos x} = 3 \;\Leftrightarrow\; 1 - \cos x = 3 + 3\cos x \;\Leftrightarrow\; -4\cos x = 2 \;\Leftrightarrow\; \cos x = -\tfrac{1}{2} \Leftrightarrow x = \tfrac{2\pi}{3}, \tfrac{4\pi}{3}$ in $[0, 2\pi)$.

38. $\sin x = \cos 2x \iff \sin x = 1 - 2\sin^2 x \iff 2\sin^2 x + \sin x - 1 = 0 \iff (2\sin x - 1)(\sin x + 1) = 0 \iff$ $\sin x = \frac{1}{2}$ or $\sin x = -1 \iff x = \frac{\pi}{6}, \frac{5\pi}{6}$ or $x = \frac{3\pi}{2}$. Thus, the solutions in $[0, 2\pi)$ are $x = \frac{\pi}{6}, \frac{3\pi}{2}, \frac{5\pi}{6}$.

39. Factor by grouping: $\tan^3 x + \tan^2 x - 3\tan x - 3 = 0 \iff (\tan x + 1)(\tan^2 x - 3) = 0 \iff \tan x = -1$ or $\tan x = \pm\sqrt{3}$ $\iff x = \frac{3\pi}{4}, \frac{7\pi}{4}$ or $x = \frac{\pi}{3}, \frac{2\pi}{3}, \frac{4\pi}{3}, \frac{5\pi}{3}$. Therefore, the solutions in $[0, 2\pi)$ are $x = \frac{\pi}{3}, \frac{2\pi}{3}, \frac{3\pi}{4}, \frac{4\pi}{3}, \frac{5\pi}{3}, \frac{7\pi}{4}$.

40. $\cos 2x \csc^2 x = 2\cos 2x \iff \cos 2x \csc^2 x - 2\cos 2x = 0 \iff \cos 2x (\csc^2 x - 2) = 0 \iff \cos 2x = 0$ or $\csc^2 x = 2 \iff \cos 2x = 0$ or $\sin^2 x = \frac{1}{2} \iff \cos 2x = 0$ or $\sin x = \pm\frac{1}{\sqrt{2}}$.
For $\cos 2x = 0$, the solutions in $[0, 4\pi)$ are $2x = \frac{\pi}{2}, \frac{3\pi}{2}, \frac{5\pi}{2}, \frac{7\pi}{2} \iff$ the solutions in $[0, 2\pi)$ are $x = \frac{\pi}{4}, \frac{3\pi}{4}, \frac{5\pi}{4}, \frac{7\pi}{4}$.
For $\sin x = \pm\frac{1}{\sqrt{2}}$, the solutions in $[0, 2\pi)$ are $x = \frac{\pi}{4}, \frac{3\pi}{4}, \frac{5\pi}{4}, \frac{7\pi}{4}$.
Thus, the solutions of the equation in $[0, 2\pi)$ are $x = \frac{\pi}{4}, \frac{3\pi}{4}, \frac{5\pi}{4}, \frac{7\pi}{4}$.

41. $\tan \frac{1}{2}x + 2\sin 2x = \csc x \iff \frac{1 - \cos x}{\sin x} + 4\sin x \cos x = \frac{1}{\sin x} \iff 1 - \cos x + 4\sin^2 x \cos x = 1 \iff$ $4\sin^2 x \cos x - \cos x = 0 \iff \cos x (4\sin^2 x - 1) = 0 \iff \cos x = 0$ or $\sin x = \pm\frac{1}{2} \iff x = \frac{\pi}{2}, \frac{3\pi}{2}$ or $x = \frac{\pi}{6},$ $\frac{5\pi}{6}, \frac{7\pi}{6}, \frac{11\pi}{6}$. Thus, the solutions in $[0, 2\pi)$ are $x = \frac{\pi}{6}, \frac{\pi}{2}, \frac{5\pi}{6}, \frac{7\pi}{6}, \frac{3\pi}{2}, \frac{11\pi}{6}$.

42. $\cos 3x + \cos 2x + \cos x = 0 \iff \cos 2x \cos x - \sin 2x \sin x + \cos 2x + \cos x = 0 \iff$ $\cos 2x \cos x + \cos 2x - \sin 2x \sin x + \cos x = 0 \iff \cos 2x (\cos x + 1) - 2\sin^2 x \cos x + \cos x = 0$ $\iff \cos 2x (\cos x + 1) + \cos x (1 - 2\sin^2 x) = 0 \iff \cos 2x (\cos x + 1) + \cos x \cos 2x = 0 \iff$ $\cos 2x (\cos x + 1 + \cos x) = 0 \iff \cos 2x (2\cos x + 1) = 0 \iff \cos 2x = 0$ or $\cos x = -\frac{1}{2} \iff 2x = \frac{\pi}{2},$ $\frac{3\pi}{2}, \frac{5\pi}{2}, \frac{7\pi}{2}$ (in $[0, 4\pi)$) or $x = \frac{2\pi}{3}, \frac{4\pi}{3}$ (in $[0, 2\pi)$). Thus, the solutions in $[0, 2\pi)$ are $x = \frac{\pi}{4}, \frac{2\pi}{3}, \frac{3\pi}{4}, \frac{5\pi}{4}, \frac{4\pi}{3}, \frac{7\pi}{4}$.

43. $\tan x + \sec x = \sqrt{3} \iff \frac{\sin x}{\cos x} + \frac{1}{\cos x} = \sqrt{3} \iff \sin x + 1 = \sqrt{3}\cos x \iff \sqrt{3}\cos x - \sin x = 1$ $\iff \frac{\sqrt{3}}{2}\cos x - \frac{1}{2}\sin x = \frac{1}{2} \iff \cos \frac{\pi}{6}\cos x - \sin \frac{\pi}{6}\sin x = \frac{1}{2} \iff \cos\left(x + \frac{\pi}{6}\right) = \frac{1}{2} \iff x + \frac{\pi}{6} = \frac{\pi}{3}, \frac{5\pi}{3} \iff x = \frac{\pi}{6},$ $\frac{3\pi}{2}$. However, $x = \frac{3\pi}{2}$ is inadmissible because $\sec \frac{3\pi}{2}$ is undefined. Thus, the only solution in $[0, 2\pi)$ is $x = \frac{\pi}{6}$.

44. $2\cos x - 3\tan x = 0 \iff 2\cos x - 3\frac{\sin x}{\cos x} = 0 \iff 2\cos^2 x - 3\sin x = 0 \ (\cos x \neq 0) \iff$ $2(1 - \sin^2 x) - 3\sin x = 0 \iff 2\sin^2 x + 3\sin x - 2 = 0 \iff (2\sin x - 1)(\sin x + 2) = 0 \iff \sin x = \frac{1}{2}$ or $\sin x = -2$ (which has no solution) $\iff x = \frac{\pi}{6}, \frac{5\pi}{6}$.

45. We graph $f(x) = \cos x$ and $g(x) = x^2 - 1$ in the viewing rectangle $[0, 6.5]$ by $[-2, 2]$. The two functions intersect at only one point, $x \approx 1.18$.

46. We graph $f(x) = e^{\sin x}$ and $g(x) = x$ in the viewing rectangle $[0, 6.5]$ by $[-1, 3]$. The two functions intersect at only one point, $x \approx 2.22$.

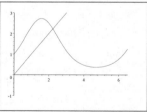

47. (a) $2000 = \frac{(400)^2 \sin \theta}{64} \iff \sin \theta = 0.8 \Rightarrow \theta = 53.1°$.

(b) $\frac{(400)^2 \sin \theta}{64} = 2500 \sin \theta \leq 2500$. Therefore it is impossible for the projectile to reach a height of 3000 ft.

(c) The function $M(\theta) = 2500 \sin \theta$ is maximized when $\sin \theta = 1$ so $\theta = 90°$. The projectile will travel the highest when it is shot straight up.

48. Since $e^{-0.2t} > 0$ we have $f(t) = e^{-0.2t} \sin 4\pi t = 0 \Leftrightarrow \sin 4\pi t = 0 \Leftrightarrow 4\pi t = k\pi \Leftrightarrow t = \dfrac{k}{4}$ where k is any integer. Thus the shock absorber is at equilibrium position every quarter second.

49. Since $15°$ is in quadrant I, $\cos 15° = \sqrt{\dfrac{1 + \cos 30°}{2}} = \sqrt{\dfrac{2 + \sqrt{3}}{4}} = \frac{1}{2}\sqrt{2 + \sqrt{3}}$.

50. $\sin \dfrac{5\pi}{12} = \sin\left(\dfrac{\pi}{4} + \dfrac{\pi}{6}\right) = \sin \dfrac{\pi}{4} \cos \dfrac{\pi}{6} + \cos \dfrac{\pi}{4} \sin \dfrac{\pi}{6} = \dfrac{1}{\sqrt{2}} \cdot \dfrac{\sqrt{3}}{2} + \dfrac{1}{\sqrt{2}} \cdot \dfrac{1}{2} = \dfrac{1 + \sqrt{3}}{2\sqrt{2}} = \dfrac{\sqrt{2} + \sqrt{6}}{4}$

51. $\tan \dfrac{\pi}{8} = \dfrac{1 - \cos \frac{\pi}{4}}{\sin \frac{\pi}{4}} = \dfrac{1 - \frac{1}{\sqrt{2}}}{\frac{1}{\sqrt{2}}} = \left(1 - \dfrac{1}{\sqrt{2}}\right)\sqrt{2} = \sqrt{2} - 1$

52. $2 \sin \dfrac{\pi}{12} \cos \dfrac{\pi}{12} = \sin\left(2 \cdot \dfrac{\pi}{12}\right) = \sin \dfrac{\pi}{6} = \dfrac{1}{2}$

53. $\sin 5° \cos 40° + \cos 5° \sin 40° = \sin(5° + 40°) = \sin 45° = \dfrac{1}{\sqrt{2}} = \dfrac{\sqrt{2}}{2}$

54. $\dfrac{\tan 66° - \tan 6°}{1 + \tan 66° \tan 6°} = \tan(66° - 6°) = \tan 60° = \sqrt{3}$

55. $\cos^2 \dfrac{\pi}{8} - \sin^2 \dfrac{\pi}{8} = \cos\left(2\left(\dfrac{\pi}{8}\right)\right) = \cos \dfrac{\pi}{4} = \dfrac{1}{\sqrt{2}} = \dfrac{\sqrt{2}}{2}$

56. $\dfrac{1}{2} \cos \dfrac{\pi}{12} + \dfrac{\sqrt{3}}{2} \sin \dfrac{\pi}{12} = \sin \dfrac{\pi}{6} \cos \dfrac{\pi}{12} + \cos \dfrac{\pi}{6} \sin \dfrac{\pi}{12} = \sin\left(\dfrac{\pi}{6} + \dfrac{\pi}{12}\right) = \sin \dfrac{\pi}{4} = \dfrac{1}{\sqrt{2}} = \dfrac{\sqrt{2}}{2}$

57. We use a product-to-sum formula: $\cos 37.5° \cos 7.5° = \dfrac{1}{2}(\cos 45° + \cos 30°) = \dfrac{1}{2}\left(\dfrac{\sqrt{2}}{2} + \dfrac{\sqrt{3}}{2}\right) = \dfrac{1}{4}\left(\sqrt{2} + \sqrt{3}\right)$.

58. $\cos 67.5° + \cos 22.5° = 2 \cos\left(\dfrac{67.5° + 22.5°}{2}\right) \cos\left(\dfrac{67.5° - 22.5°}{2}\right) = 2 \cos 45° \cos 22.5° = 2 \cdot \dfrac{1}{\sqrt{2}} \cdot \sqrt{\dfrac{1 + \cos 45°}{2}}$

$$= \sqrt{1 + \cos 45°} = \sqrt{1 + \dfrac{1}{\sqrt{2}}} = \sqrt{\dfrac{2 + \sqrt{2}}{2}}$$

In Solutions 59–64, x and y are in quadrant I, so we know that $\sec x = \dfrac{3}{2} \Rightarrow \cos x = \dfrac{2}{3}$, so $\sin x = \dfrac{\sqrt{5}}{3}$ and $\tan x = \dfrac{\sqrt{5}}{2}$. **Also,** $\csc y = 3 \Rightarrow \sin y = \dfrac{1}{3}$, **and so** $\cos y = \dfrac{2\sqrt{2}}{3}$, **and** $\tan y = \dfrac{1}{2\sqrt{2}} = \dfrac{\sqrt{2}}{4}$.

59. $\sin(x + y) = \sin x \cos y + \cos x \sin y = \dfrac{\sqrt{5}}{3} \cdot \dfrac{2\sqrt{2}}{3} + \dfrac{2}{3} \cdot \dfrac{1}{3} = \dfrac{2}{9}\left(1 + \sqrt{10}\right)$.

60. $\cos(x - y) = \cos x \cos y + \sin x \sin y = \dfrac{2}{3} \cdot \dfrac{2\sqrt{2}}{3} + \dfrac{\sqrt{5}}{3} \cdot \dfrac{1}{3} = \dfrac{1}{9}\left(4\sqrt{2} + \sqrt{5}\right)$.

61. $\tan(x + y) = \dfrac{\tan x + \tan y}{1 - \tan x \tan y} = \dfrac{\frac{\sqrt{5}}{2} + \frac{\sqrt{2}}{4}}{1 - \left(\frac{\sqrt{5}}{2}\right)\left(\frac{\sqrt{2}}{4}\right)} = \dfrac{\frac{\sqrt{5}}{2} + \frac{\sqrt{2}}{4}}{1 - \left(\frac{\sqrt{5}}{2}\right)\left(\frac{\sqrt{2}}{4}\right)} \cdot \dfrac{8}{8} = \dfrac{2\left(2\sqrt{5} + \sqrt{2}\right)}{8 - \sqrt{10}} \cdot \dfrac{8 + \sqrt{10}}{8 + \sqrt{10}}$

$$= \dfrac{2}{3}\left(\sqrt{2} + \sqrt{5}\right)$$

62. $\sin 2x = 2 \sin x \cos x = 2 \cdot \dfrac{\sqrt{5}}{3} \cdot \dfrac{2}{3} = \dfrac{4\sqrt{5}}{9}$.

63. $\cos \dfrac{y}{2} = \sqrt{\dfrac{1 + \cos y}{2}} = \sqrt{\dfrac{1 + \left(\frac{2\sqrt{2}}{3}\right)}{2}} = \sqrt{\dfrac{3 + 2\sqrt{2}}{6}}$ (since cosine is positive in quadrant I)

64. $\tan \dfrac{y}{2} = \dfrac{1 - \cos y}{\sin y} = \dfrac{1 - \frac{2\sqrt{2}}{3}}{\frac{1}{3}} = \dfrac{3 - 2\sqrt{2}}{1} = 3 - 2\sqrt{2}$

65. $\sin^{-1} \dfrac{\sqrt{3}}{2} = \dfrac{\pi}{3}$

66. $\tan^{-1} \dfrac{\sqrt{3}}{3} = \dfrac{\pi}{6}$

67. $\cos\left(\tan^{-1}\sqrt{3}\right) = \cos \dfrac{\pi}{3} = \dfrac{1}{2}$

68. $\sin\left(\cos^{-1} \dfrac{\sqrt{3}}{2}\right) = \sin \dfrac{\pi}{6} = \dfrac{1}{2}$

69. Let $u = \sin^{-1} \frac{2}{5}$ and so $\sin u = \frac{2}{5}$. Then from the triangle, $\tan\left(\sin^{-1} \frac{2}{5}\right) = \tan u = \frac{2}{\sqrt{21}}$.

70. Let $u = \cos^{-1} \frac{3}{8}$ then $\cos u = \frac{3}{8}$. From the triangle, we have $\sin\left(\cos^{-1} \frac{3}{8}\right) = \sin u = \frac{\sqrt{55}}{8}$.

71. $\cos\left(2\sin^{-1} \frac{1}{3}\right) = 1 - 2\sin^2\left(\sin^{-1} \frac{1}{3}\right) = 1 - 2\left(\frac{1}{3}\right)^2 = \frac{7}{9}$

72. Let $u = \sin^{-1} \frac{5}{13}$ and $v = \cos^{-1} \frac{4}{5}$. Then $\sin u = \frac{5}{13}$ and $\cos v = \frac{4}{5}$. So from the triangles, we have

$$
\begin{aligned}
\cos\left(\sin^{-1} \frac{5}{13} - \cos^{-1} \frac{4}{5}\right) &= \cos(u - v) \\
&= \cos u \cos v + \sin u \sin v \\
&= \frac{12}{13} \cdot \frac{4}{5} + \frac{5}{13} \cdot \frac{3}{5} = \frac{63}{65}
\end{aligned}
$$

73. Let $\theta = \tan^{-1} x \iff \tan\theta = x$. Then from the triangle, we have $\sin\left(\tan^{-1} x\right) = \sin\theta = \dfrac{x}{\sqrt{1 + x^2}}$.

74. Let $\theta = \sin^{-1} x$. Then $\sin\theta = x$. From the triangle, we have $\sec\left(\sin^{-1} x\right) = \sec\theta = \dfrac{1}{\sqrt{1 - x^2}}$.

75. $\cos\theta = \dfrac{x}{3} \Rightarrow \theta = \cos^{-1}\left(\dfrac{x}{3}\right)$

76. $\tan\theta = \dfrac{x}{2} \Rightarrow \theta = \tan^{-1}\left(\dfrac{x}{2}\right)$

77. (a) $\tan\theta = \dfrac{10}{x} \iff \theta = \tan^{-1}\left(\dfrac{10}{x}\right)$.

(b) $\theta = \tan^{-1}\left(\dfrac{10}{x}\right)$, for $x > 0$, is shown in the graph. There is no maximum value since the function is undefined at 0. (But when $x = 0$, the driver no longer can see the sign.)

78. (a)   Let γ be the angle formed by the top of the tower, the car, and the base of the building, and let β be the angle formed by base of the tower, the car, and the base of the diagram. Then $\tan \gamma = \dfrac{420}{x}$ $\Leftrightarrow$

$\gamma = \tan^{-1}\left(\dfrac{420}{x}\right)$ and $\tan \beta = \dfrac{380}{x} \Leftrightarrow \beta = \tan^{-1}\left(\dfrac{380}{x}\right)$. Thus,

$\theta = \gamma - \beta = \tan^{-1}\left(\dfrac{420}{x}\right) - \tan^{-1}\left(\dfrac{380}{x}\right)$.

(b)   We graph $\theta(x)$ and find that θ is maximized when $x = 400$.

Chapter 7 Test

1. (a) $\tan \theta \sin \theta + \cos \theta = \dfrac{\sin \theta}{\cos \theta} \sin \theta + \cos \theta = \dfrac{\sin^2 \theta}{\cos \theta} + \dfrac{\cos^2 \theta}{\cos \theta} = \dfrac{1}{\cos \theta} = \sec \theta$

(b) $\dfrac{\tan x}{1 - \cos x} = \dfrac{\tan x}{1 - \cos x} \cdot \dfrac{1 + \cos x}{1 + \cos x} = \dfrac{\tan x \,(1 + \cos x)}{1 - \cos^2 x} = \dfrac{\dfrac{\sin x}{\cos x}\,(1 + \cos x)}{\sin^2 x} = \dfrac{1}{\sin x} \cdot$

$\dfrac{1 + \cos x}{\cos x} = \csc x \,(1 + \sec x)$

(c) $\dfrac{2 \tan x}{1 + \tan^2 x} = \dfrac{2 \tan x}{\sec^2 x} = \dfrac{2 \sin x}{\cos x} \cdot \cos^2 x = 2 \sin x \cos x = \sin 2x$

2. $\dfrac{x}{\sqrt{4 - x^2}} = \dfrac{2 \sin \theta}{\sqrt{4 - (2 \sin \theta)^2}} = \dfrac{2 \sin \theta}{\sqrt{4 - 4 \sin^2 \theta}} = \dfrac{2 \sin \theta}{2\sqrt{1 - \sin^2 \theta}} = \dfrac{\sin \theta}{\sqrt{\cos^2 \theta}} = \dfrac{\sin \theta}{|\cos \theta|} = \dfrac{\sin \theta}{\cos \theta} = \tan \theta$ (because

$\cos \theta > 0$ for $-\dfrac{\pi}{2} < \theta < \dfrac{\pi}{2}$)

3. (a) $\sin 8° \cos 22° + \cos 8° \sin 22° = \sin (8° + 22°) = \sin 30° = \dfrac{1}{2}$

(b) $\sin 75° = \sin (45° + 30°) = \sin 45° \cos 30° + \cos 45° \sin 30° = \dfrac{\sqrt{2}}{2} \cdot \dfrac{\sqrt{3}}{2} + \dfrac{\sqrt{2}}{2} \cdot \dfrac{1}{2} = \dfrac{1}{4}\left(\sqrt{6} + \sqrt{2}\right)$

(c) $\sin \dfrac{\pi}{12} = \sin \left(\dfrac{\pi}{2}\right) = \sqrt{\dfrac{1 - \cos \frac{\pi}{6}}{2}} = \sqrt{\dfrac{1 - \frac{\sqrt{3}}{2}}{2}} = \sqrt{\dfrac{2 - \sqrt{3}}{4}} = \dfrac{1}{2}\sqrt{2 - \sqrt{3}}$

4. From the figures, we have $\cos(\alpha + \beta) = \cos \alpha \cos \beta - \sin \alpha \sin \beta = \dfrac{2}{\sqrt{5}} \cdot \dfrac{\sqrt{5}}{3} - \dfrac{1}{\sqrt{5}} \cdot \dfrac{2}{3} = \dfrac{2\sqrt{5} - 2}{3\sqrt{5}} = \dfrac{10 - 2\sqrt{5}}{15}$.

5. (a) $\sin 3x \cos 5x = \dfrac{1}{2}\left[\sin(3x + 5x) + \sin(3x - 5x)\right] = \dfrac{1}{2}\left(\sin 8x - \sin 2x\right)$

(b) $\sin 2x - \sin 5x = 2 \cos \left(\dfrac{2x + 5x}{2}\right) \sin \left(\dfrac{2x - 5x}{2}\right) = -2 \cos \dfrac{7x}{2} \sin \dfrac{3x}{2}$

6. $\sin \theta = -\dfrac{4}{5}$. Since θ is in quadrant III, $\cos \theta = -\dfrac{3}{5}$. Then $\tan \dfrac{\theta}{2} = \dfrac{1 - \cos \theta}{\sin \theta} = \dfrac{1 - \left(-\frac{3}{5}\right)}{-\frac{4}{5}} = -\dfrac{1 + \frac{3}{5}}{\frac{4}{5}} = -\dfrac{5 + 3}{4} = -2$.

7. $y = \sin x$ has domain $(-\infty, \infty)$ and $y = \sin^{-1} x$ has domain $[-1, 1]$.

8. (a) $\tan \theta = \dfrac{x}{4} \Rightarrow \theta = \tan^{-1}\left(\dfrac{x}{4}\right)$

(b) $\cos \theta = \dfrac{3}{x} \Rightarrow \theta = \cos^{-1}\left(\dfrac{3}{x}\right)$

9. (a) $2\cos^2 x + 5\cos x + 2 = 0 \quad \Leftrightarrow \quad (2\cos x + 1)(\cos x + 2) = 0 \quad \Leftrightarrow \quad \cos x = -\frac{1}{2}$ or $\cos x = -2$ (which is impossible). So in the interval $[0, 2\pi)$, the solutions are $x = \frac{2\pi}{3}, \frac{4\pi}{3}$.

(b) $\sin 2x - \cos x = 0 \quad \Leftrightarrow \quad 2\sin x \cos x - \cos x = 0 \Leftrightarrow \cos x (2\sin x - 1) = 0 \quad \Leftrightarrow \quad \cos x = 0$ or $\sin x = \frac{1}{2}$
$\Leftrightarrow \quad x = \frac{\pi}{2}, \frac{3\pi}{2}$ or $x = \frac{\pi}{6}, \frac{5\pi}{6}$. Therefore, the solutions in $[0, 2\pi)$ are $x = \frac{\pi}{6}, \frac{\pi}{2}, \frac{5\pi}{6}, \frac{3\pi}{2}$.

10. $5\cos 2x = 2 \quad \Leftrightarrow \quad \cos 2x = \frac{2}{5} \Leftrightarrow 2x = \cos^{-1} 0.4 \approx 1.159279$. The solutions in $[0, 4\pi)$ are $2x \approx 1.159279$,
$2\pi - 1.159279$, $2\pi + 1.159279$, $4\pi - 1.159279 \quad \Leftrightarrow \quad 2x \approx 1.159279, 5.123906, 7.442465, 11.407091 \quad \Leftrightarrow$
$x \approx 0.57964, 2.56195, 3.72123, 5.70355$ in $[0, 2\pi)$.

11. Let $u = \tan^{-1}\frac{9}{40}$ so $\tan u = \frac{9}{40}$. From the triangle, $r = \sqrt{9^2 + 40^2} = 41$. So
$\cos\left(\tan^{-1}\frac{9}{40}\right) = \cos u = \frac{40}{41}$.

Focus on Modeling: Traveling and Standing Waves

1. (a) Substituting $x = 0$, we get $y(0, t) = 5\sin\left(2 \cdot 0 - \frac{\pi}{2}t\right) = 5\sin\left(-\frac{\pi}{2}t\right) = -5\sin\frac{\pi}{2}t$.

(b)

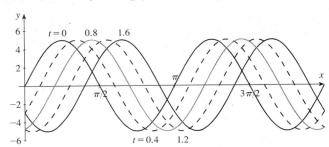

(c) We express the function in the standard form $y(x, t) = A\sin k(x - vt)$: $y(x, t) = 5\sin\left(2x - \frac{\pi}{2}t\right) = 5\sin 2\left(x - \frac{\pi}{4}t\right)$. Comparing this to the standard form, we see that the velocity of the wave is $v = \frac{\pi}{4}$.

2. (a) $y = 0.2\sin(1.047x - 0.524t) + 0.2\sin(1.047x + 0.524t) = 2(0.2)\sin 1.047x \cos 0.524t = 0.4\sin 1.047x \cos 0.524t$. The nodes occur when $1.047x = m\pi \Leftrightarrow x = \frac{\pi}{1.047}m \approx 3m$. So the nodes are at $3, 6, 9, 12, \ldots$.

(b)

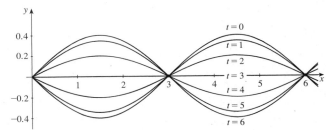

Note that when $t = 3$, $\cos(0.524 \cdot 3) \approx -0.001$, so $|y(x, 3)| \leq 0.0004$. Thus, the graph of $y(x, 3)$ cannot be distinguished from the x-axis in the diagram. Yes, this is a standing wave.

3. From the graph, we see that the amplitude is $A = 2.7$ and the period is 9.2, so $k = \frac{2\pi}{9.2} \approx 0.68$. Since $v = 6$, we have $kv = \frac{2\pi}{9.2} \cdot 6 \approx 4.10$, so the equation we seek is $y(x, t) = 2.7\sin(0.68x - 4.10t)$.

4. (a) We are given $A = 5$, period $\frac{2\pi}{3}$, and $v = 0.5$. Since the period is $\frac{2\pi}{3}$, we have $k = \frac{2\pi}{2\pi/3} = 3$. Thus, expressing the function in standard form, we have $y(x, t) = 5\sin 3(x - 0.5t) = 5\sin(3x - 1.5t)$.

(b)

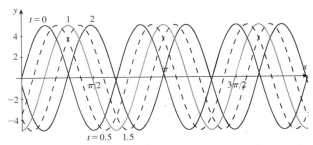

5. From the graphs, we see that the amplitude is $A = 0.6$. The nodes occur at $x = 0, 1, 2, 3$. Since $\sin \alpha x = 0$ when $\alpha x = k\pi$ (k any integer), we have $\alpha = \pi$. Then since the frequency is $\beta/2\pi$, we get $20 = \beta/2\pi \Leftrightarrow \beta = 40\pi$. Thus, an equation for this model is $f(x, t) = 0.6\sin \pi x \cos 40\pi t$.

6. From the graph, we see that the amplitude is $A = 7$. Now $\sin \alpha x = 0$ when $\alpha x = k\pi$ (k an integer). So for $k = 1$, we must have $\alpha\left(\frac{\pi}{2}\right) = \pi \Leftrightarrow \alpha = 2$. Then since the period is 4π, we have $2\pi/\beta = 4\pi \Leftrightarrow \beta = \frac{1}{2}$. Thus, an equation for this model is $f(x, t) = 7\sin 2x \cos \frac{1}{2}t$.

7. (a) The first standing wave has $\alpha = 1$, the second has $\alpha = 2$, the third has $\alpha = 3$, and the fourth has $\alpha = 4$.

(b) α is equal to the number of nodes minus 1. The first string has two nodes and $\alpha = 1$; the second string has three nodes and $\alpha = 2$, and so forth.

(c) Since the frequency is $\beta/2\pi$, we have $440 = \beta/2\pi \quad\Leftrightarrow\quad \beta = 880\pi$.

(d) The first standing wave has equation $y = \sin x \cos 880\pi t$, the second has equation $y = \sin 2x \cos 880\pi t$, the third has equation $y = \sin 3x \cos 880\pi t$, and the fourth has equation $y = \sin 4x \cos 880\pi t$.

8. (a) The nodes of the tube occur when $\cos \frac{1}{2}x = 0$ and $0 \le x \le 37.7$. So $\frac{1}{2}x = (2k + 1)\frac{\pi}{2} \Leftrightarrow x = (2k + 1)\pi$. Thus, the nodes are at $x = \pi, 3\pi, 5\pi, 7\pi, 9\pi$, and 11π. We stop there since $13\pi > 37.7$. Note that the endpoints of the tube ($x = 0$ and $x = 37.7$) are not nodes.

(b) In the function $y = A \cos \alpha x \cos \beta t$, the frequency is $\beta/2\pi$. In this case, the frequency is $\frac{50\pi}{2\pi} = 25$ Hz.

8 Polar Coordinates and Vectors

8.1 Polar Coordinates

1.

2.

3.

4.

5.

6.

Answers to Exercises 7–12 will vary.

7. $\left(3, \frac{\pi}{2}\right)$ also has polar coordinates $\left(3, \frac{5\pi}{2}\right)$ or $\left(-3, \frac{3\pi}{2}\right)$

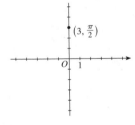

8. $\left(2, \frac{3\pi}{4}\right)$ also has polar coordinates $\left(2, \frac{11\pi}{4}\right)$ or $\left(-2, \frac{7\pi}{4}\right)$.

9. $\left(-1, \frac{7\pi}{6}\right)$ also has polar coordinates $\left(1, \frac{\pi}{6}\right)$ or $\left(-1, -\frac{5\pi}{6}\right)$.

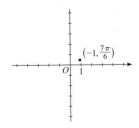

10. $\left(-2, -\frac{\pi}{3}\right)$ also has polar coordinates $\left(2, \frac{2\pi}{3}\right)$ or $\left(-2, \frac{5\pi}{3}\right)$.

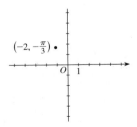

11. $(-5, 0)$ also has polar coordinates $(5, \pi)$ or $(-5, 2\pi)$.

12. $(3, 1)$ also has polar coordinates $(3, 1 + 2\pi)$ or $(-3, 1 + \pi)$.

13. Q has coordinates $\left(4, \frac{3\pi}{4}\right)$.

14. R has coordinates $\left(4, -\frac{3\pi}{4}\right) = \left(4, \frac{5\pi}{4}\right)$.

15. Q has coordinates $\left(-4, -\frac{\pi}{4}\right) = \left(4, \frac{3\pi}{4}\right)$.

16. P has coordinates $\left(-4, \frac{13\pi}{4}\right) = \left(-4, \frac{5\pi}{4}\right) = \left(4, \frac{\pi}{4}\right)$.

17. P has coordinates $\left(4, -\frac{23\pi}{4}\right) = \left(4, \frac{\pi}{4}\right)$.

18. Q has coordinates $\left(-4, \frac{23\pi}{4}\right) = (-4, -\pi/4) = \left(4, \frac{3\pi}{4}\right)$.

19. P has coordinates $\left(-4, \frac{101\pi}{4}\right) = \left(-4, \frac{5\pi}{4}\right) = \left(4, \frac{\pi}{4}\right)$.

20. S has coordinates $\left(4, \frac{103\pi}{4}\right) = \left(4, \frac{7\pi}{4}\right)$.

21. $P = (-3, 3)$ in rectangular coordinates, so $r^2 = x^2 + y^2 = (-3)^2 + 3^2 = 18$ and we can take $r = 3\sqrt{2}$.

$\tan\theta = \dfrac{y}{x} = \dfrac{3}{-3} = -1$, so since P is in quadrant 2 we take $\theta = \frac{3\pi}{4}$. Thus, polar coordinates for P are $\left(3\sqrt{2}, \frac{3\pi}{4}\right)$.

22. $Q = (0, -3)$ in rectangular coordinates, so $r = 3$ and $\theta = \frac{3\pi}{2}$. Polar coordinates for Q are $\left(3, \frac{3\pi}{2}\right)$.

23. Here $r = 5$ and $\theta = -\frac{2\pi}{3}$, so $x = r\cos\theta = 5\cos\left(-\frac{2\pi}{3}\right) = -\frac{5}{2}$ and $y = r\sin\theta = 5\sin\left(-\frac{2\pi}{3}\right) = -\frac{5\sqrt{3}}{2}$. R has rectangular coordinates $\left(-\frac{5}{2}, -\frac{5\sqrt{3}}{2}\right)$.

24. $r = 2$ and $\theta = \frac{5\pi}{6}$, so S has rectangular coordinates $(r\cos\theta, r\sin\theta) = \left(2\cos\frac{5\pi}{6}, 2\sin\frac{5\pi}{6}\right) = (-\sqrt{3}, 1)$.

25. $(r, \theta) = \left(4, \frac{\pi}{6}\right)$. So $x = r\cos\theta = 4\cos\frac{\pi}{6} = 4 \cdot \frac{\sqrt{3}}{2} = 2\sqrt{3}$ and $y = r\sin\theta = 4\sin\frac{\pi}{6} = 4 \cdot \frac{1}{2} = 2$. Thus, the rectangular coordinates are $(2\sqrt{3}, 2)$.

26. $(r, \theta) = \left(6, \frac{2\pi}{3}\right)$. So $x = r\cos\theta = 6\cos\frac{2\pi}{3} = -6 \cdot \frac{1}{2} = -3$ and $y = r\sin\theta = 6\sin\frac{2\pi}{3} = 6 \cdot \frac{\sqrt{3}}{2} = 3\sqrt{3}$. Thus, the rectangular coordinates are $(-3, 3\sqrt{3})$.

27. $(r, \theta) = \left(\sqrt{2}, -\frac{\pi}{4}\right)$. So $x = r\cos\theta = \sqrt{2}\cos\left(-\frac{\pi}{4}\right) = \sqrt{2} \cdot \frac{1}{\sqrt{2}} = 1$, and $y = r\sin\theta = \sqrt{2}\sin\left(-\frac{\pi}{4}\right) = \sqrt{2}\left(-\frac{1}{\sqrt{2}}\right) = -1$. Thus, the rectangular coordinates are $(1, -1)$.

28. $(r, \theta) = \left(-1, \frac{5\pi}{2}\right)$. So $x = r\cos\theta = -1\cos\frac{5\pi}{2} = -1 \cdot 0 = 0$ and $y = r\sin\theta = -1\sin\frac{5\pi}{2} = -1 \cdot 1 = -1$. Thus, the rectangular coordinates are $(0, -1)$.

29. $(r, \theta) = (5, 5\pi)$. So $x = r\cos\theta = 5\cos 5\pi = -5$, and $y = r\sin\theta = 5\sin 5\pi = 0$. Thus, the rectangular coordinates are $(-5, 0)$.

30. $(r, \theta) = (0, 13\pi)$. So $(x, y) = (0, 0)$ because $r = 0$.

31. $(r, \theta) = \left(6\sqrt{2}, \frac{11\pi}{6}\right)$. So $x = r\cos\theta = 6\sqrt{2}\cos\frac{11\pi}{6} = 3\sqrt{6}$ and $y = r\sin\theta = 6\sqrt{2}\sin\frac{11\pi}{6} = -3\sqrt{2}$. Thus, the rectangular coordinates are $(3\sqrt{6}, -3\sqrt{2})$.

32. $(r, \theta) = \left(\sqrt{3}, -\frac{5\pi}{3}\right)$. So $x = r\cos\theta = \sqrt{3}\cos\left(-\frac{5\pi}{3}\right) = \frac{\sqrt{3}}{2}$ and $y = r\sin\theta = \sqrt{3}\sin\left(-\frac{5\pi}{3}\right) = \frac{3}{2}$. Thus, the rectangular coordinates are $\left(\frac{\sqrt{3}}{2}, \frac{3}{2}\right)$.

33. $(x, y) = (-1, 1)$. Since $r^2 = x^2 + y^2$, we have $r^2 = (-1)^2 + 1^2 = 2$, so $r = \sqrt{2}$. Now $\tan\theta = \dfrac{y}{x} = \dfrac{1}{-1} = -1$, so, since the point is in the second quadrant, $\theta = \frac{3\pi}{4}$. Thus, polar coordinates are $\left(\sqrt{2}, \frac{3\pi}{4}\right)$.

34. $(x, y) = \left(3\sqrt{3}, -3\right)$. Since $r^2 = x^2 + y^2$, we have $r^2 = \left(3\sqrt{3}\right)^2 + (-3)^2 = 36$, so $r = 6$. Now

$\tan\theta = \dfrac{y}{x} = -\dfrac{3}{3\sqrt{3}} = -\dfrac{1}{\sqrt{3}}$, so, since the point is in the fourth quadrant, $\theta = \dfrac{11\pi}{6}$. Thus, polar coordinates are $\left(6, \dfrac{11\pi}{6}\right)$.

35. $(x, y) = \left(\sqrt{8}, \sqrt{8}\right)$. Since $r^2 = x^2 + y^2$, we have $r^2 = \left(\sqrt{8}\right)^2 + \left(\sqrt{8}\right)^2 = 16$, so $r = 4$. Now $\tan\theta = \dfrac{y}{x} = \dfrac{\sqrt{8}}{\sqrt{8}} = 1$, so,

since the point is in the first quadrant, $\theta = \dfrac{\pi}{4}$. Thus, polar coordinates are $\left(4, \dfrac{\pi}{4}\right)$.

36. $(x, y) = \left(-\sqrt{6}, -\sqrt{2}\right)$. Since $r^2 = x^2 + y^2$, we have $r^2 = \left(-\sqrt{6}\right)^2 + \left(-\sqrt{2}\right)^2 = 8$, so $r = 2\sqrt{2}$. Now

$\tan\theta = \dfrac{y}{x} = \dfrac{-\sqrt{2}}{-\sqrt{6}} = \dfrac{1}{\sqrt{3}}$, so, since the point is in the third quadrant, $\theta = \dfrac{7\pi}{6}$. Thus, polar coordinates are $\left(2\sqrt{2}, \dfrac{7\pi}{6}\right)$.

37. $(x, y) = (3, 4)$. Since $r^2 = x^2 + y^2$, we have $r^2 = 3^2 + 4^2 = 25$, so $r = 5$. Now $\tan\theta = \dfrac{y}{x} = \dfrac{4}{3}$, so, since the point is in

the first quadrant, $\theta = \tan^{-1}\dfrac{4}{3}$. Thus, polar coordinates are $\left(5, \tan^{-1}\dfrac{4}{3}\right)$.

38. $(x, y) = (1, -2)$. Since $r^2 = x^2 + y^2$, we have $r^2 = 1^2 + (-2)^2 = 2$, so $r = \sqrt{5}$. Now, $\tan\theta = \dfrac{y}{x} = \dfrac{-2}{1} = -2$, and

since the point is in the fourth quadrant, $\theta = 2\pi + \tan^{-1}(-2)$ (since we need $0 \le \theta < 2\pi$). Thus, polar coordinates are

$\left(\sqrt{5}, 2\pi + \tan^{-1}(-2)\right)$.

39. $(x, y) = (-6, 0)$. $r^2 = \left(-6^2\right) = 36$, so $r = 6$. Now $\tan\theta = \dfrac{y}{x} = 0$, so since the point is on the negative x-axis, $\theta = \pi$.

Thus, polar coordinates are $(6, \pi)$.

40. $(x, y) = \left(0, -\sqrt{3}\right)$. $r = \sqrt{3}$ and since the point is on the negative y-axis, $\theta = \dfrac{3\pi}{2}$. Thus, polar coordinates are $\left(\sqrt{3}, \dfrac{3\pi}{2}\right)$.

41. $x = y$ $\Leftrightarrow$ $r\cos\theta = r\sin\theta$ $\Leftrightarrow$ $\tan\theta = 1$, and so $\theta = \dfrac{\pi}{4}$.

42. $x^2 + y^2 = 9$. By substitution, $(r\cos\theta)^2 + (r\sin\theta)^2 = 9$ $\Leftrightarrow$ $r^2\left(\cos^2\theta + \sin^2\theta\right) = 9$ $\Leftrightarrow$ $r^2 = 9$ $\Leftrightarrow$

$r = 3$.

43. $y = x^2$. We substitute and then solve for r: $r\sin\theta = (r\cos\theta)^2 = r^2\cos^2\theta$ $\Leftrightarrow$ $\sin\theta = r\cos^2\theta$ $\Leftrightarrow$

$r = \dfrac{\sin\theta}{\cos^2\theta} = \tan\theta\sec\theta$.

44. $y = 5$. By substitution, $r\sin\theta = 5$ $\Leftrightarrow$ $r = \dfrac{5}{\sin\theta} = 5\csc\theta$.

45. $x = 4$. We substitute and then solve for r: $r\cos\theta = 4$ $\Leftrightarrow$ $r = \dfrac{4}{\cos\theta} = 4\sec\theta$.

46. $x^2 - y^2 = 1$. By substitution, $(r\cos\theta)^2 - (r\sin\theta)^2 = 1$ $\Leftrightarrow$ $r^2\left(\cos^2\theta - \sin^2\theta\right) = 1$ $\Leftrightarrow$ $r^2\cos 2\theta = 1$ $\Leftrightarrow$

$r^2 = \dfrac{1}{\cos 2\theta} = \sec 2\theta$.

47. $r = 7$. But $r^2 = x^2 + y^2$, so $x^2 + y^2 = r^2 = 49$. Hence, the equivalent equation in rectangular coordinates is

$x^2 + y^2 = 49$.

48. $\theta = \pi$ $\Rightarrow$ $\tan\theta = 0$ $\Rightarrow$ $\dfrac{y}{x} = 0$ $\Rightarrow$ $y = 0$.

49. $r\cos\theta = 6$. But $x = r\cos\theta$, and so $x = 6$ is the equation.

50. $r = 6\cos\theta$ $\Leftrightarrow$ $r^2 = 6r\cos\theta$. By substitution, $x^2 + y^2 = 6x$ $\Leftrightarrow$ $\left(x^2 - 6x + 9\right) + y^2 = 9$ $\Leftrightarrow$

$(x - 3)^2 + y^2 = 9$.

51. $r^2 = \tan\theta$. Substituting $r^2 = x^2 + y^2$ and $\tan\theta = \dfrac{y}{x}$, we get $x^2 + y^2 = \dfrac{y}{x}$.

52. $r^2 = \sin 2\theta = 2\sin\theta\cos\theta$ $\Leftrightarrow$ $r^4 = 2r^2\sin\theta\cos\theta = 2(r\cos\theta)(r\sin\theta)$. By substitution, $\left(x^2 + y^2\right)^2 = 2xy$ $\Leftrightarrow$

$x^4 + 2x^2y^2 + y^4 - 2xy = 0$.

53. $r = \dfrac{1}{\sin\theta - \cos\theta}$ $\Rightarrow$ $r(\sin\theta - \cos\theta) = 1$ $\Leftrightarrow$ $r\sin\theta - r\cos\theta = 1$, and since $r\cos\theta = x$ and $r\sin\theta = y$, we

get $y - x = 1$.

54. $r = \dfrac{1}{1 + \sin\theta}$ $\Leftrightarrow$ $r(1 + \sin\theta) = 1$ $\Leftrightarrow$ $r + r\sin\theta = 1$. Thus $r = 1 - r\sin\theta$, and squaring both sides gives

$r^2 = (1 - r\sin\theta)^2$ $\Leftrightarrow$ $x^2 + y^2 = (1 - y)^2 = 1 - 2y + y^2$ $\Leftrightarrow$ $x^2 + 2y - 1 = 0$.

55. $r = 1 + \cos\theta$. If we multiply both sides of this equation by r we get $r^2 = r + r\cos\theta$. Thus $r^2 - r\cos\theta = r$, and squaring both sides gives $\left(r^2 - r\cos\theta\right)^2 = r^2$ $\Leftrightarrow$ $\left(x^2 + y^2 - x\right)^2 = x^2 + y^2$

56. $r = \dfrac{4}{1 + 2\sin\theta}$ $\Leftrightarrow$ $r(1 + 2\sin\theta) = 4$ $\Leftrightarrow$ $r + 2r\sin\theta = 4$. Thus $r = 4 - 2r\sin\theta$. Squaring both

sides, we get $r^2 = (4 - 2r\sin\theta)^2$. Substituting, $x^2 + y^2 = (4 - 2y)^2$ $\Leftrightarrow$ $x^2 + y^2 = 16 - 16y + 4y^2$ $\Leftrightarrow$ $x^2 - 3y^2 + 16y - 16 = 0$.

57. $r = 2\sec\theta$ $\Leftrightarrow$ $r = 2 \cdot \dfrac{1}{\cos\theta}$ $\Leftrightarrow$ $r\cos\theta = 2$ $\Leftrightarrow$ $x = 2$.

58. $r = 2 - \cos\theta$ $\Leftrightarrow$ $r^2 = 2r - r\cos\theta$ $\Leftrightarrow$ $r^2 + r\cos\theta = 2r$ $\Leftrightarrow$ $\left(r^2 + r\cos\theta\right)^2 = (2r)^2$ $\Leftrightarrow$ $\left(r^2 + r\cos\theta\right)^2 = 4r^2$ $\Rightarrow$ $\left(x^2 + y^2 - x\right)^2 = 4\left(x^2 + y^2\right)$

59. $\sec\theta = 2$ $\Leftrightarrow$ $\cos\theta = \frac{1}{2}$ $\Leftrightarrow$ $\theta = \pm\frac{\pi}{3}$ $\Leftrightarrow$ $\tan\theta = \pm\sqrt{3}$ $\Leftrightarrow$ $\dfrac{y}{x} = \pm\sqrt{3}$ $\Leftrightarrow$ $y = \pm\sqrt{3}x$.

60. $\cos 2\theta = 1$ means that $2\theta = 0$ $\Rightarrow$ $\theta = 0$ $\Rightarrow$ $\tan\theta = 0$ $\Rightarrow$ $\dfrac{y}{x} = 0$ $\Rightarrow$ $y = 0$

61. (a) In rectangular coordinates, the points (r_1, θ_1) and (r_2, θ_2) are $(x_1, y_1) = (r_1\cos\theta_1, r_1\sin\theta_1)$ and $(x_2, y_2) = (r_2\cos\theta_2, r_2\sin\theta_2)$. Then, the distance between the points is

$$
\begin{aligned}
D &= \sqrt{(x_1 - x_2)^2 + (y_1 - y_2)^2} = \sqrt{(r_1\cos\theta_1 - r_2\cos\theta_2)^2 + (r_1\sin\theta_1 - r_2\sin\theta_2)^2} \\
&= \sqrt{r_1^2\left(\cos^2\theta_1 + \sin^2\theta_1\right) + r_2^2\left(\cos^2\theta_2 + \sin^2\theta_2\right) - 2r_1 r_2\left(\cos\theta_1\cos\theta_2 + \sin\theta_1\sin\theta_2\right)} \\
&= \sqrt{r_1^2 + r_2^2 - 2r_1 r_2\cos(\theta_2 - \theta_1)}
\end{aligned}
$$

(b) The distance between the points $\left(3, \frac{3\pi}{4}\right)$ and $\left(-1, \frac{7\pi}{6}\right)$ is

$$
D = \sqrt{3^2 + (-1)^2 - 2(3)(-1)\cos\left(\frac{7\pi}{6} - \frac{3\pi}{4}\right)} = \sqrt{9 + 1 + 6\cos\frac{5\pi}{12}} \approx 3.40
$$

8.2   Graphs of Polar Equations

1. VI   **2.** III   **3.** II   **4.** IV   **5.** I   **6.** V

7. Polar axis: $2 - \sin(-\theta) = 2 + \sin\theta \neq r$, so the graph is not symmetric about the polar axis.

Pole: $2 - \sin(\theta + \pi) = 2 - (\sin\pi\cos\theta + \cos\pi\sin\theta) = 2 - (-\sin\theta) = 2 + \sin\theta \neq r$, so the graph is not symmetric about the pole.

Line $\theta = \frac{\pi}{2}$: $2 - \sin(\pi - \theta) = 2 - (\sin\pi\cos\theta - \cos\pi\sin\theta) = 2 - \sin\theta = r$, so the graph is symmetric about $\theta = \frac{\pi}{2}$.

8. Polar axis: $4 + 8\cos(-\theta) = 4 + 8\cos\theta = r$, so the graph is symmetric about the polar axis.

Pole: $4 + 8\cos(\theta + \pi) = 4 + 8(\cos\pi\cos\theta - \sin\pi\sin\theta) = 4 + 8(-\cos\theta) \neq r$, so the graph is not symmetric about the pole.

Line $\theta = \frac{\pi}{2}$: $4 + 8\cos(\pi - \theta) = 4 + 8(\cos\pi\cos\theta + \sin\pi\sin\theta) = 4 + 8(-\cos\theta) \neq r$, so the graph is not symmetric about $\theta = \frac{\pi}{2}$.

9. Polar axis: $3 \sec(-\theta) = 3 \sec \theta = r$, so the graph is symmetric about the polar axis.

Pole: $3 \sec(\theta + \pi) = \dfrac{3}{\cos(\theta + \pi)} = \dfrac{1}{\cos \pi \cos \theta - \sin \pi \sin \theta} = \dfrac{3}{-\cos \theta} = -3 \sec \theta \neq r$, so the graph is not symmetric about the pole.

Line $\theta = \frac{\pi}{2}$: $3 \sec(\pi - \theta) = \dfrac{3}{\cos(\pi - \theta)} = \dfrac{1}{\cos \pi \cos \theta + \sin \pi \sin \theta} = \dfrac{3}{-\cos \theta} = -3 \sec \theta \neq r$, so the graph is not symmetric about $\theta = \frac{\pi}{2}$.

10. Polar axis: $5 \cos(-\theta) \csc(-\theta) = 5 \cos \theta (-\csc \theta) \neq r$, so the graph is not symmetric about the polar axis.

Pole: $5 \cos(\theta + \pi) \csc(\theta + \pi) = 5 \cos(\theta + \pi) \dfrac{1}{\sin(\theta + \pi)}$

$= 5 (\cos \pi \cos \theta - \sin \pi \sin \theta) \dfrac{1}{\sin \pi \cos \theta + \cos \pi \sin \theta} = 5 (-\cos \theta) \dfrac{1}{-\sin \theta} = 5 \cos \theta \csc \theta = r$,

so the graph is symmetric about the pole.

Line $\theta = \frac{\pi}{2}$: $5 \cos(\pi - \theta) \csc(\pi - \theta) = 5 \cos(\pi - \theta) \dfrac{1}{\sin(\pi - \theta)}$

$= 5 (\cos \pi \cos \theta + \sin \pi \sin \theta) \dfrac{1}{\sin \pi \cos \theta - \cos \pi \sin \theta} = 5 (-\cos \theta) \dfrac{1}{\sin \theta} = -5 \cos \theta \csc \theta \neq r$,

so the graph is not symmetric about $\theta = \frac{\pi}{2}$.

11. Polar axis: $\dfrac{4}{3 - 2 \sin(-\theta)} = \dfrac{4}{3 + 2 \sin \theta} \neq r$, so the graph is not symmetric about the polar axis.

Pole: $\dfrac{4}{3 - 2 \sin(\theta + \pi)} = \dfrac{4}{3 - 2 (\sin \pi \cos \theta + \cos \pi \sin \theta)} = \dfrac{4}{3 - 2 (-\sin \theta)} = \dfrac{4}{3 + 2 \sin \theta} \neq r$, so the graph is not symmetric about the pole.

Line $\theta = \frac{\pi}{2}$: $\dfrac{4}{3 - 2 \sin(\pi - \theta)} = \dfrac{4}{3 - 2 (\sin \pi \cos \theta - \cos \pi \sin \theta)} = \dfrac{4}{3 - 2 \sin \theta} = r$, so the graph is symmetric about $\theta = \frac{\pi}{2}$.

12. Polar axis: $\dfrac{5}{1 + 3 \cos(-\theta)} = \dfrac{5}{1 + 3 \cos \theta} = r$, so the graph is symmetric about the polar axis.

Pole: $\dfrac{5}{1 + 3 \cos(\theta + \pi)} = \dfrac{5}{1 + 3 (\cos \pi \cos \theta - \sin \pi \sin \theta)} = \dfrac{5}{1 + 3 (-\cos \theta)} = \dfrac{5}{1 - 3 \cos \theta} \neq r$, so the graph is not symmetric about the pole.

Line $\theta = \frac{\pi}{2}$: $\dfrac{5}{1 + 3 \cos(\pi - \theta)} = \dfrac{5}{1 + 3 (\cos \pi \cos \theta + \sin \pi \sin \theta)} = \dfrac{5}{1 - 3 \cos \theta} \neq r$, so the graph is not symmetric about $\theta = \frac{\pi}{2}$.

13. Polar axis: $4 \cos 2 (-\theta) = 4 \cos 2\theta = r^2$, so the graph is symmetric about the polar axis.

Pole: $(-r)^2 = r^2$, so the graph is symmetric about the pole.

Line $\theta = \frac{\pi}{2}$: $4 \cos 2 (\pi - \theta) = 4 \cos(2\pi - 2\theta) = 4 \cos(-2\theta) = 4 \cos 2\theta = r^2$, so the graph is symmetric about $\theta = \frac{\pi}{2}$.

14. Polar axis: $9 \sin(-\theta) = -9 \sin \theta \neq r^2$, so the graph is not symmetric about the polar axis.

Pole: $(-r)^2 = r^2$, so the graph is symmetric about the pole.

Line $\theta = \frac{\pi}{2}$: $9 \sin(\pi - \theta) = 9 (\sin \pi \cos \theta - \cos \pi \sin \theta) = 9 \sin \theta = r^2$, so the graph is symmetric about $\theta = \frac{\pi}{2}$.

15. $r = 2$. Circle.

16. $r = -1$. Circle.

17. $\theta = -\frac{\pi}{2}$. Line.

18. $\theta = \frac{5\pi}{6}$. Line.

19. $r = 6 \sin \theta$. Circle.

20. $r = \cos \theta$. Circle.

21. $r = -2 \cos \theta$. Circle.

22. $r = 2 \sin \theta + 2 \cos \theta \quad \Leftrightarrow \quad r^2 = 2r \sin \theta + 2r \cos \theta$
$\quad \Leftrightarrow \quad x^2 + y^2 = 2x + 2y \quad \Leftrightarrow$
$(x - 1)^2 + (y - 1)^2 = 2$. Circle.

23. $r = 2 - 2 \cos \theta$. Cardioid.

24. $r = 1 + \sin \theta$. Cardioid.

25. $r = -3\,(1 + \sin\theta)$. Cardioid.

26. $r = \cos\theta - 1$. Cardioid.

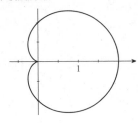

27. $r = \theta, \theta \geq 0$

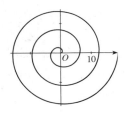

28. $r\theta = 1, \theta > 0$

29. $r = \sin 2\theta$

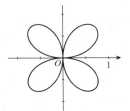

30. $r = 2\cos 3\theta$

31. $r^2 = \cos 2\theta$

32. $r^2 = 4\sin 2\theta$

33. $r = 2 + \sin\theta$

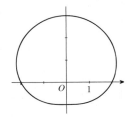

34. $r = 1 - 2\cos\theta$

35. $r = 2 + \sec\theta$

36. $r = \sin\theta\tan\theta$

37. $r = \cos\left(\dfrac{\theta}{2}\right), \theta \in [0, 4\pi]$

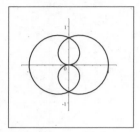

38. $r = \sin\left(\dfrac{8\theta}{5}\right), \theta \in [0, 10\pi]$

39. $r = 1 + 2\sin\left(\dfrac{\theta}{2}\right), \theta \in [0, 4\pi]$

40. $r = \sqrt{1 - 0.8\sin^2\theta}, \theta \in [0, 2\pi]$

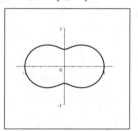

41. $r = 1 + \sin n\theta$. The number of loops is n.

| $n = 1$ | $n = 2$ | $n = 3$ | $n = 4$ | $n = 5$ |

42. $r = 1 + c\sin 2\theta$

| $c = 0.3$ | $c = 0.6$ | $c = 1$ | $c = 1.5$ | $c = 2$ |

As c increases, the graph becomes "pinched" along the line $\theta = \frac{3\pi}{4}$, eventually growing more "leaves" with that line as their axis.

43. The graph of $r = \sin\left(\dfrac{\theta}{2}\right)$ is IV, since the graph must contain the points $(0,0)$, $\left(\dfrac{1}{\sqrt{2}}, \dfrac{\pi}{2}\right)$, $(1,\pi)$, and so on.

44. The graph of $r = \dfrac{1}{\sqrt{\theta}}$ is I, since as θ increase, r decreases $(\theta > 0)$. So this is a spiral into the origin.

45. The graph of $r = \theta \sin\theta$ is III, since for $\theta = \frac{\pi}{2}, \frac{5\pi}{2}, \frac{7\pi}{2}, \ldots$ the values of r are also $\frac{\pi}{2}, \frac{5\pi}{2}, \frac{7\pi}{2}, \ldots$ Thus the graph must cross the vertical axis at an infinite number of points.

46. The graph of $r = 1 + 3\cos(3\theta)$ is II, since when $\theta = 0$, $r = 1 + 3 = 4$ and when $\theta = \pi$, $r = 1 - 3 = -2$, so there should be two intercepts on the positive-axis.

47. $\left(x^2 + y^2\right)^3 = 4x^2y^2 \quad \Leftrightarrow \quad \left(r^2\right)^3 = 4\left(r\cos\theta\right)^2\left(r\sin\theta\right)^2 \quad \Leftrightarrow$

$r^6 = 4r^4\cos^2\theta\sin^2\theta \quad \Leftrightarrow \quad r^2 = 4\cos^2\theta\sin^2\theta \quad \Leftrightarrow$

$r = 2\cos\theta\sin\theta = \sin 2\theta$. The equation is $r = \sin 2\theta$, a rose.

48. $\left(x^2 + y^2\right)^3 = \left(x^2 - y^2\right)^2 \quad \Leftrightarrow \quad \left(r^2\right)^3 = \left[(r\cos\theta)^2 - (r\sin\theta)^2\right]^2 \quad \Leftrightarrow$

$r^6 = \left(r^2\cos^2\theta - r^2\sin^2\theta\right)^2 \quad \Leftrightarrow \quad r^6 = \left[r^2\left(\cos^2\theta - \sin^2\theta\right)\right]^2 \quad \Leftrightarrow$

$r^6 = r^4\left(\cos^2\theta - \sin^2\theta\right)^2 \quad \Leftrightarrow \quad r^2 = \left(\cos 2\theta\right)^2 \quad \Leftrightarrow \quad r = \pm\cos 2\theta$. The

equations $r = \cos 2\theta$ and $r = -\cos 2\theta$ have the same graph, a rose.

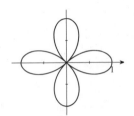

49. $\left(x^2 + y^2\right)^2 = x^2 - y^2 \quad \Leftrightarrow \quad \left(r^2\right)^2 = (r\cos\theta)^2 - (r\sin\theta)^2 \quad \Leftrightarrow$

$r^4 = r^2\cos^2\theta - r^2\sin^2\theta \quad \Leftrightarrow \quad r^4 = r^2\left(\cos^2\theta - \sin^2\theta\right) \quad \Leftrightarrow$

$r^2 = \cos^2\theta - \sin^2\theta = \cos 2\theta$. The graph is $r^2 = \cos 2\theta$, a leminiscate.

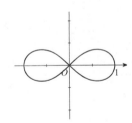

50. $x^2 + y^2 = \left(x^2 + y^2 - x\right)^2 \quad \Leftrightarrow \quad r^2 = \left(r^2 - r\cos\theta\right)^2 \quad \Leftrightarrow$

$r^2 = \left[r\left(r - \cos\theta\right)\right]^2 \quad \Leftrightarrow \quad r^2 = r^2\left(r - \cos\theta\right)^2 \quad \Leftrightarrow \quad 1 = \left(r - \cos\theta\right)^2$

$\Leftrightarrow \quad \pm 1 = r - \cos\theta \quad \Leftrightarrow \quad r = \cos\theta \pm 1$. Both $r = \cos\theta + 1$ and

$r = \cos\theta - 1$ give the same graph. To see this, replace θ with $\theta + \pi$:

$\cos\left(\theta + \pi\right) - 1 = -\cos\theta - 1 = -\left(\cos\theta + 1\right)$. This is a cardioid.

51. $r = a\cos\theta + b\sin\theta \quad \Leftrightarrow \quad r^2 = ar\cos\theta + br\sin\theta \quad \Leftrightarrow \quad x^2 + y^2 = ax + by \quad \Leftrightarrow \quad x^2 - ax + y^2 - by = 0 \quad \Leftrightarrow$

$x^2 - ax + \frac{1}{4}a^2 + y^2 - by + \frac{1}{4}b^2 = \frac{1}{4}a^2 + \frac{1}{4}b^2 \quad \Leftrightarrow$

$\left(x - \frac{1}{2}a\right)^2 + \left(y - \frac{1}{2}b\right)^2 = \frac{1}{4}\left(a^2 + b^2\right)$. Thus, in rectangular coordinates the center is $\left(\frac{1}{2}a, \frac{1}{2}b\right)$ and the radius is

$\frac{1}{2}\sqrt{a^2 + b^2}$.

52. (a)

(b) $r = \tan\theta\sec\theta = \dfrac{\sin\theta}{\cos\theta}\left(\dfrac{1}{\cos\theta}\right) = \dfrac{y/r}{(x/r)^2} = \dfrac{ry}{x^2}$ $\Leftrightarrow$ $\dfrac{y}{x^2} = 1$

$\Leftrightarrow$ $y = x^2$.

53. (a)

At $\theta = 0$, the satellite is at the "rightmost" point in its orbit, $(5625, 0)$. As θ increases, it travels counterclockwise. Note that it is moving fastest when $\theta = \pi$.

(b) The satellite is closest to earth when $\theta = \pi$. Its height above the earth's surface at this point is

$22500/\left(4 - \cos\pi\right) - 3960 = 4500 - 3960 = 540$ mi.

54. (a)

The satellite starts out at the same point, $(5625, 0)$, but its orbit decays. It narrowly misses the earth at its first perigee (closest approach to the earth), and crashes during its second orbit.

(b) The satellite crashes when $\theta \approx 8.37$ rad $\approx 480°$.

55. The graphs of $r = 1 + \sin\left(\theta - \frac{\pi}{6}\right)$ and $r = 1 + \sin\left(\theta - \frac{\pi}{3}\right)$ have the same shape as $r = 1 + \sin\theta$, rotated through angles of $\frac{\pi}{6}$ and $\frac{\pi}{3}$, respectively. Similarly, the graph of $r = f\left(\theta - \alpha\right)$ is the graph of $r = f\left(\theta\right)$ rotated by the angle α.

56. The circle $r = 2$ (in polar coordinates) has rectangular coordinate equation $x^2 + y^2 = 4$. The polar coordinate form is simpler. The graph of the equation $r = \sin 2\theta$ is a four-leafed rose. Multiplying both sides by r^2, we get $r^3 = r^2 2\cos\theta\sin\theta = 2\left(r\cos\theta\right)\left(r\sin\theta\right)$ which is $\left(x^2 + y^2\right)^{3/2} = 2xy$ in rectangular form. The polar form is definitely simpler.

57. $y = 2$ $\Leftrightarrow$ $r\sin\theta = 2$ $\Leftrightarrow$ $r = 2\csc\theta$. The rectangular coordinate system gives the simpler equation here. It is easier to study lines in rectangular coordinates.

8.3   Polar Form of Complex Numbers; DeMoivre's Theorem

1. $|4i| = \sqrt{0^2 + 4^2} = 4$

2. $|-3i| = \sqrt{0 + 9} = 3$

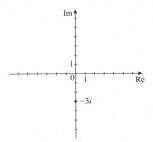

3. $|-2| = \sqrt{4 + 0} = 2$

4. $|6| = 6$

5. $|5 + 2i| = \sqrt{5^2 + 2^2} = \sqrt{29}$

6. $|7 - 3i| = \sqrt{49 + 9} = \sqrt{58}$

7. $\left|\sqrt{3} + i\right| = \sqrt{3 + 1} = 2$

8. $\left|-1 - \frac{\sqrt{3}}{3}i\right| = \sqrt{1 + \frac{1}{3}} = \sqrt{\frac{4}{3}} = \frac{2\sqrt{3}}{3}$

9. $\left|\dfrac{3+4i}{5}\right| = \sqrt{\dfrac{9}{25} + \dfrac{16}{25}} = 1$

10. $\left|\dfrac{-\sqrt{2}+i\sqrt{2}}{2}\right| = \sqrt{\dfrac{1}{2} + \dfrac{1}{2}} = 1$

11. $z = 1+i, 2z = 2+2i, -z = -1-i, \frac{1}{2}z = \frac{1}{2} + \frac{1}{2}i$

12. $z = -1+\sqrt{3}i, 2z = -2+2\sqrt{3}i, -z = 1-\sqrt{3}i,$
$\frac{1}{2}z = -\frac{1}{2} + \frac{\sqrt{3}}{2}i$

13. $z = 8+2i, \overline{z} = 8-2i$

14. $z = -5+6i, \overline{z} = -5-6i$

15. $z_1 = 2-i, z_2 = 2+i, z_1+z_2 = 2-i+2+i = 4,$
$z_1 z_2 = (2-i)(2+i) = 4-i^2 = 5$

16. $z_1 = -1+i, z_2 = 2-3i,$
$z_1+z_2 = -1+i+2-3i = 1-2i,$
$z_1 z_2 = (-1+i)(2-3i) = -2+3i+2i-3i^2 = 1+5i$

17. $\{z = a + bi \mid a \leq 0, b \geq 0\}$

18. $\{z = a + bi \mid a > 1, b > 1\}$

19. $\{z \mid |z| = 3\}$

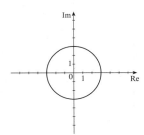

20. $\{z \mid |z| \geq 1\}$

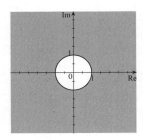

21. $\{z \mid |z| < 2\}$

22. $\{z \mid 2 \leq |z| \leq 5\}$

23. $\{z = a + bi \mid a + b < 2\}$

24. $\{z = a + bi \mid a \geq b\}$

25. $1 + i$. Then $\tan \theta = \frac{1}{1} = 1$ with θ in quadrant I $\Rightarrow$ $\theta = \frac{\pi}{4}$, and $r = \sqrt{1^2 + 1^2} = \sqrt{2}$. Hence, $1 + i = \sqrt{2} \left(\cos \frac{\pi}{4} + i \sin \frac{\pi}{4} \right)$.

26. $1 + \sqrt{3}i$. Then $\tan \theta = \sqrt{3}$ with θ in quadrant I $\Rightarrow$ $\theta = \frac{\pi}{3}$, and $r = \sqrt{1 + 3} = 2$. Hence, $1 - \sqrt{3}i = 2 \left(\cos \frac{\pi}{3} + i \sin \frac{\pi}{3} \right)$.

27. $\sqrt{2} - \sqrt{2}i$. Then $\tan \theta = \frac{\sqrt{2}}{\sqrt{2}} = -1$ with θ in quadrant IV $\Rightarrow$ $\theta = \frac{7\pi}{4}$, and $r = \sqrt{2 + 2} = 2$. Hence, $\sqrt{2} - \sqrt{2}i = 2 \left(\cos \frac{7\pi}{4} + i \sin \frac{7\pi}{4} \right)$.

28. $1 - i$. Then $\tan \theta = -1$ with θ in quadrant IV $\Rightarrow$ $\theta = \frac{7\pi}{4}$, and $r = \sqrt{1 + 1} = \sqrt{2}$. Hence, $1 - i = \sqrt{2} \left(\cos \frac{7\pi}{4} + i \sin \frac{7\pi}{4} \right)$.

29. $2\sqrt{3} - 2i$. Then $\tan\theta = \frac{-2}{2\sqrt{3}} = -\frac{1}{\sqrt{3}}$ with θ in quadrant IV $\Rightarrow$ $\theta = \frac{11\pi}{6}$, and $r = \sqrt{12+4} = 4$. Hence,
$2\sqrt{3} - 2i = 4\left(\cos\frac{11\pi}{6} + i\sin\frac{11\pi}{6}\right)$.

30. $-1 + i$. Then $\tan\theta = -1$ with θ in quadrant II $\Rightarrow$ $\theta = \frac{3\pi}{4}$, and $r = \sqrt{1+1} = \sqrt{2}$. Hence,
$-1 + i = \sqrt{2}\left(\cos\frac{3\pi}{4} + i\sin\frac{3\pi}{4}\right)$.

31. $-3i$. Then $\theta = \frac{3\pi}{2}$, and $r = \sqrt{0+9} = 3$. Hence, $3i = 3\left(\cos\frac{3\pi}{2} + i\sin\frac{3\pi}{2}\right)$.

32. $-3 - 3\sqrt{3}i$. Then $\tan\theta = \sqrt{3}$ with θ in quadrant III $\Rightarrow$ $\theta = \frac{4\pi}{3}$, and $r = \sqrt{9+27} = 6$. Hence,
$-3 - 3\sqrt{3}i = 6\left(\cos\frac{4\pi}{3} + i\sin\frac{4\pi}{3}\right)$.

33. $5 + 5i$. Then $\tan\theta = \frac{5}{5} = 1$ with θ in quadrant I $\Rightarrow$ $\theta = \frac{\pi}{4}$, and $r = \sqrt{25+25} = 5\sqrt{2}$. Hence,
$5 + 5i = 5\sqrt{2}\left(\cos\frac{\pi}{4} + i\sin\frac{\pi}{4}\right)$.

34. 4. Then $\theta = 0$, and $r = \sqrt{16+0} = 4$. Hence, $4 = 4\left(\cos 0 + i\sin 0\right)$.

35. $4\sqrt{3} - 4i$. Then $\tan\theta = \frac{-4}{4\sqrt{3}} = -\frac{1}{\sqrt{3}}$ with θ in quadrant IV $\Rightarrow$ $\theta = \frac{11\pi}{6}$, and $r = \sqrt{48+16} = 8$. Hence,
$4\sqrt{3} - 4i = 8\left(\cos\frac{11\pi}{6} + i\sin\frac{11\pi}{6}\right)$.

36. $8i$. Then $\theta = \frac{\pi}{2}$, and $r = 8$. Hence, $8i = 8\left(\cos\frac{\pi}{2} + i\sin\frac{\pi}{2}\right)$.

37. -20. Then $\theta = \pi$, and $r = 20$. Hence, $-20 = 20\left(\cos\pi + i\sin\pi\right)$.

38. $\sqrt{3} + i$. Then $\tan\theta = \frac{1}{\sqrt{3}}$ with θ in quadrant I $\Rightarrow$ $\theta = \frac{\pi}{6}$, and $r = \sqrt{3+1} = 2$. Hence, $\sqrt{3} + i = 2\left(\cos\frac{\pi}{6} + i\sin\frac{\pi}{6}\right)$.

39. $3 + 4i$. Then $\tan\theta = \frac{4}{3}$ with θ in quadrant I $\Rightarrow$ $\theta = \tan^{-1}\frac{4}{3}$, and $r = \sqrt{9+16} = 5$. Hence,
$3 + 4i = 5\left[\cos\left(\tan^{-1}\frac{4}{3}\right) + i\sin\left(\tan^{-1}\frac{4}{3}\right)\right]$.

40. $i(2 - 2i) = 2 + 2i$. Then $\tan\theta = 1$ with θ in quadrant I $\Rightarrow$ $\theta = \frac{\pi}{4}$, and $r = \sqrt{4+4} = 2\sqrt{2}$. Hence,
$i(2 - 2i) = 2\sqrt{2}\left(\cos\frac{\pi}{4} + i\sin\frac{\pi}{4}\right)$.

41. $3i(1 + i) = -3 + 3i$. Then $\tan\theta = \frac{3}{-3} = -1$ with θ in quadrant II $\Rightarrow$ $\theta = \frac{3\pi}{4}$, and $r = \sqrt{9+9} = 3\sqrt{2}$. Hence,
$3i(1 + i) = 3\sqrt{2}\left(\cos\frac{3\pi}{4} + i\sin\frac{3\pi}{4}\right)$.

42. $2(1 - i) = 2 - 2i$. Then $\tan\theta = -1$ with θ in quadrant IV $\Rightarrow$ $\theta = \frac{7\pi}{4}$, and $r = \sqrt{4+4} = 2\sqrt{2}$. Hence,
$2(1 - i) = 2\sqrt{2}\left(\cos\frac{7\pi}{4} + i\sin\frac{7\pi}{4}\right)$.

43. $4\left(\sqrt{3} + i\right) = 4\sqrt{3} + 4i$. Then $\tan\theta = \frac{4}{4\sqrt{3}} = \frac{1}{\sqrt{3}}$ with θ in quadrant I $\Rightarrow$ $\theta = \frac{\pi}{6}$, and $r = \sqrt{48+16} = 8$. Hence,
$4\left(\sqrt{3} + i\right) = 8\left(\cos\frac{\pi}{6} + i\sin\frac{\pi}{6}\right)$.

44. $-3 - 3i$. Then $\tan\theta = 1$ with θ in quadrant III $\Rightarrow$ $\theta = \frac{5\pi}{4}$, and $r = \sqrt{9+9} = 3\sqrt{2}$. Hence,
$-3 - 3i = 3\sqrt{2}\left(\cos\frac{5\pi}{4} + i\sin\frac{5\pi}{4}\right)$.

45. $2 + i$. Then $\tan\theta = \frac{1}{2}$ with θ in quadrant I $\Rightarrow$ $\theta = \tan^{-1}\frac{1}{2}$, and $r = \sqrt{4+1} = \sqrt{5}$. Hence,
$2 + i = \sqrt{5}\left[\cos\left(\tan^{-1}\frac{1}{2}\right) + i\sin\left(\tan^{-1}\frac{1}{2}\right)\right]$.

46. $3 + \sqrt{3}i$. Then $\tan\theta = \frac{1}{\sqrt{3}}$ with θ in quadrant I $\Rightarrow$ $\theta = \frac{\pi}{6}$, and $r = \sqrt{9+3} = 2\sqrt{3}$. Hence,
$3 + \sqrt{3}i = 2\sqrt{3}\left(\cos\frac{\pi}{6} + i\sin\frac{\pi}{6}\right)$.

47. $\sqrt{2} + \sqrt{2}i$. Then $\tan\theta = \frac{\sqrt{2}}{\sqrt{2}} = 1$ with θ in quadrant I $\Rightarrow$ $\theta = \frac{\pi}{4}$, and $r = \sqrt{2+2} = 2$. Hence,
$2 + \sqrt{2}i = 2\left(\cos\frac{\pi}{4} + i\sin\frac{\pi}{4}\right)$.

48. $-\pi i$. Then $\theta = \frac{3\pi}{2}$, and $r = \pi$. Hence $-\pi i = \pi\left(\cos\frac{3\pi}{2} + i\sin\frac{3\pi}{2}\right)$.

49. $z_1 = \cos\pi + i\sin\pi$, $z_2 = \cos\frac{\pi}{3} + i\sin\frac{\pi}{3}$, $z_1 z_2 = \cos\left(\pi + \frac{\pi}{3}\right) + i\sin\left(\pi + \frac{\pi}{3}\right) = \cos\frac{4\pi}{3} + i\sin\frac{4\pi}{3}$,

$z_1/z_2 = \cos\left(\pi - \frac{\pi}{3}\right) + i\sin\left(\pi - \frac{\pi}{3}\right) = \cos\frac{2\pi}{3} + i\sin\frac{2\pi}{3}$

50. $z_1 = \cos\frac{\pi}{4} + i\sin\frac{\pi}{4}$, $z_2 = \cos\frac{3\pi}{4} + i\sin\frac{3\pi}{4}$, $z_1 z_2 = \cos\left(\frac{\pi}{4} + \frac{3\pi}{4}\right) + i\sin\left(\frac{\pi}{4} + \frac{3\pi}{4}\right) = \cos\pi + i\sin\pi$,

$z_1/z_2 = \cos\left(\frac{\pi}{4} - \frac{3\pi}{4}\right) + i\sin\left(\frac{\pi}{4} - \frac{3\pi}{4}\right) = \cos\left(-\frac{\pi}{2}\right) + i\sin\left(-\frac{\pi}{2}\right) = \cos\frac{\pi}{2} - i\sin\frac{\pi}{2}$

51. $z_1 = 3\left(\cos\frac{\pi}{6} + i\sin\frac{\pi}{6}\right)$, $z_2 = 5\left(\cos\frac{4\pi}{3} + i\sin\frac{4\pi}{3}\right)$,

$z_1 z_2 = 3 \cdot 5\left[\cos\left(\frac{\pi}{6} + \frac{4\pi}{3}\right) + i\sin\left(\frac{\pi}{6} + \frac{4\pi}{3}\right)\right] = 15\left(\cos\frac{9\pi}{6} + i\sin\frac{9\pi}{6}\right) = 15\left(\cos\frac{3\pi}{2} + i\sin\frac{3\pi}{2}\right)$,

$z_1/z_2 = \frac{3}{5}\left[\cos\left(\frac{\pi}{6} - \frac{4\pi}{3}\right) + i\sin\left(\frac{\pi}{6} - \frac{4\pi}{3}\right)\right] = \frac{3}{5}\left[\cos\left(-\frac{7\pi}{6}\right) + i\sin\left(-\frac{7\pi}{6}\right)\right] = \frac{3}{5}\left[\cos\left(\frac{7\pi}{6}\right) - i\sin\left(\frac{7\pi}{6}\right)\right]$

52. $z_1 = 7\left(\cos\frac{9\pi}{8} + i\sin\frac{9\pi}{8}\right)$, $z_2 = 2\left(\cos\frac{\pi}{8} + i\sin\frac{\pi}{8}\right)$,

$z_1 z_2 = 7 \cdot 2\left[\cos\left(\frac{9\pi}{8} + \frac{\pi}{8}\right) + i\sin\left(\frac{9\pi}{8} + \frac{\pi}{8}\right)\right] = 14\left(\cos\frac{5\pi}{4} + i\sin\frac{5\pi}{4}\right)$,

$z_1/z_2 = \frac{7}{2}\left[\cos\left(\frac{9\pi}{8} - \frac{\pi}{8}\right) + i\sin\left(\frac{9\pi}{8} - \frac{\pi}{8}\right)\right] = \frac{7}{2}\left(\cos\pi + i\sin\pi\right)$

53. $z_1 = 4\left(\cos 120° + i\sin 120°\right)$, $z_2 = 2\left(\cos 30° + i\sin 30°\right)$,

$z_1 z_2 = 4 \cdot 2\left[\cos\left(120° + 30°\right) + i\sin\left(120° + 30°\right)\right] = 8\left(\cos 150° + i\sin 150°\right)$,

$z_1/z_2 = \frac{4}{2}\left[\cos\left(120° - 30°\right) + i\sin\left(120° - 30°\right)\right] = 2\left(\cos 90° + i\sin 90°\right)$

54. $z_1 = \sqrt{2}\left(\cos 75° + i\sin 75°\right)$, $z_2 = 3\sqrt{2}\left(\cos 60° + i\sin 60°\right)$,

$z_1 z_2 = \sqrt{2} \cdot 3\sqrt{2} \cdot \left[\cos\left(75° + 60°\right) + i\sin\left(75° + 60°\right)\right] = 6\left(\cos 135° + i\sin 135°\right)$,

$z_1/z_2 = \frac{\sqrt{2}}{3\sqrt{2}}\left[\cos\left(75° - 60°\right) + i\sin\left(75° - 60°\right)\right] = \frac{1}{3}\left(\cos 15° + i\sin 15°\right)$

55. $z_1 = 4\left(\cos 200° + i\sin 200°\right)$, $z_2 = 25\left(\cos 150° + i\sin 150°\right)$,

$z_1 z_2 = 4 \cdot 25\left[\cos\left(200° + 150°\right) + i\sin\left(200° + 150°\right)\right] = 100\left(\cos 350° + i\sin 350°\right)$,

$z_1/z_2 = \frac{4}{25}\left[\cos\left(200° - 150°\right) + i\sin\left(200° - 150°\right)\right] = \frac{4}{25}\left(\cos 50° + i\sin 50°\right)$

56. $z_1 = \frac{4}{5}\left(\cos 25° + i\sin 25°\right)$, $z_2 = \frac{1}{5}\left(\cos 155° + i\sin 155°\right)$,

$z_1 z_2 = \frac{4}{5} \cdot \frac{1}{5} \cdot \left[\cos\left(25° + 155°\right) + i\sin\left(25° + 155°\right)\right] = \frac{4}{25}\left(\cos 180° + i\sin 180°\right)$,

$z_1/z_2 = \frac{4/5}{1/5}\left[\cos\left(25° - 155°\right) + i\sin\left(25° - 155°\right)\right] = 4\left[\cos\left(-130°\right) + i\sin\left(-130°\right)\right] = 4\left(\cos 130° - i\sin 130°\right)$

57. $z_1 = \sqrt{3} + i$, so $\tan\theta_1 = \frac{1}{\sqrt{3}}$ with θ_1 in quadrant I $\Rightarrow$ $\theta_1 = \frac{\pi}{6}$, and $r_1 = \sqrt{3 + 1} = 2$.

$z_2 = 1 + \sqrt{3}i$, so $\tan\theta_2 = \sqrt{3}$ with θ_2 in quadrant I $\Rightarrow$ $\theta_2 = \frac{\pi}{3}$, and $r_1 = \sqrt{1 + 3} = 2$.

Hence, $z_1 = 2\left(\cos\frac{\pi}{6} + i\sin\frac{\pi}{6}\right)$ and $z_2 = 2\left(\cos\frac{\pi}{3} + i\sin\frac{\pi}{3}\right)$.

Thus, $z_1 z_2 = 2 \cdot 2\left[\cos\left(\frac{\pi}{6} + \frac{\pi}{3}\right) + i\sin\left(\frac{\pi}{6} + \frac{\pi}{3}\right)\right] = 4\left(\cos\frac{\pi}{2} + i\sin\frac{\pi}{2}\right)$,

$z_1/z_2 = \frac{2}{2}\left[\cos\left(\frac{\pi}{6} - \frac{\pi}{3}\right) + i\sin\left(\frac{\pi}{6} - \frac{\pi}{3}\right)\right] = \cos\left(-\frac{\pi}{6}\right) + i\sin\left(-\frac{\pi}{6}\right) = \cos\frac{\pi}{6} - i\sin\frac{\pi}{6}$, and

$1/z_1 = \frac{1}{2}\left[\cos\left(-\frac{\pi}{6}\right) + i\sin\left(-\frac{\pi}{6}\right)\right] = \frac{1}{2}\left(\cos\frac{\pi}{6} - i\sin\frac{\pi}{6}\right)$.

58. $z_1 = \sqrt{2} - \sqrt{2}i$, so $\tan\theta_1 = -1$ with θ_1 in quadrant IV $\Rightarrow$ $\theta_1 = \frac{7\pi}{4}$, and $r_1 = \sqrt{2 + 2} = 2$.

$z_2 = 1 - i$, so $\tan\theta_2 = -1$ with θ_2 in quadrant IV $\Rightarrow$ $\theta_2 = \frac{7\pi}{4}$, and $r_2 = \sqrt{1 + 1} = \sqrt{2}$.

Hence, $z_1 = 2\left(\cos\frac{7\pi}{4} + i\sin\frac{7\pi}{4}\right)$ and $z_2 = \sqrt{2}\left(\cos\frac{7\pi}{4} + i\sin\frac{7\pi}{4}\right)$.

Thus, $z_1 z_2 = 2 \cdot \sqrt{2}\left[\cos\left(\frac{7\pi}{4} + \frac{7\pi}{4}\right) + i\sin\left(\frac{7\pi}{4} + \frac{7\pi}{4}\right)\right] = 2\sqrt{2}\left(\cos\frac{7\pi}{2} + i\sin\frac{7\pi}{2}\right) = 2\sqrt{2}\left(\cos\frac{\pi}{2} - i\sin\frac{\pi}{2}\right)$,

$z_1/z_2 = \frac{2}{\sqrt{2}}\left[\cos\left(\frac{7\pi}{4} - \frac{7\pi}{4}\right) + i\sin\left(\frac{7\pi}{4} - \frac{7\pi}{4}\right)\right] = \sqrt{2}\left(\cos 0 + i\sin 0\right)$, and

$1/z_1 = \frac{1}{2}\left[\cos\left(-\frac{7\pi}{4}\right) + i\sin\left(-\frac{7\pi}{4}\right)\right] = \frac{1}{2}\left(\cos\frac{7\pi}{4} - i\sin\frac{7\pi}{4}\right)$.

59. $z_1 = 2\sqrt{3} - 2i$, so $\tan\theta_1 = \frac{-2}{2\sqrt{3}} = -\frac{1}{\sqrt{3}}$ with θ_1 in quadrant IV $\Rightarrow$ $\theta_1 = \frac{11\pi}{6}$, and $r_1 = \sqrt{12+4} = 4$.

$z_2 = -1 + i$, so $\tan\theta_2 = -1$ with θ_2 in quadrant II $\Rightarrow$ $\theta_2 = \frac{3\pi}{4}$, and $r_2 = \sqrt{1+1} = \sqrt{2}$.

Hence, $z_1 = 4\left(\cos\frac{11\pi}{6} + i\sin\frac{11\pi}{6}\right)$ and $z_2 = \sqrt{2}\left(\cos\frac{3\pi}{4} + i\sin\frac{3\pi}{4}\right)$.

Thus, $z_1 z_2 = 4 \cdot \sqrt{2}\left[\cos\left(\frac{11\pi}{6} + \frac{3\pi}{4}\right) + i\sin\left(\frac{11\pi}{6} + \frac{3\pi}{4}\right)\right] = 4\sqrt{2}\left(\cos\frac{7\pi}{12} + i\sin\frac{7\pi}{12}\right)$,

$z_1/z_2 = \frac{4}{\sqrt{2}}\left[\cos\left(\frac{11\pi}{6} - \frac{3\pi}{4}\right) + i\sin\left(\frac{11\pi}{6} - \frac{3\pi}{4}\right)\right] = 2\sqrt{2}\left(\cos\frac{13\pi}{12} + i\sin\frac{13\pi}{12}\right)$, and

$1/z_1 = \frac{1}{4}\left(\cos\left(-\frac{11\pi}{6}\right) + i\sin\left(-\frac{11\pi}{6}\right)\right) = \frac{1}{4}\left(\cos\frac{11\pi}{6} - i\sin\frac{11\pi}{6}\right)$.

60. $z_1 = -\sqrt{2}i$, so $\theta_1 = \frac{3\pi}{2}$, and $r_1 = \sqrt{2}$.

$z_2 = -3 - 3\sqrt{3}i$, so $\tan\theta_2 = \sqrt{3}$ with θ_2 in quadrant IV $\Rightarrow$ $\theta_2 = \frac{4\pi}{3}$, and $r_2 = \sqrt{9+27} = 6$.

Hence, $z_1 = \sqrt{2}\left(\cos\frac{3\pi}{2} + i\sin\frac{3\pi}{2}\right)$ and $z_2 = 6\left(\cos\frac{4\pi}{3} + i\sin\frac{4\pi}{3}\right)$.

Thus, $z_1 z_2 = \sqrt{2} \cdot 6\left[\cos\left(\frac{3\pi}{2} + \frac{4\pi}{3}\right) + i\sin\left(\frac{3\pi}{2} + \frac{4\pi}{3}\right)\right] = 6\sqrt{2}\left(\cos\frac{5\pi}{6} + i\sin\frac{5\pi}{6}\right)$,

$z_1/z_2 = \frac{\sqrt{2}}{6}\left[\cos\left(\frac{3\pi}{2} - \frac{4\pi}{3}\right) + i\sin\left(\frac{3\pi}{2} - \frac{4\pi}{3}\right)\right] = \frac{\sqrt{2}}{6}\left(\cos\frac{\pi}{6} + i\sin\frac{\pi}{6}\right)$, and

$1/z_1 = \frac{1}{\sqrt{2}}\left[\cos\left(-\frac{3\pi}{2}\right) + i\sin\left(-\frac{3\pi}{2}\right)\right] = \frac{1}{\sqrt{2}}\left(\cos\frac{3\pi}{2} - i\sin\frac{3\pi}{2}\right)$.

61. $z_1 = 5 + 5i$, so $\tan\theta_1 = \frac{5}{5} = 1$ with θ_1 in quadrant I $\Rightarrow$ $\theta_1 = \frac{\pi}{4}$, and $r_1 = \sqrt{25+25} = 5\sqrt{2}$.

$z_2 = 4$, so $\theta_2 = 0$, and $r_2 = 4$.

Hence, $z_1 = 5\sqrt{2}\left(\cos\frac{\pi}{4} + i\sin\frac{\pi}{4}\right)$ and $z_2 = 4\left(\cos 0 + i\sin 0\right)$.

Thus, $z_1 z_2 = 5\sqrt{2} \cdot 4\left[\cos\left(\frac{\pi}{4} + 0\right) + i\sin\left(\frac{\pi}{4} + 0\right)\right] = 20\sqrt{2}\left(\cos\frac{\pi}{4} + i\sin\frac{\pi}{4}\right)$, $z_1/z_2 = \frac{5\sqrt{2}}{4}\left(\cos\frac{\pi}{4} + i\sin\frac{\pi}{4}\right)$, and

$1/z_1 = \frac{1}{5\sqrt{2}}\left(\cos\left(-\frac{\pi}{4}\right) + i\sin\left(-\frac{\pi}{4}\right)\right) = \frac{\sqrt{2}}{10}\left(\cos\frac{\pi}{4} - i\sin\frac{\pi}{4}\right)$.

62. $z_1 = 4\sqrt{3} - 4i$, so $\tan\theta_1 = \frac{-4}{4\sqrt{3}} = -\frac{1}{\sqrt{3}}$ with θ_1 in quadrant III $\Rightarrow$ $\theta_1 = \frac{11\pi}{6}$, and $r_1 = \sqrt{48+16} = 8$.

$z_2 = 8i$, so $\theta_2 = \frac{\pi}{2}$, and $r_2 = 8$.

Hence, $z_1 = 8\left(\cos\frac{11\pi}{6} + i\sin\frac{11\pi}{6}\right)$ and $z_2 = 8\left(\cos\frac{\pi}{2} + i\sin\frac{\pi}{2}\right)$.

Thus, $z_1 z_2 = 8 \cdot 8\left[\cos\left(\frac{11\pi}{6} + \frac{\pi}{2}\right) + i\sin\left(\frac{11\pi}{6} + \frac{\pi}{2}\right)\right] = 64\left(\cos\frac{\pi}{3} + i\sin\frac{\pi}{3}\right)$,

$z_1/z_2 = \frac{8}{8}\left[\cos\left(\frac{11\pi}{6} - \frac{\pi}{2}\right) + i\sin\left(\frac{11\pi}{6} - \frac{\pi}{2}\right)\right] = \cos\frac{4\pi}{3} + i\sin\frac{4\pi}{3}$, and $1/z_1 = \frac{1}{8}\left(\cos\frac{11\pi}{6} - i\sin\frac{11\pi}{6}\right)$.

63. $z_1 = -20$, so $\theta_1 = \pi$, and $r_1 = 20$.

$z_2 = \sqrt{3} + i$, so $\tan\theta_2 = \frac{1}{\sqrt{3}}$ with θ_2 in quadrant I $\Rightarrow$ $\theta_2 = \frac{\pi}{6}$, and $r_2 = \sqrt{3+1} = 2$.

Hence, $z_1 = 20\left(\cos\pi + i\sin\pi\right)$ and $z_2 = 2\left(\cos\frac{\pi}{6} + i\sin\frac{\pi}{6}\right)$.

Thus, $z_1 z_2 = 20 \cdot 2\left[\cos\left(\pi + \frac{\pi}{6}\right) + i\sin\left(\pi + \frac{\pi}{6}\right)\right] = 40\left(\cos\frac{7\pi}{6} + i\sin\frac{7\pi}{6}\right)$,

$z_1/z_2 = \frac{20}{2}\left[\cos\left(\pi - \frac{\pi}{6}\right) + i\sin\left(\pi - \frac{\pi}{6}\right)\right] = 10\left(\cos\frac{5\pi}{6} + i\sin\frac{5\pi}{6}\right)$, and

$1/z_1 = \frac{1}{20}\left[\cos\left(-\pi\right) + i\sin\left(-\pi\right)\right] = \frac{1}{20}\left(\cos\pi - i\sin\pi\right)$.

64. $z_1 = 3 + 4i$, so $\tan\theta_1 = \frac{4}{3}$ with θ_1 in quadrant I $\Rightarrow$ $\theta_1 = \tan^{-1}\frac{4}{3}$, and $r_1 = \sqrt{9+16} = 5$.

$z_2 = 2 - 2i$, so $\tan\theta_2 = -1$ with θ_2 in quadrant IV $\Rightarrow$ $\theta_2 = \frac{7\pi}{4}$, and $r_2 = \sqrt{4+4} = 2\sqrt{2}$.

Hence, $z_1 = 5\left[\cos\left(\tan^{-1}\frac{4}{3}\right) + i\sin\left(\tan^{-1}\frac{4}{3}\right)\right] \approx 5\left(\cos 53.13° + i\sin 53.13°\right)$ and $z_2 = 2\sqrt{2}\left(\cos\frac{7\pi}{4} + i\sin\frac{7\pi}{4}\right)$.

Thus, $z_1 z_2 = 5 \cdot 2\sqrt{2}\left[\cos\left(\tan^{-1}\frac{4}{3} + \frac{7\pi}{4}\right) + i\sin\left(\tan^{-1}\frac{4}{3} + \frac{7\pi}{4}\right)\right]$,

$z_1/z_2 = \frac{5}{2\sqrt{2}}\left[\cos\left(\tan^{-1}\frac{4}{3} - \frac{7\pi}{4}\right) + i\sin\left(\tan^{-1}\frac{4}{3} - \frac{7\pi}{4}\right)\right] = \frac{5\sqrt{2}}{4}\left[\cos\left(\tan^{-1}\frac{4}{3} - \frac{7\pi}{4}\right) + i\sin\left(\tan^{-1}\frac{4}{3} - \frac{7\pi}{4}\right)\right]$, and

$1/z_1 = \frac{1}{5}\left[\cos\left(\tan^{-1}\frac{4}{3}\right) - i\sin\left(\tan^{-1}\frac{4}{3}\right)\right]$.

65. From Exercise 25, $1 + i = \sqrt{2}\left(\cos\frac{\pi}{4} + i\sin\frac{\pi}{4}\right)$. Thus,

$$(1+i)^{20} = \left(\sqrt{2}\right)^{20}\left[\cos 20\left(\frac{\pi}{4}\right) + i\sin 20\left(\frac{\pi}{4}\right)\right] = \left(2^{1/2}\right)^{20}\left(\cos 5\pi + i\sin 5\pi\right) = 2^{10}\left(-1 + 0i\right) = -1024.$$

66. $1 - \sqrt{3}i = 2\left(\cos\frac{5\pi}{3} + i\sin\frac{5\pi}{3}\right)$, so

$$\left(1 - \sqrt{3}i\right)^5 = 2^5\left(\cos\frac{25\pi}{3} + i\sin\frac{25\pi}{3}\right) = 32\left(\cos\frac{\pi}{3} + i\sin\frac{\pi}{3}\right) = 32\left(\frac{1}{2} + i\frac{\sqrt{3}}{2}\right) = 16 + 16\sqrt{3}i.$$

67. $r = \sqrt{12 + 4} = 4$ and $\tan\theta = \frac{2}{2\sqrt{3}} = \frac{1}{\sqrt{3}} \Rightarrow \theta = \frac{\pi}{6}$. Thus, $2\sqrt{3} + 2i = 4\left(\cos\frac{\pi}{6} + i\sin\frac{\pi}{6}\right)$. So

$$\left(2\sqrt{3} + 2i\right)^5 = 4^5\left(\cos\frac{5\pi}{6} + i\sin\frac{5\pi}{6}\right) = 1024\left(-\frac{\sqrt{3}}{2} + \frac{1}{2}i\right) = 512\left(-\sqrt{3} + i\right).$$

68. From Exercise 28, $1 - i = \sqrt{2}\left(\cos\frac{7\pi}{4} + i\sin\frac{7\pi}{4}\right)$. Thus, $(1 - i)^8 = \left(\sqrt{2}\right)^8\left(\cos 14\pi + i\sin 14\pi\right) = 16\left(1 + 0i\right) = 16.$

69. $r = \sqrt{\frac{1}{2} + \frac{1}{2}} = 1$ and $\tan\theta = 1 \Rightarrow \theta = \frac{\pi}{4}$. Thus $\frac{\sqrt{2}}{2} + \frac{\sqrt{2}}{2}i = \cos\frac{\pi}{4} + i\sin\frac{\pi}{4}$. Therefore,

$$\left(\frac{\sqrt{2}}{2} + \frac{\sqrt{2}}{2}i\right)^{12} = \cos 12\left(\frac{\pi}{4}\right) + i\sin 12\left(\frac{\pi}{4}\right) = \cos 3\pi + i\sin 3\pi = -1.$$

70. $r = \sqrt{3 + 1} = 2$ and $\tan\theta = \frac{-1}{\sqrt{3}}$ with θ in quadrant IV $\Rightarrow \theta = \frac{11\pi}{6}$. Thus $\sqrt{3} - i = 2\left(\cos\frac{11\pi}{6} + i\sin\frac{11\pi}{6}\right)$, so

$$\left(\sqrt{3} - i\right)^{-10} = \left(\frac{1}{2}\right)^{10}\left(\cos\frac{-110\pi}{6} + i\sin\frac{-110\pi}{6}\right) = \frac{1}{1024}\left(\cos\frac{2\pi}{3} - i\sin\frac{2\pi}{3}\right) = \frac{1}{1024}\left(-\frac{1}{2} + \frac{\sqrt{3}}{2}i\right) = \frac{1}{2048}\left(-1 + \sqrt{3}i\right).$$

71. $r = \sqrt{4 + 4} = 4\sqrt{2}$ and $\tan\theta = -1$ with θ in quadrant IV $\Rightarrow \theta = \frac{7\pi}{4}$. Thus $2 - 2i = 2\sqrt{2}\left(\cos\frac{7\pi}{4} + i\sin\frac{7\pi}{4}\right)$, so

$$(2 - 2i)^8 = \left(2\sqrt{2}\right)^8\left(\cos 14\pi + i\sin 14\pi\right) = 4096\left(1 - 0i\right) = 4096.$$

72. $r = \sqrt{\frac{1}{4} + \frac{3}{4}} = 1$ and $\tan\theta = \sqrt{3}$ with θ in quadrant III $\Rightarrow \theta = -\frac{4\pi}{3}$. Thus $-\frac{1}{2} - \frac{\sqrt{3}}{2}i = \cos\frac{4\pi}{3} + i\sin\frac{4\pi}{3}$, so

$$\left(-\frac{1}{2} - \frac{\sqrt{3}}{2}i\right)^{15} = \cos\frac{60\pi}{3} + i\sin\frac{60\pi}{3} = \cos 20\pi + i\sin 20\pi = 1.$$

73. $r = \sqrt{1 + 1} = \sqrt{2}$ and $\tan\theta = 1$ with θ in quadrant III $\Rightarrow \theta = \frac{5\pi}{4}$. Thus $-1 - i = \sqrt{2}\left(\cos\frac{5\pi}{4} + i\sin\frac{5\pi}{4}\right)$, so

$$(-1 - i)^7 = \left(\sqrt{2}\right)^7\left(\cos\frac{35\pi}{4} + i\sin\frac{35\pi}{4}\right) = 8\sqrt{2}\left(\cos\frac{3\pi}{4} + i\sin\frac{3\pi}{4}\right) = 8\sqrt{2}\left(\frac{1}{\sqrt{2}} - i\frac{1}{\sqrt{2}}\right) = 8\left(-1 + i\right).$$

74. $r = \sqrt{9 + 3} = 2\sqrt{3}$ and $\tan\theta = \frac{\sqrt{3}}{3}$ with θ in quadrant I $\Rightarrow \theta = \frac{\pi}{6}$. Thus $3 + \sqrt{3}i = 2\sqrt{3}\left(\cos\frac{\pi}{6} + i\sin\frac{\pi}{6}\right)$, so

$$\left(3 + \sqrt{3}i\right)^4 = 144\left(\cos\frac{2\pi}{3} + i\sin\frac{2\pi}{3}\right) = 144\left(-\frac{1}{2} + \frac{\sqrt{3}}{2}i\right) = 72\left(-1 + \sqrt{3}i\right).$$

75. $r = \sqrt{12 + 4} = 4$ and $\tan\theta = \frac{2}{2\sqrt{3}} = \frac{1}{\sqrt{3}} \Rightarrow \theta = \frac{\pi}{6}$. Thus $2\sqrt{3} + 2i = 4\left(\cos\frac{\pi}{6} + i\sin\frac{\pi}{6}\right)$, so

$$\left(2\sqrt{3} + 2i\right)^{-5} = \left(\frac{1}{4}\right)^5\left(\cos\frac{-5\pi}{6} + i\sin\frac{-5\pi}{6}\right) = \frac{1}{1024}\left(-\frac{\sqrt{3}}{2} - \frac{1}{2}i\right) = \frac{1}{2048}\left(-\sqrt{3} - i\right)$$

76. $r = \sqrt{1 + 1} = \sqrt{2}$ and $\tan\theta = -1$ with θ in quadrant IV $\Rightarrow \theta = \frac{7\pi}{4}$. Thus $1 - i = \sqrt{2}\left(\cos\frac{7\pi}{4} + i\sin\frac{7\pi}{4}\right)$, so

$$(1 - i)^{-8} = \frac{1}{16}\left(\cos\frac{-56\pi}{4} + i\sin\frac{-56\pi}{4}\right) = \frac{1}{16}\left(\cos 14\pi - i\sin 14\pi\right) = \frac{1}{16}.$$

77. $r = \sqrt{48 + 16} = 8$ and $\tan\theta = \frac{4}{4\sqrt{3}} = \frac{1}{\sqrt{3}} \Rightarrow \theta = \frac{\pi}{6}$. Thus

$4\sqrt{3} + 4i = 8\left(\cos\frac{\pi}{6} + i\sin\frac{\pi}{6}\right)$. So,

$$\left(4\sqrt{3} + 4i\right)^{1/2} = \sqrt{8}\left[\cos\left(\frac{\pi/6 + 2k\pi}{2}\right) + i\sin\left(\frac{\pi/6 + 2k\pi}{2}\right)\right] \text{ for } k = 0, 1.$$

Thus the two roots are $w_0 = 2\sqrt{2}\left(\cos\frac{\pi}{12} + i\sin\frac{\pi}{12}\right)$ and

$w_1 = 2\sqrt{2}\left(\cos\frac{13\pi}{12} + i\sin\frac{13\pi}{12}\right)$.

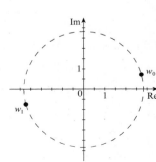

78. $r = \sqrt{48 + 16} = 8$ and $\tan\theta = \frac{4}{4\sqrt{3}} = \frac{1}{\sqrt{3}} \Rightarrow \theta = \frac{\pi}{6}$. Thus

$4\sqrt{3} + 4i = 8\left(\cos\frac{\pi}{6} + i\sin\frac{\pi}{6}\right)$. So

$\left(4\sqrt{3} + 4i\right)^{1/3} = 2\left[\cos\left(\frac{\pi/6 + 2k\pi}{3}\right) + i\sin\left(\frac{\pi/6 + 2k\pi}{3}\right)\right]$ for $k = 0, 1, 2$.

Thus the three roots are $w_0 = 2\left(\cos\frac{\pi}{18} + i\sin\frac{\pi}{18}\right)$,

$w_1 = 2\left(\cos\frac{13\pi}{18} + i\sin\frac{13\pi}{8}\right)$, and $w_2 = 2\left(\cos\frac{25\pi}{18} + i\sin\frac{25\pi}{18}\right)$.

79. $-81i = 81\left(\cos\frac{3\pi}{2} + i\sin\frac{3\pi}{2}\right)$. Thus,

$(-81i)^{1/4} = 81^{1/4}\left[\cos\left(\frac{3\pi/2 + 2k\pi}{4}\right) + i\sin\left(\frac{3\pi/2 + 2k\pi}{4}\right)\right]$ for $k = 0, 1,$

$2, 3$. The four roots are $w_0 = 3\left(\cos\frac{3\pi}{8} + i\sin\frac{3\pi}{8}\right)$, $w_1 = 3\left(\cos\frac{7\pi}{8} + i\sin\frac{7\pi}{8}\right)$,

$w_2 = 3\left(\cos\frac{11\pi}{8} + i\sin\frac{11\pi}{8}\right)$, and $w_3 = 3\left(\cos\frac{15\pi}{8} + i\sin\frac{15\pi}{8}\right)$.

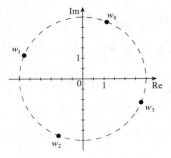

80. $32 = 32\left(\cos 0 + i\sin 0\right)$. Thus, $32^{1/5}\left(\cos\frac{2k\pi}{5} + i\sin\frac{2k\pi}{5}\right)$ for $k = 0, 1, 2, 3,$

4. Thus the five roots are $w_0 = 2\left(\cos 0 + i\sin 0\right)$, $w_1 = 2\left(\cos\frac{2\pi}{5} + i\sin\frac{2\pi}{5}\right)$,

$w_2 = 2\left(\cos\frac{4\pi}{5} + i\sin\frac{4\pi}{5}\right)$, $w_3 = 2\left(\cos\frac{6\pi}{5} + i\sin\frac{6\pi}{5}\right)$, and

$w_4 = 2\left(\cos\frac{8\pi}{5} + i\sin\frac{8\pi}{5}\right)$.

81. $1 = \cos 0 + i\sin 0$. Thus, $1^{1/8} = \cos\frac{2k\pi}{8} + i\sin\frac{2k\pi}{8}$, for $k = 0, 1, 2, 3, 4, 5, 6,$

7. So the eight roots are $w_0 = \cos 0 + i\sin 0 = 1$,

$w_1 = \cos\frac{\pi}{4} + i\sin\frac{\pi}{4} = \frac{\sqrt{2}}{2} + i\frac{\sqrt{2}}{2}$, $w_2 = \cos\frac{\pi}{2} + i\sin\frac{\pi}{2} = i$,

$w_3 = \cos\frac{3\pi}{4} + i\sin\frac{3\pi}{4} = -\frac{\sqrt{2}}{2} + i\frac{\sqrt{2}}{2}$, $w_4 = \cos\pi + i\sin\pi = -1$,

$w_5 = \cos\frac{5\pi}{4} + i\sin\frac{5\pi}{4} = -\frac{\sqrt{2}}{2} - i\frac{\sqrt{2}}{2}$, $w_6 = \cos\frac{3\pi}{2} + i\sin\frac{3\pi}{2} = -i$, and

$w_7 = \cos\frac{7\pi}{4} + i\sin\frac{7\pi}{4} = \frac{\sqrt{2}}{2} - i\frac{\sqrt{2}}{2}$.

82. From Exercise 25, $1 + i = \sqrt{2}\left(\cos\frac{\pi}{4} + i\sin\frac{\pi}{4}\right)$. So

$$(1+i)^{1/3} = \left(\sqrt{2}\right)^{1/3}\left[\cos\left(\frac{\pi/4 + 2k\pi}{3}\right) + i\sin\left(\frac{\pi/4 + 2k\pi}{3}\right)\right] \text{ for } k = 0,$$

1, 2. Thus the three roots are $w_0 = 2^{1/6}\left(\cos\frac{\pi}{12} + i\sin\frac{\pi}{12}\right)$,

$w_1 = 2^{1/6}\left(\cos\frac{9\pi}{12} + i\sin\frac{9\pi}{12}\right)$, and $w_2 = 2^{1/6}\left(\cos\frac{17\pi}{12} + i\sin\frac{17\pi}{12}\right)$.

83. $i = \cos\frac{\pi}{2} + i\sin\frac{\pi}{2}$, so $i^{1/3} = \cos\left(\frac{\pi/2 + 2k\pi}{3}\right) + i\sin\left(\frac{\pi/2 + 2k\pi}{3}\right)$ for

$k = 0$, 1, 2. Thus the three roots are $w_0 = \cos\frac{\pi}{6} + i\sin\frac{\pi}{6} = \frac{\sqrt{3}}{2} + \frac{1}{2}i$,

$w_1 = \cos\frac{5\pi}{6} + i\sin\frac{5\pi}{6} = -\frac{\sqrt{3}}{2} + \frac{1}{2}i$, and $w_2 = \cos\frac{3\pi}{2} + i\sin\frac{3\pi}{2} = -i$.

84. $i = \cos\frac{\pi}{2} + i\sin\frac{\pi}{2}$, so $i^{1/5} = \cos\left(\frac{\pi/2 + 2k\pi}{5}\right) + i\sin\left(\frac{\pi/2 + 2k\pi}{5}\right)$ for

$k = 0$, 1, 2, 3, 4. Thus the five roots are $w_0 = \cos\frac{\pi}{10} + i\sin\frac{\pi}{10}$,

$w_1 = \cos\frac{\pi}{2} + i\sin\frac{\pi}{2}$, $w_2 = \cos\frac{9\pi}{10} + i\sin\frac{9\pi}{10}$, $w_3 = \cos\frac{13\pi}{10} + i\sin\frac{13\pi}{10}$, and

$w_4 = \cos\frac{17\pi}{10} + i\sin\frac{17\pi}{10}$.

85. $-1 = \cos\pi + i\sin\pi$. Then $(-1)^{1/4} = \cos\left(\frac{\pi + 2k\pi}{4}\right) + i\sin\left(\frac{\pi + 2k\pi}{4}\right)$ for

$k = 0$, 1, 2, 3. So the four roots are $w_0 = \cos\frac{\pi}{4} + i\sin\frac{\pi}{4} = \frac{\sqrt{2}}{2} + i\frac{\sqrt{2}}{2}$,

$w_1 = \cos\frac{3\pi}{4} + i\sin\frac{3\pi}{4} = -\frac{\sqrt{2}}{2} + i\frac{\sqrt{2}}{2}$, $w_2 = \cos\frac{5\pi}{4} + i\sin\frac{5\pi}{4} = -\frac{\sqrt{2}}{2} - i\frac{\sqrt{2}}{2}$,

and $w_3 = \cos\frac{7\pi}{4} + i\sin\frac{7\pi}{4} = \frac{\sqrt{2}}{2} - i\frac{\sqrt{2}}{2}$.

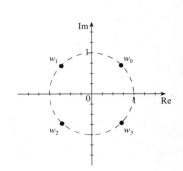

86. $r = \sqrt{16^2 (1+3)} = 32$ and $\tan \theta = \frac{16\sqrt{3}}{16} = \sqrt{3}$ with θ in quadrant III $\Rightarrow$

$\theta = \frac{4\pi}{3}$. Thus $-16 - 16\sqrt{3}i = 32 \left(\cos \frac{4\pi}{3} + i \sin \frac{4\pi}{3} \right)$. So

$$(-16 - 16\sqrt{3}i)^{1/5} = 32^{1/5} \left[\cos \left(\frac{4\pi/3 + 2k\pi}{5} \right) + i \sin \left(\frac{4\pi/3 + 2k\pi}{5} \right) \right] \text{ for}$$

$k = 0, 1, 2, 3, 4$. The five roots are $w_0 = 2 \left(\cos \frac{4\pi}{15} + i \sin \frac{4\pi}{15} \right)$,

$w_1 = 2 \left(\cos \frac{2\pi}{3} + i \sin \frac{2\pi}{3} \right)$, $w_2 = 2 \left(\cos \frac{16\pi}{15} + i \sin \frac{16\pi}{15} \right)$,

$w_3 = 2 \left(\cos \frac{22\pi}{15} + i \sin \frac{22\pi}{15} \right)$, and $w_4 = 2 \left(\cos \frac{28\pi}{15} + i \sin \frac{28\pi}{15} \right)$.

87. $z^4 + 1 = 0 \quad \Leftrightarrow \quad z = (-1)^{1/4} = \frac{\sqrt{2}}{2} (\pm 1 \pm i)$ (from Exercise 85)

88. $z^8 - i = 0 \quad \Rightarrow \quad x = i^{1/8}$. Since $i = \cos \frac{\pi}{2} + i \sin \frac{\pi}{2}$, then, $z = i^{1/8} = \cos \left(\frac{\pi/2 + 2k\pi}{8} \right) + i \sin \left(\frac{\pi/2 + 2k\pi}{8} \right)$

for $k = 0, 1, 2, 3, 4, 5, 6, 7$. Thus there are eight solutions: $z = \cos \frac{\pi}{16} + i \sin \frac{\pi}{16}, \cos \frac{5\pi}{16} + i \sin \frac{5\pi}{16}, \cos \frac{9\pi}{16} + i \sin \frac{9\pi}{16},$

$\cos \frac{13\pi}{16} + i \sin \frac{13\pi}{16}, \cos \frac{17\pi}{16} + i \sin \frac{17\pi}{16}, \cos \frac{21\pi}{16} + i \sin \frac{21\pi}{16}, \cos \frac{25\pi}{16} + i \sin \frac{25\pi}{16},$ and $\cos \frac{29\pi}{16} + i \sin \frac{29\pi}{16}$.

89. $z^3 - 4\sqrt{3} - 4i = 0 \quad \Leftrightarrow \quad z = \left(4\sqrt{3} + 4i \right)^{1/3}$. Since $4\sqrt{3} + 4i = 8 \left(\cos \frac{\pi}{6} + i \sin \frac{\pi}{6} \right)$,

$\left(4\sqrt{3} + 4i \right)^{1/3} = 8^{1/3} \left[\cos \left(\frac{\pi/6 + 2k\pi}{3} \right) + i \sin \left(\frac{\pi/6 + 2k\pi}{3} \right) \right]$, for $k = 0, 1, 2$. Thus the three roots are

$z = 2 \left(\cos \frac{\pi}{18} + i \sin \frac{\pi}{18} \right), z = 2 \left(\cos \frac{13\pi}{18} + i \sin \frac{13\pi}{8} \right)$, and $z = 2 \left(\cos \frac{25\pi}{18} + i \sin \frac{25\pi}{18} \right)$.

90. $z^6 - 1 = 0 \quad \Leftrightarrow \quad z = 1^{1/6}$. Since $1 = \cos 0 + i \sin 0, z = 1^{1/6} = \cos \frac{2k\pi}{6} + i \sin \frac{2k\pi}{6}$ for $k = 0, 1, 2, 3, 4, 5$. Thus

there are six solutions: $z = \pm 1, \pm \frac{1}{2} \pm \frac{\sqrt{3}}{2}i$.

91. $z^3 + 1 = -i \quad \Rightarrow \quad z = (-1 - i)^{1/3}$. Since $-1 - i = \sqrt{2} \left(\cos \frac{5\pi}{4} + i \sin \frac{5\pi}{4} \right)$,

$z = (-1 - i)^{1/3} = 2^{1/6} \left[\cos \left(\frac{5\pi/4 + 2k\pi}{3} \right) + i \sin \left(\frac{5\pi/4 + 2k\pi}{3} \right) \right]$ for $k = 0, 1, 2$. Thus the three solutions to this

equation are $z = 2^{1/6} \left(\cos \frac{5\pi}{12} + i \sin \frac{5\pi}{12} \right), 2^{1/6} \left(\cos \frac{13\pi}{12} + i \sin \frac{13\pi}{12} \right)$, and $2^{1/6} \left(\cos \frac{21\pi}{12} + i \sin \frac{21\pi}{12} \right)$.

92. $z^3 - 1 = 0 \quad \Rightarrow \quad z = 1^{1/3}$. Since $1 = \cos 0 + i \sin 0, z = 1^{1/3} = \cos \frac{2k\pi}{3} + i \sin \frac{2k\pi}{3}$ for $k = 0, 1, 2$. Thus the three

solutions to this equation are $z = \cos 0 + i \sin 0, \cos \frac{2\pi}{3} + i \sin \frac{2\pi}{3}$, and $\cos \frac{4\pi}{3} + i \sin \frac{4\pi}{3}$ or $z = 1, -\frac{1}{2} + \frac{\sqrt{3}}{2}i, -\frac{1}{2} - \frac{\sqrt{3}}{2}i$.

93. (a) $w = \cos \frac{2\pi}{n} + i \sin \frac{2\pi}{n}$ for a positive integer n. Then, $w^k = \cos \frac{2k\pi}{n} + i \sin \frac{2k\pi}{n}$. Now $w^0 = \cos 0 + i \sin 0 = 1$

and for $k \neq 0, \left(w^k \right)^n = \cos 2k\pi + i \sin 2k\pi = 1$. So the nth roots of 1 are $\cos \frac{2k\pi}{n} + i \sin \frac{2k\pi}{n} = w^k$ for

$k = 0, 1, 2, \ldots, n - 1$. In other words, the nth roots of 1 are $w^0, w^1, w^2, w^3, \ldots, w^{n-1}$ or $1, w, w^2, w^3, \ldots, w^{n-1}$.

(b) For $k = 0, 1, \ldots, n - 1$, we have $\left(sw^k \right)^n = s^n \left(w^k \right)^n = z \cdot 1 = z$, so sw^k are nth roots of z for $k = 0, 1, \ldots, n - 1$.

94. The cube roots of 1 are $w^0 = 1$, $w^1 = \cos\frac{2\pi}{3} + i\sin\frac{2\pi}{3} = -\frac{1}{2} + \frac{\sqrt{3}}{2}i$, and $w^2 = \cos\frac{4\pi}{3} + i\sin\frac{4\pi}{3} = \frac{1}{2} - \frac{\sqrt{3}}{2}i$, so their sum is $w^0 + w^1 + w^2 = 1 + \left(-\frac{1}{2} + \frac{\sqrt{3}}{2}i\right) + \left(\frac{1}{2} - \frac{\sqrt{3}}{2}i\right) = 0$.

The fourth roots of 1 are $w^0 = 1$, $w^1 = i$, $w^2 = -1$, and $w^3 = -i$, so their sum is $w^0 + w^1 + w^2 + w^3 = 1 + i - 1 - i = 0$.

The fifth roots of 1 are $w^0 = 1$, $w^1 = \cos\frac{2\pi}{5} + i\sin\frac{2\pi}{5}$, $w^2 = \cos\frac{4\pi}{5} + i\sin\frac{4\pi}{5}$, $w^3 = \cos\frac{6\pi}{5} + i\sin\frac{6\pi}{5}$, and $w^4 = \cos\frac{8\pi}{5} + i\sin\frac{8\pi}{5}$, so their sum is

$1 + \left(\cos\frac{2\pi}{5} + i\sin\frac{2\pi}{5}\right) + \left(\cos\frac{4\pi}{5} + i\sin\frac{4\pi}{5}\right) + \left(\cos\frac{6\pi}{5} + i\sin\frac{6\pi}{5}\right) + \left(\cos\frac{8\pi}{5} + i\sin\frac{8\pi}{5}\right)$

$= 1 + 2\cos\frac{2\pi}{5} + 2\cos\frac{6\pi}{5}$ (most terms cancel) $= 1 + 2\left[\left(\frac{\sqrt{5}}{4} - \frac{1}{4}\right) + \left(-\frac{\sqrt{5}}{4} - \frac{1}{4}\right)\right] = 0$

The sixth roots of 1 are $w^0 = 1$, $w^1 = \cos\frac{\pi}{3} + i\sin\frac{\pi}{3} = \frac{1}{2} + \frac{\sqrt{3}}{2}i$, $w^2 = \cos\frac{2\pi}{3} + i\sin\frac{2\pi}{3} = -\frac{1}{2} + \frac{\sqrt{3}}{2}i$, $w^3 = -1$, $w^4 = \cos\frac{4\pi}{3} + i\sin\frac{4\pi}{3} = -\frac{1}{2} - \frac{\sqrt{3}}{2}i$, and $w^5 = \cos\frac{5\pi}{3} + i\sin\frac{5\pi}{3} = \frac{1}{2} - \frac{\sqrt{3}}{2}i$, so their sum is

$1 + \left(\frac{1}{2} + \frac{\sqrt{3}}{2}i\right) + \left(-\frac{1}{2} + \frac{\sqrt{3}}{2}i\right) - 1 + \left(-\frac{1}{2} - \frac{\sqrt{3}}{2}i\right) + \left(\frac{1}{2} - \frac{\sqrt{3}}{2}i\right) = 0$.

The eight roots of 1 are $w^0 = 1$, $w^1 = \cos\frac{\pi}{4} + i\sin\frac{\pi}{4} = \frac{\sqrt{2}}{2} + \frac{\sqrt{2}}{2}i$, $w^2 = i$, $w^3 = \cos\frac{3\pi}{4} + i\sin\frac{3\pi}{4} = -\frac{\sqrt{2}}{2} + \frac{\sqrt{2}}{2}i$, $w^4 = -1$, $w^5 = \cos\frac{5\pi}{4} + i\sin\frac{5\pi}{4} = -\frac{\sqrt{2}}{2} - \frac{\sqrt{2}}{2}i$, $w^6 = -i$, and $w^7 = \cos\frac{7\pi}{4} + i\sin\frac{7\pi}{4} = \frac{\sqrt{2}}{2} - \frac{\sqrt{2}}{2}i$, so their sum is

$1 + \left(\frac{\sqrt{2}}{2} + \frac{\sqrt{2}}{2}i\right) + i + \left(-\frac{\sqrt{2}}{2} + \frac{\sqrt{2}}{2}\right) - 1 + \left(-\frac{\sqrt{2}}{2} - \frac{\sqrt{2}}{2}i\right) - i + \left(\frac{\sqrt{2}}{2} - \frac{\sqrt{2}}{2}i\right) = 0$.

It seems that the sum of any set of nth roots is 0.

To prove this, factor $w^n - 1 = \left(w^1 - 1\right)\left(1 + w^1 + w^2 + w^3 + \cdots + w^{n-1}\right)$. Since this is 0 and $w^1 \neq 0$, we must have $1 + w^1 + w^2 + w^3 + \cdots + w^{n-1} = 0$.

95. The cube roots of 1 are $w^0 = 1$, $w^1 = \cos\frac{2\pi}{3} + i\sin\frac{2\pi}{3}$, and $w^2 = \cos\frac{4\pi}{3} + i\sin\frac{4\pi}{3}$, so their product is $w^0 \cdot w^1 \cdot w^2 = (1)\left(\cos\frac{2\pi}{3} + i\sin\frac{2\pi}{3}\right)\left(\cos\frac{4\pi}{3} + i\sin\frac{4\pi}{3}\right) = \cos 2\pi + i\sin 2\pi = 1$.

The fourth roots of 1 are $w^0 = 1$, $w^1 = i$, $w^2 = -1$, and $w^3 = -i$, so their product is $w^0 \cdot w^1 \cdot w^2 \cdot w^3 = (1) \cdot (i) \cdot (-1) \cdot (-i) = i^2 = -1$.

The fifth roots of 1 are $w^0 = 1$, $w^1 = \cos\frac{2\pi}{5} + i\sin\frac{2\pi}{5}$, $w^2 = \cos\frac{4\pi}{5} + i\sin\frac{4\pi}{5}$, $w^3 = \cos\frac{6\pi}{5} + i\sin\frac{6\pi}{5}$, and $w^4 = \cos\frac{8\pi}{5} + i\sin\frac{8\pi}{5}$, so their product is $1\left(\cos\frac{2\pi}{5} + i\sin\frac{2\pi}{5}\right)\left(\cos\frac{4\pi}{5} + i\sin\frac{4\pi}{5}\right)\left(\cos\frac{6\pi}{5} + i\sin\frac{6\pi}{5}\right)\left(\cos\frac{8\pi}{5} + i\sin\frac{8\pi}{5}\right) = \cos 4\pi + i\sin 4\pi = 1$.

The sixth roots of 1 are $w^0 = 1$, $w^1 = \cos\frac{\pi}{3} + i\sin\frac{\pi}{3}$, $w^2 = \cos\frac{2\pi}{3} + i\sin\frac{2\pi}{3} = -\frac{1}{2} + \frac{\sqrt{3}}{2}i$, $w^3 = -1$, $w^4 = \cos\frac{4\pi}{3} + i\sin\frac{4\pi}{3} = -\frac{1}{2} - \frac{\sqrt{3}}{2}i$, and $w^5 = \cos\frac{5\pi}{3} + i\sin\frac{5\pi}{3} = \frac{1}{2} - \frac{\sqrt{3}}{2}i$, so their product is $1\left(\cos\frac{\pi}{3} + i\sin\frac{\pi}{3}\right)\left(\cos\frac{2\pi}{3} + i\sin\frac{2\pi}{3}\right)(-1)\left(\cos\frac{4\pi}{3} + i\sin\frac{4\pi}{3}\right)\left(\cos\frac{5\pi}{3} + i\sin\frac{5\pi}{3}\right) = \cos 5\pi + i\sin 5\pi = -1$.

The eight roots of 1 are $w^0 = 1$, $w^1 = \cos\frac{\pi}{4} + i\sin\frac{\pi}{4}$, $w^2 = i$, $w^3 = \cos\frac{3\pi}{4} + i\sin\frac{3\pi}{4}$, $w^4 = -1$, $w^5 = \cos\frac{5\pi}{4} + i\sin\frac{5\pi}{4}$, $w^6 = -i$, $w^7 = \cos\frac{7\pi}{4} + i\sin\frac{7\pi}{4}$, so their product is $1\left(\cos\frac{\pi}{4} + i\sin\frac{\pi}{4}\right)i\left(\cos\frac{3\pi}{4} + i\sin\frac{3\pi}{4}\right)(-1)\left(\cos\frac{5\pi}{4} + i\sin\frac{5\pi}{4}\right)(-i)\left(\cos\frac{7\pi}{4} + i\sin\frac{7\pi}{4}\right) = i^2 \cdot (\cos 2\pi + i\sin 2\pi) = -1$.

The product of the nth roots of 1 is -1 if n is even and 1 if n is odd.

The proof requires the fact that the sum of the first m integers is $\frac{m(m+1)}{2}$.

Let $w = \cos\frac{2\pi}{n} + i\sin\frac{2\pi}{n}$. Then $w^k = \cos\frac{2k\pi}{n} + i\sin\frac{2k\pi}{n}$ for $k = 0, 1, 2, \ldots, n-1$. The argument of the product of the n roots of unity can be found by adding the arguments of each w^k. So the argument of the product is

$\theta = 0 + \frac{2(1)\pi}{n} + \frac{2(2)\pi}{n} + \frac{2(3)\pi}{n} + \cdots + \frac{2(n-2)\pi}{n} + \frac{2(n-1)\pi}{n} = \frac{2\pi}{n}[0 + 1 + 2 + 3 + \cdots + (n-2) + (n-1)]$.

Since this is the sum of the first $n-1$ integers, this sum is $\frac{2\pi}{n} \cdot \frac{(n-1)n}{2} = (n-1)\pi$. Thus the product of the n roots of unity is $\cos((n-1)\pi) + i\sin((n-1)\pi) = -1$ if n is even and 1 if n is odd.

96. (a) $z = \frac{-(1+i)\pm\sqrt{(1+i)^2-4(1)(i)}}{2(1)} = \frac{-1-i\pm\sqrt{2i-4i}}{2} = \frac{-1-i\pm\sqrt{-2i}}{2}$. Since $-2i = 2\left(\cos\frac{3\pi}{2} + i\sin\frac{3\pi}{2}\right)$, we apply

DeMoivre's Theorem to find $\sqrt{-2i}$, we have $w_1 = \sqrt{2}\left(\cos\frac{3\pi}{4} + i\sin\frac{3\pi}{4}\right) = \sqrt{2}\left(-\frac{\sqrt{2}}{2} + \frac{\sqrt{2}}{2}i\right) = -1 + i$

and $w_2 = \sqrt{2}\left(\cos\frac{7\pi}{4} + i\sin\frac{7\pi}{4}\right) = \sqrt{2}\left(\frac{\sqrt{2}}{2} - \frac{\sqrt{2}}{2}i\right) = 1 - i$. (Notice that $w_2 = -w_1$.) So

$z = \frac{-1-i+(-1+i)}{2} = \frac{-1-i-1+i}{2} = \frac{-2}{2} = -1$ or $z = \frac{-1-i+(1-i)}{2} = -\frac{-1-i+1-i}{2} - \frac{-2i}{2} = -i$.

Checking: $(-1)^2 + (1+i)(-1) + i = 1 - 1 - i + i = 0$ and $(-i)^2 + (1+i)(-i) + i = -1 - i - i^2 + i = 0$.

Alternatively we could have factored

$z^2 + (1+i)z + i = z^2 + z + zi + i = z^2 + zi + z + i = (z^2 + zi) + (z + i) = z(z + i) + (z + i)$

$= (z + i)(z + 1) = 0$

so $z + i = 0 \iff z = -i$ or $z + 1 = 0 \iff z = -1$.

(b) $z = \frac{-(-i)\pm\sqrt{(-i)^2-4(1)(1)}}{2(1)} = \frac{i\pm\sqrt{i^2-4}}{2} = \frac{i\pm\sqrt{-5}}{2} = \frac{i\pm\sqrt{5}i}{2}$.

So $z = \frac{i+\sqrt{5}i}{2} = \frac{1+\sqrt{5}}{2}i$ or $z = \frac{i-\sqrt{5}i}{2} = \frac{1-\sqrt{5}}{2}i$. Checking:

$\left(\frac{1+\sqrt{5}}{2}i\right)^2 - i\left(\frac{1+\sqrt{5}}{2}i\right) + 1 = -\frac{1+2\sqrt{5}+5}{4} + \frac{1+\sqrt{5}}{2} + 1 = -\frac{6+2\sqrt{5}}{4} + \frac{1+\sqrt{5}}{2} + \frac{2}{2} = -\frac{3+\sqrt{5}}{2} + \frac{3+\sqrt{5}}{2} = 0$

$\left(\frac{1-\sqrt{5}}{2}i\right)^2 - i\left(\frac{1-\sqrt{5}}{2}i\right) + 1 = -\frac{1-2\sqrt{5}+5}{4} + \frac{1-\sqrt{5}}{2} + 1 = -\frac{6-2\sqrt{5}}{4} + \frac{1-\sqrt{5}}{2} + \frac{2}{2} = -\frac{3-\sqrt{5}}{2} + \frac{3-\sqrt{5}}{2} = 0$

This polynomial does not factor as nicely as the polynomial in part (a).

(c) $z = \frac{(2-i)\pm\sqrt{(2-i)^2-4(1)\left(-\frac{1}{4}i\right)}}{2(1)} = \frac{2-i\pm\sqrt{4-4i+i^2+i}}{2} = \frac{2-i\pm\sqrt{3-3i}}{2}$.

To apply DeMoivre's Theorem, we have $3 - 3i = 3\sqrt{2}\left(\cos\frac{7\pi}{4} + i\sin\frac{7\pi}{4}\right)$, so one root of $\sqrt{3-3i}$

is $w_1 = \sqrt{3\sqrt{2}}\left(\cos\frac{7\pi}{8} + i\sin\frac{7\pi}{8}\right)$. Now using the half-angle formulas and the fact that $\cos\frac{7\pi}{8} < 0$

and $\sin\frac{7\pi}{8} > 0$, we have $\cos\frac{7\pi}{8} = \cos\frac{\frac{7\pi}{4}}{2} = -\sqrt{\frac{1+\cos\frac{7\pi}{4}}{2}} = -\sqrt{\frac{1+\frac{\sqrt{2}}{2}}{2}} = -\sqrt{\frac{2+\sqrt{2}}{4}}$ and

$\sin\frac{7\pi}{8} = \sin\frac{\frac{7\pi}{4}}{2} = \sqrt{\frac{1-\cos\frac{7\pi}{4}}{2}} = \sqrt{\frac{1-\frac{\sqrt{2}}{2}}{2}} = \sqrt{\frac{2-\sqrt{2}}{4}}$. So

$w_1 = \sqrt{3\sqrt{2}}\left(\cos\frac{7\pi}{8} + i\sin\frac{7\pi}{8}\right) = \sqrt{3\sqrt{2}}\left(-\sqrt{\frac{2+\sqrt{2}}{4}}\right) + \sqrt{3\sqrt{2}}\sqrt{\frac{2-\sqrt{2}}{4}}i$

$= -\sqrt{\frac{3\sqrt{2}+3}{2}} + \sqrt{\frac{3\sqrt{2}-3}{2}}i$

$w_2 = -w_1 = \sqrt{\frac{3\sqrt{2}+3}{2}} - \sqrt{\frac{3\sqrt{2}-3}{2}}i$. Then

$z = \frac{2-i+\left(-\sqrt{\frac{3\sqrt{2}+3}{2}} + \sqrt{\frac{3\sqrt{2}-3}{2}}i\right)}{2} = 1 - \frac{1}{2}i - \sqrt{\frac{3\sqrt{2}+3}{8}} + \sqrt{\frac{3\sqrt{2}-3}{8}}i$

$= \left(1 - \sqrt{\frac{3\sqrt{2}+3}{8}}\right) + \left(-\frac{1}{2} + \sqrt{\frac{3\sqrt{2}-3}{8}}\right)i$

or

$z = \frac{2-i+\left(\sqrt{\frac{3\sqrt{2}+3}{2}} - \sqrt{\frac{3\sqrt{2}-3}{2}}i\right)}{2} = 1 - \frac{1}{2}i + \sqrt{\frac{3\sqrt{2}+3}{8}} + \sqrt{\frac{3\sqrt{2}-3}{8}}i$

$= \left(1 + \sqrt{\frac{3\sqrt{2}+3}{8}}\right) + \left(-\frac{1}{2} - \sqrt{\frac{3\sqrt{2}-3}{8}}\right)i$

I have discovered a most wondrous proof of this fact, but unfortunately the margin is too small to contain it.

8.4   **Vectors**

1. $2\mathbf{u} = 2\langle -2, 3\rangle = \langle -4, 6\rangle$

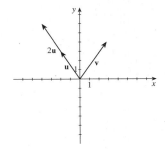

2. $-\mathbf{v} = -\langle 3, 4\rangle = \langle -3, -4\rangle$

3. $\mathbf{u} + \mathbf{v} = \langle -2, 3\rangle + \langle 3, 4\rangle = \langle -2 + 3, 3 + 4\rangle = \langle 1, 7\rangle$

4. $\mathbf{u} - \mathbf{v} = \langle -2, 3\rangle - \langle 3, 4\rangle = \langle -2 - 3, 3 - 4\rangle = \langle -5, -1\rangle$

5. $\mathbf{v} - 2\mathbf{u} = \langle 3, 4\rangle -$
$2\langle -2, 3\rangle = \langle 3 - 2(-2), 4 - 2(3)\rangle = \langle 7, -2\rangle$

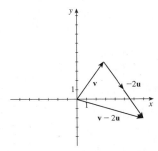

6. $2\mathbf{u} + \mathbf{v} = 2\langle -2, 3\rangle +$
$\langle 3, 4\rangle = \langle 2(-2) + 3, 2(3) + 4\rangle = \langle -1, 10\rangle$

In Solutions 7–16, $\mathbf{v}$ represents the vector with initial point P and terminal point Q.

7. $P(2, 1), Q(5, 4)$. $\mathbf{v} = \langle 5 - 2, 4 - 1\rangle = \langle 3, 3\rangle$

8. $P(2, 1), Q(-3, 4)$. $\mathbf{v} = \langle -3 - 2, 4 - 1\rangle = \langle -5, 3\rangle$

9. $P(1, 2), Q(4, 1)$. $\mathbf{v} = \langle 4 - 1, 1 - 2\rangle = \langle 3, -1\rangle$

10. $P(3, 1), Q(1, -2)$. $\mathbf{v} = \langle 3 - 1, -2 - 1\rangle = \langle 2, -3\rangle$

11. $P(3, 2), Q(8, 9)$. $\mathbf{v} = \langle 8 - 3, 9 - 2\rangle = \langle 5, 7\rangle$

12. $P(1, 1), Q(9, 9)$. $\mathbf{v} = \langle 9 - 1, 9 - 1\rangle = \langle 8, 8\rangle$

13. $P(5, 3), Q(1, 0)$. $\mathbf{v} = \langle 1 - 5, 0 - 3\rangle = \langle -4, -3\rangle$

14. $P(-1, 3), Q(-6, -1)$.
$\mathbf{v} = \langle -6 - (-1), -1 - 3\rangle = \langle -5, -4\rangle$

15. $P(-1, -1), Q(-1, 1)$.
$\mathbf{v} = \langle -1 - (-1), 1 - (-1)\rangle = \langle 0, 2\rangle$

16. $P(-8, -6), Q(-1, -1)$.
$\mathbf{v} = \langle -1 - (-8), -1 - (-6)\rangle = \langle 7, 5\rangle$

17. $\mathbf{u} = \langle 2, 7 \rangle$, $\mathbf{v} = \langle 3, 1 \rangle$. $2\mathbf{u} = 2 \cdot \langle 2, 7 \rangle = \langle 4, 14 \rangle$; $-3\mathbf{v} = -3 \cdot \langle 3, 1 \rangle = \langle -9, -3 \rangle$; $\mathbf{u} + \mathbf{v} = \langle 2, 7 \rangle + \langle 3, 1 \rangle = \langle 5, 8 \rangle$;
$3\mathbf{u} - 4\mathbf{v} = \langle 6, 21 \rangle - \langle 12, 4 \rangle = \langle -6, 17 \rangle$

18. $\mathbf{u} = \langle -2, 5 \rangle$, $\mathbf{v} = \langle 2, -8 \rangle$. $2\mathbf{u} = 2 \cdot \langle -2, 5 \rangle = \langle -4, 10 \rangle$; $-3\mathbf{v} = -3 \cdot \langle 2, -8 \rangle = \langle -6, 24 \rangle$;
$\mathbf{u} + \mathbf{v} = \langle -2, 5 \rangle + \langle 2, -8 \rangle = \langle 0, -3 \rangle$; $3\mathbf{u} - 4\mathbf{v} = \langle -6, 15 \rangle - \langle 8, -32 \rangle = \langle -14, 47 \rangle$

19. $\mathbf{u} = \langle 0, -1 \rangle$, $\mathbf{v} = \langle -2, 0 \rangle$. $2\mathbf{u} = 2 \cdot \langle 0, -1 \rangle = \langle 0, -2 \rangle$; $-3\mathbf{v} = -3 \cdot \langle -2, 0 \rangle = \langle 6, 0 \rangle$;
$\mathbf{u} + \mathbf{v} = \langle 0, -1 \rangle + \langle -2, 0 \rangle = \langle -2, -1 \rangle$; $3\mathbf{u} - 4\mathbf{v} = \langle 0, -3 \rangle - \langle -8, 0 \rangle = \langle 8, -3 \rangle$

20. $\mathbf{u} = \mathbf{i}$, $\mathbf{v} = -2\mathbf{j}$. $2\mathbf{u} = 2\mathbf{i}$; $-3\mathbf{v} = -3(-2\mathbf{j}) = 6\mathbf{j}$; $\mathbf{u} + \mathbf{v} = \mathbf{i} - 2\mathbf{j}$; $3\mathbf{u} - 4\mathbf{v} = 3\mathbf{i} + 8\mathbf{j}$

21. $\mathbf{u} = 2\mathbf{i}$, $\mathbf{v} = 3\mathbf{i} - 2\mathbf{j}$. $2\mathbf{u} = 2 \cdot 2\mathbf{i} = 4\mathbf{i}$; $-3\mathbf{v} = -3(3\mathbf{i} - 2\mathbf{j}) = -9\mathbf{i} + 6\mathbf{j}$; $\mathbf{u} + \mathbf{v} = 2\mathbf{i} + 3\mathbf{i} - 2\mathbf{j} = 5\mathbf{i} - 2\mathbf{j}$;
$3\mathbf{u} - 4\mathbf{v} = 3 \cdot 2\mathbf{i} - 4(3\mathbf{i} - 2\mathbf{j}) = -6\mathbf{i} + 8\mathbf{j}$

22. $\mathbf{u} = \mathbf{i} + \mathbf{j}$, $\mathbf{v} = \mathbf{i} - \mathbf{j}$. $2\mathbf{u} = 2\mathbf{i} + 2\mathbf{j}$, $-3\mathbf{v} = -3\mathbf{i} + 3\mathbf{j}$, $\mathbf{u} + \mathbf{v} = \mathbf{i} + \mathbf{j} + \mathbf{i} - \mathbf{j} = 2\mathbf{i}$; $3\mathbf{u} - 4\mathbf{v} = 3(\mathbf{i} + \mathbf{j}) - 4(\mathbf{i} - \mathbf{j}) = -\mathbf{i} + 7\mathbf{j}$

23. $\mathbf{u} = 2\mathbf{i} + \mathbf{j}$, $\mathbf{v} = 3\mathbf{i} - 2\mathbf{j}$. Then $|\mathbf{u}| = \sqrt{2^2 + 1^2} = \sqrt{5}$; $|\mathbf{v}| = \sqrt{3^2 + 2^2} = \sqrt{13}$; $2\mathbf{u} = 4\mathbf{i} + 2\mathbf{j}$;
$|2\mathbf{u}| = \sqrt{4^2 + 2^2} = 2\sqrt{5}$; $\frac{1}{2}\mathbf{v} = \frac{3}{2}\mathbf{i} - \mathbf{j}$; $\left|\frac{1}{2}\mathbf{v}\right| = \sqrt{\left(\frac{3}{2}\right)^2 + 1^2} = \frac{1}{2}\sqrt{13}$; $\mathbf{u} + \mathbf{v} = 5\mathbf{i} - \mathbf{j}$; $|\mathbf{u} + \mathbf{v}| = \sqrt{5^2 + 1^2} = \sqrt{26}$;
$\mathbf{u} - \mathbf{v} = 2\mathbf{i} + \mathbf{j} - 3\mathbf{i} + 2\mathbf{j} = -\mathbf{i} + 3\mathbf{j}$; $\quad |\mathbf{u} - \mathbf{v}| = \sqrt{1^2 + 3^2} = \sqrt{10}$; $|\mathbf{u}| - |\mathbf{v}| = \sqrt{5} - \sqrt{13}$

24. $\mathbf{u} = -2\mathbf{i} + 3\mathbf{j}$, $\mathbf{v} = \mathbf{i} - 2\mathbf{j}$. Then $|\mathbf{u}| = \sqrt{4 + 9} = \sqrt{13}$; $|\mathbf{v}| = \sqrt{1 + 4} = \sqrt{5}$; $2\mathbf{u} = -4\mathbf{i} + 6\mathbf{j}$; $|2\mathbf{u}| = \sqrt{16 + 36} = 2\sqrt{13}$;
$\frac{1}{2}\mathbf{v} = \frac{1}{2}\mathbf{i} - \mathbf{j}$; $\left|\frac{1}{2}\mathbf{v}\right| = \sqrt{\frac{1}{4} + 1} = \frac{1}{2}\sqrt{5}$; $\mathbf{u} + \mathbf{v} = -\mathbf{i} + \mathbf{j}$; $|\mathbf{u} + \mathbf{v}| = \sqrt{1 + 1} = \sqrt{2}$; $\mathbf{u} - \mathbf{v} = -3\mathbf{i} + 5\mathbf{j}$;
$|\mathbf{u} - \mathbf{v}| = \sqrt{9 + 25} = \sqrt{34}$; $|\mathbf{u}| - |\mathbf{v}| = \sqrt{13} - \sqrt{5}$

25. $\mathbf{u} = \langle 10, -1 \rangle$, $\mathbf{v} = \langle -2, -2 \rangle$. Then $|\mathbf{u}| = \sqrt{10^2 + 1^2} = \sqrt{101}$; $|\mathbf{v}| = \sqrt{(-2)^2 + (-2)^2} = 2\sqrt{2}$; $2\mathbf{u} = \langle 20, -2 \rangle$;
$|2\mathbf{u}| = \sqrt{20^2 + 2^2} = \sqrt{404} = 2\sqrt{101}$; $\frac{1}{2}\mathbf{v} = \langle -1, -1 \rangle$; $\left|\frac{1}{2}\mathbf{v}\right| = \sqrt{(-1)^2 + (-1)^2} = \sqrt{2}$; $\mathbf{u} + \mathbf{v} = \langle 8, -3 \rangle$;
$|\mathbf{u} + \mathbf{v}| = \sqrt{8^2 + 3^2} = \sqrt{73}$; $\mathbf{u} - \mathbf{v} = \langle 12, 1 \rangle$; $|\mathbf{u} - \mathbf{v}| = \sqrt{12^2 + 1^2} = \sqrt{145}$; $|\mathbf{u}| - |\mathbf{v}| = \sqrt{101} - 2\sqrt{2}$

26. $\mathbf{u} = \langle -6, 6 \rangle$, $\mathbf{v} = \langle -2, -1 \rangle$. Then $|\mathbf{u}| = \sqrt{36 + 36} = 6\sqrt{2}$; $|\mathbf{v}| = \sqrt{4 + 1} = \sqrt{5}$; $2\mathbf{u} = \langle -12, 12 \rangle$;
$|2\mathbf{u}| = \sqrt{144 + 144} = 12\sqrt{2}$; $\frac{1}{2}\mathbf{v} = \langle -1, -\frac{1}{2} \rangle$; $\left|\frac{1}{2}\mathbf{v}\right| = \sqrt{1 + \frac{1}{4}} = \frac{1}{2}\sqrt{5}$; $\mathbf{u} + \mathbf{v} = \langle -8, 5 \rangle$;
$|\mathbf{u} + \mathbf{v}| = \sqrt{64 + 25} = \sqrt{89}$; $\mathbf{u} - \mathbf{v} = \langle -4, 7 \rangle$; $|\mathbf{u} - \mathbf{v}| = \sqrt{16 + 49} = \sqrt{63}$; $|\mathbf{u}| - |\mathbf{v}| = 6\sqrt{2} - \sqrt{5}$

In Solutions 27–32, x represents the horizontal component and y the vertical component.

27. $|\mathbf{v}| = 40$, direction $\theta = 30°$. $x = 40\cos 30° = 20\sqrt{3}$ and $y = 40\sin 30° = 20$. Thus, $\mathbf{v} = x\mathbf{i} + y\mathbf{j} = 20\sqrt{3}\mathbf{i} + 20\mathbf{j}$.

28. $|\mathbf{v}| = 50$, direction $\theta = 120°$. $x = 50\cos 120° = -25$ and $y = 50\sin 120° = 25\sqrt{3}$. Thus, $\mathbf{v} = x\mathbf{i} + y\mathbf{j} = -25\mathbf{i} + 25\sqrt{3}\mathbf{j}$.

29. $|\mathbf{v}| = 1$, direction $\theta = 225°$. $x = \cos 225° = -\frac{1}{\sqrt{2}}$ and $y = \sin 225° = -\frac{1}{\sqrt{2}}$. Thus,
$\mathbf{v} = x\mathbf{i} + y\mathbf{j} = -\frac{1}{\sqrt{2}}\mathbf{i} - \frac{1}{\sqrt{2}}\mathbf{j} = -\frac{\sqrt{2}}{2}\mathbf{i} - \frac{\sqrt{2}}{2}\mathbf{j}$.

30. $|\mathbf{v}| = 800$, direction $\theta = 125°$. $x = 800\cos 125° \approx -458.86$ and $y = 800\sin 125° \approx 655.32$. Thus,
$\mathbf{v} = x\mathbf{i} + y\mathbf{j} = (800\cos 125°)\mathbf{i} + (800\sin 125°)\mathbf{j} \approx -458.86\mathbf{i} + 655.32\mathbf{j}$.

31. $|\mathbf{v}| = 4$, direction $\theta = 10°$. $x = 4\cos 10° \approx 3.94$ and $y = 4\sin 10° \approx 0.69$. Thus,
$\mathbf{v} = x\mathbf{i} + y\mathbf{j} = (4\cos 10°)\mathbf{i} + (4\sin 10°)\mathbf{j} \approx 3.94\mathbf{i} + 0.69\mathbf{j}$.

32. $|\mathbf{v}| = \sqrt{3}$, direction $\theta = 300°$. $x = \sqrt{3}\cos 300° = \frac{\sqrt{3}}{2}$ and $y = \sqrt{3}\sin 300° = -\frac{3}{2}$. Thus, $\mathbf{v} = x\mathbf{i} + y\mathbf{j} = \frac{\sqrt{3}}{2}\mathbf{i} - \frac{3}{2}\mathbf{j}$.

33. $\mathbf{v} = \langle 3, 4 \rangle$. The magnitude is $|\mathbf{v}| = \sqrt{3^2 + 4^2} = 5$. The direction is θ where $\tan \theta = \frac{4}{3}$ $\Leftrightarrow$ $\theta = \tan^{-1}\left(\frac{4}{3}\right) \approx 53.13°$.

34. $\mathbf{v} = \left\langle -\frac{\sqrt{2}}{2}, -\frac{\sqrt{2}}{2} \right\rangle$. The magnitude is $|\mathbf{v}| = \sqrt{\frac{1}{2} + \frac{1}{2}} = 1$. The direction is θ where $\tan \theta = 1$ with θ in quadrant III $\Leftrightarrow$
$\theta = \tan^{-1} 1 = 225°$.

35. $\mathbf{v} = \langle -12, 5 \rangle$. The magnitude is $|\mathbf{v}| = \sqrt{(-12)^2 + 5^2} = \sqrt{169} = 13$. The direction is θ where $\tan \theta = -\frac{5}{12}$ with θ in
quadrant II $\Leftrightarrow$ $\theta = \tan^{-1}\left(-\frac{5}{12}\right) \approx 157.38°$.

36. $\mathbf{v} = \langle 40, 9 \rangle$. The magnitude is $|\mathbf{v}| = \sqrt{1600 + 81} = 41$. The direction is θ where $\tan \theta = \frac{9}{40}$ with θ in quadrant I $\Leftrightarrow$
$\theta = \tan^{-1}\frac{9}{40} \approx 12.68°$.

37. $\mathbf{v} = \mathbf{i} + \sqrt{3}\mathbf{j}$. The magnitude is $|\mathbf{v}| = \sqrt{1^2 + \left(\sqrt{3}\right)^2} = 2$. The direction is θ where $\tan\theta = \sqrt{3}$ with θ in quadrant I $\Leftrightarrow$
$\theta = \tan^{-1}\sqrt{3} = 60°$.

38. $\mathbf{v} = \mathbf{i} + \mathbf{j}$. The magnitude is $|\mathbf{v}| = \sqrt{1+1} = \sqrt{2}$. The direction is θ where $\tan\theta = 1$ with θ in quadrant I $\Leftrightarrow$
$\theta = \tan^{-1} 1 = 45°$.

39. $|\mathbf{v}| = 30$, direction $\theta = 30°$. $x = 30\cos 30° = 30 \cdot \dfrac{\sqrt{3}}{2} \approx 25.98$, $y = 30\sin 30° = 15$. So the horizontal component of
force is $15\sqrt{3}$ lb and the vertical component is -15 lb.

40. $|\mathbf{v}| = 500$, direction $\theta = 70°$. $x = 500\cos 70° \approx 171.01$, $y = 500\sin 70° \approx 469.85$. So the east component of the
velocity is 171.01 mi/h and the north component is 469.85 mi/h.

41. The flow of the river can be represented by the vector $\mathbf{v} = -3\mathbf{j}$ and the swimmer can be represented by the vector $\mathbf{u} = 2\mathbf{i}$.
Therefore the true velocity is $\mathbf{u} + \mathbf{v} = 2\mathbf{i} - 3\mathbf{j}$.

42. The ocean currents can be represented by the vector $\mathbf{v} = 3\mathbf{i}$ and the salmon can be represented by the vector
$\mathbf{u} = \frac{5\sqrt{2}}{2}\mathbf{i} + \frac{5\sqrt{2}}{2}\mathbf{j}$. Therefore $\mathbf{u} + \mathbf{v} = \left(\frac{5\sqrt{2}}{2} + 3\right)\mathbf{i} + \frac{5\sqrt{2}}{2}\mathbf{j}$ represents the true velocity of the fish.

43. (a) The velocity of the wind is $\langle 0, 40\rangle$.

(b) The velocity of the jet relative to the air is $\langle 425, 0\rangle$.

(c) The true velocity of the jet is $\mathbf{v} = 425\mathbf{i} + 40\mathbf{j} = \langle 425, 40\rangle$.

(d) The true speed of the jet is $|\mathbf{v}| = \sqrt{425^2 + 40^2} \approx 427$ mi/h, and the true direction is $\theta = \tan^{-1}\left(\frac{40}{425}\right) \approx 5.4°$ $\Rightarrow$
θ is N 84.6° E.

44. (a) The velocity of the wind is $\mathbf{w} = \langle 55\cos 60°, 55\sin 60°\rangle = \left\langle \frac{55}{2}, \frac{55\sqrt{3}}{2}\right\rangle$.

(b) The velocity of the jet is $\mathbf{w} = \langle 765\cos 45°, 765\sin 45°\rangle = \left\langle \frac{765\sqrt{2}}{2}, \frac{765\sqrt{2}}{2}\right\rangle$.

(c) The true velocity of the jet is $\mathbf{v} + \mathbf{w} = \left\langle \frac{55}{2} + \frac{765\sqrt{2}}{2}, \frac{55\sqrt{3}}{2} + \frac{765\sqrt{2}}{2}\right\rangle \approx \langle 568.44, 588.57\rangle$.

(d) The true speed of the jet is $|\mathbf{w} + \mathbf{v}| \approx \sqrt{568.44^2 + 588.57^2} \approx 818$ mi/h. The direction of the vector $\mathbf{w} + \mathbf{v}$ is
$\theta \approx \tan^{-1}\left(\frac{588.57}{568.44}\right) \approx 46°$. Thus the true direction of the jet is approximately N 44° E.

45. If the direction of the plane is N 30° W, the airplane's velocity is $\mathbf{u} = \langle u_x, u_y\rangle$ where $u_x = -765\cos 60° = -382.5$,
and $u_y = 765\sin 60° \approx 662.51$. If the direction of the wind is N 30° E, the wind velocity is
$\mathbf{w} = \langle w_x, w_y\rangle$ where $w_x = 55\cos 60° = 27.5$, and $w_y = 55\sin 60° \approx 47.63$. Thus, the actual flight
path is $\mathbf{v} = \mathbf{u} + \mathbf{w} = \langle -382.5 + 27.5, 662.51 + 47.63\rangle = \langle -355, 710.14\rangle$, and so the true speed is
$|\mathbf{v}| = \sqrt{355^2 + 710.14^2} \approx 794$ mi/h, and the true direction is $\theta = \tan^{-1}\left(-\frac{710.14}{355}\right) \approx 116.6°$ so θ is N 26.6° W.

46. Let $\mathbf{v}$ be the velocity vector of the jet and let θ be the direction of this vector. Thus $\mathbf{v} = (765\cos\theta)\mathbf{i} + (765\sin\theta)\mathbf{j}$. If w
is the velocity vector of the wind then the true course of the jet is $\mathbf{v} + \mathbf{w} = \left(765\cos\theta + \frac{55}{2}\right)\mathbf{i} + \left(765\sin\theta + \frac{55\sqrt{3}}{2}\right)\mathbf{j}$.
To achieve a course of true north, the east-west component (the $\mathbf{i}$ component) of the jet's velocity vector must be 0. That is
$765\cos\theta + \frac{55}{2} = 0$ $\Leftrightarrow$ $\cos\theta = -\frac{27.5}{765}$ $\Leftrightarrow$ $\theta = \cos^{-1}\left(-\frac{27.5}{765}\right) \approx 92.1°$. Thus the pilot should head his plane in
the direction N 2.1° W.

47. (a) The velocity of the river is represented by the vector $\mathbf{r} = \langle 10, 0\rangle$.

(b) Since the boater direction is 60° from the shore at 20 mi/h, the velocity of the boat is represented by the vector
$\mathbf{b} = \langle 20\cos 60°, 20\sin 60°\rangle \approx \langle 10, 17.32\rangle$.

(c) $\mathbf{w} = \mathbf{r} + \mathbf{b} = \langle 10 + 10, 0 + 17.32\rangle = \langle 20, 17.32\rangle$

(d) The true speed of the boat is $|\mathbf{w}| = \sqrt{20^2 + 17.32^2} \approx 26.5$ mi/h, and the true direction is
$\theta = \tan^{-1}\left(\frac{17.32}{20}\right) \approx 40.9° \approx$ N 49.1° E.

48. Let $\mathbf{w}$ be the velocity vector of the water, let $\mathbf{v}$ be the velocity vector of the boat, and let θ be the direction of $\mathbf{v}$. Then $\mathbf{v} = (20 \cos \theta) \, \mathbf{i} + (20 \sin \theta) \, \mathbf{j}$ and $\mathbf{w} = 10 \mathbf{i}$. The true course of the boat is $\mathbf{v} + \mathbf{w} = (20 \cos \theta + 10) \, \mathbf{i} + (20 \sin \theta) \, \mathbf{j}$. To achieve a course of true north, the east-west component of the boat's velocity vector must be 0. Thus, $20 \cos \theta + 10 = 0$
$\Leftrightarrow \quad \cos \theta = \dfrac{-10}{20} = -\frac{1}{2} \quad \Leftrightarrow \quad \theta = \cos^{-1} \left(-\frac{1}{2} \right) = 120°$. Thus the boater should head her boat in the direction N 30° W.

49. (a) Let $\mathbf{b} = \langle b_x, b_y \rangle$ represent the velocity of the boat relative to the water. Then $\mathbf{b} = \langle 24 \cos 18°, 24 \sin 18° \rangle$.

(b) Let $\mathbf{w} = \langle w_x, w_y \rangle$ represent the velocity of the water. Then $\mathbf{w} = \langle 0, w \rangle$ where w is the speed of the water. So the true velocity of the boat is $\mathbf{b} + \mathbf{w} = \langle 24 \cos 18°, 24 \sin 18° - w \rangle$. For the direction to be due east, we must have $24 \sin 18° - w = 0 \quad \Leftrightarrow \quad w = 7.42$ mi/h. Therefore, the true speed of the water is 7.4 mi/h. Since $\mathbf{b} + \mathbf{w} = \langle 24 \cos 18°, 0 \rangle$, the true speed of the boat is $|\mathbf{b} + \mathbf{w}| = 24 \cos 18° \approx 22.8$ mi/h.

50. Let w represent the velocity of the woman and l the velocity of the ocean liner. Then $\mathbf{w} = \langle -2, 0 \rangle$, and $\mathbf{l} = \langle 0, 25 \rangle$, and so $\mathbf{r} = \langle -2 + 0, 0 + 25 \rangle$. Hence, relative to the water, the woman's speed is $|\mathbf{r}| = \sqrt{4 + 625} \approx 25.08$ mi/h, and her direction is $\theta = \tan^{-1} \frac{25}{-2} \approx 94.57°$ or approximately N 4.57° W.

51. $\mathbf{F}_1 = \langle 2, 5 \rangle$ and $\mathbf{F}_2 = \langle 3, -8 \rangle$.

(a) $\mathbf{F}_1 + \mathbf{F}_2 = \langle 2 + 3, 5 - 8 \rangle = \langle 5, -3 \rangle$

(b) The additional force required is $\mathbf{F}_3 = \langle 0, 0 \rangle - \langle 5, -3 \rangle = \langle -5, 3 \rangle$.

52. $\mathbf{F}_1 = \langle 3, -7 \rangle$, $\mathbf{F}_2 = \langle 4, -2 \rangle$, and $\mathbf{F}_3 = \langle -7, 9 \rangle$.

(a) $\mathbf{F}_1 + \mathbf{F}_2 + \mathbf{F}_3 = \langle 3 + 4 - 7, -7 - 2 + 9 \rangle = \langle 0, 0 \rangle$

(b) No additional force is required.

53. $\mathbf{F}_1 = 4 \mathbf{i} - \mathbf{j}$, $\mathbf{F}_2 = 3 \mathbf{i} - 7 \mathbf{j}$, $\mathbf{F}_3 = -8 \mathbf{i} + 3 \mathbf{j}$, and $\mathbf{F}_4 = \mathbf{i} + \mathbf{j}$.

(a) $\mathbf{F}_1 + \mathbf{F}_2 + \mathbf{F}_3 + \mathbf{F}_4 = (4 + 3 - 8 + 1) \, \mathbf{i} + (-1 - 7 + 3 + 1) \, \mathbf{j} = 0 \mathbf{i} - 4 \mathbf{j}$

(b) The additional force required is $\mathbf{F}_5 = 0 \mathbf{i} + 0 \mathbf{j} - (0 \mathbf{i} - 4 \mathbf{j}) = 4 \mathbf{j}$.

54. $\mathbf{F}_1 = \mathbf{i} - \mathbf{j}$, $\mathbf{F}_2 = \mathbf{i} + \mathbf{j}$, and $\mathbf{F}_3 = -2 \mathbf{i} + \mathbf{j}$.

(a) $\mathbf{F}_1 + \mathbf{F}_2 + \mathbf{F}_3 = (1 + 1 - 2) \, \mathbf{i} + (-1 + 1 + 1) \, \mathbf{j} = 0 \mathbf{i} + \mathbf{j}$

(b) The additional force required is $\mathbf{F}_4 = 0 \mathbf{i} + 0 \mathbf{j} - (0 \mathbf{i} + \mathbf{j}) = -\mathbf{j}$.

55. $\mathbf{F}_1 = \langle 10 \cos 60°, 10 \sin 60° \rangle = \langle 5, 5\sqrt{3} \rangle$, $\mathbf{F}_2 = \langle -8 \cos 30°, 8 \sin 30° \rangle = \langle -4\sqrt{3}, 4 \rangle$, and $\mathbf{F}_3 = \langle -6 \cos 20°, -6 \sin 20° \rangle \approx \langle -5.638, -2.052 \rangle$.

(a) $\mathbf{F}_1 + \mathbf{F}_2 + \mathbf{F}_3 = \langle 5 - 4\sqrt{3} - 5.638, 5\sqrt{3} + 4 - 2.052 \rangle \approx \langle -7.57, 10.61 \rangle$.

(b) The additional force required is $\mathbf{F}_4 = \langle 0, 0 \rangle - \langle -7.57, 10.61 \rangle = \langle 7.57, -10.61 \rangle$.

56. $\mathbf{F}_1 = \langle 3, -1 \rangle$, $\mathbf{F}_2 = \langle 1, 2 \rangle$, $\mathbf{F}_3 = \langle -2, -1 \rangle$, and $\mathbf{F}_4 = \langle 0, -4 \rangle$.

(a) $\mathbf{F}_1 + \mathbf{F}_2 + \mathbf{F}_3 + \mathbf{F}_4 = \langle 3 + 1 - 2 + 0, -1 + 2 - 1 - 4 \rangle = \langle 2, -4 \rangle$

(b) The additional force required is $\mathbf{F}_5 = \langle 0, 0 \rangle - \langle 2, -4 \rangle = \langle -2, 4 \rangle$.

57. From the figure we see that $\mathbf{T}_1 = -|\mathbf{T}_1|\cos 50°\mathbf{i} + |\mathbf{T}_1|\sin 50°\mathbf{j}$ and $\mathbf{T}_2 = |\mathbf{T}_2|\cos 30°\mathbf{i} + |\mathbf{T}_2|\sin 30°\mathbf{j}$. Since $\mathbf{T}_1 + \mathbf{T}_2 = 100\mathbf{j}$ we get $-|\mathbf{T}_1|\cos 50° + |\mathbf{T}_2|\cos 30° = 0$ and $|\mathbf{T}_1|\sin 50° + |\mathbf{T}_2|\sin 30° = 100$. From the first equation, $|\mathbf{T}_2| = |\mathbf{T}_1|\dfrac{\cos 50°}{\cos 30°}$, and substituting into the second equation gives $|\mathbf{T}_1|\sin 50° + |\mathbf{T}_1|\dfrac{\cos 50°\sin 30°}{\cos 30°} = 100$

$\Leftrightarrow \quad |\mathbf{T}_1|\left(\sin 50°\cos 30° + \cos 50°\sin 30°\right) = 100\cos 30° \quad \Leftrightarrow \quad |\mathbf{T}_1|\sin\left(50° + 30°\right) = 100\cos 30° \quad \Leftrightarrow$

$|\mathbf{T}_1| = 100\dfrac{\cos 30°}{\sin 80°} \approx 87.9416$.

Similarly, solving for $|\mathbf{T}_1|$ in the first equation gives $|\mathbf{T}_1| = |\mathbf{T}_2|\dfrac{\cos 30°}{\cos 50°}$ and substituting gives

$|\mathbf{T}_2|\dfrac{\cos 30°\sin 50°}{\cos 50°} + |\mathbf{T}_2|\sin 30° = 100 \quad \Leftrightarrow \quad |\mathbf{T}_2|\left(\cos 30°\sin 50° + \cos 50°\sin 30°\right) = 100\cos 50° \quad \Leftrightarrow$

$|\mathbf{T}_2| = \dfrac{100\cos 50°}{\sin 80°} \approx 65.2704$. Thus, $\mathbf{T}_1 \approx \left(-87.9416\cos 50°\right)\mathbf{i} + \left(87.9416\sin 50°\right)\mathbf{j} \approx -56.5\mathbf{i} + 67.4\mathbf{j}$ and $\mathbf{T}_2 \approx \left(65.2704\cos 30°\right)\mathbf{i} + \left(65.2704\sin 30°\right)\mathbf{j} \approx 56.5\mathbf{i} + 32.6\mathbf{j}$.

58. From the figure we see that $\mathbf{T}_1 = -|\mathbf{T}_1|\cos 22.3°\mathbf{i} + |\mathbf{T}_1|\sin 22.3°\mathbf{j}$ and $\mathbf{T}_2 = |\mathbf{T}_2|\cos 41.5°\mathbf{i} + |\mathbf{T}_2|\sin 41.5°\mathbf{j}$. Since $\mathbf{T}_1 + \mathbf{T}_2 = 18,278\mathbf{j}$, we get $-|\mathbf{T}_1|\cos 22.3° + |\mathbf{T}_2|\cos 41.5° = 0$ and $|\mathbf{T}_1|\sin 22.3° + |\mathbf{T}_2|\sin 41.5° = 18,278$. From the first equation, $|\mathbf{T}_2| = |\mathbf{T}_1|\dfrac{\cos 22.3°}{\cos 41.5°}$, and substituting into the second equation gives

$|\mathbf{T}_1|\sin 22.3° + |\mathbf{T}_1|\dfrac{\cos 22.3°\sin 41.5°}{\cos 41.5°} = 18,278 \quad \Leftrightarrow$

$|\mathbf{T}_1|\left(\sin 22.3°\cos 41.5° + \cos 22.3°\sin 41.5°\right) = 18,278\cos 41.5° \quad \Leftrightarrow$

$|\mathbf{T}_1|\sin\left(22.3° + 41.5°\right) = 18,278\cos 41.5° \quad \Leftrightarrow \quad |\mathbf{T}_1| = 18,278\dfrac{\cos 41.5°}{\sin 63.8°} \approx 15,257$.

Similarly, solving for $|\mathbf{T}_1|$ in the first equation gives $|\mathbf{T}_1| = |\mathbf{T}_2|\dfrac{\cos 41.5°}{\cos 22.3°}$

and substituting gives $|\mathbf{T}_2|\dfrac{\cos 41.5°\sin 22.3°}{\cos 22.3°} + |\mathbf{T}_2|\sin 41.5° = 18,278 \quad \Leftrightarrow$

$|\mathbf{T}_2|\left(\sin 22.3°\cos 41.5° + \sin 41.5°\cos 22.3°\right) = 18,278\cos 22.3° \quad \Leftrightarrow \quad |\mathbf{T}_2| = \dfrac{18,278\cos 22.3°}{\sin 63.8°} \approx 18,847$.

Thus, $\mathbf{T}_1 \approx \left(-15,257\cos 22.3°\right)\mathbf{i} + \left(15,257\sin 22.3°\right)\mathbf{j} \approx -14,116\mathbf{i} + 5,789\mathbf{j}$ and $\mathbf{T}_2 \approx \left(18,847\cos 41.5°\right)\mathbf{i} + \left(18,847\sin 41.5°\right)\mathbf{j} \approx 14,116\mathbf{i} + 12,488\mathbf{j}$.

59. When we add two (or more vectors), the resultant vector can be found by first placing the initial point of the second vector at the terminal point of the first vector. The resultant vector can then found by using the new terminal point of the second vector and the initial point of the first vector. When the n vectors are placed head to tail in the plane so that they form a polygon, the initial point and the terminal point are the same. Thus the sum of these n vectors is the zero vector.

8.5 The Dot Product

1. (a) $\mathbf{u}\cdot\mathbf{v} = \langle 2,0\rangle\cdot\langle 1,1\rangle = 2 + 0 = 2$

  (b) $\cos\theta = \dfrac{\mathbf{u}\cdot\mathbf{v}}{|\mathbf{u}|\,|\mathbf{v}|} = \dfrac{2}{2\cdot\sqrt{2}} = \dfrac{1}{\sqrt{2}} \Rightarrow \theta = 45°$

2. (a) $\mathbf{u}\cdot\mathbf{v} = \langle 1,\sqrt{3}\rangle\cdot\langle -\sqrt{3},1\rangle = -\sqrt{3} + \sqrt{3} = 0$

  (b) $\cos\theta = \dfrac{\mathbf{u}\cdot\mathbf{v}}{|\mathbf{u}|\,|\mathbf{v}|} = 0 \Rightarrow \theta = 90°$

3. (a) $\mathbf{u}\cdot\mathbf{v} = \langle 2,7\rangle\cdot\langle 3,1\rangle = 6 + 7 = 13$

  (b) $\cos\theta = \dfrac{\mathbf{u}\cdot\mathbf{v}}{|\mathbf{u}|\,|\mathbf{v}|} = \dfrac{13}{\sqrt{53}\cdot\sqrt{10}} \Rightarrow \theta \approx 56°$

4. (a) $\mathbf{u}\cdot\mathbf{v} = \langle -6,6\rangle\cdot\langle 1,-1\rangle = -6 + (-6) = -12$

  (b) $\cos\theta = \dfrac{\mathbf{u}\cdot\mathbf{v}}{|\mathbf{u}|\,|\mathbf{v}|} = \dfrac{-12}{6\sqrt{2}\cdot\sqrt{2}} = -1 \Rightarrow \theta = 180°$

5. (a) $\mathbf{u} \cdot \mathbf{v} = \langle 3, -2 \rangle \cdot \langle 1, 2 \rangle = 3 + (-4) = -1$

(b) $\cos \theta = \dfrac{\mathbf{u} \cdot \mathbf{v}}{|\mathbf{u}| \, |\mathbf{v}|} = \dfrac{-1}{\sqrt{13} \cdot \sqrt{5}} \Rightarrow \theta \approx 97°$

6. (a) $\mathbf{u} \cdot \mathbf{v} = \langle 2, 1 \rangle \cdot \langle 3, -2 \rangle = 6 + (-2) = 4$

(b) $\cos \theta = \dfrac{\mathbf{u} \cdot \mathbf{v}}{|\mathbf{u}| \, |\mathbf{v}|} = \dfrac{4}{\sqrt{5} \cdot \sqrt{13}} \Rightarrow \theta \approx 60.3°$

7. (a) $\mathbf{u} \cdot \mathbf{v} = \langle 0, -5 \rangle \cdot \langle -1, -\sqrt{3} \rangle = 0 + 5\sqrt{3} = 5\sqrt{3}$

(b) $\cos \theta = \dfrac{\mathbf{u} \cdot \mathbf{v}}{|\mathbf{u}| \, |\mathbf{v}|} = \dfrac{5\sqrt{3}}{5 \cdot 2} = \dfrac{\sqrt{3}}{2} \Rightarrow \theta = 30°$

8. (a) $\mathbf{u} \cdot \mathbf{v} = \langle 1, 1 \rangle \cdot \langle 1, -1 \rangle = 1 + (-1) = 0$

(b) $\cos \theta = \dfrac{\mathbf{u} \cdot \mathbf{v}}{|\mathbf{u}| \, |\mathbf{v}|} = \dfrac{0}{\sqrt{2} \cdot \sqrt{2}} = 0 \Rightarrow \theta = 90°$

9. $\mathbf{u} \cdot \mathbf{v} = -12 + 12 = 0 \Rightarrow$ vectors are orthogonal

10. $\mathbf{u} \cdot \mathbf{v} = 0 + 0 = 0 \Rightarrow$ vectors are orthogonal

11. $\mathbf{u} \cdot \mathbf{v} = -8 + 12 = 4 \neq 0 \Rightarrow$ vectors are not orthogonal

12. $\mathbf{u} \cdot \mathbf{v} = 0 + 0 = 0 \Rightarrow$ vectors are orthogonal

13. $\mathbf{u} \cdot \mathbf{v} = -24 + 24 = 0 \Rightarrow$ vectors are orthogonal

14. $\mathbf{u} \cdot \mathbf{v} = -4 + 0 = -4 \Rightarrow$ vectors are not orthogonal

15. $\mathbf{u} \cdot \mathbf{v} + \mathbf{u} \cdot \mathbf{w} = \langle 2, 1 \rangle \cdot \langle 1, -3 \rangle + \langle 2, 1 \rangle \cdot \langle 3, 4 \rangle$
$= 2 - 3 + 6 + 4 = 9$

16. $\mathbf{u} \cdot (\mathbf{v} + \mathbf{w}) = \langle 2, 1 \rangle \cdot [\langle 1, -3 \rangle + \langle 3, 4 \rangle]$
$= \langle 2, 1 \rangle \cdot \langle 4, 1 \rangle = 8 + 1 = 9$

17. $(\mathbf{u} + \mathbf{v}) \cdot (\mathbf{u} - \mathbf{v}) = [\langle 2, 1 \rangle + \langle 1, -3 \rangle] \cdot [\langle 2, 1 \rangle - \langle 1, -3 \rangle]$
$= \langle 3, -2 \rangle \cdot \langle 1, 4 \rangle = 3 - 8 = -5$

18. $(\mathbf{u} \cdot \mathbf{v})(\mathbf{u} \cdot \mathbf{w}) = (\langle 2, 1 \rangle \cdot \langle 1, -3 \rangle)(\langle 2, 1 \rangle \cdot \langle 3, 4 \rangle)$
$= (-1)(10) = -10$

19. $x = \dfrac{\mathbf{u} \cdot \mathbf{v}}{|\mathbf{v}|} = \dfrac{12 - 24}{5} = -\dfrac{12}{5}$

20. $x = \dfrac{\mathbf{u} \cdot \mathbf{v}}{|\mathbf{v}|} = \dfrac{-\frac{3}{\sqrt{2}} + \frac{5}{\sqrt{2}}}{1} = \dfrac{2}{\sqrt{2}} = \sqrt{2}$

21. $x = \dfrac{\mathbf{u} \cdot \mathbf{v}}{|\mathbf{v}|} = \dfrac{0 - 24}{1} = -24$

22. $x = \dfrac{\mathbf{u} \cdot \mathbf{v}}{|\mathbf{v}|} = \dfrac{56 + 0}{10} = \dfrac{28}{5}$

23. (a) $\mathbf{u}_1 = \text{proj}_{\mathbf{v}} \mathbf{u} = \left(\dfrac{\mathbf{u} \cdot \mathbf{v}}{|\mathbf{v}|^2} \right) \mathbf{v} = \left(\dfrac{\langle -2, 4 \rangle \cdot \langle 1, 1 \rangle}{1^2 + 1^2} \right) \langle 1, 1 \rangle = \langle 1, 1 \rangle.$

(b) $\mathbf{u}_2 = \mathbf{u} - \mathbf{u}_1 = \langle -2, 4 \rangle - \langle 1, 1 \rangle = \langle -3, 3 \rangle$

24. (a) $\mathbf{u}_1 = \text{proj}_{\mathbf{v}} \mathbf{u} = \left(\dfrac{\mathbf{u} \cdot \mathbf{v}}{|\mathbf{v}|^2} \right) \mathbf{v} = \left(\dfrac{\langle 7, -4 \rangle \cdot \langle 2, 1 \rangle}{2^2 + 1^2} \right) \langle 2, 1 \rangle = 2 \langle 2, 1 \rangle = \langle 4, 2 \rangle$

(b) $\mathbf{u}_2 = \mathbf{u} - \mathbf{u}_1 = \langle 7, -4 \rangle - \langle 4, 2 \rangle = \langle 3, -6 \rangle$

25. (a) $\mathbf{u}_1 = \text{proj}_{\mathbf{v}} \mathbf{u} = \left(\dfrac{\mathbf{u} \cdot \mathbf{v}}{|\mathbf{v}|^2} \right) \mathbf{v} = \left(\dfrac{\langle 1, 2 \rangle \cdot \langle 1, -3 \rangle}{1^2 + (-3)^2} \right) \langle 1, -3 \rangle = -\dfrac{1}{2} \langle 1, -3 \rangle = \left\langle -\dfrac{1}{2}, \dfrac{3}{2} \right\rangle$

(b) $\mathbf{u}_2 = \mathbf{u} - \mathbf{u}_1 = \langle 1, 2 \rangle - \left\langle -\dfrac{1}{2}, \dfrac{3}{2} \right\rangle = \left\langle \dfrac{3}{2}, \dfrac{1}{2} \right\rangle$

26. (a) $\mathbf{u}_1 = \text{proj}_{\mathbf{v}} \mathbf{u} = \left(\dfrac{\mathbf{u} \cdot \mathbf{v}}{|\mathbf{v}|^2} \right) \mathbf{v} = \left(\dfrac{\langle 11, 3 \rangle \cdot \langle -3, -2 \rangle}{(-3)^2 + (-2)^2} \right) \langle -3, -2 \rangle = -3 \langle -3, -2 \rangle = \langle 9, 6 \rangle$

(b) $\mathbf{u}_2 = \mathbf{u} - \mathbf{u}_1 = \langle 11, 3 \rangle - \langle 9, 6 \rangle = \langle 2, -3 \rangle$

27. (a) $\mathbf{u}_1 = \text{proj}_{\mathbf{v}} \mathbf{u} = \left(\dfrac{\mathbf{u} \cdot \mathbf{v}}{|\mathbf{v}|^2} \right) \mathbf{v} = \left(\dfrac{\langle 2, 9 \rangle \cdot \langle -3, 4 \rangle}{(-3)^3 + 4^2} \right) \langle -3, 4 \rangle = \dfrac{6}{5} \langle -3, 4 \rangle = \left\langle -\dfrac{18}{5}, \dfrac{24}{5} \right\rangle$

(b) $\mathbf{u}_2 = \mathbf{u} - \mathbf{u}_1 = \langle 2, 9 \rangle - \left\langle -\dfrac{18}{5}, \dfrac{24}{5} \right\rangle = \left\langle \dfrac{28}{5}, \dfrac{21}{5} \right\rangle$

28. (a) $\mathbf{u}_1 = \text{proj}_{\mathbf{v}} \mathbf{u} = \left(\dfrac{\mathbf{u} \cdot \mathbf{v}}{|\mathbf{v}|^2} \right) \mathbf{v} = \left(\dfrac{\langle 1, 1 \rangle \cdot \langle 2, -1 \rangle}{2^2 + (-1)^2} \right) \langle 2, -1 \rangle = \dfrac{1}{5} \langle 2, -1 \rangle = \left\langle \dfrac{2}{5}, -\dfrac{1}{5} \right\rangle$

(b) $\mathbf{u}_2 = \mathbf{u} - \mathbf{u}_1 = \langle 1, 1 \rangle - \left\langle \dfrac{2}{5}, -\dfrac{1}{5} \right\rangle = \left\langle \dfrac{3}{5}, \dfrac{6}{5} \right\rangle$

29. $W = \mathbf{F} \cdot \mathbf{d} = \langle 4, -5 \rangle \cdot \langle 3, 8 \rangle = -28$

30. $W = \mathbf{F} \cdot \mathbf{d} = \langle 400, 50 \rangle \cdot \langle 201, 0 \rangle = 80,400$

31. $W = \mathbf{F} \cdot \mathbf{d} = \langle 10, 3 \rangle \cdot \langle 4, -5 \rangle = 25$

32. $W = \mathbf{F} \cdot \mathbf{d} = \langle -4, 20 \rangle \cdot \langle 5, 15 \rangle = 280$

33. Let $\mathbf{u} = \langle u_1, u_2 \rangle$ and $\mathbf{v} = \langle v_1, v_2 \rangle$. Then
$\mathbf{u} \cdot \mathbf{v} = \langle u_1, u_2 \rangle \cdot \langle v_1, v_2 \rangle = u_1 v_1 + u_2 v_2 = v_1 u_1 + v_2 u_2 = \langle v_1, v_2 \rangle \cdot \langle u_1, u_2 \rangle = \mathbf{v} \cdot \mathbf{u}$

34. Let $\mathbf{u} = \langle u_1, u_2 \rangle$ and $\mathbf{v} = \langle v_1, v_2 \rangle$. Then
$(a\mathbf{u}) \cdot \mathbf{v} = (a \langle u_1, u_2 \rangle) \cdot \langle v_1, v_2 \rangle = \langle au_1, au_2 \rangle \cdot \langle v_1, v_2 \rangle = au_1 v_1 + au_2 v_2 = a(u_1 v_1 + u_2 v_2) = a(\mathbf{u} \cdot \mathbf{v})$
$= u_1 a v_1 + u_2 a v_2 = \langle u_1, u_2 \rangle \cdot \langle av_1, av_2 \rangle = \mathbf{u} \cdot (a\mathbf{v})$

35. Let $\mathbf{u} = \langle u_1, u_2 \rangle$, $\mathbf{v} = \langle v_1, v_2 \rangle$, and $\mathbf{w} = \langle w_1, w_2 \rangle$. Then

$$(\mathbf{u} + \mathbf{v}) \cdot \mathbf{w} = (\langle u_1, u_2 \rangle + \langle v_1, v_2 \rangle) \cdot \langle w_1, w_2 \rangle = \langle u_1 + v_1, u_2 + v_2 \rangle \cdot \langle w_1, w_2 \rangle$$
$$= u_1 w_1 + v_1 w_1 + u_2 w_2 + v_2 w_2 = u_1 w_1 + u_2 w_2 + v_1 w_1 + v_2 w_2$$
$$= \langle u_1, u_2 \rangle \cdot \langle w_1, w_2 \rangle + \langle v_1, v_2 \rangle \cdot \langle w_1, w_2 \rangle = \mathbf{u} \cdot \mathbf{w} + \mathbf{v} \cdot \mathbf{w}$$

36. Let $\mathbf{u} = \langle u_1, u_2 \rangle$ and $\mathbf{v} = \langle v_1, v_2 \rangle$. Then

$$(\mathbf{u} - \mathbf{v}) \cdot (\mathbf{u} + \mathbf{v}) = (\langle u_1, u_2 \rangle - \langle v_1, v_2 \rangle) \cdot (\langle u_1, u_2 \rangle + \langle v_1, v_2 \rangle) = \langle u_1 - v_1, u_2 - v_2 \rangle \cdot \langle u_1 + v_1, u_2 +, v_2 \rangle$$
$$= u_1^2 - v_1^2 + u_2^2 - v_2^2 = (u_1^2 + u_2^2) - (v_1^2 + v_2^2) = \left(\sqrt{u_1^2 + u_2^2} \right)^2 - \left(\sqrt{v_1^2 + v_2^2} \right)^2 = |\mathbf{u}|^2 - |\mathbf{v}|^2$$

37. We use the definition that $\text{proj}_\mathbf{v} \, \mathbf{u} = \left(\dfrac{\mathbf{u} \cdot \mathbf{v}}{|\mathbf{v}|^2} \right) \mathbf{v}$. Then

$$\text{proj}_\mathbf{v} \, \mathbf{u} \cdot (\mathbf{u} - \text{proj}_\mathbf{v} \, \mathbf{u}) = \left(\dfrac{\mathbf{u} \cdot \mathbf{v}}{|\mathbf{v}|^2} \right) \mathbf{v} \cdot \left[\mathbf{u} - \left(\dfrac{\mathbf{u} \cdot \mathbf{v}}{|\mathbf{v}|^2} \right) \mathbf{v} \right] = \left(\dfrac{\mathbf{u} \cdot \mathbf{v}}{|\mathbf{v}|^2} \right) (\mathbf{v} \cdot \mathbf{u}) - \left(\dfrac{\mathbf{u} \cdot \mathbf{v}}{|\mathbf{v}|^2} \right) \mathbf{v} \cdot \left(\dfrac{\mathbf{u} \cdot \mathbf{v}}{|\mathbf{v}|^2} \right) \mathbf{v}$$
$$= \dfrac{(\mathbf{u} \cdot \mathbf{v})^2}{|\mathbf{v}|^2} - \dfrac{(\mathbf{u} \cdot \mathbf{v})^2}{|\mathbf{v}|^4} |\mathbf{v}|^2 = \dfrac{(\mathbf{u} \cdot \mathbf{v})^2}{|\mathbf{v}|^2} - \dfrac{(\mathbf{u} \cdot \mathbf{v})^2}{|\mathbf{v}|^2} = 0$$

Thus $\mathbf{u}$ and $\mathbf{u} - \text{proj}_\mathbf{v} \, \mathbf{u}$ are orthogonal.

38. $\mathbf{v} \cdot \text{proj}_\mathbf{v} \, \mathbf{u} = \mathbf{v} \cdot \left(\dfrac{\mathbf{u} \cdot \mathbf{v}}{|\mathbf{v}|^2} \right) \mathbf{v} = \dfrac{(\mathbf{u} \cdot \mathbf{v})(\mathbf{v} \cdot \mathbf{v})}{|\mathbf{v}|^2} = \mathbf{u} \cdot \mathbf{v}$.

39. $W = \mathbf{F} \cdot \mathbf{d} = \langle 4, -7 \rangle \cdot \langle 4, 0 \rangle = 16$ ft-lb

40. The displacement of the object is $\mathbf{D} = \langle 11, 13 \rangle - \langle 2, 5 \rangle = \langle 9, 8 \rangle$. Hence, the work done is
$W = \mathbf{F} \cdot \mathbf{D} = \langle 2, 8 \rangle \cdot \langle 9, 8 \rangle = 18 + 64 = 82$ ft-lb.

41. The distance vector is $\mathbf{D} = \langle 200, 0 \rangle$ and the force vector is $\mathbf{F} = \langle 50 \cos 30°, 50 \sin 30° \rangle$. Hence, the work done is
$W = \mathbf{F} \cdot \mathbf{D} = \langle 200, 0 \rangle \cdot \langle 50 \cos 30°, 50 \sin 30° \rangle = 200 \cdot 50 \cos 30° \approx 8660$ ft-lb.

42. $W = \mathbf{F} \cdot \mathbf{d}$, and in this problem $\mathbf{F} = \langle 0, -2500 \rangle$, $\mathbf{d} = \langle 500 \cos 12°, 500 \sin 12° \rangle$ Thus,
$W = \langle 0, -2500 \rangle \cdot \langle 500 \cos 12°, 500 \sin 12° \rangle \approx 0 - (2500)(104.0) = -260{,}000$ ft-lb. This is the work done by gravity;
the car does (positive) work in overcoming the force of gravity. So the work done by the car is 260,000 ft-lb.

43. Since the weight of the car is 2755 lb, the force exerted perpendicular to the earth is 2755 lb. Resolving this into a force $\mathbf{u}$
perpendicular to the driveway gives $|\mathbf{u}| = 2766 \cos 65° \approx 1164$ lb. Thus, a force of about 1164 lb is required.

44. (a) Since the force parallel to the driveway is $490 = |\mathbf{w}| \sin 10°$ $\quad \Leftrightarrow \quad$ $|\mathbf{w}| = \dfrac{490}{\sin 10°} \approx 2821.8$, and thus the weight of
the car is about 2822 lb.

(b) The force exerted against the driveway is $2821.8 \cos 10° \approx 2779$ lb.

45. Since the force required parallel to the plane is 80 lb and the weight of the package is 200 lb, it follows that $80 = 200 \sin \theta$,
where θ is the angle of inclination of the plane. Then $\theta = \sin^{-1} \left(\frac{80}{200} \right) \approx 23.58°$, and so the angle of inclination is
approximately $23.6°$.

46. Let $\mathbf{R}$ represent the force exerted by the rope and $\mathbf{d}$ the force causing the cart to roll down the ramp. Gravity acting on
the cart exerts a force $\mathbf{w}$ of 40 lb directly downward. So the magnitude of the part of the force $\mathbf{w}$ causing the cart to roll
down the ramp is $|\mathbf{d}| = 40 \cos 15°$. The angle between $\mathbf{R}$ and $\mathbf{d}$ is $45°$, so the magnitude of the force holding the cart up is
$|\mathbf{R}| \cos 45°$. Equating these two, we have $|\mathbf{R}| \cos 45° = 40 \cos 15°$, so $|\mathbf{R}| = \dfrac{40 \cos 15°}{\cos 45°} \approx 54.6$ lb.

47. (a) $2(0) + 4(2) = 8$, so $Q(0, 2)$ lies on L. $2(2) + 4(1) = 4 + 4 = 8$, so $R(2, 1)$ lies on L.

(b) $\mathbf{u} = \overrightarrow{QP} = \langle 0, 2 \rangle - \langle 3, 4 \rangle = \langle -3, -2 \rangle$.

$\mathbf{v} = \overrightarrow{QR} = \langle 0, 2 \rangle - \langle 2, 1 \rangle = \langle -2, 1 \rangle$.

$\mathbf{w} = \operatorname{proj}_{\mathbf{v}} \mathbf{u} = \left(\dfrac{\mathbf{u} \cdot \mathbf{v}}{|\mathbf{v}|^2} \right) \mathbf{v} = \dfrac{\langle -3, -2 \rangle \cdot \langle 2, 1 \rangle}{(-2)^2 + 1^2} \langle -2, 1 \rangle$

$= -\frac{8}{5} \langle -2, 1 \rangle = \left\langle \frac{16}{5}, -\frac{8}{5} \right\rangle$

(c) From the graph, we can see that $\mathbf{u} - \mathbf{w}$ is orthogonal to $\mathbf{v}$ (and thus to L). Thus, the distance from P to L is $|\mathbf{u} - \mathbf{w}|$.

Chapter 8 Review

1. (a)

(b) $x = 12 \cos \frac{\pi}{6} = 12 \cdot \frac{\sqrt{3}}{2} = 6\sqrt{3}$,

$y = 12 \sin \frac{\pi}{6} = 12 \cdot \frac{1}{2} = 6$. Thus, the rectangular coordinates of P are $\left(6\sqrt{3}, 6 \right)$.

2. (a)

(b) $x = 8 \cos \left(-\frac{3\pi}{4} \right) = 8 \left(-\frac{\sqrt{2}}{2} \right) = -4\sqrt{2}$,

$y = 8 \sin \left(-\frac{3\pi}{4} \right) = 8 \left(-\frac{\sqrt{2}}{2} \right) = -4\sqrt{2}$. Thus, the rectangular coordinates of P are $\left(-4\sqrt{2}, -4\sqrt{2} \right)$.

3. (a)

(b) $x = -3 \cos \frac{7\pi}{4} = -3 \left(\frac{\sqrt{2}}{2} \right) = -\frac{3\sqrt{2}}{2}$,

$y = -3 \sin \frac{7\pi}{4} = -3 \left(-\frac{\sqrt{2}}{2} \right) = \frac{3\sqrt{2}}{2}$. Thus, the rectangular coordinates of P are $\left(-\frac{3\sqrt{2}}{2}, \frac{3\sqrt{2}}{2} \right)$.

4. (a)

(b) $x = -\sqrt{3} \cos \frac{2\pi}{3} = -\sqrt{3} \left(-\frac{1}{2} \right) = \frac{\sqrt{3}}{2}$,

$y = -\sqrt{3} \sin \frac{2\pi}{3} = -\sqrt{3} \left(\frac{\sqrt{3}}{2} \right) = -\frac{3}{2}$. Thus, the rectangular coordinates of P are $\left(\frac{\sqrt{3}}{2}, -\frac{3}{2} \right)$.

5. (a)

(b) $x = 4\sqrt{3} \cos \left(-\frac{5\pi}{3} \right) = 4\sqrt{3} \left(\frac{1}{2} \right) = 2\sqrt{3}$,

$y = 4\sqrt{3} \sin \left(-\frac{5\pi}{3} \right) = 4\sqrt{3} \left(\frac{\sqrt{3}}{2} \right) = 6$. Thus, the rectangular coordinates of P are $\left(2\sqrt{3}, 6 \right)$.

6. (a)

(b) $x = -6\sqrt{2} \cos \left(-\frac{\pi}{4} \right) = -6\sqrt{2} \left(\frac{\sqrt{2}}{2} \right) = -6$,

$y = -6\sqrt{2} \sin \left(-\frac{\pi}{4} \right) = -6\sqrt{2} \left(-\frac{\sqrt{2}}{2} \right) = 6$. Thus, the rectangular coordinates of P are $(-6, 6)$.

7. (a)

(b) $r = \sqrt{8^2 + 8^2} = \sqrt{128} = 8\sqrt{2}$ and $\bar{\theta} = \tan^{-1} \frac{8}{8}$.

Since P is in quadrant I, $\theta = \frac{\pi}{4}$. Polar coordinates for

P are $\left(8\sqrt{2}, \frac{\pi}{4}\right)$.

(c) $\left(-8\sqrt{2}, \frac{5\pi}{4}\right)$

8. (a)

(b) $r = \sqrt{\left(-\sqrt{2}\right)^2 + \left(\sqrt{6}\right)^2} = \sqrt{8} = 2\sqrt{2}$ and

$\bar{\theta} = \tan^{-1} \frac{\sqrt{6}}{-\sqrt{2}} = \tan^{-1}\left(-\sqrt{3}\right) = -\frac{\pi}{3}$. Since x is

negative and y is positive, $\theta = \frac{2\pi}{3}$. Polar coordinates

for P are $\left(2\sqrt{2}, \frac{2\pi}{3}\right)$.

(c) $\left(-2\sqrt{2}, \frac{5\pi}{3}\right)$

9. (a)

(b) $r = \sqrt{\left(-6\sqrt{2}\right)^2 + \left(-6\sqrt{2}\right)^2} = \sqrt{144} = 12$ and

$\bar{\theta} = \tan^{-1} \frac{-6\sqrt{2}}{-6\sqrt{2}} = \frac{\pi}{4}$. Since P is in quadrant III,

$\theta = \frac{5\pi}{4}$. Polar coordinates for P are $\left(12, \frac{5\pi}{4}\right)$.

(c) $\left(-12, \frac{\pi}{4}\right)$

10. (a)

(b) $r = \sqrt{\left(3\sqrt{3}\right)^2 + 3^2} = \sqrt{36} = 6$ and

$\bar{\theta} = \tan^{-1} \frac{3}{3\sqrt{3}} = \tan^{-1} \frac{\sqrt{3}}{3} = \frac{\pi}{6}$. Since P is in

quadrant I, $\theta = \frac{\pi}{6}$. Polar coordinates for P are $\left(6, \frac{\pi}{6}\right)$.

(c) $\left(-6, \frac{7\pi}{6}\right)$

11. (a)

(b) $r = \sqrt{(-3)^2 + \left(\sqrt{3}\right)^2} = \sqrt{12} = 2\sqrt{3}$ and

$\bar{\theta} = \tan^{-1} \frac{\sqrt{3}}{-3}$. Since P is in quadrant II, $\theta = \frac{5\pi}{6}$.

Polar coordinates for P are $\left(2\sqrt{3}, \frac{5\pi}{6}\right)$.

(c) $\left(-2\sqrt{3}, \frac{11\pi}{6}\right)$

12. (a)

(b) $r = \sqrt{4^2 + (-4)^2} = \sqrt{32} = 4\sqrt{2}$ and

$\bar{\theta} = \tan^{-1} \frac{-4}{4}$. Since P is in quadrant IV, $\theta = \frac{7\pi}{4}$.

Polar coordinates for P are $\left(4\sqrt{2}, \frac{7\pi}{4}\right)$.

(c) $\left(-4\sqrt{2}, \frac{3\pi}{4}\right)$

13. (a) $x + y = 4$ $\Leftrightarrow$ $r \cos \theta + r \sin \theta = 4$ $\Leftrightarrow$

$r (\cos \theta + \sin \theta) = 4$ $\Leftrightarrow$ $r = \dfrac{4}{\cos \theta + \sin \theta}$

(b) The rectangular equation is easier to graph.

14. (a) $xy = 1$ $\Leftrightarrow$ $(r \cos \theta)(r \sin \theta) = 1$ $\Leftrightarrow$

$r^2 (\cos \theta \sin \theta) = 1$ $\Leftrightarrow$

$r^2 = \dfrac{1}{\cos \theta \sin \theta} = \dfrac{2}{\sin 2\theta}$ or $r^2 = 2 \csc \theta.$

(b) The rectangular equation is easier to graph.

15. (a) $x^2 + y^2 = 4x + 4y$ $\Leftrightarrow$ $r^2 = 4r \cos \theta + 4r \sin \theta$

$\Leftrightarrow$ $r^2 = r (4 \cos \theta + 4 \sin \theta)$ $\Leftrightarrow$

$r = 4 \cos \theta + 4 \sin \theta$

(b) The polar equation is easier to graph.

16. (a) $\left(x^2 + y^2\right)^2 = 2xy \Leftrightarrow \left(r^2\right)^2 = 2 (r \cos \theta)(r \sin \theta)$

$\Leftrightarrow r^4 = 2r^2 \cos \theta \sin \theta \Leftrightarrow r^2 = 2 \cos \theta \sin \theta \Leftrightarrow$

$r^2 = \sin 2\theta$

(b) The polar equation is easier to graph.

17. (a)

(b) $r = 3 + 3 \cos \theta$ $\Leftrightarrow$ $r^2 = 3r + 3r \cos \theta$, which

gives $x^2 + y^2 = 3\sqrt{x^2 + y^2} + 3x$ $\Leftrightarrow$

$x^2 - 3x + y^2 = 3\sqrt{x^2 + y^2}$. Squaring both sides

gives $\left(x^2 - 3x + y^2\right)^2 = 9 \left(x^2 + y^2\right).$

18. (a)

(b) $r = 3 \sin \theta$ $\Leftrightarrow$ $r^2 = 3r \sin \theta$, so $x^2 + y^2 = 3y$

$\Leftrightarrow$ $x^2 + \left(y^2 - 3y + \frac{9}{4}\right) = \frac{9}{4}$ $\Leftrightarrow$

$x^2 + \left(y - \frac{3}{2}\right)^2 = \frac{9}{4}.$

19. (a)

(b) $r = 2 \sin 2\theta$ $\Leftrightarrow$ $r = 2 \cdot 2 \sin \theta \cos \theta$ $\Leftrightarrow$

$r^3 = 4r^2 \sin \theta \cos \theta$ $\Leftrightarrow$

$\left(r^2\right)^{3/2} = 4 (r \sin \theta)(r \cos \theta)$ and so, since

$x = r \cos \theta$ and $y = r \sin \theta$, we get

$\left(x^2 + y^2\right)^{3/2} = 4xy.$

20. (a)

(b) $r = 4 \cos 3\theta = 4 (\cos 2\theta \cos \theta - \sin 2\theta \sin \theta)$

$= 4 \left[\cos \theta \left(\cos^2 \theta - \sin^2 \theta\right) - 2 \sin^2 \theta \cos \theta\right]$ $\Leftrightarrow$

$r = 4 \left(\cos^3 \theta - 3 \sin^2 \theta \cos \theta\right)$ $\Leftrightarrow$

$r^4 = 4r^3 \left(\cos^3 \theta - 3 \sin^2 \theta \cos \theta\right)$, which gives

$\left(x^2 + y^2\right)^2 = 4x^3 - 12xy^2.$

21. (a)

(b) $r^2 = \sec 2\theta = \dfrac{1}{\cos 2\theta} = \dfrac{1}{\cos^2 \theta - \sin^2 \theta} \quad \Leftrightarrow$

$r^2 \left(\cos^2 \theta - \sin^2 \theta \right) = 1 \quad \Leftrightarrow$

$r^2 \cos^2 \theta - r^2 \sin^2 \theta = 1 \quad \Leftrightarrow$

$(r \cos \theta)^2 - (r \sin \theta)^2 = 1 \quad \Leftrightarrow \quad x^2 - y^2 = 1.$

22. (a)

(b) $r^2 = 4 \sin 2\theta = 8 \sin \theta \cos \theta \quad \Leftrightarrow$

$r^4 = 8r^2 \sin \theta \cos \theta$, so $\left(x^2 + y^2 \right)^2 = 8xy.$

23. (a)

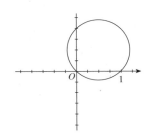

(b) $r = \sin \theta + \cos \theta \quad \Leftrightarrow \quad r^2 = r \sin \theta + r \cos \theta$, so $x^2 + y^2 = y + x$

$\Leftrightarrow \quad \left(x^2 - x + \tfrac{1}{4} \right) + \left(y^2 - y + \tfrac{1}{4} \right) = \tfrac{1}{2} \quad \Leftrightarrow$

$\left(x - \tfrac{1}{2} \right)^2 + \left(y - \tfrac{1}{2} \right)^2 = \tfrac{1}{2}.$

24. (a)

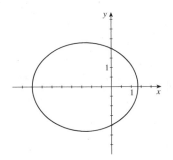

(b) $r = \dfrac{4}{2 + \cos \theta} \quad \Leftrightarrow \quad 2r + r \cos \theta = 4$, so $2\sqrt{x^2 + y^2} + x = 4 \quad \Leftrightarrow$

$2\sqrt{x^2 + y^2} = 4 - x.$ Squaring both sides gives

$4 \left(x^2 + y^2 \right) = (4 - x)^2 = 16 - 8x + x^2 \quad \Leftrightarrow \quad 3x^2 + 8x + 4y^2 = 16$

$\Leftrightarrow \quad 3 \left(x + \tfrac{4}{3} \right)^2 + 4y^2 = 16 + \tfrac{16}{3} \quad \Leftrightarrow \quad \dfrac{\left(x + \tfrac{4}{3} \right)^2}{\tfrac{64}{9}} + \dfrac{y^2}{\tfrac{16}{9}} = 1.$

25. $r = \cos (\theta/3),\ \theta \in [0, 3\pi].$

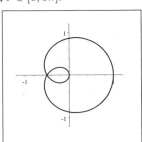

26. $r = \sin (9\theta/4),\ \theta \in [0, 8\pi]$

27. $r = 1 + 4\cos(\theta/3)$, $\theta \in [0, 6\pi]$.

28. $r = \theta \sin\theta$, $\theta \in [-3\pi, 3\pi]$. Note that this graph is not bounded.

29. (a)

(b) $4 + 4i$ has $r = \sqrt{16 + 16} = 4\sqrt{2}$, and
$\theta = \tan^{-1}\frac{4}{4} = \frac{\pi}{4}$ (in quadrant I).

(c) $4 + 4i = 4\sqrt{2}\left(\cos\frac{\pi}{4} + i\sin\frac{\pi}{4}\right)$

30. (a)

(b) $-10i$ has $r = 10$ and $\theta = \frac{3\pi}{2}$.

(c) $-10i = 10\left(\cos\frac{3\pi}{2} + i\sin\frac{3\pi}{2}\right)$

31. (a)

(b) $5 + 3i$. Then $r = \sqrt{25 + 9} = \sqrt{34}$, and $\theta = \tan^{-1}\frac{3}{5}$.

(c) $5 + 3i = \sqrt{34}\left[\cos\left(\tan^{-1}\frac{3}{5}\right) + i\sin\left(\tan^{-1}\frac{3}{5}\right)\right]$

32. (a)

(b) $1 + \sqrt{3}i$ has $r = \sqrt{1 + 3} = 2$, and
$\theta = \tan^{-1}\sqrt{3} = \frac{\pi}{3}$ (since θ is in quadrant I).

(c) $1 + \sqrt{3}i = 2\left(\cos\frac{\pi}{3} + i\sin\frac{\pi}{3}\right)$

33. (a)

(b) $-1 + i$ has $r = \sqrt{1 + 1} = \sqrt{2}$ and $\tan\theta = \frac{1}{-1}$ with

θ in quadrant II $\Leftrightarrow$ $\theta = \frac{3\pi}{4}$.

(c) $-1 + i = \sqrt{2}\left(\cos\frac{3\pi}{4} + i\sin\frac{3\pi}{4}\right)$

34. (a)

(b) -20 has $r = 20$ and $\theta = \pi$.

(c) $-20 = 20(\cos\pi + i\sin\pi)$

35. $1 - \sqrt{3}i$ has $r = \sqrt{1 + 3} = 2$ and $\tan\theta = \frac{-\sqrt{3}}{1} = -\sqrt{3}$ with θ in
quadrant III $\Leftrightarrow$ $\theta = \frac{5\pi}{3}$. Therefore, $1 - \sqrt{3}i = 2\left(\cos\frac{5\pi}{3} + i\sin\frac{5\pi}{3}\right)$, and so
$\left(1 - \sqrt{3}i\right)^4 = 2^4\left(\cos\frac{20\pi}{3} + i\sin\frac{20\pi}{3}\right) = 16\left(\cos\frac{2\pi}{3} + i\sin\frac{2\pi}{3}\right) = 16\left(-\frac{1}{2} + i\frac{\sqrt{3}}{2}\right) = 8\left(-1 + i\sqrt{3}\right).$

36. $1 + i$ has $r = \sqrt{1+1} = \sqrt{2}$ and $\theta = \frac{\pi}{4}$. Thus, $1 + i = \sqrt{2}\left(\cos\frac{\pi}{4} + i\sin\frac{\pi}{4}\right)$, and so

$(1+i)^8 = \left(\sqrt{2}\right)^8 (\cos 2\pi + i\sin 2\pi) = 16(1 + i \cdot 0) = 16$.

37. $\sqrt{3}+i$ has $r = \sqrt{3+1} = 2$ and $\tan\theta = \frac{1}{\sqrt{3}}$ with θ in quadrant I $\Leftrightarrow$ $\theta = \frac{\pi}{6}$. Therefore, $\sqrt{3}+i = 2\left(\cos\frac{\pi}{6} + i\sin\frac{\pi}{6}\right)$,

and so

$\left(\sqrt{3}+i\right)^{-4} = 2^{-4}\left(\cos\frac{-4\pi}{6} + i\sin\frac{-4\pi}{6}\right) = \frac{1}{16}\left(\cos\frac{2\pi}{3} - i\sin\frac{2\pi}{3}\right) = \frac{1}{16}\left(-\frac{1}{2} - i\frac{\sqrt{3}}{2}\right)$

$= \frac{1}{32}\left(-1 - i\sqrt{3}\right) = -\frac{1}{32}\left(1 + i\sqrt{3}\right)$

38. $\frac{1}{2} + \frac{\sqrt{3}}{2}i$ has $r = \sqrt{\frac{1}{4} + \frac{3}{4}} = 1$ and $\theta = \tan^{-1}\frac{\sqrt{3}/2}{1/2} = \frac{\pi}{3}$ (since θ is in quadrant I). So $\frac{1}{2} + \frac{\sqrt{3}}{2}i = \cos\frac{\pi}{3} + i\sin\frac{\pi}{3}$. Thus

$\left(\frac{1}{2} + \frac{\sqrt{3}}{2}i\right)^{20} = 1^{20}\left(\cos\frac{20\pi}{3} + i\sin\frac{20\pi}{3}\right) = \cos\frac{2\pi}{3} + i\sin\frac{2\pi}{3} = -\frac{1}{2} + \frac{\sqrt{3}}{2}i = \frac{1}{2}\left(-1 + i\sqrt{3}\right)$

39. $-16i$ has $r = 16$ and $\theta = \frac{3\pi}{2}$. Thus, $-16i = 16\left(\cos\frac{3\pi}{2} + i\sin\frac{3\pi}{2}\right)$ and so

$(-16i)^{1/2} = 16^{1/2}\left[\cos\left(\frac{3\pi + 4k\pi}{2}\right) + i\sin\left(\frac{3\pi + 4k\pi}{2}\right)\right]$ for $k = 0, 1$. Thus

the roots are $w_0 = 4\left(\cos\frac{3\pi}{4} + i\sin\frac{3\pi}{4}\right) = 4\left(-\frac{1}{\sqrt{2}} + i\frac{1}{\sqrt{2}}\right) = 2\sqrt{2}\left(-1 + i\right)$ and

$w_1 = 4\left(\cos\frac{7\pi}{4} + i\sin\frac{7\pi}{4}\right) = 4\left(\frac{1}{\sqrt{2}} - i\frac{1}{\sqrt{2}}\right) = 2\sqrt{2}\left(1 - i\right)$.

40. $4 + 4\sqrt{3}i$ has $r = \sqrt{16+48} = 8$ and $\theta = \tan^{-1}\frac{4\sqrt{3}}{4} = \frac{\pi}{3}$. Therefore, $4 + 4\sqrt{3}i = 8\left(\cos\frac{\pi}{3} + i\sin\frac{\pi}{3}\right)$.

Thus $\left(4 + 4\sqrt{3}i\right)^{1/3} = \sqrt[3]{8}\left[\cos\left(\frac{\pi + 6k\pi}{9}\right) + i\sin\left(\frac{\pi + 6k\pi}{9}\right)\right]$ for $k = 0, 1, 2$. Thus the three roots are

$w_0 = 2\left(\cos\frac{\pi}{9} + i\sin\frac{\pi}{9}\right)$, $w_1 = 2\left(\cos\frac{7\pi}{9} + i\sin\frac{7\pi}{9}\right)$, and $w_2 = 2\left(\cos\frac{13\pi}{9} + i\sin\frac{13\pi}{9}\right)$.

41. $1 = \cos 0 + i\sin 0$. Then $1^{1/6} = 1\left(\cos\frac{2k\pi}{6} + i\sin\frac{2k\pi}{6}\right)$ for $k = 0, 1, 2, 3, 4, 5$. Thus the six roots are

$w_0 = 1(\cos 0 + i\sin 0) = 1$, $w_1 = 1\left(\cos\frac{\pi}{3} + i\sin\frac{\pi}{3}\right) = \frac{1}{2} + i\frac{\sqrt{3}}{2}$, $w_2 = 1\left(\cos\frac{2\pi}{3} + i\sin\frac{2\pi}{3}\right) = -\frac{1}{2} + i\frac{\sqrt{3}}{2}$,

$w_3 = 1(\cos\pi + i\sin\pi) = -1$, $w_4 = 1\left(\cos\frac{4\pi}{3} + i\sin\frac{4\pi}{3}\right) = -\frac{1}{2} - i\frac{\sqrt{3}}{2}$, and $w_5 = 1\left(\cos\frac{5\pi}{3} + i\sin\frac{5\pi}{3}\right) = \frac{1}{2} - i\frac{\sqrt{3}}{2}$.

42. $i = \cos\frac{\pi}{2} + i\sin\frac{\pi}{2}$. Then $i^{1/8} = \cos\left(\frac{\pi/2 + 2k\pi}{8}\right) + i\sin\left(\frac{\pi/2 + 2k\pi}{8}\right) = \cos\left(\frac{\pi + 4k\pi}{16}\right) + i\sin\left(\frac{\pi + 4k\pi}{16}\right)$ for

$k = 0, 1, 2, 3, 4, 5, 6, 7$. Thus the eight roots are $w_0 = \cos\frac{\pi}{16} + i\sin\frac{\pi}{16}$, $w_1 = \cos\frac{5\pi}{16} + i\sin\frac{5\pi}{16}$, $w_2 = \cos\frac{9\pi}{16} + i\sin\frac{9\pi}{16}$,

$w_3 = \cos\frac{13\pi}{16} + i\sin\frac{13\pi}{16}$, $w_4 = \cos\frac{17\pi}{16} + i\sin\frac{17\pi}{16}$, $w_5 = \cos\frac{21\pi}{16} + i\sin\frac{21\pi}{16}$, $w_6 = \cos\frac{25\pi}{16} + i\sin\frac{25\pi}{16}$, and

$w_7 = \cos\frac{29\pi}{16} + i\sin\frac{29\pi}{16}$.

43. $\mathbf{u} = \langle -2, 3\rangle$ and $\mathbf{v} = \langle 8, 1\rangle$. Then $|\mathbf{u}| = \sqrt{(-2)^2 + 3^2} = \sqrt{13}$, $\mathbf{u} + \mathbf{v} = \langle -2 + 8, 3 + 1\rangle = \langle 6, 4\rangle$,

$\mathbf{u} - \mathbf{v} = \langle -2 - 8, 3 - 1\rangle = \langle -10, 2\rangle$, $2\mathbf{u} = \langle -4, 6\rangle$, and $3\mathbf{u} - 2\mathbf{v} = \langle -6, 9\rangle - \langle 16, 2\rangle = \langle -6 - 16, 9 - 2\rangle = \langle -22, 7\rangle$.

44. $\mathbf{u} = 2\mathbf{i} + \mathbf{j}$ and $\mathbf{v} = \mathbf{i} - 2\mathbf{j}$. Then $|\mathbf{u}| = \sqrt{2^2 + 1^2} = \sqrt{5}$, $\mathbf{u} + \mathbf{v} = (2 + 1)\mathbf{i} + (1 - 2)\mathbf{j} = 3\mathbf{i} - \mathbf{j}$,

$\mathbf{u} - \mathbf{v} = (2 - 1)\mathbf{i} + (1 + 2)\mathbf{j} = \mathbf{i} + 3\mathbf{j}$, $2\mathbf{u} = 4\mathbf{i} + 2\mathbf{j}$, and $3\mathbf{u} - 2\mathbf{v} = (6 - 2)\mathbf{i} + (3 + 4)\mathbf{j} = 4\mathbf{i} + 7\mathbf{j}$.

45. $P(0, 3)$ and $Q(3, -1)$. $\mathbf{u} = \langle 3 - 0, -1 - 3\rangle = \langle 3, -4\rangle = 3\mathbf{i} - 4\mathbf{j}$

46. $\mathbf{u} = (|\mathbf{u}|\cos\theta)\,\mathbf{i} + (|\mathbf{u}|\sin\theta)\,\mathbf{j} = 20\cos 60°\mathbf{i} + 20\sin 60°\mathbf{j} = 10\mathbf{i} + 10\sqrt{3}\mathbf{j}$

47. Let $Q(x, y)$ be the terminal point. Then $\langle x - 5, y - 6\rangle = \langle 5, -8\rangle$ $\Leftrightarrow$ $x - 5 = 5$ and $y - 6 = -8$ $\Leftrightarrow$ $x = 10$

and $y = -2$. Therefore, the terminal point is $Q(10, -2)$.

48. $\tan\theta = \frac{-5}{2}$ with θ in quadrant IV $\Leftrightarrow$ $\theta = \tan^{-1}(-2.5) \approx -68.2°$.

49. (a) The resultant force **r** is the sum of the forces; to find this we first resolve the two vectors:

$$\mathbf{v}_1 = 2.0 \times 10^4 \text{ lb N } 50° \text{ E} = \left\langle 2.0 \times 10^4 \cdot \cos 40°, 2.0 \times 10^4 \cdot \sin 40° \right\rangle \approx \langle 15321, 12856 \rangle \text{ and}$$

$$\mathbf{v}_2 = 3.4 \times 10^4 \text{ lb S } 75° \text{ E} = \left\langle 3.4 \times 10^4 \cdot \cos(-15°), 3.4 \times 10^4 \cdot \sin(-15°) \right\rangle \approx \langle 32841, -8800 \rangle. \text{ Thus}$$

$$\mathbf{r} = \mathbf{v}_1 + \mathbf{v}_2 \approx \langle 15321, 12856 \rangle + \langle 32841, -8800 \rangle = \langle 48163, 4056 \rangle \approx \langle 4.82, 0.41 \rangle \times 10^4 = (4.82\mathbf{i} + 0.41\mathbf{j}) \times 10^4.$$

(b) The magnitude is $|\mathbf{r}| = \sqrt{48163^2 + 4056^2} \approx 4.8 \times 10^4$ lb. We have $\theta \approx \tan^{-1}\left(\frac{4056}{48163}\right) \approx 4.8°$. Thus the direction of **r** is approximately N 85.2° E.

50. (a) The initial velocity of the airplane is $\mathbf{v} = 600 \cos 30° \, \mathbf{i} + 600 \sin 30° \, \mathbf{j} = \langle 300\sqrt{3}, 300 \rangle$. The wind has a velocity $\mathbf{w} = 50 \cos 120° \, \mathbf{i} + 50 \sin 120° \, \mathbf{j} = \langle -25, 25\sqrt{3} \rangle$. Thus, the resultant velocity is $\mathbf{r} = \langle 300\sqrt{3} - 25, 300 + 25\sqrt{3} \rangle$.

(b) The true speed of the plane is $|\mathbf{r}| = \sqrt{\left(300\sqrt{3} - 25\right)^2 + \left(300 + 25\sqrt{3}\right)^2} \approx 602.1$ mi/h. Since

$$\tan \theta = \frac{300 + 25\sqrt{3}}{300\sqrt{3} - 25} \approx 0.69408, \, \theta \approx \tan^{-1}(0.69408) \approx 34.8°, \text{ and the true direction is N } 55.2° \text{ E}.$$

51. $\mathbf{u} = \langle 4, -3 \rangle$ and $\mathbf{v} = \langle 9, -8 \rangle$. Then $|\mathbf{u}| = \sqrt{(4)^2 + (-3)^2} = \sqrt{25} = 5$,

$\mathbf{u} \cdot \mathbf{u} = \langle 4, -3 \rangle \cdot \langle 4, -3 \rangle = (4)(4) + (-3)(-3) = 16 + 9 = 25$, and

$\mathbf{u} \cdot \mathbf{v} = \langle 4, -3 \rangle \cdot \langle 9, -8 \rangle = (4)(9) + (-3)(-8) = 36 + 24 = 60$.

52. $\mathbf{u} = \langle 5, 12 \rangle$ and $\mathbf{v} = \langle 10, -4 \rangle$. Then $|\mathbf{u}| = \sqrt{(5)^2 + (12)^2} = \sqrt{169} = 13$,

$\mathbf{u} \cdot \mathbf{u} = \langle 5, 12 \rangle \cdot \langle 5, 12 \rangle = (5)(5) + (12)(12) = 25 + 144 = 169$, and

$\mathbf{u} \cdot \mathbf{v} = \langle 5, 12 \rangle \cdot \langle 10, -4 \rangle = (5)(10) + (12)(-4) = 50 - 48 = 2$.

53. $\mathbf{u} = -2\mathbf{i} + 2\mathbf{j}$ and $\mathbf{v} = \mathbf{i} + \mathbf{j}$. Then $|\mathbf{u}| = \sqrt{(-2)^2 + (2)^2} = \sqrt{8} = 2\sqrt{2}$,

$\mathbf{u} \cdot \mathbf{u} = -2\mathbf{i} + 2\mathbf{j} \cdot -2\mathbf{i} + 2\mathbf{j} = (-2)(-2) + (2)(2) = 4 + 4 = 8$, and

$\mathbf{u} \cdot \mathbf{v} = -2\mathbf{i} + 2\mathbf{j} \cdot \mathbf{i} + \mathbf{j} = (-2)(1) + (2)(1) = -2 + 2 = 0$.

54. $\mathbf{u} = 10\mathbf{j}$ and $\mathbf{v} = 5\mathbf{i} - 3\mathbf{j}$. Then $|\mathbf{u}| = \sqrt{(0)^2 + (10)^2} = \sqrt{100} = 10$,

$\mathbf{u} \cdot \mathbf{u} = 10\mathbf{j} \cdot 10\mathbf{j} = (0)(0) + (10)(10) = 100$, and $\mathbf{u} \cdot \mathbf{v} = 10\mathbf{j} \cdot 5\mathbf{i} - 3\mathbf{j} = (0)(5) + (10)(-3) = -30$.

55. $\mathbf{u} = \langle -4, 2 \rangle$ and $\mathbf{v} = \langle 3, 6 \rangle$. Since $\mathbf{u} \cdot \mathbf{v} = -12 + 12 = 0$, the vectors are orthogonal.

56. $\mathbf{u} = \langle 5, 3 \rangle$ and $\mathbf{v} = \langle -2, 6 \rangle$. Then $\cos \theta = \dfrac{\mathbf{u} \cdot \mathbf{v}}{|\mathbf{u}| \, |\mathbf{v}|} = \dfrac{-10 + 18}{\sqrt{34} \cdot \sqrt{40}} = \dfrac{5}{2\sqrt{340}} = \dfrac{5}{4\sqrt{85}}$. Thus, $\theta = \cos^{-1} \dfrac{5}{4\sqrt{85}} \approx 82.2°$.

57. $\mathbf{u} = 2\mathbf{i} + \mathbf{j}$ and $\mathbf{v} = \mathbf{i} + 3\mathbf{j}$. Then $\cos \theta = \dfrac{\mathbf{u} \cdot \mathbf{v}}{|\mathbf{u}| \, |\mathbf{v}|} = \dfrac{2 + 3}{\sqrt{5}\sqrt{10}} = \dfrac{\sqrt{2}}{2}$. Thus, $\theta = \cos^{-1} \dfrac{\sqrt{2}}{2} = 45°$.

58. $\mathbf{u} = \mathbf{i} - \mathbf{j}$ and $\mathbf{v} = \mathbf{i} + \mathbf{j}$. Then $\cos \theta = \dfrac{\mathbf{u} \cdot \mathbf{v}}{|\mathbf{u}| \, |\mathbf{v}|} = \dfrac{1 - 1}{\sqrt{2} \cdot \sqrt{2}} = 0$, so the vectors are orthogonal.

59. (a) $\mathbf{u} = \langle 3, 1 \rangle$ and $\mathbf{v} = \langle 6, -1 \rangle$. Then the component of **u** along **v** is $\dfrac{\mathbf{u} \cdot \mathbf{v}}{|\mathbf{v}|} = \dfrac{\langle 3, 1 \rangle \cdot \langle 6, -1 \rangle}{\sqrt{\langle 6, -1 \rangle \cdot \langle 6, -1 \rangle}} = \dfrac{18 - 1}{\sqrt{36 + 1}} = \dfrac{17\sqrt{37}}{37}$.

(b) $\mathbf{u}_1 = \text{proj}_\mathbf{v} \, \mathbf{u} = \left(\dfrac{\mathbf{u} \cdot \mathbf{v}}{|\mathbf{v}|^2} \right) \mathbf{v} = \left(\dfrac{\langle 3, 1 \rangle \cdot \langle 6, -1 \rangle}{6^2 + (-1)^2} \right) \langle 6, -1 \rangle = \dfrac{17}{37} \langle 6, -1 \rangle = \left\langle \dfrac{102}{37}, -\dfrac{17}{37} \right\rangle$.

(c) $\mathbf{u}_2 = \mathbf{u} - \mathbf{u}_1 = \langle 3, 1 \rangle - \left\langle \dfrac{102}{37}, -\dfrac{17}{37} \right\rangle = \left\langle \dfrac{9}{37}, \dfrac{54}{37} \right\rangle$.

60. (a) $\mathbf{u} = \langle -8, 6 \rangle$ and $\mathbf{v} = \langle 20, 20 \rangle$. Then the component of **u** along **v** is

$$\frac{\mathbf{u} \cdot \mathbf{v}}{|\mathbf{v}|} = \frac{\langle -8, 6 \rangle \cdot \langle 20, 20 \rangle}{\sqrt{\langle 20, 20 \rangle \cdot \langle 20, 20 \rangle}} = \frac{-160 + 120}{\sqrt{400 + 400}} = \frac{-40}{\sqrt{800}} = \frac{-40}{20\sqrt{2}} = -\sqrt{2}.$$

(b) $\mathbf{u}_1 = \text{proj}_\mathbf{v} \, \mathbf{u} = \left(\dfrac{\mathbf{u} \cdot \mathbf{v}}{|\mathbf{v}|^2} \right) \mathbf{v} = \left(\dfrac{\langle -8, 6 \rangle \cdot \langle 20, 20 \rangle}{20^2 + 20^2} \right) \langle 20, 20 \rangle = -\dfrac{1}{20} \langle 20, 20 \rangle = \langle -1, -1 \rangle$.

(c) $\mathbf{u}_2 = \mathbf{u} - \mathbf{u}_1 = \langle -8, 6 \rangle - \langle -1, -1 \rangle = \langle -7, 7 \rangle$.

61. The displacement is $\mathbf{D} = \langle 7 - 1, -1 - 1 \rangle = \langle 6, -2 \rangle$. Thus, $W = \mathbf{F} \cdot \mathbf{D} = \langle 2, 9 \rangle \cdot \langle 6, -2 \rangle = -6$.

62. $W = \mathbf{F} \cdot \mathbf{D} = 3800$ ft-lb. But $\mathbf{F} \cdot \mathbf{D} = |\mathbf{F}|\,|\mathbf{D}| \cos\theta \quad \Leftrightarrow \quad \cos\theta = \dfrac{\mathbf{F} \cdot \mathbf{D}}{|\mathbf{F}|\,|\mathbf{D}|} = \dfrac{3800}{(250)\,(20)} = 0.76$. Therefore,

$\theta = \cos^{-1}(0.76) \approx 40.5°$.

Chapter 8 Test

1. (a) $x = 8 \cos \frac{5\pi}{4} = 8 \left(-\frac{\sqrt{2}}{2} \right) = -4\sqrt{2}$, $y = 8 \sin \frac{5\pi}{4} = 8 \left(-\frac{\sqrt{2}}{2} \right) = -4\sqrt{2}$. So the point has rectangular coordinates

$\left(-4\sqrt{2}, -4\sqrt{2} \right)$.

(b) $P = (-6, 2\sqrt{3})$ in rectangular coordinates. So $\tan\theta = \frac{2\sqrt{3}}{-6}$ and the reference angle is $\overline{\theta} = \frac{\pi}{6}$. Since P is in

quadrant II, we have $\theta = \frac{5\pi}{6}$. Next, $r^2 = (-6)^2 + \left(2\sqrt{3}\right)^2 = 36 + 12 = 48$, so $r = 4\sqrt{3}$. Thus, polar coordinates for

the point are $\left(4\sqrt{3}, \frac{5\pi}{6} \right)$ or $\left(-4\sqrt{3}, \frac{11\pi}{6} \right)$.

2. (a)

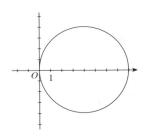

(b) $r = 8 \cos\theta \quad \Leftrightarrow \quad r^2 = 8r \cos\theta \quad \Leftrightarrow \quad x^2 + y^2 = 8x \quad \Leftrightarrow$

$x^2 - 8x + y^2 = 0 \quad \Leftrightarrow \quad x^2 - 8x + 16 + y^2 = 16 \quad \Leftrightarrow$

$(x - 4)^2 + y^2 = 16$

3. (a)

Im

$\bullet\, 1 + \sqrt{3}i$

1

1   Re

(b) $1 + \sqrt{3}i$ has $r = \sqrt{1 + 3} = 2$ and $\theta = \tan^{-1}\left(\sqrt{3}\right) = \frac{\pi}{3}$. So, in

trigonometric form, $1 + \sqrt{3}i = 2 \left(\cos \frac{\pi}{3} + i \sin \frac{\pi}{3} \right)$.

(c) $z = 1 + \sqrt{3}i = 2 \left(\cos \frac{\pi}{3} + i \sin \frac{\pi}{3} \right) \quad \Rightarrow$

$z^9 = 2^9 \left(\cos \frac{9\pi}{3} + i \sin \frac{9\pi}{3} \right) = 512 \left(\cos 3\pi + i \sin 3\pi \right)$

$= 512 \left(-1 + i\,(0) \right) = -512$

4. $z_1 = 4 \left(\cos \frac{7\pi}{12} + i \sin \frac{7\pi}{12} \right)$ and $z_2 = 2 \left(\cos \frac{5\pi}{12} + i \sin \frac{5\pi}{12} \right)$.

Then $z_1 z_2 = 4 \cdot 2 \left[\cos\left(\dfrac{7\pi + 5\pi}{12} \right) + i \sin\left(\dfrac{7\pi + 5\pi}{12} \right) \right] = 8 \left(\cos\pi + i \sin\pi \right) = -8$ and

$z_1/z_2 = \frac{4}{2} \left[\cos\left(\dfrac{7\pi - 5\pi}{12} \right) + i \sin\left(\dfrac{7\pi - 5\pi}{12} \right) \right] = 2 \left(\cos \frac{\pi}{6} + i \sin \frac{\pi}{6} \right) = 2 \left(\frac{\sqrt{3}}{2} + \frac{1}{2}i \right) = \sqrt{3} + i$.

5. $27i$ has $r = 27$ and $\theta = \frac{\pi}{2}$, so $27i = 27 \left(\cos \frac{\pi}{2} + i \sin \frac{\pi}{2} \right)$. Thus,

$(27i)^{1/3} = \sqrt[3]{27} \left[\cos\left(\dfrac{\frac{\pi}{2} + 2k\pi}{3} \right) + i \sin\left(\dfrac{\frac{\pi}{2} + 2k\pi}{3} \right) \right]$

$= 3 \left[\cos\left(\dfrac{\pi + 4k\pi}{6} \right) + i \sin\left(\dfrac{\pi + 4k\pi}{6} \right) \right]$

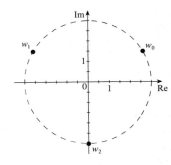

for $k = 0, 1, 2$. Thus, the three roots are

$w_0 = 3 \left(\cos \frac{\pi}{6} + i \sin \frac{\pi}{6} \right) = 3 \left(\frac{\sqrt{3}}{2} + \frac{1}{2}i \right) = \frac{3}{2} \left(\sqrt{3} + i \right)$,

$w_1 = 3 \left(\cos \frac{5\pi}{6} + i \sin \frac{5\pi}{6} \right) = 3 \left(-\frac{\sqrt{3}}{2} + \frac{1}{2}i \right) = \frac{3}{2} \left(-\sqrt{3} + i \right)$, and

$w_2 = 3 \left(\cos \frac{9\pi}{6} + i \sin \frac{9\pi}{6} \right) = -3i$.

6. (a) $\mathbf{u}$ has initial point $P(3, -1)$ and terminal point $Q(-3, 9)$. Therefore, $\mathbf{u} = \langle -3 - 3, 9 - (-1) \rangle = \langle -6, 10 \rangle = -6\mathbf{i} + 10\mathbf{j}$.

(b) $\mathbf{u} = \langle -6, 10 \rangle \quad \Rightarrow \quad |\mathbf{u}| = \sqrt{(-6)^2 + 10^2} = \sqrt{4 \cdot (9 + 25)} = 2\sqrt{34}$

7. $\mathbf{u} = \langle 1, 3 \rangle$ and $\mathbf{v} = \langle -6, 2 \rangle$.

(a) $\mathbf{u} - 3\mathbf{v} = \langle 1, 3 \rangle - \langle -18, 6 \rangle = \langle 19, -3 \rangle$

(b) $|\mathbf{u} + \mathbf{v}| = |\langle 1 - 6, 3 + 2 \rangle| = |\langle -5, 5 \rangle| = \sqrt{(-5)^2 + 5^2} = 5\sqrt{2}$

(c) $\mathbf{u} \cdot \mathbf{v} = (1)(-6) + (3)(2) = -6 + 6 = 0$

(d) Since $\mathbf{u} \cdot \mathbf{v} = 0$, it is true that $\mathbf{u}$ and $\mathbf{v}$ are perpendicular.

8. (a)

(b) $|\mathbf{u}| = \sqrt{\left(-4\sqrt{3}\right)^2 + 4^2} = \sqrt{48 + 16} = 8$ and $\tan\theta = \frac{4}{-4\sqrt{3}} = -\frac{\sqrt{3}}{3}$, so $\theta = \frac{5\pi}{6}$ (since the terminal point of $\mathbf{u}$ is in quadrant III).

9. Let $\mathbf{r}$ represent the velocity of the river and $\mathbf{b}$ the velocity of the boat. Then $\mathbf{r} = \langle 8, 0 \rangle$ and $\mathbf{b} = \langle 12\sin 30°, 12\cos 30° \rangle = \langle 6, 6\sqrt{3} \rangle$.

(a) The resultant (or true) velocity is $\mathbf{v} = \mathbf{r} + \mathbf{b} = \langle 14, 6\sqrt{3} \rangle = 14\mathbf{i} + 6\sqrt{3}\mathbf{j}$.

(b) $|\mathbf{v}| = \sqrt{14^2 + \left(6\sqrt{3}\right)^2} = \sqrt{196 + 108} = \sqrt{304} \approx 17.44$ and $\theta = \tan^{-1}\left(\frac{6\sqrt{3}}{14}\right) = \tan^{-1}\left(\frac{3\sqrt{3}}{7}\right) \approx 36.6°$.

Therefore, the true speed of the boat is approximately 17.4 mi/h and the true direction is approximately N 53.4° E.

10. (a) $\cos\theta = \dfrac{\langle 3, 2 \rangle \cdot \langle 5, -1 \rangle}{|\langle 3, 2 \rangle| \, |\langle 5, -1 \rangle|} = \dfrac{15 - 2}{\sqrt{13}\sqrt{26}} = \dfrac{13}{13\sqrt{2}} = \dfrac{1}{\sqrt{2}} \quad \Rightarrow \quad \theta = \frac{\pi}{4}$ rad $= 45°$.

(b) The component of $\mathbf{u}$ along $\mathbf{v}$ is $\dfrac{\mathbf{u} \cdot \mathbf{v}}{|\mathbf{v}|} = \dfrac{\langle 3, 2 \rangle \cdot \langle 5, -1 \rangle}{\sqrt{26}} = \dfrac{15 - 2}{\sqrt{26}} = \dfrac{13}{\sqrt{26}} = \dfrac{\sqrt{26}}{2}$.

(c) $\text{proj}_{\mathbf{v}}\,\mathbf{u} = \left(\dfrac{\mathbf{u} \cdot \mathbf{v}}{|\mathbf{v}|^2}\right)\mathbf{v} = \left(\dfrac{\langle 3, 2 \rangle \cdot \langle 5, -1 \rangle}{5^2 + (-1)^2}\right)\langle 5, -1 \rangle = \frac{13}{26}\langle 5, -1 \rangle = \frac{1}{2}\langle 5, -1 \rangle = \langle \frac{5}{2}, -\frac{1}{2} \rangle$.

11. The displacement vector is $\mathbf{D} = \langle 7, -13 \rangle - \langle 2, 2 \rangle = \langle 5, -15 \rangle$. Therefore, the work done is $W = \mathbf{F} \cdot \mathbf{D} = \langle 3, -5 \rangle \cdot \langle 5, -15 \rangle = 15 + 75 = 90$.

Focus on Modeling: Mapping the World

1. (a) Since we want $x = 36$ when $\alpha = 360°$, we substitute these values and solve for R: $36 = \frac{\pi}{180} \cdot 360R$ $\Leftrightarrow$ $R = \frac{36}{2\pi} \approx 5.73$ inches.

(b) The circumference of the earth at the equator is $2\pi (3960)$. Since the length of the equator on the map is 36 inches, each inch represents $\frac{1}{36}$ of that length, or $\frac{1}{36} \cdot 7920\pi \approx 691.2$ miles.

2. The distance from the equator to $70°$ N is $y = 5.73 \tan 70° \approx 15.74$. So the map should be $2 \cdot 15.74 = 31.48$ inches tall.

3. (a) $x = \frac{\pi}{180} (-122.3)(5.73) \approx -12.33$; $y = 5.73 \tan 47.6° \approx 6.28$.

(b) $x = \frac{\pi}{180} (37.6)(5.73) \approx 3.76$; $y = 5.73 \tan 55.8° \approx 8.43$

(c) $x = \frac{\pi}{180} (151.2)(5.73) \approx 15.12$; $y = 5.73 \tan (-33.9°) \approx -3.85$

(d) $x = \frac{\pi}{180} (-43.1)(5.73) \approx -4.31$; $y = 5.73 \tan (-22.9°) \approx -2.42$

4. (a) Since the outside of the map corresponds to the equator, we use $\beta = 0$ in the formula, with $r = 20$. Thus,
$$20 = 2R \tan 45° \quad \Leftrightarrow \quad R = \frac{10}{\tan 45°} = 10.$$

(b) $\theta = 151.2°$ and $r = 2(10) \tan \left(\frac{-33.9°}{2} + 45° \right) = 20 \tan 28.05° \approx 10.66$. So Sydney, Australia corresponds to the point $(10.66, 151.2°)$.

5. The formula for the length of a circular arc is $s = r\theta$, where θ is measured in radians. Using this formula, we find that the distance along a meridian between the latitudes $\beta°$ and $(\beta + 1)°$ is $\frac{\pi}{180} R \approx 0.01745R$.

(a) The projected distance on the cylinder is $R \tan 21° - R \tan 10° \approx 0.01989R$. Thus, the ratio is $\frac{0.01989R}{0.01745R} \approx 1.14$.

(b) The projected distance on the cylinder is $R \tan 41° - R \tan 40° \approx 0.03019R$. Thus, the ratio is $\frac{0.03019R}{0.01745R} \approx 1.73$.

(c) The projected distance on the cylinder is $R \tan 81° - R \tan 80° \approx 0.64247R$. Thus, the ratio is $\frac{0.64247R}{0.01745R} \approx 36.82$.

6. We first need to determine the radius r of the circle at latitude β.

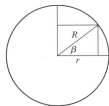

From the figure, we see that $\cos \beta = r/R$, so $r = R \cos \beta$. Using the formula for the length of a circular arc, we find that the distance between two points on the sphere at latitude β that are $1°$ longitude apart is $\frac{\pi}{180} r = \frac{\pi}{180} R \cos \beta$. On the cylinder, the distance between two points that are $1°$ longitude apart is $\frac{\pi}{180} R$. Thus, the ratio of the projected distance on the cylinder to the distance on the sphere is $\dfrac{\frac{\pi}{180} R}{\frac{\pi}{180} R \cos \beta} = \sec \beta$.

(a) At $20°$ N, the ratio is $\sec 20° \approx 1.06$.

(b) At $40°$ N, the ratio is $\sec 40° \approx 1.31$.

(c) At $80°$ N, the ratio is $\sec 80° \approx 5.76$.

7. The projected distance on the plane between latitude β_1° and β_2° is

$$2R \tan \left(\tfrac{1}{2}\beta_1 + 45^\circ \right) - 2R \tan \left(\tfrac{1}{2}\beta_2 + 45^\circ \right) = 2R \left[\tan \left(\tfrac{1}{2}\beta_1 + 45^\circ \right) - \tan \left(\tfrac{1}{2}\beta_2 + 45^\circ \right) \right]$$

In Problem 5 we found that on the sphere, the distance along a meridian between the latitudes β° and $(\beta + 1)^\circ$ is $\frac{\pi}{180} R \approx 0.01745R.$

(a) The projected distance on the plane is

$$2R \left[\tan \left(\tfrac{1}{2}(-20^\circ) + 45^\circ \right) - \tan \left(\tfrac{1}{2}(-21^\circ) + 45^\circ \right) \right] = 2R \left(\tan 35^\circ - R \tan 34.5^\circ \right)$$
$$\approx 0.02583R$$

Thus, the ratio is $\dfrac{0.02583R}{0.01745R} \approx 1.48.$

(b) The projected distance on the plane is

$$2R \left[\tan \left(\tfrac{1}{2}(-40) + 45^\circ \right) - \tan \left(\tfrac{1}{2}(-41) + 45^\circ \right) \right] = 2R \left(\tan 25^\circ - R \tan 24.5^\circ \right)$$
$$\approx 0.02116R$$

Thus, the ratio is $\dfrac{0.02116R}{0.01745R} \approx 1.21.$

(c) The projected distance on the plane is

$$2R \left[\tan \left(\tfrac{1}{2}(-80) + 45^\circ \right) - \tan \left(\tfrac{1}{2}(-81) + 45^\circ \right) \right] = 2R \left(\tan 5^\circ - R \tan 4.5^\circ \right)$$
$$\approx 0.01757R$$

Thus, the ratio is $\dfrac{0.01757R}{0.01745R} \approx 1.01.$

8. Using the formula for the length of a circular arc, we find that the projected distance on the plane between two points that are 1° longitude apart (at latitude β°) is $\frac{\pi}{180} r$, where $r = 2R \tan \left(\tfrac{1}{2}\beta + 45^\circ \right)$. Thus, the ratio of the projected distance on the plane to the distance on the sphere is $\dfrac{\frac{\pi}{180} 2R \tan \left(\tfrac{1}{2}\beta + 45^\circ \right)}{\frac{\pi}{180} R \cos \beta} = \dfrac{2 \tan \left(\tfrac{1}{2}\beta + 45^\circ \right)}{\cos \beta}.$

(a) At 20° S, the ratio is $\dfrac{2 \tan \left(\tfrac{1}{2}(-20^\circ) + 45^\circ \right)}{\cos 20^\circ} = \dfrac{2 \tan 35^\circ}{\cos 20^\circ} \approx 1.49.$

(b) At 40° S, the ratio is $\dfrac{2 \tan \left(\tfrac{1}{2}(-40^\circ) + 45^\circ \right)}{\cos 40^\circ} = \dfrac{2 \tan 25^\circ}{\cos 40^\circ} \approx 1.22.$

(c) At 80° S, the ratio is $\dfrac{2 \tan \left(\tfrac{1}{2}(-80^\circ) + 45^\circ \right)}{\cos 40^\circ} = \dfrac{2 \tan 5^\circ}{\cos 80^\circ} \approx 1.01.$

9 Systems of Equations and Inequalities

9.1 Systems of Equations

1. $\begin{cases} x - y = 2 \\ 2x + 3y = 9 \end{cases}$ Solving the first equation for x, we get $x = y + 2$, and substituting this into the second equation gives

$2(y+2)+3y = 9 \iff 5y+4 = 9 \iff 5y = 5 \iff y = 1$. Substituting for y we get $x = y+2 = (1)+2 = 3$. Thus, the solution is $(3, 1)$.

2. $\begin{cases} 2x + y = 7 \\ x + 2y = 2 \end{cases}$ Solving the first equation for y, we get $y = 7 - 2x$, and substituting this into the second equation

gives $x + 2(7 - 2x) = 2 \iff x + 14 - 4x = 2 \iff -3x = -12 \iff x = 4$. Substituting for x we get $y = 7 - 2x = 7 - 2(4) = -1$. Thus, the solution is $(4, -1)$.

3. $\begin{cases} y = x^2 \\ y = x + 12 \end{cases}$ Substituting $y = x^2$ into the second equation gives $x^2 = x + 12 \iff$

$0 = x^2 - x - 12 = (x - 4)(x + 3) \Rightarrow x = 4$ or $x = -3$. So since $y = x^2$, the solutions are $(-3, 9)$ and $(4, 16)$.

4. $\begin{cases} x^2 + y^2 = 25 \\ y = 2x \end{cases}$ Substituting for y in the first equation gives $x^2 + (2x)^2 = 25 \iff 5x^2 = 25 \iff x^2 = 5 \Rightarrow$

$x = \pm\sqrt{5}$ When $x = \sqrt{5}$ then $y = 2\sqrt{5}$, and when $x = -\sqrt{5}$ then $y = 2(-\sqrt{5}) = -2\sqrt{5}$. Thus the solutions are $(\sqrt{5}, 2\sqrt{5})$ and $(-\sqrt{5}, -2\sqrt{5})$.

5. $\begin{cases} x^2 + y^2 = 8 \\ x + y = 0 \end{cases}$ Solving the second equation for y gives $y = -x$, and substituting this into the first equation gives

$x^2 + (-x)^2 = 8 \iff 2x^2 = 8 \iff x = \pm 2$. So since $y = -x$, the solutions are $(2, -2)$ and $(-2, 2)$.

6. $\begin{cases} x^2 + y = 9 \\ x - y + 3 = 0 \end{cases}$ Solving the first equation for y, we get $y = 9 - x^2$. Substituting this into the second equation gives

$x - (9 - x^2) + 3 = 0 \iff x^2 + x - 6 = 0 \iff (x + 3)(x - 2) = 0 \iff x = -3$ or $x = 2$. If $x = -3$, then $y = 9 - (-3)^2 = 0$, and if $x = 2$, then $y = 9 - (2)^2 = 5$. Thus the solutions are $(-3, 0)$ and $(2, 5)$.

7. $\begin{cases} x + y^2 = 0 \\ 2x + 5y^2 = 75 \end{cases}$ Solving the first equation for x gives $x = -y^2$, and substituting this into the second equation

gives $2(-y^2) + 5y^2 = 75 \iff 3y^2 = 75 \iff y^2 = 25 \iff y = \pm 5$. So since $x = -y^2$, the solutions are $(-25, -5)$ and $(-25, 5)$.

8. $\begin{cases} x^2 - y = 1 \\ 2x^2 + 3y = 17 \end{cases}$ Solving the first equation for y, we get $y = x^2 - 1$. Substituting this into the second equation gives

$2x^2 + 3(x^2 - 1) = 17 \iff 2x^2 + 3x^2 - 3 = 17 \iff 5x^2 = 20 \iff x^2 = 4 \iff x = \pm 2$. If $x = -2$, then $y = (-2)^2 - 1 = 3$, and if $x = 2$, then $y = (2)^2 - 1 = 3$. Thus the solutions are $(-2, 3)$ and $(2, 3)$.

9. $\begin{cases} x + 2y = 5 \\ 2x + 3y = 8 \end{cases}$ Multiplying the first equation by 2 and the second by -1 gives the system

$\begin{cases} 2x + 4y = 10 \\ -2x - 3y = -8 \end{cases}$ Adding, we get $y = 2$, and substituting into the first equation in the original system gives

$x + 2(2) = 5 \Leftrightarrow x + 4 = 5 \quad \Leftrightarrow \quad x = 1$. The solution is $(1, 2)$.

10. $\begin{cases} 4x - 3y = 11 \\ 8x + 4y = 12 \end{cases}$ Multiplying the first equation by 2 gives the system $\begin{cases} 8x - 6y = 22 \\ 8x + 4y = 12 \end{cases}$ Subtracting the equations

gives $-10y = 10 \Leftrightarrow y = -1$. Substituting this value into the second equation gives $8x + 4(-1) = 12 \quad \Leftrightarrow$
$8x = 16 \Leftrightarrow x = 2$. Thus, the solution is $(2, -1)$.

11. $\begin{cases} x^2 - 2y = 1 \\ x^2 + 5y = 29 \end{cases}$ Subtracting the first equation from the second equation gives $7y = 28 \Rightarrow y = 4$. Substituting $y = 4$ into

the first equation of the original system gives $x^2 - 2(4) = 1 \quad \Leftrightarrow \quad x^2 = 9 \quad \Leftrightarrow \quad x = \pm 3$. The solutions are $(3, 4)$ and
$(-3, 4)$.

12. $\begin{cases} 3x^2 + 4y = 17 \\ 2x^2 + 5y = 2 \end{cases}$ Multiplying the first equation by 2 and the second by 3 gives the system

$\begin{cases} 6x^2 + 8y = 34 \\ -6x^2 - 15y = -6 \end{cases}$ Adding we get $-7y = 28 \quad \Leftrightarrow \quad y = -4$. Substituting this value into the second equation gives

$2x^2 + 5(-4) = 2 \Rightarrow 2x^2 = 22 \quad \Leftrightarrow \quad x^2 = 11 \Leftrightarrow x = \pm\sqrt{11}$. Thus the solutions are $(\sqrt{11}, -4)$ and $(-\sqrt{11}, -4)$.

13. $\begin{cases} 3x^2 - y^2 = 11 \\ x^2 + 4y^2 = 8 \end{cases}$ Multiplying the first equation by 4 gives the system $\begin{cases} 12x^2 - 4y^2 = 44 \\ x^2 + 4y^2 = 8 \end{cases}$ Adding the equations

gives $13x^2 = 52 \Leftrightarrow x = \pm 2$. Substituting into the first equation we get $3(4) - y^2 = 11 \quad \Leftrightarrow \quad y = \pm 1$. Thus, the
solutions are $(2, 1)$, $(2, -1)$, $(-2, 1)$, and $(-2, -1)$.

14. $\begin{cases} 2x^2 + 4y = 13 \\ x^2 - y^2 = \frac{7}{2} \end{cases}$ Multiplying the second equation by 2 gives the system $\begin{cases} 2x^2 + 4y = 13 \\ 2x^2 - 2y^2 = 7 \end{cases}$ Subtracting the

equations gives $4y + 2y^2 = 6 \Leftrightarrow y^2 + 2y - 3 = 0 \quad \Leftrightarrow \quad (y + 3)(y - 1) = 0 \quad \Leftrightarrow \quad y = -3, y = 1$. If $y = -3$, then

$2x^2 + 4(-3) = 13 \quad \Leftrightarrow \quad x^2 = \frac{25}{2} \Leftrightarrow x = \pm\frac{5\sqrt{2}}{2}$. If $y = 1$, then $2x^2 + 4(1) = 13 \quad \Leftrightarrow \quad x^2 = \frac{9}{2} \Leftrightarrow x = \pm\frac{3\sqrt{2}}{2}$.

Hence, the solutions are $\left(\pm\frac{5\sqrt{2}}{2}, -3\right)$ and $\left(\pm\frac{3\sqrt{2}}{2}, 1\right)$.

15. $\begin{cases} x - y^2 + 3 = 0 \\ 2x^2 + y^2 - 4 = 0 \end{cases}$ Adding the two equations gives $2x^2 + x - 1 = 0$. Using the quadratic formula we have

$x = \dfrac{-1 \pm \sqrt{1 - 4(2)(-1)}}{2(2)} = \dfrac{-1 \pm \sqrt{9}}{4} = \dfrac{-1 \pm 3}{4}$. So $x = \dfrac{-1 - 3}{4} = -1$ or $x = \dfrac{-1 + 3}{4} = \frac{1}{2}$. Substituting $x = -1$

into the first equation gives $-1 - y^2 + 3 = 0 \Leftrightarrow y^2 = 2 \quad \Leftrightarrow \quad y = \pm\sqrt{2}$. Substituting $x = \frac{1}{2}$ into the first equation

gives $\frac{1}{2} - y^2 + 3 = 0 \quad \Leftrightarrow \quad y^2 = \frac{7}{2} \quad \Leftrightarrow \quad y = \pm\sqrt{\frac{7}{2}}$. Thus the solutions are $(-1, \pm\sqrt{2})$ and $\left(\frac{1}{2}, \pm\sqrt{\frac{7}{2}}\right)$.

16. $\begin{cases} x^2 - y^2 = 1 \\ 2x^2 - y^2 = x + 3 \end{cases}$ Subtracting the first equation from the second equation gives $x^2 = x + 2$ $\Leftrightarrow$

$x^2 - x - 2 = 0 \Leftrightarrow (x - 2)(x + 1) = 0$ $\Leftrightarrow$ $x = 2, x = -1$. Solving the first equation for y^2 we have $y^2 = x^2 - 1$.
When $x = -1$, $y^2 = (-1)^2 - 1 = 0$ so $y = 0$ and when $x = 2$, $y^2 = (2)^2 - 1 = 3$ so $y = \pm\sqrt{3}$. Thus, the solutions are
$(-1, 0)$, $\left(2, -\sqrt{3}\right)$, and $\left(2, \sqrt{3}\right)$.

17. $\begin{cases} 2x + y = -1 \\ x - 2y = -8 \end{cases}$ By inspection of the graph, it appears that $(-2, 3)$ is the solution to the system. We check this in both

equations to verify that it is a solution. $2(-2) + 3 = -4 + 3 = -1$ and $-2 - 2(3) = -2 - 6 = -8$. Since both equations
are satisfied, the solution is $(-2, 3)$.

18. $\begin{cases} x + y = 2 \\ 2x + y = 5 \end{cases}$ By inspection of the graph, it appears that $(3, -1)$ is the solution to the system. We check this in both

equations to verify that it is a solution. $3 + (-1) = 2$ and $2(3) + (-1) = 6 - 1 = 5$. Since both equations are satisfied,
the solution is $(3, -1)$.

19. $\begin{cases} x^2 + y = 8 \\ x - 2y = -6 \end{cases}$ By inspection of the graph, it appears that $(2, 4)$ is a solution, but is difficult to get accurate values

for the other point. Multiplying the first equation by 2 gives the system $\begin{cases} 2x^2 + 2y = 16 \\ x - 2y = -6 \end{cases}$ Adding the equations

gives $2x^2 + x = 10 \Leftrightarrow 2x^2 + x - 10 = 0$ $\Leftrightarrow$ $(2x + 5)(x - 2) = 0$. So $x = -\frac{5}{2}$ or $x = 2$. If $x = -\frac{5}{2}$, then
$-\frac{5}{2} - 2y = -6$ $\Leftrightarrow$ $-2y = -\frac{7}{2} \Leftrightarrow y = \frac{7}{4}$, and if $x = 2$, then $2 - 2y = -6 \Leftrightarrow -2y = -8$ $\Leftrightarrow$ $y = 4$. Hence, the
solutions are $\left(-\frac{5}{2}, \frac{7}{4}\right)$ and $(2, 4)$.

20. $\begin{cases} x - y^2 = -4 \\ x - y = 2 \end{cases}$ By inspection of the graph, it appears that $(0, -2)$ and $(5, 3)$ are solutions to the system. We check

each point in both equations to verify that it is a solution. For $(0, -2)$: $(0) - (-2)^2 = -4$ and $(0) - (-2) = 2$.
For $(5, 3)$: $5 - 3^2 = 5 - 9 = -4$ and $5 - 3 = 2$. Thus, the solutions are $(0, -2)$ and $(5, 3)$.

21. $\begin{cases} x^2 + y = 0 \\ x^3 - 2x - y = 0 \end{cases}$ By inspection of the graph, it appears that $(-2, -4)$, $(0, 0)$, and $(1, -1)$ are solutions to the

system. We check each point in both equations to verify that it is a solution.
For $(-2, -4)$: $(-2)^2 + (-4) = 4 - 4 = 0$ and $(-2)^3 - 2(-2) - (-4) = -8 + 4 + 4 = 0$.
For $(0, 0)$: $(0)^2 + (0) = 0$ and $(0)^3 - 2(0) - (0) = 0$.
For $(1, -1)$: $(1)^2 + (-1) = 1 - 1 = 0$ and $(1)^3 - 2(1) - (-1) = 1 - 2 + 1 = 0$.
Thus, the solutions are $(-2, -4)$, $(0, 0)$, and $(1, -1)$.

22. $\begin{cases} x^2 + y^2 = 4x \\ x = y^2 \end{cases}$ By inspection of the graph, it appears that $(0, 0)$ is a solution, but is difficult to get accurate values for

the other points. Substituting for y^2 we have $x^2 + x = 4x \Leftrightarrow x^2 - 3x = 0$ $\Leftrightarrow$ $x(x - 3) = 0$. So $x = 0$ or $x = 3$.
If $x = 0$, then $y^2 = 0$ so $y = 0$. And is $x = 3$ then $y^2 = 3$ so $y = \pm\sqrt{3}$. Hence, the solutions are $(0, 0)$, $\left(3, -\sqrt{3}\right)$, and
$\left(3, \sqrt{3}\right)$.

23. $\begin{cases} y + x^2 = 4x \\ y + 4x = 16 \end{cases}$ Subtracting the second equation from the first equation gives $x^2 - 4x = 4x - 16$ $\Leftrightarrow$

$x^2 - 8x + 16 = 0 \Leftrightarrow (x - 4)^2 = 0$ $\Leftrightarrow$ $x = 4$. Substituting this value for x into either of the original equations gives $y = 0$. Therefore, the solution is $(4, 0)$.

24. $\begin{cases} x - y^2 = 0 \\ y - x^2 = 0 \end{cases}$ Solving the first equation for x and the second equation for y gives $\begin{cases} x = y^2 \\ y = x^2 \end{cases}$ Substituting for y in

the first equation gives $x = x^4$ $\Leftrightarrow$ $x(x^3 - 1) = 0$ $\Leftrightarrow$ $x = 0, x = 1$. Thus, the solutions are $(0, 0)$ and $(1, 1)$.

25. $\begin{cases} x - 2y = 2 \\ y^2 - x^2 = 2x + 4 \end{cases}$ Now $x - 2y = 2$ $\Leftrightarrow$ $x = 2y + 2$. Substituting for x gives $y^2 - x^2 = 2x + 4$ $\Leftrightarrow$

$y^2 - (2y + 2)^2 = 2(2y + 2) + 4$ $\Leftrightarrow$ $y^2 - 4y^2 - 8y - 4 = 4y + 4 + 4$ $\Leftrightarrow$ $y^2 + 4y + 4 = 0 \Leftrightarrow (y + 2)^2 = 0$ $\Leftrightarrow$ $y = -2$. Since $x = 2y + 2$, we have $x = 2(-2) + 2 = -2$. Thus, the solution is $(-2, -2)$.

26. $\begin{cases} y = 4 - x^2 \\ y = x^2 - 4 \end{cases}$ Setting the two equations equal, we get $4 - x^2 = x^2 - 4$ $\Leftrightarrow$ $2x^2 = 8$ $\Leftrightarrow$ $x = \pm 2$. Therefore, the solutions are $(2, 0)$ and $(-2, 0)$.

27. $\begin{cases} x - y = 4 \\ xy = 12 \end{cases}$ Now $x - y = 4$ $\Leftrightarrow$ $x = 4 + y$. Substituting for x gives $xy = 12$ $\Leftrightarrow$

$(4 + y)y = 12 \Leftrightarrow y^2 + 4y - 12 = 0$ $\Leftrightarrow$ $(y + 6)(y - 2) = 0$ $\Leftrightarrow$ $y = -6, y = 2$. Since $x = 4 + y$, the solutions are $(-2, -6)$ and $(6, 2)$.

28. $\begin{cases} xy = 24 \\ 2x^2 - y^2 + 4 = 0 \end{cases}$ Since $x = 0$ is not a solution, from the first equation we get $y = \dfrac{24}{x}$. Substituting

into the second equation, we get $2x^2 + 4 = \left(\dfrac{24}{x}\right)^2$ $\Rightarrow$ $2x^4 + 4x^2 = 576$ $\Leftrightarrow$

$x^4 + 2x^2 - 288 = 0 \Leftrightarrow (x^2 + 18)(x^2 - 16) = 0$. Since $x^2 + 18$ cannot be 0 if x is real, we have $x^2 - 16 = 0$ $\Leftrightarrow$

$x = \pm 4$. When $x = 4$, we have $y = \frac{24}{4} = 6$ and when $x = -4$, we have $y = \dfrac{24}{-4} = -6$. Thus the solutions are $(4, 6)$ and $(-4, -6)$.

29. $\begin{cases} x^2 y = 16 \\ x^2 + 4y + 16 = 0 \end{cases}$ Now $x^2 y = 16$ $\Leftrightarrow$ $x^2 = \dfrac{16}{y}$. Substituting for x^2 gives

$\dfrac{16}{y} + 4y + 16 = 0 \Rightarrow 4y^2 + 16y + 16 = 0$ $\Leftrightarrow$ $y^2 + 4y + 4 = 0$ $\Leftrightarrow$ $(y + 2)^2 = 0$ $\Leftrightarrow$ $y = -2$. Therefore,

$x^2 = \dfrac{16}{-2} = -8$, which has no real solution, and so the system has no solution.

30. $\begin{cases} x + \sqrt{y} = 0 \\ y^2 - 4x^2 = 12 \end{cases}$ Solving the first equation for x, we get $x = -\sqrt{y}$. Substituting for x gives

$y^2 - 4(-\sqrt{y})^2 = 12 \Leftrightarrow y^2 - 4y - 12 = 0$ $\Leftrightarrow$ $(y - 6)(y + 2) = 0 \Rightarrow y = 6, y = -2$. Since $x = -\sqrt{-2}$ is not a real solution, the only solution is $(-\sqrt{6}, 6)$.

31. $\begin{cases} x^2 + y^2 = 9 \\ x^2 - y^2 = 1 \end{cases}$ Adding the equations gives $2x^2 = 10$ $\Leftrightarrow$ $x^2 = 5$ $\Leftrightarrow$ $x = \pm\sqrt{5}$. Now

$x = \pm\sqrt{5} \Rightarrow y^2 = 9 - 5 = 4$ $\Leftrightarrow$ $y = \pm 2$, and so the solutions are $(\sqrt{5}, 2)$, $(\sqrt{5}, -2)$, $(-\sqrt{5}, 2)$, and $(-\sqrt{5}, -2)$.

32. $\begin{cases} x^2 + 2y^2 = 2 \\ 2x^2 - 3y = 15 \end{cases}$ Multiplying the first equation by 2 gives the system $\begin{cases} 2x^2 + 4y^2 = 4 \\ 2x^2 - 3y = 15 \end{cases}$ Subtracting the two

equations gives $4y^2 + 3y = -11 \Leftrightarrow 4y^2 + 3y + 11 = 0 \Rightarrow y = \dfrac{-3 \pm \sqrt{9 - 4\,(4)\,(11)}}{2\,(4)}$ which is not a real number.

Therefore, there are no real solutions.

33. $\begin{cases} 2x^2 - 8y^3 = 19 \\ 4x^2 + 16y^3 = 34 \end{cases}$ Multiplying the first equation by 2 gives the system $\begin{cases} 4x^2 - 16y^3 = 38 \\ 4x^2 + 16y^3 = 34 \end{cases}$ Adding the two

equations gives $8x^2 = 72 \Leftrightarrow x = \pm 3$, and then substituting into the first equation we have $2\,(9) - 8y^3 = 19 \Leftrightarrow$
$y^3 = -\frac{1}{8} \Leftrightarrow y = -\frac{1}{2}$. Therefore, the solutions are $\left(3, -\frac{1}{2}\right)$ and $\left(-3, -\frac{1}{2}\right)$.

34. $\begin{cases} x^4 - y^3 = 15 \\ 3x^4 + 5y^3 = 53 \end{cases}$ Multiplying the first equation by 3 gives the system $\begin{cases} 3x^4 - 3y^3 = 45 \\ 3x^4 + 5y^3 = 53 \end{cases}$ Subtracting the

equations gives $8y^3 = 8 \Leftrightarrow y^3 = 1 \Rightarrow y = 1$, and then $x^4 - 1 = 15 \Leftrightarrow x = \pm 2$. Therefore, the solutions are $(2, 1)$ and
$(-2, 1)$.

35. $\begin{cases} \dfrac{2}{x} - \dfrac{3}{y} = 1 \\ -\dfrac{4}{x} + \dfrac{7}{y} = 1 \end{cases}$ If we let $u = \dfrac{1}{x}$ and $v = \dfrac{1}{y}$, the system is equivalent to $\begin{cases} 2u - 3v = 1 \\ -4u + 7v = 1 \end{cases}$ Multiplying the first

equation by 4 gives the system $\begin{cases} 4u - 6v = 2 \\ -4u + 7v = 1 \end{cases}$ Adding the equations gives $v = 3$, and then substituting into the first

equation gives $2u - 9 = 1 \Leftrightarrow u = 5$. Thus, the solution is $\left(\frac{1}{5}, \frac{1}{3}\right)$.

36. $\begin{cases} \dfrac{4}{x^2} + \dfrac{6}{y^4} = \dfrac{7}{2} \\ \dfrac{1}{x^2} - \dfrac{2}{y^4} = 0 \end{cases}$ If we let $u = \dfrac{1}{x^2}$ and $v = \dfrac{1}{y^4}$, the system is equivalent to $\begin{cases} 4u + 6v = \frac{7}{2} \\ u - 2v = 0 \end{cases}$, and multiplying the

second equation by 3, gives $\begin{cases} 4u + 6v = \frac{7}{2} \\ 3u - 6v = 0 \end{cases}$ Adding the equations gives $7u = \frac{7}{2} \Leftrightarrow u = \frac{1}{2}$, and $v = \frac{1}{4}$. Therefore,

$x^2 = \dfrac{1}{u} = 2 \Leftrightarrow x = \pm\sqrt{2}$, and $y^4 = \dfrac{1}{v} = 4 \Leftrightarrow y = \pm\sqrt{2}$. Thus, the solutions are $\left(\sqrt{2}, \sqrt{2}\right)$, $\left(\sqrt{2}, -\sqrt{2}\right)$,
$\left(-\sqrt{2}, \sqrt{2}\right)$, and $\left(-\sqrt{2}, -\sqrt{2}\right)$.

37. $\begin{cases} y = 2x + 6 \\ y = -x + 5 \end{cases}$

The solution is approximately $(-0.33, 5.33)$.

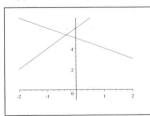

38. $\begin{cases} y = -2x + 12 \\ y = x + 3 \end{cases}$

The solution is $(3, 6)$.

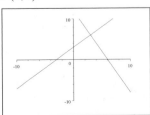

39. $\begin{cases} y = x^2 + 8x \\ y = 2x + 16 \end{cases}$

The solutions are $(-8, 0)$ and $(2, 20)$.

40. $\begin{cases} y = x^2 - 4x \\ 2x - y = 2 \end{cases} \Leftrightarrow \begin{cases} y = x^2 - 4x \\ y = 2x - 2 \end{cases}$

The solutions are approximately $(0.35, -1.30)$ and $(5.65, 9.30)$.

41. $\begin{cases} x^2 + y^2 = 25 \\ x + 3y = 2 \end{cases} \Leftrightarrow \begin{cases} y = \pm\sqrt{25 - x^2} \\ y = -\frac{1}{3}x + \frac{2}{3} \end{cases}$

The solutions are $(-4.51, 2.17)$ and $(4.91, -0.97)$.

42. $\begin{cases} x^2 + y^2 = 17 \\ x^2 - 2x + y^2 = 13 \end{cases} \Leftrightarrow \begin{cases} y = \pm\sqrt{17 - x^2} \\ y = \pm\sqrt{13 + 2x - x^2} \end{cases}$

The solutions are approximately $(2, \pm 3.61)$.

43. $\begin{cases} \dfrac{x^2}{9} + \dfrac{y^2}{18} = 1 \\ y = -x^2 + 6x - 2 \end{cases} \Leftrightarrow \begin{cases} y = \pm\sqrt{18 - 2x^2} \\ y = -x^2 + 6x - 2 \end{cases}$

The solutions are $(1.23, 3.87)$ and $(-0.35, -4.21)$.

44. $\begin{cases} x^2 - y^2 = 3 \\ y = x^2 - 2x - 8 \end{cases} \Leftrightarrow \begin{cases} y = \pm\sqrt{x^2 - 3} \\ y = x^2 - 2x - 8 \end{cases}$

The solutions are approximately $(-2.22, 1.40)$, $(-1.88, -0.72)$, $(3.45, -2.99)$, and $(4.65, 4.31)$.

45. $\begin{cases} x^4 + 16y^4 = 32 \\ x^2 + 2x + y = 0 \end{cases} \Leftrightarrow \begin{cases} y = \pm\dfrac{\sqrt[4]{32 - x^4}}{2} \\ y = -x^2 - 2x \end{cases}$

The solutions are $(-2.30, -0.70)$ and $(0.48, -1.19)$.

46. $\begin{cases} y = e^x + e^{-x} \\ y = 5 - x^2 \end{cases}$

The solution are approximately $(1.19, 3.59)$ and $(-1.19, 3.59)$.

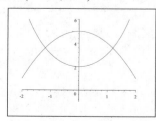

47. Let w and l be the lengths of the sides, in cm. Then we have the system $\begin{cases} lw = 180 \\ 2l + 2w = 54 \end{cases}$ We solve the second equation

for w giving, $w = 27 - l$, and substitute into the first equation to get $l(27 - l) = 180 \Leftrightarrow l^2 - 27l + 180 = 0 \Leftrightarrow$
$(l - 15)(l - 12) = 0 \Rightarrow l = 15$ or $l = 12$. If $l = 15$, then $w = 27 - 15 = 12$, and if $l = 12$, then $w = 27 - 12 = 15$.
Therefore, the dimensions of the rectangle are 12 cm by 15 cm.

48. Let b be the length of the base of the triangle, in feet, and h be the height of the triangle,

in feet. Then $\begin{cases} \frac{1}{2}bh = 84 \\ b^2 + h^2 = 25^2 = 625 \end{cases}$ The first equation gives $b = \dfrac{168}{h}$. By substitution,

$\left(\dfrac{168}{h}\right)^2 + h^2 = 625 \Leftrightarrow h^4 - 625h^2 + 168^2 = 0 \Leftrightarrow (h^2 - 49)(h^2 - 576) = 0 \Rightarrow h = 7$ or $h = 24$. Thus, the

lengths of the other two sides are 7 ft and 24 ft.

49. Let l and w be the length and width, respectively, of the rectangle. Then, the system of equations

is $\begin{cases} 2l + 2w = 70 \\ \sqrt{l^2 + w^2} = 25 \end{cases}$ Solving the first equation for l, we have $l = 35 - w$, and substituting into

the second gives $\sqrt{l^2 + w^2} = 25 \Leftrightarrow l^2 + w^2 = 625 \Leftrightarrow (35 - w)^2 + w^2 = 625 \Leftrightarrow$
$1225 - 70w + w^2 + w^2 = 625 \Leftrightarrow 2w^2 - 70w + 600 = 0 \Leftrightarrow (w - 15)(w - 20) = 0 \Rightarrow w = 15$ or $w = 20$. So the
dimensions of the rectangle are 15 and 20.

50. Let w be the width and l be the length of the rectangle, in inches. From the figure, the diagonals of the rectangle are simply

diameters of the circle. Then, $\begin{cases} wl = 160 \\ w^2 + l^2 = 20^2 = 400 \end{cases} \Leftrightarrow w = \dfrac{160}{l}$. By substitution, $\dfrac{160^2}{l^2} + l^2 = 400 \Leftrightarrow$

$l^4 - 400l^2 + 160^2 = 0 \Leftrightarrow (l^2 - 80)(l^2 - 320) = 0 \Rightarrow l = \sqrt{80} = 4\sqrt{5}$ or $l = \sqrt{320} = 8\sqrt{5}$. Therefore, the dimensions
of the rectangle are $4\sqrt{5}$ in. and $8\sqrt{5}$ in..

51. At the points where the rocket path and the hillside meet, we have $\begin{cases} y = \frac{1}{2}x \\ y = -x^2 + 401x \end{cases}$ Substituting for y in the second

equation gives $\frac{1}{2}x = -x^2 + 401x \Leftrightarrow x^2 - \frac{801}{2}x = 0 \Leftrightarrow x\left(x - \frac{801}{2}\right) = 0 \Rightarrow x = 0$, $x = \frac{801}{2}$. When $x = 0$, the
rocket has not left the pad. When $x = \frac{801}{2}$, then $y = \frac{1}{2}\left(\frac{801}{2}\right) = \frac{801}{4}$. So the rocket lands at the point $\left(\frac{801}{2}, \frac{801}{4}\right)$. The

distance from the base of the hill is $\sqrt{\left(\frac{801}{2}\right)^2 + \left(\frac{801}{4}\right)^2} \approx 447.77$ meters.

52. Let x be the circumference and y be length of the stove pipe. Using the circumference we can determine

the radius, $2\pi r = x \Leftrightarrow r = \dfrac{x}{2\pi}$. Thus the volume is $\pi\left(\dfrac{x}{2\pi}\right)^2 y = \dfrac{1}{4\pi}x^2 y$. So the system is given by

$\begin{cases} xy = 1200 \\ \frac{1}{4\pi}x^2 y = 600 \end{cases}$ Substituting for xy in the second equation gives $\frac{1}{4\pi}x^2 y = \frac{1}{4\pi}x(xy) = \frac{1}{4\pi}x(1200) = 600 \Leftrightarrow$

$x = 2\pi$. So $y = \dfrac{1200}{x} = \dfrac{1200}{2\pi} = \dfrac{600}{\pi}$. Thus the dimensions of the sheet metal are $2\pi \approx 6.3$ in and $\dfrac{600}{\pi} \approx 191.0$ in.

53. The point P is at an intersection of the circle of radius 26 centered at $A\,(22, 32)$

and the circle of radius 20 centered at $B\,(28, 20)$. We have the system

$$\begin{cases} (x - 22)^2 + (y - 32)^2 = 26^2 \\ (x - 28)^2 + (y - 20)^2 = 20^2 \end{cases} \Leftrightarrow$$

$$\begin{cases} x^2 - 44x + 484 + y^2 - 64y + 1024 = 676 \\ x^2 - 56x + 784 + y^2 - 40y + 400 = 400 \end{cases} \Leftrightarrow$$

$$\begin{cases} x^2 - 44x + y^2 - 64y = -832 \\ x^2 - 56x + y^2 - 40y = -784 \end{cases}$$ Subtracting the two equations, we get $12x - 24y = -48 \Leftrightarrow x - 2y = -4$,

which is the equation of a line. Solving for x, we have $x = 2y - 4$. Substituting into the first equation gives
$(2y - 4)^2 - 44\,(2y - 4) + y^2 - 64y = -832 \quad \Leftrightarrow \quad 4y^2 - 16y + 16 - 88y + 176 + y^2 - 64y = -832$
$\Leftrightarrow \quad 5y^2 - 168y + 192 = -832 \quad \Leftrightarrow \quad 5y^2 - 168y + 1024 = 0$. Using the quadratic formula, we have
$y = \frac{168 \pm \sqrt{168^2 - 4(5)(1024)}}{2(5)} = \frac{168 \pm \sqrt{7744}}{10} = \frac{168 \pm 88}{10} \quad \Leftrightarrow \quad y = 8$ or $y = 25.60$. Since the y-coordinate of the
point P must be less than that of point A, we have $y = 8$. Then $x = 2\,(8) - 4 = 12$. So the coordinates of P
are $(12, 8)$. To solve graphically, we must solve each equation for y. This gives $(x - 22)^2 + (y - 32)^2 = 26^2$
$\Leftrightarrow (y - 32)^2 = 26^2 - (x - 22)^2 \Rightarrow y - 32 = \pm\sqrt{676 - (x - 22)^2} \Leftrightarrow y = 32 \pm \sqrt{676 - (x - 22)^2}$. We use the
function $y = 32 - \sqrt{676 - (x - 22)^2}$ because the intersection we at interested in is below the point A. Likewise, solving
the second equation for y, we would get the function $y = 20 - \sqrt{400 - (x - 28)^2}$. In a three-dimensional situation, you
would need a minimum of three satellites, since a point on the earth can be uniquely specified as the intersection of three
spheres centered at the satellites.

54. The graphs of $y = x^2$ and $y = x + k$ for various values of k are shown. If we solve

the system $\begin{cases} y = x^2 \\ y = x + k \end{cases}$ we get $x^2 - x - k = 0$. Using the quadratic formula,

we have $x = \dfrac{-1 \pm \sqrt{1 + 4k}}{2}$. So there is no solution if $\sqrt{1 + 4k}$ is undefined, that

is, if $1 + 4k < 0 \quad \Leftrightarrow \quad k < -\frac{1}{4}$. There is be exactly one solution if $1 + 4k = 0$
$\Leftrightarrow \quad k < -\frac{1}{4}$, and there are two solutions if $1 + 4k > 0 \quad \Leftrightarrow \quad k > -\frac{1}{4}$.

55. (a) $\begin{cases} \log x + \log y = \frac{3}{2} \\ 2\log x - \log y = 0 \end{cases}$ Adding the two equations gives $3\log x = \frac{3}{2} \Leftrightarrow \log x = \frac{1}{2} \quad \Leftrightarrow \quad x = \sqrt{10}$. Substituting

into the second equation we get $2\log 10^{1/2} - \log y = 0 \Leftrightarrow \log 10 - \log y = 0 \quad \Leftrightarrow \quad \log y = 1 \Leftrightarrow y = 10$. Thus,
the solution is $\left(\sqrt{10}, 10\right)$.

(b) $\begin{cases} 2^x + 2^y = 10 \\ 4^x + 4^y = 68 \end{cases} \Leftrightarrow \begin{cases} 2^x + 2^y = 10 \\ 2^{2x} + 2^{2y} = 68 \end{cases}$ If we let $u = 2^x$ and $v = 2^y$, the system becomes $\begin{cases} u + v = 10 \\ u^2 + v^2 = 68 \end{cases}$

Solving the first equation for u, and substituting this into the second equation gives $u + v = 10 \quad \Leftrightarrow \quad u = 10 - v$, so
$(10 - v)^2 + v^2 = 68 \quad \Leftrightarrow \quad 100 - 20v + v^2 + v^2 = 68 \quad \Leftrightarrow \quad v^2 - 10v + 16 = 0 \Leftrightarrow (v - 8)\,(v - 2) = 0 \Rightarrow v = 2$
or $v = 8$. If $v = 2$, then $u = 8$, and so $y = 1$ and $x = 3$. If $v = 8$, then $u = 2$, and so $y = 3$ and $x = 1$. Thus, the
solutions are $(1, 3)$ and $(3, 1)$.

(c) $\begin{cases} x - y = \quad 3 \\ x^3 - y^3 = 387 \end{cases}$ Solving the first equation for x gives $x = 3 + y$ and using the hint,

$x^3 - y^3 = 387 \iff (x - y)(x^2 + xy + y^2) = 387$. Next, substituting for x, we get

$3\left[(3+y)^2 + y(3+y) + y^2\right] = 387 \iff 9 + 6y + y^2 + 3y + y^2 + y^2 = 129 \iff 3y^2 + 9y + 9 = 129 \iff$

$(y+8)(y-5) = 0 \Rightarrow y = -8$ or $y = 5$. If $y = -8$, then $x = 3 + (-8) = -5$, and if $y = 5$, then $x = 3 + 5 = 8$.

Thus the solutions are $(-5, -8)$ and $(8, 5)$.

(d) $\begin{cases} x^2 + xy = 1 \\ xy + y^2 = 3 \end{cases}$ Adding the equations gives $x^2 + xy + xy + y^2 = 4 \iff x^2 + 2xy + y^2 = 4 \iff$

$(x+y)^2 = 4 \Rightarrow x + y = \pm 2$. If $x + y = 2$, then from the first equation we get $x(x+y) = 1 \Rightarrow x \cdot 2 = 1 \Rightarrow x = \frac{1}{2}$,

and so $y = 2 - \frac{1}{2} = \frac{3}{2}$. If $x + y = -2$, then from the first equation we get $x(x+y) = 1 \Rightarrow$

$x \cdot (-2) = 1 \Rightarrow x = -\frac{1}{2}$, and so $y = -2 - \left(-\frac{1}{2}\right) = -\frac{3}{2}$. Thus the solutions are $\left(\frac{1}{2}, \frac{3}{2}\right)$ and $\left(-\frac{1}{2}, -\frac{3}{2}\right)$.

9.2 Systems of Linear Equations in Two Variables

1. $\begin{cases} x + y = 4 \\ 2x - y = 2 \end{cases}$

The solution is $x = 2$, $y = 2$.

2. $\begin{cases} 2x + \quad y = 11 \\ x - 2y = \quad 4 \end{cases}$

The solution is $x = 5.2$, $y = 0.6$.

3. $\begin{cases} 2x - 3y = 12 \\ -x + \frac{3}{2}y = \quad 4 \end{cases}$

The lines are parallel, so there is no intersection and hence no solution.

4. $\begin{cases} 2x + 6y = \quad 0 \\ -3x - 9y = 18 \end{cases}$

The lines are parallel, so there is no intersection and hence no solution.

5. $\begin{cases} -x + \frac{1}{2}y = \Big| -5 \\ 2x - y = \Big| 10 \end{cases}$

There are infinitely many solutions.

6. $\begin{cases} 12x + 15y = -18 \\ 2x + \frac{5}{2}y = -3 \end{cases}$

There are infinitely many solutions. The lines are the same.

7. $\begin{cases} x + y = 4 \\ -x + y = 0 \end{cases}$ Adding the two equations gives $2y = 4 \Leftrightarrow y = 2$. Substituting for y in the first equation gives

$x + 2 = 4 \Leftrightarrow x = 2$. Hence, the solution is $(2, 2)$.

8. $\begin{cases} x - y = 3 \\ x + 3y = 7 \end{cases}$ Subtracting the first equation from the second equation gives $4y = 4 \quad \Leftrightarrow \quad y = 1$. Substituting, we

have $x - 1 = 3 \Leftrightarrow x = 4$. Hence, the solution is $(4, 1)$.

9. $\begin{cases} 2x - 3y = 9 \\ 4x + 3y = 9 \end{cases}$ Adding the two equations gives $6x = 18 \Leftrightarrow x = 3$. Substituting for x in the second equation gives

$4(3) + 3y = 9 \quad \Leftrightarrow \quad 12 + 3y = 9 \quad \Leftrightarrow \quad 3y = -3 \quad \Leftrightarrow \quad x = -1$. Hence, the solution is $(3, -1)$.

10. $\begin{cases} 3x + 2y = 0 \\ -x - 2y = 8 \end{cases}$ Adding the two equations gives $2x = 8 \Leftrightarrow x = 4$. Substituting for x in the second equation gives

$3(4) + 2y = 0 \quad \Leftrightarrow \quad 12 + 2y = 0 \quad \Leftrightarrow \quad y = -6$. Hence, the solution is $(4, -6)$.

11. $\begin{cases} x + 3y = 5 \\ 2x - y = 3 \end{cases}$ Solving the first equation for x gives $x = -3y + 5$. Substituting for x in the second equation gives

$2(-3y + 5) - y = 3 \Leftrightarrow -6y + 10 - y = 3 \quad \Leftrightarrow \quad -7y = -7 \Leftrightarrow y = 1$. Then $x = -3(1) + 5 = 2$. Hence, the solution is $(2, 1)$.

12. $\begin{cases} x + y = 7 \\ 2x - 3y = -1 \end{cases}$ Adding 3 times the first equation to the second equation gives $5x = 20 \quad \Leftrightarrow \quad x = 4$. So

$4 + y = 7 \Leftrightarrow y = 3$, and the solution is $(4, 3)$.

13. $-x + y = 2 \quad \Leftrightarrow \quad y = x + 2$. Substituting for y into $4x - 3y = -3$ gives $4x - 3(x + 2) = -3 \quad \Leftrightarrow$
$4x - 3x - 6 = -3 \Leftrightarrow x = 3$, and so $y = (3) + 2 = 5$. Hence, the solution is $(3, 5)$.

14. $9x - y = -6 \quad \Leftrightarrow \quad y = 9x + 6$. Substituting for y into $4x - 3y = 28$ gives $4x - 3(9x + 6) = 28 \quad \Leftrightarrow$
$-23x = 46 \Leftrightarrow x = -2$, and so $y = 9(-2) + 6 = -12$. Thus, the solution is $(-2, -12)$.

15. $x + 2y = 7 \quad \Leftrightarrow \quad x = 7 - 2y$. Substituting for x into $5x - y = 2$ gives $5(7 - 2y) - y = 2$
$\Leftrightarrow \quad 35 - 10y - y = 2 \Leftrightarrow -11y = -33 \quad \Leftrightarrow \quad y = 3$, and so $x = 7 - 2(3) = 1$. Hence, the solution is $(1, 3)$.

16. $-4x + 12y = 0 \quad \Leftrightarrow \quad x = 3y$. Substituting for x into $12x + 4y = 160$ gives $12(3y) + 4y = 160 \quad \Leftrightarrow$
$40y = 160 \Leftrightarrow y = 4$, and so $x = 3(4) = 12$. Therefore, the solution is $(12, 4)$.

17. $\frac{1}{2}x + \frac{1}{3}y = 2$ $\Leftrightarrow$ $x + \frac{2}{3}y = 4$ $\Leftrightarrow$ $x = 4 - \frac{2}{3}y$. Substituting for x into $\frac{1}{5}x - \frac{2}{3}y = 8$ gives $\frac{1}{5}\left(4 - \frac{2}{3}y\right) - \frac{2}{3}y = 8$
$\Leftrightarrow$ $\frac{4}{5} - \frac{2}{15}y - \frac{10}{15}y = 8 \Leftrightarrow 12 - 2y - 10y = 120$ $\Leftrightarrow$ $y = -9$, and so $x = 4 - \frac{2}{3}(-9) = 10$. Hence, the solution is
$(10, -9)$.

18. $0.2x - 0.2y = -1.8$ $\Leftrightarrow$ $x = y - 9$. Substituting for x into $-0.3x + 0.5y = 3.3$ gives
$-0.3(y - 9) + 0.5y = 3.3 \Leftrightarrow 0.2y = 0.6$ $\Leftrightarrow$ $y = 3$, and so $x = (3) - 9 = -6$. Hence, the solution is $(-6, 3)$.

19. Adding twice the first equation to the second gives $0 = 0$, which is always true. Writing the equation in slope-intercept
form, we have $3x - 2y = 8$ $\Leftrightarrow$ $y = \frac{3}{2}x - 4$, so the solutions are all pairs of the form $\left(x, \frac{3}{2}x - 4\right)$ where x is a real
number.

20. $\begin{cases} 4x + 2y = 16 \\ x - 5y = 70 \end{cases}$ Adding the first equation to -4 times the second equation gives $22y = -264$ $\Leftrightarrow$ $y = -12$, so
$4x + 2(-12) = 16$ $\Leftrightarrow$ $x = 10$, and the solution is $(10, -12)$.

21. $\begin{cases} x + 4y = 8 \\ 3x + 12y = 2 \end{cases}$ Adding -3 times the first equation to the second equation gives $0 = -22$, which is never true. Thus,
the system has no solution.

22. $\begin{cases} -3x + 5y = 2 \\ 9x - 15y = 6 \end{cases}$ Adding 3 times the first equation to the second equation gives $0 = 12$, which is false. Therefore,
there is no solution to this system.

23. $\begin{cases} 2x - 6y = 10 \\ -3x + 9y = -15 \end{cases}$ Adding 3 times the first equation to 2 times the second equation gives $0 = 0$. Writing the equation
in slope-intercept form, we have $2x - 6y = 10$ $\Leftrightarrow$ $-6y = -2x + 10$ $\Leftrightarrow$ $y = \frac{1}{3}x - \frac{5}{3}$, so the solutions are all
pairs of the form $\left(x, \frac{1}{3}x - \frac{5}{3}\right)$ where x is a real number.

24. $\begin{cases} 2x - 3y = -8 \\ 14x - 21y = 3 \end{cases}$ Adding 7 times the first equation to -1 times the second equation gives $0 = -59$, which is false.
Therefore, there is no solution to this system.

25. $\begin{cases} 6x + 4y = 12 \\ 9x + 6y = 18 \end{cases}$ Adding 3 times the first equation to -2 times the second equation gives $0 = 0$. Writing the equation in
slope-intercept form, we have $6x + 4y = 12$ $\Leftrightarrow$ $4y = -6x + 12$ $\Leftrightarrow$ $y = -\frac{3}{2}x + 3$, so the solutions are all pairs
of the form $\left(x, -\frac{3}{2}x + 3\right)$ where x is a real number.

26. $\begin{cases} 25x - 75y = 100 \\ -10x + 30y = -40 \end{cases}$ Adding $\frac{1}{25}$ times the first equation to $\frac{1}{10}$ times the second equation gives $0 = 0$, which is always
true. We now put the equation in slope-intercept form. We have $x - 3y = 4 \Leftrightarrow -3y = -x + 4$ $\Leftrightarrow$ $y = \frac{1}{3}x - \frac{4}{3}$, so
the solutions are all pairs of the form $\left(x, \frac{1}{3}x - \frac{4}{3}\right)$ where x is a real number.

27. $\begin{cases} 8s - 3t = -3 \\ 5s - 2t = -1 \end{cases}$ Adding 2 times the first equation to 3 times the second equation gives $s = -3$, so
$8(-3) - 3t = -3 \Leftrightarrow -24 - 3t = -3$ $\Leftrightarrow$ $t = -7$. Thus, the solution is $(-3, -7)$.

28. $\begin{cases} u - 30v = -5 \\ -3u + 80v = 5 \end{cases}$ Adding 3 times the first equation to the second equation gives $-10v = -10$ $\Leftrightarrow$ $v = 1$, so
$u - 30(1) = -5$ $\Leftrightarrow$ $u = 25$. Thus, the solution is $(u, v) = (25, 1)$.

29. $\begin{cases} \frac{1}{2}x + \frac{3}{5}y = 3 \\ \frac{5}{3}x + 2y = 10 \end{cases}$ Adding 10 times the first equation to -3 times the second equation gives $0 = 0$. Writing the equation

in slope-intercept form, we have $\frac{1}{2}x + \frac{3}{5}y = 3$ $\Leftrightarrow$ $\frac{3}{5}y = -\frac{1}{2}x + 3$ $\Leftrightarrow$ $y = -\frac{5}{6}x + 5$, so the solutions are all pairs

of the form $\left(x, -\frac{5}{6}x + 5\right)$ where x is a real number.

30. $\begin{cases} \frac{3}{2}x - \frac{1}{3}y = \frac{1}{2} \\ 2x - \frac{1}{2}y = -\frac{1}{2} \end{cases}$ Adding -6 times the first equation to 4 times the second equation gives $-x = -5$ $\Leftrightarrow$ $x = 5$.

So $9(5) - 2y = 3$ $\Leftrightarrow$ $y = 21$. Thus, the solution is $(5, 21)$.

31. $\begin{cases} 0.4x + 1.2y = 14 \\ 12x - 5y = 10 \end{cases}$ Adding 30 times the first equation to -1 times the second equation gives $41y = 410$ $\Leftrightarrow$

$y = 10$, so $12x - 5(10) = 10$ $\Leftrightarrow$ $12x = 60$ $\Leftrightarrow$ $x = 5$. Thus, the solution is $(5, 10)$.

32. $\begin{cases} 26x - 10y = -4 \\ -0.6x + 1.2y = 3 \end{cases}$ Adding 3 times the first equation to 25 times the second equation gives $63x = 63$ $\Leftrightarrow$

$x = 1$, so $26(1) - 10y = -4$ $\Leftrightarrow$ $-10y = -30$ $\Leftrightarrow$ $y = 3$. Thus, the solution is $(1, 3)$.

33. $\begin{cases} \frac{1}{3}x - \frac{1}{4}y = 2 \\ -8x + 6y = 10 \end{cases}$ Adding 24 times the first equation to the second equation gives $0 = 58$, which is never true. Thus,

the system has no solution.

34. $\begin{cases} -\frac{1}{10}x + \frac{1}{2}y = 4 \\ 2x - 10y = -80 \end{cases}$ Adding 20 times the first equation to the second equation gives $0 = 0$, which is always true.

We now put the equation in slope-intercept form. We have $2x - 10y = -80$ $\Leftrightarrow$ $-10y = -2x - 80 \Leftrightarrow y = \frac{1}{5}x + 8$,

so the solutions are all pairs of the form $\left(x, \frac{1}{5}x + 8\right)$ where x is a real number.

35. $\begin{cases} 0.21x + 3.17y = 9.51 \\ 2.35x - 1.17y = 5.89 \end{cases}$

The solution is approximately $(3.87, 2.74)$.

36. $\begin{cases} 18.72x - 14.91y = 12.33 \\ 6.21x - 12.92y = 17.82 \end{cases}$

The solution is approximately $(-0.71, -1.72)$.

37. $\begin{cases} 2371x - 6552y = 13{,}591 \\ 9815x + 992y = 618{,}555 \end{cases}$

The solution is approximately $(61.00, 20.00)$.

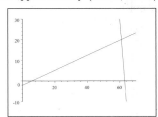

38. $\begin{cases} -435x + 912y = 0 \\ 132x + 455y = 994 \end{cases}$

The solution is approximately $(2.85, 1.36)$.

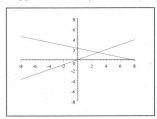

39. Subtracting the first equation from the second, we get $ay - y = 1 \Leftrightarrow y(a-1) = 1 \Leftrightarrow y = \dfrac{1}{a-1}, a \neq 1$. So

$x + \left(\dfrac{1}{a-1}\right) = 0 \Leftrightarrow x = \dfrac{1}{1-a} = -\dfrac{1}{a-1}$. Thus, the solution is $\left(-\dfrac{1}{a-1}, \dfrac{1}{a-1}\right)$.

40. Subtracting the first equation from a times the second, we get $(a-b)y = a \Leftrightarrow y = \dfrac{a}{a-b}, a \neq b$. So

$x + \left(\dfrac{a}{a-b}\right) = 1 \Leftrightarrow x = \dfrac{b}{b-a}$. Hence, the solution is $\left(\dfrac{b}{b-a}, \dfrac{a}{a-b}\right)$.

41. Subtracting b times the first equation from a times the second, we get $(a^2 - b^2)y = a - b \Leftrightarrow y = \dfrac{a-b}{a^2-b^2} = \dfrac{1}{a+b}$,

$a^2 - b^2 \neq 0$. So $ax + \dfrac{b}{a+b} = 1 \Leftrightarrow ax = \dfrac{a}{a+b} \Leftrightarrow x = \dfrac{1}{a+b}$. Thus, the solution is $\left(\dfrac{1}{a+b}, \dfrac{1}{a+b}\right)$.

42. Subtracting a times the first equation from the second, we get $b(b-a)y = 1 \Leftrightarrow y = \dfrac{1}{b(b-a)}$. So

$ax + \dfrac{b}{b(b-a)} = 0 \Leftrightarrow x = -\dfrac{1}{a(b-a)}$. Hence, the solution is $\left(-\dfrac{1}{a(b-a)}, \dfrac{1}{b(b-a)}\right) = \left(\dfrac{1}{a^2-ab}, \dfrac{1}{b^2-ab}\right)$.

43. Let the two numbers be x and y. Then $\begin{cases} x + y = 34 \\ x - y = 10 \end{cases}$ Adding these two equations gives $2x = 44 \Leftrightarrow x = 22$. So

$22 + y = 34 \Leftrightarrow y = 12$. Therefore, the two numbers are 22 and 12.

44. Let x be the larger number and y be the other number. This gives $\begin{cases} x + y = 2(x-y) \\ x = 6 + 2y \end{cases} \Rightarrow$

$\begin{cases} -x + 3y = 0 \\ x - 2y = 6 \end{cases}$ Adding these two equations gives $y = 6$, so $x = 6 + 2(6) = 18$. Therefore, the two numbers are 18

and 6.

45. Let d be the number of dimes and q be the number of quarters. This gives $\begin{cases} d + q = 14 \\ 0.10d + 0.25q = 2.75 \end{cases}$ Subtracting the

first equation from 10 times the second gives $1.5q = 13.5 \Leftrightarrow q = 9$. So $d + 9 = 14 \Leftrightarrow d = 5$. Thus, the number of

dimes is 5 and the number of quarters is 9.

46. Let c be the number of children and a be the number of adults. This gives $\begin{cases} c + a = 2200 \\ 1.50c + 4.00a = 5050 \end{cases}$ Subtracting 3 times

the first equation from 2 times the second gives $\Rightarrow 5a = 3500 \Leftrightarrow a = 700$, so $c + 700 = 2200 \Leftrightarrow c = 1500$.

Therefore, the number of children admitted was 1500 and the number of adults was 700.

47. Let x be the speed of the plane in still air and y be the speed of the wind. This gives $\begin{cases} 2x - 2y = 180 \\ 1.2x + 1.2y = 180 \end{cases}$ Subtracting

6 times the first equation from 10 times the second gives $24x = 2880$ $\Leftrightarrow$ $x = 120$, so $2(120) - 2y = 180$ $\Leftrightarrow$
$-2y = -60$ $\Leftrightarrow$ $y = 30$. Therefore, the speed of the plane is 120 mi/h and the wind speed is 30 mi/h.

48. Let x be speed of the boat in still water and y be speed of the river flow. $\begin{cases} \text{Downriver:} \quad x + y = 20 \\ \text{Upriver: } 2.5x - 2.5y = 20 \end{cases}$ Adding

5 times the first equation to 2 times the second gives $10x = 140$ $\Leftrightarrow$ $x = 14$, so $14 + y = 20 \Leftrightarrow y = 6$. Therefore, the
boat's speed is 14 mph and the current in the river flows at 6 mph.

49. Let x be the cycling speed and y be the running speed. (Remember to divide by 60 to convert minutes to decimal hours.)

We have $\begin{cases} 0.5x + 0.5y = 12.5 \\ 0.75x + 0.2y = 16 \end{cases}$ Subtracting 2 times the first equation from 5 times the second, we get $2.75x = 55$

$\Leftrightarrow$ $x = 20$, so $20 + y = 25$ $\Leftrightarrow$ $y = 5$. Thus, the cycling speed is 20 mi/h and the running speed is 5 mi/h.

50. Let x and y be the number of milliliters of the two brine solutions.

$\begin{cases} \text{Quantity:} \quad x + y = 1000 \\ \text{Concentrations: } 0.05x + 0.20y = 0.14 \end{cases}$ Subtracting the first equation from 20 times the second gives $3y = 1800$

$\Leftrightarrow$ $y = 600$, so $x + 600 = 1000 \Leftrightarrow x = 400$. Therefore, 400 milliliters of the 5% solution and 600 milliliters of the
20% solution should be mixed.

51. Let a and b be the number of grams of food A and food B. Then $\begin{cases} 0.12a + 0.20b = 32 \\ 100a + 50b = 22{,}000 \end{cases}$ Subtracting 250 times the

first equation from the second, we get $70a = 14{,}000$ $\Leftrightarrow$ $a = 200$, so $0.12(200) + 0.20b = 32$ $\Leftrightarrow$ $0.20b = 8$
$\Leftrightarrow$ $b = 40$. Thus, she should use 200 grams of food A and 40 grams of food B.

52. Let x be the number of pounds of Kenyan coffee and y be the number of pounds of Sri Lankan coffee. This gives

$\begin{cases} 3.50x + 5.60y = 11.55 \\ x + y = 3 \end{cases}$ Adding -10 times the first equation and -35 times the second gives $21y = 10.5$ $\Leftrightarrow$

$y = 0.5$, so $x + (2.5) = 3$ $\Leftrightarrow$ $x = 2.5$. Thus, 2.5 pounds of Kenyan coffee and 0.5 pounds of Sri Lankan coffee
should be mixed.

53. Let x and y be the sulfuric acid concentrations in the first and second containers.

$\begin{cases} 300x + 600y = 900\,(0.15) \\ 100x + 500y = 600\,(0.125) \end{cases}$ Subtracting the first equation from 3 times the second gives $900y = 90$ $\Leftrightarrow$

$y = 0.10$, so $100x + 500\,(0.10) = 75$ $\Leftrightarrow$ $x = 0.25$. Thus, the concentrations of sulfuric acid are 25% in the first
container and 10% in the second.

54. Let x be the amount invested at 5% and y the amount invested at 8%. $\begin{cases} \text{Total invested:} \quad x + y = 20{,}000 \\ \text{Interest earned: } 0.05x + 0.08y = 1180 \end{cases}$

Subtracting 5 times the first equation from 100 times the second gives $3y = 18{,}000$ $\Leftrightarrow$ $y = 6{,}000$, so
$x + 6{,}000 = 20{,}000$ $\Leftrightarrow$ $x = 14{,}000$. She invests $14,000 at 5% and $6,000 at 8%.

55. Let x be the amount invested at 6% and y the amount invested at 10%. The ratio of the amounts invested gives
$x = 2y$. Then the interest earned is $0.06x + 0.10y = 3520$ $\Leftrightarrow$ $6x + 10y = 352{,}000$. Substituting gives
$6(2y) + 10y = 352{,}000 \Leftrightarrow 22y = 352{,}000$ $\Leftrightarrow$ $y = 16{,}000$. Then $x = 2(16{,}000) = 32{,}000$. Thus, he invests
$32,000 at 6% and $16,000 at 10%.

56. Let x be the length of time John drives and y be the length of time Mary drives. Then $y = x + 0.25$, so $-x + y = 0.25$, and multiplying by 40, we get $-40x + 40y = 10$. Comparing the distances, we get $60x = 40y + 35$, or $60x - 40y = 35$.

This gives the system $\begin{cases} -40x + 40y = 10 \\ 60x - 40y = 35 \end{cases}$ Adding, we get $20x = 45$ $\Leftrightarrow$ $x = 2.25$, so $y = 2.25 + 0.25 = 2.5$.

Thus, John drives for $2\frac{1}{4}$ hours and Mary drives for $2\frac{1}{2}$ hours.

57. Let x be the tens digit and y be the ones digit of the number. $\begin{cases} x + y = 7 \\ 10y + x = 27 + 10x + y \end{cases}$ Adding 9 times the first equation to the second gives $18x = 36$ $\Leftrightarrow$ $x = 2$, so $2 + y = 7$ $\Leftrightarrow$ $y = 5$. Thus, the number is 25.

58. First let us find the intersection point of the two lines. The y-coordinate of the intersection point is the height of the triangle.

We have $\begin{cases} y = 2x - 4 \\ y = -4x + 20 \end{cases}$ Adding 2 times the first equation to the second gives $3y = 12$, so the triangle has height 4.

Furthermore, $y = 2x - 4$ intersects the x-axis at $x = 2$, and $y = -4x + 20$ intersects the x-axis at $x = 5$. Thus the base has length $5 - 2 = 3$. Therefore, the area of the triangle is $A = \frac{1}{2}bh = \frac{1}{2} \cdot 3 \cdot 4 = 6$.

59. $n = 5$, so $\sum_{k=1}^{n} x_k = 1 + 2 + 3 + 5 + 7 = 18$,

$\sum_{k=1}^{n} y_k = 3 + 5 + 6 + 6 + 9 = 29$,

$\sum_{k=1}^{n} x_k y_k = 1\,(3) + 2\,(5) + 3\,(6) + 5\,(6) + 7\,(9) = 124$, and

$\sum_{k=1}^{n} x_k^2 = 1^2 + 2^2 + 3^2 + 5^2 + 7^2 = 88$. Thus we get the system

$\begin{cases} 18a + 5b = 29 \\ 88a + 18b = 124 \end{cases}$ Subtracting 18 times the first equation from 5 times the second, we get $116a = 98$ $\Leftrightarrow$ $a \approx 0.845$. Then

$b = \frac{1}{5}\left[-18\,(0.845) + 29\right] \approx 2.758$. So the regression line is $y = 0.845x + 2.758$.

9.3 Systems of Linear Equations in Several Variables

1. The equation $6x - \sqrt{3}y + \frac{1}{2}z = 0$ is linear.

2. The equation $x^2 + y^2 + z^2 = 4$ is not linear, since it contains squares of variables.

3. The system $\begin{cases} xy - 3y + z = 5 \\ x - y^2 + 5z = 0 \\ 2x + yz = 3 \end{cases}$ is not a linear system, since the first equation contains a product of variables. In fact both the second and the third equation are not linear.

4. The system $\begin{cases} x - 2y + 3z = 10 \\ 2x + 5y = 2 \\ y + 2z = 4 \end{cases}$ is linear.

5. $\begin{cases} x - 2y + 4z = 3 \\ y + 2z = 7 \\ z = 2 \end{cases}$ Substituting $z = 2$ into the second equation gives $y + 2\,(2) = 7$ $\Leftrightarrow$ $y = 3$. Substituting $z = 2$

and $y = 3$ into the first equation gives $x - 2\,(3) + 4\,(2) = 3 \Leftrightarrow x = 1$. Thus, the solution is $(1, 3, 2)$.

6.
$$\begin{cases} x + y - 3z = 8 \\ \quad\ y - 3z = 5 \\ \qquad\qquad z = -1 \end{cases}$$
Substituting $z = -1$ into the second equation gives $y - 3(-1) = 5 \Leftrightarrow y = 2$. Substituting

$z = -1$ and $y = 2$ into the first equation gives $x + 2 - 3(-1) = 8 \Leftrightarrow x = 3$. Thus, the solution is $(3, 2, -1)$.

7.
$$\begin{cases} x + 2y + z = 7 \\ \quad -y + 3z = 9 \\ \qquad\quad 2z = 6 \end{cases}$$
Solving we get $2z = 6 \Leftrightarrow z = 3$. Substituting $z = 3$ into the second equation gives

$-y + 3(3) = 9 \Leftrightarrow y = 0$. Substituting $z = 3$ and $y = 0$ into the first equation gives $x + 2(0) + 3 = 7 \Leftrightarrow x = 4$.
Thus, the solution is $(4, 0, 3)$.

8.
$$\begin{cases} x - 2y + 3z = 10 \\ \quad 2y - z = 2 \\ \qquad\quad 3z = 12 \end{cases}$$
Solving we get $3z = 12 \Leftrightarrow z = 4$. Substituting $z = 4$ into the second equation gives

$2y - 4 = 2 \Leftrightarrow y = 3$. Substituting $z = 4$ and $y = 3$ into the first equation gives $x - 2(3) + 3(4) = 10 \Leftrightarrow x = 4$.
Thus, the solution is $(4, 3, 4)$.

9.
$$\begin{cases} 2x - y + 6z = 5 \\ \quad\ y + 4z = 0 \\ \qquad\ -2z = 1 \end{cases}$$
Solving we get $-2z = 1 \Leftrightarrow z = -\frac{1}{2}$. Substituting $z = -\frac{1}{2}$ into the second equation gives

$y + 4\left(-\frac{1}{2}\right) = 0 \Leftrightarrow y = 2$. Substituting $z = -\frac{1}{2}$ and $y = 2$ into the first equation gives $2x - (2) + 6\left(-\frac{1}{2}\right) = 5 \Leftrightarrow$
$x = 5$. Thus, the solution is $\left(5, 2, -\frac{1}{2}\right)$.

10.
$$\begin{cases} 4x + \quad 3z = 10 \\ \quad 2y - z = -6 \\ \qquad\quad \frac{1}{2}z = 2 \end{cases}$$
Solving we get $\frac{1}{2}z = 4 \Leftrightarrow z = 8$. Substituting $z = 8$ into the second equation gives

$2y - 8 = -6 \Leftrightarrow 2y = 2 \Leftrightarrow y = 1$. Substituting $z = 8$ into the first equation gives $4x + 3(8) = 10 \Leftrightarrow$
$4x = -14 \Leftrightarrow x = -\frac{7}{2}$. Thus, the solution is $\left(-\frac{7}{2}, 1, 8\right)$.

11.
$$\begin{cases} x - 2y - z = 4 \\ x - y + 3z = 0 \\ 2x + y + z = 0 \end{cases}$$
Subtract the first equation from the second equation:
$$\begin{cases} x - 2y - z = 4 \\ \quad\ y + 4z = -4 \\ 2x + y + z = 0 \end{cases}$$

Or, subtract $\frac{1}{2}$ times the third equation from the second equation:
$$\begin{cases} x - 2y - z = 4 \\ \quad -\frac{3}{2}y + \frac{5}{2}z = 0 \\ 2x + y + z = 0 \end{cases}$$

12.
$$\begin{cases} x + y - 3z = 3 \\ -2x + 3y + z = 2 \\ x - y + 2z = 0 \end{cases}$$
Add 2 times the first equation to the second equation:
$$\begin{cases} x + y - 3z = 3 \\ \quad 5y - 5z = 8 \\ x - y + 2z = 0 \end{cases}$$

Or, add 2 times the third equation to the second equation:
$$\begin{cases} x + y - 3z = 3 \\ \quad y + 5z = 2 \\ x - y + 2z = 0 \end{cases}$$

13. $\begin{cases} 2x - y + 3z = 2 \\ x + 2y - z = 4 \\ -4x + 5y + z = 10 \end{cases}$ Add 2 times the first equation to the third equation: $\begin{cases} 2x - y + 3z = 2 \\ x + 2y - z = 4 \\ 3y + 7z = 14 \end{cases}$

Or, add 4 times the second equation to the third equation: $\begin{cases} 2x - y + 3z = 2 \\ x + 2y - z = 4 \\ 13y - 3z = 26 \end{cases}$

14. $\begin{cases} x - 4y + z = 3 \\ y - 3z = 10 \\ 3y - 8z = 24 \end{cases}$ Add $\frac{3}{4}$ times the first equation to the third equation: $\begin{cases} x - 4y + z = 3 \\ y - 3z = 10 \\ \frac{3}{4}x - \frac{29}{4}z = \frac{105}{4} \end{cases}$

Or, subtract 3 times the second equation from the third equation: $\begin{cases} x - 4y + z = 3 \\ y - 3z = 10 \\ z = -6 \end{cases}$

15. $\begin{cases} x + y + z = 4 \\ x + 3y + 3z = 10 \\ 2x + y - z = 3 \end{cases} \Leftrightarrow \begin{cases} x + y + z = 4 \\ 2y + 2z = 6 \quad (-1) \times \text{Eq. 1} + \text{Eq. 2} \\ y + 3z = 5 \quad 2 \times \text{Eq. 1} + (-1) \times \text{Eq. 3} \end{cases} \Leftrightarrow \begin{cases} x + y + z = 4 \\ y + 3z = 5 \quad \text{Eq. 3} \\ 2y + 2z = 6 \quad \text{Eq. 2} \end{cases}$

$\Leftrightarrow \begin{cases} x + y + z = 4 \\ y + 3z = 5 \\ -4z = -4 \quad (-2) \times \text{Eq. 2} + \text{Eq. 3} \end{cases} \Leftrightarrow z = 1 \text{ and } y + 3(1) = 8 \Leftrightarrow y = 2. \text{ Then } x + 2 + 1 = 4 \quad \Leftrightarrow$

$x = 1.$ So the solution is $(1, 2, 1)$.

16. $\begin{cases} x + y + z = 0 \\ -x + 2y + 5z = 3 \\ 3x - y = 6 \end{cases} \Leftrightarrow \begin{cases} x + y + z = 0 \\ y + 2z = 1 \quad \frac{1}{3} \times \text{Eq. 1} + \frac{1}{3} \times \text{Eq. 2} \\ -4y - 3z = 6 \quad (-3) \times \text{Eq. 1} + \text{Eq. 3} \end{cases} \Leftrightarrow \begin{cases} x + y + z = 0 \\ y + 2z = 1 \\ 5z = 10 \quad 4 \times \text{Eq. 2} + \text{Eq. 3} \end{cases}$

So $z = 2$ and $y + 2(2) = 1 \Leftrightarrow y = -3$. Then $x + (-3) + 2 = 0 \quad \Leftrightarrow \quad x = 1$. So the solution is $(1, -3, 2)$.

17. $\begin{cases} x - 4z = 1 \\ 2x - y - 6z = 4 \\ 2x + 3y - 2z = 8 \end{cases} \Leftrightarrow \begin{cases} x - 4z = 1 \\ -y + 2z = 2 \quad (-2) \times \text{Eq. 1} + \text{Eq. 2} \\ 3y + 6z = 6 \quad (-2) \times \text{Eq. 1} + \text{Eq. 3} \end{cases} \Leftrightarrow \begin{cases} x - 4z = 1 \\ -y + 2z = 2 \\ 12z = 12 \quad 3 \times \text{Eq. 2} + \text{Eq. 3} \end{cases}$

So $z = 1$ and $-y + 2(1) = 2 \Leftrightarrow y = 0$. Then $x - 4(1) = 1 \quad \Leftrightarrow \quad x = 5$. So the solution is $(5, 0, 1)$.

18. $\begin{cases} x - y + 2z = 2 \\ 3x + y + 5z = 8 \\ 2x - y - 2z = -7 \end{cases} \Leftrightarrow \begin{cases} x - y + 2z = 2 \\ y - 6z = -11 \quad (-3) \times \text{Eq. 1} + \text{Eq. 3} \\ 4y - z = 2 \quad (-2) \times \text{Eq. 1} + \text{Eq. 2} \end{cases} \Leftrightarrow \begin{cases} x - y + 2z = 2 \\ y - 6z = -11 \\ 23z = 46 \quad (-4) \times \text{Eq. 2} + \text{Eq. 2} \end{cases}$

So $z = 2$ and $y - 6(2) = -11 \Leftrightarrow y = 1$. Then $x + 1 + 2 = 2 \quad \Leftrightarrow \quad x = -1$. So the solution is $(-1, 1, 2)$.

19. $\begin{cases} 2x + 4y - z = 2 \\ x + 2y - 3z = -4 \\ 3x - y + z = 1 \end{cases} \Leftrightarrow \begin{cases} x + 2y - 3z = -4 \\ 2x + 4y - z = 2 \\ 3x - y + z = 1 \end{cases} \Leftrightarrow \begin{cases} x + 2y - 3z = -4 \\ -7y + 10z = 13 \\ 5z = 10 \end{cases}$ So $z = 2$ and

$-7y + 10(2) = 13 \quad \Leftrightarrow \quad y = 1$. Then $x + 2(1) - 3(2) = -4 \quad \Leftrightarrow \quad x = 0$. So the solution is $(0, 1, 2)$.

20. $\begin{cases} 2x + y - z = -8 \\ -x + y + z = 3 \\ -2x + 4z = 18 \end{cases} \Leftrightarrow \begin{cases} -x + y + z = 3 \\ 2x + y - z = -8 \\ -2x + 4z = 18 \end{cases} \Leftrightarrow \begin{cases} -x + y + z = 3 \\ y - z = -6 \\ 3y + z = -2 \end{cases} \Leftrightarrow \begin{cases} -x + y + z = 3 \\ y - z = -6 \\ 4z = 16 \end{cases}$

So $z = 4$ and $y - 4 = -6 \Leftrightarrow y = -2$. Then $-x + (-2) + 4 = 3 \Leftrightarrow x = -1$. So the solution is $(-1, -2, 4)$.

21. $\begin{cases} y - 2z = 0 \\ 2x + 3y = 2 \\ -x - 2y + z = -1 \end{cases} \Leftrightarrow \begin{cases} -x - 2y + z = -1 \\ y - 2z = 0 \\ 2x + 3y = 2 \end{cases} \Leftrightarrow \begin{cases} -x - 2y + z = -1 \\ y - 2z = 0 \\ -y + 2z = 0 \end{cases} \Leftrightarrow \begin{cases} -x - 2y + z = -1 \\ y - 2z = 0 \\ 0 = 0 \end{cases}$

The system is dependent, so when $z = t$ we solve for y to get $y - 2t = 0 \Leftrightarrow y = 2t$. Then $-x - 2(2t) + t = -1 \Leftrightarrow -x - 3t = -1 \Leftrightarrow x = -3t + 1$. So the solutions are $(-3t + 1, 2t, t)$, where t is any real number.

22. $\begin{cases} 2y + z = 3 \\ 5x + 4y + 3z = -1 \\ x - 3y = -2 \end{cases} \Leftrightarrow \begin{cases} x - 3y = -2 \\ 2y + z = 3 \\ 5x + 4y + 3z = -1 \end{cases} \Leftrightarrow \begin{cases} x - 3y = -2 \\ 2y + z = 3 \\ 19y + 3z = 9 \end{cases} \Leftrightarrow \begin{cases} x - 3y = -2 \\ 2y + z = 3 \\ -13z = -39 \end{cases}$

So $z = 3$ and $2y + 3 = 3 \Leftrightarrow y = 0$. Then $x - 3(0) = -2 \Leftrightarrow x = -2$. So the solution is $(-2, 0, 3)$.

23. $\begin{cases} x + 2y - z = 1 \\ 2x + 3y - 4z = -3 \\ 3x + 6y - 3z = 4 \end{cases} \Leftrightarrow \begin{cases} x + 2y - z = 1 \\ -y - 2z = -5 \\ 0 = 1 \end{cases}$ Since $0 = 1$ is false, this system is inconsistent.

24. $\begin{cases} -x + 2y + 5z = 4 \\ x - 2z = 0 \\ 4x - 2y - 11z = 2 \end{cases} \Leftrightarrow \begin{cases} x - 2z = 0 \\ -x + 2y + 5z = 4 \\ 4x - 2y - 11z = 2 \end{cases} \Leftrightarrow \begin{cases} x - 2z = 0 \\ 2y + 3z = 4 \\ -2y - 3z = 2 \end{cases} \Leftrightarrow \begin{cases} x - 2z = 0 \\ 2y + 3z = 4 \\ 0 = 6 \end{cases}$

Since $0 = 6$ is false, this system is inconsistent.

25. $\begin{cases} 2x + 3y - z = 1 \\ x + 2y = 3 \\ x + 3y + z = 4 \end{cases} \Leftrightarrow \begin{cases} x + 2y = 3 \\ 2x + 3y - z = 1 \\ x + 3y + z = 4 \end{cases} \Leftrightarrow \begin{cases} x + 2y = 3 \\ -y - z = -5 \\ y + z = 1 \end{cases} \Leftrightarrow \begin{cases} x + 2y = 3 \\ -y - z = -5 \\ 0 = -4 \end{cases}$

Since $0 = -4$ is false, this system is inconsistent.

26. $\begin{cases} x - 2y - 3z = 5 \\ 2x + y - z = 5 \\ 4x - 3y - 7z = 5 \end{cases} \Leftrightarrow \begin{cases} x - 2y - 3z = 5 \\ 5y + 5z = -5 \\ 5y + 5z = -15 \end{cases} \Leftrightarrow \begin{cases} x - 2y - 3z = 5 \\ 5y + 5z = -5 \\ 0 = -10 \end{cases}$

Since $0 = -10$ is false, this system is inconsistent.

27. $\begin{cases} x + y - z = 0 \\ x + 2y - 3z = -3 \\ 2x + 3y - 4z = -3 \end{cases} \Leftrightarrow \begin{cases} x + y - z = 0 \\ y - 2z = -3 \\ y - 2z = -3 \end{cases} \Leftrightarrow \begin{cases} x + y - z = 0 \\ y - 2z = -3 \\ 0 = 0 \end{cases}$

So $z = t$ and $y - 2t = -3 \Leftrightarrow y = 2t - 3$. Then $x + (2t - 3) - t = 0 \Leftrightarrow x = -t + 3$. So the solutions are $(-t + 3, 2t - 3, t)$, where t is any real number.

28. $\begin{cases} x - 2y + z = 3 \\ 2x - 5y + 6z = 7 \\ 2x - 3y - 2z = 5 \end{cases} \Leftrightarrow \begin{cases} x - 2y + z = 3 \\ -y + 4z = 1 \\ y - 4z = -1 \end{cases} \Leftrightarrow \begin{cases} x - 2y + z = 3 \\ -y + 4z = 1 \\ 0 = 0 \end{cases}$

Then we have $-y + 4t = 1 \Leftrightarrow y = 4t - 1$. Substituting into the first equation, we have $x - 2(4t - 1) + t = 3 \Leftrightarrow x = 7t + 1$. So the solutions are $(7t + 1, 4t - 1, t)$, where t is any real number.

29. $\begin{cases} x + 3y - 2z = 0 \\ 2x \qquad + 4z = 4 \\ 4x + 6y \qquad = 4 \end{cases}$ $\Leftrightarrow$ $\begin{cases} x + 3y - 2z = 0 \\ -6y + 8z = 4 \\ -6y + 8z = 4 \end{cases}$ $\Leftrightarrow$ $\begin{cases} x + 3y - 2z = 0 \\ -6y + 8z = 4 \\ 0 = 0 \end{cases}$

So $z = t$ and $-6y + 8t = 4$ $\Leftrightarrow$ $-6y = -8t + 4 \Leftrightarrow y = \frac{4}{3}t - \frac{2}{3}$. Then $x + 3\left(\frac{4}{3}t - \frac{2}{3}\right) - 2t = 0$ $\Leftrightarrow$ $x = -2t + 2$.
So the solutions are $\left(-2t + 2, \frac{4}{3}t - \frac{2}{3}, t\right)$, where t is any real number.

30. $\begin{cases} 2x + 4y - z = 3 \\ x + 2y + 4z = 6 \\ x + 2y - 2z = 0 \end{cases}$ $\Leftrightarrow$ $\begin{cases} x + 2y - 2z = 0 \\ 2x + 4y - z = 3 \\ x + 2y + 4z = 6 \end{cases}$ $\Leftrightarrow$ $\begin{cases} x + 2y - 2z = 0 \\ 3z = 3 \\ 6z = 6 \end{cases}$ $\Leftrightarrow$ $\begin{cases} x + 2y - 2z = 0 \\ 3z = 3 \\ 0 = 0 \end{cases}$

So $z = 1$, and substituting into the first equation we have $x + 2t - 2(1) = 0$ $\Leftrightarrow$ $x = -2t + 2$. Thus, the solutions are $(-2t + 2, t, 1)$, where t is any real number.

31. $\begin{cases} x \qquad + z + 2w = 6 \\ y - 2z \qquad = -3 \\ x + 2y - z \qquad = -2 \\ 2x + y + 3z - 2w = 0 \end{cases}$ $\Leftrightarrow$ $\begin{cases} x \qquad + z + 2w = 6 \\ y - 2z \qquad = -3 \\ 2y - 2z - 2w = -8 \\ y + z - 6w = -12 \end{cases}$ $\Leftrightarrow$ $\begin{cases} x \qquad + z + 2w = 6 \\ y - 2z \qquad = -3 \\ z - w = -1 \\ 3z - 6w = -9 \end{cases}$ $\Leftrightarrow$

$\begin{cases} x \qquad + z + 2w = 6 \\ y - 2z \qquad = -3 \\ z - w = -1 \\ -3w = -6 \end{cases}$ So $w = 2$ and $z - 2 = -1$ $\Leftrightarrow$ $z = 1$. Then $y - 2(1) = -3$ $\Leftrightarrow$ $y = -1$ and

$x + 1 + 2(2) = 6$ $\Leftrightarrow$ $x = 1$. Thus, the solution is $(1, -1, 1, 2)$.

32. $\begin{cases} x + y + z + w = 0 \\ x + y + 2z + 2w = 0 \\ 2x + 2y + 3z + 4w = 1 \\ 2x + 3y + 4z + 5w = 2 \end{cases}$ $\Leftrightarrow$ $\begin{cases} x + y + z + w = 0 \\ z + w = 0 \\ z + 2w = 1 \\ y + 2z + 3w = 2 \end{cases}$ $\Leftrightarrow$ $\begin{cases} x + y + z + w = 0 \\ y + 2z + 3w = 2 \\ z + w = 0 \\ z + 2w = 1 \end{cases}$ $\Leftrightarrow$

$\begin{cases} x + y + z + w = 0 \\ y + 2z + 3w = 2 \\ z + w = 0 \\ w = 1 \end{cases}$ So $w = 1$ and $z + 1 = 0$ $\Leftrightarrow$ $z = -1$. Then $y + 2(-1) + 3(1) = 2$ $\Leftrightarrow$ $y = 1$

and $x + 1 + (-1) + 1 = 0$ $\Leftrightarrow$ $x = -1$. So the solution is $(-1, 1, -1, 1)$.

33. Let x be the amount invested at 4%, y the amount invested at 5%, and z the amount invested at 6%. We set up

a model and get the following equations: $\begin{cases} \text{Total money:} & x + y + z = 100{,}000 \\ \text{Annual income:} & 0.04x + 0.05y + 0.06z = 0.051(100{,}000) \\ \text{Equal amounts:} & x = y \end{cases}$ $\Leftrightarrow$

$\begin{cases} x + y + z = 100{,}000 \\ 4x + 5y + 6z = 510{,}000 \\ x - y = 0 \end{cases}$ $\Leftrightarrow$ $\begin{cases} x + y + z = 100{,}000 \\ y + 2z = 110{,}000 \\ -2y - z = -100{,}000 \end{cases}$ $\Leftrightarrow$ $\begin{cases} x + y + z = 100{,}000 \\ y + 2z = 110{,}000 \\ 3z = 120{,}000 \end{cases}$ So

$z = 40{,}000$ and $y + 2(40{,}000) = 110{,}000$ $\Leftrightarrow$ $y = 30{,}000$. Since $x = y$, $x = 30{,}000$. She must invest \$30,000 in short-term bonds, \$30,000 in intermediate-term bonds, and \$40,000 in long-term bonds.

34. Let x be the amount invested at 4%, y the amount invested at 6%, and z the amount invested at 8%. We set up a model and get the following equations:
$$\begin{cases} \text{Total money:} & x + y + z = 100{,}000 \\ \text{Annual income:} & 0.04x + 0.06y + 0.08z = 6{,}700 \\ \text{Equal amounts:} & y = z \end{cases} \Leftrightarrow \begin{cases} x + y + z = 100{,}000 \\ 4x + 6y + 8z = 670{,}000 \\ y - z = 0 \end{cases}$$

$$\Leftrightarrow \begin{cases} x + y + z = 100{,}000 \\ 2y + 4z = 270{,}000 \\ y - z = 0 \end{cases} \Leftrightarrow \begin{cases} x + y + z = 100{,}000 \\ 2y + 4z = 270{,}000 \\ -6z = -270{,}000 \end{cases}$$ So $z = 45{,}000$ and $y = z = 45{,}000$. Since

$x + 45{,}000 + 45{,}000 = 100{,}000 \Leftrightarrow x = 10{,}000$. She must invest \$10,000 in short-term bonds, \$45,000 in intermediate-term bonds, and \$45,000 in long-term bonds.

35. Let a, b, and c be the number of ounces of Type A, Type B, and Type C pellets used. The requirements for the different vitamins gives the following system:
$$\begin{cases} 2a + 3b + c = 9 \\ 3a + b + 3c = 14 \\ 8a + 5b + 7c = 32 \end{cases} \Leftrightarrow \begin{cases} 2a + 3b + c = 9 \\ -7b + 3c = 1 \\ -7b + 3c = -4 \end{cases}$$

Equations 2 and 3 are inconsistent, so there is no solution.

36. $$\begin{cases} I_1 + I_2 - I_3 = 0 \\ 16I_1 - 8I_2 = 4 \\ 8I_2 + 4I_3 = 5 \end{cases} \Leftrightarrow \begin{cases} I_1 + I_2 - I_3 = 0 \\ -24I_2 + 16I_3 = 4 \\ 8I_2 + 4I_3 = 5 \end{cases} \Leftrightarrow \begin{cases} I_1 + I_2 - I_3 = 0 \\ 8I_2 + 4I_3 = 5 \\ 28I_3 = 19 \end{cases}$$
So $I_3 = \frac{19}{28} \approx 0.68$ and $8I_2 + 4\left(\frac{19}{28}\right) = 5 \Leftrightarrow I_2 = \frac{2}{7} \approx 0.29$. Then $I_1 + \frac{2}{7} - \frac{19}{28} = 0 \Leftrightarrow I_1 = \frac{11}{28} \approx 0.39$.

37. Let x, y, and z be the number of acres of land planted with corn, wheat, and soybeans. We set up a model and get the following equations:
$$\begin{cases} \text{Total acres:} & x + y + z = 1200 \\ \text{Market demand:} & 2x = y \\ \text{Total cost:} & 45x + 60y + 50z = 63{,}750 \end{cases}$$ Substituting $2x$ for y, we get

$$\begin{cases} x + 2x + z = 1200 \\ 2x = y \\ 45x + 60\,(2x) + 50z = 63{,}750 \end{cases} \Leftrightarrow \begin{cases} 3x + z = 1200 \\ 2x - y = 0 \\ 165x + 50z = 63{,}750 \end{cases} \Leftrightarrow \begin{cases} 3x + z = 1200 \\ 2x - y = 0 \\ 15x = 3750 \end{cases}$$ So

$15x = 3{,}750 \Leftrightarrow x = 250$ and $y = 2\,(250) = 500$. Substituting into the original equation, we have $250 + 500 + z = 1200 \Leftrightarrow z = 450$. Thus the farmer should plant 250 acres of corn, 500 acres of wheat, and 450 acres of soybeans.

38. Let a, b, and c be the number of shares of Stock A, Stock B, and Stock C in the investor's portfolio. Since the total value remains unchanged, we get the following system:
$$\begin{cases} 10a + 25b + 29c = 74{,}000 \\ 12a + 20b + 32c = 74{,}000 \\ 16a + 15b + 32c = 74{,}000 \end{cases} \Leftrightarrow \begin{cases} 10a + 25b + 29c = 74{,}000 \\ 50b + 14c = 74{,}000 \\ 125b + 72c = 222{,}000 \end{cases} \Leftrightarrow \begin{cases} 10a + 25b + 29c = 74{,}000 \\ 50b + 14c = 74{,}000 \\ -74c = -74{,}000 \end{cases}$$
So $c = 1{,}000$. Back-substituting we have $50b + 14\,(1000) = 74{,}000 \Leftrightarrow 50b = 60{,}000 \Leftrightarrow b = 1{,}200$. And finally $10a + 25\,(1200) + 29\,(1000) = 74{,}000 \Leftrightarrow 10a + 30{,}000 + 29{,}000 = 74{,}000 \Leftrightarrow 10a = 15{,}000 \Leftrightarrow a = 1{,}500$. Thus the portfolio consists of 1,500 shares of Stock A, 1,200 shares of Stock B, and 1,000 shares of Stock C.

39. (a) We begin by substituting $\dfrac{x_0 + x_1}{2}$, $\dfrac{y_0 + y_1}{2}$, and $\dfrac{z_0 + z_1}{2}$ into the left-hand side of the first equation:

$$a_1 \left(\frac{x_0 + x_1}{2} \right) + b_1 \left(\frac{y_0 + y_1}{2} \right) + c_1 \left(\frac{z_0 + z_1}{2} \right) = \tfrac{1}{2} \left[(a_1 x_0 + b_1 y_0 + c_1 z_0) + (a_1 x_1 + b_1 y_1 + c_1 z_1) \right]$$

$$= \tfrac{1}{2} \left[d_1 + d_1 \right] = d_1$$

Thus the given ordered triple satisfies the first equation. We can show that it satisfies the second and the third in exactly the same way. Thus it is a solution of the system.

(b) We have shown in part (a) that if the system has two different solutions, we can find a third one by averaging the two solutions. But then we can find a fourth and a fifth solution by averaging the new one with each of the previous two. Then we can find four more by repeating this process with these new solutions, and so on. Clearly this process can continue indefinitely, so there are infinitely many solutions.

9.4   Systems of Linear Equations: Matrices

1. 3×2　　　**2.** 2×4　　　**3.** 2×1　　　**4.** 3×1　　　**5.** 1×3　　　**6.** 2×2

7. (a) Yes, this matrix is in row-echelon form.

(b) Yes, this matrix is in reduced row-echelon form.

(c) $\begin{cases} x = -3 \\ y = 5 \end{cases}$

8. (a) Yes, this matrix is in row-echelon form.

(b) No, this matrix not in reduced row-echelon form. The entry above the leading 1 in the second row is not 0.

(c) $\begin{cases} x + 3y = -3 \\ y = 5 \end{cases}$

9. (a) Yes, this matrix is in row-echelon form.

(b) No, this matrix is not in reduced row-echelon form, since the leading 1 in the second row does not have a zero above it.

(c) $\begin{cases} x + 2y + 8z = 0 \\ y + 3z = 2 \\ 0 = 0 \end{cases}$

10. (a) Yes, the matrix is in row-echelon form.

(b) Yes, the matrix is in reduced row-echelon form.

(c) $\begin{cases} x - 7z = 0 \\ y + 3z = 0 \\ 0 = 1 \end{cases}$

11. (a) No, this matrix is not in row-echelon form, since the row of zeros is not at the bottom.

(b) No, this matrix is not in reduced row-echelon form.

(c) $\begin{cases} x = 0 \\ 0 = 0 \\ y + 5z = 1 \end{cases}$

12. (a) Yes, the matrix is in row-echelon form.

(b) Yes, the matrix is in reduced row-echelon form.

(c) $\begin{cases} x = 1 \\ y = 2 \\ z = 3 \end{cases}$

13. (a) Yes, this matrix is in row-echelon form.

(b) Yes, this matrix is in reduced row-echelon form.

(c) $\begin{cases} x + 3y - w = 0 \\ z + 2w = 2 \\ 0 = 1 \\ 0 = 0 \end{cases}$

Notice that this system has no solution.

14. (a) No, this matrix is not in row-echelon form, since the fourth column has the leading 1 of two rows.

(b) No, this matrix is not in reduced row-echelon form.

(c) $\begin{cases} x + 3y + w = 0 \\ y + 4w = 0 \\ w + u = 2 \\ w = 0 \end{cases}$

15. $\begin{bmatrix} 1 & -2 & 1 & 1 \\ 0 & 1 & 2 & 5 \\ 1 & 1 & 3 & 8 \end{bmatrix}$ $\xrightarrow{R_3 - R_1 \to R_3}$ $\begin{bmatrix} 1 & -2 & 1 & 1 \\ 0 & 1 & 2 & 5 \\ 0 & 3 & 2 & 7 \end{bmatrix}$ $\xrightarrow{R_3 - 3R_2 \to R_3}$ $\begin{bmatrix} 1 & -2 & 1 & 1 \\ 0 & 1 & 2 & 5 \\ 0 & 0 & -4 & -8 \end{bmatrix}$. Thus, $-4z = -8$ $\Leftrightarrow$

$z = 2$; $y + 2(2) = 5$ $\Leftrightarrow$ $y = 1$; and $x - 2(1) + (2) = 1$ $\Leftrightarrow$ $x = 1$. Therefore, the solution is $(1, 1, 2)$.

16. $\begin{bmatrix} 1 & 1 & 6 & 3 \\ 1 & 1 & 3 & 3 \\ 1 & 2 & 4 & 7 \end{bmatrix}$ $\xrightarrow{R_2 - R_1 \to R_2}$ $\begin{bmatrix} 1 & 1 & 6 & 3 \\ 0 & 0 & -3 & 0 \\ 1 & 2 & 4 & 7 \end{bmatrix}$ $\xrightarrow[R_3 - R_1 \to R_3]{-\frac{1}{3}R_2}$ $\begin{bmatrix} 1 & 1 & 6 & 3 \\ 0 & 0 & 1 & 0 \\ 0 & 1 & -2 & 4 \end{bmatrix}$ $\xrightarrow{R_3 \leftrightarrow R_2}$ $\begin{bmatrix} 1 & 1 & 6 & 3 \\ 0 & 1 & -2 & 4 \\ 0 & 0 & 1 & 0 \end{bmatrix}$.

Thus, $z = 0$; $y - 2z = y - 0 = y = 4$; and $x + y + 6z = 3$ $\Leftrightarrow$ $x + 4 - 0 = 3$ $\Leftrightarrow$ $x = -1$. Therefore, the solution is $(-1, 4, 0)$.

17. $\begin{bmatrix} 1 & 1 & 1 & 2 \\ 2 & -3 & 2 & 4 \\ 4 & 1 & -3 & 1 \end{bmatrix}$ $\xrightarrow[R_3 - 4R_1 \to R_3]{R_2 - 2R_1 \to R_2}$ $\begin{bmatrix} 1 & 1 & 1 & 2 \\ 0 & -5 & 0 & 0 \\ 0 & -3 & -7 & -7 \end{bmatrix}$ $\xrightarrow{R_3 - \frac{3}{5}R_2 \to R_3}$ $\begin{bmatrix} 1 & 1 & 1 & 2 \\ 0 & -5 & 0 & 0 \\ 0 & 0 & -7 & -7 \end{bmatrix}$. Thus, $-7z = -7$

$\Leftrightarrow$ $z = 1$; $-5y = 0 \Leftrightarrow y = 0$; and $x + 0 + 1 = 2$ $\Leftrightarrow$ $x = 1$. Therefore, the solution is $(1, 0, 1)$.

18. $\begin{bmatrix} 1 & 1 & 1 & 4 \\ -1 & 2 & 3 & 17 \\ 2 & -1 & 0 & -7 \end{bmatrix}$ $\xrightarrow[R_3 - 2R_1 \to R_3]{R_2 + R_1 \to R_2}$ $\begin{bmatrix} 1 & 1 & 1 & 4 \\ 0 & 3 & 4 & 21 \\ 0 & -3 & -2 & -15 \end{bmatrix}$ $\xrightarrow[R_3 - 2R_1 \to R_3]{R_3 + R_2 \to R_3}$ $\begin{bmatrix} 1 & 1 & 1 & 4 \\ 0 & 3 & 4 & 21 \\ 0 & 0 & 2 & 6 \end{bmatrix}$. Thus, $2z = 6$ $\Leftrightarrow$

$z = 3$; $3y + 4(3) = 21 \Leftrightarrow y = 3$; and $x + (3) + (3) = 4 \Leftrightarrow x = -2$. The solution is $(-2, 3, 3)$.

19. $\begin{bmatrix} 1 & 2 & -1 & -2 \\ 1 & 0 & 1 & 0 \\ 2 & -1 & -1 & -3 \end{bmatrix}$ $\xrightarrow[R_3 - 2R_1 \to R_3]{R_2 - R_1 \to R_2}$ $\begin{bmatrix} 1 & 2 & -1 & -2 \\ 0 & -2 & 2 & 2 \\ 0 & -5 & 1 & 1 \end{bmatrix}$ $\xrightarrow{-\frac{1}{2}R_2}$ $\begin{bmatrix} 1 & 2 & -1 & -2 \\ 0 & 1 & 1 & 1 \\ 0 & -5 & 1 & 1 \end{bmatrix}$ $\xrightarrow{R_3 + 5R_2 \to R_3}$

$\begin{bmatrix} 1 & 2 & -1 & -2 \\ 0 & 1 & 1 & 1 \\ 0 & 0 & 6 & 6 \end{bmatrix}$. Thus, $6z = 6$ $\Leftrightarrow$ $z = 1$; $y + (1) = 1 \Leftrightarrow y = 0$; and $x + 2(0) - (1) = -2 \Leftrightarrow x = -1$.

Therefore, the solution is $(-1, 0, 1)$.

20. $\begin{bmatrix} 0 & 2 & 1 & 4 \\ 1 & 1 & 0 & 4 \\ 3 & 3 & -1 & 10 \end{bmatrix}$ $\xrightarrow{R_1 \leftrightarrow R_2}$ $\begin{bmatrix} 1 & 1 & 0 & 4 \\ 0 & 2 & 1 & 4 \\ 3 & 3 & -1 & 10 \end{bmatrix}$ $\xrightarrow{R_3 - 3R_1 \to R_3}$ $\begin{bmatrix} 1 & 1 & 0 & 4 \\ 0 & 2 & 1 & 4 \\ 0 & 0 & -1 & -2 \end{bmatrix}$. Thus, $-z = -2$ $\Leftrightarrow$

$z = 2$; $2y + (2) = 4$ $\Leftrightarrow$ $y = 1$; and $x + (1) = 4$ $\Leftrightarrow$ $x = 3$. The solution is $(3, 1, 2)$

21. $\begin{bmatrix} 1 & 2 & -1 & 9 \\ 2 & 0 & -1 & -2 \\ 3 & 5 & 2 & 22 \end{bmatrix}$ $\xrightarrow[R_3 - 3R_1 \to R_3]{R_2 - 2R_1 \to R_2}$ $\begin{bmatrix} 1 & 2 & -1 & 9 \\ 0 & -4 & 1 & -20 \\ 0 & -1 & 5 & -5 \end{bmatrix}$ $\xrightarrow{4R_3 - R_2 \to R_3}$ $\begin{bmatrix} 1 & 2 & -1 & 9 \\ 0 & -4 & 1 & -20 \\ 0 & 0 & 19 & 0 \end{bmatrix}$ Thus, $19x_3 = 0$

$\Leftrightarrow$ $x_3 = 0$; $-4x_2 = -20 \Leftrightarrow x_2 = 5$; and $x_1 + 2(5) = 9 \Leftrightarrow x_1 = -1$. Therefore, the solution is $(-1, 5, 0)$.

22. $\begin{bmatrix} 2 & 1 & 0 & 7 \\ 2 & -1 & 1 & 6 \\ 3 & -2 & 4 & 11 \end{bmatrix}$ $\xrightarrow[2R_3 - 3R_1 \to R_3]{R_2 - R_1 \to R_2}$ $\begin{bmatrix} 2 & 1 & 0 & 7 \\ 0 & -2 & 1 & -1 \\ 0 & -7 & 8 & 1 \end{bmatrix}$ $\xrightarrow{2R_3 - 7R_2 \to R_3}$ $\begin{bmatrix} 2 & 1 & 0 & 7 \\ 0 & -2 & 1 & -1 \\ 0 & 0 & 9 & 9 \end{bmatrix}$ Then, $9x_3 = 9$ $\Leftrightarrow$

$x_3 = 1$; $-2x_2 + 1 = -1 \Leftrightarrow x_2 = 1$; and $2x_1 + 1 = 7$ $\Leftrightarrow$ $x_1 = 3$. Therefore, the solution is $(x_1, x_2, x_3) = (3, 1, 1)$.

23. $\begin{bmatrix} 2 & -3 & -1 & 13 \\ -1 & 2 & -5 & 6 \\ 5 & -1 & -1 & 49 \end{bmatrix}$ $\xrightarrow[2R_3 - 5R_1 \to R_3]{2R_2 + R_1 \to R_2}$ $\begin{bmatrix} 2 & -3 & -1 & 13 \\ 0 & 1 & -11 & 25 \\ 0 & 13 & 3 & 33 \end{bmatrix}$ $\xrightarrow{R_3 - 13R_2 \to R_3}$ $\begin{bmatrix} 2 & -3 & -1 & 13 \\ 0 & 1 & -11 & 25 \\ 0 & 0 & 146 & -292 \end{bmatrix}$ Thus,

$146z = -292 \quad \Leftrightarrow \quad z = -2; \, y - 11\,(-2) = 25 \quad \Leftrightarrow \quad y = 3;$ and $2x - 3 \cdot 3 + 2 = 13 \Leftrightarrow x = 10$. Therefore, the solution is $(10, 3, -2)$.

24. $\begin{bmatrix} 10 & 10 & -20 & 60 \\ 15 & 20 & 30 & -25 \\ -5 & 30 & -10 & 45 \end{bmatrix}$ $\xrightarrow[2R_3 + R_1 \to R_3]{2R_2 - 3R_1 \to R_2}$ $\begin{bmatrix} 10 & 10 & -20 & 60 \\ 0 & 10 & 120 & -230 \\ 0 & 70 & -40 & 150 \end{bmatrix}$ $\xrightarrow{R_3 - 7R_2 \to R_3}$ $\begin{bmatrix} 10 & 10 & -20 & 60 \\ 0 & 10 & 120 & -230 \\ 0 & 0 & -880 & 1760 \end{bmatrix}$ Thus,

$-880z = 1760 \quad \Leftrightarrow \quad z = -2; \, 10y + 120\,(-2) = -230 \quad \Leftrightarrow \quad y = 1;$ and $10x + 10 + 40 = 60 \Leftrightarrow x = 1$. Therefore, the solution is $(1, 1, -2)$.

25. $\begin{bmatrix} 1 & 1 & 1 & 2 \\ 0 & 1 & -3 & 1 \\ 2 & 1 & 5 & 0 \end{bmatrix}$ $\xrightarrow{R_3 - 2R_1 \to R_3}$ $\begin{bmatrix} 1 & 1 & 1 & 2 \\ 0 & 1 & -3 & 1 \\ 0 & -1 & 3 & -4 \end{bmatrix}$ $\xrightarrow{R_3 + R_2 \to R_3}$ $\begin{bmatrix} 1 & 1 & 1 & 3 \\ 0 & 1 & -3 & 1 \\ 0 & 0 & 0 & -3 \end{bmatrix}$. The third row of the

matrix states $0 = -3$, which is impossible. Hence, the system is inconsistent, and there is no solution.

26. $\begin{bmatrix} 1 & 0 & 3 & 3 \\ 2 & 1 & -2 & 5 \\ 0 & -1 & 8 & 1 \end{bmatrix}$ $\xrightarrow{R_2 - 2R_1 \to R_2}$ $\begin{bmatrix} 1 & 0 & 3 & 3 \\ 0 & 1 & -8 & -1 \\ 0 & -1 & 8 & 1 \end{bmatrix}$ $\xrightarrow{R_3 + R_2 \to R_3}$ $\begin{bmatrix} 1 & 0 & 3 & 3 \\ 0 & 1 & -8 & -1 \\ 0 & 0 & 0 & 0 \end{bmatrix}$. The system is

dependent; there are infinitely many solutions, given by $x + 3t = 3 \quad \Leftrightarrow \quad x = 3 - 3t;$ and $y - 8t = -1 \Leftrightarrow y = 8t - 1$. The solutions are $(3 - 3t, 8t - 1, t)$, where t is any real number.

27. $\begin{bmatrix} 2 & -3 & -9 & -5 \\ 1 & 0 & 3 & 2 \\ -3 & 1 & -4 & -3 \end{bmatrix}$ $\xrightarrow{R_1 \leftrightarrow R_2}$ $\begin{bmatrix} 1 & 0 & 3 & 2 \\ 2 & -3 & -9 & -5 \\ -3 & 1 & -4 & -3 \end{bmatrix}$ $\xrightarrow[R_3 + 3R_1 \to R_3]{R_2 - 2R_1 \to R_2}$ $\begin{bmatrix} 1 & 0 & 3 & 2 \\ 0 & -3 & -15 & -9 \\ 0 & 1 & 5 & 3 \end{bmatrix}$ $\xrightarrow{-\frac{1}{3}R_2}$

$\begin{bmatrix} 1 & 0 & 3 & 2 \\ 0 & 1 & 5 & 3 \\ 0 & 1 & 5 & 3 \end{bmatrix}$ $\xrightarrow{R_3 - R_2 \to R_3}$ $\begin{bmatrix} 1 & 0 & 3 & 2 \\ 0 & 1 & 5 & 3 \\ 0 & 0 & 0 & 0 \end{bmatrix}$. Therefore, this system has infinitely many solutions, given by $x + 3t = 2$

$\Leftrightarrow \quad x = 2 - 3t$, and $y + 5t = 3 \quad \Leftrightarrow \quad y = 3 - 5t$. Hence, the solutions are $(2 - 3t, 3 - 5t, t)$, where t is any real number.

28. $\begin{bmatrix} 1 & -2 & 5 & 3 \\ -2 & 6 & -11 & 1 \\ 3 & -16 & 20 & -26 \end{bmatrix}$ $\xrightarrow[R_3 - 3R_1 \to R_3]{R_2 + 2R_1 \to R_2}$ $\begin{bmatrix} 1 & -2 & 5 & 3 \\ 0 & 2 & -1 & 7 \\ 0 & -10 & 5 & -35 \end{bmatrix}$ $\xrightarrow{R_3 + 5R_2 \to R_3}$ $\begin{bmatrix} 1 & -2 & 5 & 3 \\ 0 & 2 & -1 & 7 \\ 0 & 0 & 0 & 0 \end{bmatrix}$ The system

is dependent; there are infinitely many solutions, given by $2y - t = 7 \quad \Leftrightarrow \quad 2y = t + 7 \quad \Leftrightarrow \quad y = \frac{1}{2}t + \frac{7}{2};$ and $x - 2\left(\frac{1}{2}t + \frac{7}{2}\right) + 5t = 3 \Leftrightarrow x - t - 7 + 5t = 3 \quad \Leftrightarrow \quad x = -4t + 10$. The solutions are $\left(-4t + 10, \frac{1}{2}t + \frac{7}{2}, t\right)$, where t is any real number.

29. $\begin{bmatrix} 1 & -1 & 3 & 3 \\ 4 & -8 & 32 & 24 \\ 2 & -3 & 11 & 4 \end{bmatrix}$ $\xrightarrow[R_3 - 2R_1 \to R_3]{R_2 - 4R_1 \to R_2}$ $\begin{bmatrix} 1 & -1 & 3 & 3 \\ 0 & -4 & 20 & 12 \\ 0 & -1 & 5 & -2 \end{bmatrix}$ $\xrightarrow[R_3 + R_2 \to R_3]{-\frac{1}{4}R_2}$ $\begin{bmatrix} 1 & -1 & 3 & 3 \\ 0 & 1 & -5 & -3 \\ 0 & 0 & 0 & -5 \end{bmatrix}$ The third row of the

matrix states $0 = -5$, which is impossible. Hence, the system is inconsistent, and there is no solution.

30.
$$\begin{bmatrix} -2 & 6 & -2 & -12 \\ 1 & -3 & 2 & 10 \\ -1 & 3 & 2 & 6 \end{bmatrix} \xrightarrow{-\frac{1}{2}R_1} \begin{bmatrix} 1 & -3 & 1 & 6 \\ 1 & -3 & 2 & 10 \\ -1 & 3 & 2 & 6 \end{bmatrix} \xrightarrow[R_3 + R_1 \to R_3]{R_2 - R_1 \to R_2} \begin{bmatrix} 1 & -3 & 1 & 6 \\ 0 & 0 & 1 & 4 \\ 0 & 0 & 3 & 12 \end{bmatrix} \xrightarrow{R_3 - 3R_2 \to R_3} \begin{bmatrix} 1 & -3 & 1 & 6 \\ 0 & 0 & 1 & 4 \\ 0 & 0 & 0 & 0 \end{bmatrix}.$$

The system is dependent; there are infinitely many solutions, given by $z = 4$, and $x - 3y + z = 6$, so $x - 3t + 4 = 6$ $\Leftrightarrow$ $x = 3t + 2$. The solutions are $(3t + 2, t, 4)$, where t is any real number.

31.
$$\begin{bmatrix} 1 & 4 & -2 & -3 \\ 2 & -1 & 5 & 12 \\ 8 & 5 & 11 & 30 \end{bmatrix} \xrightarrow[R_3 - 8R_1 \to R_3]{R_2 - 2R_1 \to R_2} \begin{bmatrix} 1 & 4 & -2 & -3 \\ 0 & -9 & 9 & 18 \\ 0 & -27 & 27 & 54 \end{bmatrix} \xrightarrow{R_3 - 3R_2 \to R_3} \begin{bmatrix} 1 & 4 & -2 & -3 \\ 0 & -9 & 9 & 18 \\ 0 & 0 & 0 & 0 \end{bmatrix}.$$

Therefore, this system has infinitely many solutions, given by $-9y + 9t = 18$ $\Leftrightarrow$ $y = -2 + t$, and $x + 4(-2 + t) - 2t = -3 \Leftrightarrow x = 5 - 2t$. Hence, the solutions are $(5 - 2t, -2 + t, t)$, where t is any real number.

32.
$$\begin{bmatrix} 3 & 2 & -3 & 10 \\ 1 & -1 & -1 & -5 \\ 1 & 4 & -1 & 20 \end{bmatrix} \xrightarrow{R_1 \leftrightarrow R_2} \begin{bmatrix} 1 & -1 & -1 & -5 \\ 3 & 2 & -3 & 10 \\ 1 & 4 & -1 & 20 \end{bmatrix} \xrightarrow[R_3 - R_1 \to R_3]{R_2 - 3R_1 \to R_2} \begin{bmatrix} 1 & -1 & -1 & -5 \\ 0 & 5 & 0 & 25 \\ 0 & 5 & 0 & 25 \end{bmatrix} \xrightarrow{R_3 - R_2 \to R_3}$$

$$\begin{bmatrix} 1 & -1 & -1 & -5 \\ 0 & 5 & 0 & 25 \\ 0 & 0 & 0 & 0 \end{bmatrix}.$$ The system is dependent; there are infinitely many solutions, given by $5s = 25$ $\Leftrightarrow$ $s = 5$, and

$r - 5 - t = -5$ $\Leftrightarrow$ $r = t$. Hence, the solutions are $(t, 5, t)$, where t is any real number.

33.
$$\begin{bmatrix} 2 & 1 & -2 & 12 \\ -1 & -\frac{1}{2} & 1 & -6 \\ 3 & \frac{3}{2} & -3 & 18 \end{bmatrix} \xrightarrow[-R_1]{R_1 \leftrightarrow R_2} \begin{bmatrix} 1 & \frac{1}{2} & -1 & 6 \\ 2 & 1 & -2 & 12 \\ 3 & \frac{3}{2} & -3 & 18 \end{bmatrix} \xrightarrow[R_3 - 3R_1 \to R_3]{R_2 - 2R_1 \to R_2} \begin{bmatrix} 1 & \frac{1}{2} & -1 & 6 \\ 0 & 0 & 0 & 0 \\ 0 & 0 & 0 & 0 \end{bmatrix}$$ Therefore, this system

has infinitely many solutions, given by $x + \frac{1}{2}s - t = 6$ $\Leftrightarrow$ $x = 6 - \frac{1}{2}s + t$. Hence, the solutions are $\left(6 - \frac{1}{2}s + t, s, t\right)$, where s and t are any real numbers.

34.
$$\begin{bmatrix} 0 & 1 & -5 & 7 \\ 3 & 2 & 0 & 12 \\ 3 & 0 & 10 & 80 \end{bmatrix} \xrightarrow{R_1 \leftrightarrow R_2} \begin{bmatrix} 3 & 2 & 0 & 12 \\ 0 & 1 & -5 & 7 \\ 3 & 0 & 10 & 80 \end{bmatrix} \xrightarrow{R_3 - R_1 \to R_3} \begin{bmatrix} 3 & 2 & 0 & 12 \\ 0 & 1 & -5 & 7 \\ 0 & -2 & 10 & 68 \end{bmatrix} \xrightarrow{R_3 + 2R_2 \to R_3} \begin{bmatrix} 3 & 2 & 0 & 12 \\ 0 & 1 & -5 & 7 \\ 0 & 0 & 0 & 82 \end{bmatrix}.$$

Therefore, the system is inconsistent and has no solution.

35.
$$\begin{bmatrix} 4 & -3 & 1 & -8 \\ -2 & 1 & -3 & -4 \\ 1 & -1 & 2 & 3 \end{bmatrix} \xrightarrow{R_1 \leftrightarrow R_3} \begin{bmatrix} 1 & -1 & 2 & 3 \\ -2 & 1 & -3 & -4 \\ 4 & -3 & 1 & -8 \end{bmatrix} \xrightarrow[R_3 - 4R_1 \to R_3]{R_2 + 2R_1 \to R_2} \begin{bmatrix} 1 & -1 & 2 & 3 \\ 0 & -1 & 1 & 2 \\ 0 & 1 & -7 & -20 \end{bmatrix} \xrightarrow{-R_2}$$

$$\begin{bmatrix} 1 & -1 & 2 & 3 \\ 0 & 1 & -1 & -2 \\ 0 & 1 & -7 & -20 \end{bmatrix} \xrightarrow{R_3 - R_2 \to R_3} \begin{bmatrix} 1 & -1 & 2 & 3 \\ 0 & 1 & -1 & -2 \\ 0 & 0 & -6 & -18 \end{bmatrix}.$$ Therefore, $-6z = -18$ $\Leftrightarrow$ $z = 3; y - (3) = -2$

$\Leftrightarrow$ $y = 1$; and $x - (1) + 2(3) = 3$ $\Leftrightarrow$ $x = -2$. Hence, the solution is $(-2, 1, 3)$.

36.
$$\begin{bmatrix} 2 & -3 & 5 & 14 \\ 4 & -1 & -2 & -17 \\ -1 & -1 & 1 & 3 \end{bmatrix} \xrightarrow[-R_1]{R_1 \leftrightarrow R_3} \begin{bmatrix} 1 & 1 & -1 & -3 \\ 4 & -1 & -2 & -17 \\ 2 & -3 & 5 & 14 \end{bmatrix} \xrightarrow[R_3 - 2R_1 \to R_3]{R_2 - 4R_1 \to R_2} \begin{bmatrix} 1 & 1 & -1 & -3 \\ 0 & -5 & 2 & -5 \\ 0 & -5 & 7 & 20 \end{bmatrix} \xrightarrow{R_3 - R_2 \to R_3} \begin{bmatrix} 1 & 1 & -1 & -3 \\ 0 & -5 & 2 & -5 \\ 0 & 0 & 5 & 25 \end{bmatrix}.$$

Thus $5z = 25$ $\Leftrightarrow$ $z = 5; -5y + 2(5) = -5$ $\Leftrightarrow$ $-5y = -15$ $\Leftrightarrow$ $y = 3$; and $x + (3) - (5) = -3$ $\Leftrightarrow$ $x = -1$. Hence, the solution is $(-1, 3, 5)$.

37. $\begin{bmatrix} 1 & 2 & -3 & -5 \\ -2 & -4 & -6 & 10 \\ 3 & 7 & -2 & -13 \end{bmatrix} \xrightarrow[R_3 - 3R_1 \to R_3]{R_2 + 2R_1 \to R_2} \begin{bmatrix} 1 & 2 & -3 & -5 \\ 0 & 0 & -12 & 0 \\ 0 & 1 & 7 & 2 \end{bmatrix} \xrightarrow{R_2 \leftrightarrow R_3} \begin{bmatrix} 1 & 2 & -3 & -5 \\ 0 & 1 & 7 & 2 \\ 0 & 0 & -12 & 0 \end{bmatrix}$. Therefore, $-12z = 0$

$\Leftrightarrow \quad z = 0; y + 7(0) = 2 \quad \Leftrightarrow \quad y = 2$; and $x + 2(2) - 3(0) = -5 \Leftrightarrow x = -9$. Hence, the solution is $(-9, 2, 0)$.

38. $\begin{bmatrix} 3 & -1 & 2 & -1 \\ 4 & -2 & 1 & -7 \\ -1 & 3 & -2 & -1 \end{bmatrix} \xrightarrow[-R_1]{R_1 \leftrightarrow R_3} \begin{bmatrix} 1 & -3 & 2 & 1 \\ 4 & -2 & 1 & -7 \\ 3 & -1 & 2 & -1 \end{bmatrix} \xrightarrow[R_3 - 3R_1 \to R_3]{R_2 - 4R_1 \to R_2} \begin{bmatrix} 1 & -3 & 2 & 1 \\ 0 & 10 & -7 & -11 \\ 0 & 8 & -4 & -4 \end{bmatrix} \xrightarrow{R_2 \leftrightarrow \frac{1}{4}R_3}$

$\begin{bmatrix} 1 & -3 & 2 & 1 \\ 0 & 2 & -1 & -1 \\ 0 & 10 & -7 & -11 \end{bmatrix} \xrightarrow{R_3 - 5R_2 \to R_3} \begin{bmatrix} 1 & -3 & 2 & 1 \\ 0 & 2 & -1 & -1 \\ 0 & 0 & -2 & -6 \end{bmatrix}$. Thus $-2z = -6 \quad \Leftrightarrow \quad z = 3$;

$2y - (3) = -1 \Leftrightarrow 2y = 2 \quad \Leftrightarrow \quad y = 1$; and $x - 3(1) + 2(3) = 1 \quad \Leftrightarrow \quad x = -2$. Hence, the solution is $(-2, 1, 3)$.

39. $\begin{bmatrix} -1 & 2 & 1 & -3 & 3 \\ 3 & -4 & 1 & 1 & 9 \\ -1 & -1 & 1 & 1 & 0 \\ 2 & 1 & 4 & -2 & 3 \end{bmatrix} \xrightarrow{-R_1} \begin{bmatrix} 1 & -2 & -1 & 3 & -3 \\ 3 & -4 & 1 & 1 & 9 \\ -1 & -1 & 1 & 1 & 0 \\ 2 & 1 & 4 & -2 & 3 \end{bmatrix} \xrightarrow[\substack{R_3 + R_1 \to R_3 \\ R_4 - 2R_1 \to R_4}]{R_2 - 3R_1 \to R_2} \begin{bmatrix} 1 & -2 & -1 & 3 & -3 \\ 0 & 2 & 4 & -8 & 18 \\ 0 & -3 & 0 & 4 & -3 \\ 0 & 5 & 6 & -8 & 9 \end{bmatrix} \xrightarrow{\frac{1}{2}R_2}$

$\begin{bmatrix} 1 & -2 & -1 & 3 & -3 \\ 0 & 1 & 2 & -4 & 9 \\ 0 & -3 & 0 & 4 & -3 \\ 0 & 5 & 6 & -8 & 9 \end{bmatrix} \xrightarrow[R_4 - 5R_2 \to R_4]{R_3 + 3R_2 \to R_3} \begin{bmatrix} 1 & -2 & -1 & 3 & -3 \\ 0 & 1 & 2 & -4 & 9 \\ 0 & 0 & 6 & -8 & 24 \\ 0 & 0 & -4 & 12 & -36 \end{bmatrix} \xrightarrow{3R_4 + 2R_3 \to R_4} \begin{bmatrix} 1 & -2 & -1 & 3 & -3 \\ 0 & 1 & 2 & -4 & 9 \\ 0 & 0 & 6 & -8 & 24 \\ 0 & 0 & 0 & 20 & -60 \end{bmatrix}$.

Therefore, $20w = -60 \quad \Leftrightarrow \quad w = -3; 6z + 24 = 24 \Leftrightarrow z = 0$. Then $y + 12 = 9 \quad \Leftrightarrow \quad y = -3$ and $x + 6 - 9 = -3$

$\Leftrightarrow \quad x = 0$. Hence, the solution is $(0, -3, 0, -3)$.

40. $\begin{bmatrix} 1 & 1 & -1 & -1 & 6 \\ 2 & 0 & 1 & -3 & 8 \\ 1 & -1 & 0 & 4 & -10 \\ 3 & 5 & -1 & -1 & 20 \end{bmatrix} \xrightarrow[\substack{R_3 - R_1 \to R_3 \\ R_4 - 3R_1 \to R_4}]{R_2 - 2R_1 \to R_2} \begin{bmatrix} 1 & 1 & -1 & -1 & 6 \\ 0 & -2 & 3 & -1 & -4 \\ 0 & -2 & 1 & 5 & -16 \\ 0 & 2 & 2 & 2 & 2 \end{bmatrix} \xrightarrow[\frac{1}{2}R_4]{\substack{R_2 + R_4 \to R_2 \\ R_3 + R_4 \to R_3}} \begin{bmatrix} 1 & 1 & -1 & -1 & 6 \\ 0 & 0 & 5 & 1 & -2 \\ 0 & 0 & 3 & 7 & -14 \\ 0 & 1 & 1 & 1 & 1 \end{bmatrix}$

$\xrightarrow[R_3 \leftrightarrow R_4]{R_4 \leftrightarrow R_2} \begin{bmatrix} 1 & 1 & -1 & -1 & 6 \\ 0 & 1 & 1 & 1 & 1 \\ 0 & 0 & 5 & 1 & -2 \\ 0 & 0 & 3 & 7 & -14 \end{bmatrix} \xrightarrow{5R_4 - 3R_3 \to R_4} \begin{bmatrix} 1 & 1 & -1 & -1 & 6 \\ 0 & 1 & 1 & 1 & 1 \\ 0 & 0 & 5 & 1 & -2 \\ 0 & 0 & 0 & 32 & -64 \end{bmatrix}$. Thus $32w = -64 \quad \Leftrightarrow \quad w = -2$;

$5z + (-2) = -2 \quad \Leftrightarrow \quad 5z = 0 \quad \Leftrightarrow \quad z = 0; y + 0 + (-2) = 1 \quad \Leftrightarrow \quad y = 3$; and $x + 3 - 0 - (-2) = 6 \Leftrightarrow x = 1$.

Hence the solution is $(1, 3, 0, -2)$.

41.
$$\begin{bmatrix} 1 & 1 & 2 & -1 & -2 \\ 0 & 3 & 1 & 2 & 2 \\ 1 & 1 & 0 & 3 & 2 \\ -3 & 0 & 1 & 2 & 5 \end{bmatrix} \xrightarrow[R_4 + 3R_1 \to R_4]{R_3 - R_1 \to R_3} \begin{bmatrix} 1 & 1 & 2 & -1 & -2 \\ 0 & 3 & 1 & 2 & 2 \\ 0 & 0 & -2 & 4 & 4 \\ 0 & 3 & 7 & -1 & -1 \end{bmatrix} \xrightarrow{R_4 - R_2 \to R_4} \begin{bmatrix} 1 & 1 & 2 & -1 & -2 \\ 0 & 3 & 1 & 2 & 2 \\ 0 & 0 & -2 & 4 & 4 \\ 0 & 0 & 6 & -3 & -3 \end{bmatrix}$$

$$\xrightarrow{R_4 + 3R_3 \to R_4} \begin{bmatrix} 1 & 1 & 2 & -1 & -2 \\ 0 & 3 & 1 & 2 & 2 \\ 0 & 0 & -2 & 4 & 4 \\ 0 & 0 & 0 & 9 & 9 \end{bmatrix}.$$ Therefore, $9w = 9 \quad \Leftrightarrow \quad w = 1; -2z + 4(1) = 4 \quad \Leftrightarrow \quad z = 0.$ Then

$3y + (0) + 2(1) = 2 \quad \Leftrightarrow \quad y = 0$ and $x + (0) + 2(0) - (1) = -2 \quad \Leftrightarrow \quad x = -1.$ Hence, the solution is $(-1, 0, 0, 1).$

42.
$$\begin{bmatrix} 1 & -3 & 2 & 1 & -2 \\ 1 & -2 & 0 & -2 & -10 \\ 0 & 0 & 1 & 5 & 15 \\ 3 & 0 & 2 & 1 & -3 \end{bmatrix} \xrightarrow[R_4 - 3R_1 \to R_4]{R_2 - R_1 \to R_2} \begin{bmatrix} 1 & -3 & 2 & 1 & -2 \\ 0 & 1 & -2 & -3 & -8 \\ 0 & 0 & 1 & 5 & 15 \\ 0 & 9 & -4 & -2 & 3 \end{bmatrix} \xrightarrow{R_4 - 9R_2 \to R_4} \begin{bmatrix} 1 & -3 & 2 & 1 & -2 \\ 0 & 1 & -2 & -3 & -8 \\ 0 & 0 & 1 & 5 & 15 \\ 0 & 0 & 14 & 25 & 75 \end{bmatrix}$$

$$\xrightarrow{R_4 - 14R_3 \to R_4} \begin{bmatrix} 1 & -3 & 2 & 1 & -2 \\ 0 & 1 & -2 & -3 & -8 \\ 0 & 0 & 1 & 5 & 15 \\ 0 & 0 & 0 & -45 & -135 \end{bmatrix}.$$ Thus $-45w = -135 \quad \Leftrightarrow \quad w = 3; z + 5(3) = 15 \quad \Leftrightarrow \quad z = 0;$

$y - 2(0) - 3(3) = -8 \Leftrightarrow y = 1;$ and $x - 3(1) + 2(0) + (3) = -2 \quad \Leftrightarrow \quad x = -2.$ Hence, the solution is $(-2, 1, 0, 3).$

43.
$$\begin{bmatrix} 1 & 0 & 1 & 1 & 4 \\ 0 & 1 & -1 & 0 & -4 \\ 1 & -2 & 3 & 1 & 12 \\ 2 & 0 & -2 & 5 & -1 \end{bmatrix} \xrightarrow[R_4 - 2R_1 \to R_4]{R_3 - R_1 \to R_3} \begin{bmatrix} 1 & 0 & 1 & 1 & 4 \\ 0 & 1 & -1 & 0 & -4 \\ 0 & -2 & 2 & 0 & 8 \\ 0 & 0 & -4 & 3 & -9 \end{bmatrix} \xrightarrow{R_3 + 2R_2 \to R_3} \begin{bmatrix} 1 & 0 & 1 & 1 & 4 \\ 0 & 1 & -1 & 0 & -4 \\ 0 & 0 & 0 & 0 & 0 \\ 0 & 0 & -4 & 3 & -9 \end{bmatrix} \xrightarrow{R_3 \leftrightarrow -R_4}$$

$$\begin{bmatrix} 1 & 0 & 1 & 1 & 4 \\ 0 & 1 & -1 & 0 & -4 \\ 0 & 0 & 4 & -3 & 9 \\ 0 & 0 & 0 & 0 & 0 \end{bmatrix}.$$ Therefore, $4z - 3t = 9 \quad \Leftrightarrow \quad 4z = 9 + 3t \Leftrightarrow z = \frac{9}{4} + \frac{3}{4}t.$ Then we have

$y - \left(\frac{9}{4} + \frac{3}{4}t\right) = -4 \quad \Leftrightarrow \quad y = \frac{-7}{4} + \frac{3}{4}t$ and $x + \left(\frac{9}{4} + \frac{3}{4}t\right) + t = 4 \quad \Leftrightarrow \quad x = \frac{7}{4} - \frac{7}{4}t.$ Hence, the solutions are

$\left(\frac{7}{4} - \frac{7}{4}t, \frac{-7}{4} + \frac{3}{4}t, \frac{9}{4} + \frac{3}{4}t, t\right),$ where t is any real number.

44.
$$\begin{bmatrix} 0 & 1 & -1 & 2 & 0 \\ 3 & 2 & 0 & 1 & 0 \\ 2 & 0 & 0 & 4 & 12 \\ -2 & 0 & -2 & 5 & 6 \end{bmatrix} \xrightarrow[\frac{1}{2}R_3]{\substack{R_2 - R_3 \to R_2 \\ R_4 + R_3 \to R_4}} \begin{bmatrix} 0 & 1 & -1 & 2 & 0 \\ 1 & 2 & 0 & -3 & -12 \\ 1 & 0 & 0 & 2 & 6 \\ 0 & 0 & -2 & 9 & 18 \end{bmatrix} \xrightarrow[R_2 - R_1 \to R_2]{R_1 \leftrightarrow R_3} \begin{bmatrix} 1 & 0 & 0 & 2 & 6 \\ 0 & 2 & 0 & -5 & -18 \\ 0 & 1 & -1 & 2 & 0 \\ 0 & 0 & -2 & 9 & 18 \end{bmatrix}$$

$$\xrightarrow[R_2 \leftrightarrow R_3]{R_2 - 2R_3 \to R_2} \begin{bmatrix} 1 & 0 & 0 & 2 & 6 \\ 0 & 1 & -1 & 2 & 0 \\ 0 & 0 & 2 & -9 & -18 \\ 0 & 0 & -2 & 9 & 18 \end{bmatrix} \xrightarrow{R_4 + R_3 \to R_4} \begin{bmatrix} 1 & 0 & 0 & 2 & 6 \\ 0 & 1 & -1 & 2 & 0 \\ 0 & 0 & 2 & -9 & -18 \\ 0 & 0 & 0 & 0 & 0 \end{bmatrix}.$$ Thus, the system has infinitely

many solutions given by $-2z + 9t = 18 \quad \Leftrightarrow \quad z = \frac{9}{2}t - 9; y - \left(\frac{9}{2}t - 9\right) + 2t = 0 \quad \Leftrightarrow \quad y = \frac{5}{2}t - 9;$ and

$x + 2t = 6 \Leftrightarrow x = -2t + 6.$ So the solutions are $\left(-2t + 6, \frac{5}{2}t - 9, \frac{9}{2}t - 9, t\right),$ where t is any real number.

45. $\begin{bmatrix} 1 & -1 & 0 & 1 & 0 \\ 3 & 0 & -1 & 2 & 0 \\ 1 & -4 & 1 & 2 & 0 \end{bmatrix} \xrightarrow[R_3 - R_1 \to R_3]{R_2 - 3R_1 \to R_2} \begin{bmatrix} 1 & -1 & 0 & 1 & 0 \\ 0 & 3 & -1 & -1 & 0 \\ 0 & -3 & 1 & 1 & 0 \end{bmatrix} \xrightarrow{R_3 + R_2 \to R_3} \begin{bmatrix} 1 & -1 & 0 & 1 & 0 \\ 0 & 3 & -1 & -1 & 0 \\ 0 & 0 & 0 & 0 & 0 \end{bmatrix}.$

Therefore, the system has infinitely many solutions, given by $3y - s - t = 0 \quad\Leftrightarrow\quad y = \frac{1}{3}(s + t)$ and $x - \frac{1}{3}(s + t) + t = 0$ $\Leftrightarrow \quad x = \frac{1}{3}(s - 2t)$. So the solutions are $\left(\frac{1}{3}(s - 2t), \frac{1}{3}(s + t), s, t\right)$, where s and t are any real numbers.

46. $\begin{bmatrix} 2 & -1 & 2 & 1 & 5 \\ -1 & 1 & 4 & -1 & 3 \\ 3 & -2 & -1 & 0 & 0 \end{bmatrix} \xrightarrow[-R_1]{R_1 \leftrightarrow R_2} \begin{bmatrix} 1 & -1 & -4 & 1 & -3 \\ 2 & -1 & 2 & 1 & 5 \\ 3 & -2 & -1 & 0 & 0 \end{bmatrix} \xrightarrow[R_3 - 3R_1 \to R_3]{R_2 - 2R_1 \to R_2} \begin{bmatrix} 1 & -1 & -4 & 1 & -3 \\ 0 & 1 & 10 & -1 & 11 \\ 0 & 1 & 11 & -3 & 9 \end{bmatrix}$

$\xrightarrow{R_3 - R_2 \to R_3} \begin{bmatrix} 1 & -1 & -4 & 1 & -3 \\ 0 & 1 & 10 & -1 & 11 \\ 0 & 0 & 1 & -2 & -2 \end{bmatrix}$. Thus, the system has infinitely many solutions, given by $z - 2t = -2 \quad\Leftrightarrow$

$z = -2 + 2t$; $y + 10(-2 + 2t) - t = 11 \Leftrightarrow y = 31 - 19t$; and $x - (31 - 19t) - 4(-2 + 2t) + t = -3 \quad\Leftrightarrow$ $x = 20 - 12t$. Hence, the solutions are $(20 - 12t, 31 - 19t, -2 + 2t, t)$, where t is any real number.

47. Let x, y, z represent the number of VitaMax, Vitron, and VitaPlus pills taken daily. The matrix representation for the system of equations is

$\begin{bmatrix} 5 & 10 & 15 & 50 \\ 15 & 20 & 0 & 50 \\ 10 & 10 & 10 & 50 \end{bmatrix} \xrightarrow[\frac{1}{5}R_3]{\genfrac{}{}{0pt}{}{\frac{1}{5}R_1}{\frac{1}{5}R_2}} \begin{bmatrix} 1 & 2 & 3 & 10 \\ 3 & 4 & 0 & 10 \\ 2 & 2 & 2 & 10 \end{bmatrix} \xrightarrow[R_3 - 2R_1 \to R_3]{R_2 - 3R_1 \to R_2} \begin{bmatrix} 1 & 2 & 3 & 10 \\ 0 & -2 & -9 & -20 \\ 0 & -2 & -4 & -10 \end{bmatrix} \xrightarrow{R_3 - R_2 \to R_3} \begin{bmatrix} 1 & 2 & 3 & 10 \\ 0 & -2 & -9 & -20 \\ 0 & 0 & 5 & 10 \end{bmatrix}.$

Thus, $5z = 10 \quad\Leftrightarrow\quad z = 2$; $-2y - 18 = -20 \Leftrightarrow y = 1$; and $x + 2 + 6 = 10 \quad\Leftrightarrow\quad x = 2$. Hence, he should take 2 VitaMax, 1 Vitron, and 2 VitaPlus pills daily.

48. Let x be the quantity, in mL, of 10% acid, y the quantity of 20% acid, and z the quantity of 40% acid. Then

$\begin{cases} 0.1x + 0.2y + 0.4z = 18 \\ x + y + z = 100 \\ x - 4z = 0 \end{cases}$ Writing this equation in matrix form, we get $\begin{bmatrix} 1 & 1 & 1 & 100 \\ 0.1 & 0.2 & 0.4 & 18 \\ 1 & 0 & -4 & 0 \end{bmatrix} \xrightarrow[R_3 - R_1 \to R_3]{\genfrac{}{}{0pt}{}{10R_2}{R_2 - R_1 \to R_2}}$

$\begin{bmatrix} 1 & 1 & 1 & 100 \\ 0 & 1 & 3 & 80 \\ 0 & -1 & -5 & -100 \end{bmatrix} \xrightarrow[-R_3]{R_3 + R_2 \to R_3} \begin{bmatrix} 1 & 1 & 1 & 100 \\ 0 & 1 & 3 & 80 \\ 0 & 0 & 2 & 20 \end{bmatrix}$. Thus $2z = 20 \quad\Leftrightarrow\quad z = 10$; $y + 30 = 80 \quad\Leftrightarrow\quad y = 50$;

and $x + 50 + 10 = 100 \quad\Leftrightarrow\quad x = 40$. So he should mix together 40 mL of 10% acid, 50 mL of 20% acid, and 10 mL of 40% acid.

49. Let x, y, and z represent the distance, in miles, of the run, swim, and cycle parts of the race respectively. Then, since time $= \dfrac{\text{distance}}{\text{speed}}$, we get the following equations from the three contestants' race times:

$\begin{cases} \left(\frac{x}{10}\right) + \left(\frac{y}{4}\right) + \left(\frac{z}{20}\right) = 2.5 \\ \left(\frac{x}{7.5}\right) + \left(\frac{y}{6}\right) + \left(\frac{z}{15}\right) = 3 \\ \left(\frac{x}{15}\right) + \left(\frac{y}{3}\right) + \left(\frac{z}{40}\right) = 1.75 \end{cases} \Leftrightarrow \begin{cases} 2x + 5y + z = 50 \\ 4x + 5y + 2z = 90 \\ 8x + 40y + 3z = 210 \end{cases}$ which has the following matrix representation:

$\begin{bmatrix} 2 & 5 & 1 & 50 \\ 4 & 5 & 2 & 90 \\ 8 & 40 & 3 & 210 \end{bmatrix} \xrightarrow[R_3 - 4R_1 \to R_3]{R_2 - 2R_1 \to R_2} \begin{bmatrix} 2 & 5 & 1 & 50 \\ 0 & -5 & 0 & -10 \\ 0 & 20 & -1 & 10 \end{bmatrix} \xrightarrow{R_3 + 4R_2 \to R_3} \begin{bmatrix} 2 & 5 & 1 & 50 \\ 0 & -5 & 0 & -10 \\ 0 & 0 & -1 & -30 \end{bmatrix}.$

Thus, $-z = -30 \quad\Leftrightarrow\quad z = 30$; $-5y = -10 \quad\Leftrightarrow\quad y = 2$; and $2x + 10 + 30 = 50 \quad\Leftrightarrow\quad x = 5$. So the race has a 5 mile run, 2 mile swim, and 30 mile cycle.

50. Let a, b, and c be the number of students in classrooms A, B, and C, respectively, where a, b, $c \geq 0$. Then, the system

of equations is $\begin{cases} a + b + c = 100 \\ \frac{1}{2}a = \frac{1}{5}b \\ \frac{1}{5}b = \frac{1}{3}c \end{cases}$ $\Leftrightarrow$ $\begin{cases} a + b + c = 100 \\ b = \frac{5}{2}a \\ c = \frac{3}{5}b = \frac{3}{2}a \end{cases}$ By substitution, $a + \frac{5}{2}a + \frac{3}{2}a = 100 \Leftrightarrow a = 20$;

$b = \frac{5}{2}(20) = 50$; and $c = \frac{3}{2}(20) = 30$. So there are 20 students in classroom A, 50 students in classroom B, and 30 students in classroom C.

51. Let t be the number of tables produced, c the number of chairs, and a the number of armoires. Then, the system of equations

is $\begin{cases} \frac{1}{2}t + c + a = 300 \\ \frac{1}{2}t + \frac{3}{2}c + a = 400 \\ t + \frac{3}{2}c + 2a = 590 \end{cases}$ $\Leftrightarrow$ $\begin{cases} t + 2c + 2a = 600 \\ t + 3c + 2a = 800 \\ 2t + 3c + 4a = 1180 \end{cases}$ and a matrix representation is

$\begin{bmatrix} 1 & 2 & 2 & 600 \\ 1 & 3 & 2 & 800 \\ 2 & 3 & 4 & 1180 \end{bmatrix}$ $\xrightarrow[R_3 - 2R_1 \to R_3]{R_2 - R_1 \to R_2}$ $\begin{bmatrix} 1 & 2 & 2 & 600 \\ 0 & 1 & 0 & 200 \\ 0 & -1 & 0 & -20 \end{bmatrix}$ $\xrightarrow{R_3 + R_2 \to R_3}$ $\begin{bmatrix} 1 & 2 & 2 & 600 \\ 0 & 1 & 0 & 200 \\ 0 & 0 & 0 & 180 \end{bmatrix}$. The third row states

$0 = 180$, which is impossible, and so the system is inconsistent. Therefore, it is impossible to use all of the available labor-hours.

52. The number of cars entering each intersection must equal the number of cars leaving that intersection. This leads

to the following equations: $\begin{cases} 200 + 180 = x + z \\ x + 70 = 20 + w \\ w + 200 = y + 30 \\ y + z = 400 + 200 \end{cases}$ Simplifying and writing this in matrix form, we get

$\begin{bmatrix} 1 & 0 & 1 & 0 & 380 \\ 1 & 0 & 0 & -1 & -50 \\ 0 & 1 & 0 & -1 & 170 \\ 0 & 1 & 1 & 0 & 600 \end{bmatrix}$ $\xrightarrow[R_4 - R_3 \to R_4]{R_2 - R_1 \to R_2}$ $\begin{bmatrix} 1 & 0 & 1 & 0 & 380 \\ 0 & 0 & -1 & -1 & -430 \\ 0 & 1 & 0 & -1 & 170 \\ 0 & 0 & 1 & 1 & 430 \end{bmatrix}$ $\xrightarrow{R_2 \leftrightarrow R_3}$ $\begin{bmatrix} 1 & 0 & 1 & 0 & 380 \\ 0 & 1 & 0 & -1 & 170 \\ 0 & 0 & -1 & -1 & -430 \\ 0 & 0 & 1 & 1 & 430 \end{bmatrix}$. Therefore,

$z + t = 430$ $\Leftrightarrow$ $z = 430 - t$; $y - t = 170 \Leftrightarrow y = 170 + t$; and $x + 430 - t = 380 \Leftrightarrow x = t - 50$. Since x, y, z, $w \geq 0$, it follows that $50 \leq t \leq 430$, and so the solutions are $(t - 50, 170 + t, 430 - t, t)$, where $50 \leq t \leq 430$.

53. *Line containing the points* $(0, 0)$ *and* $(1, 12)$: Using the general form of a line, $y = ax + b$, we substitute for x and y and solve for a and b. The point $(0, 0)$ gives $0 = a(0) + b$ $\Rightarrow$ $b = 0$; the point $(1, 12)$ gives $12 = a(1) + b$ $\Rightarrow$ $a = 12$. Since $a = 12$ and $b = 0$, the equation of the line is $y = 12x$.

Quadratic containing the points $(0, 0)$, $(1, 12)$, *and* $(3, 6)$: Using the general form of a quadratic, $y = ax^2 + bx + c$, we substitute for x and y and solve for a, b, and c. The point $(0, 0)$ gives $0 = a(0)^2 + b(0) + c$ $\Rightarrow$ $c = 0$; the point $(1, 12)$ gives $12 = a(1)^2 + b(1) + c$ $\Rightarrow$ $a + b = 12$; the point $(3, 6)$ gives $6 = a(3)^2 + b(3) + c$ $\Rightarrow$ $9a + 3b = 6$. Subtracting the third equation from -3 times the third gives $6a = -30$ $\Leftrightarrow$ $a = -5$. So $a + b = 12$ $\Leftrightarrow$ $b = 12 - a$ $\Rightarrow$ $b = 17$. Since $a = -5$, $b = 17$, and $c = 0$, the equation of the quadratic is $y = -5x^2 + 17x$.

Cubic containing the points $(0, 0)$, $(1, 12)$, $(2, 40)$, *and* $(3, 6)$*:* Using the general form of a cubic, $y = ax^3 + bx^2 + cx + d$, we substitute for x and y and solve for a, b, c, and d. The point $(0, 0)$ gives $0 = a\,(0)^3 + b\,(0)^2 + c\,(0) + d \quad \Rightarrow \quad d = 0$; the point the point $(1, 12)$ gives $12 = a\,(1)^3 + b\,(1)^2 + c\,(1) + d \quad \Rightarrow \quad a + b + c + d = 12$; the point $(2, 40)$ gives $40 = a\,(2)^3 + b\,(2)^2 + c\,(2) + d \quad \Rightarrow \quad 8a + 4b + 2c + d = 40$; the point $(3, 6)$ gives $6 = a\,(3)^3 + b\,(3)^2 + c\,(3) + d$

$\Rightarrow \quad 27a + 9b + 3c + d = 6$. Since $d = 0$, the system reduces to $\begin{cases} a + b + c = 12 \\ 8a + 4b + 2c = 40 \\ 27a + 9b + 3c = 6 \end{cases}$ which has representation

$$\begin{bmatrix} 1 & 1 & 1 & 12 \\ 8 & 4 & 2 & 40 \\ 27 & 9 & 3 & 6 \end{bmatrix} \xrightarrow[R_3 - 27R_1 \to R_3]{R_2 - 8R_1 \to R_2} \begin{bmatrix} 1 & 1 & 1 & 12 \\ 0 & -4 & -6 & -56 \\ 0 & -18 & -24 & -318 \end{bmatrix} \xrightarrow[-\frac{1}{6}R_3]{-\frac{1}{2}R_2} \begin{bmatrix} 1 & 1 & 1 & 12 \\ 0 & 2 & 3 & 28 \\ 0 & 3 & 4 & 53 \end{bmatrix} \xrightarrow{2R_3 - 3R_2 \to R_3} \begin{bmatrix} 1 & 1 & 1 & 12 \\ 0 & 2 & 3 & 28 \\ 0 & 0 & -1 & 22 \end{bmatrix}.$$

So $c = -22$ and back-substituting we have $2b + 3\,(-22) = 28 \quad \Leftrightarrow \quad b = 47$ and $a + 47 + (-22) = 0 \Leftrightarrow a = -13$. So the cubic is $y = -13x^3 + 47x^2 - 22x$.

Fourth-degree polynomial containing the points $(0, 0)$, $(1, 12)$, $(2, 40)$, $(3, 6)$, *and* $(-1, -14)$*:* Using the general form of a fourth-degree polynomial, $y = ax^4 + bx^3 + cx^2 + dx + e$, we substitute for x and y and solve for a, b, c, d, and e. The point $(0, 0)$ gives $0 = a\,(0)^4 + b\,(0)^3 + c\,(0)^2 + d\,(0) + e \quad \Rightarrow \quad e = 0$; the point $(1, 12)$ gives $12 = a\,(1)^4 + b\,(1)^3 + c\,(1)^2 + d\,(1) + e$; the point $(2, 40)$ gives $40 = a\,(2)^4 + b\,(2)^3 + c\,(2)^2 + d\,(2) + e$; the point $(3, 6)$ gives $6 = a\,(3)^4 + b\,(3)^3 + c\,(3)^2 + d\,(3) + e$; the point $(-1, -14)$ gives $-14 = a\,(-1)^4 + b\,(-1)^3 + c\,(-1)^2 + d\,(-1) + e$. Since the first equation is $e = 0$, we eliminate e from the other equations to get the system $\begin{cases} a + b + c + d = 12 \\ 16a + 8b + 4c + 2d = 40 \\ 81a + 27b + 9c + 3d = 6 \\ a - b + c - d = -14 \end{cases}$

which has the matrix representation

$$\begin{bmatrix} 1 & 1 & 1 & 1 & 12 \\ 16 & 8 & 4 & 2 & 40 \\ 81 & 27 & 9 & 3 & 6 \\ 1 & -1 & 1 & -1 & -14 \end{bmatrix} \xrightarrow[\substack{R_3 - 81R_1 \to R_3 \\ R_4 - R_1 \to R_4}]{R_2 - 16R_1 \to R_2} \begin{bmatrix} 1 & 1 & 1 & 1 & 12 \\ 0 & -8 & -12 & -14 & -152 \\ 0 & -54 & -72 & -78 & -966 \\ 0 & -2 & 0 & -2 & -26 \end{bmatrix} \xrightarrow[\substack{R_2 \to R_3 \\ R_3 \to R_4}]{-\frac{1}{2}R_4 \to R_2}$$

$$\begin{bmatrix} 1 & 1 & 1 & 1 & 12 \\ 0 & 1 & 0 & 1 & 13 \\ 0 & -8 & -12 & -14 & -152 \\ 0 & -54 & -72 & -78 & -966 \end{bmatrix} \xrightarrow[R_4 + 54R_2 \to R_4]{R_3 + 8R_2 \to R_3} \begin{bmatrix} 1 & 1 & 1 & 1 & 12 \\ 0 & 1 & 0 & 1 & 13 \\ 0 & 0 & -12 & -6 & -48 \\ 0 & 0 & -72 & -24 & -264 \end{bmatrix} \xrightarrow{R_4 - 6R_3 \to R_4} \begin{bmatrix} 1 & 1 & 1 & 1 & 12 \\ 0 & 1 & 0 & 1 & 13 \\ 0 & 0 & -12 & -6 & -48 \\ 0 & 0 & 0 & 12 & 24 \end{bmatrix}.$$

So $d = 2$. Then $-12c - 6\,(2) = -48 \quad \Leftrightarrow \quad c = 3$ and $b + 2 = 13 \quad \Leftrightarrow \quad b = 11$. Finally, $a + 11 + 3 + 2 = 12 \quad \Leftrightarrow \quad a = -4$. So the fourth-degree polynomial containing these points is $y = -4x^4 + 11x^3 + 3x^2 + 2x$.

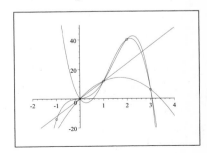

9.5   The Algebra of Matrices

1. The matrices have different dimensions, so they cannot be equal.

2. Since $\frac{1}{4} = 0.25$, $\ln 1 = 0$, $2 = \sqrt{4}$, and $3 = \frac{6}{2}$, the corresponding entries are equal, so the matrices are equal.

3. $\begin{bmatrix} 2 & 6 \\ -5 & 3 \end{bmatrix} + \begin{bmatrix} -1 & -3 \\ 6 & 2 \end{bmatrix} = \begin{bmatrix} 1 & 3 \\ 1 & 5 \end{bmatrix}$

4. $\begin{bmatrix} 0 & 1 & 1 \\ 1 & 1 & 0 \end{bmatrix} - \begin{bmatrix} 2 & 1 & -1 \\ 1 & 3 & -2 \end{bmatrix} = \begin{bmatrix} -2 & 0 & 2 \\ 0 & -2 & 2 \end{bmatrix}$

5. $3 \begin{bmatrix} 1 & 2 \\ 4 & -1 \\ 1 & 0 \end{bmatrix} = \begin{bmatrix} 3 & 6 \\ 12 & -3 \\ 3 & 0 \end{bmatrix}$

6. $2 \begin{bmatrix} 1 & 1 & 0 \\ 1 & 0 & 1 \\ 0 & 1 & 1 \end{bmatrix} + \begin{bmatrix} 1 & 1 \\ 2 & 1 \\ 3 & 1 \end{bmatrix}$ is undefined because these matrices have incompatible dimensions.

7. $\begin{bmatrix} 2 & 6 \\ 1 & 3 \\ 2 & 4 \end{bmatrix} \begin{bmatrix} 1 & -2 \\ 3 & 6 \\ -2 & 0 \end{bmatrix}$ is undefined because these matrices have incompatible dimensions.

8. $\begin{bmatrix} 2 & 1 & 2 \\ 6 & 3 & 4 \end{bmatrix} \begin{bmatrix} 1 & -2 \\ 3 & 6 \\ -2 & 0 \end{bmatrix} = \begin{bmatrix} 1 & 2 \\ 7 & 64 \end{bmatrix}$

9. $\begin{bmatrix} 1 & 2 \\ -1 & 4 \end{bmatrix} \begin{bmatrix} 1 & -2 & 3 \\ 2 & 2 & -1 \end{bmatrix} = \begin{bmatrix} 5 & 2 & 1 \\ 7 & 10 & -7 \end{bmatrix}$

10. $\begin{bmatrix} 2 & -3 \\ 0 & 1 \\ 1 & 2 \end{bmatrix} \begin{bmatrix} 5 \\ 1 \end{bmatrix} = \begin{bmatrix} 7 \\ 1 \\ 7 \end{bmatrix}$

11. $2X + A = B \quad \Leftrightarrow \quad X = \frac{1}{2}(B - A) = \frac{1}{2}\left(\begin{bmatrix} 2 & 5 \\ 3 & 7 \end{bmatrix} - \begin{bmatrix} 4 & 6 \\ 1 & 3 \end{bmatrix} \right) = \frac{1}{2}\begin{bmatrix} -2 & -1 \\ 2 & 4 \end{bmatrix} = \begin{bmatrix} -1 & -\frac{1}{2} \\ 1 & 2 \end{bmatrix}$.

12. $3X - B = C \quad \Leftrightarrow \quad 3X = C + B$. but C is a 3×2 matrix and B is a 2×2 matrix, so $C + B$ is impossible. Thus, there is no solution.

13. $2(B - X) = D$. Since B is a 2×2 matrix, $B - X$ is defined only when X is a 2×2 matrix, so $2(B - X)$ is a 2×2 matrix. But D is a 3×2 matrix. Thus, there is no solution.

14. $5(X - C) = D \quad \Leftrightarrow \quad X - C = \frac{1}{5}D \quad \Leftrightarrow$

$X = \frac{1}{5}D + C = \frac{1}{5}\begin{bmatrix} 10 & 20 \\ 30 & 20 \\ 10 & 0 \end{bmatrix} + \begin{bmatrix} 2 & 3 \\ 1 & 0 \\ 0 & 2 \end{bmatrix} = \begin{bmatrix} 2 & 4 \\ 6 & 4 \\ 2 & 0 \end{bmatrix} + \begin{bmatrix} 2 & 3 \\ 1 & 0 \\ 0 & 2 \end{bmatrix} = \begin{bmatrix} 4 & 7 \\ 7 & 4 \\ 2 & 2 \end{bmatrix}$.

15. $\frac{1}{5}(X + D) = C \quad \Leftrightarrow \quad X + D = 5C \quad \Leftrightarrow$

$X = 5C - D = 5\begin{bmatrix} 2 & 3 \\ 1 & 0 \\ 0 & 2 \end{bmatrix} - \begin{bmatrix} 10 & 20 \\ 30 & 20 \\ 10 & 0 \end{bmatrix} = \begin{bmatrix} 10 & 15 \\ 5 & 0 \\ 0 & 10 \end{bmatrix} - \begin{bmatrix} 10 & 20 \\ 30 & 20 \\ 10 & 0 \end{bmatrix} = \begin{bmatrix} 0 & -5 \\ -25 & -20 \\ -10 & 10 \end{bmatrix}$.

16. $2A = B - 3X \quad \Leftrightarrow \quad 2A - B = -3X \quad \Leftrightarrow$

$X = -\frac{1}{3}(2A - B)$

$= -\frac{1}{3}\left(2\begin{bmatrix} 4 & 6 \\ 1 & 3 \end{bmatrix} - \begin{bmatrix} 2 & 5 \\ 3 & 7 \end{bmatrix}\right) = -\frac{1}{3}\left(\begin{bmatrix} 8 & 12 \\ 2 & 6 \end{bmatrix} - \begin{bmatrix} 2 & 5 \\ 3 & 7 \end{bmatrix}\right) = -\frac{1}{3}\begin{bmatrix} 6 & 7 \\ -1 & -1 \end{bmatrix} = \begin{bmatrix} -2 & -\frac{7}{3} \\ \frac{1}{3} & \frac{1}{3} \end{bmatrix}$

In Solutions 17–38, the matrices A, B, C, D, E, F, and G are defined as follows:

$$A = \begin{bmatrix} 2 & -5 \\ 0 & 7 \end{bmatrix} \qquad B = \begin{bmatrix} 3 & \frac{1}{2} & 5 \\ 1 & -1 & 3 \end{bmatrix} \qquad C = \begin{bmatrix} 2 & -\frac{5}{2} & 0 \\ 0 & 2 & -3 \end{bmatrix}$$

$$D = \begin{bmatrix} 7 & 3 \end{bmatrix} \qquad E = \begin{bmatrix} 1 \\ 2 \\ 0 \end{bmatrix} \qquad F = \begin{bmatrix} 1 & 0 & 0 \\ 0 & 1 & 0 \\ 0 & 0 & 1 \end{bmatrix} \qquad G = \begin{bmatrix} 5 & -3 & 10 \\ 6 & 1 & 0 \\ -5 & 2 & 2 \end{bmatrix}$$

17. $B + C = \begin{bmatrix} 3 & \frac{1}{2} & 5 \\ 1 & -1 & 3 \end{bmatrix} + \begin{bmatrix} 2 & -\frac{5}{2} & 0 \\ 0 & 2 & -3 \end{bmatrix} = \begin{bmatrix} 5 & -2 & 5 \\ 1 & 1 & 0 \end{bmatrix}$

18. $B + F$ is undefined because $B\ (2 \times 3)$ and $F\ (3 \times 3)$ have incompatible dimensions.

19. $C - B = \begin{bmatrix} 2 & -\frac{5}{2} & 0 \\ 0 & 2 & -3 \end{bmatrix} - \begin{bmatrix} 3 & \frac{1}{2} & 5 \\ 1 & -1 & 3 \end{bmatrix} = \begin{bmatrix} -1 & -3 & -5 \\ -1 & 3 & -6 \end{bmatrix}$

20. $5A = 5\begin{bmatrix} 2 & -5 \\ 0 & 7 \end{bmatrix} = \begin{bmatrix} 10 & -25 \\ 0 & 35 \end{bmatrix}$

21. $3B + 2C = 3\begin{bmatrix} 3 & \frac{1}{2} & 5 \\ 1 & -1 & 3 \end{bmatrix} + 2\begin{bmatrix} 2 & -\frac{5}{2} & 0 \\ 0 & 2 & -3 \end{bmatrix} = \begin{bmatrix} 13 & -\frac{7}{2} & 15 \\ 3 & 1 & 3 \end{bmatrix}$

22. $C - 5A$ is undefined because $C\ (2 \times 3)$ and $A\ (2 \times 2)$ have incompatible dimensions.

23. $2C - 6B = 2\begin{bmatrix} 2 & -\frac{5}{2} & 0 \\ 0 & 2 & -3 \end{bmatrix} - 6\begin{bmatrix} 3 & \frac{1}{2} & 5 \\ 1 & -1 & 3 \end{bmatrix} = \begin{bmatrix} -14 & -8 & -30 \\ -6 & 10 & -24 \end{bmatrix}$

24. $DA = \begin{bmatrix} 7 & 3 \end{bmatrix}\begin{bmatrix} 2 & -5 \\ 0 & 7 \end{bmatrix} = \begin{bmatrix} 14 & -14 \end{bmatrix}$

25. AD is undefined because $A\ (2 \times 2)$ and $D\ (1 \times 2)$ have incompatible dimensions.

26. BC is undefined because $B\ (2 \times 3)$ and $C\ (2 \times 3)$ have incompatible dimensions.

27. $BF = \begin{bmatrix} 3 & \frac{1}{2} & 5 \\ 1 & -1 & 3 \end{bmatrix}\begin{bmatrix} 1 & 0 & 0 \\ 0 & 1 & 0 \\ 0 & 0 & 1 \end{bmatrix} = \begin{bmatrix} 3 & \frac{1}{2} & 5 \\ 1 & -1 & 3 \end{bmatrix}$

28. $GF = \begin{bmatrix} 5 & -3 & 10 \\ 6 & 1 & 0 \\ -5 & 2 & 2 \end{bmatrix}\begin{bmatrix} 1 & 0 & 0 \\ 0 & 1 & 0 \\ 0 & 0 & 1 \end{bmatrix} = \begin{bmatrix} 5 & -3 & 10 \\ 6 & 1 & 0 \\ -5 & 2 & 2 \end{bmatrix}$

29. $(DA)B = \begin{bmatrix} 7 & 3 \end{bmatrix}\begin{bmatrix} 2 & -5 \\ 0 & 7 \end{bmatrix}\begin{bmatrix} 3 & \frac{1}{2} & 5 \\ 1 & -1 & 3 \end{bmatrix} = \begin{bmatrix} 14 & -14 \end{bmatrix}\begin{bmatrix} 3 & \frac{1}{2} & 5 \\ 1 & -1 & 3 \end{bmatrix} = \begin{bmatrix} 28 & 21 & 28 \end{bmatrix}$

30. $D(AB) = \begin{bmatrix} 7 & 3 \end{bmatrix} \begin{bmatrix} 2 & -5 \\ 0 & 7 \end{bmatrix} \begin{bmatrix} 3 & \frac{1}{2} & 5 \\ 1 & -1 & 3 \end{bmatrix} = \begin{bmatrix} 7 & 3 \end{bmatrix} \begin{bmatrix} 1 & 6 & -5 \\ 7 & -7 & 21 \end{bmatrix} = \begin{bmatrix} 28 & 21 & 28 \end{bmatrix}$

31. $GE = \begin{bmatrix} 5 & -3 & 10 \\ 6 & 1 & 0 \\ -5 & 2 & 2 \end{bmatrix} \begin{bmatrix} 1 \\ 2 \\ 0 \end{bmatrix} = \begin{bmatrix} -1 \\ 8 \\ -1 \end{bmatrix}$

32. $A^2 = \begin{bmatrix} 2 & -5 \\ 0 & 7 \end{bmatrix} \begin{bmatrix} 2 & -5 \\ 0 & 7 \end{bmatrix} = \begin{bmatrix} 4 & -45 \\ 0 & 49 \end{bmatrix}$

33. $A^3 = \begin{bmatrix} 2 & -5 \\ 0 & 7 \end{bmatrix} \begin{bmatrix} 2 & -5 \\ 0 & 7 \end{bmatrix} \begin{bmatrix} 2 & -5 \\ 0 & 7 \end{bmatrix} = \begin{bmatrix} 4 & -45 \\ 0 & 49 \end{bmatrix} \begin{bmatrix} 2 & -5 \\ 0 & 7 \end{bmatrix} = \begin{bmatrix} 8 & -335 \\ 0 & 343 \end{bmatrix}$

34. $DB + DC = D(B+C) = \begin{bmatrix} 7 & 3 \end{bmatrix} \left(\begin{bmatrix} 3 & \frac{1}{2} & 5 \\ 1 & -1 & 3 \end{bmatrix} + \begin{bmatrix} 2 & -\frac{5}{2} & 0 \\ 0 & 2 & -3 \end{bmatrix} \right) = \begin{bmatrix} 7 & 3 \end{bmatrix} \begin{bmatrix} 5 & -2 & 5 \\ 1 & 1 & 0 \end{bmatrix} = \begin{bmatrix} 38 & -11 & 35 \end{bmatrix}$

35. B^2 is undefined because the dimensions 2×3 and 2×3 are incompatible.

36. $F^2 = \begin{bmatrix} 1 & 0 & 0 \\ 0 & 1 & 0 \\ 0 & 0 & 1 \end{bmatrix} \begin{bmatrix} 1 & 0 & 0 \\ 0 & 1 & 0 \\ 0 & 0 & 1 \end{bmatrix} = \begin{bmatrix} 1 & 0 & 0 \\ 0 & 1 & 0 \\ 0 & 0 & 1 \end{bmatrix}$

37. $BF + FE$ is undefined because the dimensions $(2 \times 3) \cdot (3 \times 3) = (2 \times 3)$ and $(3 \times 3) \cdot (3 \times 1) = (3 \times 1)$ are incompatible.

38. $ABE = \begin{bmatrix} 2 & -5 \\ 0 & 7 \end{bmatrix} \begin{bmatrix} 3 & \frac{1}{2} & 5 \\ 1 & -1 & 3 \end{bmatrix} \begin{bmatrix} 1 \\ 2 \\ 0 \end{bmatrix} = \begin{bmatrix} 1 & 6 & -5 \\ 7 & -7 & 21 \end{bmatrix} \begin{bmatrix} 1 \\ 2 \\ 0 \end{bmatrix} = \begin{bmatrix} 13 \\ -7 \end{bmatrix}$

39. $\begin{bmatrix} x & 2y \\ 4 & 6 \end{bmatrix} = \begin{bmatrix} 2 & -2 \\ 2x & -6y \end{bmatrix}$. Thus we must solve the system $\begin{cases} x = 2 \\ 2y = -2 \\ 4 = 2x \\ 6 = -6y \end{cases}$ So $x = 2$ and $2y = -2 \iff y = -1$.

Since these values for x and y also satisfy the last two equations, the solution is $x = 2$, $y = -1$.

40. $3 \cdot \begin{bmatrix} x & y \\ y & x \end{bmatrix} = \begin{bmatrix} 6 & -9 \\ -9 & 6 \end{bmatrix}$. Since $3 \cdot \begin{bmatrix} x & y \\ y & x \end{bmatrix} = \begin{bmatrix} 3x & 3y \\ 3y & 3x \end{bmatrix}$, we must solve the system $\begin{cases} 3x = 6 \\ 3y = -9 \\ 3x = 6 \\ 3y = -9 \end{cases}$ So $3x = 6 \iff$

$x = 2$ and $3y = -9 \iff y = -3$. Thus, the solution is $x = 2$, $y = -3$.

41. $2 \begin{bmatrix} x & y \\ x+y & x-y \end{bmatrix} = \begin{bmatrix} 2 & -4 \\ -2 & 6 \end{bmatrix}$. Since $2 \begin{bmatrix} x & y \\ x+y & x-y \end{bmatrix} = \begin{bmatrix} 2x & 2y \\ 2(x+y) & 2(x-y) \end{bmatrix}$, Thus we must solve the

system $\begin{cases} 2x = 2 \\ 2y = -4 \\ 2(x+y) = -2 \\ 2(x-y) = 6 \end{cases}$ So $x = 1$ and $y = -2$. Since these values for x and y also satisfy the last two equations, the

solution is $x = 1$, $y = -2$.

42. $\begin{bmatrix} x & y \\ -y & x \end{bmatrix} - \begin{bmatrix} y & x \\ x & -y \end{bmatrix} = \begin{bmatrix} 4 & -4 \\ -6 & 6 \end{bmatrix} \Leftrightarrow \begin{bmatrix} x-y & y-x \\ -x-y & x+y \end{bmatrix} = \begin{bmatrix} 4 & -4 \\ -6 & 6 \end{bmatrix}$. Thus we must solve the

system $\begin{cases} x-y = 4 \\ y-x = -4 \\ -x-y = -6 \\ x+y = 6 \end{cases}$ Adding the first equation to the last equation gives $2x = 10 \quad \Leftrightarrow \quad x = 5$ and $5 + y = 6$

$\Leftrightarrow \quad y = 1$. So the solution is $x = 5$, $y = 1$.

43. $\begin{cases} 2x - 5y = 7 \\ 3x + 2y = 4 \end{cases}$ written as a matrix equation is $\begin{bmatrix} 2 & -5 \\ 3 & 2 \end{bmatrix} \begin{bmatrix} x \\ y \end{bmatrix} = \begin{bmatrix} 7 \\ 4 \end{bmatrix}$.

44. $\begin{cases} 6x - y + z = 12 \\ 2x + z = 7 \\ y - 2z = 4 \end{cases}$ written as a matrix equation is $\begin{bmatrix} 6 & -1 & 1 \\ 2 & 0 & 1 \\ 0 & 1 & -2 \end{bmatrix} \begin{bmatrix} x \\ y \\ z \end{bmatrix} = \begin{bmatrix} 12 \\ 7 \\ 4 \end{bmatrix}$.

45. $\begin{cases} 3x_1 + 2x_2 - x_3 + x_4 = 0 \\ x_1 - x_3 = 5 \\ 3x_2 + x_3 - x_4 = 4 \end{cases}$ written as a matrix equation is $\begin{bmatrix} 3 & 2 & -1 & 1 \\ 1 & 0 & -1 & 0 \\ 0 & 3 & 1 & -1 \end{bmatrix} \begin{bmatrix} x_1 \\ x_2 \\ x_3 \\ x_4 \end{bmatrix} = \begin{bmatrix} 0 \\ 5 \\ 4 \end{bmatrix}$.

46. $\begin{cases} x - y + z = 2 \\ 4x - 2y - z = 2 \\ x + y + 5z = 2 \\ -x - y - z = 2 \end{cases}$ written as a matrix equation is $\begin{bmatrix} 1 & -1 & 1 \\ 4 & -2 & -1 \\ 1 & 1 & 5 \\ -1 & -1 & -1 \end{bmatrix} \begin{bmatrix} x \\ y \\ z \end{bmatrix} = \begin{bmatrix} 2 \\ 2 \\ 2 \\ 2 \end{bmatrix}$.

47. $A = \begin{bmatrix} 1 & 0 & 6 & -1 \\ 2 & \frac{1}{2} & 4 & 0 \end{bmatrix}$, $B = \begin{bmatrix} 1 & 7 & -9 & 2 \end{bmatrix}$, and $C = \begin{bmatrix} 1 \\ 0 \\ -1 \\ -2 \end{bmatrix}$. ABC is undefined because the dimensions of A (2×4)

and B (1×4) are not compatible. $ACB = \begin{bmatrix} -3 \\ -2 \end{bmatrix} \begin{bmatrix} 1 & 7 & -9 & 2 \end{bmatrix} = \begin{bmatrix} -3 & -21 & 27 & -6 \\ -2 & -14 & 18 & -4 \end{bmatrix}$. BAC is undefined

because the dimensions of B (1×4) and A (2×4) are not compatible. BCA is undefined because the dimensions of C (4×1) and A (2×4) are not compatible. CAB is undefined because the dimensions of C (4×1) and A (2×4) are not compatible. CBA is undefined because the dimensions of B (1×4) and A (2×4) are not compatible.

48. (a) Let $A = \begin{bmatrix} a & b \\ c & d \end{bmatrix}$ and $B = \begin{bmatrix} e & f \\ g & h \end{bmatrix}$. Then $A + B = \begin{bmatrix} a+e & b+f \\ c+g & d+h \end{bmatrix}$, and

$$(A+B)^2 = \begin{bmatrix} a+e & b+f \\ c+g & d+h \end{bmatrix} \begin{bmatrix} a+e & b+f \\ c+g & d+h \end{bmatrix}$$

$$= \begin{bmatrix} (a+e)^2 + (b+f)(c+g) & (a+e)(b+f) + (b+f)(d+h) \\ (c+g)(a+e) + (d+h)(c+g) & (c+g)(b+f) + (d+h)^2 \end{bmatrix};$$

$$A^2 = \begin{bmatrix} a & b \\ c & d \end{bmatrix} \begin{bmatrix} a & b \\ c & d \end{bmatrix} = \begin{bmatrix} a^2 + bc & ab + bd \\ ac + cd & bc + d^2 \end{bmatrix}; \; B^2 = \begin{bmatrix} e & f \\ g & h \end{bmatrix} \begin{bmatrix} e & f \\ g & h \end{bmatrix} = \begin{bmatrix} e^2 + fg & ef + fh \\ eg + gh & fg + h^2 \end{bmatrix};$$

$$AB = \begin{bmatrix} a & b \\ c & d \end{bmatrix} \begin{bmatrix} e & f \\ g & h \end{bmatrix} = \begin{bmatrix} ae + bg & af + bh \\ ce + dg & cf + dh \end{bmatrix}; \; BA = \begin{bmatrix} e & f \\ g & h \end{bmatrix} \begin{bmatrix} a & b \\ c & d \end{bmatrix} = \begin{bmatrix} ae + cf & be + df \\ ag + ch & bg + dh \end{bmatrix}. \text{ Then}$$

$$A^2 + AB + BA + B^2 = \begin{bmatrix} a^2 + bc + ae + bg + ae + cf + e^2 + fg & ab + bd + ef + fh + af + bh + be + df \\ ac + cd + eg + gh + ce + dg + ag + ch & bc + d^2 + fg + h^2 + cf + dh + bg + dh \end{bmatrix}$$

$$= \begin{bmatrix} a^2 + 2ae + e^2 + b(c+g) + f(c+g) & a(b+f) + e(b+f) + b(d+h) + f(d+h) \\ c(a+e) + g(a+e) + d(c+g) + h(c+g) & c(b+f) + g(b+f) + d^2 + 2dh + h^2 \end{bmatrix}$$

$$= \begin{bmatrix} (a+e)^2 + (b+f)(c+g) & (a+e)(b+f) + (b+f)(d+h) \\ (c+g)(a+e) + (d+h)(c+g) & (c+g)(b+f) + (d+h)^2 \end{bmatrix} = (A+B)^2$$

(b) No. From Exercise 46, $(A + B)^2 = (A + B)(A + B) = A^2 + AB + BA + B^2 \neq A^2 + 2AB + B^2$ unless $AB = BA$ which is, in general, not true, as we saw in Example 3.

49. (a) $BA = \begin{bmatrix} \$0.90 & \$0.80 & \$1.10 \end{bmatrix} \begin{bmatrix} 4000 & 1000 & 3500 \\ 400 & 300 & 200 \\ 700 & 500 & 9000 \end{bmatrix} = \begin{bmatrix} \$4690 & \$1690 & \$13,210 \end{bmatrix}$

(b) The entries in the product matrix represent the total food sales in Santa Monica, Long Beach, and Anaheim, respectively.

50. (a) $AB = \begin{bmatrix} 12 & 10 & 0 \\ 4 & 4 & 20 \\ 8 & 9 & 12 \end{bmatrix} \begin{bmatrix} \$1000 & \$500 \\ \$2000 & \$1200 \\ \$1500 & \$1000 \end{bmatrix} = \begin{bmatrix} \$32,000 & \$18,000 \\ \$42,000 & \$26,800 \\ \$44,000 & \$26,800 \end{bmatrix}$

(b) The daily profit in January from the Biloxi plant is the $(2, 1)$ matrix entry, namely $42,000.

(c) The total daily profit from all three plants in February was $18,000 + \$26,800 + \$26,800 = \$71,600$.

51. (a) $AB = \begin{bmatrix} 6 & 10 & 14 & 28 \end{bmatrix} \begin{bmatrix} 2000 & 2500 \\ 3000 & 1500 \\ 2500 & 1000 \\ 1000 & 500 \end{bmatrix} = \begin{bmatrix} 105,000 & 58,000 \end{bmatrix}$

(b) That day they canned 105,000 ounces of tomato sauce and 58,000 ounces of tomato paste.

52. (a) $AC = \begin{bmatrix} 120 & 50 & 60 \\ 40 & 25 & 30 \\ 60 & 30 & 20 \end{bmatrix} \begin{bmatrix} 0.10 \\ 0.50 \\ 1.00 \end{bmatrix} = \begin{bmatrix} 97.00 \\ 46.50 \\ 41.00 \end{bmatrix}$ Amy's stand sold $97 worth of produce on Saturday, Beth's stand

sold $46.50 worth, and Chad's stand sold $41 worth.

(b) $BC = \begin{bmatrix} 100 & 60 & 30 \\ 35 & 20 & 20 \\ 60 & 25 & 30 \end{bmatrix} \begin{bmatrix} 0.10 \\ 0.50 \\ 1.00 \end{bmatrix} = \begin{bmatrix} 70.00 \\ 33.50 \\ 48.50 \end{bmatrix}$ Amy's stand sold $70 worth of produce on Sunday, Beth's stand

sold $33.50 worth, and Chad's stand sold $48.50 worth.

(c) $A + B = \begin{bmatrix} 120 & 50 & 60 \\ 40 & 25 & 30 \\ 60 & 30 & 20 \end{bmatrix} + \begin{bmatrix} 100 & 60 & 30 \\ 35 & 20 & 20 \\ 60 & 25 & 30 \end{bmatrix} = \begin{bmatrix} 220 & 110 & 90 \\ 75 & 45 & 50 \\ 120 & 55 & 50 \end{bmatrix}$ This represents the melons, squash, and

tomatoes they sold during the weekend.

(d) $(A + B) C = \left(\begin{bmatrix} 120 & 50 & 60 \\ 40 & 25 & 30 \\ 60 & 30 & 20 \end{bmatrix} + \begin{bmatrix} 100 & 60 & 30 \\ 35 & 20 & 20 \\ 60 & 25 & 30 \end{bmatrix} \right) \begin{bmatrix} 0.10 \\ 0.50 \\ 1.00 \end{bmatrix} = \begin{bmatrix} 220 & 110 & 90 \\ 75 & 45 & 50 \\ 120 & 55 & 50 \end{bmatrix} \begin{bmatrix} 0.10 \\ 0.50 \\ 1.00 \end{bmatrix} = \begin{bmatrix} 167.00 \\ 80.00 \\ 89.50 \end{bmatrix}$

During the weekend, Amy's stand sold $167 worth, Beth's stand sold $80 worth, and Chad's stand sold $89.50 worth

of produce. Notice that $(A + B) C = AC + BC = \begin{bmatrix} 97.00 \\ 46.50 \\ 41.00 \end{bmatrix} + \begin{bmatrix} 70.00 \\ 33.50 \\ 48.50 \end{bmatrix} = \begin{bmatrix} 167.00 \\ 80.00 \\ 89.50 \end{bmatrix}$.

53. (a) $\begin{bmatrix} 1 & 0 & 1 & 0 & 1 & 1 \\ 0 & 3 & 0 & 1 & 2 & 1 \\ 1 & 2 & 0 & 0 & 3 & 0 \\ 1 & 3 & 2 & 3 & 2 & 0 \\ 0 & 3 & 0 & 0 & 2 & 1 \\ 1 & 2 & 0 & 1 & 3 & 1 \end{bmatrix}$ **(b)** $\begin{bmatrix} 2 & 1 & 2 & 1 & 2 & 2 \\ 1 & 3 & 1 & 2 & 3 & 2 \\ 2 & 3 & 1 & 1 & 3 & 1 \\ 2 & 3 & 3 & 3 & 3 & 1 \\ 1 & 3 & 1 & 1 & 3 & 2 \\ 2 & 3 & 1 & 2 & 3 & 2 \end{bmatrix}$ **(c)** $\begin{bmatrix} 2 & 3 & 2 & 3 & 2 & 2 \\ 3 & 0 & 3 & 2 & 1 & 2 \\ 2 & 1 & 3 & 3 & 0 & 3 \\ 2 & 0 & 1 & 0 & 1 & 3 \\ 3 & 0 & 3 & 3 & 1 & 2 \\ 2 & 1 & 3 & 2 & 0 & 2 \end{bmatrix}$

(d) $\begin{bmatrix} 3 & 3 & 3 & 3 & 3 & 3 \\ 3 & 0 & 3 & 3 & 0 & 3 \\ 3 & 0 & 3 & 3 & 0 & 3 \\ 3 & 0 & 0 & 0 & 0 & 3 \\ 3 & 0 & 3 & 3 & 0 & 3 \\ 3 & 0 & 3 & 3 & 0 & 3 \end{bmatrix}$ **(e)**

54. Suppose A is $n \times m$ and B is $i \times j$. If the product AB is defined, then $m = i$. If the product BA is defined, then $j = n$. Thus if both products are defined and if A is $n \times m$, then B must be $m \times n$.

55. $A = \begin{bmatrix} 1 & 1 \\ 0 & 1 \end{bmatrix}$; $A^2 = \begin{bmatrix} 1 & 1 \\ 0 & 1 \end{bmatrix} \begin{bmatrix} 1 & 1 \\ 0 & 1 \end{bmatrix} = \begin{bmatrix} 1 & 2 \\ 0 & 1 \end{bmatrix}$; $A^3 = A \cdot A^2 = \begin{bmatrix} 1 & 1 \\ 0 & 1 \end{bmatrix} \begin{bmatrix} 1 & 2 \\ 0 & 1 \end{bmatrix} = \begin{bmatrix} 1 & 3 \\ 0 & 1 \end{bmatrix}$;

$A^4 = A \cdot A^3 = \begin{bmatrix} 1 & 1 \\ 0 & 1 \end{bmatrix} \begin{bmatrix} 1 & 3 \\ 0 & 1 \end{bmatrix} = \begin{bmatrix} 1 & 4 \\ 0 & 1 \end{bmatrix}$. Therefore, it seems that $A^n = \begin{bmatrix} 1 & n \\ 0 & 1 \end{bmatrix}$.

56. $A = \begin{bmatrix} 1 & 1 \\ 1 & 1 \end{bmatrix}$; $A^2 = \begin{bmatrix} 1 & 1 \\ 1 & 1 \end{bmatrix} \begin{bmatrix} 1 & 1 \\ 1 & 1 \end{bmatrix} = \begin{bmatrix} 2 & 2 \\ 2 & 2 \end{bmatrix}$; $A^3 = A \cdot A^2 = \begin{bmatrix} 1 & 1 \\ 1 & 1 \end{bmatrix} \begin{bmatrix} 2 & 2 \\ 2 & 2 \end{bmatrix} = \begin{bmatrix} 4 & 4 \\ 4 & 4 \end{bmatrix}$;

$A^4 = A \cdot A^3 = \begin{bmatrix} 1 & 1 \\ 1 & 1 \end{bmatrix} \begin{bmatrix} 4 & 4 \\ 4 & 4 \end{bmatrix} = \begin{bmatrix} 8 & 8 \\ 8 & 8 \end{bmatrix}$. From this pattern, we see that $A^n = \begin{bmatrix} 2^{n-1} & 2^{n-1} \\ 2^{n-1} & 2^{n-1} \end{bmatrix}$.

57. Let $A = \begin{bmatrix} a & b \\ c & d \end{bmatrix}$. For the first matrix, we have $A^2 = \begin{bmatrix} a & b \\ c & d \end{bmatrix}$.

$\begin{bmatrix} a & b \\ c & d \end{bmatrix} = \begin{bmatrix} a^2 + bc & ab + bd \\ ac + cd & bc + d^2 \end{bmatrix} = \begin{bmatrix} a^2 + bc & b(a+d) \\ c(a+d) & bc + d^2 \end{bmatrix}$. So $A^2 = \begin{bmatrix} 4 & 0 \\ 0 & 9 \end{bmatrix}$ $\Leftrightarrow$ $\begin{cases} a^2 + bc = 4 \\ b(a+d) = 0 \\ c(a+d) = 0 \\ bc + d^2 = 9 \end{cases}$

If $a + d = 0$, then $a = -d$, so $4 = a^2 + bc = (-d)^2 + bc = d^2 + bc = 9$, which is a contradiction. Thus $a + d \neq 0$. Since $b(a+d) = 0$ and $c(a+d) = 0$, we must have $b = 0$ and $c = 0$. So the first equation becomes $a^2 = 4$ $\Rightarrow$ $a = \pm 2$, and the fourth equation becomes $d^2 = 9$ $\Rightarrow$ $d = \pm 3$.

Thus the square roots of $\begin{bmatrix} 4 & 0 \\ 0 & 9 \end{bmatrix}$ are $A_1 = \begin{bmatrix} 2 & 0 \\ 0 & 3 \end{bmatrix}$, $A_2 = \begin{bmatrix} 2 & 0 \\ 0 & -3 \end{bmatrix}$, $A_3 = \begin{bmatrix} -2 & 0 \\ 0 & 3 \end{bmatrix}$, and $A_4 = \begin{bmatrix} -2 & 0 \\ 0 & -3 \end{bmatrix}$.

For the second matrix, we have $A^2 = \begin{bmatrix} 1 & 5 \\ 0 & 9 \end{bmatrix}$ $\Leftrightarrow$ $\begin{cases} a^2 + bc = 1 \\ b(a+d) = 5 \\ c(a+d) = 0 \\ bc + d^2 = 9 \end{cases}$ Since $a + d \neq 0$ and $c(a+d) = 0$, we must

have $c = 0$. The equations then simplify into the system $\begin{cases} a^2 = 1 \\ b(a+d) = 5 \\ d^2 = 9 \end{cases}$ $\Rightarrow$ $\begin{cases} a = \pm 1 \\ b(a+d) = 5 \\ d = \pm 3 \end{cases}$

We consider the four possible values of a and d. If $a = 1$ and $d = 3$, then $b(a+d) = 5$ $\Rightarrow$ $b(4) = 5$ $\Rightarrow$ $b = \frac{5}{4}$. If $a = 1$ and $d = -3$, then $b(a+d) = 5$ $\Rightarrow$ $b(-2) = 5$ $\Rightarrow$ $b = -\frac{5}{2}$. If $a = -1$ and $d = 3$, then $b(a+d) = 5$ $\Rightarrow$ $b(2) = 5$ $\Rightarrow$ $b = \frac{5}{2}$. If $a = -1$ and $d = -3$, then $b(a+d) = 5$ $\Rightarrow$ $b(-4) = 5$ $\Rightarrow$ $b = -\frac{5}{4}$. Thus,

the square roots of $\begin{bmatrix} 1 & 5 \\ 0 & 9 \end{bmatrix}$ are $A_1 = \begin{bmatrix} 1 & \frac{5}{4} \\ 0 & 3 \end{bmatrix}$, $A_2 = \begin{bmatrix} 1 & -\frac{5}{2} \\ 0 & -3 \end{bmatrix}$, $A_3 = \begin{bmatrix} -1 & \frac{5}{2} \\ 0 & 3 \end{bmatrix}$, and $A_4 = \begin{bmatrix} -1 & -\frac{5}{4} \\ 0 & -3 \end{bmatrix}$.

9.6   Inverses of Matrices and Matrix Equations

1. $A = \begin{bmatrix} 4 & 1 \\ 7 & 2 \end{bmatrix}$; $B = \begin{bmatrix} 2 & -1 \\ -7 & 4 \end{bmatrix}$.

$AB = \begin{bmatrix} 4 & 1 \\ 7 & 2 \end{bmatrix} \begin{bmatrix} 2 & -1 \\ -7 & 4 \end{bmatrix} = \begin{bmatrix} 1 & 0 \\ 0 & 1 \end{bmatrix}$ and $BA = \begin{bmatrix} 2 & -1 \\ -7 & 4 \end{bmatrix} \begin{bmatrix} 4 & 1 \\ 7 & 2 \end{bmatrix} = \begin{bmatrix} 1 & 0 \\ 0 & 1 \end{bmatrix}$.

2. $A = \begin{bmatrix} 2 & -3 \\ 4 & -7 \end{bmatrix}$; $B = \begin{bmatrix} \frac{7}{2} & -\frac{3}{2} \\ 2 & -1 \end{bmatrix}$. $AB = \begin{bmatrix} 2 & -3 \\ 4 & -7 \end{bmatrix} \begin{bmatrix} \frac{7}{2} & -\frac{3}{2} \\ 2 & -1 \end{bmatrix} = \begin{bmatrix} 1 & 0 \\ 0 & 1 \end{bmatrix}$ and

$BA = \begin{bmatrix} \frac{7}{2} & -\frac{3}{2} \\ 2 & -1 \end{bmatrix} \begin{bmatrix} 2 & -3 \\ 4 & -7 \end{bmatrix} = \begin{bmatrix} 1 & 0 \\ 0 & 1 \end{bmatrix}$.

3. $A = \begin{bmatrix} 1 & 3 & -1 \\ 1 & 4 & 0 \\ -1 & -3 & 2 \end{bmatrix}$; $B = \begin{bmatrix} 8 & -3 & 4 \\ -2 & 1 & -1 \\ 1 & 0 & 1 \end{bmatrix}$. $AB = \begin{bmatrix} 1 & 3 & -1 \\ 1 & 4 & 0 \\ -1 & -3 & 2 \end{bmatrix} \begin{bmatrix} 8 & -3 & 4 \\ -2 & 1 & -1 \\ 1 & 0 & 1 \end{bmatrix} = \begin{bmatrix} 1 & 0 & 0 \\ 0 & 1 & 0 \\ 0 & 0 & 1 \end{bmatrix}$ and

$BA = \begin{bmatrix} 8 & -3 & 4 \\ -2 & 1 & -1 \\ 1 & 0 & 1 \end{bmatrix} \begin{bmatrix} 1 & 3 & -1 \\ 1 & 4 & 0 \\ -1 & -3 & 2 \end{bmatrix} = \begin{bmatrix} 1 & 0 & 0 \\ 0 & 1 & 0 \\ 0 & 0 & 1 \end{bmatrix}$.

4. $A = \begin{bmatrix} 3 & 2 & 4 \\ 1 & 1 & -6 \\ 2 & 1 & 12 \end{bmatrix}$; $B = \begin{bmatrix} 9 & -10 & -8 \\ -12 & 14 & 11 \\ -\frac{1}{2} & \frac{1}{2} & \frac{1}{2} \end{bmatrix}$. $AB = \begin{bmatrix} 3 & 2 & 4 \\ 1 & 1 & -6 \\ 2 & 1 & 12 \end{bmatrix} \begin{bmatrix} 9 & -10 & -8 \\ -12 & 14 & 11 \\ -\frac{1}{2} & \frac{1}{2} & \frac{1}{2} \end{bmatrix} = \begin{bmatrix} 1 & 0 & 0 \\ 0 & 1 & 0 \\ 0 & 0 & 1 \end{bmatrix}$ and

$BA = \begin{bmatrix} 9 & -10 & -8 \\ -12 & 14 & 11 \\ -\frac{1}{2} & \frac{1}{2} & \frac{1}{2} \end{bmatrix} \begin{bmatrix} 3 & 2 & 4 \\ 1 & 1 & -6 \\ 2 & 1 & 12 \end{bmatrix} = \begin{bmatrix} 1 & 0 & 0 \\ 0 & 1 & 0 \\ 0 & 0 & 1 \end{bmatrix}$.

5. $A = \begin{bmatrix} 7 & 4 \\ 3 & 2 \end{bmatrix} \Leftrightarrow A^{-1} = \frac{1}{14 - 12} \begin{bmatrix} 2 & -4 \\ -3 & 7 \end{bmatrix} = \begin{bmatrix} 1 & -2 \\ -\frac{3}{2} & \frac{7}{2} \end{bmatrix}$. Then,

$AA^{-1} = \begin{bmatrix} 7 & 4 \\ 3 & 2 \end{bmatrix} \begin{bmatrix} 1 & -2 \\ -\frac{3}{2} & \frac{7}{2} \end{bmatrix} = \begin{bmatrix} 1 & 0 \\ 0 & 1 \end{bmatrix}$ and $A^{-1}A = \begin{bmatrix} 1 & -2 \\ -\frac{3}{2} & \frac{7}{2} \end{bmatrix} \begin{bmatrix} 7 & 4 \\ 3 & 2 \end{bmatrix} = \begin{bmatrix} 1 & 0 \\ 0 & 1 \end{bmatrix}$.

6. $B = \begin{bmatrix} 1 & 3 & 2 \\ 0 & 2 & 2 \\ -2 & -1 & 0 \end{bmatrix}$. We begin with a 3×6 matrix whose left half is B and whose right half is I_3.

$\begin{bmatrix} 1 & 3 & 2 & 1 & 0 & 0 \\ 0 & 2 & 2 & 0 & 1 & 0 \\ -2 & -1 & 0 & 0 & 0 & 1 \end{bmatrix} \xrightarrow{R_3 + 2R_1 \to R_3} \begin{bmatrix} 1 & 3 & 2 & 1 & 0 & 0 \\ 0 & 2 & 2 & 0 & 1 & 0 \\ 0 & 5 & 4 & 2 & 0 & 1 \end{bmatrix} \xrightarrow{2R_3 - 5R_2 \to R_3} \begin{bmatrix} 1 & 3 & 2 & 1 & 0 & 0 \\ 0 & 2 & 2 & 0 & 1 & 0 \\ 0 & 0 & -2 & 4 & -5 & 2 \end{bmatrix} \begin{array}{c} \frac{1}{2}R_2 \\ \xrightarrow{} \\ -\frac{1}{2}R_3 \end{array}$

$\begin{bmatrix} 1 & 3 & 2 & 1 & 0 & 0 \\ 0 & 1 & 1 & 0 & \frac{1}{2} & 0 \\ 0 & 0 & 1 & -2 & \frac{5}{2} & -1 \end{bmatrix} \begin{array}{c} \xrightarrow{R_1 - 3R_2 \to R_1} \\ \xrightarrow{R_2 - R_3 \to R_2} \end{array} \begin{bmatrix} 1 & 0 & -1 & 1 & -\frac{3}{2} & 0 \\ 0 & 1 & 0 & 2 & -2 & 1 \\ 0 & 0 & 1 & -2 & \frac{5}{2} & -1 \end{bmatrix} \xrightarrow{R_1 + R_3 \to R_1} \begin{bmatrix} 1 & 0 & 0 & -1 & 1 & -1 \\ 0 & 1 & 0 & 2 & -2 & 1 \\ 0 & 0 & 1 & -2 & \frac{5}{2} & -1 \end{bmatrix}$.

Then $B^{-1} = \begin{bmatrix} -1 & 1 & -1 \\ 2 & -2 & 1 \\ -2 & \frac{5}{2} & -1 \end{bmatrix}$; $B^{-1}B = \begin{bmatrix} -1 & 1 & -1 \\ 2 & -2 & 1 \\ -2 & \frac{5}{2} & -1 \end{bmatrix} \begin{bmatrix} 1 & 3 & 2 \\ 0 & 2 & 2 \\ -2 & -1 & 0 \end{bmatrix} = \begin{bmatrix} 1 & 0 & 0 \\ 0 & 1 & 0 \\ 0 & 0 & 1 \end{bmatrix}$; and

$BB^{-1} = \begin{bmatrix} 1 & 3 & 2 \\ 0 & 2 & 2 \\ -2 & -1 & 0 \end{bmatrix} \begin{bmatrix} -1 & 1 & -1 \\ 2 & -2 & 1 \\ -2 & \frac{5}{2} & -1 \end{bmatrix} = \begin{bmatrix} 1 & 0 & 0 \\ 0 & 1 & 0 \\ 0 & 0 & 1 \end{bmatrix}$.

7. $\begin{bmatrix} 5 & 3 \\ 3 & 2 \end{bmatrix}^{-1} = \dfrac{1}{10-9} \begin{bmatrix} 2 & -3 \\ -3 & 5 \end{bmatrix} = \begin{bmatrix} 2 & -3 \\ -3 & 5 \end{bmatrix}$

8. $\begin{bmatrix} 3 & 4 \\ 7 & 9 \end{bmatrix}^{-1} = \dfrac{1}{27-28} \begin{bmatrix} 9 & -4 \\ -7 & 3 \end{bmatrix} = -\begin{bmatrix} 9 & -4 \\ -7 & 3 \end{bmatrix} = \begin{bmatrix} -9 & 4 \\ 7 & -3 \end{bmatrix}$

9. $\begin{bmatrix} 2 & 5 \\ -5 & -13 \end{bmatrix}^{-1} = \dfrac{1}{-26+25} \begin{bmatrix} -13 & -5 \\ 5 & 2 \end{bmatrix} = \begin{bmatrix} 13 & 5 \\ -5 & -2 \end{bmatrix}$

10. $\begin{bmatrix} -7 & 4 \\ 8 & -5 \end{bmatrix}^{-1} = \dfrac{1}{35-32} \begin{bmatrix} -5 & -4 \\ -8 & -7 \end{bmatrix} = \begin{bmatrix} -\frac{5}{3} & -\frac{4}{3} \\ -\frac{8}{3} & -\frac{7}{3} \end{bmatrix}$

11. $\begin{bmatrix} 6 & -3 \\ -8 & 4 \end{bmatrix}^{-1} = \dfrac{1}{24-24} \begin{bmatrix} 4 & 3 \\ 8 & 6 \end{bmatrix}$, which is not defined, and so there is no inverse.

12. $\begin{bmatrix} \frac{1}{2} & \frac{1}{3} \\ 5 & 4 \end{bmatrix}^{-1} = \dfrac{1}{2-\frac{5}{3}} \begin{bmatrix} 4 & -\frac{1}{3} \\ -5 & \frac{1}{2} \end{bmatrix} = \begin{bmatrix} 12 & -1 \\ -15 & \frac{3}{2} \end{bmatrix}$

13. $\begin{bmatrix} 0.4 & -1.2 \\ 0.3 & 0.6 \end{bmatrix}^{-1} = \dfrac{1}{0.24+0.36} \begin{bmatrix} 0.6 & 1.2 \\ -0.3 & 0.4 \end{bmatrix} = \begin{bmatrix} 1 & 2 \\ -\frac{1}{2} & \frac{2}{3} \end{bmatrix}$

14. $\begin{bmatrix} 4 & 2 & 3 & 1 & 0 & 0 \\ 3 & 3 & 2 & 0 & 1 & 0 \\ 1 & 0 & 1 & 0 & 0 & 1 \end{bmatrix} \xrightarrow[4R_3 - R_1 \to R_3]{4R_2 - 3R_1 \to R_2} \begin{bmatrix} 4 & 2 & 3 & 1 & 0 & 0 \\ 0 & 6 & -1 & -3 & 4 & 0 \\ 0 & -2 & 1 & -1 & 0 & 4 \end{bmatrix} \xrightarrow[3R_3 + R_2 \to R_3]{R_1 + R_3 \to R_1} \begin{bmatrix} 4 & 0 & 4 & 0 & 0 & 4 \\ 0 & 6 & -1 & -3 & 4 & 0 \\ 0 & 0 & 2 & -6 & 4 & 12 \end{bmatrix} \xrightarrow[\frac{1}{2}R_3]{\frac{1}{4}R_1}$

$\begin{bmatrix} 1 & 0 & 1 & 0 & 0 & 1 \\ 0 & 6 & -1 & -3 & 4 & 0 \\ 0 & 0 & 1 & -3 & 2 & 6 \end{bmatrix} \xrightarrow[R_2 + R_3 \to R_2]{R_1 - R_3 \to R_1} \begin{bmatrix} 1 & 0 & 0 & 3 & -2 & -5 \\ 0 & 6 & 0 & -6 & 6 & 6 \\ 0 & 0 & 1 & -3 & 2 & 6 \end{bmatrix} \xrightarrow{\frac{1}{6}R_2} \begin{bmatrix} 1 & 0 & 0 & 3 & -2 & -5 \\ 0 & 1 & 0 & -1 & 1 & 1 \\ 0 & 0 & 1 & -3 & 2 & 6 \end{bmatrix}.$

Therefore, the inverse matrix is $\begin{bmatrix} 3 & -2 & -5 \\ -1 & 1 & 1 \\ -3 & 2 & 6 \end{bmatrix}$.

15. $\begin{bmatrix} 2 & 4 & 1 & 1 & 0 & 0 \\ -1 & 1 & -1 & 0 & 1 & 0 \\ 1 & 4 & 0 & 0 & 0 & 1 \end{bmatrix} \xrightarrow[2R_3 - R_1 \to R_3]{2R_2 + R_1 \to R_2} \begin{bmatrix} 2 & 4 & 1 & 1 & 0 & 0 \\ 0 & 6 & -1 & 1 & 2 & 0 \\ 0 & 4 & -1 & -1 & 0 & 2 \end{bmatrix} \xrightarrow[3R_1 - 2R_2 \to R_1]{3R_3 - 2R_2 \to R_3} \begin{bmatrix} 6 & 0 & 5 & 1 & -4 & 0 \\ 0 & 6 & -1 & 1 & 2 & 0 \\ 0 & 0 & -1 & -5 & -4 & 6 \end{bmatrix}$

$\xrightarrow[R_2 - R_3 \to R_2]{R_1 + 5R_3 \to R_1} \begin{bmatrix} 6 & 0 & 0 & -24 & -24 & 30 \\ 0 & 6 & 0 & 6 & 6 & -6 \\ 0 & 0 & -1 & -5 & -4 & 6 \end{bmatrix} \xrightarrow[\frac{1}{6}R_2, \, -R_3]{\frac{1}{6}R_1} \begin{bmatrix} 1 & 0 & 0 & -4 & -4 & 5 \\ 0 & 1 & 0 & 1 & 1 & -1 \\ 0 & 0 & 1 & 5 & 4 & -6 \end{bmatrix}.$

Therefore, the inverse matrix is $\begin{bmatrix} -4 & -4 & 5 \\ 1 & 1 & -1 \\ 5 & 4 & -6 \end{bmatrix}$.

16. $\begin{bmatrix} 5 & 7 & 4 & 1 & 0 & 0 \\ 3 & -1 & 3 & 0 & 1 & 0 \\ 6 & 7 & 5 & 0 & 0 & 1 \end{bmatrix}$ $\xrightarrow[R_1 \leftrightarrow R_3]{R_3 - R_1 \to R_3}$ $\begin{bmatrix} 1 & 0 & 1 & -1 & 0 & 1 \\ 3 & -1 & 3 & 0 & 1 & 0 \\ 5 & 7 & 4 & 1 & 0 & 0 \end{bmatrix}$ $\xrightarrow[R_3 - 5R_1 \to R_3]{R_2 - 3R_1 \to R_2}$ $\begin{bmatrix} 1 & 0 & 1 & -1 & 0 & 1 \\ 0 & -1 & 0 & 3 & 1 & -3 \\ 0 & 7 & -1 & 6 & 0 & -5 \end{bmatrix}$

$\xrightarrow{R_3 + 7R_2 \to R_3}$ $\begin{bmatrix} 1 & 0 & 1 & -1 & 0 & 1 \\ 0 & -1 & 0 & 3 & 1 & -3 \\ 0 & 0 & -1 & 27 & 7 & -26 \end{bmatrix}$ $\xrightarrow[-R_2, -R_3]{R_1 + R_3 \to R_1}$ $\begin{bmatrix} 1 & 0 & 0 & 26 & 7 & -25 \\ 0 & 1 & 0 & -3 & -1 & 3 \\ 0 & 0 & 1 & -27 & -7 & 26 \end{bmatrix}.$

Therefore, the inverse matrix is $\begin{bmatrix} 26 & 7 & -25 \\ -3 & -1 & 3 \\ -27 & -7 & 26 \end{bmatrix}.$

17. $\begin{bmatrix} 1 & 2 & 3 & 1 & 0 & 0 \\ 4 & 5 & -1 & 0 & 1 & 0 \\ 1 & -1 & -10 & 0 & 0 & 1 \end{bmatrix}$ $\xrightarrow[R_3 - R_1 \to R_3]{R_2 - 4R_1 \to R_2}$ $\begin{bmatrix} 1 & 2 & 3 & 1 & 0 & 0 \\ 0 & -3 & -13 & -4 & 1 & 0 \\ 0 & -3 & -13 & -1 & 0 & 1 \end{bmatrix}$ $\xrightarrow{R_3 - R_2 \to R_3}$ $\begin{bmatrix} 1 & 2 & 3 & 1 & 0 & 0 \\ 0 & -3 & -13 & -4 & 1 & 0 \\ 0 & 0 & 0 & 3 & -1 & 1 \end{bmatrix}.$

Since the left half of the last row consists entirely of zeros, there is no inverse matrix.

18. $\begin{bmatrix} 2 & 1 & 0 & 1 & 0 & 0 \\ 1 & 1 & 4 & 0 & 1 & 0 \\ 2 & 1 & 2 & 0 & 0 & 1 \end{bmatrix}$ $\xrightarrow{R_1 \leftrightarrow R_2}$ $\begin{bmatrix} 1 & 1 & 4 & 0 & 1 & 0 \\ 2 & 1 & 0 & 1 & 0 & 0 \\ 2 & 1 & 2 & 0 & 0 & 1 \end{bmatrix}$ $\xrightarrow[R_3 - 2R_1 \to R_3]{R_2 - 2R_1 \to R_2}$ $\begin{bmatrix} 1 & 1 & 4 & 0 & 1 & 0 \\ 0 & -1 & -8 & 1 & -2 & 0 \\ 0 & -1 & -6 & 0 & -2 & 1 \end{bmatrix}$ $\xrightarrow[R_3 - R_2 \to R_3]{R_1 + R_2 \to R_1}$

$\begin{bmatrix} 1 & 0 & -4 & 1 & -1 & 0 \\ 0 & -1 & -8 & 1 & -2 & 0 \\ 0 & 0 & 2 & -1 & 0 & 1 \end{bmatrix}$ $\xrightarrow[R_2 + 4R_3 \to R_2]{R_1 + 2R_3 \to R_1}$ $\begin{bmatrix} 1 & 0 & 0 & -1 & -1 & 2 \\ 0 & -1 & 0 & -3 & -2 & 4 \\ 0 & 0 & 2 & -1 & 0 & 1 \end{bmatrix}$ $\xrightarrow[\frac{1}{2} R_3]{-R_2}$ $\begin{bmatrix} 1 & 0 & 0 & -1 & -1 & 2 \\ 0 & 1 & 0 & 3 & 2 & -4 \\ 0 & 0 & 1 & -\frac{1}{2} & 0 & \frac{1}{2} \end{bmatrix}.$

Therefore, the inverse matrix is $\begin{bmatrix} -1 & -1 & 2 \\ 3 & 2 & -4 \\ -\frac{1}{2} & 0 & \frac{1}{2} \end{bmatrix}.$

19. $\begin{bmatrix} 0 & -2 & 2 & 1 & 0 & 0 \\ 3 & 1 & 3 & 0 & 1 & 0 \\ 1 & -2 & 3 & 0 & 0 & 1 \end{bmatrix}$ $\xrightarrow{R_1 \leftrightarrow R_3}$ $\begin{bmatrix} 1 & -2 & 3 & 0 & 0 & 1 \\ 3 & 1 & 3 & 0 & 1 & 0 \\ 0 & -2 & 2 & 1 & 0 & 0 \end{bmatrix}$ $\xrightarrow{R_2 - 3R_1 \to R_2}$ $\begin{bmatrix} 1 & -2 & 3 & 0 & 0 & 1 \\ 0 & 7 & -6 & 0 & 1 & -3 \\ 0 & -2 & 2 & 1 & 0 & 0 \end{bmatrix}$

$\xrightarrow[R_2 + 3R_3 \to R_2]{R_1 - R_3 \to R_1}$ $\begin{bmatrix} 1 & 0 & 1 & -1 & 0 & 1 \\ 0 & 1 & 0 & 3 & 1 & -3 \\ 0 & -2 & 2 & 1 & 0 & 0 \end{bmatrix}$ $\xrightarrow{R_3 + 2R_2 \to R_3}$ $\begin{bmatrix} 1 & 0 & 1 & -1 & 0 & 1 \\ 0 & 1 & 0 & 3 & 1 & -3 \\ 0 & 0 & 2 & 7 & 2 & -6 \end{bmatrix}$ $\xrightarrow{\frac{1}{2} R_3}$

$\begin{bmatrix} 1 & 0 & 1 & -1 & 0 & 1 \\ 0 & 1 & 0 & 3 & 1 & -3 \\ 0 & 0 & 1 & \frac{7}{2} & 1 & -3 \end{bmatrix}$ $\xrightarrow{R_1 - R_3 \to R_1}$ $\begin{bmatrix} 1 & 0 & 0 & -\frac{9}{2} & -1 & 4 \\ 0 & 1 & 0 & 3 & 1 & -3 \\ 0 & 0 & 1 & \frac{7}{2} & 1 & -3 \end{bmatrix}.$ Therefore, the inverse matrix is $\begin{bmatrix} -\frac{9}{2} & -1 & 4 \\ 3 & 1 & -3 \\ \frac{7}{2} & 1 & -3 \end{bmatrix}.$

20. $\begin{bmatrix} 3 & -2 & 0 & 1 & 0 & 0 \\ 5 & 1 & 1 & 0 & 1 & 0 \\ 2 & -2 & 0 & 0 & 0 & 1 \end{bmatrix}$ $\xrightarrow{R_1 - R_3 \to R_1}$ $\begin{bmatrix} 1 & 0 & 0 & 1 & 0 & -1 \\ 5 & 1 & 1 & 0 & 1 & 0 \\ 2 & -2 & 0 & 0 & 0 & 1 \end{bmatrix}$ $\xrightarrow[R_3 - 2R_1 \to R_3]{R_2 - 5R_1 \to R_2}$ $\begin{bmatrix} 1 & 0 & 0 & 1 & 0 & -1 \\ 0 & 1 & 1 & -5 & 1 & 5 \\ 0 & -2 & 0 & -2 & 0 & 3 \end{bmatrix}$ $\xrightarrow{R_3 + 2R_2 \to R_3}$

$\begin{bmatrix} 1 & 0 & 0 & 1 & 0 & -1 \\ 0 & 1 & 1 & -5 & 1 & 5 \\ 0 & 0 & 2 & -12 & 2 & 13 \end{bmatrix}$ $\xrightarrow[R_2 - R_3 \to R_2]{\frac{1}{2} R_3}$ $\begin{bmatrix} 1 & 0 & 0 & 1 & 0 & -1 \\ 0 & 1 & 0 & 1 & 0 & -\frac{3}{2} \\ 0 & 0 & 1 & -6 & 1 & \frac{13}{2} \end{bmatrix}.$ Therefore, the inverse matrix is $\begin{bmatrix} 1 & 0 & -1 \\ 1 & 0 & -\frac{3}{2} \\ -6 & 1 & \frac{13}{2} \end{bmatrix}.$

21.
$$\begin{bmatrix} 1 & 2 & 0 & 3 & 1 & 0 & 0 & 0 \\ 0 & 1 & 1 & 1 & 0 & 1 & 0 & 0 \\ 0 & 1 & 0 & 1 & 0 & 0 & 1 & 0 \\ 1 & 2 & 0 & 2 & 0 & 0 & 0 & 1 \end{bmatrix} \xrightarrow[R_4 - R_1 \to R_4]{R_3 - R_2 \to R_3} \begin{bmatrix} 1 & 2 & 0 & 3 & 1 & 0 & 0 & 0 \\ 0 & 1 & 1 & 1 & 0 & 1 & 0 & 0 \\ 0 & 0 & -1 & 0 & 0 & -1 & 1 & 0 \\ 0 & 0 & 0 & -1 & -1 & 0 & 0 & 1 \end{bmatrix} \xrightarrow[-R_4]{-R_3} \begin{bmatrix} 1 & 2 & 0 & 3 & 1 & 0 & 0 & 0 \\ 0 & 1 & 1 & 1 & 0 & 1 & 0 & 0 \\ 0 & 0 & 1 & 0 & 0 & 1 & -1 & 0 \\ 0 & 0 & 0 & 1 & 1 & 0 & 0 & -1 \end{bmatrix}$$

$$\xrightarrow[R_2 - R_3 \to R_2]{R_1 - 2R_2 \to R_1} \begin{bmatrix} 1 & 0 & -2 & 1 & 1 & -2 & 0 & 0 \\ 0 & 1 & 0 & 1 & 0 & 0 & 1 & 0 \\ 0 & 0 & 1 & 0 & 0 & 1 & -1 & 0 \\ 0 & 0 & 0 & 1 & 1 & 0 & 0 & -1 \end{bmatrix} \xrightarrow[R_2 - R_4 \to R_2]{R_1 + 2R_3 \to R_1} \begin{bmatrix} 1 & 0 & 0 & 1 & 1 & 0 & -2 & 0 \\ 0 & 1 & 0 & 0 & -1 & 0 & 1 & 1 \\ 0 & 0 & 1 & 0 & 0 & 1 & -1 & 0 \\ 0 & 0 & 0 & 1 & 1 & 0 & 0 & -1 \end{bmatrix} \xrightarrow{R_1 \to R_1 - R_4}$$

$$\begin{bmatrix} 1 & 0 & 0 & 0 & 0 & 0 & -2 & 1 \\ 0 & 1 & 0 & 0 & -1 & 0 & 1 & 1 \\ 0 & 0 & 1 & 0 & 0 & 1 & -1 & 0 \\ 0 & 0 & 0 & 1 & 1 & 0 & 0 & -1 \end{bmatrix}. \text{ Therefore, the inverse matrix is } \begin{bmatrix} 0 & 0 & -2 & 1 \\ -1 & 0 & 1 & 1 \\ 0 & 1 & -1 & 0 \\ 1 & 0 & 0 & -1 \end{bmatrix}.$$

22.
$$\begin{bmatrix} 1 & 0 & 1 & 0 & 1 & 0 & 0 & 0 \\ 0 & 1 & 0 & 1 & 0 & 1 & 0 & 0 \\ 1 & 1 & 1 & 0 & 0 & 0 & 1 & 0 \\ 1 & 1 & 1 & 1 & 0 & 0 & 0 & 1 \end{bmatrix} \xrightarrow[R_3 - R_1 \to R_3]{R_4 - R_1 \to R_4} \begin{bmatrix} 1 & 0 & 1 & 0 & 1 & 0 & 0 & 0 \\ 0 & 1 & 0 & 1 & 0 & 1 & 0 & 0 \\ 0 & 1 & 0 & 0 & -1 & 0 & 1 & 0 \\ 0 & 1 & 0 & 1 & -1 & 0 & 0 & 1 \end{bmatrix} \xrightarrow[R_3 - R_2 \to R_3]{R_4 - R_2 \to R_4} \begin{bmatrix} 1 & 0 & 1 & 0 & 1 & 0 & 0 & 0 \\ 0 & 1 & 0 & 1 & 0 & 1 & 0 & 0 \\ 0 & 0 & 0 & -1 & -1 & -1 & 1 & 0 \\ 0 & 0 & 0 & 0 & -1 & -1 & 0 & 1 \end{bmatrix}.$$

Therefore, there is no inverse matrix.

23. $\begin{cases} 5x + 3y = 4 \\ 3x + 2y = 0 \end{cases}$ is equivalent to the matrix equation $\begin{bmatrix} 5 & 3 \\ 3 & 2 \end{bmatrix} \begin{bmatrix} x \\ y \end{bmatrix} = \begin{bmatrix} 4 \\ 0 \end{bmatrix}$. Using the inverse from Exercise 3,

$\begin{bmatrix} x \\ y \end{bmatrix} = \begin{bmatrix} 2 & -3 \\ -3 & 5 \end{bmatrix} \begin{bmatrix} 4 \\ 0 \end{bmatrix} = \begin{bmatrix} 8 \\ -12 \end{bmatrix}$. Therefore, $x = 8$ and $y = -12$.

24. $\begin{cases} 3x + 4y = 10 \\ 7x + 9y = 20 \end{cases}$ is equivalent to the matrix equation $\begin{bmatrix} 3 & 4 \\ 7 & 9 \end{bmatrix} \begin{bmatrix} x \\ y \end{bmatrix} = \begin{bmatrix} 10 \\ 20 \end{bmatrix} \Leftrightarrow$

$\begin{bmatrix} x \\ y \end{bmatrix} = \begin{bmatrix} -9 & 4 \\ 7 & -3 \end{bmatrix} \begin{bmatrix} 10 \\ 20 \end{bmatrix} = \begin{bmatrix} -10 \\ 10 \end{bmatrix}$. Therefore, $x = -10$ and $y = 10$.

25. $\begin{cases} 2x + 5y = 2 \\ -5x - 13y = 20 \end{cases}$ is equivalent to the matrix equation $\begin{bmatrix} 2 & 5 \\ -5 & -13 \end{bmatrix} \begin{bmatrix} x \\ y \end{bmatrix} = \begin{bmatrix} 2 \\ 20 \end{bmatrix}$. Using the inverse from

Exercise 5, $\begin{bmatrix} x \\ y \end{bmatrix} = \begin{bmatrix} 13 & 5 \\ -5 & -2 \end{bmatrix} \begin{bmatrix} 2 \\ 20 \end{bmatrix} = \begin{bmatrix} 126 \\ -50 \end{bmatrix}$. Therefore, $x = 126$ and $y = -50$.

26. $\begin{cases} -7x + 4y = 0 \\ 8x - 5y = 100 \end{cases}$ is equivalent to the matrix equation $\begin{bmatrix} -7 & 4 \\ 8 & -5 \end{bmatrix} \begin{bmatrix} x \\ y \end{bmatrix} = \begin{bmatrix} 0 \\ 100 \end{bmatrix} \Leftrightarrow$

$\begin{bmatrix} x \\ y \end{bmatrix} = \begin{bmatrix} -\frac{5}{3} & -\frac{4}{3} \\ -\frac{8}{3} & -\frac{7}{3} \end{bmatrix} \begin{bmatrix} 0 \\ 100 \end{bmatrix} = \begin{bmatrix} -\frac{400}{3} \\ -\frac{700}{3} \end{bmatrix}$. Therefore, $x = -\frac{400}{3}$ and $y = -\frac{700}{3}$.

27. $\begin{cases} 2x + 4y + z = 7 \\ -x + y - z = 0 \\ x + 4y = -2 \end{cases}$ is equivalent to the matrix equation $\begin{bmatrix} 2 & 4 & 1 \\ -1 & 1 & -1 \\ 1 & 4 & 0 \end{bmatrix} \begin{bmatrix} x \\ y \\ z \end{bmatrix} = \begin{bmatrix} 7 \\ 0 \\ -2 \end{bmatrix}$. Using the inverse from

Exercise 11, $\begin{bmatrix} x \\ y \\ z \end{bmatrix} = \begin{bmatrix} -4 & -4 & 5 \\ 1 & 1 & -1 \\ 5 & 4 & -6 \end{bmatrix} \begin{bmatrix} 7 \\ 0 \\ -2 \end{bmatrix} = \begin{bmatrix} -38 \\ 9 \\ 47 \end{bmatrix}$. Therefore, $x = -38$, $y = 9$, and $z = 47$.

28. $\begin{cases} 5x + 7y + 4z = 1 \\ 3x - y + 3z = 1 \\ 6x + 7y + 5z = 1 \end{cases}$ is equivalent to the matrix equation $\begin{bmatrix} 5 & 7 & 4 \\ 3 & -1 & 3 \\ 6 & 7 & 5 \end{bmatrix} \begin{bmatrix} x \\ y \\ z \end{bmatrix} = \begin{bmatrix} 1 \\ 1 \\ 1 \end{bmatrix}$ $\Leftrightarrow$

$\begin{bmatrix} x \\ y \\ z \end{bmatrix} = \begin{bmatrix} 26 & 7 & -25 \\ -3 & -1 & 3 \\ -27 & -7 & 26 \end{bmatrix} \begin{bmatrix} 1 \\ 1 \\ 1 \end{bmatrix} = \begin{bmatrix} 8 \\ -1 \\ -8 \end{bmatrix}$. Therefore, $x = 8$, $y = -1$, and $z = -8$.

29. $\begin{cases} -2y + 2z = 12 \\ 3x + y + 3z = -2 \\ x - 2y + 3z = 8 \end{cases}$ is equivalent to the matrix equation $\begin{bmatrix} 0 & -2 & 2 \\ 3 & 1 & 3 \\ 1 & -2 & 3 \end{bmatrix} \begin{bmatrix} x \\ y \\ z \end{bmatrix} = \begin{bmatrix} 12 \\ -2 \\ 8 \end{bmatrix}$. Using the inverse from

Exercise 15, $\begin{bmatrix} x \\ y \\ z \end{bmatrix} = \begin{bmatrix} -\frac{9}{2} & -1 & 4 \\ 3 & 1 & -3 \\ \frac{7}{2} & 1 & -3 \end{bmatrix} \begin{bmatrix} 12 \\ -2 \\ 8 \end{bmatrix} = \begin{bmatrix} -20 \\ 10 \\ 16 \end{bmatrix}$. Therefore, $x = -20$, $y = 10$, and $z = 16$.

30. $\begin{cases} x + 2y + 3w = 0 \\ y + z + w = 1 \\ y + w = 2 \\ x + 2y + 2w = 3 \end{cases}$ is equivalent to the matrix equation $\begin{bmatrix} 1 & 2 & 0 & 3 \\ 0 & 1 & 1 & 1 \\ 0 & 1 & 0 & 1 \\ 1 & 2 & 0 & 2 \end{bmatrix} \begin{bmatrix} x \\ y \\ z \\ w \end{bmatrix} = \begin{bmatrix} 0 \\ 1 \\ 2 \\ 3 \end{bmatrix}$ $\Leftrightarrow$

$\begin{bmatrix} x \\ y \\ z \\ w \end{bmatrix} = \begin{bmatrix} 0 & 0 & -2 & 1 \\ -1 & 0 & 1 & 1 \\ 0 & 1 & -1 & 0 \\ 1 & 0 & 0 & -1 \end{bmatrix} \begin{bmatrix} 0 \\ 1 \\ 2 \\ 3 \end{bmatrix} = \begin{bmatrix} -1 \\ 5 \\ -1 \\ -3 \end{bmatrix}$. Therefore, $x = -1$, $y = 5$, $z = -1$, and $w = -3$.

31. Using a calculator, we get the result $(3, 2, 1)$.

32. Using a calculator, we get the result $(-1, 2, 3)$.

33. Using a calculator, we get the result $(3, -2, 2)$.

34. Using a calculator, we get the result $(6, 12, 24)$.

35. Using a calculator, we get the result $(8, 1, 0, 3)$.

36. Using a calculator, we get the result $(8, 4, 2, 1)$.

37. This has the form $MX = C$, so $M^{-1}(MX) = M^{-1}C$ and $M^{-1}(MX) = (M^{-1}M)X = X$.

Now $M^{-1} = \begin{bmatrix} 3 & -2 \\ -4 & 3 \end{bmatrix}^{-1} = \frac{1}{9-8} \begin{bmatrix} 3 & 2 \\ 4 & 3 \end{bmatrix} = \begin{bmatrix} 3 & 2 \\ 4 & 3 \end{bmatrix}$. Since $X = M^{-1}C$, we get

$\begin{bmatrix} x & y & z \\ u & v & w \end{bmatrix} = \begin{bmatrix} 3 & 2 \\ 4 & 3 \end{bmatrix} \begin{bmatrix} 1 & 0 & -1 \\ 2 & 1 & 3 \end{bmatrix} = \begin{bmatrix} 7 & 2 & 3 \\ 10 & 3 & 5 \end{bmatrix}$.

38. Using the inverse matrix from Exercise 19, we see that $\begin{bmatrix} -\frac{9}{2} & -1 & 4 \\ 3 & 1 & -3 \\ \frac{7}{2} & 1 & -3 \end{bmatrix} \begin{bmatrix} 3 & 6 \\ 6 & 12 \\ 0 & 0 \end{bmatrix} = \begin{bmatrix} -\frac{39}{2} & -39 \\ 15 & 30 \\ \frac{33}{2} & 33 \end{bmatrix}.$

Hence, $\begin{bmatrix} x & u \\ y & v \\ z & w \end{bmatrix} = \begin{bmatrix} -\frac{39}{2} & -39 \\ 15 & 30 \\ \frac{33}{2} & 33 \end{bmatrix}.$

39. $\begin{bmatrix} a & -a \\ a & a \end{bmatrix}^{-1} = \dfrac{1}{a^2 - (-a^2)} \begin{bmatrix} a & a \\ -a & a \end{bmatrix} = \dfrac{1}{2a^2} \begin{bmatrix} a & a \\ -a & a \end{bmatrix} = \dfrac{1}{2a} \begin{bmatrix} 1 & 1 \\ -1 & 1 \end{bmatrix}$

40. $\left[\begin{array}{cccc|cccc} a & 0 & 0 & 0 & 1 & 0 & 0 & 0 \\ 0 & b & 0 & 0 & 0 & 1 & 0 & 0 \\ 0 & 0 & c & 0 & 0 & 0 & 1 & 0 \\ 0 & 0 & 0 & d & 0 & 0 & 0 & 1 \end{array} \right]$ $\begin{array}{c} \frac{1}{a}R_1 \\ \frac{1}{b}R_2 \\ \frac{1}{c}R_3 \\ \frac{1}{d}R_4 \\ \longrightarrow \end{array}$ $\left[\begin{array}{cccc|cccc} 1 & 0 & 0 & 0 & 1/a & 0 & 0 & 0 \\ 0 & 1 & 0 & 0 & 0 & 1/b & 0 & 0 \\ 0 & 0 & 1 & 0 & 0 & 0 & 1/c & 0 \\ 0 & 0 & 0 & 1 & 0 & 0 & 0 & 1/d \end{array} \right].$

Thus the matrix $\begin{bmatrix} a & 0 & 0 & 0 \\ 0 & b & 0 & 0 \\ 0 & 0 & c & 0 \\ 0 & 0 & 0 & d \end{bmatrix}$ has inverse $\begin{bmatrix} 1/a & 0 & 0 & 0 \\ 0 & 1/b & 0 & 0 \\ 0 & 0 & 1/c & 0 \\ 0 & 0 & 0 & 1/d \end{bmatrix}.$

41. $\begin{bmatrix} 2 & x \\ x & x^2 \end{bmatrix}^{-1} = \dfrac{1}{2x^2 - x^2} \begin{bmatrix} x^2 & -x \\ -x & 2 \end{bmatrix} = \dfrac{1}{x^2} \begin{bmatrix} x^2 & -x \\ -x & 2 \end{bmatrix} = \begin{bmatrix} 1 & -1/x \\ -1/x & 2/x^2 \end{bmatrix}.$ The inverse does not exist when $x = 0.$

42. $\begin{bmatrix} e^x & -e^{2x} \\ e^{2x} & e^{3x} \end{bmatrix}^{-1} = \dfrac{1}{e^{4x} + e^{4x}} \begin{bmatrix} e^{3x} & e^{2x} \\ -e^{2x} & e^x \end{bmatrix} = \dfrac{1}{2} \begin{bmatrix} e^{-x} & e^{-2x} \\ -e^{-2x} & e^{-3x} \end{bmatrix}.$ The inverse exists for all $x.$

43. $\left[\begin{array}{ccc|ccc} 1 & e^x & 0 & 1 & 0 & 0 \\ e^x & -e^{2x} & 0 & 0 & 1 & 0 \\ 0 & 0 & 2 & 0 & 0 & 1 \end{array} \right]$ $\xrightarrow{R_2 - e^x R_1 \to R_2}$ $\left[\begin{array}{ccc|ccc} 1 & e^x & 0 & 1 & 0 & 0 \\ 0 & -2e^{2x} & 0 & -e^x & 1 & 0 \\ 0 & 0 & 2 & 0 & 0 & 1 \end{array} \right]$ $\begin{array}{c} -\frac{1}{2}e^{-2x}R_2 \\ \frac{1}{2}R_3 \\ \longrightarrow \end{array}$

$\left[\begin{array}{ccc|ccc} 1 & e^x & 0 & 1 & 0 & 0 \\ 0 & 1 & 0 & \frac{1}{2}e^{-x} & -\frac{1}{2}e^{-2x} & 0 \\ 0 & 0 & 1 & 0 & 0 & \frac{1}{2} \end{array} \right]$ $\xrightarrow{R_1 - e^x R_2 \to R_1}$ $\left[\begin{array}{ccc|ccc} 1 & 0 & 0 & \frac{1}{2} & \frac{1}{2}e^{-x} & 0 \\ 0 & 1 & 0 & \frac{1}{2}e^{-x} & -\frac{1}{2}e^{-2x} & 0 \\ 0 & 0 & 1 & 0 & 0 & \frac{1}{2} \end{array} \right].$

Therefore, the inverse matrix is $\begin{bmatrix} \frac{1}{2} & \frac{1}{2}e^{-x} & 0 \\ \frac{1}{2}e^{-x} & -\frac{1}{2}e^{-2x} & 0 \\ 0 & 0 & \frac{1}{2} \end{bmatrix}.$ The inverse exists for all $x.$

44. $\begin{bmatrix} x & 1 \\ -x & \frac{1}{x-1} \end{bmatrix}^{-1} = \dfrac{1}{\frac{x}{x-1} + x} \begin{bmatrix} \frac{1}{x-1} & -1 \\ x & x \end{bmatrix} = \dfrac{x-1}{x^2} \begin{bmatrix} \frac{1}{x-1} & -1 \\ x & x \end{bmatrix} = \begin{bmatrix} \frac{1}{x^2} & -\frac{x-1}{x^2} \\ \frac{x-1}{x} & \frac{x-1}{x} \end{bmatrix}.$

The inverse exists for $x \neq 0, 1.$

45. $\begin{bmatrix} \cos\theta & \sin\theta \\ -\sin\theta & \cos\theta \end{bmatrix}^{-1} = \dfrac{1}{\cos^2\theta + \sin^2\theta} \begin{bmatrix} \cos\theta & -\sin\theta \\ \sin\theta & \cos\theta \end{bmatrix} = \begin{bmatrix} \cos\theta & -\sin\theta \\ \sin\theta & \cos\theta \end{bmatrix}$

46. $\begin{bmatrix} \sec\theta & \tan\theta \\ \tan\theta & \sec\theta \end{bmatrix}^{-1} = \dfrac{1}{\sec^2\theta - \tan^2\theta} \begin{bmatrix} \sec\theta & -\tan\theta \\ -\tan\theta & \sec\theta \end{bmatrix} = \begin{bmatrix} \sec\theta & -\tan\theta \\ -\tan\theta & \sec\theta \end{bmatrix}$

47. (a) $\begin{bmatrix} 3 & 1 & 3 & 1 & 0 & 0 \\ 4 & 2 & 4 & 0 & 1 & 0 \\ 3 & 2 & 4 & 0 & 0 & 1 \end{bmatrix} \xrightarrow[R_1 \leftrightarrow R_2]{R_3 - R_1 \to R_3} \begin{bmatrix} 4 & 2 & 4 & 0 & 1 & 0 \\ 3 & 1 & 3 & 1 & 0 & 0 \\ 0 & 1 & 1 & -1 & 0 & 1 \end{bmatrix} \xrightarrow{R_1 - R_2 \to R_1} \begin{bmatrix} 1 & 1 & 1 & -1 & 1 & 0 \\ 3 & 1 & 3 & 1 & 0 & 0 \\ 0 & 1 & 1 & -1 & 0 & 1 \end{bmatrix}$

$\xrightarrow{R_2 - 3R_1 \to R_2} \begin{bmatrix} 1 & 1 & 1 & -1 & 1 & 0 \\ 0 & -2 & 0 & 4 & -3 & 0 \\ 0 & 1 & 1 & -1 & 0 & 1 \end{bmatrix} \xrightarrow[\substack{-\frac{1}{2}R_2 \\ R_3 - R_2 \to R_3}]{R_1 - R_2 \to R_1} \begin{bmatrix} 1 & 0 & 1 & 1 & -\frac{1}{2} & 0 \\ 0 & 1 & 0 & -2 & \frac{3}{2} & 0 \\ 0 & 0 & 1 & 1 & -\frac{3}{2} & 1 \end{bmatrix} \xrightarrow{R_1 - R_3 \to R_1}$

$\begin{bmatrix} 1 & 0 & 0 & 0 & 1 & -1 \\ 0 & 1 & 0 & -2 & \frac{3}{2} & 0 \\ 0 & 0 & 1 & 1 & -\frac{3}{2} & 1 \end{bmatrix}$. Therefore, the inverse of the matrix is $\begin{bmatrix} 0 & 1 & -1 \\ -2 & \frac{3}{2} & 0 \\ 1 & -\frac{3}{2} & 1 \end{bmatrix}$.

(b) $\begin{bmatrix} A \\ B \\ C \end{bmatrix} = \begin{bmatrix} 0 & 1 & -1 \\ -2 & \frac{3}{2} & 0 \\ 1 & -\frac{3}{2} & 1 \end{bmatrix} \begin{bmatrix} 10 \\ 14 \\ 13 \end{bmatrix} = \begin{bmatrix} 1 \\ 1 \\ 2 \end{bmatrix}$.

Therefore, he should feed the rats 1 oz of food A, 1 oz of food B, and 2 oz of food C.

(c) $\begin{bmatrix} A \\ B \\ C \end{bmatrix} = \begin{bmatrix} 0 & 1 & -1 \\ -2 & \frac{3}{2} & 0 \\ 1 & -\frac{3}{2} & 1 \end{bmatrix} \begin{bmatrix} 9 \\ 12 \\ 10 \end{bmatrix} = \begin{bmatrix} 2 \\ 0 \\ 1 \end{bmatrix}$.

Therefore, he should feed the rats 2 oz of food A, no food B, and 1 oz of food C.

(d) $\begin{bmatrix} A \\ B \\ C \end{bmatrix} = \begin{bmatrix} 0 & 1 & -1 \\ -2 & \frac{3}{2} & 0 \\ 1 & -\frac{3}{2} & 1 \end{bmatrix} \begin{bmatrix} 2 \\ 4 \\ 11 \end{bmatrix} = \begin{bmatrix} -7 \\ 2 \\ 7 \end{bmatrix}$.

Since $A < 0$, there is no combination of foods giving the required supply.

48. $\begin{bmatrix} 3 & 1 & 4 & 1 & 0 & 0 \\ 4 & 2 & 6 & 0 & 1 & 0 \\ 3 & 2 & 5 & 0 & 0 & 1 \end{bmatrix} \xrightarrow[R_3 - R_1 \to R_3]{R_2 - R_1 \to R_2} \begin{bmatrix} 3 & 1 & 4 & 1 & 0 & 0 \\ 1 & 1 & 2 & -1 & 1 & 0 \\ 0 & 1 & 1 & -1 & 0 & 1 \end{bmatrix} \xrightarrow{R_1 \leftrightarrow R_2} \begin{bmatrix} 1 & 1 & 2 & -1 & 1 & 0 \\ 3 & 1 & 4 & 1 & 0 & 0 \\ 0 & 1 & 1 & -1 & 0 & 1 \end{bmatrix} \xrightarrow{R_2 - 3R_1 \to R_2}$

$\begin{bmatrix} 1 & 1 & 2 & -1 & 1 & 0 \\ 0 & -2 & -2 & 4 & -3 & 0 \\ 0 & 1 & 1 & -1 & 0 & 1 \end{bmatrix} \xrightarrow{R_3 + \frac{1}{2}R_2 \to R_3} \begin{bmatrix} 1 & 1 & 2 & -1 & 1 & 0 \\ 0 & -2 & -2 & 4 & -3 & 0 \\ 0 & 0 & 0 & 1 & -\frac{3}{2} & 1 \end{bmatrix}$.

Since the inverse matrix does not exist, it would not be possible to use matrix inversion in the solutions of parts (b), (c), and

(d).

49. (a) $\begin{cases} x + y + 2z = 675 \\ 2x + y + z = 600 \\ x + 2y + z = 625 \end{cases}$

(b) $\begin{bmatrix} 1 & 1 & 2 \\ 2 & 1 & 1 \\ 1 & 2 & 1 \end{bmatrix} \begin{bmatrix} x \\ y \\ z \end{bmatrix} = \begin{bmatrix} 675 \\ 600 \\ 625 \end{bmatrix}$

(c) $\begin{bmatrix} 1 & 1 & 2 & 1 & 0 & 0 \\ 2 & 1 & 1 & 0 & 1 & 0 \\ 1 & 2 & 1 & 0 & 0 & 1 \end{bmatrix} \xrightarrow[R_3 - R_1 \to R_3]{R_2 - 2R_1 \to R_2} \begin{bmatrix} 1 & 1 & 2 & 1 & 0 & 0 \\ 0 & -1 & -3 & -2 & 1 & 0 \\ 0 & 1 & -1 & -1 & 0 & 1 \end{bmatrix} \xrightarrow[R_3 + R_2 \to R_3]{R_1 + R_2 \to R_1} \begin{bmatrix} 1 & 0 & -1 & -1 & 1 & 0 \\ 0 & -1 & -3 & -2 & 1 & 0 \\ 0 & 0 & -4 & -3 & 1 & 1 \end{bmatrix}$

$\xrightarrow[-\frac{1}{4}R_3]{-R_2} \begin{bmatrix} 1 & 0 & -1 & -1 & 1 & 0 \\ 0 & 1 & 3 & 2 & -1 & 0 \\ 0 & 0 & 1 & \frac{3}{4} & -\frac{1}{4} & -\frac{1}{4} \end{bmatrix} \xrightarrow[R_2 - 3R_3 \to R_2]{R_1 + R_3 \to R_1} \begin{bmatrix} 1 & 0 & 0 & -\frac{1}{4} & \frac{3}{4} & -\frac{1}{4} \\ 0 & 1 & 0 & -\frac{1}{4} & -\frac{1}{4} & \frac{3}{4} \\ 0 & 0 & 1 & \frac{3}{4} & -\frac{1}{4} & -\frac{1}{4} \end{bmatrix}$. Therefore, the inverse of the

matrix is $\begin{bmatrix} -\frac{1}{4} & \frac{3}{4} & -\frac{1}{4} \\ -\frac{1}{4} & -\frac{1}{4} & \frac{3}{4} \\ \frac{3}{4} & -\frac{1}{4} & -\frac{1}{4} \end{bmatrix}$ and $\begin{bmatrix} x \\ y \\ z \end{bmatrix} = \begin{bmatrix} -\frac{1}{4} & \frac{3}{4} & -\frac{1}{4} \\ -\frac{1}{4} & -\frac{1}{4} & \frac{3}{4} \\ \frac{3}{4} & -\frac{1}{4} & -\frac{1}{4} \end{bmatrix} \begin{bmatrix} 675 \\ 600 \\ 625 \end{bmatrix} = \begin{bmatrix} 125 \\ 150 \\ 200 \end{bmatrix}$. Thus, he earns $125 on a

standard set, $150 on a deluxe set, and $200 on a leather-bound set.

50. No. Consider the following counterexample: $A = \begin{bmatrix} 0 & 1 \\ 0 & 0 \end{bmatrix}$ and $B = \begin{bmatrix} 0 & 2 \\ 0 & 0 \end{bmatrix}$. Then, $AB = O$, but neither $A = O$ nor

$B = O$. There are infinitely many matrices for which $A^2 = O$. One example is $A = \begin{bmatrix} 0 & 1 \\ 0 & 0 \end{bmatrix}$. Then, $A^2 = O$, but $A \neq O$.

9.7   Determinants and Cramer's Rule

1. The matrix $\begin{bmatrix} 2 & 0 \\ 0 & 3 \end{bmatrix}$ has determinant

$|D| = (2)(3) - (0)(0) = 6.$

2. The matrix $\begin{bmatrix} 0 & -1 \\ 2 & 0 \end{bmatrix}$ has determinant

$|D| = (0)(0) - (-1)(2) = 2.$

3. The matrix $\begin{bmatrix} 4 & 5 \\ 0 & -1 \end{bmatrix}$ has determinant

$|D| = (4)(-1) - (5)(0) = -4.$

4. The matrix $\begin{bmatrix} -2 & 1 \\ 3 & -2 \end{bmatrix}$ has determinant

$|D| = (-2)(-2) - (1)(3) = 1.$

5. The matrix $\begin{bmatrix} 2 & 5 \end{bmatrix}$ does not have a determinant because the matrix is not square.

6. The matrix $\begin{bmatrix} 3 \\ 0 \end{bmatrix}$ does not have a determinant because the matrix is not square.

7. The matrix $\begin{bmatrix} \frac{1}{2} & \frac{1}{8} \\ 1 & \frac{1}{2} \end{bmatrix}$ has determinant

$|D| = \frac{1}{2} \cdot \frac{1}{2} - 1 \cdot \frac{1}{8} = \frac{1}{4} - \frac{1}{8} = \frac{1}{8}.$

8. The matrix $\begin{bmatrix} 2.2 & -1.4 \\ 0.5 & 1.0 \end{bmatrix}$ has determinant

$|D| = (2.2)(1.0) - (0.5)(-1.4) = 2.2 + 0.7 = 2.9.$

In Solutions 9–14, $A = \begin{bmatrix} 1 & 0 & \frac{1}{2} \\ -3 & 5 & 2 \\ 0 & 0 & 4 \end{bmatrix}$.

9. $M_{11} = 5 \cdot 4 - 0 \cdot 2 = 20$, $A_{11} = (-1)^2 M_{11} = 20$ **10.** $M_{33} = 1 \cdot 5 + 3 \cdot 0 = 5$, $A_{33} = (-1)^6 M_{33} = 5$

11. $M_{12} = -3 \cdot 4 - 0 \cdot 2 = -12$, $A_{12} = (-1)^3 M_{12} = 12$ **12.** $M_{13} = -3 \cdot 0 - 0 \cdot 5 = 0$, $A_{13} = (-1)^4 M_{13} = 0$

13. $M_{23} = 1 \cdot 0 - 0 \cdot 0 = 0$, $A_{23} = (-1)^5 M_{23} = 0$ **14.** $M_{32} = 1 \cdot 2 + 3 \cdot \frac{1}{2} = \frac{7}{2}$, $A_{32} = (-1)^5 M_{32} = -\frac{7}{2}$

15. $M = \begin{bmatrix} 2 & 1 & 0 \\ 0 & -2 & 4 \\ 0 & 1 & -3 \end{bmatrix}$. Therefore, expanding by the first column, $|M| = 2 \begin{vmatrix} -2 & 4 \\ 1 & -3 \end{vmatrix} = 2(6-4) = 4$. Since $|M| \neq 0$,

the matrix has an inverse.

16. $M = \begin{bmatrix} 0 & -1 & 0 \\ 2 & 6 & 4 \\ 1 & 0 & 3 \end{bmatrix}$. Therefore, expanding by the first row, $|M| = -(-1) \begin{vmatrix} 2 & 4 \\ 1 & 3 \end{vmatrix} = 6 - 4 = 2$. Since $|M| \neq 0$, the

matrix has an inverse.

17. $M = \begin{bmatrix} 1 & 3 & 7 \\ 2 & 0 & -1 \\ 0 & 2 & 6 \end{bmatrix}$. Therefore, expanding by the third row,

$|M| = -2 \begin{vmatrix} 1 & 7 \\ 2 & -1 \end{vmatrix} + 6 \begin{vmatrix} 1 & 3 \\ 2 & 0 \end{vmatrix} = -2(-1-14) + 6(0-6) = 30 - 36 = -6$. Since $|M| \neq 0$, the matrix has an

inverse.

18. $M = \begin{bmatrix} -2 & -\frac{3}{2} & \frac{1}{2} \\ 2 & 4 & 0 \\ \frac{1}{2} & 2 & 1 \end{bmatrix}$. Therefore, $|M| = \frac{1}{2} \begin{vmatrix} 2 & 4 \\ \frac{1}{2} & 2 \end{vmatrix} + 1 \begin{vmatrix} -2 & -\frac{3}{2} \\ 2 & 4 \end{vmatrix} = \frac{1}{2}(4-2) + (-8+3) = 1 - 5 = -4$, and the

matrix has an inverse.

19. $M = \begin{bmatrix} 30 & 0 & 20 \\ 0 & -10 & -20 \\ 40 & 0 & 10 \end{bmatrix}$. Therefore, expanding by the first row,

$|M| = 30 \begin{vmatrix} -10 & -20 \\ 0 & 10 \end{vmatrix} + 20 \begin{vmatrix} 0 & -10 \\ 40 & 0 \end{vmatrix} = 30(-100+0) + 20(0+400) = -3000 + 8000 = 5000$, and so M^{-1}

exists.

20. $M = \begin{bmatrix} 1 & 2 & 5 \\ -2 & -3 & 2 \\ 3 & 5 & 3 \end{bmatrix}$. Therefore,

$|M| = 1 \begin{vmatrix} -3 & 2 \\ 5 & 3 \end{vmatrix} - 2 \begin{vmatrix} -2 & 2 \\ 3 & 3 \end{vmatrix} + 5 \begin{vmatrix} -2 & -3 \\ 3 & 5 \end{vmatrix} = (-9-10) - 2(-6-6) + 5(-10+9) = -19 + 24 - 5 = 0$, and

so the matrix does not have an inverse.

21. $M = \begin{bmatrix} 1 & 3 & 3 & 0 \\ 0 & 2 & 0 & 1 \\ -1 & 0 & 0 & 2 \\ 1 & 6 & 4 & 1 \end{bmatrix}$. Therefore, expanding by the third row,

$|M| = -1 \begin{vmatrix} 3 & 3 & 0 \\ 2 & 0 & 1 \\ 6 & 4 & 1 \end{vmatrix} - 2 \begin{vmatrix} 1 & 3 & 3 \\ 0 & 2 & 0 \\ 1 & 6 & 4 \end{vmatrix} = 1 \begin{vmatrix} 3 & 3 \\ 6 & 4 \end{vmatrix} - 1 \begin{vmatrix} 3 & 3 \\ 2 & 0 \end{vmatrix} - 4 \begin{vmatrix} 1 & 3 \\ 1 & 4 \end{vmatrix} = -6 + 6 - 4 = -4$, and so M^{-1} exists.

22. $M = \begin{bmatrix} 1 & 2 & 0 & 2 \\ 3 & -4 & 0 & 4 \\ 0 & 1 & 6 & 0 \\ 1 & 0 & 2 & 0 \end{bmatrix}$. Therefore, $|M| = -1 \begin{vmatrix} 2 & 0 & 2 \\ -4 & 0 & 4 \\ 1 & 6 & 0 \end{vmatrix} - 2 \begin{vmatrix} 1 & 2 & 2 \\ 3 & -4 & 4 \\ 0 & 1 & 0 \end{vmatrix} = 6 \begin{vmatrix} 2 & 2 \\ -4 & 4 \end{vmatrix} + 2 \begin{vmatrix} 1 & 2 \\ 3 & 4 \end{vmatrix} = 6 \cdot 16 - 2 \cdot 2 = 92$,

and so M^{-1} exists.

23. $|M| = \begin{vmatrix} 0 & 0 & 4 & 6 \\ 2 & 1 & 1 & 3 \\ 2 & 1 & 2 & 3 \\ 3 & 0 & 1 & 7 \end{vmatrix} = \begin{vmatrix} 0 & 0 & 4 & 6 \\ 2 & 1 & 1 & 3 \\ 0 & 0 & 1 & 0 \\ 3 & 0 & 1 & 7 \end{vmatrix}$, by replacing R_3 with $R_3 - R_2$. Then, expanding by the third row,

$|M| = 1 \begin{vmatrix} 0 & 0 & 6 \\ 2 & 1 & 3 \\ 3 & 0 & 7 \end{vmatrix} = 6 \begin{vmatrix} 2 & 1 \\ 3 & 0 \end{vmatrix} = 6(2 \cdot 0 - 3 \cdot 1) = -18$.

24. $M = \begin{bmatrix} -2 & 3 & -1 & 7 \\ 4 & 6 & -2 & 3 \\ 7 & 7 & 0 & 5 \\ 3 & -12 & 4 & 0 \end{bmatrix}$. Then $|M| = \begin{vmatrix} -2 & 3 & -1 & 7 \\ 4 & 6 & -2 & 3 \\ 7 & 7 & 0 & 5 \\ 3 & -12 & 4 & 0 \end{vmatrix} = \begin{vmatrix} -2 & 0 & -1 & 7 \\ 4 & 0 & -2 & 3 \\ 7 & 7 & 0 & 5 \\ 3 & 0 & 4 & 0 \end{vmatrix}$,

by replacing C_2 with $C_2 + 3C_3$. So expanding about the second column,

$|M| = -7 \begin{vmatrix} -2 & -1 & 7 \\ 4 & -2 & 3 \\ 3 & 4 & 0 \end{vmatrix} = -7 \left(7 \begin{vmatrix} 4 & -2 \\ 3 & 4 \end{vmatrix} - 3 \begin{vmatrix} -2 & -1 \\ 3 & 4 \end{vmatrix} \right) = -7(7 \cdot 22 + 3 \cdot 5) = -1183$.

25. $M = \begin{bmatrix} 1 & 2 & 3 & 4 & 5 \\ 0 & 2 & 4 & 6 & 8 \\ 0 & 0 & 3 & 6 & 9 \\ 0 & 0 & 0 & 4 & 8 \\ 0 & 0 & 0 & 0 & 5 \end{bmatrix}$, so $|M| = 5 \begin{vmatrix} 1 & 2 & 3 & 4 \\ 0 & 2 & 4 & 6 \\ 0 & 0 & 3 & 6 \\ 0 & 0 & 0 & 4 \end{vmatrix} = 5 \cdot 4 \begin{vmatrix} 1 & 2 & 3 \\ 0 & 2 & 4 \\ 0 & 0 & 3 \end{vmatrix} = 20 \cdot 3 \begin{vmatrix} 1 & 2 \\ 0 & 2 \end{vmatrix} = 60 \cdot 2 = 120$.

26. $M = \begin{bmatrix} 2 & -1 & 6 & 4 \\ 7 & 2 & -2 & 5 \\ 4 & -2 & 10 & 8 \\ 6 & 1 & 1 & 4 \end{bmatrix}$. Then, $|M| = \begin{vmatrix} 2 & -1 & 6 & 4 \\ 7 & 2 & -2 & 5 \\ 4 & -2 & 10 & 8 \\ 6 & 1 & 1 & 4 \end{vmatrix} = \begin{vmatrix} 0 & -1 & 6 & 4 \\ 11 & 2 & -2 & 5 \\ 0 & -2 & 10 & 8 \\ 8 & 1 & 1 & 4 \end{vmatrix}$, by replacing C_1 with $C_1 + 2C_2$. So

$|M| = -11 \begin{vmatrix} -1 & 6 & 4 \\ -2 & 10 & 8 \\ 1 & 1 & 4 \end{vmatrix} - 8 \begin{vmatrix} -1 & 6 & 4 \\ 2 & -2 & 5 \\ -2 & 10 & 8 \end{vmatrix} = -11 \begin{vmatrix} -1 & 6 & 0 \\ -2 & 10 & 0 \\ 1 & 1 & 8 \end{vmatrix} - 8 \begin{vmatrix} -1 & 6 & 0 \\ 2 & -2 & 13 \\ -2 & 10 & 0 \end{vmatrix} = -88 \begin{vmatrix} -1 & 6 \\ -2 & 10 \end{vmatrix} + 104 \begin{vmatrix} -1 & 6 \\ -2 & 10 \end{vmatrix}$

$= -88 \cdot 2 + 104 \cdot 2 = 32$

27. $B = \begin{bmatrix} 4 & 1 & 0 \\ -2 & -1 & 1 \\ 4 & 0 & 3 \end{bmatrix}$

(a) $|B| = 2 \begin{vmatrix} 1 & 0 \\ 0 & 3 \end{vmatrix} - 1 \begin{vmatrix} 4 & 0 \\ 4 & 3 \end{vmatrix} - 1 \begin{vmatrix} 4 & 1 \\ 4 & 0 \end{vmatrix} = 6 - 12 + 4 = -2$

(b) $|B| = -1 \begin{vmatrix} 4 & 1 \\ 4 & 0 \end{vmatrix} + 3 \begin{vmatrix} 4 & 1 \\ -2 & -1 \end{vmatrix} = 4 - 6 = -2$

(c) Yes, as expected, the results agree.

28. $\begin{cases} x + 2y + 6z = 5 \\ -3x - 6y + 5z = 8 \\ 2x + 6y + 9z = 7 \end{cases}$

(a) If $x = -1, y = 0$, and $z = 1$, then $x + 2y + 6z = (-1) + 2(0) + 6(1) = 5$, $-3x - 6y + 5z = -3(-1) - 6(0) + 5(1) = 8$, and $2x + 6y + 9z = 2(-1) + 6(0) + 9(1) = 7$. Therefore, $x = -1, y = 0, z = 1$ is a solution of the system.

(b) $M = \begin{bmatrix} 1 & 2 & 6 \\ -3 & -6 & 5 \\ 2 & 6 & 9 \end{bmatrix}$. Then, $|M| = \begin{vmatrix} 1 & 2 & 6 \\ -3 & -6 & 5 \\ 2 & 6 & 9 \end{vmatrix} = \begin{vmatrix} 1 & 0 & 6 \\ -3 & 0 & 5 \\ 2 & 2 & 9 \end{vmatrix}$ (replacing C_2 with $C_2 - 2C_1$), so

$|M| = -2 \begin{vmatrix} 1 & 6 \\ -3 & 5 \end{vmatrix} = -2(5 + 18) = -46$.

(c) We can write the system as a matrix equation: $\begin{bmatrix} 1 & 2 & 6 \\ -3 & -6 & 5 \\ 2 & 6 & 9 \end{bmatrix} \begin{bmatrix} x \\ y \\ z \end{bmatrix} = \begin{bmatrix} 5 \\ 8 \\ 7 \end{bmatrix}$ or $MX = B$. Since $|M| \neq 0$, M has

an inverse. If we multiply both sides of the matrix equation by M^{-1}, then we get a unique solution for X, given by $X = M^{-1}B$. Thus, the equation has no other solution.

(d) Yes, since $|M| \neq 0$.

29. $\begin{cases} 2x - y = -9 \\ x + 2y = 8 \end{cases}$ Then $|D| = \begin{vmatrix} 2 & -1 \\ 1 & 2 \end{vmatrix} = 5$, $|D_x| = \begin{vmatrix} -9 & -1 \\ 8 & 2 \end{vmatrix} = -10$, and $|D_y| = \begin{vmatrix} 2 & -9 \\ 1 & 8 \end{vmatrix} = 25$.

Hence, $x = \dfrac{|D_x|}{|D|} = \dfrac{-10}{5} = -2$, $y = \dfrac{|D_y|}{|D|} = \dfrac{25}{5} = 5$, and so the solution is $(-2, 5)$.

30. $\begin{cases} 6x + 12y = 33 \\ 4x + 7y = 20 \end{cases}$ Then $|D| = \begin{vmatrix} 6 & 12 \\ 4 & 7 \end{vmatrix} = -6$, $|D_x| = \begin{vmatrix} 33 & 12 \\ 20 & 7 \end{vmatrix} = -9$, and $|D_y| = \begin{vmatrix} 6 & 33 \\ 4 & 20 \end{vmatrix} = -12$.

Hence, $x = \dfrac{|D_x|}{|D|} = \dfrac{-9}{-6} = \dfrac{3}{2}$ and $y = \dfrac{|D_y|}{|D|} = \dfrac{-12}{-6} = 2$, and so the solution is $\left(\dfrac{3}{2}, 2\right)$.

31. $\begin{cases} x - 6y = 3 \\ 3x + 2y = 1 \end{cases}$ Then, $|D| = \begin{vmatrix} 1 & -6 \\ 3 & 2 \end{vmatrix} = 20$, $|D_x| = \begin{vmatrix} 3 & -6 \\ 1 & 2 \end{vmatrix} = 12$, and $|D_y| = \begin{vmatrix} 1 & 3 \\ 3 & 1 \end{vmatrix} = -8$.

Hence, $x = \dfrac{|D_x|}{|D|} = \dfrac{12}{20} = 0.6$, $y = \dfrac{|D_y|}{|D|} = \dfrac{-8}{20} = -0.4$, and so the solution is $(0.6, -0.4)$.

32. $\begin{cases} \frac{1}{2}x + \frac{1}{3}y = 1 \\ \frac{1}{4}x - \frac{1}{6}y = -\frac{3}{2} \end{cases}$ Then, $|D| = \begin{vmatrix} \frac{1}{2} & \frac{1}{3} \\ \frac{1}{4} & -\frac{1}{6} \end{vmatrix} = -\frac{1}{6}$, $|D_x| = \begin{vmatrix} 1 & \frac{1}{3} \\ -\frac{3}{2} & -\frac{1}{6} \end{vmatrix} = \frac{1}{3}$, and $|D_y| = \begin{vmatrix} \frac{1}{2} & 1 \\ \frac{1}{4} & -\frac{3}{2} \end{vmatrix} = -1.$

Hence, $x = \dfrac{|D_x|}{|D|} = \dfrac{\frac{1}{3}}{-\frac{1}{6}} = -2$, $y = \dfrac{|D_y|}{|D|} = \dfrac{-1}{-\frac{1}{6}} = 6$, and so the solution is $(-2, 6)$.

33. $\begin{cases} 0.4x + 1.2y = 0.4 \\ 1.2x + 1.6y = 3.2 \end{cases}$ Then, $|D| = \begin{vmatrix} 0.4 & 1.2 \\ 1.2 & 1.6 \end{vmatrix} = -0.8$, $|D_x| = \begin{vmatrix} 0.4 & 1.2 \\ 3.2 & 1.6 \end{vmatrix} = -3.2$, and $|D_y| = \begin{vmatrix} 0.4 & 0.4 \\ 1.2 & 3.2 \end{vmatrix} = 0.8.$

Hence, $x = \dfrac{|D_x|}{|D|} = \dfrac{-3.2}{-0.8} = 4$, $y = \dfrac{|D_y|}{|D|} = \dfrac{0.8}{-0.8} = -1$, and so the solution is $(4, -1)$.

34. $\begin{cases} 10x - 17y = 21 \\ 20x - 31y = 39 \end{cases}$.   Then, $|D| = \begin{vmatrix} 10 & -17 \\ 20 & -31 \end{vmatrix} = 30$, $|D_x| = \begin{vmatrix} 21 & -17 \\ 39 & -31 \end{vmatrix} = 12$, and $|D_y| = \begin{vmatrix} 10 & 21 \\ 20 & 39 \end{vmatrix} = -30.$

Hence, $x = \dfrac{|D_x|}{|D|} = \dfrac{12}{30} = \dfrac{2}{5}$, $y = \dfrac{|D_y|}{|D|} = \dfrac{-30}{30} = -1$, and so the solution is $\left(\frac{2}{5}, -1\right)$.

35. $\begin{cases} x - y + 2z = 0 \\ 3x + z = 11 \\ -x + 2y = 0 \end{cases}$ Then expanding by the second row,

$|D| = \begin{vmatrix} 1 & -1 & 2 \\ 3 & 0 & 1 \\ -1 & 2 & 0 \end{vmatrix} = -3 \begin{vmatrix} -1 & 2 \\ 2 & 0 \end{vmatrix} - 1 \begin{vmatrix} 1 & -1 \\ -1 & 2 \end{vmatrix} = 12 - 1 = 11$, $|D_x| = \begin{vmatrix} 0 & -1 & 2 \\ 11 & 0 & 1 \\ 0 & 2 & 0 \end{vmatrix} = -11 \begin{vmatrix} -1 & 2 \\ 2 & 0 \end{vmatrix} = 44$,

$|D_y| = \begin{vmatrix} 1 & 0 & 2 \\ 3 & 11 & 1 \\ -1 & 0 & 0 \end{vmatrix} = 11 \begin{vmatrix} 1 & 2 \\ -1 & 0 \end{vmatrix} = 22$, and $|D_z| = \begin{vmatrix} 1 & -1 & 0 \\ 3 & 0 & 11 \\ -1 & 2 & 0 \end{vmatrix} = -11 \begin{vmatrix} 1 & -1 \\ -1 & 2 \end{vmatrix} = -11.$

Therefore, $x = \frac{44}{11} = 4$, $y = \frac{22}{11} = 2$, $z = \frac{-11}{11} = -1$, and so the solution is $(4, 2, -1)$.

36. $\begin{cases} 5x - 3y + z = 6 \\ 4y - 6z = 22 \\ 7x + 10y = -13 \end{cases}$ Then $|D| = \begin{vmatrix} 5 & -3 & 1 \\ 0 & 4 & -6 \\ 7 & 10 & 0 \end{vmatrix} = 1 \begin{vmatrix} 0 & 4 \\ 7 & 10 \end{vmatrix} + 6 \begin{vmatrix} 5 & -3 \\ 7 & 10 \end{vmatrix} = -28 + 426 = 398$,

$|D_x| = \begin{vmatrix} 6 & -3 & 1 \\ 22 & 4 & -6 \\ -13 & 10 & 0 \end{vmatrix} = 1 \begin{vmatrix} 22 & 4 \\ -13 & 10 \end{vmatrix} + 6 \begin{vmatrix} 6 & -3 \\ -13 & 10 \end{vmatrix} = 272 + 126 = 398$,

$|D_y| = \begin{vmatrix} 5 & 6 & 1 \\ 0 & 22 & -6 \\ 7 & -13 & 0 \end{vmatrix} = 1 \begin{vmatrix} 0 & 22 \\ 7 & -13 \end{vmatrix} + 6 \begin{vmatrix} 5 & 6 \\ 7 & -13 \end{vmatrix} = -154 - 642 = -796$, and

$|D_z| = \begin{vmatrix} 5 & -3 & 6 \\ 0 & 4 & 22 \\ 7 & 10 & -13 \end{vmatrix} = 4 \begin{vmatrix} 5 & 6 \\ 7 & -13 \end{vmatrix} - 22 \begin{vmatrix} 5 & -3 \\ 7 & 10 \end{vmatrix} = -428 - 1562 = -1990.$

Therefore, the solution is $x = \frac{398}{398} = 1$, $y = \frac{-796}{398} = -2$, and $z = \frac{-1990}{398} = -5$.

37. $\begin{cases} 2x_1 + 3x_2 - 5x_3 = 1 \\ x_1 + \ x_2 - \ x_3 = 2 \\ 2x_2 + \ x_3 = 8 \end{cases}$

Then, expanding by the third row,

$$|D| = \begin{vmatrix} 2 & 3 & -5 \\ 1 & 1 & -1 \\ 0 & 2 & 1 \end{vmatrix} = -2 \begin{vmatrix} 2 & -5 \\ 1 & -1 \end{vmatrix} + \begin{vmatrix} 2 & 3 \\ 1 & 1 \end{vmatrix} = -6 - 1 = -7,$$

$$|D_{x_1}| = \begin{vmatrix} 1 & 3 & -5 \\ 2 & 1 & -1 \\ 8 & 2 & 1 \end{vmatrix} = \begin{vmatrix} 1 & -1 \\ 2 & 1 \end{vmatrix} - 3 \begin{vmatrix} 2 & -1 \\ 8 & 1 \end{vmatrix} - 5 \begin{vmatrix} 2 & 1 \\ 8 & 2 \end{vmatrix} = 3 - 30 + 20 = -7,$$

$$|D_{x_2}| = \begin{vmatrix} 2 & 1 & -5 \\ 1 & 2 & -1 \\ 0 & 8 & 1 \end{vmatrix} = -8 \begin{vmatrix} 2 & -5 \\ 1 & -1 \end{vmatrix} + \begin{vmatrix} 2 & 1 \\ 1 & 2 \end{vmatrix} = -24 + 3 = -21, \text{ and}$$

$$|D_{x_3}| = \begin{vmatrix} 2 & 3 & 1 \\ 1 & 1 & 2 \\ 0 & 2 & 8 \end{vmatrix} = -2 \begin{vmatrix} 2 & 1 \\ 1 & 2 \end{vmatrix} + 8 \begin{vmatrix} 2 & 3 \\ 1 & 1 \end{vmatrix} = -6 - 8 = -14.$$

Thus, $x_1 = \frac{-7}{-7} = 1$, $x_2 = \frac{-21}{-7} = 3$, $x_3 = \frac{-14}{-7} = 2$, and so the solution is $(1, 3, 2)$.

38. $\begin{cases} -2a \ + \ c = \ 2 \\ a + 2b - \ c = \ 9 \\ 3a + 5b + 2c = 22 \end{cases}$

Then $|D| = \begin{vmatrix} -2 & 0 & 1 \\ 1 & 2 & -1 \\ 3 & 5 & 2 \end{vmatrix} = -2 \begin{vmatrix} 2 & -1 \\ 5 & 2 \end{vmatrix} + 1 \begin{vmatrix} 1 & 2 \\ 3 & 5 \end{vmatrix} = -18 - 1 = -19,$

$$|D_a| = \begin{vmatrix} 2 & 0 & 1 \\ 9 & 2 & -1 \\ 22 & 5 & 2 \end{vmatrix} = 2 \begin{vmatrix} 2 & -1 \\ 5 & 2 \end{vmatrix} + 1 \begin{vmatrix} 9 & 2 \\ 22 & 5 \end{vmatrix} = 18 + 1 = 19,$$

$$|D_b| = \begin{vmatrix} -2 & 2 & 1 \\ 1 & 9 & -1 \\ 3 & 22 & 2 \end{vmatrix} = -2 \begin{vmatrix} 9 & -1 \\ 22 & 2 \end{vmatrix} - 2 \begin{vmatrix} 1 & -1 \\ 3 & 2 \end{vmatrix} + 1 \begin{vmatrix} 1 & 9 \\ 3 & 22 \end{vmatrix} = -80 - 10 - 5 = -95, \text{ and}$$

$$|D_c| = \begin{vmatrix} -2 & 0 & 2 \\ 1 & 2 & 9 \\ 3 & 5 & 22 \end{vmatrix} = -2 \begin{vmatrix} 2 & 9 \\ 5 & 22 \end{vmatrix} + 2 \begin{vmatrix} 1 & 2 \\ 3 & 5 \end{vmatrix} = 2 - 2 = 0.$$

Hence, the solution is $a = -1$, $b = 5$, and $c = 0$.

39. $\begin{cases} \frac{1}{3}x - \frac{1}{5}y + \frac{1}{2}z = \frac{7}{10} \\ -\frac{2}{3}x + \frac{2}{5}y + \frac{3}{2}z = \frac{11}{10} \\ x - \frac{4}{5}y + z = \frac{9}{5} \end{cases}$ $\Leftrightarrow$ $\begin{cases} 10x - 6y + 15z = 21 \\ -20x + 12y + 45z = 33 \\ 5x - 4y + 5z = 9 \end{cases}$ Then

$$|D| = \begin{vmatrix} 10 & -6 & 15 \\ -20 & 12 & 45 \\ 5 & -4 & 5 \end{vmatrix} = 10 \begin{vmatrix} 12 & 45 \\ -4 & 5 \end{vmatrix} + 6 \begin{vmatrix} -20 & 45 \\ 5 & 5 \end{vmatrix} + 15 \begin{vmatrix} -20 & 12 \\ 5 & -4 \end{vmatrix} = 2400 - 1950 + 300 = 750,$$

$$|D_x| = \begin{vmatrix} 21 & -6 & 15 \\ 33 & 12 & 45 \\ 9 & -4 & 5 \end{vmatrix} = 21 \begin{vmatrix} 12 & 45 \\ -4 & 5 \end{vmatrix} + 6 \begin{vmatrix} 33 & 45 \\ 9 & 5 \end{vmatrix} + 15 \begin{vmatrix} 33 & 12 \\ 9 & -4 \end{vmatrix} = 5040 - 1440 - 3600 = 0,$$

$$|D_y| = \begin{vmatrix} 10 & 21 & 15 \\ -20 & 33 & 45 \\ 5 & 9 & 5 \end{vmatrix} = 10 \begin{vmatrix} 33 & 45 \\ 9 & 5 \end{vmatrix} - 21 \begin{vmatrix} -20 & 45 \\ 5 & 5 \end{vmatrix} + 15 \begin{vmatrix} -20 & 33 \\ 5 & 9 \end{vmatrix} = -2400 + 6825 - 5175 = -750, \text{ and}$$

$$|D_z| = \begin{vmatrix} 10 & -6 & 21 \\ -20 & 12 & 33 \\ 5 & -4 & 9 \end{vmatrix} = 10 \begin{vmatrix} 12 & 33 \\ -4 & 9 \end{vmatrix} + 6 \begin{vmatrix} -20 & 33 \\ 5 & 9 \end{vmatrix} + 21 \begin{vmatrix} -20 & 12 \\ 5 & -4 \end{vmatrix} = 2400 - 2070 + 420 = 750.$$

Therefore, $x = 0$, $y = -1$, $z = 1$, and so the solution is $(0, -1, 1)$.

40. $\begin{cases} 2x - y = 5 \\ 5x + 3z = 19 \\ 4y + 7z = 17 \end{cases}$ Then $|D| = \begin{vmatrix} 2 & -1 & 0 \\ 5 & 0 & 3 \\ 0 & 4 & 7 \end{vmatrix} = 2 \begin{vmatrix} 0 & 3 \\ 4 & 7 \end{vmatrix} + 1 \begin{vmatrix} 5 & 3 \\ 0 & 7 \end{vmatrix} = -24 + 35 = 11,$

$$|D_x| = \begin{vmatrix} 5 & -1 & 0 \\ 19 & 0 & 3 \\ 17 & 4 & 7 \end{vmatrix} = 5 \begin{vmatrix} 0 & 3 \\ 4 & 7 \end{vmatrix} + 1 \begin{vmatrix} 19 & 3 \\ 17 & 7 \end{vmatrix} = -60 + 82 = 22,$$

$$|D_y| = \begin{vmatrix} 2 & 5 & 0 \\ 5 & 19 & 3 \\ 0 & 17 & 7 \end{vmatrix} = 2 \begin{vmatrix} 19 & 3 \\ 17 & 7 \end{vmatrix} - 5 \begin{vmatrix} 5 & 3 \\ 0 & 7 \end{vmatrix} = 164 - 175 = -11, \text{ and}$$

$$|D_z| = \begin{vmatrix} 2 & -1 & 5 \\ 5 & 0 & 19 \\ 0 & 4 & 17 \end{vmatrix} = -4 \begin{vmatrix} 2 & 5 \\ 5 & 19 \end{vmatrix} + 17 \begin{vmatrix} 2 & -1 \\ 5 & 0 \end{vmatrix} = -52 + 85 = 33. \text{ Thus, the solution is } x = 2, y = -1, \text{ and } z = 3.$$

41. $\begin{cases} 3y + 5z = 4 \\ 2x - z = 10 \\ 4x + 7y = 0 \end{cases}$ Then $|D| = \begin{vmatrix} 0 & 3 & 5 \\ 2 & 0 & -1 \\ 4 & 7 & 0 \end{vmatrix} = -3 \begin{vmatrix} 2 & -1 \\ 4 & 0 \end{vmatrix} + 5 \begin{vmatrix} 2 & 0 \\ 4 & 7 \end{vmatrix} = -12 + 70 = 58,$

$$|D_x| = \begin{vmatrix} 4 & 3 & 5 \\ 10 & 0 & -1 \\ 0 & 7 & 0 \end{vmatrix} = -7 \begin{vmatrix} 4 & 5 \\ 10 & -1 \end{vmatrix} = 378, \quad |D_y| = \begin{vmatrix} 0 & 4 & 5 \\ 2 & 10 & -1 \\ 4 & 0 & 0 \end{vmatrix} = 4 \begin{vmatrix} 4 & 5 \\ 10 & -1 \end{vmatrix} = -216, \text{ and}$$

$$|D_z| = \begin{vmatrix} 0 & 3 & 4 \\ 2 & 0 & 10 \\ 4 & 7 & 0 \end{vmatrix} = 4 \begin{vmatrix} 3 & 4 \\ 0 & 10 \end{vmatrix} - 7 \begin{vmatrix} 0 & 4 \\ 2 & 10 \end{vmatrix} = 120 + 56 = 176.$$

Thus, $x = \frac{189}{29}$, $y = -\frac{108}{29}$, and $z = \frac{88}{29}$, and so the solution is $\left(\frac{189}{29}, -\frac{108}{29}, \frac{88}{29}\right)$.

42. $\begin{cases} 2x - 5y \quad\;\; = 4 \\ x + y - z = 8 \\ 3x \quad\;\; + 5z = 0 \end{cases}$ Then $|D| = \begin{vmatrix} 2 & -5 & 0 \\ 1 & 1 & -1 \\ 3 & 0 & 5 \end{vmatrix} = 2\begin{vmatrix} 1 & -1 \\ 0 & 5 \end{vmatrix} + 5\begin{vmatrix} 1 & -1 \\ 3 & 5 \end{vmatrix} = 10 + 40 = 50,$

$|D_x| = \begin{vmatrix} 4 & -5 & 0 \\ 8 & 1 & -1 \\ 0 & 0 & 5 \end{vmatrix} = 5\begin{vmatrix} 4 & -5 \\ 8 & 1 \end{vmatrix} = 220,\; |D_y| = \begin{vmatrix} 2 & 4 & 0 \\ 1 & 8 & -1 \\ 3 & 0 & 5 \end{vmatrix} = 2\begin{vmatrix} 8 & -1 \\ 0 & 5 \end{vmatrix} - 4\begin{vmatrix} 1 & -1 \\ 3 & 5 \end{vmatrix} = 80 - 32 = 48,$ and

$|D_z| = \begin{vmatrix} 2 & -5 & 4 \\ 1 & 1 & 8 \\ 3 & 0 & 0 \end{vmatrix} = 3\begin{vmatrix} -5 & 4 \\ 1 & 8 \end{vmatrix} = -132.$ Thus, $x = \frac{22}{5}$, $y = \frac{24}{25}$, and $z = -\frac{66}{25}$.

43. $\begin{cases} x + y + z + w = 0 \\ \quad\quad\;\; 2z + w = 0 \\ \quad y - z \quad\;\; = 0 \\ x \quad\;\; + 2z \quad\;\; = 1 \end{cases}$ Then

$|D| = \begin{vmatrix} 1 & 1 & 1 & 1 \\ 2 & 0 & 0 & 1 \\ 0 & 1 & -1 & 0 \\ 1 & 0 & 2 & 0 \end{vmatrix} = -1\begin{vmatrix} 2 & 0 & 1 \\ 0 & -1 & 0 \\ 1 & 2 & 0 \end{vmatrix} - 1\begin{vmatrix} 1 & 1 & 1 \\ 2 & 0 & 1 \\ 1 & 2 & 0 \end{vmatrix} = -\left(2\begin{vmatrix} -1 & 0 \\ 2 & 0 \end{vmatrix} + 1\begin{vmatrix} 0 & 1 \\ -1 & 0 \end{vmatrix} \right) - \left(-1\begin{vmatrix} 2 & 1 \\ 1 & 0 \end{vmatrix} - 2\begin{vmatrix} 1 & 1 \\ 2 & 1 \end{vmatrix} \right)$

$= -2(0) - 1(1) + 1(-1) + 2(-1) = -4,$

$|D_x| = \begin{vmatrix} 0 & 1 & 1 & 1 \\ 0 & 0 & 0 & 1 \\ 0 & 1 & -1 & 0 \\ 1 & 0 & 2 & 0 \end{vmatrix} = -1\begin{vmatrix} 1 & 1 & 1 \\ 0 & 0 & 1 \\ 1 & -1 & 0 \end{vmatrix} = -1(-1)\begin{vmatrix} 1 & 1 \\ 1 & -1 \end{vmatrix} = -2,$

$|D_y| = \begin{vmatrix} 1 & 0 & 1 & 1 \\ 2 & 0 & 0 & 1 \\ 0 & 0 & -1 & 0 \\ 1 & 1 & 2 & 0 \end{vmatrix} = 1\begin{vmatrix} 1 & 1 & 1 \\ 2 & 0 & 1 \\ 0 & -1 & 0 \end{vmatrix} = 1\begin{vmatrix} 0 & 1 \\ -1 & 0 \end{vmatrix} - 2\begin{vmatrix} 1 & 1 \\ -1 & 0 \end{vmatrix} = 1 - 2(1) = -1,$

$|D_z| = \begin{vmatrix} 1 & 1 & 0 & 1 \\ 2 & 0 & 0 & 1 \\ 0 & 1 & 0 & 0 \\ 1 & 0 & 1 & 0 \end{vmatrix} = -1\begin{vmatrix} 1 & 1 & 1 \\ 2 & 0 & 1 \\ 0 & 1 & 0 \end{vmatrix} = -1\begin{vmatrix} 0 & 1 \\ 1 & 0 \end{vmatrix} + 2\begin{vmatrix} 1 & 1 \\ 1 & 0 \end{vmatrix} = -1(-1) + 2(-1) = -1,$ and

$|D_w| = \begin{vmatrix} 1 & 1 & 1 & 0 \\ 2 & 0 & 0 & 0 \\ 0 & 1 & -1 & 0 \\ 1 & 0 & 2 & 1 \end{vmatrix} = 1\begin{vmatrix} 1 & 1 & 1 \\ 2 & 0 & 0 \\ 0 & 1 & -1 \end{vmatrix} = -2\begin{vmatrix} 1 & 1 \\ 1 & -1 \end{vmatrix} = -2(-2) = 4.$ Hence, we have $x = \frac{|D_x|}{|D|} = \frac{-2}{-4} = \frac{1}{2},$

$y = \frac{|D_y|}{|D|} = \frac{-1}{-4} = \frac{1}{4},\; z = \frac{|D_z|}{|D|} = \frac{-1}{-4} = \frac{1}{4},$ and $w = \frac{|D_w|}{|D|} = \frac{4}{-4} = -1,$ and the solution is $\left(\frac{1}{2}, \frac{1}{4}, \frac{1}{4}, -1 \right)$.

44. $\begin{cases} x+y=1 \\ y+z=2 \\ z+w=3 \\ w-x=4 \end{cases}$ Then $|D| = \begin{vmatrix} 1 & 1 & 0 & 0 \\ 0 & 1 & 1 & 0 \\ 0 & 0 & 1 & 1 \\ -1 & 0 & 0 & 1 \end{vmatrix} = 1 \begin{vmatrix} 1 & 1 & 0 \\ 0 & 1 & 1 \\ 0 & 0 & 1 \end{vmatrix} - 1 \begin{vmatrix} 0 & 1 & 0 \\ 0 & 1 & 1 \\ -1 & 0 & 1 \end{vmatrix} = 1 \begin{vmatrix} 1 & 1 \\ 0 & 1 \end{vmatrix} - (-1) \begin{vmatrix} 1 & 0 \\ 1 & 1 \end{vmatrix} = 1+1=2,$

$|D_x| = \begin{vmatrix} 1 & 1 & 0 & 0 \\ 2 & 1 & 1 & 0 \\ 3 & 0 & 1 & 1 \\ 4 & 0 & 0 & 1 \end{vmatrix} = 1 \begin{vmatrix} 1 & 1 & 0 \\ 0 & 1 & 1 \\ 0 & 0 & 1 \end{vmatrix} - 1 \begin{vmatrix} 2 & 1 & 0 \\ 3 & 1 & 1 \\ 4 & 0 & 1 \end{vmatrix} = \begin{vmatrix} 1 & 1 \\ 0 & 1 \end{vmatrix} - \left(2 \begin{vmatrix} 1 & 1 \\ 0 & 1 \end{vmatrix} - 1 \begin{vmatrix} 3 & 1 \\ 4 & 1 \end{vmatrix}\right) = 1-3=-2,$

$|D_y| = \begin{vmatrix} 1 & 1 & 0 & 0 \\ 0 & 2 & 1 & 0 \\ 0 & 3 & 1 & 1 \\ -1 & 4 & 0 & 1 \end{vmatrix} = 1 \begin{vmatrix} 2 & 1 & 0 \\ 3 & 1 & 1 \\ 4 & 0 & 1 \end{vmatrix} - 1 \begin{vmatrix} 0 & 1 & 0 \\ 0 & 1 & 1 \\ -1 & 0 & 1 \end{vmatrix} = \left(2 \begin{vmatrix} 1 & 1 \\ 0 & 1 \end{vmatrix} - 1 \begin{vmatrix} 3 & 1 \\ 4 & 1 \end{vmatrix}\right) - (-1) \begin{vmatrix} 1 & 0 \\ 1 & 1 \end{vmatrix} = 3+1=4,$

$|D_z| = \begin{vmatrix} 1 & 1 & 1 & 0 \\ 0 & 1 & 2 & 0 \\ 0 & 0 & 3 & 1 \\ -1 & 0 & 4 & 1 \end{vmatrix} = 1 \begin{vmatrix} 1 & 2 & 0 \\ 0 & 3 & 1 \\ 0 & 4 & 1 \end{vmatrix} + 1 \begin{vmatrix} 1 & 1 & 0 \\ 1 & 2 & 0 \\ 0 & 3 & 1 \end{vmatrix} = 1 \begin{vmatrix} 3 & 1 \\ 4 & 1 \end{vmatrix} + 1 \begin{vmatrix} 1 & 1 \\ 1 & 2 \end{vmatrix} = -1+1=0,$

$|D_w| = \begin{vmatrix} 1 & 1 & 0 & 1 \\ 0 & 1 & 1 & 2 \\ 0 & 0 & 1 & 3 \\ -1 & 0 & 0 & 4 \end{vmatrix} = 1 \begin{vmatrix} 1 & 1 & 2 \\ 0 & 1 & 3 \\ 0 & 0 & 4 \end{vmatrix} + 1 \begin{vmatrix} 1 & 0 & 1 \\ 1 & 1 & 2 \\ 0 & 1 & 3 \end{vmatrix} = \begin{vmatrix} 1 & 3 \\ 0 & 4 \end{vmatrix} + \left(1 \begin{vmatrix} 1 & 2 \\ 1 & 3 \end{vmatrix} - 1 \begin{vmatrix} 0 & 1 \\ 1 & 3 \end{vmatrix}\right) = 4+2=6.$

Hence, the solution is $x = \dfrac{|D_x|}{|D|} = \dfrac{-2}{2} = -1$, $y = \dfrac{|D_y|}{|D|} = \dfrac{4}{2} = 2$, $z = \dfrac{|D_z|}{|D|} = \dfrac{0}{2} = 0$, and $w = \dfrac{|D_w|}{|D|} = \dfrac{6}{2} = 3$.

45. $\begin{vmatrix} a & 0 & 0 & 0 & 0 \\ 0 & b & 0 & 0 & 0 \\ 0 & 0 & c & 0 & 0 \\ 0 & 0 & 0 & d & 0 \\ 0 & 0 & 0 & 0 & e \end{vmatrix} = a \begin{vmatrix} b & 0 & 0 & 0 \\ 0 & c & 0 & 0 \\ 0 & 0 & d & 0 \\ 0 & 0 & 0 & e \end{vmatrix} = ab \begin{vmatrix} c & 0 & 0 \\ 0 & d & 0 \\ 0 & 0 & e \end{vmatrix} = abc \begin{vmatrix} d & 0 \\ 0 & e \end{vmatrix} = abcde$

46. $\begin{vmatrix} a & a & a & a & a \\ 0 & a & a & a & a \\ 0 & 0 & a & a & a \\ 0 & 0 & 0 & a & a \\ 0 & 0 & 0 & 0 & a \end{vmatrix} = a \begin{vmatrix} a & a & a & a \\ 0 & a & a & a \\ 0 & 0 & a & a \\ 0 & 0 & 0 & a \end{vmatrix} = a^2 \begin{vmatrix} a & a & a \\ 0 & a & a \\ 0 & 0 & a \end{vmatrix} = a^3 \begin{vmatrix} a & a \\ 0 & a \end{vmatrix} = a^5$

47. $\begin{vmatrix} x & 12 & 13 \\ 0 & x-1 & 23 \\ 0 & 0 & x-2 \end{vmatrix} = 0 \quad \Leftrightarrow \quad (x-2) \begin{vmatrix} x & 12 \\ 0 & x-1 \end{vmatrix} = 0 \quad \Leftrightarrow \quad (x-2) \cdot x (x-1) = 0 \quad \Leftrightarrow \quad x=0, 1, \text{ or } 2$

48. $\begin{vmatrix} x & 1 & 1 \\ 1 & 1 & x \\ x & 1 & x \end{vmatrix} = x \begin{vmatrix} 1 & x \\ 1 & x \end{vmatrix} - \begin{vmatrix} 1 & x \\ x & x \end{vmatrix} + \begin{vmatrix} 1 & 1 \\ x & 1 \end{vmatrix} = x(0) - (x - x^2) + 1 - x = x^2 - 2x + 1 = 0 \Leftrightarrow (x-1)^2 = 0 \Leftrightarrow x = 1$

49.
$$\begin{vmatrix} 1 & 0 & x \\ x^2 & 1 & 0 \\ x & 0 & 1 \end{vmatrix} = 0 \quad \Leftrightarrow \quad 1 \begin{vmatrix} 1 & 0 \\ 0 & 1 \end{vmatrix} + x \begin{vmatrix} x^2 & 1 \\ x & 0 \end{vmatrix} = 0 \quad \Leftrightarrow \quad 1 - x^2 = 0 \quad \Leftrightarrow \quad x^2 = 1 \quad \Leftrightarrow \quad x = \pm 1$$

50.
$$\begin{vmatrix} a & b & x-a \\ x & x+b & x \\ 0 & 1 & 1 \end{vmatrix} = -1 \begin{vmatrix} a & x-a \\ x & x \end{vmatrix} + \begin{vmatrix} a & b \\ x & x+b \end{vmatrix} = -1\left[ax - x\left(x - a\right)\right] + a\left(x + b\right) - bx$$

$$= -ax + x^2 - ax + ax + ab - bx = x^2 - ax - bx + ab = \left(x - a\right)\left(x - b\right) = 0 \Leftrightarrow x = a \text{ or } x = b$$

51. Area $= \pm \dfrac{1}{2} \begin{vmatrix} 0 & 0 & 1 \\ 6 & 2 & 1 \\ 3 & 8 & 1 \end{vmatrix} = \pm \dfrac{1}{2} \begin{vmatrix} 6 & 2 \\ 3 & 8 \end{vmatrix} = \pm \dfrac{1}{2}\left(48 - 6\right) = \dfrac{1}{2}\left(42\right) = 21$

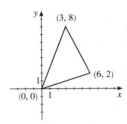

52. Area $= \pm \dfrac{1}{2} \begin{vmatrix} 1 & 0 & 1 \\ 3 & 5 & 1 \\ -2 & 2 & 1 \end{vmatrix} = \pm \dfrac{1}{2}\left(1 \begin{vmatrix} 5 & 1 \\ 2 & 1 \end{vmatrix} + 1 \begin{vmatrix} 3 & 5 \\ -2 & 2 \end{vmatrix}\right)$

$= \pm \dfrac{1}{2}\left[\left(5 - 2\right) + \left(6 + 10\right)\right] = \pm \dfrac{1}{2}\left[3 + 16\right] = \dfrac{1}{2}\left(19\right) = \dfrac{19}{2}$

53. Area $= \pm \dfrac{1}{2} \begin{vmatrix} -1 & 3 & 1 \\ 2 & 9 & 1 \\ 5 & -6 & 1 \end{vmatrix} = \pm \dfrac{1}{2}\left[-1 \begin{vmatrix} 9 & 1 \\ -6 & 1 \end{vmatrix} - 3 \begin{vmatrix} 2 & 1 \\ 5 & 1 \end{vmatrix} + 1 \begin{vmatrix} 2 & 9 \\ 5 & -6 \end{vmatrix}\right]$

$= \pm \dfrac{1}{2}\left[-1\left(9 + 6\right) - 3\left(2 - 5\right) + 1\left(-12 - 45\right)\right]$

$= \pm \dfrac{1}{2}\left[-15 - 3\left(-3\right) + \left(-57\right)\right] = \pm \dfrac{1}{2}\left(-63\right) = \dfrac{63}{2}$

54. Area $= \pm \dfrac{1}{2} \begin{vmatrix} -2 & 5 & 1 \\ 7 & 2 & 1 \\ 3 & -4 & 1 \end{vmatrix} = \pm \dfrac{1}{2}\left(-2 \begin{vmatrix} 2 & 1 \\ -4 & 1 \end{vmatrix} - 5 \begin{vmatrix} 7 & 1 \\ 3 & 1 \end{vmatrix} + 1 \begin{vmatrix} 7 & 2 \\ 3 & -4 \end{vmatrix}\right)$

$= \pm \dfrac{1}{2}\left[-2\left(2 + 4\right) - 5\left(7 - 3\right) + \left(-28 - 6\right)\right] = \pm \dfrac{1}{2}\left[-2\left(6\right) - 5\left(4\right) + \left(-34\right)\right]$

$= \pm \dfrac{1}{2}\left(-12 - 20 - 34\right) = \dfrac{1}{2}\left(66\right) = 33$

55. $\begin{vmatrix} 1 & x & x^2 \\ 1 & y & y^2 \\ 1 & z & z^2 \end{vmatrix} = 1 \begin{vmatrix} y & y^2 \\ z & z^2 \end{vmatrix} - 1 \begin{vmatrix} x & x^2 \\ z & z^2 \end{vmatrix} + 1 \begin{vmatrix} x & x^2 \\ y & y^2 \end{vmatrix} = yz^2 - y^2z - \left(xz^2 - x^2z\right) + \left(xy^2 - xy^2\right)$

$= yz^2 - y^2z - xz^2 - x^2z + xy^2 - xy^2 + xyz - xyz = xyz - xz^2 - y^2z + yz^2 - x^2y + x^2z + zy^2 - xyz$

$= z\left(xy - xz - y^2 + yz\right) - x\left(xy - xz - y^2 + yz\right) = \left(z - x\right)\left(xy - xz - y^2 + yz\right)$

$= \left(z - x\right)\left[x\left(y - z\right) - y\left(y - z\right)\right] = \left(z - x\right)\left(x - y\right)\left(y - z\right)$

56. (a) Let x be the amount of apples, y the amount of peaches, and z the amount of pears (in pounds).

We get the model
$$\begin{cases} x + y + z = 18 \\ 0.75x + 0.90y + 0.60z = 13.80 \\ -0.75x + 0.90y + 0.60z = 1.80 \end{cases}$$

(b) $|D| = \begin{vmatrix} 1 & 1 & 1 \\ 0.75 & 0.90 & 0.60 \\ -0.75 & 0.90 & 0.60 \end{vmatrix} = 1 \cdot \begin{vmatrix} 0.90 & 0.60 \\ 0.90 & 0.60 \end{vmatrix} - 1 \cdot \begin{vmatrix} 0.75 & 0.60 \\ -0.75 & 0.60 \end{vmatrix} + 1 \cdot \begin{vmatrix} 0.75 & 0.90 \\ -0.75 & 0.90 \end{vmatrix} = 0 - 0.90 + 1.35 = 0.45,$

$|D_x| = \begin{vmatrix} 18 & 1 & 1 \\ 13.80 & 0.90 & 0.60 \\ 1.80 & 0.90 & 0.60 \end{vmatrix} = 18 \cdot \begin{vmatrix} 0.90 & 0.60 \\ 0.90 & 0.60 \end{vmatrix} - 1 \cdot \begin{vmatrix} 13.80 & 0.60 \\ 1.80 & 0.60 \end{vmatrix} + 1 \cdot \begin{vmatrix} 13.80 & 0.90 \\ 1.80 & 0.90 \end{vmatrix} = 0 - 7.2 + 10.8 = 3.6,$

$|D_y| = \begin{vmatrix} 1 & 18 & 1 \\ 0.75 & 13.80 & 0.60 \\ -0.75 & 1.80 & 0.60 \end{vmatrix} = 1 \cdot \begin{vmatrix} 13.80 & 0.60 \\ 1.80 & 0.60 \end{vmatrix} - 18 \cdot \begin{vmatrix} 0.75 & 0.60 \\ -0.75 & 0.60 \end{vmatrix} + 1 \cdot \begin{vmatrix} 0.75 & 13.80 \\ -0.75 & 1.80 \end{vmatrix}$

$= 7.2 - 16.2 + 11.7 = 2.7,$ and

$|D_z| = \begin{vmatrix} 1 & 1 & 18 \\ 0.75 & 0.90 & 13.80 \\ -0.75 & 0.90 & 1.80 \end{vmatrix} = 1 \cdot \begin{vmatrix} 0.90 & 13.80 \\ 0.90 & 1.80 \end{vmatrix} - 1 \cdot \begin{vmatrix} 0.75 & 13.80 \\ -0.75 & 1.80 \end{vmatrix} + 18 \cdot \begin{vmatrix} 0.75 & 0.90 \\ -0.75 & 0.90 \end{vmatrix}$

$= -10.8 - 11.7 + 24.3 = 1.8.$

So $x = \dfrac{|D_x|}{|D|} = \dfrac{3.6}{0.45} = 8$; $y = \dfrac{|D_y|}{|D|} = \dfrac{27}{0.45} = 6$; and $z = \dfrac{|D_z|}{|D|} = \dfrac{1.8}{0.45} = 4$.

Thus, Muriel buys 8 pounds of apples, 6 pounds of peaches, and 4 pounds of pears.

57. (a) Using the points $(10, 25)$, $(15, 33.75)$, and $(40, 40)$, we substitute for x and y and get the system

$$\begin{cases} 100a + 10b + c = 25 \\ 225a + 15b + c = 33.75 \\ 1600a + 40b + c = 40 \end{cases}$$

(b) $|D| = \begin{vmatrix} 100 & 10 & 1 \\ 225 & 15 & 1 \\ 1600 & 40 & 1 \end{vmatrix} = 1 \cdot \begin{vmatrix} 225 & 15 \\ 1600 & 40 \end{vmatrix} - 1 \cdot \begin{vmatrix} 100 & 10 \\ 1600 & 40 \end{vmatrix} + 1 \cdot \begin{vmatrix} 100 & 10 \\ 225 & 15 \end{vmatrix}$

$= (9000 - 24{,}000) - (4000 - 16{,}000) + (1500 - 2250) = -15{,}000 + 12{,}000 - 750 = -3750,$

$|D_a| = \begin{vmatrix} 25 & 10 & 1 \\ 33.75 & 15 & 1 \\ 40 & 40 & 1 \end{vmatrix} = 1 \cdot \begin{vmatrix} 33.75 & 15 \\ 40 & 40 \end{vmatrix} - 1 \cdot \begin{vmatrix} 25 & 10 \\ 40 & 40 \end{vmatrix} + 1 \cdot \begin{vmatrix} 25 & 10 \\ 33.75 & 15 \end{vmatrix}$

$= (1350 - 600) - (1000 - 400) + (375 - 337.5) = 750 - 600 + 37.5 = 187.5,$

$|D_b| = \begin{vmatrix} 100 & 25 & 1 \\ 225 & 33.75 & 1 \\ 1600 & 40 & 1 \end{vmatrix} = 1 \cdot \begin{vmatrix} 225 & 33.75 \\ 1600 & 40 \end{vmatrix} - 1 \cdot \begin{vmatrix} 100 & 25 \\ 1600 & 40 \end{vmatrix} + 1 \cdot \begin{vmatrix} 100 & 25 \\ 225 & 33.75 \end{vmatrix}$

$= (9000 - 54{,}000) - (4000 - 40{,}000) + (3375 - 5625) = -45{,}000 + 36{,}000 - 2250 = -11{,}250,$ and

$$|D_c| = \begin{vmatrix} 100 & 10 & 25 \\ 225 & 15 & 33.75 \\ 1600 & 40 & 40 \end{vmatrix} = 25 \cdot \begin{vmatrix} 225 & 15 \\ 1600 & 40 \end{vmatrix} - 33.75 \cdot \begin{vmatrix} 100 & 10 \\ 1600 & 40 \end{vmatrix} + 40 \cdot \begin{vmatrix} 100 & 10 \\ 225 & 15 \end{vmatrix}$$

$$= 25 \cdot (9,000 - 24,000) - 33.75 \cdot (4,000 - 16,000) + 40 \cdot (1,500 - 2,250)$$

$$= 25 \cdot (-15,000) + 33.75 \cdot 12,000 + 40 \cdot (-750) = -375,000 + 405,000 - 30,000 = 0.$$

Thus, $a = \dfrac{|D_a|}{|D|} = \dfrac{187.5}{-3750} = 0.05$, $b = \dfrac{|D_b|}{|D|} = \dfrac{-11,250}{-3,750} = 3$, and $c = \dfrac{|D_c|}{|D|} = \dfrac{0}{-3,750} = 0$. Thus, the model is $y = 0.05x^2 + 3x$.

58. Using the determinant formula for the area of a triangle (Exercise 59), we have

$$\text{Area} = \pm \frac{1}{2} \begin{vmatrix} 1000 & 2000 & 1 \\ 5000 & 4000 & 1 \\ 2000 & 6000 & 1 \end{vmatrix} = \pm \frac{1}{2} \left(1 \cdot \begin{vmatrix} 5000 & 4000 \\ 2000 & 6000 \end{vmatrix} - 1 \cdot \begin{vmatrix} 1000 & 2000 \\ 2000 & 6000 \end{vmatrix} + 1 \cdot \begin{vmatrix} 1000 & 2000 \\ 5000 & 4000 \end{vmatrix} \right)$$

$$= \pm \frac{1}{2} \cdot (22,000,000 - 2,000,000 - 6,000,000) = \pm \frac{1}{2} \cdot 14,000,000 = \pm 7,000,000$$

Thus, the area is 7,000,000 ft^2.

59. (a) The coordinates of the vertices of the surrounding rectangle are (a_1, b_1), (a_2, b_1), (a_2, b_3), and (a_1, b_3). The area of the surrounding rectangle is given by $(a_2 - a_1) \cdot (b_3 - b_1) = a_2 b_3 + a_1 b_1 - a_2 b_1 - a_1 b_3 = a_1 b_1 + a_2 b_3 - a_1 b_3 - a_2 b_1$.

(b) The area of the three blue triangles are as follows:

Area of $\triangle((a_1, b_1), (a_2, b_1), (a_2, b_2))$: $\frac{1}{2}(a_2 - a_1) \cdot (b_2 - b_1) = \frac{1}{2}(a_2 b_2 + a_1 b_1 - a_2 b_1 - a_1 b_2)$

Area of $\triangle((a_2, b_2), (a_2, b_3), (a_3, b_3))$: $\frac{1}{2}(a_2 - a_3) \cdot (b_3 - b_2) = \frac{1}{2}(a_2 b_3 + a_3 b_2 - a_2 b_2 - a_3 b_3)$

Area of $\triangle((a_1, b), (a_1, b_3), (a_3, b_3))$: $\frac{1}{2}(a_3 - a_1) \cdot (b_3 - b_1) = \frac{1}{2}(a_3 b_3 + a_1 b_1 - a_3 b_1 - a_1 b_3)$.

Thus the sum of the areas of the blue triangles, B, is

$$B = \frac{1}{2}(a_2 b_2 + a_1 b_1 - a_2 b_1 - a_1 b_2) + \frac{1}{2}(a_2 b_3 + a_3 b_2 - a_2 b_2 - a_3 b_3) + \frac{1}{2}(a_3 b_3 + a_1 b_1 - a_3 b_1 - a_1 b_3)$$

$$= \frac{1}{2}(a_1 b_1 + a_1 b_1 + a_2 b_2 + a_2 b_3 + a_3 b_2 + a_3 b_3) - \frac{1}{2}(a_1 b_2 + a_1 b_3 + a_2 b_1 + a_2 b_2 + a_3 b_1 + a_3 b_3)$$

$$= a_1 b_1 + \frac{1}{2}(a_2 b_3 + a_3 b_2) - \frac{1}{2}(a_1 b_2 + a_1 b_3 + a_2 b_1 + a_3 b_1)$$

So the area of the red triangle A is the area of the rectangle minus the sum of the areas of the blue triangles, that is,

$$A = (a_1 b_1 + a_2 b_3 - a_1 b_3 - a_2 b_1) - \left[a_1 b_1 + \frac{1}{2}(a_2 b_3 + a_3 b_2) - \frac{1}{2}(a_1 b_2 + a_1 b_3 + a_2 b_1 + a_3 b_1) \right]$$

$$= a_1 b_1 + a_2 b_3 - a_1 b_3 - a_2 b_1 - a_1 b_1 - \frac{1}{2}(a_2 b_3 + a_3 b_2) + \frac{1}{2}(a_1 b_2 + a_1 b_3 + a_2 b_1 + a_3 b_1)$$

$$= \frac{1}{2}(a_1 b_2 + a_2 b_3 + a_3 b_1) - \frac{1}{2}(a_1 b_3 + a_2 b_1 + a_3 b_2)$$

(c) We first find $Q = \begin{vmatrix} a_1 & b_1 & 1 \\ a_2 & b_2 & 1 \\ a_3 & b_3 & 1 \end{vmatrix}$ by expanding about the third column.

$$Q = 1 \begin{vmatrix} a_2 & b_2 \\ a_3 & b_3 \end{vmatrix} - 1 \begin{vmatrix} a_1 & b_1 \\ a_3 & b_3 \end{vmatrix} + 1 \begin{vmatrix} a_1 & b_1 \\ a_2 & b_2 \end{vmatrix} = a_2 b_3 - a_3 b_2 - (a_1 b_3 - a_3 b_1) + a_1 b_2 - a_2 b_1$$

$$= a_1 b_2 + a_2 b_3 + a_3 b_1 - a_1 b_3 - a_2 b_1 - a_3 b_2$$

So $\frac{1}{2}Q = \frac{1}{2}(a_1 b_2 + a_2 b_3 + a_3 b_1) - \frac{1}{2}(a_1 b_3 - a_2 b_1 - a_3 b_2)$, the area of the red triangle. Since $\frac{1}{2}Q$ is not always positive, the area is $\pm \frac{1}{2}Q$.

60. (a) If three points lie on a line then the area of the "triangle" they determine is 0, that is, $\pm\frac{1}{2}Q = \pm\frac{1}{2}\begin{vmatrix} a_1 & b_1 & 1 \\ a_2 & b_2 & 1 \\ a_3 & b_3 & 1 \end{vmatrix} = 0$

$\Leftrightarrow$ $Q = 0$. If the points are not collinear, then the point form a triangle, and the area of the triangle determined by these points is nonzero. If $Q = 0$, then $\pm\frac{1}{2}Q = \pm\frac{1}{2}(0) = 0$, so the "triangle" has no area, and the points are collinear.

(b) (i) $\begin{vmatrix} -6 & 4 & 1 \\ 2 & 10 & 1 \\ 6 & 13 & 1 \end{vmatrix} = \begin{vmatrix} 2 & 10 \\ 6 & 13 \end{vmatrix} - \begin{vmatrix} -6 & 4 \\ 6 & 13 \end{vmatrix} + \begin{vmatrix} -6 & 4 \\ 2 & 10 \end{vmatrix}$

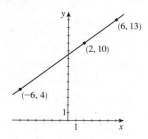

$= (26 - 60) - (-78 - 24) + (-60 - 8)$

$= -34 + 104 - 68 = 0$

Thus, these points are collinear.

(ii) $\begin{vmatrix} -5 & 10 & 1 \\ 2 & 6 & 1 \\ 15 & -2 & 1 \end{vmatrix} = \begin{vmatrix} 2 & 6 \\ 15 & -2 \end{vmatrix} - \begin{vmatrix} -5 & 10 \\ 15 & -2 \end{vmatrix} + \begin{vmatrix} -5 & 10 \\ 2 & 6 \end{vmatrix}$

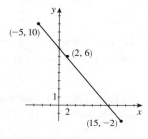

$= (-4 - 90) - (10 - 150) + (-30 - 20)$

$= -94 + 140 - 50 = -4$

These points are not collinear. Note that this is difficult to determine from the diagram.

61. (a) Let $|M| = \begin{vmatrix} x & y & 1 \\ x_1 & y_1 & 1 \\ x_2 & y_2 & 1 \end{vmatrix}$. Then, expanding by the third column,

$|M| = \begin{vmatrix} x_1 & y_1 \\ x_2 & y_2 \end{vmatrix} - \begin{vmatrix} x & y \\ x_2 & y_2 \end{vmatrix} + \begin{vmatrix} x & y \\ x_1 & y_1 \end{vmatrix} = (x_1 y_2 - x_2 y_1) - (x y_2 - x_2 y) + (x y_1 - x_1 y)$

$= x_1 y_2 - x_2 y_1 - x y_2 + x_2 y + x y_1 - x_1 y = x_2 y - x_1 y - x y_2 + x y_1 + x_1 y_2 - x_2 y_1$

$= (x_2 - x_1)y - (y_2 - y_1)x + x_1 y_2 - x_2 y_1$

So $|M| = 0$ $\Leftrightarrow$ $(x_2 - x_1)y - (y_2 - y_1)x + x_1 y_2 - x_2 y_1 = 0 \Leftrightarrow (x_2 - x_1)y = (y_2 - y_1)x - x_1 y_2 + x_2 y_1$ $\Leftrightarrow$

$(x_2 - x_1)y = (y_2 - y_1)x - x_1 y_2 + x_1 y_1 - x_1 y_1 + x_2 y_1$ $\Leftrightarrow$ $y = \dfrac{y_2 - y_1}{x_2 - x_1}x - \dfrac{x_1(y_2 - y_1)}{x_2 - x_1} + \dfrac{y_1(x_2 - x_1)}{x_2 - x_1}$

$\Leftrightarrow$ $y = \dfrac{y_2 - y_1}{x_2 - x_1}(x - x_1) + y_1$ $\Leftrightarrow$ $y - y_1 = \dfrac{y_2 - y_1}{x_2 - x_1}(x - x_1)$, which is the "two-point" form of the equation

for the line passing through the points (x_1, y_1) and (x_2, y_2).

(b) Using the result of part (a), the line has equation

$\begin{vmatrix} x & y & 1 \\ 20 & 50 & 1 \\ -10 & 25 & 1 \end{vmatrix} = 0$ $\Leftrightarrow$ $\begin{vmatrix} 20 & 50 \\ -10 & 25 \end{vmatrix} - \begin{vmatrix} x & y \\ -10 & 25 \end{vmatrix} + \begin{vmatrix} x & y \\ 20 & 50 \end{vmatrix} = 0$ $\Leftrightarrow$

$(500 + 500) - (25x + 10y) + (50x - 20y) = 0$ $\Leftrightarrow$ $25x - 30y + 1000 = 0$ $\Leftrightarrow$ $5x - 6y + 200 = 0$.

62. (a) If A is a matrix with a row or column consisting entirely of zeros, then if we expand the determinant by this row or column, we get $|A| = 0 \cdot |A_{1j}| - 0 \cdot |A_{2j}| + \cdots - 0 \cdot |A_{nj}| = 0$.

  (b) Use the principle that if matrix B is a square matrix obtained from A by adding a multiple of one row to another, or a multiple of one column to another, then $|A| = |B|$. If we let B be the matrix obtained by subtracting the two rows (or columns) that are the same, then matrix B will have a row or column that consists entirely of zeros. So $|B| = 0 \quad \Rightarrow \quad |A| = 0$.

  (c) Again use the principle that if matrix B is a square matrix obtained from A by adding a multiple of one row to another, or a multiple of one column to another, then $|A| = |B|$. If we let B be the matrix obtained by subtracting the proper multiple of the row (or column) from the other similar row (or column), then matrix B will have a row or column that consists entirely of zeros. So $|B| = 0 \quad \Rightarrow \quad |A| = 0$.

63. Gaussian elimination is superior, since it takes much longer to evaluate six 5×5 determinants than it does to perform one five-equation Gaussian elimination.

9.8 **Partial Fractions**

1. $\dfrac{1}{(x-1)(x+2)} = \dfrac{A}{x-1} + \dfrac{B}{x+2}$

2. $\dfrac{x}{x^2 + 3x - 4} = \dfrac{x}{(x-1)(x+4)} = \dfrac{A}{(x-1)} + \dfrac{B}{(x+4)}$

3. $\dfrac{x^2 - 3x + 5}{(x-2)^2(x+4)} = \dfrac{A}{x-2} + \dfrac{B}{(x-2)^2} + \dfrac{C}{x+4}$

4. $\dfrac{1}{x^4 - x^3} = \dfrac{1}{x^3(x-1)} = \dfrac{A}{x} + \dfrac{B}{x^2} + \dfrac{C}{x^3} + \dfrac{D}{x-1}$

5. $\dfrac{x^2}{(x-3)(x^2+4)} = \dfrac{A}{x-3} + \dfrac{Bx+C}{x^2+4}$

6. $\dfrac{1}{x^4 - 1} = \dfrac{1}{(x^2-1)(x^2+1)} = \dfrac{1}{(x-1)(x+1)(x^2+1)} = \dfrac{A}{x-1} + \dfrac{B}{x+1} + \dfrac{Cx+D}{x^2+1}$

7. $\dfrac{x^3 - 4x^2 + 2}{(x^2+1)(x^2+2)} = \dfrac{Ax+B}{x^2+1} + \dfrac{Cx+D}{x^2+2}$

8. $\dfrac{x^4 + x^2 + 1}{x^2(x^2+4)^2} = \dfrac{A}{x} + \dfrac{B}{x^2} + \dfrac{Cx+D}{x^2+4} + \dfrac{Ex+F}{(x^2+4)^2}$

9. $\dfrac{x^3 + x + 1}{x(2x-5)^3(x^2+2x+5)^2} = \dfrac{A}{x} + \dfrac{B}{2x-5} + \dfrac{C}{(2x-5)^2} + \dfrac{D}{(2x-5)^3} + \dfrac{Ex+F}{x^2+2x+5} + \dfrac{Gx+H}{(x^2+2x+5)^2}$

10. Since $(x^3 - 1)(x^2 - 1) = (x-1)(x^2+x+1)(x-1)(x+1) = (x-1)^2(x+1)(x^2+x+1)$, we have
$$\dfrac{1}{(x^3-1)(x^2-1)} = \dfrac{1}{(x-1)^2(x+1)(x^2+x+1)} = \dfrac{A}{x-1} + \dfrac{B}{(x-1)^2} + \dfrac{C}{x+1} + \dfrac{Dx+E}{x^2+x+1}.$$

11. $\dfrac{2}{(x-1)(x+1)} = \dfrac{A}{x-1} + \dfrac{B}{x+1}$. Multiplying by $(x-1)(x+1)$, we get $2 = A(x+1) + B(x-1) \quad \Leftrightarrow$

$2 = Ax + A + Bx - B$. Thus $\begin{cases} A + B = 0 \\ A - B = 2 \end{cases}$ Adding we get $2A = 2 \quad \Leftrightarrow \quad A = 1$. Now $A + B = 0 \quad \Leftrightarrow$

$B = -A$, so $B = -1$. Thus, the required partial fraction decomposition is $\dfrac{2}{(x-1)(x+1)} = \dfrac{1}{x-1} - \dfrac{1}{x+1}$.

12. $\dfrac{2x}{(x-1)(x+1)} = \dfrac{A}{x-1} + \dfrac{B}{x+1}$. Multiplying by $(x-1)(x+1)$, we get $2x = A(x+1) + B(x-1) \quad \Leftrightarrow$

$2x = Ax + A + Bx - B$. Thus $\begin{cases} A + B = 2 \\ A - B = 0 \end{cases}$ Adding we $2A = 2 \quad \Leftrightarrow \quad A = 1$. Since $A - B = 0 \quad \Leftrightarrow \quad B = A$,

$B = 1$. The required partial fraction decomposition is $\dfrac{2x}{(x-1)(x+1)} = \dfrac{1}{x-1} + \dfrac{1}{x+1}$.

13. $\dfrac{5}{(x-1)(x+4)} = \dfrac{A}{x-1} + \dfrac{B}{x+4}$. Multiplying by $(x-1)(x+4)$, we get $5 = A(x+4) + B(x-1)$ $\Leftrightarrow$

$5 = Ax + 4A + Bx - B$. Thus $\begin{cases} A + B = 0 \\ 4A - B = 5 \end{cases}$ Now $A + B = 0$ $\Leftrightarrow$ $B = -A$, so substituting, we

get $4A - (-A) = 5$ $\Leftrightarrow$ $5A = 5 \Leftrightarrow A = 1$ and $B = -1$. The required partial fraction decomposition is

$\dfrac{5}{(x-1)(x+4)} = \dfrac{1}{x-1} - \dfrac{1}{x+4}$.

14. $\dfrac{x+6}{x(x+3)} = \dfrac{A}{x} + \dfrac{B}{x+3}$. Multiplying by $x(x+3)$ we get $x + 6 = A(x+3) + xB$ $\Leftrightarrow$

$x + 6 = Ax + 3A + Bx = (A+B)x + 3A$. Thus $\begin{cases} A + B = 1 \\ 3A \quad\;\; = 6 \end{cases}$ Now $3A = 6$ $\Leftrightarrow$ $A = 2$, and

$2 + B = 1 \Leftrightarrow B = -1$. The required partial fraction decomposition is $\dfrac{x+6}{x(x+3)} = \dfrac{2}{x} - \dfrac{1}{x+3}$.

15. $\dfrac{12}{x^2 - 9} = \dfrac{12}{(x-3)(x+3)} = \dfrac{A}{x-3} + \dfrac{B}{x+3}$. Multiplying by $(x-3)(x+3)$, we get $12 = A(x+3) + B(x-3)$

$\Leftrightarrow$ $12 = Ax + 3A + Bx - 3B$. Thus $\begin{cases} A + B = 0 \\ 3A - 3B = 12 \end{cases}$ $\Leftrightarrow$ $\begin{cases} A + B = 0 \\ A - B = 4 \end{cases}$ Adding, we get $2A = 4$ $\Leftrightarrow$

$A = 2$. So $2 + B = 0$ $\Leftrightarrow$ $B = -2$. The required partial fraction decomposition is $\dfrac{12}{x^2 - 9} = \dfrac{2}{x-3} - \dfrac{2}{x+3}$.

16. $\dfrac{x-12}{x^2 - 4x} = \dfrac{x-12}{x(x-4)} = \dfrac{A}{x} + \dfrac{B}{x-4}$. Multiplying by $x(x-4)$, we get

$x - 12 = A(x-4) + Bx = Ax - 4A + Bx = (A+B)x - 4A$. Thus we must solve the system

$\begin{cases} A + B = \quad 1 \\ -4A \quad\quad = -12 \end{cases}$ This gives $-4A = -12$ $\Leftrightarrow$ $A = 3$, and $3 + B = 1$ $\Leftrightarrow$ $B = -2$. Thus

$\dfrac{x-12}{x^2 - 4x} = \dfrac{3}{x} - \dfrac{2}{x-4}$.

17. $\dfrac{4}{x^2 - 4} = \dfrac{4}{(x-2)(x+2)} = \dfrac{A}{x-2} + \dfrac{B}{x+2}$. Multiplying by $x^2 - 4$, we get

$4 = A(x+2) + B(x-2) = (A+B)x + (2A - 2B)$, and so $\begin{cases} A + B = 0 \\ 2A - 2B = 4 \end{cases}$ $\Leftrightarrow$ $\begin{cases} A + B = 0 \\ A - B = 2 \end{cases}$ Adding we

get $2A = 2$ $\Leftrightarrow$ $A = 1$, and $B = -1$. Therefore, $\dfrac{4}{x^2 - 4} = \dfrac{1}{x-2} - \dfrac{1}{x+2}$.

18. $\dfrac{2x+1}{x^2 + x - 2} = \dfrac{2x+1}{(x+2)(x-1)} = \dfrac{A}{x+2} + \dfrac{B}{x-1}$. Thus, $2x + 1 = A(x-1) + B(x+2) = (A+B)x + (-A + 2B)$,

and so $\begin{cases} A + B = 2 \\ -A + 2B = 1 \end{cases}$ Adding the two equations, we get $3B = 3 \Leftrightarrow B = 1$. Thus $A + 1 = 2$ $\Leftrightarrow$ $A = 1$.

Therefore, $\dfrac{2x+1}{x^2 + x - 2} = \dfrac{1}{x+2} + \dfrac{1}{x-1}$.

19. $\dfrac{x+14}{x^2 - 2x - 8} = \dfrac{x+14}{(x-4)(x+2)} = \dfrac{A}{x-4} + \dfrac{B}{x+2}$. Hence, $x + 14 = A(x+2) + B(x-4) = (A+B)x + (2A - 4B)$,

and so $\begin{cases} A + B = 1 \\ 2A - 4B = 14 \end{cases}$ $\Leftrightarrow$ $\begin{cases} 2A + 2B = 2 \\ A - 2B = 7 \end{cases}$ Adding, we get $3A = 9$ $\Leftrightarrow$ $A = 3$. So $(3) + B = 1$ $\Leftrightarrow$

$B = -2$. Therefore, $\dfrac{x+14}{x^2 - 2x - 8} = \dfrac{3}{x-4} - \dfrac{2}{x+2}$.

20. $\dfrac{8x-3}{2x^2-x} = \dfrac{8x-3}{x(2x-1)} = \dfrac{A}{x} + \dfrac{B}{2x-1}$. Hence, $8x-3 = A(2x-1) + Bx = (2A+B)x + (-A)$,

giving $\begin{cases} 2A + B = & 8 \\ -A & = -3 \end{cases}$ So $-A = -3 \Leftrightarrow A = 3$, and $2(3) + B = 8 \Leftrightarrow B = 2$. Therefore,

$\dfrac{8x-3}{2x^2-x} = \dfrac{3}{x} + \dfrac{2}{2x-1}$.

21. $\dfrac{x}{8x^2-10x+3} = \dfrac{x}{(4x-3)(2x-1)} = \dfrac{A}{4x-3} + \dfrac{B}{2x-1}$. Hence,

$x = A(2x-1) + B(4x-3) = (2A+4B)x + (-A-3B)$, and so $\begin{cases} 2A + 4B = 1 \\ -A - 3B = 0 \end{cases}$ $\Leftrightarrow$ $\begin{cases} 2A + 4B = 1 \\ -2A - 6B = 0 \end{cases}$

Adding, we get $-2B = 1 \Leftrightarrow B = -\frac{1}{2}$, and $A = \frac{3}{2}$. Therefore, $\dfrac{x}{8x^2-10x+3} = \dfrac{\frac{3}{2}}{4x-3} - \dfrac{\frac{1}{2}}{2x-1}$.

22. $\dfrac{7x-3}{x^3+2x^2-3x} = \dfrac{7x-3}{x(x+3)(x-1)} = \dfrac{A}{x} + \dfrac{B}{x+3} + \dfrac{C}{x-1}$. Hence,

$7x-3 = A(x+3)(x-1) + Bx(x-1) + Cx(x+3) = A(x^2+2x-3) + B(x^2-x) + C(x^2+3x)$

$= (A+B+C)x^2 + (2A-B+3C)x - 3A$

Thus $\begin{cases} A + B + \ C = & 0 \\ 2A - B + 3C = & 7 \\ -3A & = -3 \end{cases}$
Coefficients of x^2
Coefficients of x
Constant terms
 So $-3A = -3 \Leftrightarrow A = 1$. Substituting, the system reduces

to $\begin{cases} 1 + B + \ C = 0 \\ 2 - B + 3C = 7 \end{cases}$ Adding these two equations, we get $3 + 4C = 7 \Leftrightarrow C = 1$. Thus $1 + B + 1 = 0 \Leftrightarrow$

$B = -2$. Therefore, $\dfrac{7x-3}{x^3+2x^2-3x} = \dfrac{1}{x} - \dfrac{2}{x+3} + \dfrac{1}{x-1}$.

23. $\dfrac{9x^2-9x+6}{2x^3-x^2-8x+4} = \dfrac{9x^2-9x+6}{(x-2)(x+2)(2x-1)} = \dfrac{A}{x-2} + \dfrac{B}{x+2} + \dfrac{C}{2x-1}$. Thus,

$9x^2-9x+6 = A(x+2)(2x-1) + B(x-2)(2x-1) + C(x-2)(x+2)$

$= A(2x^2+3x-2) + B(2x^2-5x+2) + C(x^2-4)$

$= (2A+2B+C)x^2 + (3A-5B)x + (-2A+2B-4C)$

This leads to the system $\begin{cases} 2A + 2B + \ C = & 9 \\ 3A - 5B & = -9 \\ -2A + 2B - 4C = & 6 \end{cases}$
Coefficients of x^2
Coefficients of x
Constant terms
 $\Leftrightarrow$ $\begin{cases} 2A + \ 2B + \ C = & 9 \\ 16B + 3C = 45 \\ 4B - 3C = 15 \end{cases}$ $\Leftrightarrow$

$\begin{cases} 2A + \ 2B + \ C = & 9 \\ 16B + \ 3C = & 45 \\ 15C = -15 \end{cases}$ Hence, $-15C = 15 \Leftrightarrow C = -1; 16B - 3 = 45 \Leftrightarrow B = 3$; and $2A + 6 - 1 = 9$

$\Leftrightarrow A = 2$. Therefore, $\dfrac{9x^2-9x+6}{2x^3-x^2-8x+4} = \dfrac{2}{x-2} + \dfrac{3}{x+2} - \dfrac{1}{2x-1}$.

24. $\dfrac{-3x^2 - 3x + 27}{(x+2)\,(2x^2 + 3x - 9)} = \dfrac{-3x^2 - 3x + 27}{(x+2)\,(2x-3)\,(x+3)} = \dfrac{A}{x+2} + \dfrac{B}{2x-3} + \dfrac{C}{x+3}$. Thus,

$$
\begin{aligned}
-3x^2 - 3x + 27 &= A\,(2x-3)\,(x+3) + B\,(x+2)\,(x+3) + C\,(x+2)\,(2x-3) \\
&= A\,\left(2x^2 + 3x - 9\right) + B\,\left(x^2 + 5x + 6\right) + C\,\left(2x^2 + x - 6\right) \\
&= (2A + B + 2C)\,x^2 + (3A + 5B + C)\,x + (-9A + 6B - 6C)
\end{aligned}
$$

So $\begin{cases} 2A + B + 2C = -3 \quad \text{Coefficients of } x^2 \\ 3A + 5B + C = -3 \quad \text{Coefficients of } x \\ -9A + 6B - 6C = 27 \quad \text{Constant terms} \end{cases} \Leftrightarrow \begin{cases} 2A + B + 2C = -3 \\ 7B - 4C = 3 \\ 21B + 6C = 27 \end{cases} \Leftrightarrow \begin{cases} 2A + B + 2C = -3 \\ 7B - 6C = 3 \\ 24C = 24 \end{cases}$

Hence, $24C = 24 \Leftrightarrow C = 1$; then $7B - 4 = 3 \Leftrightarrow B = 1$; and $2A + 1 + 2 = -3 \Leftrightarrow A = -3$.

Therefore, $\dfrac{-3x^2 - 3x + 27}{(x+2)\,(2x^2 + 3x - 9)} = \dfrac{-3}{x+2} + \dfrac{1}{2x-3} + \dfrac{1}{x+3}$.

25. $\dfrac{x^2 + 1}{x^3 + x^2} = \dfrac{x^2 + 1}{x^2\,(x+1)} = \dfrac{A}{x} + \dfrac{B}{x^2} + \dfrac{C}{x+1}$. Hence,

$x^2 + 1 = Ax\,(x+1) + B\,(x+1) + Cx^2 = (A + C)\,x^2 + (A + B)\,x + B$, and so $B = 1$; $A + 1 = 0 \Leftrightarrow A = -1$;

and $-1 + C = 1 \Leftrightarrow C = 2$. Therefore, $\dfrac{x^2 + 1}{x^3 + x^2} = \dfrac{-1}{x} + \dfrac{1}{x^2} + \dfrac{2}{x+1}$.

26. $\dfrac{3x^2 + 5x - 13}{(3x+2)\,(x^2 - 4x + 4)} = \dfrac{3x^2 + 5x - 13}{(3x+2)\,(x-2)^2} = \dfrac{A}{3x+2} + \dfrac{B}{x-2} + \dfrac{C}{(x-2)^2}$. Thus,

$$
\begin{aligned}
3x^2 + 5x - 13 &= A\,(x-2)^2 + B\,(3x+2)\,(x-2) + C\,(3x+2) \\
&= A\,\left(x^2 - 4x + 4\right) + B\,\left(3x^2 - 4x - 4\right) + C\,(3x+2) \\
&= (A + 3B)\,x^2 + (-4A - 4B + 3C)\,x + (4A - 4B + 2C)
\end{aligned}
$$

This leads to the following system: $\begin{cases} A + 3B = 3 \quad \text{Coefficients of } x^2 \\ -4A - 4B + 3C = 5 \quad \text{Coefficients of } x \\ 4A - 4B + 2C = -13 \quad \text{Constant terms} \end{cases} \Leftrightarrow$

$\begin{cases} A + 3B = 3 \\ 8B + 3C = 17 \\ -8B + 5C = -8 \end{cases} \Leftrightarrow \begin{cases} A + 3B = 3 \\ 8B + 3C = 17 \\ 8C = 9 \end{cases}$ Hence, $8C = 9 \Leftrightarrow C = \frac{9}{8}$;

$8B + 3\left(\frac{9}{8}\right) = 8B + \frac{27}{8} = 17 \Leftrightarrow B = \frac{109}{64}$; and $A + 3\left(\frac{109}{64}\right) = A + \frac{327}{64} = 3 \Leftrightarrow A = -\frac{135}{64}$. Therefore,

$\dfrac{3x^2 + 5x - 13}{(3x+2)\,(x-2)^2} = \dfrac{-\frac{135}{64}}{3x+2} + \dfrac{\frac{109}{64}}{x-2} + \dfrac{\frac{9}{8}}{(x-2)^2}$.

27. $\dfrac{2x}{4x^2 + 12x + 9} = \dfrac{2x}{(2x+3)^2} = \dfrac{A}{2x+3} + \dfrac{B}{(2x+3)^2}$. Hence, $2x = A\,(2x+3) + B = 2Ax + (3A + B)$. So $2A = 2$

$\Leftrightarrow A = 1$; and $3\,(1) + B = 0 \Leftrightarrow B = -3$. Therefore, $\dfrac{2x}{4x^2 + 12x + 9} = \dfrac{1}{2x+3} - \dfrac{3}{(2x+3)^2}$.

28. $\dfrac{x-4}{(2x-5)^2} = \dfrac{A}{2x-5} + \dfrac{B}{(2x-5)^2}$. Hence, $x - 4 = A\,(2x-5) + B = 2Ax + (-5A + B)$, and so $\begin{cases} 2A = 1 \\ -5A + B = -4 \end{cases}$

$\Rightarrow A = \frac{1}{2}$ and $-5\left(\frac{1}{2}\right) + B = -4 \Leftrightarrow B = -\frac{3}{2}$. Therefore, $\dfrac{x-4}{(2x-5)^2} = \dfrac{\frac{1}{2}}{2x-5} - \dfrac{\frac{3}{2}}{(2x-5)^2}$.

29. $\dfrac{4x^2 - x - 2}{x^4 + 2x^3} = \dfrac{4x^2 - x - 2}{x^3\,(x+2)} = \dfrac{A}{x} + \dfrac{B}{x^2} + \dfrac{C}{x^3} + \dfrac{D}{x+2}$. Hence,

$$4x^2 - x - 2 \;=\; Ax^2\,(x+2) + Bx\,(x+2) + C\,(x+2) + Dx^3$$

$$= (A+D)\,x^3 + (2A+B)\,x^2 + (2B+C)\,x + 2C$$

So $2C = -2 \;\Leftrightarrow\; C = -1;\; 2B - 1 = -1 \;\Leftrightarrow\; B = 0;\; 2A + 0 = 4 \;\Leftrightarrow\; A = 2;$ and $2 + D = 0 \;\Leftrightarrow$

$D = -2$. Therefore, $\dfrac{4x^2 - x - 2}{x^4 + 2x^3} = \dfrac{2}{x} - \dfrac{1}{x^3} - \dfrac{2}{x+2}$.

30. $\dfrac{x^3 - 2x^2 - 4x + 3}{x^4} = \dfrac{A}{x} + \dfrac{B}{x^2} + \dfrac{C}{x^3} + \dfrac{D}{x^4}$. Hence, $x^3 - 2x^2 - 4x + 3 = Ax^3 + Bx^2 + Cx + D$. Thus $A = 1;$

$B = -2;\; C = -4;$ and $D = 3$. Therefore, $\dfrac{x^3 - 2x^2 - 4x + 3}{x^4} = \dfrac{1}{x} - \dfrac{2}{x^2} - \dfrac{4}{x^3} + \dfrac{3}{x^4}$.

31. $\dfrac{-10x^2 + 27x - 14}{(x-1)^3\,(x+2)} = \dfrac{A}{x+2} + \dfrac{B}{x-1} + \dfrac{C}{(x-1)^2} + \dfrac{D}{(x-1)^3}$. Thus,

$$-10x^2 + 27x - 14 \;=\; A\,(x-1)^3 + B\,(x+2)\,(x-1)^2 + C\,(x+2)\,(x-1) + D\,(x+2)$$

$$= A\,(x^3 - 3x^2 + 3x - 1) + B\,(x+2)\,(x^2 - 2x + 1) + C\,(x^2 + x - 2) + D\,(x+2)$$

$$= A\,(x^3 - 3x^2 + 3x - 1) + B\,(x^3 - 3x + 2) + C\,(x^2 + x - 2) + D\,(x+2)$$

$$= (A+B)\,x^3 + (-3A+C)\,x^2 + (3A - 3B + C + D)\,x + (-A + 2B - 2C + 2D)$$

which leads to the system

$$
\begin{cases}
A + B & = 0 & \text{Coefficients of } x^3 \\
-3A \quad + C & = -10 & \text{Coefficients of } x^2 \\
3A - 3B + C + D = 27 & & \text{Coefficients of } x \\
-A + 2B - 2C + 2D = -14 & & \text{Constant terms}
\end{cases}
\Leftrightarrow
\begin{cases}
A + B & = 0 \\
3B + C & = -10 \\
-3B + 2C + D = 17 \\
3B - 5C + 7D = -15
\end{cases}
\Leftrightarrow
$$

$$
\begin{cases}
A + B & = 0 \\
3B + C & = -10 \\
3C + D = 7 \\
-3C + 8D = 2
\end{cases}
\Leftrightarrow
\begin{cases}
A + B & = 0 \\
3B + C & = -10 \\
3C + D = 7 \\
9D = 9
\end{cases}
$$

Hence, $9D = 9 \;\Leftrightarrow\; D = 1, 3C + 1 = 7 \;\Leftrightarrow\; C = 2, 3B + 2 = -10 \;\Leftrightarrow\; B = -4,$ and $A - 4 = 0 \;\Leftrightarrow$

$A = 4$. Therefore, $\dfrac{-10x^2 + 27x - 14}{(x-1)^3\,(x+2)} = \dfrac{4}{x+2} - \dfrac{4}{x-1} + \dfrac{2}{(x-1)^2} + \dfrac{1}{(x-1)^3}$.

32. $\dfrac{-2x^2 + 5x - 1}{x^4 - 2x^3 + 2x - 1} = \dfrac{-2x^2 + 5x - 1}{(x - 1)\,(x^3 - x^2 - x + 1)} = \dfrac{-2x^2 + 5x - 1}{(x - 1)^3\,(x + 1)} = \dfrac{A}{x + 1} + \dfrac{B}{x - 1} + \dfrac{C}{(x - 1)^2} + \dfrac{D}{(x - 1)^3}.$

Thus,

$$
\begin{aligned}
-2x^2 + 5x - 1 &= A\,(x - 1)^3 + B\,(x + 1)\,(x - 1)^2 + C\,(x + 1)\,(x - 1) + D\,(x + 1) \\
&= A\,(x^3 - 3x^2 + 3x - 1) + B\,(x + 1)\,(x^2 - 2x + 1) + C\,(x^2 - 1) + D\,(x + 1) \\
&= A\,(x^3 - 3x^2 + 3x - 1) + B\,(x^3 - x^2 - x + 1) + C\,(x^2 - 1) + D\,(x + 1) \\
&= (A + B)\,x^3 + (-3A - B + C)\,x^2 + (3A - B + D)\,x + (-A + B - C + D)
\end{aligned}
$$

which leads to the system $\begin{cases} A + B &= 0 \quad \text{Coefficients of } x^3 \\ -3A - B + C &= -2 \quad \text{Coefficients of } x^2 \\ 3A - B \quad + D &= 5 \quad \text{Coefficients of } x \\ -A + B - C + D &= -1 \quad \text{Constant terms} \end{cases}$ $\Leftrightarrow$ $\begin{cases} A + B &= 0 \\ 2B + C &= -2 \\ -2B + C + D &= 3 \\ 2B - 3C + 4D &= 2 \end{cases}$

$\Leftrightarrow$ $\begin{cases} A + B &= 0 \\ 2B + C &= -2 \\ 2C + D &= 1 \\ -2C + 5D &= 5 \end{cases}$ $\Leftrightarrow$ $\begin{cases} A + B &= 0 \\ 2B + C &= -2 \\ 2C + D &= 1 \\ 6D &= 6 \end{cases}$ Hence, $6D = 6 \Leftrightarrow D = 1,$

$2C + 1 = 1 \Leftrightarrow C = 0,\ 2B + 0 = -2 \Leftrightarrow B = -1,$ and $A - 1 = 0 \Leftrightarrow A = 1.$ Therefore,

$$\dfrac{-2x^2 + 5x - 1}{x^4 - 2x^3 + 2x - 1} = \dfrac{1}{x + 1} - \dfrac{1}{x - 1} + \dfrac{1}{(x - 1)^3}.$$

33. $\dfrac{3x^3 + 22x^2 + 53x + 41}{(x + 2)^2\,(x + 3)^2} = \dfrac{A}{x + 2} + \dfrac{B}{(x + 2)^2} + \dfrac{C}{x + 3} + \dfrac{D}{(x + 3)^2}.$ Thus,

$$
\begin{aligned}
3x^3 + 22x^2 + 53x + 41 &= A\,(x + 2)\,(x + 3)^2 + B\,(x + 3)^2 + C\,(x + 2)^2\,(x + 3) + D\,(x + 2)^2 \\
&= A\,(x^3 + 8x^2 + 21x + 18) + B\,(x^2 + 6x + 9) \\
&\qquad + C\,(x^3 + 7x^2 + 16x + 12) + D\,(x^2 + 4x + 4) \\
&= (A + C)\,x^3 + (8A + B + 7C + D)\,x^2 \\
&\qquad + (21A + 6B + 16C + 4D)\,x + (18A + 9B + 12C + 4D)
\end{aligned}
$$

so we must solve the system $\begin{cases} A \quad + C &= 3 \quad \text{Coefficients of } x^3 \\ 8A + B + 7C + D &= 22 \quad \text{Coefficients of } x^2 \\ 21A + 6B + 16C + 4D &= 53 \quad \text{Coefficients of } x \\ 18A + 9B + 12C + 4D &= 41 \quad \text{Constant terms} \end{cases}$ $\Leftrightarrow$

$\begin{cases} A \quad + C &= 3 \\ B - C + D &= -2 \\ 6B - 5C + 4D &= -10 \\ 9B - 6C + 4D &= -13 \end{cases}$ $\Leftrightarrow$ $\begin{cases} A \quad + C &= 3 \\ B - C + D &= -2 \\ C - 2D &= 2 \\ 3C - 5D &= 5 \end{cases}$ $\Leftrightarrow$ $\begin{cases} A \quad + C &= 3 \\ B - C + D &= -2 \\ C - 2D &= 2 \\ D &= -1 \end{cases}$ Hence,

$D = -1,\ C + 2 = 2 \Leftrightarrow C = 0,\ B - 0 - 1 = -2 \Leftrightarrow B = -1,$ and $A + 0 = 3 \Leftrightarrow A = 3.$ Therefore,

$$\dfrac{3x^3 + 22x^2 + 53x + 41}{(x + 2)^2\,(x + 3)^2} = \dfrac{3}{x + 2} - \dfrac{1}{(x + 2)^2} - \dfrac{1}{(x + 3)^2}.$$

34. $\dfrac{3x^2 + 12x - 20}{x^4 - 8x^2 + 16} = \dfrac{3x^2 + 12x - 20}{(x^2 - 4)^2} = \dfrac{3x^2 + 12x - 20}{(x + 2)^2 (x - 2)^2} = \dfrac{A}{x + 2} + \dfrac{B}{(x + 2)^2} + \dfrac{C}{x - 2} + \dfrac{D}{(x - 2)^2}$. Thus,

$$3x^2 + 12x - 20 = A(x + 2)(x - 2)^2 + B(x - 2)^2 + C(x + 2)^2(x - 2) + D(x + 2)^2$$
$$= A(x^3 - 2x^2 - 4x + 8) + B(x^2 - 4x + 4) + C(x^3 + 2x^2 - 4x - 8) + D(x^2 + 4x + 4)$$
$$= (A + C)x^3 + (-2A + B + 2C + D)x^2 + (-4A - 4B - 4C + 4D)x + (8A + 4B - 8C + 4D)$$

which leads to the system $\begin{cases} A \quad\quad\; + C \quad\quad\quad = \quad 0 & \text{Coefficients of } x^3 \\ -2A + \; B + 2C + \; D = \quad 3 & \text{Coefficients of } x^2 \\ -4A - 4B - 4C + 4D = \quad 12 & \text{Coefficients of } x \\ 8A + 4B - 8C + 4D = -20 & \text{Constant terms} \end{cases} \Leftrightarrow$

$\begin{cases} A \quad + \quad C \quad\quad\quad = 0 \\ \quad\;\; B + \; 4C + \quad D = 3 \\ \quad\; 6B + \; 8C - \; 2D = -6 \\ \quad -4B - 16C + 12D = 4 \end{cases} \Leftrightarrow \begin{cases} A \quad + \quad C \quad\quad = 0 \\ \quad\;\; B + 4C + \; D = 3 \\ \quad\quad 16C + \; 8D = 24 \\ \quad\; -32C + 32D = 0 \end{cases} \Leftrightarrow \begin{cases} A \quad + \quad C \quad\quad = 0 \\ \quad\;\; B + 4C + \; D = 3 \\ \quad\quad 16C + 8D = 24 \\ \quad\quad\quad\quad 48D = 48 \end{cases}$

Hence, $48D = 48 \quad\Leftrightarrow\quad D = 1, 16C + 8 = 24 \quad\Leftrightarrow\quad C = 1; B + 4 + 1 = 3 \quad\Leftrightarrow\quad B = -2$, and $A + 1 = 0 \quad\Leftrightarrow$

$A = -1$. Therefore, $\dfrac{3x^2 + 12x - 20}{x^4 - 8x^2 + 16} = -\dfrac{1}{x + 2} - \dfrac{2}{(x + 2)^2} + \dfrac{1}{x - 2} + \dfrac{1}{(x - 2)^2}$.

35. $\dfrac{x - 3}{x^3 + 3x} = \dfrac{x - 3}{x(x^2 + 3)} = \dfrac{A}{x} + \dfrac{Bx + C}{x^2 + 3}$. Hence, $x - 3 = A(x^2 + 3) + Bx^2 + Cx = (A + B)x^2 + Cx + 3A$. So

$3A = -3 \Leftrightarrow A = -1; C = 1$; and $-1 + B = 0 \quad\Leftrightarrow\quad B = 1$. Therefore, $\dfrac{x - 3}{x^3 + 3x} = -\dfrac{1}{x} + \dfrac{x + 1}{x^2 + 3}$.

36. $\dfrac{3x^2 - 2x + 8}{x^3 - x^2 + 2x - 2} = \dfrac{3x^2 - 2x + 8}{(x^2 + 2)(x - 1)} = \dfrac{Ax + B}{x^2 + 2} + \dfrac{C}{x - 1}$. Thus,

$3x^2 - 2x + 8 = (Ax + B)(x - 1) + C(x^2 + 2) = (A + C)x^2 + (-A + B)x + (-B + 2C)$, which leads to the

system $\begin{cases} A + \quad\quad C = \quad 3 & \text{Coefficients of } x^2 \\ -A + B \quad\quad = -2 & \text{Coefficients of } x \\ \quad -B + 2C = \quad 8 & \text{Constant terms} \end{cases} \Leftrightarrow \begin{cases} A + \quad\quad C = 3 & \text{Coefficients of } x^2 \\ \quad\;\; B + \; C = 1 & \text{Coefficients of } x \\ \quad\quad 2C = 6 & \text{Constant terms} \end{cases}$

Hence, $2C = 6 \quad\Leftrightarrow\quad C = 3, B + 3 = 1 \quad\Leftrightarrow\quad B = -2$; and $A + 3 = 3 \quad\Leftrightarrow\quad A = 0$. Therefore,

$\dfrac{3x^2 - 2x + 8}{x^3 - x^2 + 2x - 2} = -\dfrac{2}{x^2 + 2} + \dfrac{3}{x - 1}$.

37. $\dfrac{2x^3 + 7x + 5}{(x^2 + x + 2)(x^2 + 1)} = \dfrac{Ax + B}{x^2 + x + 2} + \dfrac{Cx + D}{x^2 + 1}$. Thus,

$$2x^3 + 7x + 5 = (Ax + B)(x^2 + 1) + (Cx + D)(x^2 + x + 2)$$
$$= Ax^3 + Ax + Bx^2 + B + Cx^3 + Cx^2 + 2Cx + Dx^2 + Dx + 2D$$
$$= (A + C)x^3 + (B + C + D)x^2 + (A + 2C + D)x + (B + 2D)$$

We must solve the system

$\begin{cases} A + \quad C \quad\quad\; = 2 & \text{Coefficients of } x^3 \\ \quad\; B + \; C + \; D = 0 & \text{Coefficients of } x^2 \\ A + \quad 2C + \; D = 7 & \text{Coefficients of } x \\ \quad\; B \quad\quad + 2D = 5 & \text{Constant terms} \end{cases} \Leftrightarrow \begin{cases} A + \quad C \quad\quad = 2 \\ \quad\; B + C + D = 0 \\ \quad\quad\;\; C + D = 5 \\ \quad\quad\;\; C - D = -5 \end{cases} \Leftrightarrow \begin{cases} A + \quad C \quad\quad = 2 \\ \quad\; B + C + \; D = 0 \\ \quad\quad\; C + \; D = 5 \\ \quad\quad\quad\;\; 2D = 10 \end{cases}$

Hence, $2D = 10 \quad\Leftrightarrow\quad D = 5, C + 5 = 5 \quad\Leftrightarrow\quad C = 0, B + 0 + 5 = 0 \quad\Leftrightarrow\quad B = -5$, and $A + 0 = 2 \quad\Leftrightarrow$

$A = 2$. Therefore, $\dfrac{2x^3 + 7x + 5}{(x^2 + x + 2)(x^2 + 1)} = \dfrac{2x - 5}{x^2 + x + 2} + \dfrac{5}{x^2 + 1}$.

38. $\dfrac{x^2 + x + 1}{2x^4 + 3x^2 + 1} = \dfrac{x^2 + x + 1}{(2x^2 + 1)(x^2 + 1)} = \dfrac{Ax + B}{2x^2 + 1} + \dfrac{Cx + D}{x^2 + 1}$. Thus,

$$x^2 + x + 1 = (Ax + B)(x^2 + 1) + (Cx + D)(2x^2 + 1) = Ax^3 + Ax + Bx^2 + B + 2Cx^3 + 2Dx^2 + Cx + D$$

$$= (A + 2C)x^3 + (B + 2D)x^2 + (A + C)x + (B + D)$$

which leads to the system

$$\begin{cases} A & + 2C & = 0 \quad \text{Coefficients of } x^3 \\ & B & + 2D = 1 \quad \text{Coefficients of } x^2 \\ A & + C & = 1 \quad \text{Coefficients of } x \\ & B & + D = 1 \quad \text{Constant terms} \end{cases} \Leftrightarrow \begin{cases} A & + 2C & = 0 \\ & B & + 2D = 1 \\ & C & = -1 \\ & D = 0 \end{cases}$$

Hence, $D = 0$, $C = -1$, $B + 0 = 1 \Leftrightarrow B = 1$, and $A - 2 = 0 \Leftrightarrow A = 2$. Therefore,

$$\dfrac{x^2 + x + 1}{2x^4 + 3x^2 + 1} = \dfrac{2x + 1}{2x^2 + 1} - \dfrac{x}{x^2 + 1}.$$

39. $\dfrac{x^4 + x^3 + x^2 - x + 1}{x(x^2 + 1)^2} = \dfrac{A}{x} + \dfrac{Bx + C}{x^2 + 1} + \dfrac{Dx + E}{(x^2 + 1)^2}$. Hence,

$$x^4 + x^3 + x^2 - x + 1 = A(x^2 + 1)^2 + (Bx + C)x(x^2 + 1) + x(Dx + E)$$

$$= A(x^4 + 2x^2 + 1) + (Bx^2 + Cx)(x^2 + 1) + Dx^2 + Ex$$

$$= A(x^4 + 2x^2 + 1) + Bx^4 + Bx^2 + Cx^3 + Cx + Dx^2 + Ex$$

$$= (A + B)x^4 + Cx^3 + (2A + B + D)x^2 + (C + E)x + A$$

So $A = 1$, $1 + B = 1 \Leftrightarrow B = 0$; $C = 1$; $2 + 0 + D = 1 \Leftrightarrow D = -1$; and $1 + E = -1 \Leftrightarrow E = -2$.

Therefore, $\dfrac{x^4 + x^3 + x^2 - x + 1}{x(x^2 + 1)^2} = \dfrac{1}{x} + \dfrac{1}{x^2 + 1} - \dfrac{x + 2}{(x^2 + 1)^2}.$

40. $\dfrac{2x^2 - x + 8}{(x^2 + 4)^2} = \dfrac{Ax + B}{x^2 + 4} + \dfrac{Cx + D}{(x^2 + 4)^2}$. Thus,

$$2x^2 - x + 8 = (Ax + B)(x^2 + 4) + Cx + D = Ax^3 + 4Ax + Bx^2 + 4B + Cx + D$$

$$= Ax^3 + Bx^2 + (4A + C)x + (4B + D)$$

and so $A = 0$, $B = 2$, $0 + C = -1 \Leftrightarrow C = -1$, and $8 + D = 8 \Leftrightarrow D = 0$. Therefore,

$$\dfrac{2x^2 - x + 8}{(x^2 + 4)^2} = \dfrac{2}{x^2 + 4} - \dfrac{1}{(x^2 + 4)^2}.$$

41. We must first get a proper rational function. Using long division, we find that $\dfrac{x^5 - 2x^4 + x^3 + x + 5}{x^3 - 2x^2 + x - 2} = x^2 +$

$\dfrac{2x^2 + x + 5}{x^3 - 2x^2 + x - 2} = x^2 + \dfrac{2x^2 + x + 5}{(x - 2)(x^2 + 1)} = x^2 + \dfrac{A}{x - 2} + \dfrac{Bx + C}{x^2 + 1}$. Hence,

$$2x^2 + x + 5 = A(x^2 + 1) + (Bx + C)(x - 2) = Ax^2 + A + Bx^2 + Cx - 2Bx - 2C$$

$$= (A + B)x^2 + (C - 2B)x + (A - 2C)$$

Equating coefficients, we get the system

$$\begin{cases} A + B & = 2 \quad \text{Coefficients of } x^2 \\ -2B + C = 1 \quad \text{Coefficients of } x \\ A - 2C = 5 \quad \text{Constant terms} \end{cases} \Leftrightarrow \begin{cases} A + B & = 2 \\ -2B + C = 1 \\ B + 2C = -3 \end{cases} \Leftrightarrow \begin{cases} A + B & = 2 \\ -2B + C = 1 \\ 5C = -5 \end{cases}$$

Therefore, $5C = -5 \Leftrightarrow C = -1$, $-2B - 1 = 1 \Leftrightarrow B = -1$, and $A - 1 = 2 \Leftrightarrow A = 3$. Therefore,

$$\dfrac{x^5 - 2x^4 + x^3 + x + 5}{x^3 - 2x^2 + x - 2} = x^2 + \dfrac{3}{x - 2} - \dfrac{x + 1}{x^2 + 1}.$$

42. $\dfrac{x^5 - 3x^4 + 3x^3 - 4x^2 + 4x + 12}{(x-2)^2 \, (x^2+2)} = \dfrac{x^5 - 3x^4 + 3x^3 - 4x^2 + 4x + 12}{x^4 - 4x^3 + 6x^2 - 8x + 8}$. We use long division to get a proper rational function:

$$
\begin{array}{r}
x + 1 \\[2pt]
\hline
\end{array}
$$

$$
x^4 - 4x^3 + 6x^2 - 8x + 8 \enclose{longdiv}{\; x^5 - 3x^4 + 3x^3 - 4x^2 + 4x + 12}
$$

$$
\underline{x^5 - 4x^4 + 6x^3 - 8x^2 + 8x}
$$

$$
x^4 - 3x^3 + 4x^2 - 4x + 12
$$

$$
\underline{x^4 - 4x^3 + 6x^2 - 8x + 8}
$$

$$
x^3 - 2x^2 + 4x + 4
$$

Thus, $\dfrac{x^5 - 3x^4 + 3x^3 - 4x^2 + 4x + 12}{(x-2)^2 \, (x^2+2)} = x + 1 + \dfrac{x^3 - 2x^2 + 4x + 4}{(x-2)^2 \, (x^2+2)} = x + 1 + \dfrac{A}{x-2} + \dfrac{B}{(x-2)^2} + \dfrac{Cx+D}{x^2+2}$, so

$$
\begin{aligned}
x^3 - 2x^2 + 4x + 4 \; &= \; A\,(x-2)\,(x^2+2) + B\,(x^2+2) + (Cx+D)\,(x-2)^2 \\
&= \; A\,(x^3 - 2x^2 + 2x - 4) + B\,(x^2+2) + (Cx+D)\,(x^2 - 4x + 4) \\
&= \; Ax^3 - 2Ax^2 + 2Ax - 4A + Bx^2 + 2B + Cx^3 - 4Cx^2 + 4Cx + Dx^2 - 4Dx + 4D \\
&= \; (A+C)\,x^3 + (-2A + B - 4C + D)\,x^2 + (2A + 4C - 4D)\,x + (-4A + 2B + 4D)
\end{aligned}
$$

which leads to the system $\begin{cases} A + C = 1 & \text{Coefficients of } x^3 \\ -2A + B - 4C + D = -2 & \text{Coefficients of } x^2 \\ 2A + 4C - 4D = 4 & \text{Coefficients of } x \\ -4A + 2B + 4D = 4 & \text{Constant terms} \end{cases}$ $\Leftrightarrow$

$$
\begin{cases} A + C = 1 \\ B - 2C + D = 0 \\ B - 3D = 2 \\ 2B + 8C - 4D = 12 \end{cases}
\Leftrightarrow
\begin{cases} A + C = 1 \\ B - 2C + D = 0 \\ 2C - 4D = 2 \\ 8C + 2D = 8 \end{cases}
\Leftrightarrow
\begin{cases} A + C = 1 \\ B - 2C + D = 0 \\ 2C - 4D = 2 \\ 18D = 0 \end{cases}
\quad \text{Then}
$$

$D = 0$; $2C = 2$ $\Leftrightarrow$ $C = 1$; $B - 2 = 0$ $\Leftrightarrow$ $B = 2$; and $A + 1 = 1$ $\Leftrightarrow$ $A = 0$. Therefore,

$$
\dfrac{x^5 - 3x^4 + 3x^3 - 4x^2 + 4x + 12}{(x-2)^2 \, (x^2+2)} = x + 1 + \dfrac{2}{(x-2)^2} + \dfrac{x}{x^2+2}.
$$

43. $\dfrac{ax+b}{x^2-1} = \dfrac{A}{x-1} + \dfrac{B}{x+1}$. Hence, $ax + b = A\,(x+1) + B\,(x-1) = (A+B)\,x + (A-B)$.

So $\begin{cases} A + B = a \\ A - B = b \end{cases}$ Adding, we get $2A = a + b$ $\Leftrightarrow$ $A = \dfrac{a+b}{2}$.

Substituting, we get $B = a - A = \dfrac{2a}{2} - \dfrac{a+b}{2} = \dfrac{a-b}{2}$. Therefore, $A = \dfrac{a+b}{2}$ and $B = \dfrac{a-b}{2}$.

44. $\dfrac{ax^3 + bx^2}{(x^2+1)^2} = \dfrac{Ax+B}{x^2+1} + \dfrac{Cx+D}{(x^2+1)^2}$. Hence,

$$
\begin{aligned}
ax^3 + bx^2 \; &= \; (Ax+B)\,(x^2+1) + Cx + D = Ax^3 + Ax + Bx^2 + B + Cx + D \\
&= \; Ax^3 + Bx^2 + (A+C)\,x + (B+D)
\end{aligned}
$$

and so $A = a$, $B = b$, $a + C = 0$ $\Leftrightarrow$ $C = -a$, and $b + D = 0 \Leftrightarrow D = -b$. Therefore, $A = a$, $B = b$, $C = -a$, and $D = -b$.

45. (a) The expression $\dfrac{x}{x^2+1} + \dfrac{1}{x+1}$ is already a partial fraction decomposition. The denominator in the first term is a quadratic which cannot be factored and the degree of the numerator is less than 2. The denominator of the second term is linear and the numerator is a constant.

(b) The term $\dfrac{x}{(x+1)^2}$ can be decomposed further, since the numerator and denominator both have linear factors.

$\dfrac{x}{(x+1)^2} = \dfrac{A}{x+1} + \dfrac{B}{(x+1)^2}$. Hence, $x = A(x+1) + B = Ax + (A+B)$. So $A = 1$, $B = -1$, and

$\dfrac{x}{(x+1)^2} = \dfrac{1}{x+1} + \dfrac{-1}{(x+1)^2}$.

(c) The expression $\dfrac{1}{x+1} + \dfrac{2}{(x+1)^2}$ is already a partial fraction decomposition, since each numerator is constant.

(d) The expression $\dfrac{x+2}{(x^2+1)^2}$ is already a partial fraction decomposition, since the denominator is the square of a quadratic which cannot be factored, and the degree of the numerator is less than 2.

46. Combining the terms, we have

$$\dfrac{2}{x-1} + \dfrac{1}{(x-1)^2} + \dfrac{1}{x+1} = \dfrac{2(x^2-1)}{(x-1)^2(x+1)} + \dfrac{1(x+1)}{(x-1)^2(x+1)} + \dfrac{1(x^2-2x+1)}{(x-1)^2(x+1)}$$

$$= \dfrac{2x^2 - 2 + x + 1 + x^2 - 2x + 1}{(x-1)^2(x+1)} = \dfrac{3x^2 - x}{(x-1)^2(x+1)}$$

Now to find the partial fraction decomposition, we have $\dfrac{3x^2-x}{(x-1)^2(x+1)} = \dfrac{A}{x-1} + \dfrac{B}{(x-1)^2} + \dfrac{C}{x+1}$, and so

$$3x^2 - x = A(x-1)(x+1) + B(x+1) + C(x-1)^2 = A(x^2-1) + B(x+1) + C(x^2-2x+1)$$

$$= Ax^2 - A + Bx + B + Cx^2 - 2Cx + C = (A+C)x^2 + (B-2C)x + (-A+B+C)$$

which result in the system $\begin{cases} A \quad\;\; + C = \;\; 3 \quad \text{Coefficients of } x^2 \\ \quad\;\; B - 2C = -1 \quad \text{Coefficients of } x \\ -A + B + \;\; C = \;\; 0 \quad \text{Constant terms} \end{cases} \Leftrightarrow \begin{cases} A \quad\;\; + C = \;\; 3 \\ \quad\;\; B - 2C = -1 \\ \quad\;\; B + 2C = \;\; 3 \end{cases} \Leftrightarrow$

$\begin{cases} A \quad\;\; + C = \;\; 3 \\ \quad\;\; B - 2C = -1 \\ \quad\quad\;\; 4C = \;\; 4 \end{cases}$ so $4C = 4 \;\Leftrightarrow\; C = 1$, $B - 2(1) = -1 \;\Leftrightarrow\; B = 1$, and $A + 1 = 3 \;\Leftrightarrow\; A = 2$.

Therefore, we get back the same expression: $\dfrac{3x^2-x}{(x-1)^2(x+1)} = \dfrac{2}{x-1} + \dfrac{1}{(x-1)^2} + \dfrac{1}{x+1}$.

9.9 Systems of Inequalities

1. $x < 3$

2. $y \geq -2$

3. $y > x$

4. $y < x + 2$

5. $y \leq 2x + 2$

6. $y < -x + 5$

7. $2x - y \leq 8$

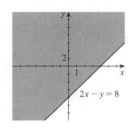

8. $3x + 4y + 12 > 0$

9. $4x + 5y < 20$

10. $-x^2 + y \geq 10$

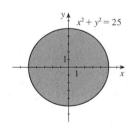

11. $y > x^2 + 1$

12. $x^2 + y^2 \geq 9$

13. $x^2 + y^2 \leq 25$

14. $x^2 + (y-1)^2 \leq 1$

15. The boundary is a solid curve, so we have the inequality $y \leq \frac{1}{2}x - 1$. We take the test point $(0, -2)$ and verify that it satisfies the inequality: $-2 \leq \frac{1}{2}(0) - 1$.

16. The boundary is a solid curve, so we have the inequality $y \leq x^2 + 2$. We take the test point $(0, 0)$ and verify that it satisfies the inequality: $0 \leq 0^2 + 2$.

17. The boundary is a broken curve, so we have the inequality $x^2 + y^2 > 4$. We take the test point $(0, 4)$ and verify that it satisfies the inequality: $0^2 + 4^2 \geq 4$.

18. The boundary is a solid curve, so we have the inequality $y \geq x^3 - 4x$. We take the test point $(1, 1)$ and verify that it satisfies the inequality: $1 \geq 1^3 - 4(1)$.

19. $\begin{cases} x + y \le 4 \\ y \ge x \end{cases}$ The vertices occur where $\begin{cases} x + y = 4 \\ y = x \end{cases}$ Substituting, we have

$2x = 4 \quad \Leftrightarrow \quad x = 2$. Since $y = x$, the vertex is $(2, 2)$, and the solution set is not bounded.

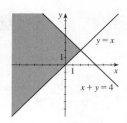

20. $\begin{cases} 2x + 3y > 12 \\ 3x - y < 21 \end{cases}$ The vertices occur where $\begin{cases} 2x + 3y = 12 \\ 3x - y = 21 \end{cases}$ $\Leftrightarrow$

$\begin{cases} 2x + 3y = 12 \\ 9x - 3y = 63 \end{cases}$ and adding the two equations gives $11x = 75 \quad \Leftrightarrow$

$x = \frac{75}{11}$. Then $2\left(\frac{75}{11}\right) + 3y = 12 \quad \Leftrightarrow \quad 3y = \frac{132-150}{11} = -\frac{18}{11} \quad \Leftrightarrow$

$y = -\frac{6}{11}$. Therefore, the vertex is $\left(\frac{75}{11}, -\frac{6}{11}\right)$, and the solution set is not bounded.

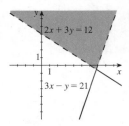

21. $\begin{cases} y < \frac{1}{4}x + 2 \\ y \ge 2x - 5 \end{cases}$ The vertex occurs where $\begin{cases} y = \frac{1}{4}x + 2 \\ y = 2x - 5 \end{cases}$ Substituting for y

gives $\frac{1}{4}x + 2 = 2x - 5 \quad \Leftrightarrow \quad \frac{7}{4}x = 7 \quad \Leftrightarrow \quad x = 4$, so $y = 3$. Hence, the vertex is $(4, 3)$, and the solution is not bounded.

22. $\begin{cases} x - y > 0 \\ 4 + y \le 2x \end{cases}$ The vertices occur where $\begin{cases} y = x \\ 4 + y = 2x \end{cases}$ Substituting for y

gives $4 + x = 2x \quad \Leftrightarrow \quad x = 4$, so $y = 4$. Hence, the vertex is $(4, 4)$, and the solution set is not bounded.

23. $\begin{cases} x \ge 0 \\ y \ge 0 \\ 3x + 5y \le 15 \\ 3x + 2y \le 9 \end{cases}$ From the graph, the points $(3, 0)$, $(0, 3)$ and $(0, 0)$ are

vertices, and the fourth vertex occurs where the lines $3x + 5y = 15$ and $3x + 2y = 9$ intersect. Subtracting these two equations gives $3y = 6 \quad \Leftrightarrow$ $y = 2$, and so $x = \frac{5}{3}$. Thus, the fourth vertex is $\left(\frac{5}{3}, 2\right)$, and the solution set is bounded.

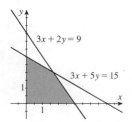

24. $\begin{cases} x > 2 \\ y < 12 \\ 2x - 4y > 8 \end{cases}$ From the graph, the vertices occur at $(2, -1)$ and $(28, 12)$.

The solution set is not bounded.

25. $\begin{cases} y < 9 - x^2 \\ y \geq x + 3 \end{cases}$ The vertices occur where $\begin{cases} y = 9 - x^2 \\ y = x + 3 \end{cases}$ Substituting for y

gives $9 - x^2 = x + 3 \quad \Leftrightarrow \quad x^2 + x - 6 = 0 \quad \Leftrightarrow$
$(x - 2)(x + 3) = 0 \Rightarrow x = -3, x = 2$. Therefore, the vertices are $(-3, 0)$ and
$(2, 5)$, and the solution set is bounded.

26. $\begin{cases} y \geq x^2 \\ x + y \geq 6 \end{cases}$ The vertices occur where $\begin{cases} y = x^2 \\ x + y = 6 \end{cases}$ Substituting for y

gives $x^2 + x = 6 \quad \Leftrightarrow \quad x^2 + x - 6 = 0 \Leftrightarrow (x + 3)(x - 2) = 0 \Rightarrow x = -3$,
$x = 2$. Since $y = x^2$, the vertices are $(-3, 9)$ and $(2, 4)$, and the solution set is not
bounded.

27. $\begin{cases} x^2 + y^2 \leq 4 \\ x - y > 0 \end{cases}$ The vertices occur where $\begin{cases} x^2 + y^2 = 4 \\ x - y = 0 \end{cases}$ Since $x - y = 0$

$\Leftrightarrow \quad x = y$, substituting for x gives $y^2 + y^2 = 4 \quad \Leftrightarrow \quad y^2 = 2 \Rightarrow y = \pm\sqrt{2}$,
and $x = \pm\sqrt{2}$. Therefore, the vertices are $\left(-\sqrt{2}, -\sqrt{2}\right)$ and $\left(\sqrt{2}, \sqrt{2}\right)$, and the
solution set is bounded.

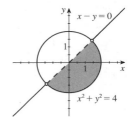

28. $\begin{cases} x > 0 \\ y > 0 \\ x + y < 10 \\ x^2 + y^2 > 9 \end{cases}$ From the graph, the vertices are $(0, 3)$, $(0, 10)$, $(3, 0)$, and

$(10, 0)$. The solution set is bounded.

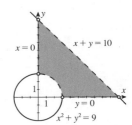

29. $\begin{cases} x^2 - y \leq 0 \\ 2x^2 + y \leq 12 \end{cases}$ The vertices occur where $\begin{cases} x^2 - y = 0 \\ 2x^2 + y = 12 \end{cases} \Leftrightarrow$

$\begin{cases} 2x^2 - 2y = 0 \\ 2x^2 + y = 12 \end{cases}$ Subtracting the equations gives $3y = 12 \quad \Leftrightarrow \quad y = 4$, and

$x = \pm 2$. Thus, the vertices are $(2, 4)$ and $(-2, 4)$, and the solution set is bounded.

30. $\begin{cases} x^2 + y^2 < 9 \\ 2x + y^2 \geq 1 \end{cases}$ The vertices occur where $\begin{cases} x^2 + y^2 = 9 \\ 2x + y^2 = 1 \end{cases}$ Subtracting the

equations gives $x^2 - 2x = 8 \quad \Leftrightarrow \quad x^2 - 2x - 8 = 0 \quad \Leftrightarrow$
$(x - 4)(x + 2) = 0 \Leftrightarrow x = -2, x = 4$. Therefore, the vertices are $\left(-2, -\sqrt{5}\right)$
and $\left(-2, \sqrt{5}\right)$, since $x = 4$ does not give a real solution for y. The solution set is
bounded.

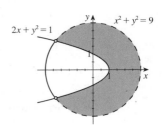

31. $\begin{cases} x + 2y \leq 14 \\ 3x - y \geq 0 \\ x - y \geq 2 \end{cases}$ We find the vertices of the region by solving pairs of the

corresponding equations: $\begin{cases} x + 2y = 14 \\ x - y = 2 \end{cases} \Leftrightarrow \begin{cases} x + 2y = 14 \\ 3y = 12 \end{cases} \Leftrightarrow y = 4$ and

$x = 6.$ $\begin{cases} 3x - y = 0 \\ x - y = 2 \end{cases} \Leftrightarrow \begin{cases} 3x - y = 0 \\ 2x - y = -2 \end{cases} \Leftrightarrow x = -1$ and $y = -3.$ Therefore,

the vertices are $(6, 4)$ and $(-1, -3)$, and the solution set is not bounded.

32. $\begin{cases} y < x + 6 \\ 3x + 2y \geq 12 \\ x - 2y \leq 2 \end{cases}$ To find where the line $y = x + 6$ intersects the lines

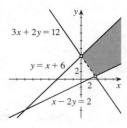

$3x + 2y = 12$ and $x - 2y = 2$, we substitute for y: $3x + 2(x + 6) = 12$ $\Leftrightarrow$
$x = 0$ and $y = 6$; $x - 2(x + 6) = 2$ $\Leftrightarrow$ $x = -14$ and $y = -8$. Next, adding
the equations $3x + 2y = 12$ and $x - 2y = 2$ yields $4x = 14$ $\Leftrightarrow$ $x = \frac{7}{2}$. So
these lines intersect at the point $\left(\frac{7}{2}, \frac{3}{4}\right)$. Since the vertex $(-14, -8)$ is not part of
the solution set, the vertices are $(0, 6)$ and $\left(\frac{7}{2}, \frac{3}{4}\right)$, and the solution set is not
bounded.

33. $\begin{cases} x \geq 0, y \geq 0 \\ x \leq 5, x + y \leq 7 \end{cases}$ The points of intersection are $(0, 7)$, $(0, 0)$, $(7, 0)$, $(5, 2)$,

and $(5, 0)$. However, the point $(7, 0)$ is not in the solution set. Therefore, the
vertices are $(0, 7)$, $(0, 0)$, $(5, 0)$, and $(5, 2)$, and the solution set is bounded.

34. $\begin{cases} x \geq 0, y \geq 0 \\ y \leq 4, 2x + y \leq 8 \end{cases}$ The points of intersection are $(0, 8)$, $(0, 4)$, $(4, 0)$, $(2, 4)$,

and $(3, 2)$. However, the point $(0, 8)$ is not in the solution set. Therefore, the
vertices are $(0, 4)$, $(2, 4)$, $(4, 0)$, and $(0, 0)$. The solution set is bounded.

35. $\begin{cases} y > x + 1 \\ x + 2y \leq 12 \\ x + 1 > 0 \end{cases}$ We find the vertices of the region by solving pairs of the

corresponding equations. Using $x = -1$ and substituting for x in the line
$y = x + 1$ gives the point $(-1, 0)$. Substituting for x in the line $x + 2y = 12$ gives

the point $\left(-1, \frac{13}{2}\right)$. $\begin{cases} y = x + 1 \\ x + 2y = 12 \end{cases} \Leftrightarrow x = y - 1$ and $y - 1 + 2y = 12$

$\Leftrightarrow$ $3y = 13$ $\Leftrightarrow$ $y = \frac{13}{3}$ and $x = \frac{10}{3}$. So the vertices are $(-1, 0)$, $\left(-1, \frac{13}{2}\right)$,
and $\left(\frac{10}{3}, \frac{13}{3}\right)$, and none of these vertices is in the solution set. The solution set is
bounded.

36. $\begin{cases} x + y > 12 \\ y < \frac{1}{2}x - 6 \\ 3x + y < 6 \end{cases}$ Graphing these inequalities, we see that there are no

points that satisfy all three, and hence the solution set is empty.

37. $\begin{cases} x^2 + y^2 \le 8 \\ x \ge 2,\ y \ge 0 \end{cases}$ The intersection points are $(2, \pm 2)$, $(2, 0)$, and $\left(2\sqrt{2}, 0\right)$.

However, since $(2, -2)$ is not part of the solution set, the vertices are $(2, 2)$, $(2, 0)$,

and $\left(2\sqrt{2}, 0\right)$. The solution set is bounded.

38. $\begin{cases} x^2 - y \ge 0 \\ x + y < 6 \\ x - y < 6 \end{cases}$ Adding the equations $x + y = 6$ and $x - y = 6$ yields $2x = 12$

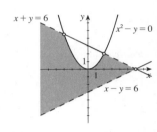

$\Leftrightarrow$ $x = 6$. So these curves intersect at the point $(6, 0)$. To find where

$x^2 - y = 0$ and $x + y = 6$ intersect, we solve the first for y, giving $y = x^2$, and

then substitute into the second equation to get $x + x^2 = 6$ $\Leftrightarrow$ $x^2 + x - 6 = 0$

$\Leftrightarrow$ $(x + 3)(x - 2) = 0$ $\Leftrightarrow$ $x = -3$ or $x = 2$. When $x = -3$, we have

$y = 9$, and when $x = 2$, we have $y = 4$, so the points of intersection are $(-3, 9)$ and $(2, 4)$. Substituting $y = x^2$ into the

equation $x - y = 6$ gives $x - x^2 = 6$, which has no solution. Thus the vertices (which are not in the solution set) are $(6, 0)$,

$(-3, 9)$, and $(2, 4)$. The solution set is not bounded.

39. $\begin{cases} x^2 + y^2 < 9 \\ x + y > 0,\ x \le 0 \end{cases}$ Substituting $x = 0$ into the equations $x^2 + y^2 = 9$ and

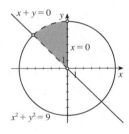

$x + y = 0$ gives the vertices $(0, \pm 3)$ and $(0, 0)$. To find the points of intersection

for the equations $x^2 + y^2 = 9$ and $x + y = 0$, we solve for $x = -y$ and substitute

into the first equation. This gives $(-y)^2 + y^2 = 9 \Rightarrow y = \pm\frac{3\sqrt{2}}{2}$. The points

$(0, -3)$ and $\left(\frac{3\sqrt{2}}{2}, -\frac{3\sqrt{2}}{2}\right)$ lie away from the solution set, so the vertices are $(0, 0)$,

$(0, 3)$, and $\left(-\frac{3\sqrt{2}}{2}, \frac{3\sqrt{2}}{2}\right)$. Note that the vertices are not solutions in this case. The solution set is bounded.

40. $\begin{cases} y \ge x^3 \\ y \le 2x + 4 \\ x + y \ge 0 \end{cases}$ The curves $y = x^3$ and $x + y = 0$ intersect when

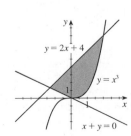

$x^3 + x = 0$ $\Leftrightarrow$ $x = 0$ $\Leftrightarrow$ $y = 0$. The lines $x + y = 0$ and $y = 2x + 4$

intersect when $-x = 2x + 4$ $\Leftrightarrow$ $3x = -4$ $\Leftrightarrow$ $x = -\frac{4}{3}$ $\Leftrightarrow$ $y = \frac{4}{3}$.

To find where $y = x^3$ and $y = 2x + 4$ intersect, we substitute for y and get

$x^3 = 2x + 4$ $\Leftrightarrow$ $x^3 - 2x - 4 = 0 \Leftrightarrow (x - 2)\left(x^2 + 2x + 2\right) = 0$ $\Rightarrow$

$x = 2$ (the other factor has no real solution). When $x = 2$ we have $y = 8$. Thus, the

vertices of the region are $(0, 0)$, $\left(-\frac{4}{3}, \frac{4}{3}\right)$, and $(2, 8)$. The solution set is bounded.

41. $\begin{cases} y \geq x - 3 \\ y \geq -2x + 6 \\ y \leq 8 \end{cases}$ Using a graphing calculator, we find the region shown. The

vertices are $(3, 0)$, $(-1, 8)$, and $(11, 8)$.

42. $\begin{cases} x + y \geq 12 \\ 2x + y \leq 24 \\ x - y \geq -6 \end{cases}$ Using the graphing calculator we find the region shown. The

vertices are $(3, 9)$, $(6, 12)$, and $(12, 0)$.

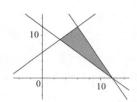

43. $\begin{cases} y \geq 6x - x^2 \\ x + y \geq 4 \end{cases}$ Using a graphing calculator, we find the region shown.

The vertices are $(0.6, 3.4)$ and $(6.4, -2.4)$.

44. $\begin{cases} y \geq x^3 \\ 2x + y \geq 0 \\ y \leq 2x + 6 \end{cases}$ Using a graphing calculator, we find the region shown.

The vertices are $(0, 0)$, $(2.2, 10.3)$ and $(-1.5, 3)$.

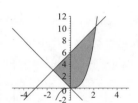

45. Let x be the number of fiction books published in a year and y the number of
nonfiction books. Then the following system of inequalities holds:

$\begin{cases} x \geq 0, y \geq 0 \\ x + y \leq 100 \\ y \geq 20, x \geq y \end{cases}$ From the graph, we see that the vertices are $(50, 50)$, $(80, 20)$

and $(20, 20)$.

46. Let x be the number of chairs made and y the number of tables. Then the following

system of inequalities holds: $\begin{cases} 2x + 3y \leq 12 \\ 2x + y \leq 8 \\ x \geq 0, y \geq 0 \end{cases}$ The intersection points are

$(0, 4)$, $(0, 8)$, $(6, 0)$, $(4, 0)$, $(0, 0)$, and $(3, 2)$. Since the points $(0, 8)$ and $(6, 0)$ are
not in the solution set, the vertices are $(0, 4)$, $(0, 0)$, $(4, 0)$, and $(3, 2)$.

47. Let x be the number of Standard Blend packages and y be the number of Deluxe Blend packages. Since there are 16 ounces per pound, we get the following system

of inequalities holds: $\begin{cases} x \geq 0 \\ y \geq 0 \\ \frac{1}{4}x + \frac{5}{8}y \leq 80 \\ \frac{3}{4}x + \frac{3}{8}y \leq 90 \end{cases}$ From the graph, we see that the

vertices are $(0, 0)$, $(120, 0)$, $(70, 100)$ and $(0, 128)$.

48. Let x be the amount of fish and y the amount of beef (in ounces) in each can. Then

the following system of inequalities holds: $\begin{cases} 12x + 6y \geq 60 \\ 3x + 9y \geq 45 \\ x \geq 0, \ y \geq 0 \end{cases}$ From the graph,

we see that the vertices are $(15, 0)$, $(3, 4)$, and $(0, 10)$.

49. $x + 2y > 4$, $-x + y < 1$, $x + 3y \leq 9$, $x < 3$.

Method 1: We shade the solution to each inequality with lines perpendicular to the boundary. As you can see, as the number of inequalities in the system increases, it gets harder to locate the region where *all* of the shaded parts overlap.

Method 2: Here, if a region is shaded then it fails to satisfy at least one inequality. As a result, the region that is left unshaded satisfies each inequality, and is the solution to the system of inequalities. In this case, this method makes it easier to identify the solution set.

To finish, we find the vertices of the solution set. The line $x = 3$ intersects the line $x + 2y = 4$ at $\left(3, \frac{1}{2}\right)$ and the line $x + 3y = 9$ at $(3, 2)$. To find where the lines $-x + y = 1$ and $x + 2y = 4$ intersect, we add the two equations, which gives $3y = 5$ $\Leftrightarrow$ $y = \frac{5}{3}$, and $x = \frac{2}{3}$. To find where the lines $-x + y = 1$ and $x + 3y = 9$ intersect, we add the two equations, which gives $4y = 10$ $\Leftrightarrow$ $y = \frac{10}{4} = \frac{5}{2}$, and $x = \frac{3}{2}$. The vertices are $\left(3, \frac{1}{2}\right)$, $(3, 2)$, $\left(\frac{2}{3}, \frac{5}{3}\right)$, and $\left(\frac{3}{2}, \frac{5}{2}\right)$, and the solution set is bounded.

Method 1

Method 2

Solution Set

Chapter 9 Review

1. $\begin{cases} 2x + 3y = 7 \\ x - 2y = 0 \end{cases}$ By inspection of the graph, it appears that $(2, 1)$ is the solution to the system. We check this in both

equations to verify that it is the solution. $2(2) + 3(1) = 4 + 3 = 7$ and $2 - 2(1) = 2 - 2 = 0$. Since both equations are satisfied, the solution is indeed $(2, 1)$.

2. $\begin{cases} 3x + y = 8 \\ y = x^2 - 5x \end{cases}$ By inspection of the graph, it appears that $(-2, 14)$ and $(4, -4)$ are solutions to the system.

We check each possible solution in both equations to verify that it is a solution: $3(-2) + (14) = -6 + 14 = 8$ and $(-2)^2 - 5(-2) = 4 + 10 = 14$; also $3(4) + (-4) = 12 - 4 = 8$ and $(4)^2 - 5(4) = 16 - 20 = -4$. Since both points satisfy both equations, the solutions are $(-2, 14)$ and $(4, -4)$.

3. $\begin{cases} x^2 + y = 2 \\ x^2 - 3x - y = 0 \end{cases}$ By inspection of the graph, it appears that $(2, -2)$ is a solution to the system, but is difficult

to get accurate values for the other point. Adding the equations, we get $2x^2 - 3x = 2 \Leftrightarrow 2x^2 - 3x - 2 = 0 \Leftrightarrow$ $(2x + 1)(x - 2) = 0$. So $2x + 1 = 0 \Leftrightarrow x = -\frac{1}{2}$ or $x = 2$. If $x = -\frac{1}{2}$, then $\left(-\frac{1}{2}\right)^2 + y = 2 \Leftrightarrow y = \frac{7}{4}$. If $x = 2$, then $2^2 + y = 2 \Leftrightarrow y = -2$. Thus, the solutions are $\left(-\frac{1}{2}, \frac{7}{4}\right)$ and $(2, -2)$.

4. $\begin{cases} x - y = -2 \\ x^2 + y^2 - 4y = 4 \end{cases}$ By inspection of the graph, it appears that $(-2, 0)$ and $(2, 4)$ are solutions to the system. We

check each possible solution in both equations to verify that it is a solution: $(-2) - (0) = -2$ and $(-2)^2 + (0)^2 - 4(0) = 4$; also $(2) - (4) = -2$ and $(2)^2 + (4)^2 - 4(4) = 4 + 16 - 16 = 4$. Since both points satisfy both equations, the solutions are $(-2, 0)$ and $(2, 4)$.

5. $\begin{cases} 3x - y = 5 \\ 2x + y = 5 \end{cases}$ Adding, we get $5x = 10 \Leftrightarrow x = 2$. So $2(2) + y = 5 \Leftrightarrow$

$y = 1$. Thus, the solution is $(2, 1)$.

6. $\begin{cases} y = 2x + 6 \\ y = -x + 3 \end{cases}$ Subtracting the second equation from the first, we get

$0 = 3x + 3 \Leftrightarrow x = -1$. So $y = -(-1) + 3 = 4$. Thus, the solution is $(-1, 4)$.

7. $\begin{cases} 2x - 7y = 28 \\ y = \frac{2}{7}x - 4 \end{cases} \Leftrightarrow \begin{cases} 2x - 7y = 28 \\ 2x - 7y = 28 \end{cases}$ Since these equations

represent the same line, any point on this line will satisfy the system. Thus the solution are $\left(x, \frac{2}{7}x - 4\right)$, where x is any real number.

8. $\begin{cases} 6x - 8y = 15 \\ -\frac{3}{2}x + 2y = -4 \end{cases}$ $\Leftrightarrow$ $\begin{cases} 6x - 8y = 15 \\ -6x + 8y = -16 \end{cases}$ Adding gives $0 = -1$ which

is false. Hence, there is no solution. The lines are parallel.

9. $\begin{cases} 2x - y = 1 \\ x + 3y = 10 \\ 3x + 4y = 15 \end{cases}$ Solving the first equation for y, we get $y = -2x + 1$.

Substituting into the second equation gives $x + 3(-2x + 1) = 10$ $\Leftrightarrow$

$-5x = 7$ $\Leftrightarrow$ $x = -\frac{7}{5}$. So $y = -\left(-\frac{7}{5}\right) + 1 = \frac{12}{5}$. Checking the point

$\left(-\frac{7}{5}, \frac{12}{5}\right)$ in the third equation we have $3\left(-\frac{7}{5}\right) + 4\left(\frac{12}{5}\right) \overset{?}{=} 15$ but

$-\frac{21}{5} + \frac{48}{5} \neq 15$. Thus, there is no solution, and the lines do not intersect at one

point.

10. $\begin{cases} 2x + 5y = 9 \\ -x + 3y = 1 \\ 7x - 2y = 14 \end{cases}$ Adding the first equation to twice the second equation gives

$11y = 11$ $\Leftrightarrow$ $y = 1$. Substituting back into the second equation, we get

$-x + 3(1) = 1$ $\Leftrightarrow$ $x = 4$. Checking point $(4, 1)$ in the third equation gives

$7(4) - 2(1) = 26 \neq 14$. Thus there is no solution, and the lines do not intersect at

one point.

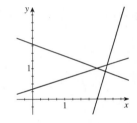

11. $\begin{cases} y = x^2 + 2x \\ y = 6 + x \end{cases}$ Substituting for y gives $6 + x = x^2 + 2x$ $\Leftrightarrow$ $x^2 + x - 6 = 0$. Factoring, we have

$(x - 2)(x + 3) = 0$. Thus $x = 2$ or -3. If $x = 2$, then $y = 8$, and if $x = -3$, then $y = 3$. Thus the solutions are $(-3, 3)$

and $(2, 8)$.

12. $\begin{cases} x^2 + y^2 = 8 \\ y = x + 2 \end{cases}$ Substituting for y in the first equation gives $x^2 + (x + 2)^2 = 8$ $\Leftrightarrow$ $2x^2 + 4x -$

$4 = 0 \Leftrightarrow 2(x^2 + 2x - 2) = 0$. Using the quadratic formula, we have $x = \dfrac{-2 \pm \sqrt{4 + 8}}{2} = \dfrac{-2 \pm 2\sqrt{3}}{2} = -1 \pm \sqrt{3}$. If

$x = -1 - \sqrt{3}$. then $y = \left(-1 - \sqrt{3}\right) + 2 = 1 - \sqrt{3}$, and if $x = -1 + \sqrt{3}$, then $y = \left(-1 + \sqrt{3}\right) + 2 = 1 + \sqrt{3}$. Thus,

the solutions are $\left(-1 - \sqrt{3}, 1 - \sqrt{3}\right)$ and $\left(-1 + \sqrt{3}, 1 + \sqrt{3}\right)$.

13. $\begin{cases} 3x + \dfrac{4}{y} = 6 \\ x - \dfrac{8}{y} = 4 \end{cases}$ Adding twice the first equation to the second gives $7x = 16$ $\Leftrightarrow$ $x = \frac{16}{7}$. So $\dfrac{16}{7} - \dfrac{8}{y} = 4$ $\Leftrightarrow$

$16y - 56 = 28y$ $\Leftrightarrow$ $-12y = 56$ $\Leftrightarrow$ $y = -\frac{14}{3}$. Thus, the solution is $\left(\frac{16}{7}, -\frac{14}{3}\right)$.

14. $\begin{cases} x^2 + y^2 = 10 \\ x^2 + 2y^2 - 7y = 0 \end{cases}$ Subtracting the first equation from the second gives $y^2 - 7y = -10 \quad \Leftrightarrow$

$y^2 - 7y + 10 = 0 \Leftrightarrow (y-2)(y-5) = 0 \Rightarrow y = 2,\ y = 5$. If $y = 2$, then $x^2 + 4 = 10 \quad \Leftrightarrow \quad x^2 = 6 \Rightarrow x = \pm\sqrt{6}$, and if $y = 5$, then $x^2 + 25 = 10 \Leftrightarrow x^2 = -15$, which leads to no real solution. Thus the solutions are $\left(\sqrt{6}, 2\right)$ and $\left(-\sqrt{6}, 2\right)$.

15. $\begin{cases} 0.32x + 0.43y = 0 \\ 7x - 12y = 341 \end{cases} \Leftrightarrow \begin{cases} y = -\dfrac{32x}{43} \\ y = \dfrac{7x - 341}{12} \end{cases}$

The solution is approximately $(21.41, -15.93)$.

16. $\begin{cases} \sqrt{12}\,x - 3\sqrt{2}\,y = 660 \\ 7137x + 3931y = 20{,}000 \end{cases} \Leftrightarrow \begin{cases} y = \dfrac{\sqrt{6}}{3}x - 110\sqrt{2} \\ y = -\dfrac{7137}{3931}x + \dfrac{20{,}000}{3931} \end{cases}$

The solution is approximately $(61.04, -105.73)$.

17. $\begin{cases} x - y^2 = 10 \\ x = \frac{1}{22}y + 12 \end{cases} \Leftrightarrow \begin{cases} y = \pm\sqrt{x - 10} \\ y = 22\,(x - 12) \end{cases}$

The solutions are $(11.94, -1.39)$ and $(12.07, 1.44)$.

18. $\begin{cases} y = 5^x + x \\ y = x^5 + 5 \end{cases}$ The solutions are approximately

$(-1.45, -1.35)$, $(1, 6)$, and $(1.51, 12.93)$.

19. (a) 2×3

(b) Yes, this matrix is in row-echelon form.

(c) No, this matrix is not in reduced row-echelon form, since the leading 1 in the second row does not have a 0 above it.

(d) $\begin{cases} x + 2y = -5 \\ y = 3 \end{cases}$

20. (a) 2×3

(b) Yes, this matrix is in row-echelon form.

(c) Yes, this matrix is in reduced row-echelon form.

(d) $\begin{cases} x = 6 \\ y = 0 \end{cases}$

21. (a) 3×4

(b) Yes, this matrix is in row-echelon form.

(c) Yes, this matrix is in reduced row-echelon form.

(d) $\begin{cases} x + 8z = 0 \\ y + 5z = -1 \\ 0 = 0 \end{cases}$

22. (a) 3×4

(b) No, this matrix is not in row-echelon form, since the leading 1 in the second row is not to the left of the one above it.

(c) Since this matrix is not in row-echelon form, it is not in reduced row-echelon form.

(d) $\begin{cases} x + 3y + 6z = 2 \\ 2x + y = 5 \\ z = 0 \end{cases}$

23. (a) 3×4

(b) No, this matrix is not in row-echelon form. The leading 1 in the second row is not to the left of the one above it.

(c) No, this matrix is not in reduced row-echelon form.

(d) $\begin{cases} \quad\ y - 3z = 4 \\ x + \ y \quad\quad = 7 \\ x + 2y + \ z = 2 \end{cases}$

24. (a) 4×4

(b) No, this matrix is not in row-echelon form. The leading 1 in the fourth row is not to the left of the one above it.

(c) No, this matrix is not in reduced row-echelon form.

(d) $\begin{cases} x + 8y + 6z = -4 \\ \quad\quad y - 3z = \ \ 5 \\ \quad\quad\quad\ 2z = -7 \\ x + \ y + \ z = \ \ 0 \end{cases}$

25. $\begin{cases} x + \ y + 2z = \ 6 \\ 2x \quad\quad + 5z = 12 \\ x + 2y + 3z = \ 9 \end{cases}$ $\Leftrightarrow$ $\begin{cases} x + \ y + 2z = 6 \\ \quad 2y - \ z = 0 \\ \quad 4y + \ z = 6 \end{cases}$ $\Leftrightarrow$ $\begin{cases} x + \ y + 2z = 6 \\ \quad 2y - \ z = 0 \\ \quad\quad 3z = 6 \end{cases}$ Therefore, $3z = 6$ $\Leftrightarrow$

$z = 2$, $2y - 2 = 0$ $\Leftrightarrow$ $y = 1$, and $x + 1 + 2\,(2) = 6$ $\Leftrightarrow$ $x = 1$. Hence, the solution is $(1, 1, 2)$.

26. $\begin{cases} x - 2y + 3z = 1 \\ x - 3y - \ z = 0 \\ 2x \quad\quad - 6z = 6 \end{cases}$ $\Leftrightarrow$ $\begin{cases} x - 2y + 3z = 1 \\ \quad\quad y + 4z = 1 \\ \quad\ 6y - 4z = 6 \end{cases}$ $\Leftrightarrow$ $\begin{cases} x - 2y + \ 3z = 1 \\ \quad\quad y + \ 4z = 1 \\ \quad\quad\ 28z = 0 \end{cases}$ Thus, $z = 0$, $y = 1$, and

$x - 2\,(1) + 3\,(0) = 1$ $\Leftrightarrow$ $x = 3$, and so the solution is $(3, 1, 0)$.

27. $\begin{cases} x - 2y + \ 3z = 1 \\ 2x - \ y + \quad z = 3 \\ 2x - 7y + 11z = 2 \end{cases}$ $\Leftrightarrow$ $\begin{cases} x - 2y + \ 3z = 1 \\ \quad\ 3y - \ 5z = 1 \\ \quad\ 6y - 10z = 1 \end{cases}$ $\Leftrightarrow$ $\begin{cases} x - 2y + 3z = \ 1 \\ \quad\ 3y - 5z = \ 1 \\ \quad\quad\quad\ 0 = -1 \end{cases}$ which is impossible.

Therefore, the system has no solution.

28. $\begin{cases} x + \ y + \ z + \ w = 2 \\ 2x \quad\quad - 3z \quad\quad = 5 \\ x - 2y \quad\quad + 4w = 9 \\ x + \ y + 2z + 3w = 5 \end{cases}$ $\Leftrightarrow$ $\begin{cases} x + \ y + \ z + \ w = \ \ 2 \\ \quad 2y + 5z + 2w = -1 \\ \quad 3y + \ z - 3w = -7 \\ \quad\quad\quad z + 2w = \ \ 3 \end{cases}$ $\Leftrightarrow$ $\begin{cases} x + \ y + \quad z + \quad w = \ \ 2 \\ \quad 2y + \ 5z + \ 2w = -1 \\ \quad\quad 13z + 12w = \ 11 \\ \quad\quad\quad z + \ 2w = \ \ 3 \end{cases}$ $\Leftrightarrow$

$\begin{cases} x + \ y + \quad z + \quad w = \ \ 2 \\ \quad 2y + \ 5z + \ 2w = -1 \\ \quad\quad 13z + 12w = \ 11 \\ \quad\quad\quad\quad 14w = \ 28 \end{cases}$ Therefore, $14w = 28$ $\Leftrightarrow$ $w = 2$, $13z + 12\,(2) = 11$ $\Leftrightarrow$ $z = -1$;

$2y + 5\,(-1) + 2\,(2) = -1$ $\Leftrightarrow$ $2y - 1 = -1$ $\Leftrightarrow$ $y = 0$; and $x - 1 + 2 = 2$ $\Leftrightarrow$ $x = 1$. So the solution is $(1, 0, -1, 2)$.

29. $\begin{bmatrix} 1 & 2 & 2 & 6 \\ 1 & -1 & 0 & -1 \\ 2 & 1 & 3 & 7 \end{bmatrix}$ $\xrightarrow{R_2 \leftrightarrow R_1}$ $\begin{bmatrix} 1 & -1 & 0 & -1 \\ 1 & 2 & 2 & 6 \\ 2 & 1 & 3 & 7 \end{bmatrix}$ $\xrightarrow[R_3 - 2R_1 \to R_3]{R_2 - R_1 \to R_2}$ $\begin{bmatrix} 1 & -1 & 0 & -1 \\ 0 & 3 & 2 & 7 \\ 0 & 3 & 3 & 9 \end{bmatrix}$ $\xrightarrow{R_3 - R_2 \to R_3}$ $\begin{bmatrix} 1 & -1 & 0 & -1 \\ 0 & 3 & 2 & 7 \\ 0 & 0 & 1 & 2 \end{bmatrix}$.

Thus, $z = 2$, $3y + 2\,(2) = 7$ $\Leftrightarrow$ $3y = 3 \Leftrightarrow y = 1$, and $x - (1) = -1$ $\Leftrightarrow$ $x = 0$, and so the solution is $(0, 1, 2)$.

30. $\begin{bmatrix} 1 & -1 & 1 & 2 \\ 1 & 1 & 3 & 6 \\ 0 & 2 & 3 & 5 \end{bmatrix}$ $\xrightarrow{R_2 - R_1 \to R_2}$ $\begin{bmatrix} 1 & -1 & 1 & 2 \\ 0 & 2 & 2 & 4 \\ 0 & 2 & 3 & 5 \end{bmatrix}$ $\xrightarrow{R_3 - R_2 \to R_3}$ $\begin{bmatrix} 1 & -1 & 1 & 2 \\ 0 & 2 & 2 & 4 \\ 0 & 0 & 1 & 1 \end{bmatrix}$. Thus, $z = 1$; $2y + 2\,(1) = 4$

$\Leftrightarrow$ $y = 1$; and $x - (1) + (1) = 2$ $\Leftrightarrow$ $x = 2$, and so the solution is $(2, 1, 1)$.

31. $\begin{bmatrix} 1 & -2 & 3 & -2 \\ 2 & -1 & 1 & 2 \\ 2 & -7 & 11 & -9 \end{bmatrix}$ $\xrightarrow[R_3 - 2R_1 \to R_3]{R_2 - 2R_1 \to R_2}$ $\begin{bmatrix} 1 & -2 & 3 & -2 \\ 0 & 3 & -5 & 6 \\ 0 & -3 & 5 & -5 \end{bmatrix}$ $\xrightarrow{R_3 + R_2 \to R_3}$ $\begin{bmatrix} 1 & -2 & 3 & -2 \\ 0 & 3 & -5 & 6 \\ 0 & 0 & 0 & 1 \end{bmatrix}$.

The last row corresponds to the equation $0 = 1$, which is always false. Thus, there is no solution.

32. $\begin{bmatrix} 1 & -1 & 1 & 2 \\ 1 & 1 & 3 & 6 \\ 3 & -1 & 5 & 10 \end{bmatrix}$ $\xrightarrow[R_3 - 3R_1 \to R_3]{R_2 - R_1 \to R_2}$ $\begin{bmatrix} 1 & -1 & 1 & 2 \\ 0 & 2 & 2 & 4 \\ 0 & 2 & 2 & 4 \end{bmatrix}$ $\xrightarrow{R_3 - R_2 \to R_3}$ $\begin{bmatrix} 1 & -1 & 1 & 2 \\ 0 & 2 & 2 & 4 \\ 0 & 0 & 0 & 0 \end{bmatrix}$ $\xrightarrow{\frac{1}{2}R_2}$ $\begin{bmatrix} 1 & -1 & 1 & 2 \\ 0 & 1 & 1 & 2 \\ 0 & 0 & 0 & 0 \end{bmatrix}$

$\xrightarrow{R_1 + R_2 \to R_1}$ $\begin{bmatrix} 1 & 0 & 2 & 4 \\ 0 & 1 & 1 & 2 \\ 0 & 0 & 0 & 0 \end{bmatrix}$. Let $z = t$. Then $y + t = 2 \iff y = 2 - t$ and $x + 2t = 4 \iff x = 4 - 2t$, and so the

solutions are $(4 - 2t, 2 - t, t)$, where t is any real number.

33. $\begin{bmatrix} 1 & 1 & 1 & 1 & 0 \\ 1 & -1 & -4 & -1 & -1 \\ 1 & -2 & 0 & 4 & -7 \\ 2 & 2 & 3 & 4 & -3 \end{bmatrix}$ $\xrightarrow[R_4 - 2R_1 \to R_4]{\substack{R_2 - R_1 \to R_2 \\ R_3 - R_1 \to R_3}}$ $\begin{bmatrix} 1 & 1 & 1 & 1 & 0 \\ 0 & -2 & -5 & -2 & -1 \\ 0 & -3 & -1 & 3 & -7 \\ 0 & 0 & 1 & 2 & -3 \end{bmatrix}$ $\xrightarrow{-R_3 + R_2 \to R_3}$ $\begin{bmatrix} 1 & 1 & 1 & 1 & 0 \\ 0 & 1 & -4 & -5 & 6 \\ 0 & -3 & -1 & 3 & -7 \\ 0 & 0 & 1 & 2 & -3 \end{bmatrix}$

$\xrightarrow{R_3 + 3R_2 \to R_3}$ $\begin{bmatrix} 1 & 1 & 1 & 1 & 0 \\ 0 & 1 & -4 & -5 & 6 \\ 0 & 0 & -13 & -12 & 11 \\ 0 & 0 & 1 & 2 & -3 \end{bmatrix}$ $\xrightarrow{R_3 \leftrightarrow R_4}$ $\begin{bmatrix} 1 & 1 & 1 & 1 & 0 \\ 0 & 1 & -4 & -5 & 6 \\ 0 & 0 & 1 & 2 & -3 \\ 0 & 0 & -13 & -12 & 11 \end{bmatrix}$ $\xrightarrow{R_4 + 13R_3 \to R_4}$ $\begin{bmatrix} 1 & 1 & 1 & 1 & 0 \\ 0 & 1 & -4 & -5 & 6 \\ 0 & 0 & 1 & 2 & -3 \\ 0 & 0 & 0 & 14 & -28 \end{bmatrix}$.

Therefore, $14w = -28 \iff w = -2$, $z + 2(-2) = -3 \iff z = 1$, $y - 4(1) - 5(-2) = 6 \iff y = 0$, and $x + 0 + 1 + (-2) = 0 \iff x = 1$. So the solution is $(1, 0, 1, -2)$.

34. $\begin{bmatrix} 1 & 0 & 3 & 0 & -1 \\ 0 & 1 & 0 & -4 & 5 \\ 0 & 2 & 1 & 1 & 0 \\ 2 & 1 & 5 & -4 & 4 \end{bmatrix}$ $\xrightarrow{R_4 - 2R_1 \to R_4}$ $\begin{bmatrix} 1 & 0 & 3 & 0 & -1 \\ 0 & 1 & 0 & -4 & 5 \\ 0 & 2 & 1 & 1 & 0 \\ 0 & 1 & -1 & -4 & 6 \end{bmatrix}$ $\xrightarrow[R_4 - R_2 \to R_4]{R_3 - 2R_2 \to R_3}$ $\begin{bmatrix} 1 & 0 & 3 & 0 & -1 \\ 0 & 1 & 0 & -4 & 5 \\ 0 & 0 & 1 & 9 & -10 \\ 0 & 0 & -1 & 0 & 1 \end{bmatrix}$ $\xrightarrow{R_3 \leftrightarrow R_4}$

$\begin{bmatrix} 1 & 0 & 3 & 0 & -1 \\ 0 & 1 & 0 & -4 & 5 \\ 0 & 0 & -1 & 0 & 1 \\ 0 & 0 & 1 & 9 & -10 \end{bmatrix}$ $\xrightarrow{R_4 + 3R_3 \to R_4}$ $\begin{bmatrix} 1 & 0 & 3 & 0 & -1 \\ 0 & 1 & 0 & -4 & 5 \\ 0 & 0 & -1 & 0 & 1 \\ 0 & 0 & 0 & 9 & -9 \end{bmatrix}$ $\xrightarrow[\frac{1}{9}R_4]{-R_3}$ $\begin{bmatrix} 1 & 0 & 3 & 0 & -1 \\ 0 & 1 & 0 & -4 & 5 \\ 0 & 0 & 1 & 0 & -1 \\ 0 & 0 & 0 & 1 & -1 \end{bmatrix}$ $\xrightarrow[R_2 + 4R_4 \to R_2]{R_1 - 3R_3 \to R_1}$

$\begin{bmatrix} 1 & 0 & 0 & 0 & 2 \\ 0 & 1 & 0 & 0 & 1 \\ 0 & 0 & 1 & 0 & -1 \\ 0 & 0 & 0 & 1 & -1 \end{bmatrix}$. Therefore, the solution is $(2, 1, -1, -1)$.

35. $\begin{cases} x - 3y + z = 4 \\ 4x - y + 15z = 5 \end{cases}$ $\iff$ $\begin{cases} x - 3y + z = 4 \\ y + z = -1 \end{cases}$ Thus, the system has infinitely many solutions given by

$z = t$, $y + t = -1 \iff y = -1 - t$, and $x + 3(1 + t) + t = 4 \iff x = 1 - 4t$. Therefore, the solutions are $(1 - 4t, -1 - t, t)$, where t is any real number.

36. $\begin{cases} 2x - 3y + 4z = 3 \\ 4x - 5y + 9z = 13 \\ 2x \qquad + 7z = 0 \end{cases}$ $\Leftrightarrow$ $\begin{cases} 2x - 3y + 4z = 3 \\ y + z = 7 \\ 3y + 3z = -3 \end{cases}$ $\Leftrightarrow$ $\begin{cases} 2x - 3y + 4z = 3 \\ y + z = 7 \\ 0 = -24 \end{cases}$

Since this last equation is impossible, the system is inconsistent and has no solution.

37. $\begin{cases} -x + 4y + z = 8 \\ 2x - 6y + z = -9 \\ x - 6y - 4z = -15 \end{cases}$ $\Leftrightarrow$ $\begin{cases} -x + 4y + z = 8 \\ 2y + 3z = 7 \\ 6y + 9z = 21 \end{cases}$ $\Leftrightarrow$ $\begin{cases} -x + 4y + z = 8 \\ 2y + 3z = 7 \\ 0 = 0 \end{cases}$

Thus, the system has infinitely many solutions. Letting $z = t$, we find $2y + 3t = 7$ $\Leftrightarrow$ $y = \frac{7}{2} - \frac{3}{2}t$, and $-x + 4\left(\frac{7}{2} - \frac{3}{2}t\right) + t = 8$ $\Leftrightarrow$ $x = 6 - 5t$. Therefore, the solutions are $\left(6 - 5t, \frac{7}{2} - \frac{3}{2}t, t\right)$, where t is any real number.

38. $\begin{cases} x \quad - z + w = 2 \\ 2x + y \quad - 2w = 12 \\ 3y + z + w = 4 \\ x + y - z \quad = 10 \end{cases}$ $\Leftrightarrow$ $\begin{cases} x \quad - z + w = 2 \\ y + 2z - 4w = 8 \\ 3y + z + w = 4 \\ y \quad - w = 8 \end{cases}$ $\Leftrightarrow$ $\begin{cases} x \quad - z + w = 2 \\ y + 2z - 4w = 8 \\ 5z - 13w = 20 \\ z + 4w = -20 \end{cases}$ $\Leftrightarrow$

$\begin{cases} x \quad - z + w = 2 \\ y + 2z - 4w = 8 \\ 5z - 13w = 20 \\ 33w = -120 \end{cases}$ Therefore, $33w = -120$ $\Leftrightarrow$ $w = -\frac{40}{11}$, $5z - 13\left(-\frac{40}{11}\right) = 20$ $\Leftrightarrow$ $z = -\frac{60}{11}$,

$y + 2\left(-\frac{60}{11}\right) - 4\left(-\frac{40}{11}\right) = 8$ $\Leftrightarrow$ $y = \frac{48}{11}$; and $x - \left(-\frac{60}{11}\right) + \left(-\frac{40}{11}\right) = 2$ $\Leftrightarrow$ $x = \frac{2}{11}$. Hence, the solution is $\left(\frac{2}{11}, \frac{48}{11}, -\frac{60}{11}, -\frac{40}{11}\right)$.

39. $\begin{bmatrix} 1 & -1 & 3 & 2 \\ 2 & 1 & 1 & 2 \\ 3 & 0 & 4 & 4 \end{bmatrix}$ $\xrightarrow[R_3 - 3R_1 \to R_3]{R_2 - 2R_1 \to R_2}$ $\begin{bmatrix} 1 & -1 & 3 & 2 \\ 0 & 3 & -5 & -2 \\ 0 & 3 & -5 & -2 \end{bmatrix}$ $\xrightarrow{R_3 - R_2 \to R_3}$ $\begin{bmatrix} 1 & -1 & 3 & 2 \\ 0 & 3 & -5 & -2 \\ 0 & 0 & 0 & 0 \end{bmatrix}$ $\xrightarrow{\frac{1}{3}R_2}$

$\begin{bmatrix} 1 & -1 & 3 & 2 \\ 0 & 1 & -\frac{5}{3} & -\frac{2}{3} \\ 0 & 0 & 0 & 0 \end{bmatrix}$ $\xrightarrow{R_1 + R_2 \to R_1}$ $\begin{bmatrix} 1 & 0 & \frac{4}{3} & \frac{4}{3} \\ 0 & 1 & -\frac{5}{3} & -\frac{2}{3} \\ 0 & 0 & 0 & 0 \end{bmatrix}$. The system is dependent, so let $z = t$: $y - \frac{5}{3}t = -\frac{2}{3}$ $\Leftrightarrow$

$y = \frac{5}{3}t - \frac{2}{3}$ and $x + \frac{4}{3}t = \frac{4}{3}$ $\Leftrightarrow$ $x = -\frac{4}{3}t + \frac{4}{3}$. So the solution is $\left(-\frac{4}{3}t + \frac{4}{3}, \frac{5}{3}t - \frac{2}{3}, t\right)$, where t is any real number.

40. $\begin{bmatrix} 1 & -1 & 0 & 1 \\ 1 & 1 & 2 & 3 \\ 1 & -3 & -2 & -1 \end{bmatrix}$ $\xrightarrow[R_3 - R_1 \to R_3]{R_2 - R_1 \to R_2}$ $\begin{bmatrix} 1 & -1 & 0 & 1 \\ 0 & 2 & 2 & 2 \\ 0 & -2 & -2 & -2 \end{bmatrix}$ $\xrightarrow{R_3 + R_2 \to R_3}$ $\begin{bmatrix} 1 & -1 & 0 & 1 \\ 0 & 2 & 2 & 2 \\ 0 & 0 & 0 & 0 \end{bmatrix}$ $\xrightarrow{\frac{1}{2}R_4}$

$\begin{bmatrix} 1 & -1 & 0 & 1 \\ 0 & 1 & 1 & 1 \\ 0 & 0 & 0 & 0 \end{bmatrix}$ $\xrightarrow{R_1 + R_2 \to R_1}$ $\begin{bmatrix} 1 & 0 & 1 & 2 \\ 0 & 1 & 1 & 1 \\ 0 & 0 & 0 & 0 \end{bmatrix}$. Since the system is dependent, let $z = t$. Then $y + t = 1$ $\Leftrightarrow$

$y = -t + 1$ and $x + t = 2$ $\Leftrightarrow$ $x = -t + 2$. So, the solution is $(-t + 2, -t + 1, t)$ where t is any real number.

41. $\begin{bmatrix} 1 & -1 & 1 & -1 & 0 \\ 3 & -1 & -1 & -1 & 2 \end{bmatrix}$ $\xrightarrow{R_2 - 3R_1 \to R_2}$ $\begin{bmatrix} 1 & -1 & 1 & -1 & 0 \\ 0 & 2 & -4 & 2 & 2 \end{bmatrix}$ $\xrightarrow{\frac{1}{2}R_4}$ $\begin{bmatrix} 1 & -1 & 1 & -1 & 0 \\ 0 & 1 & -2 & 1 & 1 \end{bmatrix}$ $\xrightarrow{R_1 + R_2 \to R_1}$

$\begin{bmatrix} 1 & 0 & -1 & 0 & 1 \\ 0 & 1 & -2 & 1 & 1 \end{bmatrix}$. Since the system is dependent, Let $z = s$ and $w = t$. Then $y - 2s + t = 1$ $\Leftrightarrow$ $y = 2s - t + 1$

and $x - s = 1$ $\Leftrightarrow$ $x = s + 1$. So the solution is $(s + 1, 2s - t + 1, s, t)$, where s and t are any real numbers.

42. $\begin{bmatrix} 1 & -1 & 3 \\ 2 & 1 & 6 \\ 1 & -2 & 9 \end{bmatrix}$ $\xrightarrow[R_3 - R_1 \rightarrow R_3]{R_2 - 2R_1 \rightarrow R_2}$ $\begin{bmatrix} 1 & -1 & 3 \\ 0 & 3 & 0 \\ 0 & -1 & 6 \end{bmatrix}$ $\xrightarrow{R_2 + 3R_3 \rightarrow R_2}$ $\begin{bmatrix} 1 & -1 & 3 \\ 0 & 0 & 18 \\ 0 & -1 & 6 \end{bmatrix}$. Since the second row corresponds to

the equation $0 = 18$, which is always false, this system has no solution.

43. $\begin{bmatrix} 1 & -1 & 1 & 0 \\ 3 & 2 & -1 & 6 \\ 1 & 4 & -3 & 3 \end{bmatrix}$ $\xrightarrow[R_3 - R_1 \rightarrow R_3]{R_2 - 3R_1 \rightarrow R_2}$ $\begin{bmatrix} 1 & -1 & 1 & 0 \\ 0 & 5 & -4 & 6 \\ 0 & 5 & -4 & 3 \end{bmatrix}$ $\xrightarrow{R_3 - R_2 \rightarrow R_3}$ $\begin{bmatrix} 1 & -1 & 1 & 0 \\ 0 & 5 & -4 & 6 \\ 0 & 0 & 0 & 3 \end{bmatrix}$. The last row of this

matrix corresponds to the equation $0 = 3$, which is always false. Hence there is no solution.

44. $\begin{bmatrix} 1 & 2 & 3 & 2 \\ 2 & -1 & -5 & 1 \\ 4 & 3 & 1 & 6 \end{bmatrix}$ $\xrightarrow[R_3 - 4R_1 \rightarrow R_3]{R_2 - 2R_1 \rightarrow R_2}$ $\begin{bmatrix} 1 & 2 & 3 & 2 \\ 0 & -5 & -11 & -3 \\ 0 & -5 & -11 & -2 \end{bmatrix}$ $\xrightarrow{R_3 - R_2 \rightarrow R_3}$ $\begin{bmatrix} 1 & 2 & 3 & 2 \\ 0 & -5 & -11 & -3 \\ 0 & 0 & 0 & 1 \end{bmatrix}$. Since the third row

corresponds to the equation $0 = 1$, which is always false, this system has no solution.

45. $\begin{bmatrix} 1 & 1 & -1 & -1 & 2 \\ 1 & -1 & 1 & -1 & 0 \\ 2 & 0 & 0 & 2 & 2 \\ 2 & 4 & -4 & -2 & 6 \end{bmatrix}$ $\xrightarrow{R_1 \leftrightarrow \frac{1}{2}R_3}$ $\begin{bmatrix} 1 & 0 & 0 & 1 & 1 \\ 1 & -1 & 1 & -1 & 0 \\ 1 & 1 & -1 & -1 & 2 \\ 2 & 4 & -4 & -2 & 6 \end{bmatrix}$ $\xrightarrow[\substack{R_3 - R_1 \rightarrow R_3 \\ R_4 - 2R_1 \rightarrow R_4}]{R_2 - R_1 \rightarrow R_2}$ $\begin{bmatrix} 1 & 0 & 0 & 1 & 1 \\ 0 & -1 & 1 & -2 & -1 \\ 0 & 1 & -1 & -2 & 1 \\ 0 & 4 & -4 & -4 & 4 \end{bmatrix}$

$\xrightarrow[R_4 + 4R_2 \rightarrow R_4]{R_3 + R_2 \rightarrow R_3}$ $\begin{bmatrix} 1 & 0 & 0 & 1 & 1 \\ 0 & -1 & 1 & -2 & -1 \\ 0 & 0 & 0 & -4 & 0 \\ 0 & 0 & 0 & -12 & 0 \end{bmatrix}$ $\xrightarrow[-\frac{1}{12}R_4]{-\frac{1}{4}R_3}$ $\begin{bmatrix} 1 & 0 & 0 & 1 & 1 \\ 0 & -1 & 1 & -2 & -1 \\ 0 & 0 & 0 & 0 & 0 \\ 0 & 0 & 0 & 1 & 0 \end{bmatrix}$ $\xrightarrow[\substack{R_2 + 2R_3 \rightarrow R_2 \\ R_4 - R_3 \rightarrow R_4}]{R_1 - R_3 \rightarrow R_1}$ $\begin{bmatrix} 1 & 0 & 0 & 0 & 1 \\ 0 & -1 & 1 & 0 & -1 \\ 0 & 0 & 0 & 1 & 0 \\ 0 & 0 & 0 & 0 & 0 \end{bmatrix}$.

This system is dependent. Let $z = t$, so $-y + t = -1 \quad \Leftrightarrow \quad y = t + 1$; $x = 1 \quad \Leftrightarrow \quad x = 1$. So the solution is

$(1, t + 1, t, 0)$, where t is any real number.

46. $\begin{bmatrix} 1 & -1 & -2 & 3 & 0 \\ 0 & 1 & -1 & 1 & 1 \\ 3 & -2 & -7 & 10 & 2 \end{bmatrix}$ $\xrightarrow{R_3 - 3R_1 \rightarrow R_3}$ $\begin{bmatrix} 1 & -1 & -2 & 3 & 0 \\ 0 & 1 & -1 & 1 & 1 \\ 0 & 1 & -1 & 1 & 2 \end{bmatrix}$ $\xrightarrow{R_3 - R_2 \rightarrow R_3}$ $\begin{bmatrix} 1 & -1 & -2 & 3 & 0 \\ 0 & 1 & -1 & 1 & 1 \\ 0 & 0 & 0 & 0 & 1 \end{bmatrix}$. Since the third

row corresponds to the equation $0 = 1$, which is always false, this system has no solution.

47. Let x be the amount in the 6% account and y the amount in the 7% account. The system is $\begin{cases} y = 2x \\ 0.06x + 0.07y = 600 \end{cases}$

Substituting gives $0.06x + 0.07(2x) = 600 \Leftrightarrow 0.2x = 600 \quad \Leftrightarrow \quad x = 3000$, so $y = 2(3000) = 6000$. Hence, the man

has \$3,000 invested at 6% and \$6,000 invested at 7%.

48. Let n be the number of nickels, d the number of dimes, and q the number of quarter in the piggy bank. We get the following

system: $\begin{cases} n + d + q = 50 \\ 5n + 10d + 25z = 560 \\ 10d = 5(5n) \end{cases}$ Since $10d = 25n$, we have $d = \frac{5}{2}n$, so substituting into the first equation we

get $n + \frac{5}{2}n + q = 50 \quad \Leftrightarrow \quad \frac{7}{2}n + q = 50 \quad \Leftrightarrow \quad q = 50 - \frac{7}{2}n$. Now substituting this into the second equation we

have $5n + 10\left(\frac{5}{2}n\right) + 25\left(50 - \frac{7}{2}n\right) = 560 \quad \Leftrightarrow \quad 5n + 25n + 1250 - \frac{175}{2}n = 560 \quad \Leftrightarrow \quad 1250 - \frac{115}{2}n = 560$

$\Leftrightarrow \quad \frac{115}{2}n = 650 \quad \Leftrightarrow \quad n = 12$. Then $d = \frac{5}{2}(12) = 30$ and $q = 50 - n - d = 50 - 12 - 30 = 8$. Thus the piggy

bank contains 12 nickels, 30 dimes, and 8 quarters.

49. Let x be the amount invested in Bank A, y the amount invested in Bank B, and z the amount invested in Bank C.

We get the following system:
$$\begin{cases} x + y + z = 60{,}000 \\ 0.02x + 0.025y + 0.03z = 1575 \\ 2x + 2z = y \end{cases} \Leftrightarrow \begin{cases} x + y + z = 60{,}000 \\ 2x + 2.5y + 3z = 157{,}500 \\ 2x - y + 2z = 0 \end{cases}$$

which has matrix representation $\begin{bmatrix} 1 & 1 & 1 & 60{,}000 \\ 2 & 2.5 & 3 & 157{,}500 \\ 2 & -1 & 2 & 0 \end{bmatrix}$ $\xrightarrow[R_3 - 2R_1 \to R_3]{R_2 - 2R_1 \to R_2}$ $\begin{bmatrix} 1 & 1 & 1 & 60{,}000 \\ 0 & 0.5 & 1 & 37{,}500 \\ 0 & -3 & 0 & -120{,}000 \end{bmatrix}$ $\xrightarrow{R_2 \leftrightarrow -\frac{1}{3}R_3}$

$\begin{bmatrix} 1 & 1 & 1 & 60{,}000 \\ 0 & 1 & 0 & 40{,}000 \\ 0 & 0.5 & 1 & 37{,}500 \end{bmatrix}$ $\xrightarrow[R_3 - 0.5R_2 \to R_3]{R_1 - R_2 \to R_1}$ $\begin{bmatrix} 1 & 0 & 1 & 20{,}000 \\ 0 & 1 & 0 & 40{,}000 \\ 0 & 0 & 1 & 17{,}500 \end{bmatrix}$ $\xrightarrow{R_1 - R_3 \to R_1}$ $\begin{bmatrix} 1 & 0 & 1 & 2{,}500 \\ 0 & 1 & 0 & 40{,}000 \\ 0 & 0 & 1 & 17{,}500 \end{bmatrix}$. Thus, she invests

$2{,}500 in Bank A, $40{,}000 in Bank B, and $17{,}500 in Bank C.

50. Let x be the amount of haddock, y the amount of sea bass, and z the amount of red snapper, in pounds. Our system

has the matrix representation $\begin{bmatrix} 1 & 1 & 1 & 560 \\ 1.25 & 0.75 & 2.00 & 575 \\ 1.25 & 0 & 2.00 & 320 \end{bmatrix}$ $\xrightarrow{R_2 - R_3 \to R_2}$ $\begin{bmatrix} 1 & 1 & 1 & 560 \\ 0 & 0.75 & 0 & 255 \\ 1.25 & 0 & 2.00 & 320 \end{bmatrix}$ $\xrightarrow{R_3 - 1.25R_1 \to R_3}$

$\begin{bmatrix} 1 & 1 & 1 & 560 \\ 0 & 0.75 & 0 & 255 \\ 0 & -1.25 & 0.75 & -380 \end{bmatrix}$ $\xrightarrow{\frac{4}{3}R_2}$ $\begin{bmatrix} 1 & 1 & 1 & 560 \\ 0 & 1 & 0 & 340 \\ 0 & -1.25 & 0.75 & -380 \end{bmatrix}$ $\xrightarrow{R_3 + 1.25R_2 \to R_3}$ $\begin{bmatrix} 1 & 1 & 1 & 560 \\ 0 & 1 & 0 & 340 \\ 0 & 0 & 0.75 & 45 \end{bmatrix}$ $\xrightarrow{\frac{4}{3}R_3}$

$\begin{bmatrix} 1 & 1 & 1 & 560 \\ 0 & 1 & 0 & 340 \\ 0 & 0 & 1 & 60 \end{bmatrix}$ $\xrightarrow{R_1 - R_3 \to R_1}$ $\begin{bmatrix} 1 & 1 & 0 & 500 \\ 0 & 1 & 0 & 340 \\ 0 & 0 & 1 & 60 \end{bmatrix}$ $\xrightarrow{R_1 - R_2 \to R_1}$ $\begin{bmatrix} 1 & 0 & 0 & 160 \\ 0 & 1 & 0 & 340 \\ 0 & 0 & 1 & 60 \end{bmatrix}$. Thus, he caught 160 lb of

haddock, 340 lb of sea bass, and 60 lb of red snapper.

In Solutions 51–62, the matrices A, B, C, D, E, F, **and** G **are defined as follows:**

$$A = \begin{bmatrix} 2 & 0 & -1 \end{bmatrix} \qquad B = \begin{bmatrix} 1 & 2 & 4 \\ -2 & 1 & 0 \end{bmatrix} \qquad C = \begin{bmatrix} \frac{1}{2} & 3 \\ 2 & \frac{3}{2} \\ -2 & 1 \end{bmatrix}$$

$$D = \begin{bmatrix} 1 & 4 \\ 0 & -1 \\ 2 & 0 \end{bmatrix} \qquad E = \begin{bmatrix} 2 & -1 \\ -\frac{1}{2} & 1 \end{bmatrix} \qquad F = \begin{bmatrix} 4 & 0 & 2 \\ -1 & 1 & 0 \\ 7 & 5 & 0 \end{bmatrix} \qquad G = \begin{bmatrix} 5 \end{bmatrix}$$

51. $A + B$ is not defined because the matrix dimensions 1×3 and 2×3 are not compatible.

52. $C - D = \begin{bmatrix} \frac{1}{2} & 3 \\ 2 & \frac{3}{2} \\ -2 & 1 \end{bmatrix} - \begin{bmatrix} 1 & 4 \\ 0 & -1 \\ 2 & 0 \end{bmatrix} = \begin{bmatrix} -\frac{1}{2} & -1 \\ 2 & \frac{5}{2} \\ -4 & 1 \end{bmatrix}$

53. $2C + 3D = 2\begin{bmatrix} \frac{1}{2} & 3 \\ 2 & \frac{3}{2} \\ -2 & 1 \end{bmatrix} + 3\begin{bmatrix} 1 & 4 \\ 0 & -1 \\ 2 & 0 \end{bmatrix} = \begin{bmatrix} 1 & 6 \\ 4 & 3 \\ -4 & 2 \end{bmatrix} + \begin{bmatrix} 3 & 12 \\ 0 & -3 \\ 6 & 0 \end{bmatrix} = \begin{bmatrix} 4 & 18 \\ 4 & 0 \\ 2 & 2 \end{bmatrix}$

54. $5B - 2C$ is not defined because the matrix dimensions 2×3 and 3×2 are not compatible.

55. $GA = \begin{bmatrix} 5 \end{bmatrix}\begin{bmatrix} 2 & 0 & -1 \end{bmatrix} = \begin{bmatrix} 10 & 0 & -5 \end{bmatrix}$

56. AG is undefined because the matrix dimensions 1×3 and 1×1 are not compatible.

57. $BC = \begin{bmatrix} 1 & 2 & 4 \\ -2 & 1 & 0 \end{bmatrix} \begin{bmatrix} \frac{1}{2} & 3 \\ 2 & \frac{3}{2} \\ -2 & 1 \end{bmatrix} = \begin{bmatrix} -\frac{7}{2} & 10 \\ 1 & -\frac{9}{2} \end{bmatrix}$

58. $CB = \begin{bmatrix} \frac{1}{2} & 3 \\ 2 & \frac{3}{2} \\ -2 & 1 \end{bmatrix} \begin{bmatrix} 1 & 2 & 4 \\ -2 & 1 & 0 \end{bmatrix} = \begin{bmatrix} -\frac{11}{2} & 4 & 2 \\ -1 & \frac{11}{2} & 8 \\ -4 & -3 & -8 \end{bmatrix}$

59. $BF = \begin{bmatrix} 1 & 2 & 4 \\ -2 & 1 & 0 \end{bmatrix} \begin{bmatrix} 4 & 0 & 2 \\ -1 & 1 & 0 \\ 7 & 5 & 0 \end{bmatrix} = \begin{bmatrix} 30 & 22 & 2 \\ -9 & 1 & -4 \end{bmatrix}$

60. $FC = \begin{bmatrix} 4 & 0 & 2 \\ -1 & 1 & 0 \\ 7 & 5 & 0 \end{bmatrix} \begin{bmatrix} \frac{1}{2} & 3 \\ 2 & \frac{3}{2} \\ -2 & 1 \end{bmatrix} = \begin{bmatrix} -2 & 14 \\ \frac{3}{2} & -\frac{3}{2} \\ \frac{27}{2} & \frac{57}{2} \end{bmatrix}$

61. $(C + D) E = \left(\begin{bmatrix} \frac{1}{2} & 3 \\ 2 & \frac{3}{2} \\ -2 & 1 \end{bmatrix} + \begin{bmatrix} 1 & 4 \\ 0 & -1 \\ 2 & 0 \end{bmatrix} \right) \begin{bmatrix} 2 & -1 \\ -\frac{1}{2} & 1 \end{bmatrix} = \begin{bmatrix} \frac{3}{2} & 7 \\ 2 & \frac{1}{2} \\ 0 & 1 \end{bmatrix} \begin{bmatrix} 2 & -1 \\ -\frac{1}{2} & 1 \end{bmatrix} = \begin{bmatrix} -\frac{1}{2} & \frac{11}{2} \\ \frac{15}{4} & -\frac{3}{2} \\ -\frac{1}{2} & 1 \end{bmatrix}$

62. $F (2C - D) = \begin{bmatrix} 4 & 0 & 2 \\ -1 & 1 & 0 \\ 7 & 5 & 0 \end{bmatrix} \left(\begin{bmatrix} 1 & 6 \\ 4 & 3 \\ -4 & 2 \end{bmatrix} - \begin{bmatrix} 1 & 4 \\ 0 & -1 \\ 2 & 0 \end{bmatrix} \right) = \begin{bmatrix} 4 & 0 & 2 \\ -1 & 1 & 0 \\ 7 & 5 & 0 \end{bmatrix} \begin{bmatrix} 0 & 2 \\ 4 & 4 \\ -6 & 2 \end{bmatrix} = \begin{bmatrix} -12 & 12 \\ 4 & 2 \\ 20 & 34 \end{bmatrix}$

63. $AB = \begin{bmatrix} 2 & -5 \\ -2 & 6 \end{bmatrix} \begin{bmatrix} 3 & \frac{5}{2} \\ 1 & 1 \end{bmatrix} = \begin{bmatrix} 1 & 0 \\ 0 & 1 \end{bmatrix}$ and $BA = \begin{bmatrix} 3 & \frac{5}{2} \\ 1 & 1 \end{bmatrix} \begin{bmatrix} 2 & -5 \\ -2 & 6 \end{bmatrix} = \begin{bmatrix} 1 & 0 \\ 0 & 1 \end{bmatrix}$.

64. $AB = \begin{bmatrix} 2 & -1 & 3 \\ 2 & -2 & 1 \\ 0 & 1 & 1 \end{bmatrix} \begin{bmatrix} -\frac{3}{2} & 2 & \frac{5}{2} \\ -1 & 1 & 2 \\ 1 & -1 & -1 \end{bmatrix} = \begin{bmatrix} 1 & 0 & 0 \\ 0 & 1 & 0 \\ 0 & 0 & 1 \end{bmatrix}$ and $BA = \begin{bmatrix} -\frac{3}{2} & 2 & \frac{5}{2} \\ -1 & 1 & 2 \\ 1 & -1 & -1 \end{bmatrix} \begin{bmatrix} 2 & -1 & 3 \\ 2 & -2 & 1 \\ 0 & 1 & 1 \end{bmatrix} = \begin{bmatrix} 1 & 0 & 0 \\ 0 & 1 & 0 \\ 0 & 0 & 1 \end{bmatrix}$.

In Solutions 65–70, $A = \begin{bmatrix} 2 & 1 \\ 3 & 2 \end{bmatrix}$, $B = \begin{bmatrix} 1 & -2 \\ -2 & 4 \end{bmatrix}$, **and** $C = \begin{bmatrix} 0 & 1 & 3 \\ -2 & 4 & 0 \end{bmatrix}$.

65. $A + 3X = B \iff 3X = B - A \iff X = \frac{1}{3} (B - A)$. Thus,

$$X = \frac{1}{3} \left(\begin{bmatrix} 1 & -2 \\ -2 & 4 \end{bmatrix} - \begin{bmatrix} 2 & 1 \\ 3 & 2 \end{bmatrix} \right) = \frac{1}{3} \begin{bmatrix} -1 & -3 \\ -5 & 2 \end{bmatrix}.$$

66. $\frac{1}{2} (X - 2B) = A \iff X - 2B = 2A \iff X = 2A + 2B = 2 (A + B)$. Thus,

$$X = 2 \left(\begin{bmatrix} 2 & 1 \\ 3 & 2 \end{bmatrix} + \begin{bmatrix} 1 & -2 \\ -2 & 4 \end{bmatrix} \right) = 2 \begin{bmatrix} 3 & -1 \\ 1 & 6 \end{bmatrix} = \begin{bmatrix} 6 & -2 \\ 2 & 12 \end{bmatrix}.$$

67. $2 (X - A) = 3B \iff X - A = \frac{3}{2} B \iff X = A + \frac{3}{2} B$. Thus,

$$X = \begin{bmatrix} 2 & 1 \\ 3 & 2 \end{bmatrix} + \frac{3}{2} \begin{bmatrix} 1 & -2 \\ -2 & 4 \end{bmatrix} = \begin{bmatrix} 2 & 1 \\ 3 & 2 \end{bmatrix} + \begin{bmatrix} \frac{3}{2} & -3 \\ -3 & 6 \end{bmatrix} = \begin{bmatrix} \frac{7}{2} & -2 \\ 0 & 8 \end{bmatrix}.$$

68. $2X + C = 5A \iff 2X = 5A - C$, but the difference $5A - C$ is not defined because the dimensions of $5A$ and C are not the same.

69. $AX = C \iff A^{-1}AX = X = A^{-1}C$. Now

$$A^{-1} = \frac{1}{4 - 3} \begin{bmatrix} 2 & -1 \\ -3 & 2 \end{bmatrix} = \begin{bmatrix} 2 & -1 \\ -3 & 2 \end{bmatrix}. \text{ Thus, } X = A^{-1}C = \begin{bmatrix} 2 & -1 \\ -3 & 2 \end{bmatrix} \begin{bmatrix} 0 & 1 & 3 \\ -2 & 4 & 0 \end{bmatrix} = \begin{bmatrix} 2 & -2 & 6 \\ -4 & 5 & -9 \end{bmatrix}.$$

70. $AX = B \iff A^{-1}AX = X = A^{-1}B$. From Exercise 69,

$$A^{-1} = \begin{bmatrix} 2 & -1 \\ -3 & 2 \end{bmatrix}. \text{ Thus, } X = A^{-1}B = \begin{bmatrix} 2 & -1 \\ -3 & 2 \end{bmatrix} \begin{bmatrix} 1 & -2 \\ -2 & 4 \end{bmatrix} = \begin{bmatrix} 4 & -8 \\ -7 & 14 \end{bmatrix}.$$

71. $D = \begin{bmatrix} 1 & 4 \\ 2 & 9 \end{bmatrix}$. Then $|D| = 1\,(9) - 2\,(4) = 1$, and so $D^{-1} = \begin{bmatrix} 9 & -4 \\ -2 & 1 \end{bmatrix}$.

72. $D = \begin{bmatrix} 2 & 2 \\ 1 & -3 \end{bmatrix}$. Then $|D| = 2\,(-3) - 1\,(2) = -8$, and so $D^{-1} = -\frac{1}{8}\begin{bmatrix} -3 & -2 \\ -1 & 2 \end{bmatrix} = \begin{bmatrix} \frac{3}{8} & \frac{1}{4} \\ \frac{1}{8} & -\frac{1}{4} \end{bmatrix}$.

73. $D = \begin{bmatrix} 4 & -12 \\ -2 & 6 \end{bmatrix}$. Then $|D| = 4\,(6) - 2\,(12) = 0$, and so D has no inverse.

74. $D = \begin{bmatrix} 2 & 4 & 0 \\ -1 & 1 & 2 \\ 0 & 3 & 2 \end{bmatrix}$. Then $|D| = 2 \begin{vmatrix} 1 & 2 \\ 3 & 2 \end{vmatrix} - 4 \begin{vmatrix} -1 & 2 \\ 0 & 2 \end{vmatrix} = 2\,(2 - 6) - 4\,(-2) = 0$, and so D has no inverse.

75. $D = \begin{bmatrix} 3 & 0 & 1 \\ 2 & -3 & 0 \\ 4 & -2 & 1 \end{bmatrix}$. Then, $|D| = 1 \begin{vmatrix} 2 & -3 \\ 4 & -2 \end{vmatrix} + 1 \begin{vmatrix} 3 & 0 \\ 2 & -3 \end{vmatrix} = -4 + 12 - 9 = -1$. So D^{-1} exists.

$$\begin{bmatrix} 3 & 0 & 1 & 1 & 0 & 0 \\ 2 & -3 & 0 & 0 & 1 & 0 \\ 4 & -2 & 1 & 0 & 0 & 1 \end{bmatrix} \xrightarrow{R_1 - R_2 \to R_1} \begin{bmatrix} 1 & 3 & 1 & 1 & -1 & 0 \\ 2 & -3 & 0 & 0 & 1 & 0 \\ 4 & -2 & 1 & 0 & 0 & 1 \end{bmatrix} \xrightarrow[R_3 - 4R_1 \to R_3]{R_2 - 2R_1 \to R_2} \begin{bmatrix} 1 & 3 & 1 & 1 & -1 & 0 \\ 0 & -9 & -2 & -2 & 3 & 0 \\ 0 & -14 & -3 & -4 & 4 & 1 \end{bmatrix} \xrightarrow[-2R_3]{-3R_2}$$

$$\begin{bmatrix} 1 & 3 & 1 & 1 & -1 & 0 \\ 0 & 27 & 6 & 6 & -9 & 0 \\ 0 & 28 & 6 & 8 & -8 & -2 \end{bmatrix} \xrightarrow{R_3 - R_2 \to R_3} \begin{bmatrix} 1 & 3 & 1 & 1 & -1 & 0 \\ 0 & 27 & 6 & 6 & -9 & 0 \\ 0 & 1 & 0 & 2 & 1 & -2 \end{bmatrix} \xrightarrow[\frac{1}{3}R_3]{R_3 \leftrightarrow R_2} \begin{bmatrix} 1 & 3 & 1 & 1 & -1 & 0 \\ 0 & 1 & 0 & 2 & 1 & -2 \\ 0 & 9 & 2 & 2 & -3 & 0 \end{bmatrix} \xrightarrow[R_1 - 3R_2 \to R_1]{R_3 - 9R_2 \to R_3}$$

$$\begin{bmatrix} 1 & 0 & 1 & -5 & -4 & 6 \\ 0 & 1 & 0 & 2 & 1 & -2 \\ 0 & 0 & 2 & -16 & -12 & 18 \end{bmatrix} \xrightarrow[R_1 - R_3 \to R_1]{\frac{1}{2}R_3} \begin{bmatrix} 1 & 0 & 0 & 3 & 2 & -3 \\ 0 & 1 & 0 & 2 & 1 & -2 \\ 0 & 0 & 1 & -8 & -6 & 9 \end{bmatrix}. \text{ Thus, } D^{-1} = \begin{bmatrix} 3 & 2 & -3 \\ 2 & 1 & -2 \\ -8 & -6 & 9 \end{bmatrix}.$$

76. $D = \begin{bmatrix} 1 & 2 & 3 \\ 2 & 4 & 5 \\ 2 & 5 & 6 \end{bmatrix}$. Then, $|D| = 1 \begin{vmatrix} 4 & 5 \\ 5 & 6 \end{vmatrix} - 2 \begin{vmatrix} 2 & 5 \\ 2 & 6 \end{vmatrix} + 3 \begin{vmatrix} 2 & 4 \\ 2 & 5 \end{vmatrix} = -1 - 4 + 6 = 1$. So D^{-1} exists.

$$\begin{bmatrix} 1 & 2 & 3 & 1 & 0 & 0 \\ 2 & 4 & 5 & 0 & 1 & 0 \\ 2 & 5 & 6 & 0 & 0 & 1 \end{bmatrix} \xrightarrow[R_3 - 2R_1 \to R_3]{R_2 - 2R_1 \to R_2} \begin{bmatrix} 1 & 2 & 3 & 1 & 0 & 0 \\ 0 & 0 & -1 & -2 & 1 & 0 \\ 0 & 1 & 0 & -2 & 0 & 1 \end{bmatrix} \xrightarrow{-R_2 \leftrightarrow R_3} \begin{bmatrix} 1 & 2 & 3 & 1 & 0 & 0 \\ 0 & 1 & 0 & -2 & 0 & 1 \\ 0 & 0 & 1 & 2 & -1 & 0 \end{bmatrix}$$

$$\xrightarrow{R_1 - 3R_3 \to R_1} \begin{bmatrix} 1 & 2 & 0 & -5 & 3 & 0 \\ 0 & 1 & 0 & -2 & 0 & 1 \\ 0 & 0 & 1 & 2 & -1 & 0 \end{bmatrix} \xrightarrow{R_1 - 2R_2 \to R_1} \begin{bmatrix} 1 & 0 & 0 & -1 & 3 & -2 \\ 0 & 1 & 0 & -2 & 0 & 1 \\ 0 & 0 & 1 & 2 & -1 & 0 \end{bmatrix}. \text{ Thus, } D^{-1} = \begin{bmatrix} -1 & 3 & -2 \\ -2 & 0 & 1 \\ 2 & -1 & 0 \end{bmatrix}.$$

77. $D = \begin{bmatrix} 1 & 0 & 0 & 1 \\ 0 & 2 & 0 & 2 \\ 0 & 0 & 3 & 3 \\ 0 & 0 & 0 & 4 \end{bmatrix}$. Thus, $|D| = \begin{vmatrix} 2 & 0 & 2 \\ 0 & 3 & 3 \\ 0 & 0 & 4 \end{vmatrix} = 2 \begin{vmatrix} 3 & 3 \\ 0 & 4 \end{vmatrix} = 24$ and D^{-1} exists. $\begin{bmatrix} 1 & 0 & 0 & 1 & 1 & 0 & 0 & 0 \\ 0 & 2 & 0 & 2 & 0 & 1 & 0 & 0 \\ 0 & 0 & 3 & 3 & 0 & 0 & 1 & 0 \\ 0 & 0 & 0 & 4 & 0 & 0 & 0 & 1 \end{bmatrix} \xrightarrow[\frac{1}{4}R_4]{\substack{\frac{1}{2}R_2 \\ \frac{1}{3}R_3}}$

$\begin{bmatrix} 1 & 0 & 0 & 1 & 1 & 0 & 0 & 0 \\ 0 & 1 & 0 & 1 & 0 & \frac{1}{2} & 0 & 0 \\ 0 & 0 & 1 & 1 & 0 & 0 & \frac{1}{3} & 0 \\ 0 & 0 & 0 & 1 & 0 & 0 & 0 & \frac{1}{4} \end{bmatrix} \xrightarrow[\substack{R_1 - R_4 \to R_1 \\ R_2 - R_4 \to R_2 \\ R_3 - R_4 \to R_3}]{} \begin{bmatrix} 1 & 0 & 0 & 0 & 1 & 0 & 0 & -\frac{1}{4} \\ 0 & 1 & 0 & 0 & 0 & \frac{1}{2} & 0 & -\frac{1}{4} \\ 0 & 0 & 1 & 0 & 0 & 0 & \frac{1}{3} & -\frac{1}{4} \\ 0 & 0 & 0 & 1 & 0 & 0 & 0 & \frac{1}{4} \end{bmatrix}$. Therefore, $D^{-1} = \begin{bmatrix} 1 & 0 & 0 & -\frac{1}{4} \\ 0 & \frac{1}{2} & 0 & -\frac{1}{4} \\ 0 & 0 & \frac{1}{3} & -\frac{1}{4} \\ 0 & 0 & 0 & \frac{1}{4} \end{bmatrix}$.

78. $D = \begin{bmatrix} 1 & 0 & 1 & 0 \\ 0 & 1 & 0 & 1 \\ 1 & 1 & 1 & 2 \\ 1 & 2 & 1 & 2 \end{bmatrix}$. Thus,

$|D| = \begin{vmatrix} 1 & 0 & 1 \\ 1 & 1 & 2 \\ 2 & 1 & 2 \end{vmatrix} + \begin{vmatrix} 0 & 1 & 1 \\ 1 & 1 & 2 \\ 1 & 2 & 2 \end{vmatrix} = \left(\begin{vmatrix} 1 & 2 \\ 1 & 2 \end{vmatrix} + \begin{vmatrix} 1 & 1 \\ 2 & 1 \end{vmatrix} \right) + \left(-\begin{vmatrix} 1 & 2 \\ 1 & 2 \end{vmatrix} + \begin{vmatrix} 1 & 1 \\ 1 & 2 \end{vmatrix} \right) = (0 - 1) + (0 + 1) = 0$.

Hence, D^{-1} does not exist.

79. $\begin{bmatrix} 12 & -5 \\ 5 & -2 \end{bmatrix} \begin{bmatrix} x \\ y \end{bmatrix} = \begin{bmatrix} 10 \\ 17 \end{bmatrix}$. If we let $A = \begin{bmatrix} 12 & -5 \\ 5 & -2 \end{bmatrix}$, then $A^{-1} = \frac{1}{-24 + 25} \begin{bmatrix} -2 & 5 \\ -5 & 12 \end{bmatrix} = \begin{bmatrix} -2 & 5 \\ -5 & 12 \end{bmatrix}$, and so

$\begin{bmatrix} x \\ y \end{bmatrix} = \begin{bmatrix} -2 & 5 \\ -5 & 12 \end{bmatrix} \begin{bmatrix} 10 \\ 17 \end{bmatrix} = \begin{bmatrix} 65 \\ 154 \end{bmatrix}$. Therefore, the solution is $(65, 154)$.

80. $\begin{bmatrix} 6 & -5 \\ 8 & -7 \end{bmatrix} \begin{bmatrix} x \\ y \end{bmatrix} = \begin{bmatrix} 1 \\ -1 \end{bmatrix}$. If we let $A = \begin{bmatrix} 6 & -5 \\ 8 & -7 \end{bmatrix}$, then

$A^{-1} = \frac{1}{-42 + 40} \begin{bmatrix} -7 & 5 \\ -8 & 6 \end{bmatrix} = -\frac{1}{2} \begin{bmatrix} -7 & 5 \\ -8 & 6 \end{bmatrix} = \begin{bmatrix} \frac{7}{2} & -\frac{5}{2} \\ 4 & -3 \end{bmatrix}$, and so $\begin{bmatrix} x \\ y \end{bmatrix} = \begin{bmatrix} \frac{7}{2} & -\frac{5}{2} \\ 4 & -3 \end{bmatrix} \begin{bmatrix} 1 \\ -1 \end{bmatrix} = \begin{bmatrix} 6 \\ 7 \end{bmatrix}$.

Therefore, the solution is $(6, 7)$.

81. $\begin{bmatrix} 2 & 1 & 5 \\ 1 & 2 & 2 \\ 1 & 0 & 3 \end{bmatrix} \begin{bmatrix} x \\ y \\ z \end{bmatrix} = \begin{bmatrix} \frac{1}{3} \\ \frac{1}{4} \\ \frac{1}{6} \end{bmatrix}$. Let $A = \begin{bmatrix} 2 & 1 & 5 \\ 1 & 2 & 2 \\ 1 & 0 & 3 \end{bmatrix}$. Then $\begin{bmatrix} 2 & 1 & 5 & 1 & 0 & 0 \\ 1 & 2 & 2 & 0 & 1 & 0 \\ 1 & 0 & 3 & 0 & 0 & 1 \end{bmatrix} \xrightarrow{R_1 \leftrightarrow R_2} \begin{bmatrix} 1 & 2 & 2 & 0 & 1 & 0 \\ 2 & 1 & 5 & 1 & 0 & 0 \\ 1 & 0 & 3 & 0 & 0 & 1 \end{bmatrix}$

$\xrightarrow[R_3 - R_1 \to R_3]{R_2 - 2R_1 \to R_2} \begin{bmatrix} 1 & 2 & 2 & 0 & 1 & 0 \\ 0 & -3 & 1 & 1 & -2 & 0 \\ 0 & -2 & 1 & 0 & -1 & 1 \end{bmatrix} \xrightarrow{R_2 - 2R_3 \to R_2} \begin{bmatrix} 1 & 2 & 2 & 0 & 1 & 0 \\ 0 & 1 & -1 & 1 & 0 & -2 \\ 0 & -2 & 1 & 0 & -1 & 1 \end{bmatrix} \xrightarrow[R_3 \to R_3 + 2R_2]{R_1 - 2R_2 \to R_1}$

$\begin{bmatrix} 1 & 0 & 4 & -2 & 1 & 4 \\ 0 & 1 & -1 & 1 & 0 & -2 \\ 0 & 0 & -1 & 2 & -1 & -3 \end{bmatrix} \xrightarrow{-R_3} \begin{bmatrix} 1 & 0 & 4 & -2 & 1 & 4 \\ 0 & 1 & -1 & 1 & 0 & -2 \\ 0 & 0 & 1 & -2 & 1 & 3 \end{bmatrix} \xrightarrow[R_2 + R_3 \to R_2]{R_1 - 4R_3 \to R_1} \begin{bmatrix} 1 & 0 & 0 & 6 & -3 & -8 \\ 0 & 1 & 0 & -1 & 1 & 1 \\ 0 & 0 & 1 & -2 & 1 & 3 \end{bmatrix}$. Hence,

$A^{-1} = \begin{bmatrix} 6 & -3 & -8 \\ -1 & 1 & 1 \\ -2 & 1 & 3 \end{bmatrix}$ and $\begin{bmatrix} x \\ y \\ z \end{bmatrix} = \begin{bmatrix} 6 & -3 & -8 \\ -1 & 1 & 1 \\ -2 & 1 & 3 \end{bmatrix} \begin{bmatrix} \frac{1}{3} \\ \frac{1}{4} \\ \frac{1}{6} \end{bmatrix} = \begin{bmatrix} -\frac{1}{12} \\ \frac{1}{12} \\ \frac{1}{12} \end{bmatrix}$, and so the solution is $\left(-\frac{1}{12}, \frac{1}{12}, \frac{1}{12} \right)$.

82. $\begin{bmatrix} 2 & 0 & 3 \\ 1 & 1 & 6 \\ 3 & -1 & 1 \end{bmatrix} \begin{bmatrix} x \\ y \\ z \end{bmatrix} = \begin{bmatrix} 5 \\ 0 \\ 5 \end{bmatrix}$. Let $A = \begin{bmatrix} 2 & 0 & 3 \\ 1 & 1 & 6 \\ 3 & -1 & 1 \end{bmatrix}$. Then $\begin{bmatrix} 2 & 0 & 3 & 1 & 0 & 0 \\ 1 & 1 & 6 & 0 & 1 & 0 \\ 3 & -1 & 1 & 0 & 0 & 1 \end{bmatrix} \xrightarrow{R_1 \leftrightarrow R_2} \begin{bmatrix} 1 & 1 & 6 & 0 & 1 & 0 \\ 2 & 0 & 3 & 1 & 0 & 0 \\ 3 & -1 & 1 & 0 & 0 & 1 \end{bmatrix}$

$\xrightarrow[R_3 - 3R_1 \to R_3]{R_2 - 2R_1 \to R_2} \begin{bmatrix} 1 & 1 & 6 & 0 & 1 & 0 \\ 0 & -2 & -9 & 1 & -2 & 0 \\ 0 & -4 & -17 & 0 & -3 & 1 \end{bmatrix} \xrightarrow{R_2 - 2R_3 \to R_2} \begin{bmatrix} 1 & 1 & 6 & 0 & 1 & 0 \\ 0 & -2 & -9 & 1 & -2 & 0 \\ 0 & 0 & 1 & -2 & 1 & 1 \end{bmatrix} \xrightarrow[R_2 - 6R_3 \to 2R_2]{R_1 + 9R_3 \to R_1}$

$\begin{bmatrix} 1 & 1 & 0 & 12 & -5 & -6 \\ 0 & -2 & 0 & -17 & 7 & 9 \\ 0 & 0 & 1 & -2 & 1 & 1 \end{bmatrix} \xrightarrow{-\frac{1}{2}R_2} \begin{bmatrix} 1 & 1 & 0 & 12 & -5 & -6 \\ 0 & 1 & 0 & \frac{17}{2} & -\frac{7}{2} & -\frac{9}{2} \\ 0 & 0 & 1 & -2 & 1 & 1 \end{bmatrix} \xrightarrow{R_1 - R_2 \to R_1} \begin{bmatrix} 1 & 0 & 0 & \frac{7}{2} & -\frac{3}{2} & -\frac{3}{2} \\ 0 & 1 & 0 & \frac{17}{2} & -\frac{7}{2} & -\frac{9}{2} \\ 0 & 0 & 1 & -2 & 1 & 1 \end{bmatrix}$.

Hence, $A^{-1} = \begin{bmatrix} \frac{7}{2} & -\frac{3}{2} & -\frac{3}{2} \\ \frac{17}{2} & -\frac{7}{2} & -\frac{9}{2} \\ -2 & 1 & 1 \end{bmatrix}$ and $\begin{bmatrix} x \\ y \\ z \end{bmatrix} = \begin{bmatrix} \frac{7}{2} & -\frac{3}{2} & -\frac{3}{2} \\ \frac{17}{2} & -\frac{7}{2} & -\frac{9}{2} \\ -2 & 1 & 1 \end{bmatrix} \begin{bmatrix} 5 \\ 0 \\ 5 \end{bmatrix} = \begin{bmatrix} 10 \\ 20 \\ -5 \end{bmatrix}$, and so the solution is $(10, 20, -5)$.

83. $|D| = \begin{vmatrix} 2 & 7 \\ 6 & 16 \end{vmatrix} = 32 - 42 = -10$, $|D_x| = \begin{vmatrix} 13 & 7 \\ 30 & 16 \end{vmatrix} = 208 - 210 = -2$, and $|D_y| = \begin{vmatrix} 2 & 13 \\ 6 & 30 \end{vmatrix} = 60 - 78 = -18$.

Therefore, $x = \frac{-2}{-10} = \frac{1}{5}$ and $y = \frac{-18}{-10} = \frac{9}{5}$, and so the solution is $\left(\frac{1}{5}, \frac{9}{5} \right)$.

84. $|D| = \begin{vmatrix} 12 & -11 \\ 7 & 9 \end{vmatrix} = 108 + 77 = 185$, $|D_x| = \begin{vmatrix} 140 & -11 \\ 20 & 9 \end{vmatrix} = 1260 + 220 = 1480$, and

$|D_y| = \begin{vmatrix} 12 & 140 \\ 7 & 20 \end{vmatrix} = 240 - 980 = -740$. Therefore, $x = \frac{1480}{185} = 8$ and $y = \frac{-740}{185} = -4$, and so the solution is $(8, -4)$.

85. $|D| = \begin{vmatrix} 2 & -1 & 5 \\ -1 & 7 & 0 \\ 5 & 4 & 3 \end{vmatrix} = 5 \begin{vmatrix} -1 & 7 \\ 5 & 4 \end{vmatrix} + 3 \begin{vmatrix} 2 & -1 \\ -1 & 7 \end{vmatrix} = -195 + 39 = -156$,

$|D_x| = \begin{vmatrix} 0 & -1 & 5 \\ 9 & 7 & 0 \\ -9 & 4 & 3 \end{vmatrix} = 5 \begin{vmatrix} 9 & 7 \\ -9 & 4 \end{vmatrix} + 3 \begin{vmatrix} 0 & -1 \\ 9 & 7 \end{vmatrix} = 495 + 27 = 522$,

$|D_y| = \begin{vmatrix} 2 & 0 & 5 \\ -1 & 9 & 0 \\ 5 & -9 & 3 \end{vmatrix} = 5 \begin{vmatrix} -1 & 9 \\ 5 & -9 \end{vmatrix} + 3 \begin{vmatrix} 2 & 0 \\ -1 & 9 \end{vmatrix} = -180 + 54 = -126$, and

$|D_z| = \begin{vmatrix} 2 & -1 & 0 \\ -1 & 7 & 9 \\ 5 & 4 & -9 \end{vmatrix} = -9 \begin{vmatrix} 2 & -1 \\ 5 & 4 \end{vmatrix} - 9 \begin{vmatrix} 2 & -1 \\ -1 & 7 \end{vmatrix} = -117 - 117 = -234$.

Therefore, $x = \frac{522}{-156} = -\frac{87}{26}$, $y = \frac{-126}{-156} = \frac{21}{26}$, and $z = \frac{-234}{-156} = \frac{3}{2}$, and so the solution is $\left(-\frac{87}{26}, \frac{21}{26}, \frac{3}{2} \right)$.

86. $|D| = \begin{vmatrix} 3 & 4 & -1 \\ 1 & 0 & -4 \\ 2 & 1 & 5 \end{vmatrix} = -4 \begin{vmatrix} 1 & -4 \\ 2 & 5 \end{vmatrix} - 1 \begin{vmatrix} 3 & -1 \\ 1 & -4 \end{vmatrix} = -52 + 11 = -41,$

$|D_x| = \begin{vmatrix} 10 & 4 & -1 \\ 20 & 0 & -4 \\ 30 & 1 & 5 \end{vmatrix} = -4 \begin{vmatrix} 20 & -4 \\ 30 & 5 \end{vmatrix} - 1 \begin{vmatrix} 10 & -1 \\ 20 & -4 \end{vmatrix} = -880 + 20 = -860,$

$|D_y| = \begin{vmatrix} 3 & 10 & -1 \\ 1 & 20 & -4 \\ 2 & 30 & 5 \end{vmatrix} = 3 \begin{vmatrix} 20 & -4 \\ 30 & 5 \end{vmatrix} - 1 \begin{vmatrix} 10 & -1 \\ 30 & 5 \end{vmatrix} + 2 \begin{vmatrix} 10 & -1 \\ 20 & -4 \end{vmatrix} = 660 - 80 - 40 = 540,$ and

$|D_z| = \begin{vmatrix} 3 & 4 & 10 \\ 1 & 0 & 20 \\ 2 & 1 & 30 \end{vmatrix} = -4 \begin{vmatrix} 1 & 20 \\ 2 & 30 \end{vmatrix} - 1 \begin{vmatrix} 3 & 10 \\ 1 & 20 \end{vmatrix} = 40 - 50 = -10.$

Therefore, $x = \frac{-860}{-41} = \frac{860}{41}$, $y = -\frac{540}{41}$, and $z = \frac{10}{41}$, and so the solution is $\left(\frac{860}{41}, -\frac{540}{41}, \frac{10}{41} \right)$.

87. The area is $\pm \frac{1}{2} \begin{vmatrix} -1 & 3 & 1 \\ 3 & 1 & 1 \\ -2 & -2 & 1 \end{vmatrix} = \pm \frac{1}{2} \left(\begin{vmatrix} 3 & 1 \\ -2 & -2 \end{vmatrix} - \begin{vmatrix} -1 & 3 \\ -2 & -2 \end{vmatrix} + \begin{vmatrix} -1 & 3 \\ 3 & 1 \end{vmatrix} \right) = \pm \frac{1}{2} (-4 - 8 - 10) = 11.$

88. The area is $\pm \frac{1}{2} \begin{vmatrix} 5 & -2 & 1 \\ 1 & 5 & 1 \\ -4 & 1 & 1 \end{vmatrix} = \pm \frac{1}{2} \left(\begin{vmatrix} 1 & 5 \\ -4 & 1 \end{vmatrix} - \begin{vmatrix} 5 & -2 \\ -4 & 1 \end{vmatrix} + \begin{vmatrix} 5 & -2 \\ 1 & 5 \end{vmatrix} \right) = \pm \frac{1}{2} (21 + 3 + 27) = \frac{51}{2}.$

89. $\frac{3x+1}{x^2 - 2x - 15} = \frac{3x+1}{(x-5)(x+3)} = \frac{A}{x-5} + \frac{B}{x+3}.$ Thus, $3x + 1 = A(x+3) + B(x-5) = x(A+B) + (3A - 5B),$

and so $\begin{cases} A + B = 3 \\ 3A - 5B = 1 \end{cases} \Leftrightarrow \begin{cases} -3A - 3B = -9 \\ 3A - 5B = 1 \end{cases}$ Adding, we have $-8B = -8 \quad \Leftrightarrow \quad B = 1,$ and $A = 2.$

Hence, $\frac{3x+1}{x^2 - 2x - 15} = \frac{2}{x-5} + \frac{1}{x+3}.$

90. $\frac{8}{x^3 - 4x} = \frac{8}{x(x^2 - 4)} = \frac{8}{x(x+2)(x-2)} = \frac{A}{x} + \frac{B}{x-2} + \frac{C}{x+2}.$ Then $8 = A(x^2 - 4) + Bx(x+2) +$

$Cx(x-2) = x^2(A+B+C) + x(2B - 2C) - 4A.$ Thus, $-4A = 8 \quad \Leftrightarrow \quad A = -2, 2B - 2C = 0 \quad \Leftrightarrow \quad B = C,$

and $-2 + 2B = 0 \quad \Leftrightarrow \quad B = 1,$ so $C = 1.$ Therefore, $\frac{8}{x^3 - 4x} = -\frac{2}{x} + \frac{1}{x-2} + \frac{1}{x+2}.$

91. $\frac{2x-4}{x(x-1)^2} = \frac{A}{x} + \frac{B}{x-1} + \frac{C}{(x-1)^2}.$ Then $2x - 4 = A(x-1)^2 + Bx(x-1) + Cx = Ax^2 - 2Ax + A + Bx^2 -$

$Bx + Cx = x^2(A+B) + x(-2A - B + C) + A.$ So $A = -4, -4 + B = 0 \quad \Leftrightarrow \quad B = 4,$ and $8 - 4 + C = 2 \quad \Leftrightarrow$

$C = -2.$ Therefore, $\frac{2x-4}{x(x-1)^2} = -\frac{4}{x} + \frac{4}{x-1} - \frac{2}{(x-1)^2}.$

92. $\dfrac{x+6}{x^3-2x^2+4x-8} = \dfrac{x+6}{(x^2+4)(x-2)} = \dfrac{Ax+B}{x^2+4} + \dfrac{C}{x-2}$. Thus,

$$x+6 = (Ax+B)(x-2) + C(x^2+4) = Ax^2 - 2Ax + Bx - 2B + Cx^2 + 4C$$
$$= x^2(A+C) + x(-2A+B) + (-2B+4C)$$

and we get the system $\begin{cases} A \quad\quad + C = 0 \\ -2A + B \quad\quad = 1 \\ \quad\quad -2B + 4C = 6 \end{cases} \Leftrightarrow \begin{cases} A \quad\quad + C = 0 \\ \quad B + 2C = 1 \\ -2B + 4C = 6 \end{cases} \Leftrightarrow \begin{cases} A \quad\quad + C = 0 \\ \quad B + 2C = 1 \\ \quad\quad 8C = 8 \end{cases}$

Thus, $8C = 8 \Leftrightarrow C = 1$, $B + 2 = 1 \Leftrightarrow B = -1$, and $A + 1 = 0 \Leftrightarrow A = -1$. So

$$\dfrac{x+6}{x^3-2x^2+4x-8} = -\dfrac{x+1}{x^2+4} + \dfrac{1}{x-2}.$$

93. $\dfrac{2x-1}{x^3+x} = \dfrac{2x-1}{x(x^2+1)} = \dfrac{A}{x} + \dfrac{Bx+C}{x^2+1}$. Then $2x - 1 = A(x^2+1) + (Bx+C)x = Ax^2 + A + Bx^2 +$

$Cx = (A+B)x^2 + Cx + A$. So $A = -1$, $C = 2$, and $A + B = 0$ gives us $B = 1$. Thus $\dfrac{2x-1}{x^3+x} = -\dfrac{1}{x} + \dfrac{x+2}{x^2+1}$.

94. Since $x^4 + x^2 - 2 = (x^2-1)(x^2+2) = (x-1)(x+1)(x^2+2)$, we have $\dfrac{5x^2-3x+10}{x^4+x^2-2} = \dfrac{A}{x-1} + \dfrac{B}{x+1} +$

$\dfrac{Cx+D}{x^2+2}$. Thus

$$5x^2 - 3x + 10 = (x+1)(x^2+2)A + (x-1)(x^2+2)B + (x^2-1)(Cx+D)$$
$$= Ax^3 + Ax^2 + 2Ax + 2A + Bx^3 - Bx^2 + 2Bx - 2B + Cx^3 + Dx^2 - Cx - D$$
$$= (A+B+C)x^3 = (A-B+D)x^2 + (2A+2B-C)x + (2A-2B-D)$$

This leads to the system $\begin{cases} A + B + C \quad\quad = 0 & \text{Coefficients of } x^3 \\ A - B \quad\quad + D = 5 & \text{Coefficients of } x^2 \\ 2A + 2B - C \quad\quad = -3 & \text{Coefficients of } x \\ 2A - 2B \quad\quad - D = 10 & \text{Constant terms} \end{cases} \Leftrightarrow \begin{cases} A + B + C \quad\quad = 0 \\ 2B + C - D = -5 \\ 3C \quad\quad = 3 \\ 4B - C + D = -13 \end{cases}$

$\Leftrightarrow \begin{cases} A + B + C \quad\quad = 0 \\ 2B + C - D = -5 \\ \quad C \quad\quad = 1 \\ 3C - 3D = 3 \end{cases}$ Thus $C = 1$, $3(1) - 3D = 3 \Leftrightarrow D = 0$, $2B + 1 - 0 = -5 \Leftrightarrow$

$B = -3$, and $A - 3 + 1 = 0 \Leftrightarrow A = 2$. Thus, $\dfrac{5x^2-3x+10}{x^4+x^2-2} = \dfrac{2}{x-1} - \dfrac{3}{x+1} + \dfrac{x}{x^2+2}$.

95. The boundary is a solid curve, so we have the inequality $x + y^2 \le 4$. We take the test point $(0,0)$ and verify that it satisfies the inequality: $0 + 0^2 \le 4$.

96. The boundary is a solid curve, so we have the inequality $x^2 + y^2 \ge 8$. We take the test point $(0,3)$ and verify that it satisfies the inequality: $0^2 + 3^2 \ge 8$.

97. $3x + y \leq 6$

98. $y \geq x^2 - 3$

99. $x^2 + y^2 > 9$

100. $x - y^4 < 4$

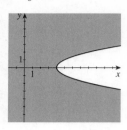

101. $\begin{cases} y \geq x^2 - 3x \\ y \leq \frac{1}{3}x - 1 \end{cases}$

102. $\begin{cases} y \geq x - 1 \\ x^2 + y^2 \leq 1 \end{cases}$

103. $\begin{cases} x + y \geq 2 \\ y - x \leq 2 \\ x \leq 3 \end{cases}$

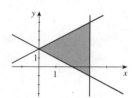

104. $\begin{cases} y \geq -2x \\ y \leq 2x \\ y \leq -\frac{1}{2}x + 2 \end{cases}$

105. $\begin{cases} x^2 + y^2 < 9 \\ x + y < 0 \end{cases}$ The vertices occur where $y = -x$. By substitution,

$x^2 + x^2 = 9$ $\Leftrightarrow$ $x = \pm\frac{3}{\sqrt{2}}$, and so $y = \mp\frac{3}{\sqrt{2}}$. Therefore, the vertices are

$\left(\frac{3}{\sqrt{2}}, -\frac{3}{\sqrt{2}}\right)$ and $\left(-\frac{3}{\sqrt{2}}, \frac{3}{\sqrt{2}}\right)$ and the solution set is bounded.

106. $\begin{cases} y - x^2 \geq 4 \\ y < 20 \end{cases}$ The vertices occur where $y = x^2 + 4$ and $y = 2$. By

substitution, $x^2 + 4 = 20$ $\Leftrightarrow$ $x^2 = 16$ $\Leftrightarrow$ $x = \pm 4$ and $y = 20$. Thus,

the vertices are $(\pm 4, 20)$ and the solution set is bounded.

107. $\begin{cases} x \geq 0, y \geq 0 \\ x + 2y \leq 12 \\ y \leq x + 4 \end{cases}$ The intersection points are $(-4, 0)$, $(0, 4)$, $\left(\frac{4}{3}, \frac{16}{3}\right)$, $(0, 6)$,

$(0, 0)$, and $(12, 0)$. Since the points $(-4, 0)$ and $(0, 6)$ are not in the solution set,

the vertices are $(0, 4)$, $\left(\frac{4}{3}, \frac{16}{3}\right)$, $(12, 0)$, and $(0, 0)$. The solution set is bounded.

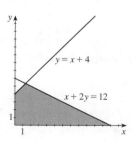

108. $\begin{cases} x \geq 4 \\ x + y \geq 24 \\ x \leq 2y + 12 \end{cases}$ The lines $x + y = 24$ and $x = 2y + 12$ intersect at the

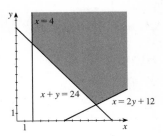

point $(20, 4)$. The lines $x = 4$ and $x = 2y + 12$ intersect at the point $(-4, 4)$, however, this vertex does not satisfy the other inequality. The lines $x + y = 24$ and $x = 4$ intersect at the point $(4, 20)$. Hence, the vertices are $(4, 20)$ and $(20, 4)$. The solution set is not bounded.

109. $\begin{cases} -x + y + z = a \\ x - y + z = b \\ x + y - z = c \end{cases} \Leftrightarrow \begin{cases} -x + y + z = a \\ \qquad 2z = a + b \\ \qquad 2y = a + c \end{cases}$ Thus, $y = \dfrac{a + c}{2}$, $z = \dfrac{a + b}{2}$, and $-x + \dfrac{a + c}{2} + \dfrac{a + b}{2} = a$

$\Leftrightarrow \quad x = \dfrac{b + c}{2}$. The solution is $\left(\dfrac{b + c}{2}, \dfrac{a + c}{2}, \dfrac{a + b}{2} \right)$.

110. $\begin{cases} ax + by + cz = a - b + c \\ bx + by + cz = \qquad c \\ cx + cy + cz = \qquad c \end{cases}$ $a \neq b \neq c \neq 0$ $\Leftrightarrow$ $\begin{cases} ax + by + cz = a - b + c \\ bx + by + cz = \qquad c \\ x + y + z = \qquad 1 \end{cases}$ Subtracting the second

equation from the first gives $(a - b) x = a - b$ $\Leftrightarrow$ $x = 1$. Subtracting the third equation from the second, $(b - c) x + (b - c) y = 0$ $\Leftrightarrow$ $y = -x = -1$. So $1 - 1 + z = 1$ $\Leftrightarrow$ $z = 1$, and the solution is $(1, -1, 1)$.

111. Solving the second equation for y, we have $y = kx$. Substituting for y in the first equation gives us

$x + kx = 12 \Leftrightarrow (1 + k) x = 12 \Leftrightarrow x = \dfrac{12}{k + 1}$. Substituting for y in the third equation gives us

$kx - x = 2k \Leftrightarrow (k - 1) x = 2k \Leftrightarrow x = \dfrac{2k}{k - 1}$. These points of intersection are the same when the

x-values are equal. Thus, $\dfrac{12}{k + 1} = \dfrac{2k}{k - 1} \Leftrightarrow 12 (k - 1) = 2k (k + 1) \Leftrightarrow 12k - 12 = 2k^2 + 2k \Leftrightarrow$

$0 = 2k^2 - 10k + 12 = 2 (k^2 - 5k + 6) = 2 (k - 3) (k + 2)$. Hence, $k = 2$ or $k = 3$.

112. The system will have infinitely many solutions when the system has solutions other than $(0, 0, 0)$. So we solve the

system with $x \neq 0$, $y \neq 0$, and $z \neq 0$. $\begin{cases} kx + y + z = 0 \\ x + 2y + kz = 0 \\ -x + 2y + 3z = 0 \end{cases} \Leftrightarrow \begin{cases} kx + \qquad y + \qquad z = 0 \\ \qquad 4y + (k + 3) z = 0 \\ \qquad (2k + 1) y + (3k + 1) z = 0 \end{cases} \Leftrightarrow$

$\begin{cases} kx + y + \qquad\qquad z = 0 \\ \qquad 4y + \qquad (k + 3) z = 0 \\ \qquad \left[(3k + 1) - \left(\dfrac{2k + 1}{4} \right) (k + 3) \right] z = 0 \end{cases}$ Since $z \neq 0$, we must have $3k + 1 - \dfrac{2k + 1}{4} (k + 3) = 0$ $\Leftrightarrow$

$2k^2 - 5k - 1 = 0$, so $k = \dfrac{5 \pm \sqrt{(-5)^2 - 4 (2) (-1)}}{2 (2)} = \dfrac{5 \pm \sqrt{33}}{4}$.

Chapter 9 Test

1. (a) The system is linear.

(b) $\begin{cases} x + 3y = 7 \\ 5x + 2y = -4 \end{cases}$ Multiplying the first equation by -5 and then adding gives $-13y = -39$ $\Leftrightarrow$ $y = 3$. So

$x + 3\,(3) = 7$ $\Leftrightarrow$ $x = -2$. Thus, the solution is $(-2, 3)$.

2. (a) The system is nonlinear.

(b) $\begin{cases} 6x + y^2 = 10 \\ 3x - y = 5 \end{cases}$ $\Leftrightarrow$ $\begin{cases} 6x + y^2 = 10 \\ y^2 + 2y = 0 \end{cases}$ Thus $y^2 + 2y = y\,(y + 2) = 0$, so either $y = 0$ or $y = -2$. If $y = 0$,

then $3x = 5$ $\Leftrightarrow$ $x = \frac{5}{3}$ and if $y = -2$, then $3x - (-2) = 5$ $\Leftrightarrow$ $3x = 3$ $\Leftrightarrow$ $x = 1$. Thus the solutions

are $\left(\frac{5}{3}, 0\right)$ and $(1, -2)$.

3. $\begin{cases} x - 2y = 1 \\ y = x^3 - 2x^2 \end{cases}$

The solutions are approximately $(-0.55, -0.78)$, $(0.43, -0.29)$, and $(2.12, 0.56)$.

4. Let w be the speed of the wind and a the speed of the airplane in still air, in kilometers per hour. Then the speed of the of the plane flying against the wind is $a - w$ and the speed of the plane flying with the wind is $a + w$. Using distance = rate × time,

we get the system $\begin{cases} 600 = 2.5\,(a - w) \\ 300 = \frac{50}{60}\,(a + w) \end{cases}$ $\Leftrightarrow$ $\begin{cases} 240 = a - w \\ 360 = a + w \end{cases}$ Adding the two equations, we get $600 = 2a$ $\Leftrightarrow$

$a = 300$. So $360 = 300 + w$ $\Leftrightarrow$ $w = 60$. Thus the speed of the airplane in still air is 300 km/h and the speed of the wind is 60 km/h.

5. This matrix is in row-echelon form, but not in reduced row-echelon form, since the leading 1 in the second row does not have a 0 above it.

6. This matrix is in reduced row-echelon form.

7. This matrix is in neither row-echelon form nor reduced row-echelon form.

8. $\begin{cases} x - y + 2z = 0 \\ 2x - 4y + 5z = -5 \\ 2y - 3z = 5 \end{cases}$ has the matrix representation $\begin{bmatrix} 1 & -1 & 2 & 0 \\ 2 & -4 & 5 & -5 \\ 0 & 2 & -3 & 5 \end{bmatrix}$ $\xrightarrow{R_2 - R_1 \to R_2}$ $\begin{bmatrix} 1 & -1 & 2 & 0 \\ 0 & -2 & 1 & -5 \\ 0 & 2 & -3 & 5 \end{bmatrix}$

$\xrightarrow{R_3 + R_2 \to R_3}$ $\begin{bmatrix} 1 & -1 & 2 & 0 \\ 0 & -2 & 1 & -5 \\ 0 & 0 & -2 & 0 \end{bmatrix}$ $\xrightarrow{-\frac{1}{2}R_3}$ $\begin{bmatrix} 1 & -1 & 2 & 0 \\ 0 & -2 & 1 & -5 \\ 0 & 0 & 1 & 0 \end{bmatrix}$. Thus $z = 0$, $-2y + 0 = -5$ $\Leftrightarrow$ $y = \frac{5}{2}$, and

$x - \frac{5}{2} + 2\,(0) = 0$ $\Leftrightarrow$ $x = \frac{5}{2}$. Thus, the solution is $\left(\frac{5}{2}, \frac{5}{2}, 0\right)$.

9. $\begin{cases} 2x - 3y + z = 3 \\ x + 2y + 2z = -1 \\ 4x + y + 5z = 4 \end{cases}$ has the matrix representation $\begin{bmatrix} 2 & -3 & 1 & 3 \\ 1 & 2 & 2 & -1 \\ 4 & 1 & 5 & 4 \end{bmatrix} \xrightarrow{R_1 \leftrightarrow R_2} \begin{bmatrix} 1 & 2 & 2 & -1 \\ 2 & -3 & 1 & 3 \\ 4 & 1 & 5 & 4 \end{bmatrix}$

$\xrightarrow[R_3 - 4R_1 \to R_3]{R_2 - 2R_1 \to R_2} \begin{bmatrix} 1 & 2 & 2 & -1 \\ 0 & -7 & -3 & 5 \\ 0 & -7 & -3 & 8 \end{bmatrix} \xrightarrow{R_3 - R_2 \to R_3} \begin{bmatrix} 1 & 2 & 2 & -1 \\ 0 & -7 & -3 & 5 \\ 0 & 0 & 0 & 3 \end{bmatrix}.$

Since the last row corresponds to the equation $0 = 3$, this system has no solution.

10. $\begin{cases} x + 3y - z = 0 \\ 3x + 4y - 2z = -1 \\ -x + 2y = 1 \end{cases}$ has the matrix representation $\begin{bmatrix} 1 & 3 & -1 & 0 \\ 3 & 4 & -2 & -1 \\ -1 & 2 & 0 & 1 \end{bmatrix} \xrightarrow[R_3 + R_1 \to R_3]{R_2 - 3R_1 \to R_2} \begin{bmatrix} 1 & 3 & -1 & 0 \\ 0 & -5 & 1 & -1 \\ 0 & 5 & -1 & 1 \end{bmatrix}$

$\xrightarrow{R_3 - R_2 \to R_3} \begin{bmatrix} 1 & 3 & -1 & 0 \\ 0 & -5 & 1 & -1 \\ 0 & 0 & 0 & 0 \end{bmatrix} \xrightarrow{-\frac{1}{5}R_2} \begin{bmatrix} 1 & 3 & -1 & 0 \\ 0 & 1 & -\frac{1}{5} & \frac{1}{5} \\ 0 & 0 & 0 & 0 \end{bmatrix} \xrightarrow{R_1 - 3R_2 \to R_1} \begin{bmatrix} 1 & 0 & -\frac{2}{5} & -\frac{3}{5} \\ 0 & 1 & -\frac{1}{5} & \frac{1}{5} \\ 0 & 0 & 0 & 0 \end{bmatrix}.$

Since this system is dependent, let $z = t$. Then $y - \frac{1}{5}t = \frac{1}{5} \iff y = \frac{1}{5}t + \frac{1}{5}$ and $x - \frac{2}{5}t = -\frac{3}{5} \iff x = \frac{2}{5}t - \frac{3}{5}$.

Thus, the solution is $\left(\frac{2}{5}t - \frac{3}{5}, \frac{1}{5}t + \frac{1}{5}, t \right)$.

11. Let x, y, and z represent the price in dollars for coffee, juice, and donuts respectively. Then the system of equations is

$\begin{cases} 2x + y + 2z = 6.25 \quad \text{Anne} \\ x \quad\quad + 3z = 3.75 \quad \text{Barry} \\ 3x + y + 4z = 9.25 \quad \text{Cathy} \end{cases} \iff \begin{cases} 2x + y + 2z = 6.25 \\ y - 4z = -1.25 \\ y - 5z = -2.00 \end{cases} \iff \begin{cases} 2x + y + 2z = 6.25 \\ y - 4z = -1.25 \\ z = 0.75 \end{cases}$

Thus, $z = 0.75$, $y - 4(0.75) = -1.25 \iff y = 1.75$, and $2x + 1.75 + 2(0.75) = 6.25 \iff x = 1.5$. Thus coffee costs $1.50, juice costs $1.75, and donuts cost $0.75.

12. $A = \begin{bmatrix} 2 & 3 \\ 2 & 4 \end{bmatrix}$, $B = \begin{bmatrix} 2 & 4 \\ -1 & 1 \\ 3 & 0 \end{bmatrix}$, and $C = \begin{bmatrix} 1 & 0 & 4 \\ -1 & 1 & 2 \\ 0 & 1 & 3 \end{bmatrix}$.

(a) $A + B$ is undefined because A is 2×2 and B is 3×2, so they have incompatible dimensions.

(b) AB is undefined because A is 2×2 and B is 3×2, so they have incompatible dimensions.

(c) $BA - 3B = \begin{bmatrix} 2 & 4 \\ -1 & 1 \\ 3 & 0 \end{bmatrix} \begin{bmatrix} 2 & 3 \\ 2 & 4 \end{bmatrix} - 3 \begin{bmatrix} 2 & 4 \\ -1 & 1 \\ 3 & 0 \end{bmatrix} = \begin{bmatrix} 12 & 22 \\ 0 & 1 \\ 6 & 9 \end{bmatrix} - \begin{bmatrix} 6 & 12 \\ -3 & 3 \\ 9 & 0 \end{bmatrix} = \begin{bmatrix} 6 & 10 \\ 3 & -2 \\ -3 & 9 \end{bmatrix}$

(d) $CBA = \begin{bmatrix} 1 & 0 & 4 \\ -1 & 1 & 2 \\ 0 & 1 & 3 \end{bmatrix} \begin{bmatrix} 2 & 4 \\ -1 & 1 \\ 3 & 0 \end{bmatrix} \begin{bmatrix} 2 & 3 \\ 2 & 4 \end{bmatrix} = \begin{bmatrix} 14 & 4 \\ 3 & -3 \\ 8 & 1 \end{bmatrix} \begin{bmatrix} 2 & 3 \\ 2 & 4 \end{bmatrix} = \begin{bmatrix} 36 & 58 \\ 0 & -3 \\ 18 & 28 \end{bmatrix}$

(e) $A = \begin{bmatrix} 2 & 3 \\ 2 & 4 \end{bmatrix} \iff A^{-1} = \frac{1}{8-6} \begin{bmatrix} 4 & -3 \\ -2 & 2 \end{bmatrix} = \begin{bmatrix} 2 & -\frac{3}{2} \\ -1 & 1 \end{bmatrix}$

(f) B^{-1} does not exist because B is not a square matrix.   **(g)** $\det(B)$ is not defined because B is not a square matrix.

(h) $\det(C) = \begin{vmatrix} 1 & 0 & 4 \\ -1 & 1 & 2 \\ 0 & 1 & 3 \end{vmatrix} = 1 \begin{vmatrix} 1 & 2 \\ 1 & 3 \end{vmatrix} + 4 \begin{vmatrix} -1 & 1 \\ 0 & 1 \end{vmatrix} = 1 - 4 = -3$

13. (a) The system $\begin{cases} 4x - 3y = 10 \\ 3x - 2y = 30 \end{cases}$ is equivalent to the matrix equation $\begin{bmatrix} 4 & -3 \\ 3 & -2 \end{bmatrix} \begin{bmatrix} x \\ y \end{bmatrix} = \begin{bmatrix} 10 \\ 30 \end{bmatrix}$.

(b) We have $|D| = \begin{vmatrix} 4 & -3 \\ 3 & -2 \end{vmatrix} = 4(-2) - 3(-3) = 1$. So $D^{-1} = \begin{bmatrix} -2 & 3 \\ -3 & 4 \end{bmatrix}$ and $\begin{bmatrix} x \\ y \end{bmatrix} = \begin{bmatrix} -2 & 3 \\ -3 & 4 \end{bmatrix} \begin{bmatrix} 10 \\ 30 \end{bmatrix} = \begin{bmatrix} 70 \\ 90 \end{bmatrix}$.

Therefore, $x = 70$ and $y = 90$.

14. $|A| = \begin{vmatrix} 1 & 4 & 1 \\ 0 & 2 & 0 \\ 1 & 0 & 1 \end{vmatrix} = 2 \begin{vmatrix} 1 & 1 \\ 1 & 1 \end{vmatrix} = 0$, $|B| = \begin{vmatrix} 1 & 4 & 0 \\ 0 & 2 & 0 \\ -3 & 0 & 1 \end{vmatrix} = 2 \begin{vmatrix} 1 & 0 \\ -3 & 1 \end{vmatrix} = 2$. Since $|A| = 0$, A does not have an inverse, and

since $|B| \neq 0$, B does have an inverse. $\begin{bmatrix} 1 & 4 & 0 & 1 & 0 & 0 \\ 0 & 2 & 0 & 0 & 1 & 0 \\ -3 & 0 & 1 & 0 & 0 & 1 \end{bmatrix}$ $\xrightarrow{R_3 + 3R_1 \to R_3}$ $\begin{bmatrix} 1 & 4 & 0 & 1 & 0 & 0 \\ 0 & 2 & 0 & 0 & 1 & 0 \\ 0 & 12 & 1 & 3 & 0 & 1 \end{bmatrix}$ $\xrightarrow[R_3 - 6R_2 \to R_3]{R_1 - 2R_2 \to R_1}$

$\begin{bmatrix} 1 & 0 & 0 & 1 & -2 & 0 \\ 0 & 2 & 0 & 0 & 1 & 0 \\ 0 & 0 & 1 & 3 & -6 & 1 \end{bmatrix}$ $\xrightarrow{\frac{1}{2}R_2}$ $\begin{bmatrix} 1 & 0 & 0 & 1 & -2 & 0 \\ 0 & 1 & 0 & 0 & \frac{1}{2} & 0 \\ 0 & 0 & 1 & 3 & -6 & 1 \end{bmatrix}$. Therefore, $B^{-1} = \begin{bmatrix} 1 & -2 & 0 \\ 0 & \frac{1}{2} & 0 \\ 3 & -6 & 1 \end{bmatrix}$.

15. $\begin{cases} 2x \quad\;\; - z = 14 \\ 3x - y + 5z = 0 \\ 4x + 2y + 3z = -2 \end{cases}$ Then $|D| = \begin{vmatrix} 2 & 0 & -1 \\ 3 & -1 & 5 \\ 4 & 2 & 3 \end{vmatrix} = 2 \begin{vmatrix} -1 & 5 \\ 2 & 3 \end{vmatrix} - 1 \begin{vmatrix} 3 & -1 \\ 4 & 2 \end{vmatrix} = -26 - 10 = -36$,

$|D_x| = \begin{vmatrix} 14 & 0 & -1 \\ 0 & -1 & 5 \\ -2 & 2 & 3 \end{vmatrix} = 14 \begin{vmatrix} -1 & 5 \\ 2 & 3 \end{vmatrix} - 1 \begin{vmatrix} 0 & -1 \\ 4 & 2 \end{vmatrix} = -182 + 2 = -180$,

$|D_y| = \begin{vmatrix} 2 & 14 & -1 \\ 3 & 0 & 5 \\ 4 & -2 & 3 \end{vmatrix} = -3 \begin{vmatrix} 14 & -1 \\ -2 & 3 \end{vmatrix} - 5 \begin{vmatrix} 2 & 14 \\ 4 & -2 \end{vmatrix} = -120 + 300 = 180$, and

$|D_z| = \begin{vmatrix} 2 & 0 & 14 \\ 3 & -1 & 0 \\ 4 & 2 & -2 \end{vmatrix} = 2 \begin{vmatrix} -1 & 0 \\ 2 & -2 \end{vmatrix} + 14 \begin{vmatrix} 3 & -1 \\ 2 & 2 \end{vmatrix} = 4 + 140 = 144$.

Therefore, $x = \frac{-180}{-36} = 5$, $y = \frac{180}{-36} = -5$, $z = \frac{144}{-36} = -4$, and so the solution is $(5, -5, -4)$.

16. $\dfrac{4x-1}{(x-1)^2(x+2)} = \dfrac{A}{x-1} + \dfrac{B}{(x-1)^2} + \dfrac{C}{x+2}$. Thus,

$$4x - 1 = A(x-1)(x+2) + B(x+2) + C(x-1)^2 = A(x^2+x-2) + B(x+2) + C(x^2-2x+1)$$

$$= (A+C)x^2 + (A+B-2C)x + (-2A+2B+C)$$

which leads to the system of equations

$$\begin{cases} A \quad\quad + C = \;\;0 \\ A + B - 2C = \;\;4 \\ -2A + 2B + \;\;C = -1 \end{cases} \Leftrightarrow \begin{cases} A \quad\quad + C = \;\;0 \\ B - 3C = \;\;4 \\ 2B + 3C = -1 \end{cases} \Leftrightarrow \begin{cases} A \quad\quad + C = \;\;0 \\ B - 3C = \;\;4 \\ 9C = -9 \end{cases}$$

Therefore, $9C = -9 \;\Leftrightarrow\; C = -1$, $B - 3(-1) = 4 \;\Leftrightarrow\; B = 1$, and $A + (-1) = 0 \;\Leftrightarrow\; A = 1$. Therefore,

$$\dfrac{4x-1}{(x-1)^2(x+2)} = \dfrac{1}{x-1} + \dfrac{1}{(x-1)^2} - \dfrac{1}{x+2}.$$

17. $\dfrac{2x-3}{x^3+3x} = \dfrac{2x-3}{x(x^2+3)} = \dfrac{A}{x} + \dfrac{Bx+C}{x^2+3}$. Then

$$2x - 3 = A(x^2+3) + (Bx+C)x = Ax^2 + 3A + Bx^2 + Cx = (A+B)x^2 + Cx + 3A.$$

So $3A = -3 \;\Leftrightarrow\; A = -1$, $C = 2$ and $A + B = 0$ gives us $B = 1$. Thus $\dfrac{2x-3}{x^3+x} = -\dfrac{1}{x} + \dfrac{x+2}{x^2+3}$.

18. $\begin{cases} 2x + y \le \;\;8 \\ x - y \ge -2 \\ x + 2y \ge \;\;4 \end{cases}$ From the graph, the points $(4,0)$ and $(0,2)$ are vertices. The

third vertex occurs where the lines $2x + y = 8$ and $x - y = -2$ intersect. Adding these two equations gives $3x = 6 \;\Leftrightarrow\; x = 2$, and so $y = 8 - 2(2) = 4$. Thus, the third vertex is $(2,4)$.

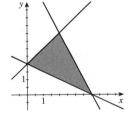

19. $\begin{cases} x^2 - 5 + y \le 0 \\ y \le 5 + 2x \end{cases}$ Substituting $y = 5 + 2x$ into the first equation gives

$x^2 - 5 + (5+2x) = 0 \;\Leftrightarrow\; x^2 + 2x = 0 \Leftrightarrow x(x+2) = 0 \;\Leftrightarrow\; x = 0$ or $x = -2$. If $x = 0$, then $y = 5 + 2(0) = 5$, and if $x = -2$, then $y = 5 + 2(-2) = 1$. Thus, the vertices are $(0,5)$ and $(-2,1)$.

Focus on Modeling: Linear Programming

1.

Vertex	$M = 200 - x - y$
$(0, 2)$	$200 - (0) - (2) = 198$
$(0, 5)$	$200 - (0) - (5) = 195$
$(4, 0)$	$200 - (4) - (0) = 196$

Thus, the maximum value is 198 and the minimum value is 195.

2.

Vertex	$N = \frac{1}{2}x + \frac{1}{4}y + 40$
$(1, 0)$	$\frac{1}{2}(1) + \frac{1}{4}(0) + 40 = 40.5$
$\left(\frac{1}{2}, \frac{1}{2}\right)$	$\frac{1}{2}\left(\frac{1}{2}\right) + \frac{1}{4}\left(\frac{1}{2}\right) + 40 = 40.375$
$(2, 2)$	$\frac{1}{2}(2) + \frac{1}{4}(2) + 40 = 41.5$
$(4, 0)$	$\frac{1}{2}(4) + \frac{1}{4}(0) + 40 = 42$

Thus, the maximum value is 42 and the minimum value is 40.375.

3. $\begin{cases} x \geq 0,\, y \geq 0 \\ 2x + y \leq 10 \\ 2x + 4y \leq 28 \end{cases}$ The objective function is $P = 140 - x + 3y$. From the graph, the vertices are $(0, 0)$, $(5, 0)$, $(2, 6)$, and $(0, 7)$.

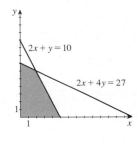

Vertex	$P = 140 - x + 3y$
$(0, 0)$	$140 - (0) + 3(0) = 140$
$(5, 0)$	$140 - (5) + 3(0) = 135$
$(2, 6)$	$140 - (2) + 3(6) = 156$
$(0, 7)$	$140 - (0) + 3(7) = 161$

Thus the maximum value is 161, and the minimum value is 135.

4. $\begin{cases} x \geq 0,\, y \geq 0 \\ x \leq 10,\, y \leq 20 \\ x + y \geq 5 \\ x + 2y \leq 18 \end{cases}$ The objective function is $Q = 70x + 82y$. From the graph, the vertices are at $(0, 9)$, $(0, 5)$, $(5, 0)$, $(10, 0)$, and $(10, 4)$. Note that the restriction $y \leq 20$ is irrelevant, superseded by $x + 2y \leq 18$ and $x \geq 0$.

Vertex	$Q = 70x + 82y$
$(0, 9)$	$70(0) + 82(9) = 738$
$(0, 5)$	$70(0) + 82(5) = 410$
$(5, 0)$	$70(5) + 82(0) = 350$
$(10, 0)$	$70(10) + 82(0) = 700$
$(10, 4)$	$70(10) + 82(4) = 1028$

Thus, the maximum value of Q is 1028 and the minimum value is 350.

5. Let t be the number of tables made daily and c be the number of chairs made daily. Then the data given can be summarized by the following table:

	Tables t	Chairs c	Available time
Carpentry	2 h	3 h	108 h
Finishing	1 h	$\frac{1}{2}$ h	20 h
Profit	$35	$20	

Thus we wish to maximize the total profit $P = 35t + 20c$ subject to the constraints $\begin{cases} 2t + 3c \le 108 \\ t + \frac{1}{2}c \le 20 \\ t \ge 0, c \ge 0 \end{cases}$

From the graph, the vertices occur at $(0, 0)$, $(20, 0)$, $(0, 36)$, and $(3, 34)$.

Vertex	$P = 35t + 20c$
$(0, 0)$	$35\,(0) + 20\,(0) = 0$
$(20, 0)$	$35\,(20) + 20\,(0) = 700$
$(0, 36)$	$35\,(0) + 20\,(36) = 720$
$(3, 34)$	$35\,(3) + 20\,(34) = 785$

Hence, 3 tables and 34 chairs should be produced daily for a maximum profit of $785.

6. Let c be the number of colonial homes built and r the number of ranch homes built. Since there are 100 lots available, $c + r \le 100$. From the capital restriction, we get $30{,}000c + 40{,}000r \le 3{,}600{,}000$, or $3c + 4r \le 360$. Thus, we wish to

maximize the profit $P = 4000c + 8000r$ subject to the constraints $\begin{cases} c \ge 0, r \ge 0 \\ c + r \le 100 \\ 3c + 4r \le 360 \end{cases}$

From the graph, the vertices occur at $(0, 0)$, $(100, 0)$, $(40, 60)$, and $(0, 90)$.

Vertex	$P = 4000c + 8000r$
$(0, 0)$	$4000\,(0) + 8000\,(0) = \phantom{000{,}00}0$
$(100, 0)$	$4000\,(100) + 8000\,(0) = 400{,}000$
$(40, 60)$	$4000\,(40) + 8000\,(60) = 640{,}000$
$(0, 90)$	$4000\,(0) + 8000\,(90) = 720{,}000$

Therefore, he should build no colonial style and 90 ranch style houses for a maximum profit of $720,000. Note that ten of the lots will be left vacant.

7. Let x be the number of crates of oranges and y the number of crates of grapefruit. Then the data given can be summarized by the following table:

	Oranges	Grapefruit	Available
Volume	4 ft^3	6 ft^3	300 ft^3
Weight	80 lb	100 lb	5600 lb
Profit	$2.50	$4.00	

In addition, $x \geq y$. Thus we wish to maximize the total profit $P = 2.5x + 4y$ subject to the constraints

$$\begin{cases} x \geq 0, \ y \geq 0, \ x \geq y \\ 4x + 6y \leq 300 \\ 80x + 100y \leq 5600 \end{cases}$$

From the graph, the vertices occur at $(0,0)$, $(30,30)$, $(45,20)$, and $(70,0)$.

Vertex	$P = 2.5x + 4y$
$(0,0)$	$2.5(0) + 4(0) = \ \ \ 0$
$(30,30)$	$2.5(30) + 4(30) = 195$
$(45,20)$	$2.5(45) + 4(20) = 192.5$
$(70,0)$	$2.5(70) + 4(0) = 175$

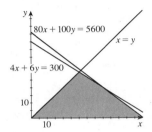

Thus, she should carry 30 crates of oranges and 30 crates of grapefruit for a maximum profit of $195.

8. Let x be the daily production of standard calculators and y the daily production of scientific calculators. Then the inequalities $\begin{cases} x \geq 100, \ y \geq 80 \\ x \leq 200, \ y \leq 170 \\ x + y \geq 200 \end{cases}$ describe the constraints. From the graph, the vertices occur at $(100, 100)$, $(100, 170)$, $(200, 170)$, $(200, 80)$, and $(120, 80)$.

(a) Minimize the objective function $C = 5x + 7y$:

Vertex	$C = 5x + 7y$
$(100, 100)$	$5(100) + 7(100) = 1200$
$(100, 170)$	$5(100) + 7(170) = 1690$
$(200, 170)$	$5(200) + 7(170) = 2190$
$(200, 80)$	$5(200) + 7(80) = 1560$
$(120, 80)$	$5(120) + 7(80) = 1160$

So to minimize cost, they should produce 120 standard and 80 scientific calculators.

(b) Maximize the objective function $P = -2x + 5y$:

Vertex	$P = -2x + 5y$
$(100, 100)$	$-2(100) + 5(100) = 300$
$(100, 170)$	$-2(100) + 5(170) = 650$
$(200, 170)$	$-2(200) + 5(170) = 450$
$(200, 80)$	$-2(200) + 5(80) = \ \ \ 0$
$(120, 80)$	$-2(120) + 5(80) = 160$

So to maximize profit, they should produce 100 standard and 170 scientific calculators.

9. Let x be the number of stereo sets shipped from Long Beach to Santa Monica and y the number of stereo sets shipped from Long Beach to El Toro. Thus, $15 - x$ sets must be shipped to Santa Monica from Pasadena and $19 - y$ sets to El Toro from Pasadena. Thus, $x \geq 0$, $y \geq 0$, $15 - x \geq 0$, $19 - y \geq 0$, $x + y \leq 24$, and $(15 - x) + (19 - y) \leq 18$. Simplifying, we get

the constraints $\begin{cases} x \geq 0, y \geq 0 \\ x \leq 15, y \leq 19 \\ x + y \leq 24 \\ x + y \geq 16 \end{cases}$

The objective function is the cost $C = 5x + 6y + 4(15 - x) + 5.5(19 - y) = x + 0.5y + 164.5$, which we wish to minimize. From the graph, the vertices occur at $(0, 16)$, $(0, 19)$, $(5, 19)$, $(15, 9)$, and $(15, 1)$.

Vertex	$C = x + 0.5y + 164.5$
$(0, 16)$	$(0) + 0.5(16) + 164.5 = 172.5$
$(0, 19)$	$(0) + 0.5(19) + 164.5 = 174$
$(5, 19)$	$(5) + 0.5(19) + 164.5 = 179$
$(15, 9)$	$(15) + 0.5(9) + 164.5 = 184$
$(15, 1)$	$(15) + 0.5(1) + 164.5 = 180$

The minimum cost is \$172.50 and occurs when $x = 0$ and $y = 16$. Hence, no stereo should be shipped from Long Beach to Santa Monica, 16 from Long Beach to El Toro, 15 from Pasadena to Santa Monica, and 3 from Pasadena to El Toro.

10. Let x be the number of sheets shipped from the east side store to customer A and y be the number of sheets shipped from the east side store to customer B. Then $50 - x$ sheets must be shipped to customer A from the west side store and $70 - y$ sheets must be shipped to customer B from the west side store. Thus, we obtain the constraints

$\begin{cases} x \geq 0, y \geq 0 \\ x \leq 50, y \leq 70 \\ x + y \leq 80 \\ 50 - x + 70 - y \leq 45 \end{cases}$ $\Leftrightarrow$ $\begin{cases} x \geq 0, y \geq 0 \\ x \leq 50, y \leq 70 \\ x + y \leq 80 \\ x + y \geq 75 \end{cases}$

The objective function is the cost $C = 0.5x + 0.6y + 0.4(50 - x) + 0.55(70 - y) = 0.1x + 0.05y + 58.5$, which we wish to minimize. From the graph, the vertices occur at $(5, 70)$, $(10, 70)$, $(50, 30)$, and $(50, 25)$.

Vertex	$C = 0.1x + 0.05y + 58.5$
$(5, 70)$	$0.1(5) + 0.05(70) + 58.5 = 62.5$
$(10, 70)$	$0.1(10) + 0.05(70) + 58.5 = 63$
$(50, 30)$	$0.1(50) + 0.05(30) + 58.5 = 65$
$(50, 25)$	$0.1(50) + 0.05(25) + 58.5 = 64.75$

Therefore, the minimum cost is \$62.50 and occurs when $x = 5$ and $y = 70$. So 5 sheets should be shipped from the east side store to customer A, 70 sheets from the east side store to customer B, 45 sheets from the west side store to customer A, and no sheet from the west side store to customer B.

11. Let x be the number of bags of standard mixtures and y be the number of bags of deluxe mixtures. Then the data can be summarized by the following table:

	Standard	Deluxe	Available
Cashews	100 g	150 g	15 kg
Peanuts	200 g	50 g	20 kg
Selling price	$1.95	$2.20	

Thus the total revenue, which we want to maximize, is given by $R = 1.95x + 2.25y$. We have the constraints

$$\begin{cases} x \geq 0, y \geq 0, x \geq y \\ 0.1x + 0.15y \leq 15 \\ 0.2x + 0.05y \leq 20 \end{cases} \Leftrightarrow \begin{cases} x \geq 0, y \geq 0, x \geq y \\ 10x + 15y \leq 1500 \\ 20x + 5y \leq 2000 \end{cases}$$

From the graph, the vertices occur at $(0, 0)$, $(60, 60)$, $(90, 40)$, and $(100, 0)$.

Vertex	$R = 1.95x + 2.25y$
$(0, 0)$	$1.96(0) + 2.25(0) = 0$
$(60, 60)$	$1.95(60) + 2.25(60) = 252$
$(90, 40)$	$1.95(90) + 2.25(40) = 265.5$
$(100, 0)$	$1.95(100) + 2.25(0) = 195$

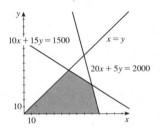

Hence, he should pack 90 bags of standard and 40 bags of deluxe mixture for a maximum revenue of $265.50.

12. Let x be the quantity of type I food and y the quantity of type II food, in ounces. Then the data can be summarized by the following table:

	Type I	Type II	Required
Fat	8 g	12 g	24 g
Carbohydrate	12 g	12 g	36 g
Protein	2 g	1 g	4 g
Cost	$0.20	$0.30	

Also, the total amount of food must be no more than 5 oz. Thus, the constraints are $\begin{cases} x \geq 0, y \geq 0, \\ x + y \leq 5, 8x + 12y \geq 24 \\ 12x + 12y \geq 36, 2x + y \geq 4 \end{cases}$

The objective function is the cost $C = 0.2x + 0.3y$, which we wish to minimize. From the graph, the vertices occur at $(1, 2)$, $(0, 4)$, $(0, 5)$, $(5, 0)$, and $(3, 0)$.

Vertex	$C = 0.2x + 0.3y$
$(1, 2)$	$0.2(1) + 0.3(2) = 0.8$
$(0, 4)$	$0.2(0) + 0.3(4) = 1.2$
$(0, 5)$	$0.2(0) + 0.3(5) = 1.5$
$(5, 0)$	$0.2(5) + 0.3(0) = 1.0$
$(3, 0)$	$0.2(3) + 0.3(0) = 0.6$

Hence, the rabbits should be fed 3 oz of type I food and no type II food, for a minimum cost of $0.60.

13. Let x be the amount in municipal bonds and y the amount in bank certificates, both in dollars. Then $12000 - x - y$ is the amount in high-risk bonds. So our constraints can be stated as

$$\begin{cases} x \geq 0, y \geq 0, x \geq 3y \\ 12,000 - x - y \geq 0 \\ 12,000 - x - y \leq 2000 \end{cases} \Leftrightarrow \begin{cases} x \geq 0, y \geq 0, x \geq 3y \\ x + y \leq 12,000 \\ x + y \geq 10,000 \end{cases}$$

From the graph, the vertices occur at $(7500, 2500)$, $(10000, 0)$, $(12000, 0)$, and $(9000, 3000)$. The objective function is

$P = 0.07x + 0.08y + 0.12\,(12000 - x - y) = 1440 - 0.05x - 0.04y$, which we wish to maximize.

Vertex	$P = 1440 - 0.05x - 0.04y$
$(7500, 2500)$	$1440 - 0.05\,(7500) - 0.04\,(2500) = 965$
$(10000, 0)$	$1440 - 0.05\,(10,000) - 0.04\,(0) = 940$
$(12000, 0)$	$1440 - 0.05\,(12,000) - 0.04\,(0) = 840$
$(9000, 3000)$	$1440 - 0.05\,(9000) - 0.04\,(3000) = 870$

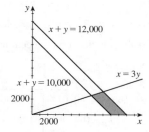

Hence, she should invest $7500 in municipal bonds, $2500 in bank certificates, and the remaining $2000 in high-risk bonds for a maximum yield of $965.

14. The only change that needs to be made to the constraints in Exercise 13 is that the 2000 in the last inequality becomes 3000. Then we have

$$\begin{cases} x \geq 0, y \geq 0, x \geq 3y \\ 12,000 - x - y \geq 0 \\ 12,000 - x - y \leq 3000 \end{cases} \Leftrightarrow \begin{cases} x \geq 0, y \geq 0, x \geq 3y \\ x + y \leq 12,000 \\ x + y \geq 9000 \end{cases}$$

From the graph, the vertices occur at $(6750, 2250)$, $(9000, 0)$, $(12000, 0)$, and $(9000, 3000)$. The objective function is

$Y = 0.07x + 0.08y + 0.12\,(12000 - x - y) = 1440 - 0.05x - 0.04y$, which we wish to maximize.

Vertex	$Y = 1440 - 0.05x - 0.04y$
$(6750, 2250)$	$1440 - 0.05\,(6750) - 0.04\,(2250) = 1012.5$
$(9000, 0)$	$1440 - 0.05\,(9000) - 0.04\,(0) = 990$
$(12000, 0)$	$1440 - 0.05\,(12,000) - 0.04\,(0) = 840$
$(9000, 3000)$	$1440 - 0.05\,(9000) - 0.04\,(3000) = 870$

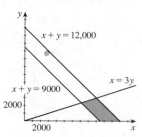

Hence, she should invest $6750 in municipal bonds, $2250 in bank certificates, and $3000 in high-risk bonds for a maximum yield of $1012.50, which is an increase of $47.50, over her yield in Exercise 13.

15. Let g be the number of games published and e be the number of educational programs published. Then the number of utility programs published is $36 - g - e$. Hence we wish to maximize profit, $P = 5000g + 8000e + 6000\,(36 - g - e) = 216{,}000 - 1000g + 2000e$, subject to the constraints

$$\begin{cases} g \geq 4,\, e \geq 0 \\ 36 - g - e \geq 0 \\ 36 - g - e \leq 2e \end{cases} \Leftrightarrow \begin{cases} g \geq 4,\, e \geq 0 \\ g + e \leq 36 \\ g + 3e \geq 36. \end{cases}$$

From the graph, the vertices are at $\left(4, \frac{32}{3}\right)$, $(4, 32)$, and $(36, 0)$. The objective function is $P = 216{,}000 - 1000g + 2000e$.

Vertex	$P = 216{,}000 - 1000g + 2000e$
$\left(4, \frac{32}{3}\right)$	$216{,}000 - 1000\,(4) + 2000\left(\frac{32}{3}\right) = 233{,}333.33$
$(4, 32)$	$216{,}000 - 1000\,(4) + 2000\,(32) = 276{,}000$
$(36, 0)$	$216{,}000 - 1000\,(36) + 2000\,(0) = 180{,}000$

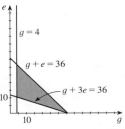

So, they should publish 4 games, 32 educational programs, and no utility program for a maximum profit of $276,000 annually.

16. $\begin{cases} x \geq 0,\, x \geq y \\ x + 2y \leq 12 \\ x + y \leq 10 \end{cases}$

(a)

(b)

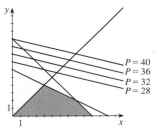

(c) These lines will first touch the feasible region at the top vertex, $(4, 4)$.

(d)

Vertex	$P = x + 4y$
$(0, 0)$	$(0) + 4\,(0) = \ \ 0$
$(10, 0)$	$(10) + 4\,(0) = 10$
$(4, 4)$	$(4) + 4\,(4) = 20$
$(8, 2)$	$(8) + 4\,(2) = 16$

The maximum value of the objective function occurs at the vertex $(4, 4)$.

10 Analytic Geometry

10.1 Parabolas

1. $y^2 = 2x$ is Graph III, which opens to the right and is not as wide as the graph for Exercise 5.

2. $y^2 = -\frac{1}{4}x$ is Graph V, the only graph that opens downward.

3. $x^2 = -6y$ is Graph II, which opens downward and is narrower than the graph for Exercise 6.

4. $2x^2 = y$ is Graph I, the only graph that opens to the right.

5. $y^2 - 8x = 0$ is Graph VI, which opens to the right and is wider than the graph for Exercise 1.

6. $12y + x^2 = 0$ is Graph IV, which opens downward and is wider than the graph for Exercise 3.

7. $y^2 = 4x$. Then $4p = 4 \iff p = 1$. The focus is $(1, 0)$, the directrix is $x = -1$, and the focal diameter is 4.

8. $x^2 = y$. Then $4p = 1 \iff p = \frac{1}{4}$. The focus is $\left(0, \frac{1}{4}\right)$, the directrix is $y = -\frac{1}{4}$, and the focal diameter is 1.

9. $x^2 = 9y$. Then $4p = 9 \iff p = \frac{9}{4}$. The focus is $\left(0, \frac{9}{4}\right)$, the directrix is $y = -\frac{9}{4}$, and the focal diameter is 9.

10. $y^2 = 3x$. Then $4p = 3 \iff p = \frac{3}{4}$. The focus is $\left(\frac{3}{4}, 0\right)$, the directrix is $x = -\frac{3}{4}$, and the focal diameter is 3.

11. $y = 5x^2 \iff x^2 = \frac{1}{5}y$. Then $4p = \frac{1}{5} \iff p = \frac{1}{20}$. The focus is $\left(0, \frac{1}{20}\right)$, the directrix is $y = -\frac{1}{20}$, and the focal diameter is $\frac{1}{5}$.

12. $y = -2x^2 \iff x^2 = -\frac{1}{2}y$. Then $4p = -\frac{1}{2} \iff p = -\frac{1}{8}$. The focus is $\left(0, -\frac{1}{8}\right)$, the directrix is $y = \frac{1}{8}$, and the focal diameter is $\frac{1}{2}$.

13. $x = -8y^2 \Leftrightarrow y^2 = -\frac{1}{8}x$. Then $4p = -\frac{1}{8} \Leftrightarrow$
$p = -\frac{1}{32}$. The focus is $\left(-\frac{1}{32}, 0\right)$, the directrix is $x = \frac{1}{32}$,
and the focal diameter is $\frac{1}{8}$.

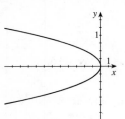

14. $x = \frac{1}{2}y^2 \Leftrightarrow y^2 = 2x$. Then $4p = 2 \Leftrightarrow p = \frac{1}{2}$.
The focus is $\left(\frac{1}{2}, 0\right)$, the directrix is $x = -\frac{1}{2}$, and the focal
diameter is 2.

15. $x^2 + 6y = 0 \Leftrightarrow x^2 = -6y$. Then $4p = -6 \Leftrightarrow$
$p = -\frac{3}{2}$. The focus is $\left(0, -\frac{3}{2}\right)$, the directrix is $y = \frac{3}{2}$, and
the focal diameter is 6.

16. $x - 7y^2 = 0 \Leftrightarrow y^2 = \frac{1}{7}x$. Then $4p = \frac{1}{7} \Leftrightarrow$
$p = \frac{1}{28}$. The focus is $\left(\frac{1}{28}, 0\right)$, the directrix is $x = -\frac{1}{28}$,
and the focal diameter is $\frac{1}{7}$.

17. $5x + 3y^2 = 0 \Leftrightarrow y^2 = -\frac{5}{3}x$. Then $4p = -\frac{5}{3} \Leftrightarrow$
$p = -\frac{5}{12}$. The focus is $\left(-\frac{5}{12}, 0\right)$, the directrix is $x = \frac{5}{12}$,
and the focal diameter is $\frac{5}{3}$.

18. $8x^2 + 12y = 0 \Leftrightarrow x^2 = -\frac{3}{2}y$. Then $4p = -\frac{3}{2} \Leftrightarrow$
$p = -\frac{3}{8}$. The focus is $\left(0, -\frac{3}{8}\right)$, the directrix is $y = \frac{3}{8}$, and
the focal diameter is $\frac{3}{2}$.

19. $x^2 = 16y$

20. $x^2 = -8y$

21. $y^2 = -\frac{1}{3}x$

22. $8y^2 = x$

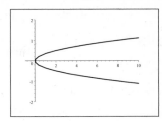

23. $4x + y^2 = 0$

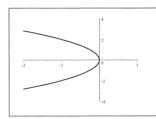

24. $x - 2y^2 = 0$

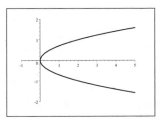

25. Since the focus is $(0, 2)$, $p = 2 \iff 4p = 8$. Hence, an equation of the parabola is $x^2 = 8y$.

26. Since the focus is $\left(0, -\frac{1}{2}\right)$, $p = -\frac{1}{2} \iff 4p = -2$. So an equation of the parabola is $x^2 = -2y$.

27. Since the focus is $(-8, 0)$, $p = -8 \iff 4p = -32$. Hence, an equation of the parabola is $y^2 = -32x$.

28. Since the focus is $(5, 0)$, $p = 5 \iff 4p = 20$. Hence, an equation of the parabola is $y^2 = 20x$.

29. Since the directrix is $x = 2$, $p = -2 \iff 4p = -8$. Hence, an equation of the parabola is $y^2 = -8x$.

30. Since the directrix is $y = 6$, $p = -6 \iff 4p = -24$. Hence, an equation of the parabola is $x^2 = -24y$.

31. Since the directrix is $y = -10$, $p = 10 \iff 4p = 40$. Hence, an equation of the parabola is $x^2 = 40y$.

32. Since the directrix is $x = -\frac{1}{8}$, $p = \frac{1}{8} \iff 4p = \frac{1}{2}$. Hence, an equation of the parabola is $y^2 = \frac{1}{2}x$.

33. The focus is on the positive x-axis, so the parabola opens horizontally with $2p = 2 \iff 4p = 4$. So an equation of the parabola is $y^2 = 4x$.

34. The directrix has y-intercept 6, and so $p = -6 \iff 4p = -24$. Therefore, an equation of the parabola is $x^2 = -24y$.

35. Since the parabola opens upward with focus 5 units from the vertex, the focus is $(5, 0)$. So $p = 5 \iff 4p = 20$. Thus an equation of the parabola is $x^2 = 20y$.

36. Since the focal diameter is 8 and the focus is on the negative y-axis, $4p = -8$. So the equation is $x^2 = -8y$.

37. $p = 2 \iff 4p = 8$. Since the parabola opens upward, its equation is $x^2 = 8y$.

38. The directrix is $x = -2$, and so $p = 2 \iff 4p = 8$. Since the parabola opens to the left, its equation is $y^2 = 8x$.

39. $p = 4 \iff 4p = 16$. Since the parabola opens to the left, its equation is $y^2 = -16x$.

40. $p = 3 \iff 4p = 12$. Since the parabola opens downward, its equation is $x^2 = -12y$.

41. The focal diameter is $4p = \frac{3}{2} + \frac{3}{2} = 3$. Since the parabola opens to the left, its equation is $y^2 = -3x$.

42. The focal diameter is $4p = 2(5) = 10$. Since the parabola opens upward, its equation is $x^2 = 10y$.

43. The equation of the parabola has the form $y^2 = 4px$. Since the parabola passes through the point $(4, -2)$, $(-2)^2 = 4p(4)$ $\iff 4p = 1$, and so an equation is $y^2 = x$.

44. Since the directrix is $x = -p$, we have $p^2 = 16$, so $p = 4$, and an equation is $y^2 = 4px$ or $y^2 = 16x$.

45. The area of the shaded region is width $\times$ height $= 4p \cdot p = 8$, and so $p^2 = 2 \iff p = -\sqrt{2}$ (because the parabola opens downward). Therefore, an equation is $x^2 = 4py = -4\sqrt{2}y \iff x^2 = -4\sqrt{2}y$.

46. The focus is $(0, p)$. Since the line has slope $\frac{1}{2}$, an equation of the line is $y = \frac{1}{2}x + p$. Therefore, the point where the line intersects the parabola has y-coordinate $\frac{1}{2}(2) + p = p + 1$. The parabola's equation is of the form $x^2 = 4py$, so $(2)^2 = 4p(p + 1) \iff p^2 + p - 1 = 0 \iff p = \dfrac{-1 + \sqrt{5}}{2}$ (since $p > 0$). Hence, an equation of the parabola is $x^2 = 2(\sqrt{5} - 1)y$.

47. (a) A parabola with directrix $y = -p$ has equation $x^2 = 4py$. If the directrix is $y = \frac{1}{2}$, then $p = -\frac{1}{2}$, so an equation is $x^2 = 4\left(-\frac{1}{2}\right)y \iff x^2 = -2y$. If the directrix is $y = 1$, then $p = -1$, so an equation is $x^2 = 4(-1)y \iff x^2 = -4y$. If the directrix is $y = 4$, then $p = -4$, so an equation is $x^2 = 4(-4)y \iff x^2 = -16y$. If the directrix is $y = 8$, then $p = -8$, so an equation is $x^2 = 4(-8)y \iff x^2 = -32y$.

(b)

As the directrix moves further from the vertex, the parabolas get flatter.

48. (a) If the focal diameter of a parabola is $4p$, it has equation $x^2 = 4py$. If the focal diameter is $4p = 1$, an equation is $x^2 = y$. If the focal diameter is $4p = 2$, an equation is $x^2 = 2y$. If the focal diameter is $4p = 4$, an equation is $x^2 = 4y$. If the focal diameter is $4p = 8$, an equation is $x^2 = 8y$.

(b)

As the focal diameter increases, the parabolas get flatter.

49. (a) Since the focal diameter is 12 cm, $4p = 12$. Hence, the parabola has equation $y^2 = 12x$.

(b) At a point 20 cm horizontally from the vertex, the parabola passes through the point $(20, y)$, and hence from part (a), $y^2 = 12(20) \iff y^2 = 240 \iff y = \pm 4\sqrt{15}$. Thus, $|CD| = 8\sqrt{15} \approx 31$ cm.

50. The equation of the parabola has the form $x^2 = 4py$. From the diagram, the parabola passes through the point $(10, 1)$, and so $(10)^2 = 4p(1) \iff 4p = 100$ and $p = 25$. Therefore, the receiver is 25 ft from the vertex.

51. With the vertex at the origin, the top of one tower will be at the point $(300, 150)$. Inserting this point into the equation $x^2 = 4py$ gives $(300)^2 = 4p(150) \iff 90000 = 600p \iff p = 150$. So an equation of the parabolic part of the cables is $x^2 = 4(150)y \iff x^2 = 600y$.

52. The equation of the parabola has the form $x^2 = 4py$. From the diagram, the parabola passes through the point $(100, 3.79)$, and so $(100)^2 = 4p(3.79) \iff 15.16p = 10000$ and $p \approx 659.63$. Therefore, the receiver is about 659.63 inches ≈ 55 feet from the vertex.

53. Many answers are possible: satellite dish TV antennas, sound surveillance equipment, solar collectors for hot water heating or electricity generation, bridge pillars, etc.

54. Yes. If a cone intersects a plane that is parallel to a line on the cone, the resulting curve is a parabola, as shown in the text.

10.2   Ellipses

1. $\dfrac{x^2}{16} + \dfrac{y^2}{4} = 1$ is Graph II. The major axis is horizontal and the vertices are $(\pm 4, 0)$.

2. $x^2 + \dfrac{y^2}{9} = 1$ is Graph IV. The major axis is vertical and the vertices are $(0, \pm 3)$.

3. $4x^2 + y^2 = 4$ is Graph I. The major axis is vertical and the vertices are $(0, \pm 2)$.

4. $16x^2 + 25y^2 = 400$ is Graph III. The major axis is horizontal and the vertices are $(\pm 5, 0)$.

5. $\dfrac{x^2}{25} + \dfrac{y^2}{9} = 1$. This ellipse has $a = 5$, $b = 3$, and so $c^2 = a^2 - b^2 = 16$ $\Leftrightarrow$
$c = 4$. The vertices are $(\pm 5, 0)$, the foci are $(\pm 4, 0)$, the eccentricity is
$e = \dfrac{c}{a} = \dfrac{4}{5} = 0.8$, the length of the major axis is $2a = 10$, and the length of the
minor axis is $2b = 6$.

6. $\dfrac{x^2}{16} + \dfrac{y^2}{25} = 1$. This ellipse has $a = 5$, $b = 4$, and so $c^2 = 25 - 16 = 9$ $\Leftrightarrow$
$c = 3$. The vertices are $(0, \pm 5)$, the foci are $(0, \pm 3)$, the eccentricity is
$e = \dfrac{c}{a} = \dfrac{3}{5} = 0.6$, the length of the major axis is $2a = 10$, and the length of the
minor axis is $2b = 8$.

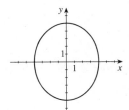

7. $9x^2 + 4y^2 = 36$ $\Leftrightarrow$ $\dfrac{x^2}{4} + \dfrac{y^2}{9} = 1$. This ellipse has $a = 3$, $b = 2$, and so
$c^2 = 9 - 4 = 5$ $\Leftrightarrow$ $c = \sqrt{5}$. The vertices are $(0, \pm 3)$, the foci are $\left(0, \pm\sqrt{5}\right)$,
the eccentricity is $e = \dfrac{c}{a} = \dfrac{\sqrt{5}}{3}$, the length of the major axis is $2a = 6$, and the
length of the minor axis is $2b = 4$.

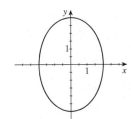

8. $4x^2 + 25y^2 = 100$ $\Leftrightarrow$ $\dfrac{x^2}{25} + \dfrac{y^2}{4} = 1$. This ellipse has $a = 5$, $b = 2$, and so
$c^2 = 25 - 4 = 21$ $\Leftrightarrow$ $c = \sqrt{21}$. The vertices are $(\pm 5, 0)$, the foci are
$\left(\pm\sqrt{21}, 0\right)$, the eccentricity is $e = \dfrac{c}{a} = \dfrac{\sqrt{21}}{5}$, the length of the major axis is
$2a = 10$, and the length of the minor axis is $2b = 4$.

9. $x^2 + 4y^2 = 16$ $\Leftrightarrow$ $\dfrac{x^2}{16} + \dfrac{y^2}{4} = 1$. This ellipse has $a = 4$, $b = 2$, and so
$c^2 = 16 - 4 = 12$ $\Leftrightarrow$ $c = 2\sqrt{3}$. The vertices are $(\pm 4, 0)$, the foci are
$\left(\pm 2\sqrt{3}, 0\right)$, the eccentricity is $e = \dfrac{c}{a} = \dfrac{2\sqrt{3}}{4} = \dfrac{\sqrt{3}}{2}$, the length of the major axis
is $2a = 8$, and the length of the minor axis is $2b = 4$.

10. $4x^2 + y^2 = 16 \Leftrightarrow \dfrac{x^2}{4} + \dfrac{y^2}{16} = 1$. This ellipse has $a = 4$, $b = 2$, and so $c^2 = 16 - 4 = 12 \Leftrightarrow c = 2\sqrt{3}$. The vertices are $(0, \pm 4)$, the foci are $\left(0, \pm 2\sqrt{3}\right)$, the eccentricity is $e = \dfrac{c}{a} = \dfrac{2\sqrt{3}}{4} = \dfrac{\sqrt{3}}{2}$, the length of the major axis is $2a = 8$, and the length of the minor axis is $2b = 4$.

11. $2x^2 + y^2 = 3 \Leftrightarrow \dfrac{x^2}{\frac{3}{2}} + \dfrac{y^2}{3} = 1$. This ellipse has $a = \sqrt{3}$, $b = \sqrt{\frac{3}{2}}$, and so $c^2 = 3 - \dfrac{3}{2} = \dfrac{3}{2} \Leftrightarrow c = \sqrt{\frac{3}{2}} = \dfrac{\sqrt{6}}{2}$. The vertices are $(0, \pm\sqrt{3})$, the foci are $\left(0, \pm\dfrac{\sqrt{6}}{2}\right)$, the eccentricity is $e = \dfrac{c}{a} = \dfrac{\frac{\sqrt{6}}{2}}{\sqrt{3}} = \dfrac{\sqrt{2}}{2}$, the length of the major axis is $2a = 2\sqrt{3}$, and the length of the minor axis is $2b = 2 \cdot \dfrac{\sqrt{6}}{2} = \sqrt{6}$.

12. $5x^2 + 6y^2 = 30 \Leftrightarrow \dfrac{x^2}{6} + \dfrac{y^2}{5} = 1$. This ellipse has $a = \sqrt{6}$, $b = \sqrt{5}$, and so $c^2 = 6 - 5 = 1 \Leftrightarrow c = 1$. The vertices are $\left(\pm\sqrt{6}, 0\right)$, the foci are $(\pm 1, 0)$, the eccentricity is $e = \dfrac{c}{a} = \dfrac{1}{\sqrt{6}} = \dfrac{\sqrt{6}}{6}$: length of the major axis: $2a = 2\sqrt{6}$, and the length of the minor axis is $2b = 2\sqrt{5}$.

13. $x^2 + 4y^2 = 1 \Leftrightarrow \dfrac{x^2}{1} + \dfrac{y^2}{\frac{1}{4}} = 1$. This ellipse has $a = 1$, $b = \frac{1}{2}$, and so $c^2 = 1 - \dfrac{1}{4} = \dfrac{3}{4} \Leftrightarrow c = \dfrac{\sqrt{3}}{2}$. The vertices are $(\pm 1, 0)$, the foci are $\left(\pm\dfrac{\sqrt{3}}{2}, 0\right)$, the eccentricity is $e = \dfrac{c}{a} = \dfrac{\sqrt{3}/2}{1} = \dfrac{\sqrt{3}}{2}$, the length of the major axis is $2a = 2$, and the length of the minor axis is $2b = 1$.

14. $9x^2 + 4y^2 = 1 \Leftrightarrow \dfrac{x^2}{1/9} + \dfrac{y^2}{1/4} = 1$. This ellipse has $a = \frac{1}{2}$, and so $c^2 = \dfrac{1}{4} - \dfrac{1}{9} = \dfrac{5}{36} \Leftrightarrow c = \dfrac{\sqrt{5}}{6}$. The vertices are $\left(0, \pm\frac{1}{2}\right)$, the foci are $\left(0, \pm\dfrac{\sqrt{5}}{6}\right)$, the eccentricity is $e = \dfrac{c}{a} = \dfrac{\sqrt{5}/6}{1/2} = \dfrac{\sqrt{5}}{3}$, the length of the major axis is $2a = 1$, and the length of the minor axis is $2b = \frac{2}{3}$.

15. $\frac{1}{2}x^2 + \frac{1}{8}y^2 = \frac{1}{4} \Leftrightarrow 2x^2 + \frac{1}{2}y^2 = 1 \Leftrightarrow \dfrac{x^2}{\frac{1}{2}} + \dfrac{y^2}{2} = 1$. This ellipse has $a = \sqrt{2}$, $b = \dfrac{1}{\sqrt{2}}$, and so $c^2 = 2 - \dfrac{1}{2} = \dfrac{3}{2} \Leftrightarrow c = \sqrt{\frac{3}{2}} = \dfrac{\sqrt{6}}{2}$. The vertices are $\left(0, \pm\sqrt{2}\right)$, the foci are $\left(0, \pm\dfrac{\sqrt{6}}{2}\right)$, the eccentricity is $e = \dfrac{c}{a} = \dfrac{\frac{\sqrt{6}}{2}}{\sqrt{2}} = \dfrac{\sqrt{3}}{2}$, the length of the major axis is $2a = 2\sqrt{2}$, and length of the minor axis is $2b = \sqrt{2}$.

16. $x^2 = 4 - 2y^2 \iff x^2 + 2y^2 = 4 \iff \dfrac{x^2}{4} + \dfrac{y^2}{2} = 1$. This ellipse has $a = 2$, $b = \sqrt{2}$, and so $c^2 = 4 - 2 = 2 \iff c = \sqrt{2}$. The vertices are $(\pm 2, 0)$, the foci are $(\pm\sqrt{2}, 0)$, the eccentricity is $e = \dfrac{c}{a} = \dfrac{\sqrt{2}}{2}$, the length of the major axis is $2a = 4$, and the length of the minor axis is $2b = 2\sqrt{2}$.

17. $y^2 = 1 - 2x^2 \iff 2x^2 + y^2 = 1 \iff \dfrac{x^2}{\frac{1}{2}} + \dfrac{y^2}{1} = 1$. This ellipse has $a = 1$, $b = \dfrac{\sqrt{2}}{2}$, and so $c^2 = 1 - \dfrac{1}{2} = \dfrac{1}{2} \iff c = \dfrac{\sqrt{2}}{2}$. The vertices are $(0, \pm 1)$, the foci are $\left(0, \pm\dfrac{\sqrt{2}}{2}\right)$, the eccentricity is $e = \dfrac{c}{a} = \dfrac{1/\sqrt{2}}{1} = \dfrac{\sqrt{2}}{2}$, the length of the major axis is $2a = 2$, and the length of the minor axis is $2b = \sqrt{2}$.

18. $20x^2 + 4y^2 = 5 \iff \dfrac{x^2}{1/4} + \dfrac{y^2}{5/4} = 1$. This ellipse has $a = \dfrac{\sqrt{5}}{2}$, $b = \dfrac{1}{2}$, and so $c^2 = \dfrac{5}{4} - \dfrac{1}{4} = 1 \iff c = 1$. The vertices are $\left(0, \pm\dfrac{\sqrt{5}}{2}\right)$, the foci are $(0, \pm 1)$, the eccentricity is $e = \dfrac{c}{a} = \dfrac{1}{\sqrt{5}/2} = \dfrac{2\sqrt{5}}{5}$, the length of the major axis is $2a = \sqrt{5}$, and the length of the minor axis is $2b = 1$.

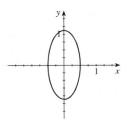

19. This ellipse has a horizontal major axis with $a = 5$ and $b = 4$, so an equation is $\dfrac{x^2}{(5)^2} + \dfrac{y^2}{(4)^2} = 1 \iff \dfrac{x^2}{25} + \dfrac{y^2}{16} = 1$.

20. This ellipse has a vertical major axis with $a = 5$ and $b = 2$. Thus an equation is $\dfrac{x^2}{2^2} + \dfrac{y^2}{5^2} = 1 \iff \dfrac{x^2}{4} + \dfrac{y^2}{25} = 1$.

21. This ellipse has a vertical major axis with $c = 2$ and $b = 2$. So $a^2 = c^2 + b^2 = 2^2 + 2^2 = 8 \iff a = 2\sqrt{2}$. So an equation is $\dfrac{x^2}{(2)^2} + \dfrac{y^2}{\left(2\sqrt{2}\right)^2} = 1 \iff \dfrac{x^2}{4} + \dfrac{y^2}{8} = 1$.

22. This ellipse has a vertical major axis with $a = 4$ and $c = 3$. So $c^2 = a^2 - b^2 \iff 9 = 16 - b^2 \iff b^2 = 7$. Thus an equation is $\dfrac{x^2}{7} + \dfrac{y^2}{4^2} = 1 \iff \dfrac{x^2}{7} + \dfrac{y^2}{16} = 1$.

23. This ellipse has a horizontal major axis with $a = 16$, so an equation of the ellipse is of the form $\dfrac{x^2}{16^2} + \dfrac{y^2}{b^2} = 1$. Substituting the point $(8, 6)$ into the equation, we get $\dfrac{64}{256} + \dfrac{36}{b^2} = 1 \iff \dfrac{36}{b^2} = 1 - \dfrac{1}{4} \iff \dfrac{36}{b^2} = \dfrac{3}{4} \iff b^2 = \dfrac{4\,(36)}{3} = 48$. Thus, an equation of the ellipse is $\dfrac{x^2}{256} + \dfrac{y^2}{48} = 1$.

24. This ellipse has a vertical major axis with $b = 2$, so an equation of the ellipse is of the form $\dfrac{x^2}{2^2} + \dfrac{y^2}{a^2} = 1$. Substituting the point $(-1, 2)$ into the equation, we get $\dfrac{1}{4} + \dfrac{4}{a^2} = 1 \iff \dfrac{4}{a^2} = 1 - \dfrac{1}{4} \iff \dfrac{4}{a^2} = \dfrac{3}{4} \iff a^2 = \dfrac{4\,(4)}{3} = \dfrac{16}{3}$. Thus, an equation of the ellipse is $\dfrac{x^2}{4} + \dfrac{y^2}{16/3} = 1 \iff \dfrac{x^2}{4} + \dfrac{3y^2}{16} = 1$.

25. $\dfrac{x^2}{25} + \dfrac{y^2}{20} = 1 \iff \dfrac{y^2}{20} = 1 - \dfrac{x^2}{25} \iff$

$y^2 = 20 - \dfrac{4x^2}{5} \implies y = \pm\sqrt{20 - \dfrac{4x^2}{5}}.$

26. $x^2 + \dfrac{y^2}{12} = 1 \iff \dfrac{y^2}{12} = 1 - x^2 \iff y^2 = 12 - 12x^2$

$\implies y = \pm\sqrt{12 - 12x^2}.$

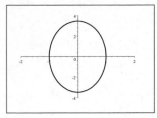

27. $6x^2 + y^2 = 36 \iff y^2 = 36 - 6x^2 \implies$
$y = \pm\sqrt{36 - 6x^2}.$

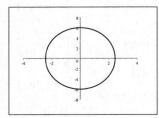

28. $x^2 + 2y^2 = 8 \iff 2y^2 = 8 - x^2 \iff y^2 = 4 - \dfrac{x^2}{2}$

$\implies y = \pm\sqrt{4 - \dfrac{x^2}{2}}.$

29. The foci are $(\pm 4, 0)$, and the vertices are $(\pm 5, 0)$. Thus, $c = 4$ and $a = 5$, and so $b^2 = 25 - 16 = 9$. Therefore, an equation of the ellipse is $\dfrac{x^2}{25} + \dfrac{y^2}{9} = 1$.

30. The foci are $(0, \pm 3)$ and the vertices are $(0, \pm 5)$. Thus, $c = 3$ and $a = 5$, and so $c^2 = a^2 - b^2 \iff 9 = 25 - b^2 \iff$ $b^2 = 25 - 9 = 16$. Therefore, an equation of the ellipse is $\dfrac{x^2}{16} + \dfrac{y^2}{25} = 1$.

31. The length of the major axis is $2a = 4 \iff a = 2$, the length of the minor axis is $2b = 2 \iff b = 1$, and the foci are on the y-axis. Therefore, an equation of the ellipse is $x^2 + \dfrac{y^2}{4} = 1$.

32. The length of the major axis is $2a = 6 \iff a = 3$, the length of the minor axis is $2b = 4 \iff b = 2$, and the foci are on the x-axis. Therefore, an equation of the ellipse is $\dfrac{x^2}{9} + \dfrac{y^2}{4} = 1$.

33. The foci are $(0, \pm 2)$, and the length of the minor axis is $2b = 6 \iff b = 3$. Thus, $a^2 = 4 + 9 = 13$. Since the foci are on the y-axis, an equation is $\dfrac{x^2}{9} + \dfrac{y^2}{13} = 1$.

34. The foci are $(\pm 5, 0)$, and the length of the major axis is $2a = 12 \iff a = 6$. Thus, $c^2 = a^2 - b^2 \iff 25 = 36 - b^2$ $\iff b^2 = 36 - 25 = 11$. Since the foci are on the x-axis, an equation is $\dfrac{x^2}{36} + \dfrac{y^2}{11} = 1$.

35. The endpoints of the major axis are $(\pm 10, 0) \iff a = 10$, and the distance between the foci is $2c = 6 \iff c = 3$. Therefore, $b^2 = 100 - 9 = 91$, and so an equation of the ellipse is $\dfrac{x^2}{100} + \dfrac{y^2}{91} = 1$.

36. Since the endpoints of the minor axis are $(0, \pm 3)$, we have $b = 3$. The distance between the foci is $2c = 8$, so $c = 4$. Thus, $a^2 = b^2 + c^2 = 9 + 16 = 25$, and an equation of the ellipse is $\dfrac{x^2}{25} + \dfrac{y^2}{9} = 1$.

37. The length of the major axis is 10, so $2a = 10$ $\Leftrightarrow$ $a = 5$, and the foci are on the x-axis, so the form of the equation

is $\dfrac{x^2}{25} + \dfrac{y^2}{b^2} = 1$. Since the ellipse passes through $\left(\sqrt{5}, 2\right)$, we know that $\dfrac{\left(\sqrt{5}\right)^2}{25} + \dfrac{(2)^2}{b^2} = 1$ $\Leftrightarrow$ $\dfrac{5}{25} + \dfrac{4}{b^2} = 1$ $\Leftrightarrow$

$\dfrac{4}{b^2} = \dfrac{4}{5}$ $\Leftrightarrow$ $b^2 = 5$, and so an equation is $\dfrac{x^2}{25} + \dfrac{y^2}{5} = 1$.

38. Since the foci are $(0, \pm 2)$, we have $c = 2$. The eccentricity is $\dfrac{1}{9} = \dfrac{c}{a}$ $\Leftrightarrow$ $a = 9c = 9\,(2) = 18$, and so

$b^2 = a^2 - c^2 = 18^2 - 2^2 = 320$. Since the foci lie on the y-axis, an equation of the ellipse is $\dfrac{x^2}{320} + \dfrac{y^2}{324} = 1$.

39. Since the foci are $(\pm 1.5, 0)$, we have $c = \dfrac{3}{2}$. Since the eccentricity is $0.8 = \dfrac{c}{a}$, we have $a = \dfrac{\frac{3}{2}}{\frac{4}{5}} = \dfrac{15}{8}$, and

so $b^2 = \dfrac{225}{64} - \dfrac{9}{4} = \dfrac{225 - 16 \cdot 9}{64} = \dfrac{81}{64}$. Therefore, an equation of the ellipse is $\dfrac{x^2}{(15/8)^2} + \dfrac{y^2}{81/64} = 1$ $\Leftrightarrow$

$\dfrac{64x^2}{225} + \dfrac{64y^2}{81} = 1$.

40. Since the length of the major axis is $2a = 4$, we have $a = 2$. The eccentricity is $\dfrac{\sqrt{3}}{2} = \dfrac{c}{a} = \dfrac{c}{2}$, so $c = \sqrt{3}$. Then

$b^2 = a^2 - c^2 = 4 - 3 = 1$, and since the foci are on the y-axis, an equation of the ellipse is $x^2 + \dfrac{y^2}{4} = 1$.

41. $\begin{cases} 4x^2 + y^2 = 4 \\ 4x^2 + 9y^2 = 36 \end{cases}$ Subtracting the first equation from the second gives

$8y^2 = 32$ $\Leftrightarrow$ $y^2 = 4$ $\Leftrightarrow$ $y = \pm 2$. Substituting $y = \pm 2$ in the first equation

gives $4x^2 + (\pm 2)^2 = 4$ $\Leftrightarrow$ $x = 0$, and so the points of intersection are $(0, \pm 2)$.

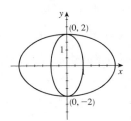

42. $\begin{cases} \dfrac{x^2}{16} + \dfrac{y^2}{9} = 1 \\ \dfrac{x^2}{9} + \dfrac{y^2}{16} = 1 \end{cases}$ $\Leftrightarrow$ $\begin{cases} 9x^2 + 16y^2 = 144 \\ 16x^2 + 9y^2 = 144 \end{cases}$ $\Leftrightarrow$ $\begin{cases} 144x^2 + 256y^2 = 2304 \\ -144x^2 - 81y^2 = -1296 \end{cases}$

Adding gives $175y^2 = 1008$ $\Rightarrow$ $y = \pm\dfrac{12}{5}$. Substituting for y gives

$9x^2 + 16\left(\dfrac{12}{5}\right)^2 = 144$ $\Leftrightarrow$ $9x^2 = 144 - \dfrac{2304}{25} = \dfrac{1296}{25}$ $\Leftrightarrow$ $x = \pm\dfrac{12}{5}$, and

so the four points of intersection are $\left(\pm\dfrac{12}{5}, \pm\dfrac{12}{5}\right)$.

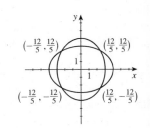

43. $\begin{cases} 100x^2 + 25y^2 = 100 \\ x^2 + \dfrac{y^2}{9} = 1 \end{cases}$ Dividing the first equation by 100 gives $x^2 + \dfrac{y^2}{4} = 1$.

Subtracting this equation from the second equation gives $\dfrac{y^2}{9} - \dfrac{y^2}{4} = 0$ $\Leftrightarrow$

$\left(\dfrac{1}{9} - \dfrac{1}{4}\right) y^2 = 0$ $\Leftrightarrow$ $y = 0$. Substituting $y = 0$ in the second equation gives

$x^2 + (0)^2 = 1$ $\Leftrightarrow$ $x = \pm 1$, and so the points of intersection are $(\pm 1, 0)$.

44. (a) The ellipse $x^2 + 4y^2 = 16$ $\Leftrightarrow$ $\dfrac{x^2}{16} + \dfrac{y^2}{4} = 1$ has $a = 4$ and $b = 2$. Thus, an equation of the ancillary circle is

$x^2 + y^2 = 4$.

(b) If (s, t) is a point on the ancillary circle, then $s^2 + t^2 = 4$ $\Leftrightarrow$ $4s^2 + 4t^2 = 16$ $\Leftrightarrow$ $(2s)^2 + 4\,(t)^2 = 16$, which

implies that $(2s, t)$ is a point on the ellipse.

45. (a) $x^2 + ky^2 = 100 \iff ky^2 = 100 - x^2 \iff y = \pm\dfrac{1}{k}\sqrt{100 - x^2}$.

For the top half, we graph $y = \dfrac{1}{k}\sqrt{100 - x^2}$ for $k = 4$, 10, 25, and 50.

(b) This family of ellipses have common major axes and vertices, and the eccentricity increases as k increases.

46. $\dfrac{x^2}{k} + \dfrac{y^2}{4+k} = 1$ is an ellipse for $k > 0$. Then $a^2 = 4 + k$, $b^2 = k$, and so $c^2 = 4 + k - k = 4 \iff c = \pm 2$. Therefore, all of the ellipses' foci are $(0, \pm 2)$ regardless of the value of k.

47. Using the perihelion, $a - c = 147{,}000{,}000$, while using the aphelion, $a + c = 153{,}000{,}000$. Adding, we have $2a = 300{,}000{,}000 \iff a = 150{,}000{,}000$. So $b^2 = a^2 - c^2 = \left(150 \times 10^6\right)^2 - \left(3 \times 10^6\right)^2 = 22{,}491 \times 10^{12} = 2.2491 \times 10^{16}$. Thus, an equation of the orbit is $\dfrac{x^2}{2.2500 \times 10^{16}} + \dfrac{y^2}{2.2491 \times 10^{16}} = 1$.

48. Using the eccentricity, $e = 0.25 = \dfrac{c}{a} \iff c = 0.25a$. Using the length of the minor axis, $2b = 10{,}000{,}000{,}000 \iff b = 5 \times 10^9$. Since $a^2 = c^2 + b^2$, $a^2 = (0.25a)^2 + 25 \times 10^{18} \iff \frac{15}{16}a^2 = 25 \times 10^{18} \iff a^2 = \frac{80}{3} \times 10^{18} \iff a = \sqrt{\frac{80}{3}} \times 10^9 = 4\sqrt{\frac{5}{3}} \times 10^9$. Then $c = 0.25\left(4\sqrt{\frac{5}{3}} \times 10^9\right) = \sqrt{\frac{5}{3}} \times 10^9$. Since the Sun is at one focus of the ellipse, the distance from Pluto to the Sun at perihelion is $a - c = 4\sqrt{\frac{5}{3}} \times 10^9 - \sqrt{\frac{5}{3}} \times 10^9 = 3\sqrt{\frac{5}{3}} \times 10^9 \approx 3.87 \times 10^9$ km; the distance from Pluto to the Sun at aphelion is $a + c = 4\sqrt{\frac{5}{3}} \times 10^9 + \sqrt{\frac{5}{3}} \times 10^9 = 5\sqrt{\frac{5}{3}} \times 10^9 \approx 6.45 \times 10^9$ km.

49. Using the perilune, $a - c = 1075 + 68 = 1143$, and using the apolune, $a + c = 1075 + 195 = 1270$. Adding, we get $2a = 2413 \iff a = 1206.5$. So $c = 1270 - 1206.5 \iff c = 63.5$. Therefore, $b^2 = (1206.5)^2 - (63.5)^2 = 1{,}451{,}610$. Since $a^2 \approx 1{,}455{,}642$, an equation of Apollo 11's orbit is $\dfrac{x^2}{1{,}455{,}642} + \dfrac{y^2}{1{,}451{,}610} = 1$.

50. Placing the origin at the center of the sheet of plywood and letting the x-axis be the long central axis, we have $2a = 8$, so that $a = 4$, and $2b = 4$, so that $b = 2$. So $c^2 = a^2 - b^2 = 4^2 - 2^2 = 12 \Rightarrow c = 2\sqrt{3} \approx 3.46$. So the tacks should be located $2(3.46) = 6.92$ feet apart and the string should be $2a = 8$ feet long.

51. From the diagram, $a = 40$ and $b = 20$, and so an equation of the ellipse whose top half is the window is $\dfrac{x^2}{1600} + \dfrac{y^2}{400} = 1$.

Since the ellipse passes through the point $(25, h)$, by substituting, we have $\dfrac{25^2}{1600} + \dfrac{h^2}{400} = 1 \iff 625 + 4y^2 = 1600$

$\iff y = \dfrac{\sqrt{975}}{2} = \dfrac{5\sqrt{39}}{2} \approx 15.61$ in. Therefore, the window is approximately 15.6 inches high at the specified point.

52. Have each friend hold one end of the string on the blackboard. These fixed points will be the foci. Then, keeping the string taut with the chalk, draw the ellipse.

53. We start with the flashlight perpendicular to the wall; this shape is a circle. As the angle of elevation increases, the shape of the light changes to an ellipse. When the flashlight is angled so that the outer edge of the light cone is parallel to the wall, the shape of the light is a parabola. Finally, as the angle of elevation increases further, the shape of the light is hyperbolic.

54. The foci are $(\pm c, 0)$, where $c^2 = a^2 - b^2$. The endpoints of one *latus rectum* are the points $(c, \pm k)$, and the length is $2k$. Substituting this point into the equation, we get $\dfrac{c^2}{a^2} + \dfrac{k^2}{b^2} = 1 \iff \dfrac{k^2}{b^2} = 1 - \dfrac{c^2}{a^2} = \dfrac{a^2 - c^2}{a^2} \iff k^2 = \dfrac{b^2\left(a^2 - c^2\right)}{a^2}$.

Since $b^2 = a^2 - c^2$, the last equation becomes $k^2 = \dfrac{b^4}{a^2} \Rightarrow k = \dfrac{b^2}{a}$. Thus, the length of the *latus rectum* is $2k = 2\left(\dfrac{b^2}{a}\right) = \dfrac{2b^2}{a}$.

55. The shape drawn on the paper is almost, but not quite, an ellipse. For example, when the bottle has radius 1 unit and the compass legs are set 1 unit apart, then it can be shown that an equation of the resulting curve is $1 + y^2 = 2\cos x$. The graph of this curve differs very slightly from the ellipse with the same major and minor axis. This example shows that in mathematics, things are not always as they appear to be.

10.3 Hyperbolas

1. $\dfrac{x^2}{4} - y^2 = 1$ is Graph III, which opens horizontally and has vertices at $(\pm 2, 0)$.

2. $y^2 - \dfrac{x^2}{9} = 1$ is Graph IV, which opens vertically and has vertices at $(0, \pm 1)$.

3. $16y^2 - x^2 = 144$ is Graph II, which pens vertically and has vertices at $(0, \pm 3)$.

4. $9x^2 - 25y^2 = 225$ is Graph I, which opens horizontally and has vertices at $(\pm 5, 0)$.

5. The hyperbola $\dfrac{x^2}{4} - \dfrac{y^2}{16} = 1$ has $a = 2$, $b = 4$, and $c^2 = 16 + 4 \;\;\Rightarrow\;\; c = 2\sqrt{5}$. The vertices are $(\pm 2, 0)$, the foci are $(\pm 2\sqrt{5}, 0)$, and the asymptotes are $y = \pm\frac{4}{2}x$ $\Leftrightarrow\;\; y = \pm 2x$.

6. The hyperbola $\dfrac{y^2}{9} - \dfrac{x^2}{16} = 1$ has $a = 3$, $b = 4$, and $c^2 = 9 + 16 = 25 \;\;\Rightarrow\;\; c = 5$. The vertices are $(0, \pm 3)$, the foci are $(0, \pm 5)$, and the asymptotes are $y = \pm\frac{3}{4}x$.

7. The hyperbola $\dfrac{y^2}{1} - \dfrac{x^2}{25} = 1$ has $a = 1$, $b = 5$, and $c^2 = 1 + 25 = 26 \;\;\Rightarrow\;\; c = \sqrt{26}$. The vertices are $(0, \pm 1)$, the foci are $(0, \pm\sqrt{26})$, and the asymptotes are $y = \pm\frac{1}{5}x$.

8. The hyperbola $\dfrac{x^2}{2} - \dfrac{y^2}{1} = 1$ has $a = \sqrt{2}$, $b = 1$, and $c^2 = 2 + 1 = 3 \;\;\Rightarrow\;\; c = \sqrt{3}$. The vertices are $(\pm\sqrt{2}, 0)$, the foci are $(\pm\sqrt{3}, 0)$, and the asymptotes are $y = \pm\frac{\sqrt{2}}{2}x$.

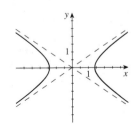

9. The hyperbola $x^2 - y^2 = 1$ has $a = 1$, $b = 1$, and $c^2 = 1 + 1 = 2 \;\Rightarrow\; c = \sqrt{2}$. The vertices are $(\pm 1, 0)$, the foci are $(\pm\sqrt{2}, 0)$, and the asymptotes are $y = \pm x$.

10. The hyperbola $9x^2 - 4y^2 = 36 \;\Leftrightarrow\; \dfrac{x^2}{4} - \dfrac{y^2}{9} = 1$ has $a = 2$, $b = 3$, and $c^2 = 4 + 9 = 13 \;\Rightarrow\; c = \sqrt{13}$. The vertices are $(\pm 2, 0)$, the foci are $(\pm\sqrt{13}, 0)$, and the asymptotes are $y = \pm\frac{3}{2}x$.

11. The hyperbola $25y^2 - 9x^2 = 225 \;\Leftrightarrow\; \dfrac{y^2}{9} - \dfrac{x^2}{25} = 1$ has $a = 3$, $b = 5$, and $c^2 = 25 + 9 = 34 \;\Rightarrow\; c = \sqrt{34}$. The vertices are $(0, \pm 3)$, the foci are $\left(0, \pm\sqrt{34}\right)$, and the asymptotes are $y = \pm\frac{3}{5}x$.

12. The hyperbola $x^2 - y^2 + 4 = 0 \;\Leftrightarrow\; y^2 - x^2 = 4 \;\Leftrightarrow\; \dfrac{y^2}{4} - \dfrac{x^2}{4} = 1$ has $a = 2$, $b = 2$, and $c^2 = 4 + 4 = 8 = 2\sqrt{2}$. The vertices are $(0, \pm 2)$, the foci are $\left(0, \pm 2\sqrt{2}\right)$, and the asymptotes are $y = \pm x$.

13. The hyperbola $x^2 - 4y^2 - 8 = 0 \;\Leftrightarrow\; \dfrac{x^2}{8} - \dfrac{y^2}{2} = 1$ has $a = \sqrt{8}$, $b = \sqrt{2}$, and $c^2 = 8 + 2 = 10 \;\Rightarrow\; c = \sqrt{10}$. The vertices are $\left(\pm 2\sqrt{2}, 0\right)$, the foci are $\left(\pm\sqrt{10}, 0\right)$, and the asymptotes are $y = \pm\frac{\sqrt{2}}{\sqrt{8}}x = \pm\frac{1}{2}x$.

14. The hyperbola $x^2 - 2y^2 = 3 \;\Leftrightarrow\; \dfrac{x^2}{3} - \dfrac{y^2}{3/2} = 1$ has $a = \sqrt{3}$, $b = \sqrt{3/2} = \frac{\sqrt{6}}{2}$, and $c^2 = 3 + \frac{3}{2} = \frac{9}{2} \;\Rightarrow\; c = \frac{3\sqrt{2}}{2}$. The vertices are $\left(\pm\sqrt{3}, 0\right)$, the foci are $\left(\pm\frac{\sqrt{6}}{2}, 0\right)$, and the asymptotes are $y = \pm\dfrac{\frac{\sqrt{6}}{2}}{\sqrt{3}}x = \pm\frac{\sqrt{2}}{2}x$.

15. The hyperbola $4y^2 - x^2 = 1$ $\Leftrightarrow$ $\dfrac{y^2}{\frac{1}{4}} - x^2 = 1$ has $a = \frac{1}{2}, b = 1$, and $c^2 = \frac{1}{4} + 1 = \frac{5}{4}$ $\Rightarrow$ $c = \dfrac{\sqrt{5}}{2}$. The vertices are $\left(0, \pm\frac{1}{2}\right)$, the foci are $\left(0, \pm\dfrac{\sqrt{5}}{2}\right)$, and the asymptotes are $y = \pm\dfrac{1/2}{1}x = \pm\frac{1}{2}x$.

16. The hyperbola $9x^2 - 16y^2 = 1$ $\Leftrightarrow$ $\dfrac{x^2}{1/9} - \dfrac{y^2}{1/16} = 1$ has $a = \frac{1}{3}, b = \frac{1}{4}$, and $c^2 = \frac{1}{9} + \frac{1}{16} = \frac{25}{144}$ $\Rightarrow$ $c = \frac{5}{12}$. The vertices are $\left(\pm\frac{1}{3}, 0\right)$, the foci are $\left(\pm\frac{5}{12}, 0\right)$, and the asymptotes are $y = \pm\dfrac{1/4}{1/3}x = \pm\frac{3}{4}x$.

17. From the graph, the foci are $(\pm 4, 0)$, and the vertices are $(\pm 2, 0)$, so $c = 4$ and $a = 2$. Thus, $b^2 = 16 - 4 = 12$, and since the vertices are on the x-axis, an equation of the hyperbola is $\dfrac{x^2}{4} - \dfrac{y^2}{12} = 1$.

18. From the graph, the foci are $(0, \pm 13)$ and the vertices are $(0, \pm 12)$, so $c = 13$ and $a = 12$. Then $b^2 = c^2 - a^2 = 169 - 144 = 25$, and since the vertices are on the y-axis, an equation of the hyperbola is $\dfrac{y^2}{144} - \dfrac{x^2}{25} = 1$.

19. From the graph, the vertices are $(0, \pm 4)$, the foci are on the y-axis, and the hyperbola passes through the point $(3, -5)$. So the equation is of the form $\dfrac{y^2}{16} - \dfrac{x^2}{b^2} = 1$. Substituting the point $(3, -5)$, we have $\dfrac{(-5)^2}{16} - \dfrac{(3)^2}{b^2} = 1$ $\Leftrightarrow$ $\dfrac{25}{16} - 1 = \dfrac{9}{b^2}$ $\Leftrightarrow$ $\dfrac{9}{16} = \dfrac{9}{b^2}$ $\Leftrightarrow$ $b^2 = 16$. Thus, an equation of the hyperbola is $\dfrac{y^2}{16} - \dfrac{x^2}{16} = 1$.

20. The vertices are $(\pm 2\sqrt{3}, 0)$, so $a = 2\sqrt{3}$, so an equation of the hyperbola is of the form $\dfrac{x^2}{(2\sqrt{3})^2} - \dfrac{y^2}{b^2} = 1$. Substituting the point $(4, 4)$ into the equation, we get $\dfrac{16}{12} - \dfrac{16}{b^2} = 1$ $\Leftrightarrow$ $\dfrac{16}{b^2} = \dfrac{16}{12} - 1$ $\Leftrightarrow$ $\dfrac{16}{b^2} = \dfrac{4}{12}$ $\Leftrightarrow$ $b^2 = 48$. Thus, an equation of the hyperbola is $\dfrac{x^2}{12} - \dfrac{y^2}{48} = 1$.

21. The vertices are $(\pm 3, 0)$, so $a = 3$. Since the asymptotes are $y = \pm\frac{1}{2}x = \pm\dfrac{b}{a}x$, we have $\dfrac{b}{3} = \dfrac{1}{2}$ $\Leftrightarrow$ $b = \dfrac{3}{2}$. Since the vertices are on the x-axis, an equation is $\dfrac{x^2}{3^2} - \dfrac{y^2}{(3/2)^2} = 1$ $\Leftrightarrow$ $\dfrac{x^2}{9} - \dfrac{4y^2}{9} = 1$.

22. From the graph, the vertices are $(0, \pm 3)$, so $a = 3$. Since the asymptotes are $y = \pm 3x = \pm\dfrac{a}{b}x$, we have $\dfrac{3}{b} = 3$ $\Leftrightarrow$ $b = 1$. Since the vertices are on the x-axis, an equation is $\dfrac{y^2}{3^2} - \dfrac{x^2}{1^2} = 1$ $\Leftrightarrow$ $\dfrac{y^2}{9} - x^2 = 1$.

23. $x^2 - 2y^2 = 8$ $\Leftrightarrow$ $2y^2 = x^2 - 8 \Leftrightarrow y^2 = \frac{1}{2}x^2 - 4$ $\Rightarrow y = \pm\sqrt{\frac{1}{2}x^2 - 4}$

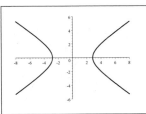

24. $3y^2 - 4x^2 = 24$ $\Leftrightarrow$ $3y^2 = 4x^2 + 24 \Leftrightarrow$ $y^2 = \frac{4}{3}x^2 + 8$ $\Rightarrow y = \pm\sqrt{\frac{4}{3}x^2 + 8}$

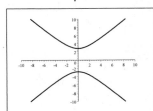

25. $\dfrac{y^2}{2} - \dfrac{x^2}{6} = 1 \;\Leftrightarrow\; \dfrac{y^2}{2} = \dfrac{x^2}{6} + 1 \Leftrightarrow y^2 = \dfrac{x^2}{3} + 2 \;\Rightarrow\;$ **26.** $\dfrac{x^2}{100} - \dfrac{y^2}{64} = 1 \;\Leftrightarrow\; 16x^2 - 25y^2 = 1600 \Leftrightarrow$

$y = \pm\sqrt{\dfrac{x^2}{3} + 2}$

$\qquad\qquad\qquad\qquad\qquad\quad 25y^2 = 16x^2 - 1600 \;\Leftrightarrow\; y^2 = \tfrac{16}{25}x^2 - 64 \;\Rightarrow$

$\qquad\qquad\qquad\qquad\qquad\qquad y = \pm\sqrt{\tfrac{16}{25}x^2 - 64}$

27. The foci are $(\pm 5, 0)$ and the vertices are $(\pm 3, 0)$, so $c = 5$ and $a = 3$. Then $b^2 = 25 - 9 = 16$, and since the vertices are on the x-axis, an equation of the hyperbola is $\dfrac{x^2}{9} - \dfrac{y^2}{16} = 1$.

28. The foci are $(0, \pm 10)$ and the vertices are $(0, \pm 8)$, so $c = 10$ and $a = 8$. Then $b^2 = c^2 - a^2 = 100 - 64 = 36$, and since the vertices are on the y-axis, an equation of the hyperbola is $\dfrac{y^2}{64} - \dfrac{x^2}{36} = 1$.

29. The foci are $(0, \pm 2)$ and the vertices are $(0, \pm 1)$, so $c = 2$ and $a = 1$. Then $b^2 = 4 - 1 = 3$, and since the vertices are on the y-axis, an equation is $y^2 - \dfrac{x^2}{3} = 1$.

30. The foci are $(\pm 6, 0)$ and the vertices are $(\pm 2, 0)$, so $c = 6$ and $a = 2$. Then $b^2 = c^2 - a^2 = 36 - 4 = 32$, and since the vertices are on the x-axis, an equation is $\dfrac{x^2}{4} - \dfrac{y^2}{32} = 1$.

31. The vertices are $(\pm 1, 0)$ and the asymptotes are $y = \pm 5x$, so $a = 1$. The asymptotes are $y = \pm\dfrac{b}{a}x$, so $\dfrac{b}{1} = 5 \;\Leftrightarrow\; b = 5$. Therefore, an equation of the hyperbola is $x^2 - \dfrac{y^2}{25} = 1$.

32. The vertices are $(0, \pm 6)$, so $a = 6$. The asymptotes are $y = \pm\tfrac{1}{3}x = \pm\dfrac{a}{b}x \;\Leftrightarrow\; \dfrac{6}{b} = \tfrac{1}{3} \;\Leftrightarrow\; b = 18$. Since the vertices are on the y-axis, an equation of the hyperbola is $\dfrac{y^2}{36} - \dfrac{x^2}{324} = 1$.

33. The foci are $(0, \pm 8)$, and the asymptotes are $y = \pm\tfrac{1}{2}x$, so $c = 8$. The asymptotes are $y = \pm\dfrac{a}{b}x$, so $\dfrac{a}{b} = \tfrac{1}{2}$ and $b = 2a$. Since $a^2 + b^2 = c^2 = 64$, we have $a^2 + 4a^2 = 64 \;\Leftrightarrow\; a^2 = \tfrac{64}{5}$ and $b^2 = 4a^2 = \tfrac{256}{5}$. Thus, an equation of the hyperbola is $\dfrac{y^2}{64/5} - \dfrac{x^2}{256/5} = 1 \;\Leftrightarrow\; \dfrac{5y^2}{64} - \dfrac{5x^2}{256} = 1$.

34. The vertices are $(0, \pm 6)$, so $a = 6$. Since the vertices are on the y-axis, the hyperbola has an equation of the form $\dfrac{y^2}{36} - \dfrac{x^2}{b^2} = 1$. Since the hyperbola passes through the point $(-5, 9)$, we have $\dfrac{81}{36} - \dfrac{25}{b^2} = 1 \;\Leftrightarrow\; \dfrac{25}{b^2} = \dfrac{45}{36} \;\Leftrightarrow\; b^2 = 20$. Thus, an equation is $\dfrac{y^2}{36} - \dfrac{x^2}{20} = 1$.

35. The asymptotes of the hyperbola are $y = \pm x$, so $b = a$. Since the hyperbola passes through the point $(5, 3)$, its foci are on the x-axis, and an equation is of the form, $\dfrac{x^2}{a^2} - \dfrac{y^2}{a^2} = 1$, so it follows that $\dfrac{25}{a^2} - \dfrac{9}{a^2} = 1 \iff a^2 = 16 = b^2$. Therefore, an equation of the hyperbola is $\dfrac{x^2}{16} - \dfrac{y^2}{16} = 1$.

36. The foci are $(\pm 3, 0)$, so $c = 3$. Since the vertices are on the x-axis, an equation of the hyperbola is of the form $\dfrac{x^2}{a^2} - \dfrac{y^2}{b^2} = 1$. Since the hyperbola passes through the point $(4, 1)$, we have $\dfrac{16}{a^2} - \dfrac{1}{b^2} = 1$. Using the foci, $c^2 = a^2 + b^2 = 9 \iff a^2 = 9 - b^2$, and substituting gives $\dfrac{16}{9 - b^2} - \dfrac{1}{b^2} = 1 \iff 16b^2 - (9 - b^2) = b^2 (9 - b^2) \iff 17b^2 - 9 = 9b^2 - b^4 \iff b^4 + 8b^2 - 9 = 0 \iff (b^2 + 9)(b^2 - 1) = 0 \iff b^2 = 1$ or $b^2 = -9$ (never). Then we have $a^2 = 9 - b^2 = 8$. Thus, an equation of the hyperbola is $\dfrac{x^2}{8} - y^2 = 1$.

37. The foci are $(\pm 5, 0)$, and the length of the transverse axis is 6, so $c = 5$ and $2a = 6 \iff a = 3$. Thus, $b^2 = 25 - 9 = 16$, and an equation is $\dfrac{x^2}{9} - \dfrac{y^2}{16} = 1$.

38. The foci are $(0, \pm 1)$, and the length of the transverse axis is 1, so $c = 1$ and $2a = 1 \iff a = \frac{1}{2}$. Then $b^2 = c^2 - a^2 = 1 - \frac{1}{4} = \frac{3}{4}$, and since the foci are on the y-axis, an equation is $\dfrac{y^2}{1/4} - \dfrac{x^2}{3/4} = 1 \iff 4y^2 - \dfrac{4x^2}{3} = 1$.

39. (a) The hyperbola $x^2 - y^2 = 5 \iff \dfrac{x^2}{5} - \dfrac{y^2}{5} = 1$ has $a = \sqrt{5}$ and $b = \sqrt{5}$. Thus, the asymptotes are $y = \pm x$, and their slopes are $m_1 = 1$ and $m_2 = -1$. Since $m_1 \cdot m_2 = -1$, the asymptotes are perpendicular.

(b) Since the asymptotes are perpendicular, they must have slopes ± 1, so $a = b$. Therefore, $c^2 = 2a^2 \iff a^2 = \dfrac{c^2}{2}$, and since the vertices are on the x-axis, an equation is $\dfrac{x^2}{\frac{1}{2}c^2} - \dfrac{y^2}{\frac{1}{2}c^2} = 1 \iff x^2 - y^2 = \dfrac{c^2}{2}$.

40. The hyperbolas $\dfrac{x^2}{a^2} - \dfrac{y^2}{b^2} = 1$ and $\dfrac{x^2}{a^2} - \dfrac{y^2}{b^2} = -1$ are conjugate to each other.

(a) $x^2 - 4y^2 + 16 = 0 \iff \dfrac{x^2}{16} - \dfrac{y^2}{4} = -1$ and $4y^2 - x^2 + 16 = 0$

$\iff \dfrac{x^2}{16} - \dfrac{y^2}{4} = 1$. So the hyperbolas are conjugate to each other.

(b) They both have the same asymptotes, $y = \pm\frac{1}{2}x$.

(c) The two general conjugate hyperbolas both have asymptotes

$y = \pm\dfrac{b}{a}x$.

41. $\sqrt{(x + c)^2 + y^2} - \sqrt{(x - c)^2 + y^2} = \pm 2a$. Let us consider the positive case only. Then $\sqrt{(x + c)^2 + y^2} = 2a + \sqrt{(x - c)^2 + y^2}$, and squaring both sides gives $x^2 + 2cx + c^2 + y^2 = 4a^2 + 4a\sqrt{(x - c)^2 + y^2} + x^2 - 2cx + c^2 + y^2 \iff 4a\sqrt{(x - c)^2 + y^2} = 4cx - 4a^2$. Dividing by 4 and squaring both sides gives $a^2 (x^2 - 2cx + c^2 + y^2) = c^2x^2 - 2a^2cx + a^4 \iff a^2x^2 - 2a^2cx + a^2c^2 + a^2y^2 = c^2x^2 - 2a^2cx + a^4 \iff a^2x^2 + a^2c^2 + a^2y^2 = c^2x^2 + a^4$. Rearranging the order, we have $c^2x^2 - a^2x^2 - a^2y^2 = a^2c^2 - a^4 \iff (c^2 - a^2) x^2 - a^2y^2 = a^2 (c^2 - a^2)$. The negative case gives the same result.

42. (a) The hyperbola $\dfrac{x^2}{9} - \dfrac{y^2}{16} = 1$ has $a = 3$, $b = 4$, so $c^2 = 9 + 16 = 25$, and $c = 5$. Therefore, the foci are $F_1\,(5, 0)$ and $F_2\,(-5, 0)$.

(b) Substituting $P\left(5, \frac{16}{3}\right)$ into an equation of the hyperbola, we get $\dfrac{25}{9} - \dfrac{256/9}{16} = \dfrac{25}{9} - \dfrac{16}{9} = 1$, so P lies on the hyperbola.

(c) $d\,(P, F_1) = \sqrt{(5-5)^2 + (16/3 - 0)^2} = \frac{16}{3}$, and $d\,(P, F_2) = \sqrt{(-5-5)^2 + (16/3 - 0)^2} = \frac{1}{3}\sqrt{900 + 256} = \frac{34}{3}$.

(d) $d\,(P, F_2) - d\,(P, F_1) = \frac{34}{3} - \frac{16}{3} = 6 = 2\,(3) = 2a$.

43. (a) From the equation, we have $a^2 = k$ and $b^2 = 16 - k$. Thus, $c^2 = a^2 + b^2 = k + 16 - k = 16 \quad \Rightarrow \quad c = \pm 4$. Thus the foci of the family of hyperbolas are $(0, \pm 4)$.

(b) $\dfrac{y^2}{k} - \dfrac{x^2}{16 - k} = 1 \quad \Leftrightarrow \quad y^2 = k\left(1 + \dfrac{x^2}{16 - k}\right) \quad \Rightarrow$

$y = \pm\sqrt{k + \dfrac{kx^2}{16 - k}}$. For the top branch, we graph $y = \sqrt{k + \dfrac{kx^2}{16 - k}}$,

$k = 1, 4, 8, 12$. As k increases, the asymptotes get steeper and the vertices move further apart.

44. $d\,(AB) = 500 = 2c \quad \Leftrightarrow \quad c = 250$.

(a) Since $\Delta t = 2640$ and $v = 980$, we have $\Delta d = d\,(PA) - d\,(PB) = v\Delta t = (980 \text{ ft/}\mu s) \cdot (2640\ \mu s) = 2{,}587{,}200 \text{ ft} = 490 \text{mi}$.

(b) $c = 250$, $2a = 490 \quad \Leftrightarrow \quad a = 245$ and the foci are on the y-axis. Then $b^2 = 250^2 - 245^2 = 2475$. Hence, an equation is $\dfrac{y^2}{60{,}025} - \dfrac{x^2}{2475} = 1$.

(c) Since P is due east of A, $c = 250$ is the y-coordinate of P. Therefore, P is at $(x, 250)$, and so $\dfrac{250^2}{245^2} - \dfrac{x^2}{2475} = 1 \quad \Leftrightarrow$

$x^2 = 2475\left(\dfrac{250^2}{245^2} - 1\right) \approx 102.05$. Then $x \approx 10.1$, and so P is approximately 10.1 miles from A.

45. Since the asymptotes are perpendicular, $a = b$. Also, since the sun is a focus and the closest distance is 2×10^9, it follows that $c - a = 2 \times 10^9$. Now $c^2 = a^2 + b^2 = 2a^2$, and so $c = \sqrt{2}a$. Thus, $\sqrt{2}a - a = 2 \times 10^9 \quad \Rightarrow \quad a = \dfrac{2 \times 10^9}{\sqrt{2} - 1}$

and $a^2 = b^2 = \dfrac{4 \times 10^{18}}{3 - 2\sqrt{2}} \approx 2.3 \times 10^{19}$. Therefore, an equation of the hyperbola is $\dfrac{x^2}{2.3 \times 10^{19}} - \dfrac{y^2}{2.3 \times 10^{19}} = 1 \quad \Leftrightarrow$

$x^2 - y^2 = 2.3 \times 10^{19}$.

46. (a) These equally spaced concentric circles can be used as a kind of measure where we count the number of rings. In the case of the red dots, the sum of the number of wave crests from each center is a constant, in this case 17. As you move out one wave crest from the left stone you move in one wave crest from the right stone. Therefore this satisfies the geometric definition of an ellipse.

(b) Similarly, in the case of the blue dots, the difference of the number of wave crests from each center is a constant. As you move out one wave crest from the left center you also move out one wave crest from the right stone. Therefore this satisfies the geometric definition of a hyperbola.

47. Some possible answers are: as cross-sections of nuclear power plant cooling towers, or as reflectors for camouflaging the location of secret installations.

48. The wall is parallel to the axis of the cone of light coming from the top of the shade, so the intersection of the wall and the cone of light is a hyperbola. In the case of the flashlight, hold it parallel to the ground to form a hyperbola.

10.4 Shifted Conics

1. The ellipse $\dfrac{(x-2)^2}{9} + \dfrac{(y-1)^2}{4} = 1$ is obtained from the ellipse $\dfrac{x^2}{9} + \dfrac{y^2}{4} = 1$
by shifting it 2 units to the right and 1 unit upward. So $a = 3$, $b = 2$, and
$c = \sqrt{9-4} = \sqrt{5}$. The center is $(2, 1)$, the foci are $(2 \pm \sqrt{5}, 1)$, the vertices are
$(2 \pm 3, 1) = (-1, 1)$ and $(5, 1)$, the length of the major axis is $2a = 6$, and the
length of the minor axis is $2b = 4$.

2. The ellipse $\dfrac{(x-3)^2}{16} + (y+3)^2 = 1$ is obtained from the ellipse $\dfrac{x^2}{16} + y^2 = 1$ by
shifting to the right 3 units and downward 3 units. So $a = 4$, $b = 1$, and
$c = \sqrt{16-1} = \sqrt{15}$. The center is $(3, -3)$, the foci are $(3 \pm \sqrt{15}, -3)$, the
vertices are $(3 \pm 4, -3) = (-1, -3)$ and $(7, -3)$, the length of the major axis is
$2a = 8$, and the length of the minor axis is $2b = 2$.

3. The ellipse $\dfrac{x^2}{9} + \dfrac{(y+5)^2}{25} = 1$ is obtained from the ellipse $\dfrac{x^2}{9} + \dfrac{y^2}{4} = 1$ by
shifting it 5 units downward. So $a = 5$, $b = 3$, and $c = \sqrt{25-9} = 4$. The center
is $(0, -5)$, the foci are $(0, -5 \pm 4) = (0, -9)$ and $(0, -1)$, the vertices are
$(0, -5 \pm 5) = (0, -10)$ and $(0, 0)$, the length of the major axis is $2a = 10$, and
the length of the minor axis is $2b = 6$.

4. The ellipse $\dfrac{(x+2)^2}{4} + y^2 = 1$ is obtained from the ellipse $\dfrac{x^2}{4} + \dfrac{y^2}{1} = 1$ by
shifting to the left 2 units. So $a = 2$, $b = 1$, and $c = \sqrt{4-1} = \sqrt{3}$. The center is
$(-2, 0)$, the foci are $(-2 \pm \sqrt{3}, 0)$, the vertices are $(-2 \pm 2, 0) = (-4, 0)$ and
$(0, 0)$, the length of the major axis is $2a = 4$, and the length of the minor axis is
$2b = 2$.

5. The parabola $(x-3)^2 = 8(y+1)$ is obtained from the parabola $x^2 = 8y$ by
shifting it 3 units to the right and 1 unit down. So $4p = 8 \Leftrightarrow p = 2$. The vertex
is $(3, -1)$, the focus is $(3, -1+2) = (3, 1)$, and the directrix is
$y = -1 - 2 = -3$.

6. The parabola $(y+5)^2 = -6x + 12 = -6(x-2)$ is obtained from the parabola
$y^2 = -6x$ by shifting to the right 2 units and down 5 units. So $4p = -6 \Leftrightarrow$
$p = -\frac{3}{2}$. The vertex is $(2, -5)$, the focus is $\left(2 - \frac{3}{2}, -5\right) = \left(\frac{1}{2}, -5\right)$, and the
directrix is $x = 2 + \frac{3}{2} = \frac{7}{2}$.

7. The parabola $-4\left(x+\frac{1}{2}\right)^2 = y \iff \left(x+\frac{1}{2}\right)^2 = -\frac{1}{4}y$ is obtained from the

parabola $x^2 = -\frac{1}{4}y$ by shifting it $\frac{1}{2}$ unit to the left. So $4p = -\frac{1}{4} \iff p = -\frac{1}{16}$.

The vertex is $\left(-\frac{1}{2}, 0\right)$, the focus is $\left(-\frac{1}{2}, 0 - \frac{1}{16}\right) = \left(-\frac{1}{2}, -\frac{1}{16}\right)$, and the directrix

is $y = 0 + \frac{1}{16} = \frac{1}{16}$.

8. The parabola $y^2 = 16x - 8 = 16\left(x - \frac{1}{2}\right)$ is obtained from the parabola $y^2 = 16x$

by shifting to the right $\frac{1}{2}$ unit. So $4p = 16 \iff p = 4$. The vertex is $\left(\frac{1}{2}, 0\right)$, the

focus is $\left(\frac{1}{2} + 4, 0\right) = \left(\frac{9}{2}, 0\right)$, and the directrix is $x = \frac{1}{2} - 4 = -\frac{7}{2}$.

9. The hyperbola $\dfrac{(x+1)^2}{9} - \dfrac{(y-3)^2}{16} = 1$ is obtained from the hyperbola

$\dfrac{x^2}{9} - \dfrac{y^2}{16} = 1$ by shifting it 1 unit to the left and 3 units up. So $a = 3$, $b = 4$, and

$c = \sqrt{9 + 16} = 5$. The center is $(-1, 3)$, the foci are $(-1 \pm 5, 3) = (-6, 3)$ and

$(4, 3)$, the vertices are $(-1 \pm 3, 3) = (-4, 3)$ and $(2, 3)$, and the asymptotes are

$(y - 3) = \pm\frac{4}{3}(x + 1) \iff y = \pm\frac{4}{3}(x + 1) + 3 \iff 3y = 4x + 13$ and

$3y = -4x + 5$.

10. The hyperbola $(x - 8)^2 - (y + 6)^2 = 1$ is obtained from the hyperbola

$x^2 - y^2 = 1$ by shifting to the right 8 units and downward 6 units. So $a = 1$,

$b = 1$, and $c = \sqrt{1 + 1} = \sqrt{2}$. The center is $(8, -6)$, the foci are $\left(8 \pm \sqrt{2}, -6\right)$,

the vertices are $(8 \pm 1, -6) = (7, -6)$ and $(9, -6)$, and the asymptotes are

$y + 6 = \pm(x - 8) \iff y = x - 14$ and $y = -x + 2$.

11. The hyperbola $y^2 - \dfrac{(x+1)^2}{4} = 1$ is obtained from the hyperbola $y^2 - \dfrac{x^2}{4} = 1$ by

shifting it 1 unit to the left. So $a = 1$, $b = 2$, and $c = \sqrt{1 + 4} = \sqrt{5}$. The center is

$(-1, 0)$, the foci are $\left(-1, \pm\sqrt{5}\right) = \left(-1, -\sqrt{5}\right)$ and $\left(-1, \sqrt{5}\right)$, the vertices are

$(-1, \pm 1) = (-1, -1)$ and $(-1, 1)$, and the asymptotes are $y = \pm\frac{1}{2}(x + 1) \iff$

$y = \frac{1}{2}(x + 1)$ and $y = -\frac{1}{2}(x + 1)$.

12. The hyperbola $\dfrac{(y-1)^2}{25} - (x + 3)^2 = 1$ is obtained from the hyperbola

$\dfrac{y^2}{25} - x^2 = 1$ by shifting to the left 3 units and upward 1 unit. So $a = 5$, $b = 1$,

and $c = \sqrt{25 + 1} = \sqrt{26}$. The center is $(-3, 1)$, the foci are $\left(-3, 1 \pm \sqrt{26}\right)$, the

vertices are $(-3, 1 \pm 5) = (-3, -4)$ and $(-3, 6)$, and the asymptotes are

$(y - 1) = \pm 5(x + 3) \iff y = 5x + 16$ and $y = -5x - 14$.

13. This is a parabola that opens down with its vertex at $(0, 4)$, so its equation is of the form $x^2 = a(y - 4)$. Since $(1, 0)$ is a point on this parabola, we have $(1)^2 = a(0 - 4) \iff 1 = -4a \iff a = -\frac{1}{4}$. Thus, an equation is $x^2 = -\frac{1}{4}(y - 4)$.

14. This is a parabola that opens to the right with its vertex at $(-6, 0)$, so its equation is of the form $y^2 = 4p(x + 6)$, with $p > 0$. Since the distance from the vertex to the directrix is $p = -6 - (-12) = 6$, an equation is $y^2 = 4(6)(x + 6) \iff y^2 = 24(x + 6)$

15. This is an ellipse with the major axis parallel to the x-axis, with one vertex at $(0, 0)$, the other vertex at $(10, 0)$, and one focus at $(8, 0)$. The center is at $\left(\frac{0+10}{2}, 0\right) = (5, 0)$, $a = 5$, and $c = 3$ (the distance from one focus to the center). So $b^2 = a^2 - c^2 = 25 - 9 = 16$. Thus, an equation is $\dfrac{(x-5)^2}{25} + \dfrac{y^2}{16} = 1$.

16. This is an ellipse with the major axis parallel to the y-axis. From the graph the center is $(2, -3)$, with $a = 3$ and $b = 2$. Thus, an equation is $\dfrac{(x-2)^2}{4} + \dfrac{(y+3)^2}{9} = 1$.

17. This is a hyperbola with center $(0, 1)$ and vertices $(0, 0)$ and $(0, 2)$. Since a is the distance form the center to a vertex, we have $a = 1$. The slope of the given asymptote is 1, so $\dfrac{a}{b} = 1 \iff b = 1$. Thus, an equation of the hyperbola is $(y - 1)^2 - x^2 = 1$.

18. From the graph, the vertices are $(2, 0)$ and $(6, 0)$. The center is the midpoint between the vertices, so the center is $\left(\dfrac{2+6}{2}, \dfrac{0+0}{2}\right) = (4, 0)$. Since a is the distance from the center to a vertex, $a = 2$. Since the vertices are on the x-axis, the equation is of the form $\dfrac{(x-4)^2}{4} - \dfrac{y^2}{b^2} = 1$. Since the point $(0, 4)$ lies on the hyperbola, we have $\dfrac{(0-4)^2}{4} - \dfrac{(4)^2}{b^2} = 1$ $\iff \dfrac{16}{4} - \dfrac{16}{b^2} = 1 \iff 3 = \dfrac{16}{b^2} \iff b^2 = \dfrac{16}{3}$. Thus, an equation of the hyperbola is $\dfrac{(x-4)^2}{4} - \dfrac{y^2}{16/3} = 1 \iff \dfrac{(x-4)^2}{4} - \dfrac{3y^2}{16} = 1$.

19. $9x^2 - 36x + 4y^2 = 0 \iff 9(x^2 - 4x + 4) - 36 + 4y^2 = 0 \iff$ $9(x-2)^2 + 4y^2 = 36 \iff \dfrac{(x-2)^2}{4} + \dfrac{y^2}{9} = 1$. This is an ellipse with $a = 3$, $b = 2$, and $c = \sqrt{9 - 4} = \sqrt{5}$. The center is $(2, 0)$, the foci are $(2, \pm\sqrt{5})$, the vertices are $(2, \pm 3)$, the length of the major axis is $2a = 6$, and the length of the minor axis is $2b = 4$.

20. $y^2 = 4(x + 2y) \iff y^2 - 8y = 4x \iff y^2 - 8y + 16 = 4x + 16 \iff$ $(y - 4)^2 = 4(x + 4)$. This is a parabola with $4p = 4 \iff p = 1$. The vertex is $(-4, 4)$, the focus is $(-4 + 1, 4) = (-3, 4)$, and the directrix is $x = -4 - 1 = -5$.

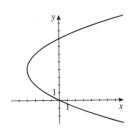

21. $x^2 - 4y^2 - 2x + 16y = 20 \quad \Leftrightarrow$

$(x^2 - 2x + 1) - 4(y^2 - 4y + 4) = 20 + 1 - 16 \quad \Leftrightarrow \quad (x-1)^2 - 4(y-2)^2 = 5$

$\Leftrightarrow \quad \dfrac{(x-1)^2}{5} - \dfrac{(y-2)^2}{\frac{5}{4}} = 1.$ This is a hyperbola with $a = \sqrt{5}$, $b = \frac{1}{2}\sqrt{5}$, and

$c = \sqrt{5 + \frac{5}{4}} = \frac{5}{2}.$ The center is $(1, 2)$, the foci are $\left(1 \pm \frac{5}{2}, 2\right) = \left(-\frac{3}{2}, 2\right)$ and

$\left(\frac{7}{2}, 2\right)$, the vertices are $\left(1 \pm \sqrt{5}, 2\right)$, and the asymptotes are $y - 2 = \pm\frac{1}{2}(x - 1)$

$\Leftrightarrow \quad y = \pm\frac{1}{2}(x - 1) + 2 \quad \Leftrightarrow \quad y = \frac{1}{2}x + \frac{3}{2}$ and $y = -\frac{1}{2}x + \frac{5}{2}$.

22. $x^2 + 6x + 12y + 9 = 0 \quad \Leftrightarrow \quad x^2 + 6x + 9 = -12y \quad \Leftrightarrow \quad (x + 3)^2 = -12y.$
This is a parabola with $4p = -12 \quad \Leftrightarrow \quad p = -3.$ The vertex is $(-3, 0)$, the focus
is $(-3, -3)$, and the directrix is $y = 3$.

23. $4x^2 + 25y^2 - 24x + 250y + 561 = 0 \quad \Leftrightarrow \quad 4\left(x^2 - 6x + 9\right) +$

$25\left(y^2 + 10y + 25\right) = -561 + 36 + 625 \Leftrightarrow \quad 4(x-3)^2 + 25(y+5)^2 = 100$

$\Leftrightarrow \quad \dfrac{(x-3)^2}{25} + \dfrac{(y+5)^2}{4} = 1.$ This is an ellipse with $a = 5$, $b = 2$, and

$c = \sqrt{25 - 4} = \sqrt{21}.$ The center is $(3, -5)$, the foci are $\left(3 \pm \sqrt{21}, -5\right)$, the

vertices are $(3 \pm 5, -5) = (-2, -5)$ and $(8, -5)$, the length of the major axis is

$2a = 10$, and the length of the minor axis is $2b = 4$.

24. $2x^2 + y^2 = 2y + 1 \quad \Leftrightarrow \quad 2x^2 + (y^2 - 2y + 1) = 1 + 1 \quad \Leftrightarrow$

$2x^2 + (y - 1)^2 = 2 \quad \Leftrightarrow \quad x^2 + \dfrac{(y-1)^2}{2} = 1.$ This is an ellipse with $a = \sqrt{2}$,

$b = 1$, and $c = \sqrt{2 - 1} = 1.$ The center is $(0, 1)$, the foci are $(0, 1 \pm 1) = (0, 0)$

and $(0, 2)$, the vertices are $\left(0, 1 \pm \sqrt{2}\right)$, the length of the major axis is $2a = 2\sqrt{2}$,

and the length of the minor axis is $2b = 2$.

25. $16x^2 - 9y^2 - 96x + 288 = 0 \quad \Leftrightarrow \quad 16\left(x^2 - 6x\right) - 9y^2 + 288 = 0 \quad \Leftrightarrow$

$16\left(x^2 - 6x + 9\right) - 9y^2 = 144 - 288 \quad \Leftrightarrow \quad 16(x-3)^2 - 9y^2 = -144 \quad \Leftrightarrow$

$\dfrac{y^2}{16} - \dfrac{(x-3)^2}{9} = 1.$ This is a hyperbola with $a = 4$, $b = 3$, and

$c = \sqrt{16 + 9} = 5.$ The center is $(3, 0)$, the foci are $(3, \pm 5)$, the vertices are

$(3, \pm 4)$, and the asymptotes are $y = \pm\frac{4}{3}(x - 3) \quad \Leftrightarrow \quad y = \frac{4}{3}x - 4$ and

$y = 4 - \frac{4}{3}x$.

26. $4x^2 - 4x - 8y + 9 = 0 \iff 4(x^2 - x) - 8y + 9 = 0 \iff$

$4\left(x^2 - x + \frac{1}{4}\right) = 8y - 9 + 1 \iff 4\left(x - \frac{1}{2}\right)^2 = 8(y - 1) \iff$

$\left(x - \frac{1}{2}\right)^2 = 2(y - 1)$. This is a parabola with $4p = 2 \iff p = \frac{1}{2}$. The vertex is

$\left(\frac{1}{2}, 1\right)$, the focus is $\left(\frac{1}{2}, \frac{3}{2}\right)$, and the directrix is $y = -\frac{1}{2} + 1 = \frac{1}{2}$.

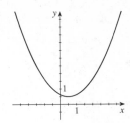

27. $x^2 + 16 = 4\left(y^2 + 2x\right) \iff x^2 - 8x - 4y^2 + 16 = 0 \iff$

$\left(x^2 - 8x + 16\right) - 4y^2 = -16 + 16 \iff 4y^2 = (x - 4)^2 \iff$

$y = \pm\frac{1}{2}(x - 4)$. Thus, the conic is degenerate, and its graph is the pair of lines

$y = \frac{1}{2}(x - 4)$ and $y = -\frac{1}{2}(x - 4)$.

28. $x^2 - y^2 = 10(x - y) + 1 \iff x^2 - 10x - y^2 + 10y = 1 \iff$

$\left(x^2 - 10x + 25\right) - \left(y^2 - 10y + 25\right) = 1 + 25 - 25 \iff$

$(x - 5)^2 - (y - 5)^2 = 1$. This is a hyperbola with $a = 1$, $b = 1$, and

$c = \sqrt{1 + 1} = \sqrt{2}$. The center is $(5, 5)$, the foci are $\left(5 \pm \sqrt{2}, 5\right)$, the vertices are

$(5 \pm 1, 5) = (4, 5)$ and $(6, 5)$, and the asymptotes are $y - 5 = \pm(x - 5) \iff$

$y = x$ and $y = -x + 10$.

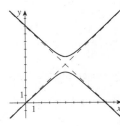

29. $3x^2 + 4y^2 - 6x - 24y + 39 = 0 \iff 3\left(x^2 - 2x\right) + 4\left(y^2 - 6y\right) = -39 \iff$

$3\left(x^2 - 2x + 1\right) + 4\left(y^2 - 6y + 9\right) = -39 + 3 + 36 \iff$

$3(x - 1)^2 + 4(y - 3)^2 = 0 \iff x = 1$ and $y = 3$. This is a degenerate conic

whose graph is the point $(1, 3)$.

30. $x^2 + 4y^2 + 20x - 40y + 300 = 0 \iff \left(x^2 + 20x\right) + 4\left(y^2 - 10y\right) = -300 \iff \left(x^2 + 20x + 100\right) +$

$4\left(y^2 - 10y + 25\right) = -300 + 100 + 100 \iff (x + 10)^2 + 4(y - 5)^2 = -100$. Since $u^2 + v^2 \geq 0$ for all $u, v \in \mathbb{R}$,

there is no (x, y) such that $(x + 10)^2 + 4(y - 5)^2 = -100$. So there is no solution, and the graph is empty.

31. $2x^2 - 4x + y + 5 = 0 \iff y = -2x^2 + 4x - 5$.

32. $4x^2 + 9y^2 - 36y = 0 \iff 4x^2 + 9\left(y^2 - 4y\right) = 0 \iff$

$4x^2 + 9\left(y^2 - 4y + 4\right) = 36 \iff 9\left(y^2 - 4y + 4\right) = 36 - 4x^2 \iff$

$y^2 - 4y + 4 = 4 - \frac{4}{9}x^2 \iff y - 2 = \pm\sqrt{4 - \frac{4}{9}x^2} \iff y = 2 \pm \sqrt{4 - \frac{4}{9}x^2}$

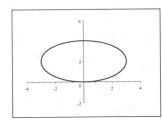

33. $9x^2 + 36 = y^2 + 36x + 6y \quad \Leftrightarrow \quad x^2 - 36x + 36 = y^2 + 6y \quad \Leftrightarrow$

$9x^2 - 36x + 45 = y^2 + 6y + 9 \quad \Leftrightarrow \quad 9\left(x^2 - 4x + 5\right) = (y+3)^2 \quad \Leftrightarrow$

$y + 3 = \pm\sqrt{9\left(x^2 - 4x + 5\right)} \quad \Leftrightarrow \quad y = -3 \pm 3\sqrt{x^2 - 4x + 5}$

34. $x^2 - 4y^2 + 4x + 8y = 0 \quad \Leftrightarrow \quad x^2 + 4x - 4\left(y^2 - 2y\right) = 0 \quad \Leftrightarrow$

$\left(x^2 + 4x + 4\right) - 4\left(y^2 - 2y + 1\right) = 0 \quad \Leftrightarrow \quad 4\left(y - 1\right)^2 = (x+2)^2 \quad \Leftrightarrow$

$2\left(y - 1\right) = \pm(x+2) \quad \Leftrightarrow \quad y - 1 = \pm\frac{1}{2}\left(x+2\right) \quad \Leftrightarrow \quad y = 1 \pm \frac{1}{2}\left(x+2\right).$ So

$y = 1 + \frac{1}{2}\left(x + 2\right) = \frac{1}{2}x + 2$ and $y = 1 - \frac{1}{2}\left(x + 2\right) = -\frac{1}{2}x.$ This is a

degenerate conic.

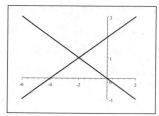

35. $4x^2 + y^2 + 4\left(x - 2y\right) + F = 0 \quad \Leftrightarrow \quad 4\left(x^2 + x\right) + \left(y^2 - 8y\right) = -F \quad \Leftrightarrow$

$4\left(x^2 + x + \frac{1}{4}\right) + \left(y^2 - 8y + 16\right) = 16 + 1 - F \quad \Leftrightarrow \quad 4\left(x + \frac{1}{2}\right)^2 + (y-1)^2 = 17 - F$

(a) For an ellipse, $17 - F > 0 \quad \Leftrightarrow \quad F < 17.$

(b) For a single point, $17 - F = 0 \quad \Leftrightarrow \quad F = 17.$

(c) For the empty set, $17 - F < 0 \quad \Leftrightarrow \quad F > 17.$

36. The parabola $x^2 + y = 100 \quad \Leftrightarrow \quad x^2 = -\left(y - 100\right)$ has $4p = -1 \quad \Leftrightarrow \quad p = -\frac{1}{4}.$ The vertex is $(0, 100)$ and so the focus

is $\left(0, 100 - \frac{1}{4}\right) = \left(0, \frac{399}{4}\right).$ Thus, one vertex of the ellipse is $(0, 100)$, and one focus is $\left(0, \frac{399}{4}\right).$ Since the second focus

of the ellipse is $(0, 0)$, the second vertex is $\left(0, -\frac{1}{4}\right).$ So $2a = 100 + \frac{1}{4} = \frac{401}{4} \quad \Leftrightarrow \quad a = \frac{401}{8}.$ Since $2c$ is the distance

between the foci of the ellipse, $2c = \frac{399}{4},\, c = \frac{399}{8},$ and then $b^2 = a^2 - c^2 = \frac{401^2}{64} - \frac{399^2}{64} = 25.$ The center of the ellipse is

$\left(0, \frac{399}{8}\right)$ and so its equation is $\dfrac{x^2}{25} + \dfrac{\left(y - \frac{399}{8}\right)^2}{\left(\frac{401}{8}\right)^2} = 1,$ which simplifies to $\dfrac{x^2}{25} + \dfrac{(8y - 399)^2}{160{,}801} = 1.$

37. (a) $x^2 = 4p\left(y + p\right),$ for

$p = -2, -\frac{3}{2}, -1, -\frac{1}{2}, \frac{1}{2}, 1, \frac{3}{2}, 2.$

(b) The graph of $x^2 = 4p\left(y + p\right)$ is obtained by shifting the graph of

$x^2 = 4py$ vertically $-p$ units so that the vertex is at $(0, -p).$ The

focus of $x^2 = 4py$ is at $(0, p)$, so this point is also shifted $-p$ units

vertically to the point $(0, p - p) = (0, 0).$ Thus, the focus is located

at the origin.

(c) The parabolas become narrower as the vertex moves toward the

origin.

38. Since $(0, 0)$ and $(1600, 0)$ are both points on the parabola, the x-coordinate of the vertex is 800. And since the highest

point it reaches is 3200, the y-coordinate of the vertex is 3200. Thus the vertex is $(800, 3200)$, and the equation

is of the form $(x - 800)^2 = 4p\left(y - 3200\right).$ Substituting the point $(0, 0)$, we get $(0 - 800)^2 = 4p\left(0 - 3200\right)$

$\Leftrightarrow \quad 640{,}000 = -12{,}800p \quad \Leftrightarrow \quad p = -50.$ So an equation is $(x - 800)^2 = 4\left(-50\right)\left(y - 3200\right) \quad \Leftrightarrow$

$(x - 800)^2 = -200\left(y - 3200\right).$

39. Since the height of the satellite above the earth varies between 140 and 440, the
length of the major axis is $2a = 140 + 2\,(3960) + 440 = 8500 \quad \Leftrightarrow \quad a = 4250$.
Since the center of the earth is at one focus, we have

$$a - c = (\text{earth radius}) + 140 = 3960 + 140 = 4100 \quad \Leftrightarrow$$

$c = a - 4100 = 4250 - 4100 = 150$. Thus, the center of the ellipse is $(-150, 0)$.
So $b^2 = a^2 - c^2 = 4250^2 - 150^2 = 18{,}062{,}500 - 22500 = 18{,}040{,}000$. Hence,

an equation is $\dfrac{(x + 150)^2}{18{,}062{,}500} + \dfrac{y^2}{18{,}040{,}000} = 1$.

40. (a) We assume that $(0, 1)$ is the focus closer to the vertex $(0, 0)$, as shown in the figure in the text. Then the center of
the ellipse is $(0, a)$ and $1 = a - c$. So $c = a - 1$ and $(a - 1)^2 = a^2 - b^2 \quad \Leftrightarrow \quad a^2 - 2a + 1 = a^2 - b^2 \quad \Leftrightarrow$
$b^2 = 2a - 1$. Thus, the equation is $\dfrac{x^2}{2a - 1} + \dfrac{(y - a)^2}{a^2} = 1$. If we choose $a = 2$, then we get $\dfrac{x^2}{3} + \dfrac{(y - 2)^2}{4} = 1$. If
we choose $a = 5$, then we get $\dfrac{x^2}{9} + \dfrac{(y - 5)^2}{25} = 1$. (Answers will vary, depending on your choices of $a > 1$.)

(b) Since a vertex is at $(0, 0)$ and a focus is at $(0, 1)$, we must have $c - a = 1$ ($a > 0$), and the center of the hyperbola is
$(0, -a)$. So $c = a + 1$ and $(a + 1)^2 = a^2 + b^2 \quad \Leftrightarrow \quad a^2 + 2a + 1 = a^2 + b^2 \quad \Leftrightarrow \quad b^2 = 2a + 1$. Thus the
equation is $\dfrac{(y + a)^2}{a^2} - \dfrac{x^2}{2a + 1} = 1$. If we let $a = 2$, then we get $\dfrac{(y + 2)^2}{4} - \dfrac{x^2}{5} = 1$. If we let $a = 5$, then we get
$\dfrac{(y + 5)^2}{25} - \dfrac{x^2}{11} = 1$. (Answers will vary, depending on your choices of a.)

(c) Since the vertex is at $(0, 0)$ and the focus is at $(0, 1)$, we must have
$p = 1$. So $(x - 0)^2 = 4\,(1)\,(y - 0) \quad \Leftrightarrow \quad x^2 = 4y$, and there is no
other possible parabola.

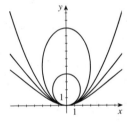

(d) Graphs will vary, depending on the choices of a in parts (a) and (b).

(e) The ellipses are inside the parabola and the hyperbolas are outside the
parabola. All touch at the origin.

10.5   Rotation of Axes

1. $(x, y) = (1, 1)$, $\phi = 45°$. Then $X = x \cos \phi + y \sin \phi = 1 \cdot \frac{1}{\sqrt{2}} + 1 \cdot \frac{1}{\sqrt{2}} = \sqrt{2}$ and
$Y = -x \sin \phi + y \cos \phi = -1 \cdot \frac{1}{\sqrt{2}} + 1 \cdot \frac{1}{\sqrt{2}} = 0$. Therefore, the XY-coordinates of the given point are $(X, Y) = \left(\sqrt{2}, 0 \right)$.

2. $(x, y) = (-2, 1)$, $\phi = 30°$. Then $X = x \cos \phi + y \sin \phi = -2 \cdot \frac{\sqrt{3}}{2} + 1 \cdot \frac{1}{2} = \frac{1}{2} \left(1 - 2\sqrt{3} \right)$ and
$Y = -x \sin \phi + y \cos \phi = 2 \cdot \frac{1}{2} + 1 \cdot \frac{\sqrt{3}}{2} = \frac{1}{2} \left(2 + \sqrt{3} \right)$. Therefore, the XY-coordinates of the given point are
$(X, Y) = \left(\frac{1}{2} \left(1 - 2\sqrt{3} \right), \frac{1}{2} \left(2 + \sqrt{3} \right) \right)$.

3. $(x, y) = \left(3, -\sqrt{3} \right)$, $\phi = 60°$. Then $X = x \cos \phi + y \sin \phi = 3 \cdot \frac{1}{2} - \sqrt{3} \cdot \frac{\sqrt{3}}{2} = 0$ and
$Y = -x \sin \phi + y \cos \phi = -3 \cdot \frac{\sqrt{3}}{2} - \sqrt{3} \cdot \frac{1}{2} = -2\sqrt{3}$. Therefore, the XY-coordinates of the given point are
$(X, Y) = \left(0, -2\sqrt{3} \right)$.

4. $(x, y) = (2, 0)$, $\phi = 15°$. Then $X = x \cos \phi + y \sin \phi = 2 \cos 15° + 0 \sin 15° \approx 1.9319$ and
$Y = -x \sin \phi + y \cos \phi = -2 \sin 15° + 0 \cos 15° \approx -0.5176$. Therefore, the XY-coordinates of the given point are
approximately $(X, Y) = (1.9319, -0.5176)$.

5. $(x, y) = (0, 2)$, $\phi = 55°$. Then $X = x \cos\phi + y \sin\phi = 0 \cos 55° + 2 \sin 55° \approx 1.6383$ and $Y = -x \sin\phi + y \cos\phi = -0 \sin 55° + 2 \cos 55° \approx 1.1472$. Therefore, the XY-coordinates of the given point are approximately $(X, Y) = (1.6383, 1.1472)$.

6. $(x, y) = (\sqrt{2}, 4\sqrt{2})$, $\phi = 45°$. Then $X = x \cos\phi + y \sin\phi = \sqrt{2} \cdot \frac{1}{\sqrt{2}} + 4\sqrt{2} \cdot \frac{1}{\sqrt{2}} = 5$ and $Y = -x \sin\phi + y \cos\phi = -\sqrt{2} \cdot \frac{1}{\sqrt{2}} + 4\sqrt{2} \cdot \frac{1}{\sqrt{2}} = 3$. Therefore, the XY-coordinates of the given point are $(X, Y) = (5, 3)$.

7. $x^2 - 3y^2 = 4$, $\phi = 60°$. Then $x = X \cos 60° - Y \sin 60° = \frac{1}{2}X - \frac{\sqrt{3}}{2}Y$ and $y = X \sin 60° + Y \cos 60° = \frac{\sqrt{3}}{2}X + \frac{1}{2}Y$. Substituting these values into the equation, we get $\left(\frac{1}{2}X - \frac{\sqrt{3}}{2}Y\right)^2 - 3\left(\frac{\sqrt{3}}{2}X + \frac{1}{2}Y\right)^2 = 4 \quad \Leftrightarrow$

$\frac{X^2}{4} - \frac{\sqrt{3}XY}{2} + \frac{3Y^2}{4} - 3\left(\frac{3X^2}{4} + \frac{\sqrt{3}XY}{2} + \frac{Y^2}{4}\right) = 4 \quad \Leftrightarrow \quad \frac{X^2}{4} - \frac{9}{4}X^2 + \frac{3Y^2}{4} - \frac{3Y^2}{4} - \frac{\sqrt{3}XY}{2} - \frac{3\sqrt{3}XY}{2} = 4$

$\Leftrightarrow \quad -2X^2 - 2\sqrt{3}XY = 4 \quad \Leftrightarrow \quad X^2 + \sqrt{3}XY = -2$.

8. $y = (x - 1)^2$, $\phi = 45°$. Then $x = X \cos 45° - Y \sin 45° = \frac{\sqrt{2}}{2}X - \frac{\sqrt{2}}{2}Y$ and $y = X \sin 45° + Y \cos 45° = \frac{\sqrt{2}}{2}X + \frac{\sqrt{2}}{2}Y$. Substituting these values into the equation, we get

$\left(\frac{\sqrt{2}}{2}X + \frac{\sqrt{2}}{2}Y\right) = \left(\frac{\sqrt{2}}{2}X - \frac{\sqrt{2}}{2}Y - 1\right)^2 = \frac{X^2}{2} - 2\frac{\sqrt{2}}{2}X\left(\frac{\sqrt{2}}{2}Y + 1\right) + \left(\frac{\sqrt{2}}{2}Y + 1\right)^2$

$\qquad = \frac{X^2}{2} - 2\frac{\sqrt{2}}{2}X\left(\frac{\sqrt{2}}{2}Y + 1\right) + \frac{Y^2}{2} + \sqrt{2}Y + 1 \quad \Leftrightarrow$

$\frac{X^2}{2} - \frac{\sqrt{2}}{2}X - \sqrt{2}X\left(\frac{\sqrt{2}}{2}Y + 1\right) + \frac{Y^2}{2} + \sqrt{2}Y + 1 - \frac{\sqrt{2}}{2}Y = 0 \quad \Leftrightarrow \quad X^2 + Y^2 - 2XY - 3\sqrt{2}X + \sqrt{2}Y + 2 = 0$.

9. $x^2 - y^2 = 2y$, $\phi = \cos^{-1}\left(\frac{3}{5}\right)$. So $\cos\phi = \frac{3}{5}$ and $\sin\phi = \frac{4}{5}$. Then

$(X \cos\phi - Y \sin\phi)^2 - (X \sin\phi + Y \cos\phi)^2 = 2(X \sin\phi + Y \cos\phi) \quad \Leftrightarrow \quad \left(\frac{3}{5}X - \frac{4}{5}Y\right)^2 -$

$\left(\frac{4}{5}X + \frac{3}{5}Y\right)^2 = 2\left(\frac{4}{5}X + \frac{3}{5}Y\right) \quad \Leftrightarrow \quad \frac{9X^2}{25} - \frac{24XY}{25} + \frac{16Y^2}{25} - \frac{16X^2}{25} - \frac{24XY}{25} - \frac{9Y^2}{25} = \frac{8X}{5} + \frac{6Y}{5} \quad \Leftrightarrow$

$-\frac{7X^2}{25} - \frac{48XY}{25} + \frac{7Y^2}{25} - \frac{8X}{5} - \frac{6Y}{5} = 0 \quad \Leftrightarrow \quad 7Y^2 - 48XY - 7X^2 - 40X - 30Y = 0$.

10. $x^2 + 2y^2 = 16$, $\phi = \sin^{-1}\left(\frac{3}{5}\right)$. So $\sin\phi = \frac{3}{5}$ and $\cos\phi = \frac{4}{5}$. Then $x = \frac{4}{5}X - \frac{3}{5}Y$ and $y = \frac{3}{5}X + \frac{4}{5}Y$. Substituting these values into the equation, we get

$\left(\frac{4}{5}X - \frac{3}{5}Y\right)^2 + 2\left(\frac{3}{5}X + \frac{4}{5}Y\right)^2 = 16 \quad \Leftrightarrow \quad \frac{16}{25}X^2 - \frac{24}{25}XY + \frac{9}{25}Y^2 + 2\left(\frac{9}{25}X^2 + \frac{24}{25}XY + \frac{16}{25}Y^2\right) = 16$

$\Leftrightarrow \quad \frac{16}{25}X^2 + \frac{18}{25}X^2 + \frac{9}{25}Y^2 + \frac{32}{25}Y^2 - \frac{24}{25}XY + \frac{48}{25}XY = 16 \quad \Leftrightarrow \quad \frac{34}{25}X^2 + \frac{41}{25}Y^2 + \frac{24}{25}XY = 16 \quad \Leftrightarrow$

$34X^2 + 41Y^2 + 24XY = 400$.

11. $x^2 + 2\sqrt{3}xy - y^2 = 4$, $\phi = 30°$. Then $x = X \cos 30° - Y \sin 30° = \frac{\sqrt{3}}{2}X - \frac{1}{2}Y = \frac{1}{2}\left(\sqrt{3}X - Y\right)$ and $y = X \sin 30° + Y \cos 30° = \frac{1}{2}X + \frac{\sqrt{3}}{2}Y = \frac{1}{2}\left(X + \sqrt{3}Y\right)$. Substituting these values into the equation, we get $\left[\frac{1}{2}\left(\sqrt{3}X - Y\right)\right]^2 + 2\sqrt{3}\left[\frac{1}{2}\left(\sqrt{3}X - Y\right)\right]\left[\frac{1}{2}\left(X + \sqrt{3}Y\right)\right] - \left[\frac{1}{2}\left(X + \sqrt{3}Y\right)\right]^2 = 4 \quad \Leftrightarrow$

$\left(\sqrt{3}X - Y\right)^2 + 2\sqrt{3}\left(\sqrt{3}X - Y\right)\left(X + \sqrt{3}Y\right) - \left(X + \sqrt{3}Y\right)^2 = 16 \quad \Leftrightarrow$

$\left(3X^2 - 2\sqrt{3}XY + Y^2\right) + \left(6X^2 + 4\sqrt{3}XY - 6Y^2\right) - \left(X^2 + 2\sqrt{3}XY + 3Y^2\right) = 16 \quad \Leftrightarrow \quad 8X^2 - 8Y^2 = 16 \quad \Leftrightarrow$

$\frac{X^2}{2} - \frac{Y^2}{2} = 1$. This is a hyperbola.

12. $xy = x + y$, $\phi = \frac{\pi}{4}$. Therefore, $x = X \cos \frac{\pi}{4} - Y \sin \frac{\pi}{4} = \frac{1}{\sqrt{2}}X - \frac{1}{\sqrt{2}}Y = \frac{1}{\sqrt{2}}(X - Y)$

and $y = X \sin \frac{\pi}{4} + Y \cos \frac{\pi}{4} = \frac{1}{\sqrt{2}}X + \frac{1}{\sqrt{2}}Y = \frac{1}{\sqrt{2}}(X + Y)$. Substituting into the equation gives

$\left[\frac{1}{\sqrt{2}}(X - Y)\right]\left[\frac{1}{\sqrt{2}}(X + Y)\right] = \frac{1}{\sqrt{2}}(X - Y) + \frac{1}{\sqrt{2}}(X + Y) \iff \frac{1}{2}(X^2 - Y^2) = \frac{2}{\sqrt{2}}X \iff$

$X^2 - Y^2 = 2\sqrt{2}X \iff \dfrac{(X - \sqrt{2})^2}{2} - \dfrac{Y^2}{2} = 1$. This is a hyperbola.

13. (a) $xy = 8 \iff 0x^2 + xy + 0y^2 = 8$. So $A = 0$, $B = 1$, and $C = 0$, and so the discriminant is $B^2 - 4AC = 1^2 - 4(0)(0) = 1$. Since the discriminant is positive, the equation represents a hyperbola.

(b) $\cot 2\phi = \dfrac{A - C}{B} = 0 \Rightarrow 2\phi = 90° \iff \phi = 45°$. Therefore,

$x = \frac{\sqrt{2}}{2}X - \frac{\sqrt{2}}{2}Y$ and $y = \frac{\sqrt{2}}{2}X + \frac{\sqrt{2}}{2}Y$. After substitution, the original

equation becomes $\left(\frac{\sqrt{2}}{2}X - \frac{\sqrt{2}}{2}Y\right)\left(\frac{\sqrt{2}}{2}X + \frac{\sqrt{2}}{2}Y\right) = 8 \iff$

$\dfrac{(X - Y)(X + Y)}{2} = 8 \iff \dfrac{X^2}{16} - \dfrac{Y^2}{16} = 1$. This is a hyperbola with $a = 4$, $b = 4$, and $c = 4\sqrt{2}$. Hence, the

vertices are $V(\pm 4, 0)$ and the foci are $F(\pm 4\sqrt{2}, 0)$.

(c)

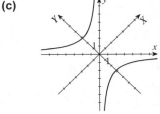

14. (a) $xy + 4 = 0 \iff 0x^2 + xy + 0y^2 + 4 = 0$. So $A = 0$, $B = 1$, and $C = 0$, and so the discriminant is $B^2 - 4AC = 1^2 - 4(0)(0) = 1$. Since the discriminant is positive, the equation represents a hyperbola.

(b) $\cot 2\phi = \dfrac{A - C}{B} = 0 \Rightarrow 2\phi = 90° \iff \phi = 45°$. Therefore,

$x = \frac{\sqrt{2}}{2}X - \frac{\sqrt{2}}{2}Y$ and $y = \frac{\sqrt{2}}{2}X + \frac{\sqrt{2}}{2}Y$. After substitution, the original

equation becomes $\left(\frac{\sqrt{2}}{2}X - \frac{\sqrt{2}}{2}Y\right)\left(\frac{\sqrt{2}}{2}X + \frac{\sqrt{2}}{2}Y\right) + 4 = 0 \iff$

$\dfrac{(X - Y)(X + Y)}{2} = -4 \iff \dfrac{Y^2}{8} - \dfrac{X^2}{8} = 1$. This is a hyperbola with $a = 2\sqrt{2}$, $b = 2\sqrt{2}$, and $c = 4$. Hence,

the vertices are $V(0, \pm 2\sqrt{2})$ and the foci are $F(0, \pm 4)$.

(c)

15. (a) $x^2 + 2xy + y^2 + x - y = 0$. So $A = 1$, $B = 2$, and $C = 1$, and so the discriminant is $B^2 - 4AC = 2^2 - 4(1)(1) = 0$. Since the discriminant is zero, the equation represents a parabola.

(b) $\cot 2\phi = \dfrac{A - C}{B} = 0 \Rightarrow 2\phi = 90° \iff \phi = 45°$. Therefore,

$x = \frac{\sqrt{2}}{2}X - \frac{\sqrt{2}}{2}Y$ and $y = \frac{\sqrt{2}}{2}X + \frac{\sqrt{2}}{2}Y$. After substitution, the original

equation becomes

$\left(\frac{\sqrt{2}}{2}X - \frac{\sqrt{2}}{2}Y\right)^2 + 2\left(\frac{\sqrt{2}}{2}X - \frac{\sqrt{2}}{2}Y\right)\left(\frac{\sqrt{2}}{2}X + \frac{\sqrt{2}}{2}Y\right)$

$+ \left(\frac{\sqrt{2}}{2}X + \frac{\sqrt{2}}{2}Y\right)^2 + \left(\frac{\sqrt{2}}{2}X - \frac{\sqrt{2}}{2}Y\right) - \left(\frac{\sqrt{2}}{2}X + \frac{\sqrt{2}}{2}Y\right) = 0 \iff$

$\frac{1}{2}X^2 - XY + \frac{1}{2}Y^2 + X^2 - Y^2 + \frac{1}{2}X^2 + XY + Y^2 - \sqrt{2}Y = 0 \iff 2X^2 - \sqrt{2}Y = 0 \iff X^2 = \frac{\sqrt{2}}{2}Y$.

This is a parabola with $4p = \frac{1}{\sqrt{2}}$ and hence the focus is $F\left(0, \frac{1}{4\sqrt{2}}\right)$.

(c)

16. (a) $13x^2 + 6\sqrt{3}xy + 7y^2 = 16$. Then $A = 13$, $B = 6\sqrt{3}$, and $C = 7$, and so

the discriminant is $B^2 - 4AC = \left(6\sqrt{3}\right)^2 - 4\,(13)\,(7) = -256$. Since the

discriminant is negative, the equation represents an ellipse.

(c)

(b) $\cot 2\phi = \dfrac{A - C}{B} = \dfrac{13 - 7}{6\sqrt{3}} = \dfrac{1}{\sqrt{2}} \;\Rightarrow\; 2\phi = 60° \;\Leftrightarrow\; \phi = 30°$.

Therefore, $x = \frac{\sqrt{3}}{2}X - \frac{1}{2}Y$ and $y = \frac{1}{2}X + \frac{\sqrt{3}}{2}Y$. After substitution, the

original equation becomes

$$13\left(\tfrac{\sqrt{3}}{2}X - \tfrac{1}{2}Y\right)^2 + 6\sqrt{3}\left(\tfrac{\sqrt{3}}{2}X - \tfrac{1}{2}Y\right)\left(\tfrac{1}{2}X + \tfrac{\sqrt{3}}{2}Y\right) + 7\left(\tfrac{1}{2}X + \tfrac{\sqrt{3}}{2}Y\right)^2 = 16 \quad\Leftrightarrow$$

$$\tfrac{13}{4}\left(3X^2 - 2\sqrt{3}XY + Y^2\right) + \tfrac{3\sqrt{3}}{2}\left(\sqrt{3}X^2 + 2XY - \sqrt{3}Y^2\right) + \tfrac{7}{4}\left(X^2 + 2\sqrt{3}XY + 3Y^2\right) = 16 \quad\Leftrightarrow$$

$$X^2\left(\tfrac{39}{4} + \tfrac{9}{2} + \tfrac{7}{4}\right) + XY\left(-\tfrac{13\sqrt{3}}{2} + \tfrac{6\sqrt{3}}{2} + \tfrac{7\sqrt{3}}{2}\right) + Y^2\left(\tfrac{13}{4} - \tfrac{9}{2} + \tfrac{21}{4}\right) = 16 \quad\Leftrightarrow\quad 16X^2 + 4Y^2 = 16 \quad\Leftrightarrow$$

$X^2 + \dfrac{Y^2}{4} = 1$. This is an ellipse with $a = 2$, $b = 1$, and $c = \sqrt{4 - 1} = \sqrt{3}$. Thus, the vertices are $V\,(0, \pm 2)$ and

the foci are $F\left(0, \pm\sqrt{3}\right)$.

17. (a) $x^2 + 2\sqrt{3}xy - y^2 + 2 = 0$. So $A = 1$, $B = 2\sqrt{3}$, and $C = -1$, and so

the discriminant is $B^2 - 4AC = \left(2\sqrt{3}\right)^2 - 4\,(1)\,(-1) > 0$. Since the

discriminant is positive, the equation represents a hyperbola.

(c)

(b) $\cot 2\phi = \dfrac{A - C}{B} = \dfrac{1 + 1}{2\sqrt{3}} = \dfrac{1}{\sqrt{3}} \;\Rightarrow\; 2\phi = 60° \;\Leftrightarrow\; \phi = 30°$.

Therefore, $x = \frac{\sqrt{3}}{2}X - \frac{1}{2}Y$ and $y = \frac{1}{2}X + \frac{\sqrt{3}}{2}Y$. After substitution, the

original equation becomes

$$\left(\tfrac{\sqrt{3}}{2}X - \tfrac{1}{2}Y\right)^2 + 2\sqrt{3}\left(\tfrac{\sqrt{3}}{2}X - \tfrac{1}{2}Y\right)\left(\tfrac{1}{2}X + \tfrac{\sqrt{3}}{2}Y\right) - \left(\tfrac{1}{2}X + \tfrac{\sqrt{3}}{2}Y\right)^2 + 2 = 0 \quad\Leftrightarrow$$

$$\tfrac{3}{4}X^2 - \tfrac{\sqrt{3}}{2}XY + \tfrac{1}{4}Y^2 + \tfrac{\sqrt{3}}{2}\left(\sqrt{3}X^2 + 2XY - \sqrt{3}Y^2\right) - \tfrac{1}{4}X^2 - \tfrac{\sqrt{3}}{2}XY - \tfrac{3}{4}Y^2 + 2 = 0 \quad\Leftrightarrow$$

$$X^2\left(\tfrac{3}{4} + \tfrac{3}{2} - \tfrac{1}{4}\right) + XY\left(-\tfrac{\sqrt{3}}{2} + \sqrt{3} - \tfrac{\sqrt{3}}{2}\right) + Y^2\left(\tfrac{1}{4} - \tfrac{3}{2} - \tfrac{3}{4}\right) = -2 \quad\Leftrightarrow\quad 2X^2 - 2Y^2 = -2 \quad\Leftrightarrow$$

$Y^2 - X^2 = 1$.

18. (a) $21x^2 + 10\sqrt{3}xy + 31y^2 = 144$. Then $A = 21$, $B = 10\sqrt{3}$, and $C = 31$,

and so the discriminant is

$B^2 - 4AC = \left(10\sqrt{3}\right)^2 - 4\,(21)\,(31) = -2304$. Since the discriminant

is negative, the equation represents an ellipse.

(c)

(b) $\cot 2\phi = \dfrac{A - C}{B} = \dfrac{21 - 31}{10\sqrt{3}} = -\dfrac{1}{\sqrt{3}} \Rightarrow 2\phi = 120° \;\Leftrightarrow\; \phi = 60°$.

Therefore, $x = \frac{1}{2}X - \frac{\sqrt{3}}{2}Y$ and $y = \frac{\sqrt{3}}{2}X + \frac{1}{2}Y$. After substitution, the

original equation becomes

$$21\left(\tfrac{1}{2}X - \tfrac{\sqrt{3}}{2}Y\right)^2 + 10\sqrt{3}\left(\tfrac{1}{2}X - \tfrac{\sqrt{3}}{2}Y\right)\left(\tfrac{\sqrt{3}}{2}X + \tfrac{1}{2}Y\right) + 31\left(\tfrac{\sqrt{3}}{2}X + \tfrac{1}{2}Y\right)^2 = 144 \quad\Leftrightarrow$$

$$\tfrac{21}{4}\left(X^2 - 2\sqrt{3}XY + 3Y^2\right) + \tfrac{5\sqrt{3}}{2}\left(\sqrt{3}X^2 - 2XY - \sqrt{3}Y^2\right) + \tfrac{31}{4}\left(3X^2 + 2\sqrt{3}XY + Y^2\right) = 144 \quad\Leftrightarrow$$

$$X^2\left(\tfrac{21}{4} + \tfrac{15}{2} + \tfrac{93}{4}\right) + XY\left(-\tfrac{21\sqrt{3}}{2} - \tfrac{10\sqrt{3}}{2} + \tfrac{31\sqrt{3}}{2}\right) + Y^2\left(\tfrac{63}{4} - \tfrac{15}{2} + \tfrac{31}{4}\right) = 144 \quad\Leftrightarrow$$

$36X^2 + 16Y^2 = 144 \quad\Leftrightarrow\quad \frac{1}{4}X^2 + \frac{1}{9}Y^2 = 1$. This is an ellipse with $a = 3$, $b = 2$, and $c = \sqrt{9 - 4} = \sqrt{5}$.

19. (a) $11x^2 - 24xy + 4y^2 + 20 = 0$. So $A = 11$, $B = -24$, and $C = 4$, and so the discriminant is $B^2 - 4AC = (-24)^2 - 4(11)(4) > 0$. Since the discriminant is positive, the equation represents a hyperbola.

(c)

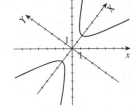

(b) $\cot 2\phi = \dfrac{A - C}{B} = \dfrac{11 - 4}{-24} = -\dfrac{7}{24} \;\Rightarrow\; \cos 2\phi = -\dfrac{7}{25}$. Therefore,

$\cos\phi = \sqrt{\dfrac{1 + (-7/25)}{2}} = \dfrac{3}{5}$ and $\sin\phi = \sqrt{\dfrac{1 - (-7/25)}{2}} = \dfrac{4}{5}$. Hence,

$x = \dfrac{3X}{5} - \dfrac{4}{5}Y$ and $y = \dfrac{4}{5}X + \dfrac{3}{5}Y$. After substitution, the original

equation becomes

Since $\cos 2\phi = -\dfrac{7}{25}$, we have
$2\phi \approx 106.26°$, so $\phi \approx 53°$.

$11\left(\dfrac{3}{5}X - \dfrac{4}{5}Y\right)^2 - 24\left(\dfrac{3}{5}X - \dfrac{4}{5}Y\right)\left(\dfrac{4}{5}X + \dfrac{3}{5}Y\right) + 4\left(\dfrac{4}{5}X + \dfrac{3}{5}Y\right)^2 + 20 = 0 \quad\Leftrightarrow$

$\dfrac{11}{25}\left(9X^2 - 24XY + 16Y^2\right) - \dfrac{24}{25}\left(12X^2 - 7XY - 12Y^2\right) + \dfrac{4}{25}\left(16X^2 + 24XY + 9Y^2\right) + 20 = 0 \quad\Leftrightarrow$

$X^2(99 - 288 + 64) + XY(-264 + 168 + 96) + Y^2(176 + 288 + 36) = -500 \quad\Leftrightarrow$

$-125X^2 + 500Y^2 = -500 \quad\Leftrightarrow\quad \dfrac{1}{4}X^2 - Y^2 = 1$.

20. (a) $25x^2 - 120xy + 144y^2 - 156x - 65y = 0$. Then $A = 25$, $B = -120$, and $C = 144$, and so the discriminant is $B^2 - 4AC = (-120)^2 - 4(25)(144) = 0$. Since the discriminant is zero, the equation represents a parabola.

(c)

(b) $\cot 2\phi = \dfrac{A - C}{B} = \dfrac{25 - 144}{-120} = \dfrac{-119}{-120} \;\Rightarrow\; \cos 2\phi = \dfrac{119}{169}$.

Therefore, $\cos\phi = \sqrt{\dfrac{1 + 119/169}{2}} = \dfrac{12}{13}$ and $\sin\phi = \sqrt{\dfrac{1 - 119/169}{2}} = \dfrac{5}{13}$.

Hence, $x = \dfrac{12X}{13} - \dfrac{5Y}{13}$ and $y = \dfrac{5X}{13} + \dfrac{12Y}{13}$. Substituting gives

Since $\cos 2\phi = \dfrac{119}{169}$, we have
$2\phi \approx 45.2°$, so $\phi \approx 23°$.

$25\left(\dfrac{12X}{13} - \dfrac{5Y}{13}\right)^2 - 120\left(\dfrac{12X}{13} - \dfrac{5Y}{13}\right)\left(\dfrac{5X}{13} + \dfrac{12Y}{13}\right) + 144\left(\dfrac{5X}{13} + \dfrac{12Y}{13}\right)^2 - 156\left(\dfrac{12X}{13} - \dfrac{5Y}{13}\right) -$

$65\left(\dfrac{5X}{13} + \dfrac{12Y}{13}\right) = 0 \quad\Leftrightarrow\quad \dfrac{X^2}{169}\left(25 \cdot 12^2 - 120 \cdot 12 \cdot 5 + 144 \cdot 5^2\right) +$

$\dfrac{Y^2}{169}\left(25 \cdot 5^2 - 120(-5)(12) + 144 \cdot 12^2\right) - \dfrac{X}{13}\left(156 \cdot 12 + 65 \cdot 5\right) + \dfrac{Y}{13}\left(156 \cdot 5 - 65 \cdot 12\right) = 0 \quad\Leftrightarrow$

$169Y^2 - 169X = 0 \quad\Leftrightarrow\quad X = Y^2$. This is a parabola with $4p = 1$.

21. (a) $\sqrt{3}x^2 + 3xy = 3$. So $A = \sqrt{3}$, $B = 3$, and $C = 0$, and so the discriminant is $B^2 - 4AC = (3)^2 - 4(\sqrt{3})(0) = 9$. Since the discriminant is positive, the equation represents a hyperbola.

(c)

(b) $\cot 2\phi = \dfrac{A - C}{B} = \dfrac{1}{\sqrt{3}} \;\Rightarrow\; 2\phi = 60° \;\Leftrightarrow\; \phi = 30°$. Therefore,

$x = \dfrac{\sqrt{3}}{2}X - \dfrac{1}{2}Y$ and $y = \dfrac{1}{2}X + \dfrac{\sqrt{3}}{2}Y$. After substitution, the equation

becomes $\sqrt{3}\left(\dfrac{\sqrt{3}}{2}X - \dfrac{1}{2}Y\right)^2 + 3\left(\dfrac{\sqrt{3}}{2}X - \dfrac{1}{2}Y\right)\left(\dfrac{1}{2}X + \dfrac{\sqrt{3}}{2}Y\right) = 3$

$\Leftrightarrow\quad \dfrac{\sqrt{3}}{4}\left(3X^2 - 2\sqrt{3}XY + Y^2\right) + \dfrac{3}{4}\left(\sqrt{3}X^2 + 2XY - \sqrt{3}Y^2\right) = 3 \quad\Leftrightarrow$

$X^2\left(\dfrac{3\sqrt{3}}{4} + \dfrac{3\sqrt{3}}{4}\right) + XY\left(\dfrac{-6}{4} + \dfrac{6}{4}\right) + Y^2\left(\dfrac{\sqrt{3}}{4} - \dfrac{3\sqrt{3}}{4}\right) = 3 \;\Leftrightarrow\; \dfrac{3\sqrt{3}}{2}X^2 - \dfrac{\sqrt{3}}{2}Y^2 = 3 \;\Leftrightarrow$

$\dfrac{\sqrt{3}}{2}X^2 - \dfrac{1}{2\sqrt{3}}Y^2 = 1$. This is a hyperbola with $a = \sqrt{\dfrac{2}{\sqrt{3}}}$ and $b = \sqrt{2\sqrt{3}}$.

22. (a) $153x^2 + 192xy + 97y^2 = 225$. Then $A = 153$, $B = 192$, and $C = 97$, and so the discriminant is

$B^2 - 4AC = (192)^2 - 4(153)(97) = -22500$. Since the discriminant is negative, the equation represents an ellipse.

(b) $\cot 2\phi = \dfrac{A - C}{B} = \dfrac{153 - 97}{192} = \dfrac{56}{192} \Rightarrow \cos 2\phi = \dfrac{56}{200}$. Therefore,

$\cos \phi = \sqrt{\dfrac{1 + 56/200}{2}} = \dfrac{16}{20} = \dfrac{4}{5}$ and $\sin \phi = \sqrt{\dfrac{1 - 56/200}{2}} = \dfrac{12}{20} = \dfrac{3}{5}$.

Substituting gives

(c)

$\phi = \cos^{-1} \dfrac{4}{5} \approx 36.9°$.

$153 \left(\dfrac{4}{5}X - \dfrac{3}{5}Y\right)^2 + 192 \left(\dfrac{4}{5}X - \dfrac{3}{5}Y\right)\left(\dfrac{3}{5}X + \dfrac{4}{5}Y\right) + 97 \left(\dfrac{3}{5}X + \dfrac{4}{5}Y\right)^2 = 225 \quad \Leftrightarrow$

$\dfrac{153}{25}\left(16X^2 - 24XY + 9Y^2\right) + \dfrac{192}{25}\left(12X^2 + 7XY - 12Y^2\right) + \dfrac{97}{25}\left(9X^2 + 24XY + 16Y^2\right) = 225 \quad \Leftrightarrow$

$X^2 \left(2448 + 2304 + 873\right) + XY \left(-3672 + 1344 + 2328\right) + Y^2 \left(1377 - 2304 + 1552\right) = 5625 \quad \Leftrightarrow$

$5625X^2 + 625Y^2 = 5625 \quad \Leftrightarrow \quad X^2 + \dfrac{1}{9}Y^2 = 1$. This is an ellipse with $a = 3$, $b = 1$, and $c = \sqrt{9 - 1} = 2\sqrt{2}$.

23. (a) $2\sqrt{3}x^2 - 6xy + \sqrt{3}x + 3y = 0$. So $A = 2\sqrt{3}$, $B = -6$, and $C = 0$, and so the discriminant is $B^2 - 4AC = (-6)^2 - 4\left(2\sqrt{3}\right)(0) = 36$. Since the discriminant is positive, the equation represents a hyperbola.

(b) $\cot 2\phi = \dfrac{A - C}{B} = \dfrac{2\sqrt{3}}{-6} = -\dfrac{1}{\sqrt{3}} \quad \Rightarrow \quad 2\phi = 120° \quad \Leftrightarrow \quad \phi = 60°$.

(c)

Therefore, $x = \dfrac{1}{2}X - \dfrac{\sqrt{3}}{2}Y$ and $y = \dfrac{\sqrt{3}}{2}X + \dfrac{1}{2}Y$, and substituting gives

$2\sqrt{3}\left(\dfrac{1}{2}X - \dfrac{\sqrt{3}}{2}Y\right)^2 - 6\left(\dfrac{1}{2}X - \dfrac{\sqrt{3}}{2}Y\right)\left(\dfrac{\sqrt{3}}{2}X + \dfrac{1}{2}Y\right) + \sqrt{3}\left(\dfrac{1}{2}X - \dfrac{\sqrt{3}}{2}Y\right) + 3\left(\dfrac{\sqrt{3}}{2}X + \dfrac{1}{2}Y\right) = 0 \quad \Leftrightarrow$

$\dfrac{\sqrt{3}}{2}\left(X^2 - 2\sqrt{3}XY + 3Y^2\right) - \dfrac{3}{2}\left(\sqrt{3}X^2 - 2XY - \sqrt{3}Y^2\right) + \dfrac{\sqrt{3}}{2}\left(X - \sqrt{3}Y\right) + \dfrac{3}{2}\left(\sqrt{3}X + Y\right) = 0 \quad \Leftrightarrow$

$X^2 \left(\dfrac{\sqrt{3}}{2} - \dfrac{3\sqrt{3}}{2}\right) + X\left(\dfrac{\sqrt{3}}{2} + \dfrac{3\sqrt{3}}{2}\right) + XY(-3 + 3) + Y^2\left(\dfrac{3\sqrt{3}}{2} + \dfrac{3\sqrt{3}}{2}\right) + Y\left(-\dfrac{3}{2} + \dfrac{3}{2}\right) = 0 \quad \Leftrightarrow$

$-\sqrt{3}X^2 + 2\sqrt{3}X + 3\sqrt{3}Y^2 = 0 \quad \Leftrightarrow \quad -X^2 + 2X + 3Y^2 = 0 \quad \Leftrightarrow \quad 3Y^2 - \left(X^2 - 2X + 1\right) = -1 \quad \Leftrightarrow$

$(X - 1)^2 - 3Y^2 = 1$. This is a hyperbola with $a = 1$, $b = \dfrac{\sqrt{3}}{3}$, $c = \sqrt{1 + \dfrac{1}{3}} = \dfrac{2}{\sqrt{3}}$, and $C(1, 0)$.

24. (a) $9x^2 - 24xy + 16y^2 = 100(x - y - 1)$. Then $A = 9$, $B = -24$, and $C = 16$, and so the discriminant is

$B^2 - 4AC = (-24)^2 - 4(9)(16) = 0$. Since the discriminant is zero, the equation represents a parabola.

(b) $\cot 2\phi = \dfrac{A - C}{B} = \dfrac{9 - 16}{-24} = \dfrac{7}{24} \quad \Rightarrow \quad \cos 2\phi = \dfrac{7}{25}$, so

$\cos \phi = \sqrt{\dfrac{1 + 7/25}{2}} = \dfrac{4}{5}$ and $\sin \phi = \sqrt{\dfrac{1 - 7/25}{2}} = \dfrac{3}{5}$, and so

$x = \dfrac{4}{5}X - \dfrac{3}{5}Y$, $y = \dfrac{3}{5}X + \dfrac{4}{5}Y$. By substitution,

(c)

Since $\cos 2\phi = \dfrac{7}{25}$,

$2\phi \approx 73.74°$, so $\phi \approx 36.9°$.

$9\left(\dfrac{4}{5}X - \dfrac{3}{5}Y\right)^2 - 24\left(\dfrac{4}{5}X - \dfrac{3}{5}Y\right)\left(\dfrac{3}{5}X + \dfrac{4}{5}Y\right) + 16\left(\dfrac{3}{5}X + \dfrac{4}{5}Y\right)^2 = 100\left(\dfrac{4}{5}X - \dfrac{3}{5}Y - \dfrac{3}{5}X - \dfrac{4}{5}Y - 1\right) \quad \Leftrightarrow$

$\dfrac{9}{25}\left(16X^2 - 24XY + 9Y^2\right) - \dfrac{24}{25}\left(12X^2 + 7XY - 12Y^2\right) + \dfrac{16}{25}\left(9X^2 + 24XY + 16Y^2\right) = 100\left(\dfrac{1}{5}X - \dfrac{7}{5}Y - 1\right)$

$\Leftrightarrow \quad 625Y^2 = 500X - 3500Y - 2500 \quad \Leftrightarrow \quad 5Y^2 + 28Y = 4X - 20 \quad \Leftrightarrow$

$5\left(Y^2 + \dfrac{28}{5}Y + \dfrac{196}{25}\right) = 4X - 20 + \dfrac{196}{5} = 4X + \dfrac{96}{5} \quad \Leftrightarrow \quad \left(Y + \dfrac{14}{5}\right)^2 = \dfrac{4}{5}\left(X + \dfrac{24}{5}\right)$. This is a parabola with $4p = \dfrac{4}{5}$ and $V\left(-\dfrac{24}{5}, -\dfrac{14}{5}\right)$.

25. (a) $52x^2 + 72xy + 73y^2 = 40x - 30y + 75$. So $A = 52$, $B = 72$, and $C = 73$, and so the discriminant is $B^2 - 4AC = (72)^2 - 4(52)(73) = -10{,}000$. Since the discriminant is decidedly negative, the equation represents an ellipse.

(b) $\cot 2\phi = \dfrac{A - C}{B} = \dfrac{52 - 73}{72} = -\dfrac{7}{24}$. Therefore, as in Exercise 19(b), we get $\cos\phi = \frac{3}{5}$, $\sin\phi = \frac{4}{5}$, and $x = \frac{3}{5}X - \frac{4}{5}Y$, $y = \frac{4}{5}X + \frac{3}{5}Y$. By substitution,

$$52\left(\tfrac{3}{5}X - \tfrac{4}{5}Y\right)^2 + 72\left(\tfrac{3}{5}X - \tfrac{4}{5}Y\right)\left(\tfrac{4}{5}X + \tfrac{3}{5}Y\right) + 73\left(\tfrac{4}{5}X + \tfrac{3}{5}Y\right)^2$$
$$= 40\left(\tfrac{3}{5}X - \tfrac{4}{5}Y\right) - 30\left(\tfrac{4}{5}X + \tfrac{3}{5}Y\right) + 75 \quad\Leftrightarrow$$
$$\tfrac{52}{25}\left(9X^2 - 24XY + 16Y^2\right) + \tfrac{72}{25}\left(12X^2 - 7XY - 12Y^2\right) + \tfrac{73}{25}\left(16X^2 + 24XY + 9Y^2\right)$$
$$= 24X - 32Y - 24X - 18Y + 75 \quad\Leftrightarrow$$
$$468X^2 + 832Y^2 + 864X^2 - 864Y^2 + 1168X^2 + 657Y^2 = -1250Y + 1875 \quad\Leftrightarrow \quad 2500X^2 + 625Y^2 + 1250Y = 1875$$
$$\Leftrightarrow \quad 100X^2 + 25Y^2 + 50Y = 75 \quad\Leftrightarrow \quad X^2 + \tfrac{1}{4}\left(Y + 1\right)^2 = 1. \text{ This is an ellipse with } a = 2, b = 1,$$
$$c = \sqrt{4 - 1} = \sqrt{3}, \text{ and center } C\,(0, -1).$$

(c)

Since $\cos 2\phi = -\frac{7}{25}$, we have $2\phi = \cos^{-1}\left(-\frac{7}{25}\right) \approx 106.26°$ and so $\phi \approx 53°$.

26. (a) $(7x + 24y)^2 = 49x^2 + 336xy + 576y^2 = 600x - 175y + 25$. So $A = 49$, $B = 336$, and $C = 576$, and so the discriminant is $B^2 - 4AC = (336)^2 - 4(49)(576) = 0$. Since the discriminant is zero, the equation represents a parabola.

(b) $\cot 2\phi = \dfrac{A - C}{B} = \dfrac{49 - 576}{336} = -\dfrac{527}{336} \quad\Rightarrow\quad \cos 2\phi = -\dfrac{527}{625}$. Therefore, $\cos\phi = \sqrt{\dfrac{1 - 527/625}{2}} = \dfrac{7}{25}$ and $\sin\phi = \sqrt{\dfrac{1 + 527/625}{2}} = \dfrac{24}{25}$. Substituting $x = \frac{7}{25}X - \frac{24}{25}Y$ and $y = \frac{24}{25}X + \frac{7}{25}Y$ gives

$$49\left(\tfrac{7}{25}X - \tfrac{24}{25}Y\right)^2 + 336\left(\tfrac{7}{25}X - \tfrac{24}{25}Y\right)\left(\tfrac{24}{25}X + \tfrac{7}{25}Y\right) + 576\left(\tfrac{24}{25}X + \tfrac{7}{25}Y\right)^2$$
$$= 600\left(\tfrac{7}{25}X - \tfrac{24}{25}Y\right) - 175\left(\tfrac{24}{25}X + \tfrac{7}{25}Y\right) + 25 \quad\Leftrightarrow$$
$$\tfrac{49}{625}\left(49X^2 - 336XY + 576Y^2\right) + \tfrac{336}{625}\left(168X^2 - 527XY - 168Y^2\right) + \tfrac{576}{625}\left(576X^2 + 336XY + 49Y^2\right)$$
$$= 168X - 576Y - 168X - 49Y + 25 \quad\Leftrightarrow$$
$$X^2\left(2401 + 56{,}448 + 331{,}776\right) + XY\left(-16{,}464 - 177{,}072 + 193{,}536\right) + Y^2\left(28{,}224 - 56{,}448 + 28{,}224\right)$$
$$= -625^2 Y + 15{,}625 \quad\Leftrightarrow$$
$$390{,}625X^2 + 390{,}625Y = 15{,}625 \quad\Leftrightarrow \quad 25X^2 + 25Y = 1 \quad\Leftrightarrow \quad X^2 = -Y + \tfrac{1}{25} = -\left(Y - \tfrac{1}{25}\right). \text{ This is a}$$
parabola with $4p = -1$ and vertex $\left(0, \frac{1}{25}\right)$.

(c)

Since $\cos 2\phi = -\frac{527}{625}$, we have $2\phi = \cos^{-1}\left(-\frac{527}{625}\right) \approx 147.48°$ and so $\phi \approx 74°$.

27. (a) The discriminant is $B^2 - 4AC = (-4)^2 + 4\,(2)\,(2) = 0$. Since the discriminant is 0, the equation represents a parabola.

(b) $2x^2 - 4xy + 2y^2 - 5x - 5 = 0 \iff 2y^2 - 4xy = -2x^2 + 5x + 5$

$\iff 2\left(y^2 - 2xy\right) = -2x^2 + 5x + 5 \iff$

$2\left(y^2 - 2xy + x^2\right) = -2x^2 + 5x + 5 + 2x^2 \iff$

$2\left(y - x\right)^2 = 5x + 5 \iff$

$\left(y - x\right)^2 = \frac{5}{2}x + \frac{5}{2} \implies y - x = \pm\sqrt{\frac{5}{2}x + \frac{5}{2}} \iff$

$y = x \pm \sqrt{\frac{5}{2}x + \frac{5}{2}}$

28. (a) The discriminant is $B^2 - 4AC = (-2)^2 + 4\,(1)\,(3) = -8 < 0$. Since the discriminant is negative, the equation represents an ellipse.

(b) $x^2 - 2xy + 3y^2 = 8 \iff 3y^2 - 2xy = 8 - x^2 \iff$

$3\left(y^2 - \frac{2}{3}xy\right) = 8 - x^2 \iff 3\left(y^2 - \frac{2}{3}xy + \frac{1}{9}x^2\right) = 8 - x^2 + \frac{1}{3}x^2 \iff$

$\iff 3\left(y - \frac{1}{3}x\right)^2 = 8 - \frac{2}{3}x^2 \iff \left(y - \frac{1}{3}x\right)^2 = \frac{8}{3} - \frac{2}{9}x^2 \implies$

$y - \frac{1}{3}x = \pm\sqrt{\frac{8}{3} - \frac{2}{9}x^2} \iff y = \frac{1}{3}x \pm \sqrt{\frac{8}{3} - \frac{2}{9}x^2}$

29. (a) The discriminant is $B^2 - 4AC = 10^2 + 4\,(6)\,(3) = 28 > 0$. Since the discriminant is positive, the equation represents a hyperbola.

(b) $6x^2 + 10xy + 3y^2 - 6y = 36 \iff 3y^2 + 10xy - 6y = 36 - 6x^2 \iff$

$3y^2 + 2\,(5x - 3)\,y = 36 - 6x^2 \iff y^2 + 2\left(\frac{5}{3}x - 1\right)y = 12 - 2x^2$

$\iff y^2 + 2\left(\frac{5}{3}x - 1\right)y + \left(\frac{5}{3}x - 1\right)^2 = \left(\frac{5}{3}x - 1\right)^2 + 12 - 2x^2 \iff$

$\left[y + \left(\frac{5}{3}x - 1\right)\right]^2 = \frac{25}{9}x^2 - \frac{10}{3}x + 1 + 12 - 2x^2 \iff$

$\left[y + \left(\frac{5}{3}x - 1\right)\right]^2 = \frac{7}{9}x^2 - \frac{10}{3}x + 13 \iff$

$y + \left(\frac{5}{3}x - 1\right) = \pm\sqrt{\frac{7}{9}x^2 - \frac{10}{3}x + 13} \iff$

$y = -\frac{5}{3}x + 1 \pm \sqrt{\frac{7}{9}x^2 - \frac{10}{3}x + 13}$

30. (a) The discriminant is $B^2 - 4AC = (-6)^2 + 4\,(9)\,(1) = 0$. Since the discriminant is 0, the equation represents a parabola.

(b) $9x^2 - 6xy + y^2 + 6x - 2y = 0 \iff y^2 - 6xy - 2y = -9x^2 - 6x$

$\iff y^2 - 2\,(3x + 1)\,y = -9x^2 - 6x \iff$

$y^2 - 2\,(3x + 1)\,y + (3x + 1)^2 = (3x + 1)^2 - 9x^2 - 6x \iff$

$\left[y - (3x + 1)\right]^2 = 1 \iff y - (3x + 1) = \pm 1 \iff$

$y = 3x + 1 \pm 1$. So $y = 3x$ or $y = 3x + 2$. This is a degenerate conic.

31. (a) $7x^2 + 48xy - 7y^2 - 200x - 150y + 600 = 0$. Then $A = 7$, $B = 48$, and $C = -7$, and so the discriminant is $B^2 - 4AC = (48)^2 - 4(7)(7) > 0$. Since the discriminant is positive, the equation represents a hyperbola. We now find the equation in terms of XY-coordinates. We have $\cot 2\phi = \dfrac{A - C}{B} = \dfrac{7}{24}$ $\Rightarrow$ $\cos \phi = \frac{4}{5}$ and $\sin \phi = \frac{3}{5}$. Therefore, $x = \frac{4}{5}X - \frac{3}{5}Y$ and $y = \frac{3}{5}X + \frac{4}{5}Y$, and substitution gives

$$7\left(\tfrac{4}{5}X - \tfrac{3}{5}Y\right)^2 + 48\left(\tfrac{4}{5}X - \tfrac{3}{5}Y\right)\left(\tfrac{3}{5}X + \tfrac{4}{5}Y\right) - 7\left(\tfrac{3}{5}X + \tfrac{4}{5}Y\right)^2 - 200\left(\tfrac{4}{5}X - \tfrac{3}{5}Y\right) - 150\left(\tfrac{3}{5}X + \tfrac{4}{5}Y\right) + 600 = 0$$

$\Leftrightarrow$ $\frac{7}{25}\left(16X^2 - 24XY + 9Y^2\right) + \frac{48}{25}\left(12X^2 + 7XY - 12Y^2\right) - \frac{7}{25}\left(9X^2 + 24XY + 16Y^2\right)$
$\quad - 160X + 120Y - 90X - 120Y + 600 = 0$

$\Leftrightarrow$ $112X^2 - 168XY + 63Y^2 + 576X^2 + 336XY - 576Y^2 - 63X^2 - 168XY - 112Y^2 - 6250X + 15{,}000 = 0$

$\Leftrightarrow$ $25X^2 - 25Y^2 - 250X + 600 = 0$ $\Leftrightarrow$ $25\left(X^2 - 10X + 25\right) - 25Y^2 = -600 + 625$ $\Leftrightarrow$

$(X - 5)^2 - Y^2 = 1$. This is a hyperbola with $a = 1$, $b = 1$, $c = \sqrt{1 + 1} = \sqrt{2}$, and center $C(5, 0)$.

(b) In the XY-plane, the center is $C(5, 0)$, the vertices are $V(5 \pm 1, 0) = V_1(4, 0)$ and $V_2(6, 0)$, and the foci are $F\left(5 \pm \sqrt{2}, 0\right)$. In the xy-plane, the center is $C\left(\frac{4}{5} \cdot 5 - \frac{3}{5} \cdot 0, \frac{3}{5} \cdot 5 + \frac{4}{5} \cdot 0\right) = C(4, 3)$, the vertices are $V_1\left(\frac{4}{5} \cdot 4 - \frac{3}{5} \cdot 0, \frac{3}{5} \cdot 4 + \frac{4}{5} \cdot 0\right) = V_1\left(\frac{16}{5}, \frac{12}{5}\right)$ and $V_2\left(\frac{4}{5} \cdot 6 - \frac{3}{5} \cdot 0, \frac{3}{5} \cdot 6 + \frac{4}{5} \cdot 0\right) = V_2\left(\frac{24}{5}, \frac{18}{5}\right)$, and the foci are $F_1\left(4 + \frac{4}{5}\sqrt{2}, 3 + \frac{3}{5}\sqrt{2}\right)$ and $F_2\left(4 - \frac{4}{5}\sqrt{2}, 3 - \frac{3}{5}\sqrt{2}\right)$.

(c) In the XY-plane, the equations of the asymptotes are $Y = X - 5$ and $Y = -X + 5$. In the xy-plane, these equations become $-x \cdot \frac{3}{5} + y \cdot \frac{4}{5} = x \cdot \frac{4}{5} + y \cdot \frac{3}{5} - 5$ $\Leftrightarrow$ $y = 7x - 25$ and $-x \cdot \frac{3}{5} + y \cdot \frac{4}{5} = -\left(x \cdot \frac{4}{5} + y \cdot \frac{3}{5}\right) + 5$ $\Leftrightarrow$ $y = -\frac{1}{7}x + \frac{25}{7}$.

32. (a) $2\sqrt{2}(x + y)^2 = 7x + 9y$ $\Leftrightarrow$ $2\sqrt{2}x^2 + 4\sqrt{2}xy + 2\sqrt{2}y^2 = 7x + 9y$. Therefore, $A = 2\sqrt{2}$, $B = 4\sqrt{2}$, and $C = 2\sqrt{2}$, and so $\cot 2\phi = \dfrac{A - C}{B} = 0$ $\Rightarrow$ $2\phi = 90°$ $\Rightarrow$ $\phi = 45°$. Thus $x = \dfrac{X - Y}{\sqrt{2}}$, $y = \dfrac{X + Y}{\sqrt{2}}$ $\Rightarrow$ $x + y = \sqrt{2}X$. Thus the equation becomes $2\sqrt{2}\left(\sqrt{2}X\right)^2 = \dfrac{16X + 2Y}{\sqrt{2}}$ $\Leftrightarrow$ $8X^2 = 16X + 2Y$ $\Leftrightarrow$ $4\left(X^2 + 2X + 1\right) = Y + 4$ $\Leftrightarrow$ $4(X + 1)^2 = Y + 4$. This is a parabola.

(b) $4p = \frac{1}{4}$ $\Rightarrow$ $p = \frac{1}{16}$. Thus, in XY-coordinates the vertex is $V(-1, -4)$ and the focus is $F\left(-1, -\frac{63}{16}\right)$. In xy-coordinates, $V\left(\frac{3}{\sqrt{2}}, \frac{-5}{\sqrt{2}}\right)$ and $F\left(\frac{47\sqrt{2}}{32}, \frac{-79\sqrt{2}}{32}\right)$.

(c) The directrix is $Y = -\frac{65}{16}$. Thus $\dfrac{-x + y}{\sqrt{2}} = -\dfrac{65}{16}$ or $y = x - \frac{65\sqrt{2}}{16}$.

33. We use the hint and eliminate Y by adding: $x = X \cos \phi - Y \sin \phi$ $\Leftrightarrow$ $x \cos \phi = X \cos^2 \phi - Y \sin \phi \cos \phi$ and $y = X \sin \phi + Y \cos \phi$ $\Leftrightarrow$ $y \sin \phi = X \sin^2 \phi + Y \sin \phi \cos \phi$, and adding these two equations gives $x \cos \phi + y \sin \phi = X\left(\cos^2 \phi + \sin^2 \phi\right)$ $\Leftrightarrow$ $x \cos \phi + y \sin \phi = X$. In a similar manner, we eliminate X by subtracting: $x = X \cos \phi - Y \sin \phi$ $\Leftrightarrow$ $-x \sin \phi = -X \cos \phi \sin \phi + Y \sin^2 \phi$ and $y = X \sin \phi + Y \cos \phi$ $\Leftrightarrow$ $y \cos \phi = X \sin \phi \cos \phi + Y \cos^2 \phi$, so $-x \sin \phi + y \cos \phi = Y\left(\cos^2 \phi + \sin^2 \phi\right)$ $\Leftrightarrow$ $-x \sin \phi + y \cos \phi = Y$. Thus, $X = x \cos \phi + y \sin \phi$ and $Y = -x \sin \phi + y \cos \phi$.

34. $\sqrt{x} + \sqrt{y} = 1$. Squaring both sides gives $x + 2\sqrt{xy} + y = 1 \iff 2\sqrt{xy} = 1 - x - y$, and squaring both sides again gives $4xy = (1 - x - y)^2 = 1 - x - y - x + x^2 + xy - y + xy + y^2 \iff 4xy = x^2 + y^2 + 2xy - 2x - 2y + 1$

$\iff x^2 + y^2 - 2xy - 2x - 2y + 1 = 0$. Then $A = 1$, $B = -2$, and $C = 1$, and so $\cot 2\phi = \dfrac{A - C}{B} = 0 \Rightarrow 2\phi = 90°$

$\iff \phi = 45°$. Therefore, $x = \frac{\sqrt{2}}{2}X - \frac{\sqrt{2}}{2}Y$ and $y = \frac{\sqrt{2}}{2}X + \frac{\sqrt{2}}{2}Y$, and substituting gives

$\left(\frac{\sqrt{2}}{2}X - \frac{\sqrt{2}}{2}Y\right)^2 - 2\left(\frac{\sqrt{2}}{2}X - \frac{\sqrt{2}}{2}Y\right)\left(\frac{\sqrt{2}}{2}X + \frac{\sqrt{2}}{2}Y\right)$

$\qquad\qquad + \left(\frac{\sqrt{2}}{2}X + \frac{\sqrt{2}}{2}Y\right)^2 - 2\left(\frac{\sqrt{2}}{2}X - \frac{\sqrt{2}}{2}Y\right) - 2\left(\frac{\sqrt{2}}{2}X + \frac{\sqrt{2}}{2}Y\right) + 1 = 0 \iff$

$\frac{1}{2}(X^2 - 2XY + Y^2) - (X^2 - Y^2) + \frac{1}{2}(X^2 + 2XY + Y^2) - 2\sqrt{2}X + 1 = 0 \iff X^2\left(\frac{1}{2} - 1 + \frac{1}{2}\right) + $

$XY(-1 + 1) + Y^2\left(\frac{1}{2} + 1 + \frac{1}{2}\right) - 2\sqrt{2}X + 1 = 0 \iff 2Y^2 = 2\sqrt{2}X - 1 \iff Y^2 = \sqrt{2}X - \frac{1}{2} = \sqrt{2}\left(X - \frac{1}{2\sqrt{2}}\right)$.

This is a parabola with $4p = \sqrt{2}$ and vertex $V\left(\dfrac{1}{2\sqrt{2}}, 0\right)$. However, in the original equation we must have $x \geq 0$ and $y \geq 0$, so we get only the part of the parabola that lies in the first quadrant.

35. $Z = \begin{bmatrix} x \\ y \end{bmatrix}$, $Z' = \begin{bmatrix} X \\ Y \end{bmatrix}$, and $R = \begin{bmatrix} \cos\phi & -\sin\phi \\ \sin\phi & \cos\phi \end{bmatrix}$.

Thus $Z = RZ' \iff \begin{bmatrix} x \\ y \end{bmatrix} = \begin{bmatrix} \cos\phi & -\sin\phi \\ \sin\phi & \cos\phi \end{bmatrix}\begin{bmatrix} X \\ Y \end{bmatrix} = \begin{bmatrix} X\cos\phi - Y\sin\phi Y \\ X\sin\phi + Y\cos\phi \end{bmatrix}$. Equating the entries in this

matrix equation gives the first pair of rotation of axes formulas. Now

$R^{-1} = \dfrac{1}{\cos^2\phi + \sin^2\phi}\begin{bmatrix} \cos\phi & \sin\phi \\ -\sin\phi & \cos\phi \end{bmatrix} = \begin{bmatrix} \cos\phi & \sin\phi \\ -\sin\phi & \cos\phi \end{bmatrix}$ and so $Z' = R^{-1}Z \iff$

$\begin{bmatrix} X \\ Y \end{bmatrix} = \begin{bmatrix} \cos\phi & \sin\phi \\ -\sin\phi & \cos\phi \end{bmatrix}\begin{bmatrix} x \\ y \end{bmatrix} = \begin{bmatrix} x\cos\phi + y\sin\phi \\ -x\sin\phi + y\cos\phi \end{bmatrix}$. Equating the entries in this matrix equation gives the

second pair of rotation of axes formulas.

36. (a) Using $A' = A\cos^2\phi + B\sin\phi\cos\phi + C\sin^2\phi$, $B' = 2(C - a)\sin\phi\cos\phi + B(\cos^2\phi - \sin^2\phi)$, and $C' = A\sin^2\phi - B\sin\phi\cos\phi + C\cos^2\phi$, we first expand the terms.

$(B')^2 = [2(C - a)\sin\phi\cos\phi + B(\cos^2\phi - \sin^2\phi)]^2$

$= 4(C - A)^2\sin^2\phi\cos^2\phi + 4B(C - A)\sin\phi\cos\phi(\cos^2\phi - \sin^2\phi) + B^2(\cos^2\phi - \sin^2\phi)^2$

$= 4(C - A)^2\sin^2\phi\cos^2\phi + 4B(C - A)\sin\phi\cos^3\phi - 4B(C - A)\sin^3\phi\cos\phi$

$\qquad\qquad\qquad\qquad + B^2\cos^4\phi - 2B^2\sin^2\phi\cos^2\phi + B^2\sin^4\phi$

$4A'C' = 4(A\cos^2\phi + B\sin\phi\cos\phi + C\sin^2\phi)(A\sin^2\phi - B\sin\phi\cos\phi + C\cos^2\phi)$

$= 4A^2\sin^2\phi\cos^2\phi - 4AB\sin\phi\cos^3\phi + 4AC\cos^4\phi + 4AB\sin^3\phi\cos\phi - 4B^2\sin^2\phi\cos^2\phi$

$\qquad\qquad + 4BC\sin\phi\cos^3\phi + 4AC\sin^4\phi - 4BC\sin^3\phi\cos\phi + 4C^2\sin^2\phi\cos^2\phi$

Since there are many terms in this expansion, we find the coefficients of like trignometric terms.

Term	$(B')^2$	$-4A'C'$	Sum
$\cos^4\phi$	B^2	$-4AC$	$B^2 - 4AC$
$\sin\phi\cos^3\phi$	$4B(C-A)$	$4AB - 4BC$	$4BC - 4AB + 4AB - 4BC = 0$
$\sin^2\phi\cos^2\phi$	$4(C-A)^2 - 2B^2$	$-4A^2 + 4B^2 - 4C^2$	$-8AC + 2B^2 = 2(B^2 - 4AC)$
$\sin^3\phi\cos\phi$	$-4B(C-A)$	$-4AB + 4BC$	$-4BC + AB - 4AB + 4BC = 0$
$\sin^4\phi$	B^2	$-4AC$	$B^2 - 4AC$

So

$$
\begin{aligned}
B'^2 - 4A'C' &= (B^2 - 4AC)\cos^4\phi + 2(B^2 - 4AC)\sin^2\phi\cos^2\phi + (B^2 - 4AC)\sin^4\phi \\
&= (B^2 - 4AC)(\cos^4\phi + 2\sin^2\phi\cos^2\phi + \sin^4\phi) = (B^2 - 4AC)(\cos^2\phi + \sin^2\phi)^2 \\
&= (B^2 - 4AC)(1^2) = B^2 - 4AC
\end{aligned}
$$

So $B^2 - 4AC = B'^2 - 4A'C'$.

(b) Using $A' = A\cos^2\phi + B\sin\phi\cos\phi + C\sin^2\phi$ and $C' = A\sin^2\phi - B\sin\phi\cos\phi + C\cos^2\phi$, we have

$$
\begin{aligned}
A' + C' &= A\cos^2\phi + B\sin\phi\cos\phi + C\sin^2\phi + A\sin^2\phi - B\sin\phi\cos\phi + C\cos^2\phi \\
&= A(\sin^2\phi + \cos^2\phi) + C(\sin^2\phi + \cos^2\phi) \\
&= A + C
\end{aligned}
$$

(c) Since $F' = F$, F is also invariant under rotation.

37. Let P be the point (x_1, y_1) and Q be the point (x_2, y_2) and let $P'(X_1, Y_1)$ and $Q'(X_2, Y_2)$ be the images of P and Q under the rotation of ϕ. So $X_1 = x_1\cos\phi + y_1\sin\phi$, $Y_1 = -x_1\sin\phi + y_1\cos\phi$, $X_2 = x_2\cos\phi + y_2\sin\phi$, and $Y_2 = -x_2\sin\phi + y_2\cos\phi$. Thus $d(P', Q') = \sqrt{(X_2 - X_1)^2 + (Y_2 - Y_1)^2}$, where

$$
\begin{aligned}
(X_2 - X_1)^2 &= [(x_2\cos\phi + y_2\sin\phi) - (x_1\cos\phi + y_1\sin\phi)]^2 = [(x_2 - x_1)\cos\phi + (y_2 - y_1)\sin\phi]^2 \\
&= (x_2 - x_1)^2\cos^2\phi + (x_2 - x_1)(y_2 - y_1)\sin\phi\cos\phi + (y_2 - y_1)^2\sin^2\phi
\end{aligned}
$$

and

$$
\begin{aligned}
(Y_2 - Y_1)^2 &= [(-x_2\sin\phi + y_2\cos\phi) - (-x_1\sin\phi + y_1\cos\phi)]^2 = [-(x_2 - x_1)\sin\phi + (y_2 - y_1)\cos\phi]^2 \\
&= (x_2 - x_1)^2\sin^2\phi - (x_2 - x_1)(y_2 - y_1)\sin\phi\cos\phi + (y_2 - y_1)^2\cos^2\phi
\end{aligned}
$$

So

$$
\begin{aligned}
(X_2 - X_1)^2 + (Y_2 - Y_1)^2 &= (x_2 - x_1)^2\cos^2\phi + (x_2 - x_1)(y_2 - y_1)\sin\phi\cos\phi + (y_2 - y_1)^2\sin^2\phi \\
&\quad + (x_2 - x_1)^2\sin^2\phi - (x_2 - x_1)(y_2 - y_1)\sin\phi\cos\phi + (y_2 - y_1)^2\cos^2\phi \\
&= (x_2 - x_1)^2\cos^2\phi + (y_2 - y_1)^2\sin^2\phi + (x_2 - x_1)^2\sin^2\phi + (y_2 - y_1)^2\cos^2\phi \\
&= (x_2 - x_1)^2(\cos^2\phi + \sin^2\phi) + (y_2 - y_1)^2(\sin^2\phi + \cos^2\phi) = (x_2 - x_1)^2 + (y_2 - y_1)^2
\end{aligned}
$$

Putting these equations together gives

$$
d(P', Q') = \sqrt{(X_2 - X_1)^2 + (Y_2 - Y_1)^2} = \sqrt{(x_2 - x_1)^2 + (y_2 - y_1)^2} = d(P, Q).
$$

10.6 Polar Equations of Conics

1. Substituting $e = \frac{2}{3}$ and $d = 3$ into the general equation of a conic with vertical directrix, we get $r = \dfrac{\frac{2}{3} \cdot 3}{1 + \frac{2}{3} \cos \theta}$ $\Leftrightarrow$

$r = \dfrac{6}{3 + 2 \cos \theta}$.

2. Substituting $e = \frac{4}{3}$ and $d = 3$ into the general equation of a conic with vertical directrix, we get $r = \dfrac{\frac{4}{3} \cdot 3}{1 - \frac{4}{3} \cos \theta}$ $\Leftrightarrow$

$r = \dfrac{12}{3 - 4 \cos \theta}$.

3. Substituting $e = 1$ and $d = 2$ into the general equation of a conic with horizontal directrix, we get $r = \dfrac{1 \cdot 2}{1 + \sin \theta}$ $\Leftrightarrow$

$r = \dfrac{2}{1 + \sin \theta}$.

4. Substituting $e = \frac{1}{2}$ and $d = 4$ into the general equation of a conic with horizontal directrix, we get $r = \dfrac{\frac{1}{2} \cdot 4}{1 - \frac{1}{2} \sin \theta}$ $\Leftrightarrow$

$r = \dfrac{4}{2 - \sin \theta}$.

5. $r = 5 \sec \theta$ $\Leftrightarrow$ $r \cos \theta = 5 \Leftrightarrow x = 5$. So $d = 5$ and $e = 4$ gives $r = \dfrac{4 \cdot 5}{1 + 4 \cos \theta}$ $\Leftrightarrow$ $r = \dfrac{20}{1 + 4 \cos \theta}$.

6. $r = 2 \csc \theta$ $\Leftrightarrow$ $r \sin \theta = 2 \Leftrightarrow y = 2$. So $d = 2$ and $e = 0.6$ gives $r = \dfrac{0.6 \cdot 2}{1 + 0.6 \sin \theta}$ $\Leftrightarrow$ $r = \dfrac{1.2}{1 + 0.6 \sin \theta}$.

7. Since this is a parabola whose focus is at the origin and vertex at $(5, \pi/2)$, the directrix must be $y = 10$. So $d = 10$ and

$e = 1$ gives $r = \dfrac{1 \cdot 10}{1 + \sin \theta} = \dfrac{10}{1 + \sin \theta}$.

8. Since the vertex is at $(2, 0)$ we have $d(P, F) = 2$. Now, since $\dfrac{d(P, F)}{d(P, \ell)} = e$ we get $\dfrac{2}{d(P, \ell)} = 0.4$ $\Leftrightarrow$

$d(P, \ell) = \dfrac{2}{0.4} = 5$. The directrix is $x = 7$, so substituting $e = 0.4$ and $d = 7$ we get $r = \dfrac{0.4 \cdot 7}{1 + 0.4 \cos \theta}$ $\Leftrightarrow$

$r = \dfrac{2.8}{1 + 0.4 \cos \theta}$.

9. $r = \dfrac{6}{1 + \cos \theta}$ is Graph II. The eccentricity is 1, so this is a parabola. When $\theta = 0$, we have $r = 3$ and when $\theta = \frac{\pi}{2}$, we have $r = 6$.

10. $r = \dfrac{2}{2 - \cos \theta}$ is Graph III. $r = \dfrac{1}{1 - \frac{1}{2} \cos \theta}$, so $e = \frac{1}{2}$ and this is an ellipse. When $\theta = 0$, $r = 2$, and when $\theta = \pi$, $r = \frac{2}{3}$.

11. $r = \dfrac{3}{1 - 2 \sin \theta}$ is Graph VI. $e = 2$, so this is a hyperbola. When $\theta = 0$, $r = 3$, and when $\theta = \pi$, $r = 3$.

12. $r = \dfrac{5}{3 - 3 \sin \theta}$ is Graph I. $r = \dfrac{\frac{5}{3}}{1 - \sin \theta}$, so $e = 1$ and this is a parabola. When $\theta = 0$, $r = \frac{5}{3}$ and when $\theta = \pi$, $r = \frac{5}{3}$.

13. $r = \dfrac{12}{3 + 2 \sin \theta}$ is Graph IV. $r = \dfrac{4}{1 + \frac{2}{3} \sin \theta}$, so $e = \frac{2}{3}$ and this is an ellipse. When $\theta = 0$, $r = 4$, and when $\theta = \pi$, $r = 4$.

14. $r = \dfrac{12}{2 + 3 \cos \theta}$ is Graph V. $r = \dfrac{6}{1 + \frac{3}{2} \cos \theta}$, so $e = \frac{3}{2}$ and this is a hyperbola. When $\theta = 0$, $r = \frac{12}{5}$, and when $\theta = \pi$, we have $r = 12$.

15. (a) $r = \dfrac{4}{1 + 3\cos\theta}$ $\Rightarrow$ $e = 3$, so the conic is a hyperbola.

(b) The vertices occur where $\theta = 0$ and $\theta = \pi$. Now $\theta = 0$ $\Rightarrow$

$r = \dfrac{4}{1 + 3\cos 0} = 1$, and $\theta = \pi$ $\Rightarrow$ $r = \dfrac{4}{1 + 3\cos\pi} = \dfrac{4}{-2} = -2$. Thus the

vertices are $(1, 0)$ and $(-2, \pi)$.

16. (a) $r = \dfrac{8}{3 + 3\cos\theta}$ $\Leftrightarrow$ $r = \dfrac{\frac{8}{3}}{1 + \cos\theta}$ $\Rightarrow$ $e = 1$, so the conic is a parabola.

(b) Substituting $\theta = 0$, we have $r = \dfrac{8}{3 + 3\cos 0} = \dfrac{8}{6} = \dfrac{4}{3}$. Thus the vertex is $\left(\frac{4}{3}, 0\right)$.

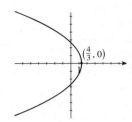

17. (a) $r = \dfrac{2}{1 - \cos\theta}$ $\Rightarrow$ $e = 1$, so the conic is a parabola.

(b) Substituting $\theta = \pi$, we have $r = \dfrac{2}{1 - \cos\pi} = \dfrac{2}{2} = 1$. Thus the vertex is $(1, \pi)$.

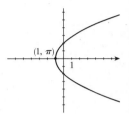

18. (a) $r = \dfrac{10}{3 - 2\sin\theta}$ $\Leftrightarrow$ $r = \dfrac{\frac{10}{3}}{1 - \frac{2}{3}\sin\theta}$ $\Rightarrow$ $e = \frac{2}{3}$, so the conic is an ellipse.

(b) The vertices occur where $\theta = \frac{\pi}{2}$ and $\theta = \frac{3\pi}{2}$. Now $\theta = \frac{\pi}{2}$ $\Rightarrow$

$r = \dfrac{10}{3 - 2\sin\frac{\pi}{2}} = \dfrac{10}{1} = 10$ and $\theta = \frac{3\pi}{2}$ $\Rightarrow$ $r = \dfrac{10}{3 - 2\sin\frac{3\pi}{2}} = \dfrac{10}{5} = 2$.

Thus, the vertices are $\left(10, \frac{\pi}{2}\right)$ and $\left(2, \frac{3\pi}{2}\right)$.

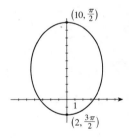

19. (a) $r = \dfrac{6}{2 + \sin\theta}$ $\Leftrightarrow$ $r = \dfrac{\frac{1}{2} \cdot 6}{1 + \frac{1}{2}\sin\theta}$ $\Rightarrow$ $e = \frac{1}{2}$, so the conic is an ellipse.

(b) The vertices occur where $\theta = \frac{\pi}{2}$ and $\theta = \frac{3\pi}{2}$. Now $\theta = \frac{\pi}{2}$ $\Rightarrow$

$r = \dfrac{6}{2 + \sin\frac{\pi}{2}} = \dfrac{6}{3} = 2$ and $\theta = \frac{3\pi}{2}$ $\Rightarrow$ $r = \dfrac{6}{2 + \sin\frac{3\pi}{2}} = \dfrac{6}{1} = 6$. Thus, the

vertices are $\left(2, \frac{\pi}{2}\right)$ and $\left(6, \frac{3\pi}{2}\right)$.

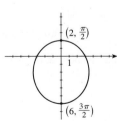

20. (a) $r = \dfrac{5}{2 - 3\sin\theta}$ $\Leftrightarrow$ $r = \dfrac{\frac{5}{2}}{1 - \frac{3}{2}\sin\theta}$ $\Rightarrow$ $e = \frac{3}{2}$, so the conic is a

hyperbola.

(b) The vertices occur where $\theta = \frac{\pi}{2}$ and $\theta = \frac{3\pi}{2}$. Now $\theta = \frac{\pi}{2}$ $\Rightarrow$

$r = \dfrac{5}{2 - 3\sin\frac{\pi}{2}} = \dfrac{5}{-1} = -5$ and $\theta = \frac{3\pi}{2}$ $\Rightarrow$ $r = \dfrac{5}{2 - 3\sin\frac{3\pi}{2}} = \dfrac{5}{5} = 1$.

Thus, the vertices are $\left(-5, \frac{\pi}{2}\right)$ and $\left(1, \frac{3\pi}{2}\right)$.

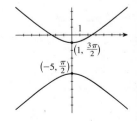

21. (a) $r = \dfrac{7}{2 - 5\sin\theta}$ $\Leftrightarrow$ $r = \dfrac{\frac{7}{2}}{1 - \frac{5}{2}\sin\theta}$ $\Rightarrow$ $e = \frac{5}{2}$, so the conic is a

hyperbola.

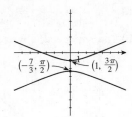

(b) The vertices occur where $\theta = \frac{\pi}{2}$ and $\theta = \frac{3\pi}{2}$. $r = \dfrac{7}{2 - 5\sin\frac{\pi}{2}} = \frac{7}{-3} = -\frac{7}{3}$ and

$\theta = \frac{3\pi}{2}$ $\Rightarrow$ $r = \dfrac{7}{2 - 5\sin\frac{3\pi}{2}} = \frac{7}{7} = 1$. Thus, the vertices are $\left(-\frac{7}{3}, \frac{\pi}{2}\right)$ and

$\left(1, \frac{3\pi}{2}\right)$.

22. (a) $r = \dfrac{8}{3 + \cos\theta}$ $\Leftrightarrow$ $r = \dfrac{\frac{8}{3}}{1 + \frac{1}{3}\cos\theta}$ $\Rightarrow$ $e = \frac{1}{3}$, so the conic is an ellipse.

(b) The vertices occur where $\theta = 0$ and $\theta = \pi$. Now $\theta = 0$ $\Rightarrow$

$r = \dfrac{8}{3 + \cos 0} = \frac{8}{4} = 2$ and $\theta = \pi$ $\Rightarrow$ $r = \dfrac{8}{3 + \cos\pi} = \frac{8}{2} = 4$. Thus, the

vertices are $(2, 0)$ and $(4, \pi)$.

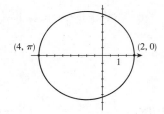

23. (a) $r = \dfrac{1}{4 - 3\cos\theta}$ $\Leftrightarrow$ $r = \dfrac{\frac{1}{4}}{1 - \frac{3}{4}\cos\theta}$ $\Rightarrow$ $e = \frac{3}{4}$. Since $ed = \frac{1}{4}$ we

have $d = \dfrac{\frac{1}{4}}{e} = \frac{4}{3} \cdot \frac{1}{4} = \frac{1}{3}$. Therefore the eccentricity is $\frac{3}{4}$ and the directrix is

$x = -\frac{1}{3}$ $\Leftrightarrow$ $r = -\frac{1}{3}\sec\theta$.

(b) We replace θ by $\theta - \frac{\pi}{3}$ to get $r = \dfrac{1}{4 - 3\cos\left(\theta - \frac{\pi}{3}\right)}$.

24. $r = \dfrac{5}{2 + 2\sin\theta}$ $\Leftrightarrow$ $r = \dfrac{\frac{5}{2}}{1 + \sin\theta}$. Thus $d = \frac{5}{2}$ and the directrix is $y = \frac{5}{2}$

$\Leftrightarrow$ $r = \frac{5}{2}\csc\theta$. The equation of the conic obtained by rotating this parabola

about its focus through an angle of $\frac{\pi}{6}$ is $r = \dfrac{5}{2 + 2\sin\left(\theta - \frac{\pi}{6}\right)}$.

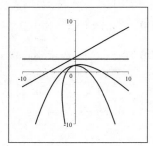

25. The ellipse is nearly circular when e is close to 0 and becomes more elongated as

$e \to 1^-$. At $e = 1$, the curve becomes a parabola.

26. (a) Shown are the graphs of the conics $r = \dfrac{d}{1 + \sin\theta}$ where $d = \frac{1}{2}$, $d = 2$, and $d = 10$. As d increases, the parabolas get flatter while the vertex moves further from the focus at the origin.

(b) Shown are the graphs of the conics $r = \dfrac{e}{1 + e\sin\theta}$ where $e = \frac{1}{2}$, $e = 1$, and $e = 2$. As e changes the conic changes from an ellipse to a parabola, and finally to a hyperbola. The vertex gets closer to the directrix (shown as a dashed line in the figure).

27. (a) Since the polar form of an ellipse with directrix $x = -d$ is $r = \dfrac{ed}{1 - e\cos\theta}$ we need to show that $ed = a\left(1 - e^2\right)$.

From the proof of the Equivalent Description of Conics we have $a^2 = \dfrac{e^2 d^2}{\left(1 - e^2\right)^2}$. Since the conic is an ellipse, $e < 1$ and so the quantities a, d, and $\left(1 - e^2\right)$ are all positive. Thus we can take the square roots of both sides and maintain equality. Thus $a^2 = \dfrac{e^2 d^2}{\left(1 - e^2\right)^2} \quad \Leftrightarrow \quad a = \dfrac{ed}{1 - e^2} \quad \Leftrightarrow \quad ed = a\left(1 - e^2\right)$. As a result, $r = \dfrac{ed}{1 - e\cos\theta} \quad \Leftrightarrow$

$r = \dfrac{a\left(1 - e^2\right)}{1 - e\cos\theta}$.

(b) Since $2a = 2.99 \times 10^8$ we have $a = 1.495 \times 10^8$, so a polar equation for the earth's orbit (using $e \approx 0.017$) is

$$r = \dfrac{1.495 \times 10^8 \left[1 - (0.017)^2\right]}{1 - 0.017\cos\theta} \approx \dfrac{1.49 \times 10^8}{1 - 0.017\cos\theta}.$$

28. (a) Using the form of the equation from Exercise 27, the perihelion distance occurs when $\theta = \pi$ and the aphelion distance occurs when $\theta = 0$. Since the focus is at the origin, the perihelion distance is $\dfrac{a\left(1 - e^2\right)}{1 + e} = \dfrac{a\left(1 - e\right)\left(1 + e\right)}{1 + e} = a\left(1 - e\right)$

and the aphelion distance is $\dfrac{a\left(1 - e^2\right)}{1 - e} = \dfrac{a\left(1 - e\right)\left(1 + e\right)}{1 - e} = a\left(1 + e\right)$.

(b) Given $e = 0.017$ and $2a = 2.99 \times 10^8$ we have $a = 1.495 \times 10^8$. Thus the perihelion distance is $1.495 \times 10^8 \left[1 - (0.017)\right] \approx 1.468 \times 10^8$ km and the aphelion distance is $1.495 \times 10^8 \left(1 + 0.017\right) \approx 1.520 \times 10^8$ km.

29. From Exercise 28, we know that at perihelion $r = 4.43 \times 10^9 = a\left(1 - e\right)$ and at aphelion $r = 7.37 \times 10^9 = a\left(1 + e\right)$.

Dividing these equations gives $\dfrac{7.37 \times 10^9}{4.43 \times 10^9} = \dfrac{a\left(1 + e\right)}{a\left(1 - e\right)} \quad \Leftrightarrow \quad 1.664 = \dfrac{1 + e}{1 - e} \quad \Leftrightarrow \quad 1.664\left(1 - e\right) = 1 + e \quad \Leftrightarrow$

$1.664 - 1 = e + 1.664 \quad \Leftrightarrow \quad 0.664 = 2.664e \quad \Leftrightarrow \quad e = \dfrac{0.664}{2.664} \approx 0.25$.

30. Since the focus is at the origin, the distance from the focus to any point on the conic is the absolute value of the r-coordinate of that point, which we can obtain from the polar equation.

31. The r-coordinate of the satellite will be its distance from the focus (the center of the earth). From the r-coordinate we can easily calculate the height of the satellite.

10.7   Plane Curves and Parametric Equations

1. (a) $x = 2t$, $y = t + 6$

(b) Since $x = 2t$, $t = \dfrac{x}{2}$ and so $y = \dfrac{x}{2} + 6 \Leftrightarrow$
$x - 2y + 12 = 0$.

2. (a) $x = 6t - 4$, $y = 3t$, $t \geq 0$

(b) Since $y = 3t$, $t = \dfrac{y}{3}$ and so $x = 6\left(\dfrac{y}{3}\right) - 4 = 2y - 4$
$\Leftrightarrow \quad 2y = x + 4$, $y \geq 0$.

3. (a) $x = t^2$, $y = t - 2$, $2 \leq t \leq 4$

(b) Since $x = t^2$, $t = \sqrt{x}$ and since $2 \leq t \leq 4$ we have
$4 \leq x \leq 16$. Thus $y = \sqrt{x} - 2$ with $4 \leq x \leq 16$.

4. (a) $x = 2t + 1$, $y = \left(t + \frac{1}{2}\right)^2$

(b) Since $y = \left(t + \frac{1}{2}\right)^2$, $4y = 4\left(t + \frac{1}{2}\right)^2 = (2t + 1)^2$,
and since $x = 2t + 1$, we have $x^2 = (2t + 1)^2 = 4y$
$\Leftrightarrow \quad y = \frac{1}{4}x^2$.

5. (a) $x = \sqrt{t}$, $y = 1 - t \quad \Rightarrow \quad t \geq 0$

(b) Since $x = \sqrt{t}$, we have $x^2 = t$, and so $y = 1 - x^2$
with $x \geq 0$.

6. (a) $x = t^2$, $y = t^4 + 1$

(b) Since $x = t^2$, we have $x^2 = t^4$ and so $y = x^2 + 1$,
$x \geq 0$.

7. (a) $x = \dfrac{1}{t}$, $y = t + 1$

(b) Since $x = \dfrac{1}{t}$ we have $t = \dfrac{1}{x}$ and so $y = \dfrac{1}{x} + 1$.

8. (a) $x = t + 1$, $y = \dfrac{t}{t + 1}$

(b) Since $x = t + 1$, we have $t = x - 1$, so $y = \dfrac{x - 1}{x}$.

9. (a) $x = 4t^2$, $y = 8t^3$

(b) Since $x = 4t^2$ we have $x\sqrt{x} = 4t^2 \cdot 2t = 8t^3$, and so
$y = \pm x\sqrt{x}$.

10. (a) $x = |t|$, $y = |1 - |t||$

(b) Since $x = |t|$, we have $y = |1 - x|$, where $x \geq 0$.

11. (a) $x = 2\sin t$, $y = 2\cos t$, $0 \leq t \leq \pi$

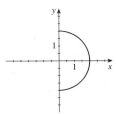

(b) $x^2 = (2\sin t)^2 = 4\sin^2 t$ and $y^2 = 4\cos^2 t$. Hence,
$x^2 + y^2 = 4\sin^2 t + 4\cos^2 t = 4 \quad \Leftrightarrow$
$x^2 + y^2 = 4$, where $x \geq 0$.

12. (a) $x = 2\cos t$, $y = 3\sin t$, $0 \leq t \leq 2\pi$

(b) We have $\cos t = x/2$ and $\sin t = y/3$, so
$(x/2)^2 + (y/3)^2 = \cos^2 t + \sin^2 t = 1 \quad \Leftrightarrow$
$\frac{1}{4}x^2 + \frac{1}{9}y^2 = 1$.

13. (a) $x = \sin^2 t$, $y = \sin^4 t$

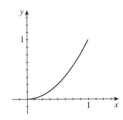

(b) Since $x = \sin^2 t$ we have $x^2 = \sin^4 t$ and so $y = x^2$.
But since $0 \leq \sin^2 t \leq 1$ we only get the part of this
parabola for which $0 \leq x \leq 1$.

14. (a) $x = \sin^2 t$, $y = \cos t$

(b) Since $y = \cos t$, we have $y^2 = \cos^2 t$ and so
$x + y^2 = \sin^2 t + \cos^2 t = 1$ or $x = 1 - y^2$ (actually
$y = \pm\sqrt{1-x}$), where $0 \leq x \leq 1$.

15. (a) $x = \cos t$, $y = \cos 2t$

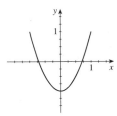

(b) Since $x = \cos t$ we have $x^2 = \cos^2 t$, so
$2x^2 - 1 = 2\cos^2 t - 1 = \cos 2t = y$. Hence, the
rectangular equation is $y = 2x^2 - 1$, $-1 \leq x \leq 1$.

16. (a) $x = \cos 2t$, $y = \sin 2t$

(b) $x^2 = \cos^2 2t$ and $y^2 = \sin^2 2t$. Then
$x^2 + y^2 = \cos^2 2t + \sin^2 2t = 1 \quad \Leftrightarrow$
$x^2 + y^2 = 1$.

17. (a) $x = \sec t, y = \tan t, 0 \le t < \frac{\pi}{2} \quad \Rightarrow \quad x \ge 1$ and $y \ge 0$.

(b) $x^2 = \sec^2 t, y^2 = \tan^2 t$, and $y^2 + 1 = \tan^2 t + 1 = \sec^2 t = x^2$. Therefore, $y^2 + 1 = x^2 \quad \Leftrightarrow \quad x^2 - y^2 = 1, x \ge 1, y \ge 0$.

18. (a) $x = \cot t, y = \csc t, 0 < t < \pi$ so $y \ge 1$.

(b) $x^2 = \cot^2 t, y^2 = \csc^2 t$, and so $x^2 + 1 = \cot^2 t + 1 = \csc^2 t = y^2$. Therefore, $y^2 = x^2 + 1$, with $y \ge 1$. This is the top half of the hyperbola $y^2 - x^2 = 1$.

19. (a) $x = e^t, y = e^{-t} \quad \Rightarrow \quad x > 0, y > 0$.

(b) $xy = e^t \cdot e^{-t} = e^0 = 1$. Hence, the equation is $xy = 1$, with $x > 0, y > 0$.

20. (a) $x = e^{2t}, y = e^t, t \ge 0$.

(b) $y^2 = e^{2t}$ so $x = y^2$, with $y \ge 1$.

21. (a) $x = \cos^2 t, y = \sin^2 t$

(b) $x + y = \cos^2 t + \sin^2 t = 1$. Hence, the equation is $x + y = 1$ with $0 \le x, y \le 1$.

22. (a) $x = \cos^3 t, y = \sin^3 t, 0 \le t \le 2\pi$

(b) $x^{2/3} = \cos^2 t$ and $y^{2/3} = \sin^2 t$, and so $x^{2/3} + y^{2/3} = 1$.

23. Since the line passes through the point $(4, -1)$ and has slope $\frac{1}{2}$, parametric equations for the line are $x = 4 + t$, $y = -1 + \frac{1}{2}t$.

24. Since the line passes through the point $(-10, -20)$ and has slope -2, parametric equations for the line are $x = -10 + t$, $y = -20 - 2t$.

25. Since the line passes through the points $(6, 7)$ and $(7, 8)$, its slope is $\dfrac{8 - 7}{7 - 6} = 1$. Thus, parametric equations for the line are $x = 6 + t, y = 7 + t$.

26. Since the line passes through the points $(0, 0)$ and $(12, 7)$, its slope is $\dfrac{7 - 0}{12 - 0} = \dfrac{7}{12}$. Thus, parametric equations for the line are $x = t, y = \frac{7}{12}t$.

27. Since $\cos^2 t + \sin^2 t = 1$, we have $a^2 \cos^2 t + a^2 \sin^2 t = a^2$. If we let $x = a \cos t$ and $y = a \sin t$, then $x^2 + y^2 = a^2$. Hence, parametric equations for the circle are $x = a \cos t$, $y = a \sin t$.

28. Since $\cos^2 t + \sin^2 t = 1$, we have $\dfrac{a^2 \cos^2 t}{a^2} + \dfrac{b^2 \sin^2 t}{b^2} = 1$. If we let $x = a \cos t$ and $y = b \sin t$, then $\dfrac{x^2}{a^2} + \dfrac{y^2}{b^2} = 1$. Hence, parametric equations for the ellipse are $x = a \cos t$, $y = b \sin t$.

29. $x = a \tan \theta \iff \tan \theta = \dfrac{x}{a} \Rightarrow \tan^2 \theta = \dfrac{x^2}{a^2}$. Also, $y = b \sec \theta \iff \sec \theta = \dfrac{y}{b} \Rightarrow \sec^2 \theta = \dfrac{y^2}{b^2}$. Since $\tan^2 \theta = \sec^2 \theta - 1$, we have $\dfrac{x^2}{a^2} = \dfrac{y^2}{b^2} - 1 \iff \dfrac{y^2}{b^2} - \dfrac{x^2}{a^2} = 1$, which is the equation of a hyperbola.

30. Substituting the given values for x and y into the equation we derived in Exercise 29, we get

$$\frac{\left(b\sqrt{t+1}\right)^2}{b^2} - \frac{\left(a\sqrt{t}\right)^2}{a^2} = (t+1) - t = 1.$$ Thus the points on this curve satisfy the equation, which is that of a hyperbola.

However, this hyperbola is only the part of $\dfrac{y^2}{b^2} - \dfrac{x^2}{a^2} = 1$ for which $x \geq 0$ and $y \geq 0$.

31. $x = t \cos t$, $y = t \sin t$, $t \geq 0$

t	x	y
0	0	0
$\frac{\pi}{4}$	$\frac{\pi\sqrt{2}}{8}$	$\frac{\pi\sqrt{2}}{8}$
$\frac{\pi}{2}$	0	$\frac{\pi}{2}$
$\frac{3\pi}{4}$	$-\frac{3\pi\sqrt{2}}{8}$	$\frac{3\pi\sqrt{2}}{8}$
π	$-\pi$	0

t	x	y
$\frac{5\pi}{4}$	$-\frac{5\pi\sqrt{2}}{8}$	$-\frac{5\pi\sqrt{2}}{8}$
$\frac{3\pi}{2}$	0	$-\frac{3\pi}{2}$
$\frac{7\pi}{4}$	$\frac{7\pi\sqrt{2}}{8}$	$-\frac{7\pi\sqrt{2}}{8}$
2π	2π	0

32. $x = \sin t$, $y = \sin 2t$

33. $x = \dfrac{3t}{1+t^3}$, $y = \dfrac{3t^2}{1+t^3}$, $t \neq -1$

t	x	y	t	x	y	t	x	y	t	x	y
-0.9	-9.96	8.97	2	0.67	1.33	-1.1	9.97	-10.97	-4	0.19	-0.76
-0.75	-3.89	2.92	2.5	0.45	1.13	-1.25	3.93	-4.92	-4.5	0.15	-0.67
-0.5	-1.71	0.86	3	0.32	0.96	-1.5	1.89	-2.84	-5	0.12	-0.60
0	0	0	4	0.18	0.74	-2	0.86	-1.71	-6	0.08	-0.50
0.5	1.33	0.67	5	0.12	0.60	-2.5	0.51	-1.28	-7	0.06	-0.43
1	1.5	1.5	6	0.08	0.50	-3	0.35	-1.04	-8	0.05	-0.38
1.5	1.03	1.54				-3.5	0.25	-0.88			

As $t \to -1^-$ we have $x \to -\infty$ and $y \to \infty$. As $t \to -1^+$ we have $x \to \infty$ and $y \to -\infty$. As $t \to \infty$ we have $x \to 0^+$ and $y \to 0^+$. As $t \to -\infty$ we have $x \to 0^+$ and $y \to 0^-$.

34. $x = \cot t$, $y = \sin^2 t$, $0 < t < \pi$

35. $x = (v_0 \cos \alpha) t$, $y = (v_0 \sin \alpha) t - 16t^2$. From the equation for x,

$t = \dfrac{x}{v_0 \cos \alpha}$. Substituting into the equation for y gives

$$y = (v_0 \sin \alpha) \frac{x}{v_0 \cos \alpha} - 16 \left(\frac{x}{v_0 \cos \alpha}\right)^2 = x \tan \alpha - \frac{16x^2}{v_0^2 \cos^2 \alpha}.$$ Thus

the equation is of the form $y = c_1 x - c_2 x^2$, where c_1 and c_2 are constants, so its graph is a parabola.

36. $v_0 = 2048$ ft/s and $\alpha = 30°$.

(a) The bullet will hit the ground when $y = 0$. Since $y = (v_0 \sin \alpha) t - 16t^2$, we have $0 = (2048 \cdot \sin 30°) t - 16t^2 \quad \Leftrightarrow$
$0 = 1024t - 16t^2 \Leftrightarrow 16t (t - 64) = 0 \quad \Leftrightarrow \quad t = 0$ or $t = 64$. Hence, the bullet will hit the ground after 64 seconds.

(b) After 64 seconds, the bullet will hit the ground at $x = (2048 \cdot \cos 30°) \cdot 64 = 65{,}536\sqrt{3} \approx 113{,}511.7$ ft≈ 21.5 miles.

(c) The maximum height attained by the bullet is the maximum value of the y parameter. Since
$y = 1024t - 16t^2 = -16 \left(t^2 - 64t\right) = -16 \left(t^2 - 64t + 1024\right) + 16{,}384 = -16 \left(t - 32\right)^2 + 16{,}384$, y is
maximized when $t = 32$, and therefore the maximum height is 16,384 ft≈ 3.1 miles.

37. $x = \sin t$, $y = 2 \cos 3t$

38. $x = 2 \sin t$, $y = \cos 4t$

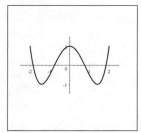

39. $x = 3 \sin 5t$, $y = 5 \cos 3t$

40. $x = \sin 4t$, $y = \cos 3t$

41. $x = \sin (\cos t)$, $y = \cos t^{3/2}$, $0 \le t \le 2\pi$

42. $x = 2 \cos t + \cos 2t$, $y = 2 \sin t - \sin 2t$

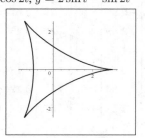

43. (a) $r = e^{\theta/12}$, $0 \le \theta \le 4\pi \quad \Rightarrow \quad x = e^{t/12} \cos t$,
$y = e^{t/12} \sin t$

(b)

44. (a) $r = \sin \theta + 2 \cos \theta \Leftrightarrow x = (\sin \theta + 2 \cos \theta) \cos \theta$,
$y = (\sin \theta + 2 \cos \theta) \sin \theta$

(b)

45. (a) $r = \dfrac{4}{2 - \cos\theta}$ $\Leftrightarrow$ $x = \dfrac{4\cos t}{2 - \cos t}, y = \dfrac{4\sin t}{2 - \cos t}$ **46. (a)** $r = 2^{\sin\theta}$ $\Rightarrow$ $x = 2^{\sin\theta}\cos\theta, y = 2^{\sin\theta}\sin\theta$

(b)

(b)

47. $x = t^3 - 2t$, $y = t^2 - t$ is Graph III, since $y = t^2 - t = \left(t^2 - t + \frac{1}{4}\right) - \frac{1}{4} = \left(t - \frac{1}{2}\right)^2 - \frac{1}{4}$, and so $y \geq -\frac{1}{4}$ on this curve, while x is unbounded.

48. $x = \sin 3t$, $y = \sin 4t$ is Graph IV, since when $t = 0$ and $t = \pi$ the curve passes through $(0, 0)$. Thus this curve must pass through $(0, 0)$ twice.

49. $x = t + \sin 2t$, $y = t + \sin 3t$ is Graph II, since the values of x and y oscillate about their values on the line $x = t$, $y = t$ $\Leftrightarrow$ $y = x$.

50. $x = \sin(t + \sin t)$, $y = \cos(t + \cos t)$ is Graph I, since this curve does not pass through the point $(0, 0)$.

51. If we modify Figure 8 so that $|PC| = b$, then by the same reasoning as in Example 6, we see that $x = |OT| - |PQ| = a\theta - b\sin\theta$ and $y = |TC| - |CQ| = a - b\cos\theta$. We graph the case where $a = 3$ and $b = 2$.

52. From the first figure, we see that $x = |OT| - |PQ| = a\theta - b\sin\theta$ and $y = |TC| - |CQ| = a - b\cos\theta$. When $a = 1$ and $b = 2$, the parametric equations become $x = \theta - 2\sin\theta$, $y = 1 - 2\cos\theta$. The curve is sketched for $0 \leq \theta \leq 4\pi$.

53. (a) We first note that the center of circle C (the small circle) has coordinates $([a-b]\cos\theta, [a-b]\sin\theta)$. Now the arc PQ has the same length as the arc

$P'Q$, so $b\phi = a\theta$ $\Leftrightarrow$ $\phi = \dfrac{a}{b}\theta$, and so $\phi - \theta = \dfrac{a}{b}\theta - \theta = \dfrac{a-b}{b}\theta$. Thus the x-coordinate of P is the x-coordinate of the center of circle C plus

$b\cos(\phi - \theta) = b\cos\left(\dfrac{a-b}{b}\theta\right)$, and the y-coordinate of P is the

y-coordinate of the center of circle C minus

$b\cdot\sin(\phi - \theta) = b\sin\left(\dfrac{a-b}{b}\theta\right)$. So $x = (a-b)\cos\theta + b\cos\left(\dfrac{a-b}{b}\theta\right)$

and $y = (a-b)\sin\theta - b\sin\left(\dfrac{a-b}{b}\theta\right)$.

(b) If $a = 4b$, $b = \dfrac{a}{4}$, and $x = \frac{3}{4}a\cos\theta + \frac{1}{4}a\cos 3\theta$, $y = \frac{3}{4}a\sin\theta - \frac{1}{4}a\sin 3\theta$.

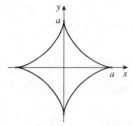

From Example 2 in Section 7.3, $\cos 3\theta = 4\cos^3\theta - 3\cos\theta$. Similarly, one can prove that $\sin 3\theta = 3\sin\theta - 4\sin^3\theta$. Substituting, we get

$x = \frac{3}{4}a\cos\theta + \frac{1}{4}a\left(4\cos^3\theta - 3\cos\theta\right) = a\cos^3\theta$

$y = \frac{3}{4}a\sin\theta - \frac{1}{4}a\left(3\sin\theta - 4\sin^3\theta\right) = a\sin^3\theta$. Thus,

$x^{2/3} + y^{2/3} = a^{2/3}\cos^2\theta + a^{2/3}\sin^2\theta = a^{2/3}$, so $x^{2/3} + y^{2/3} = a^{2/3}$.

54. The coordinates of C are $([a+b]\cos\theta, [a+b]\sin\theta)$. Let ϕ be $\angle OCP$ as shown in the figure. Then the arcs traced out by rolling the circle along the outside are equal, that is, $b\phi = a\theta$ $\Leftrightarrow$ $\phi = \dfrac{a}{b}\theta$. P is displaced from C by amounts equal to the legs of the right triangle CPT, where CP is the hypotenuse. Since $\triangle OCQ$ is a right triangle, it follows that

$\angle OCQ = \frac{\pi}{2} - \theta$. Thus, $\alpha = \phi - \left(\dfrac{\pi}{2} - \theta\right) = \dfrac{a}{b}\theta - \dfrac{\pi}{2} + \theta = \left(\dfrac{a+b}{b}\right)\theta - \dfrac{\pi}{2}$. So

$$x = (a+b)\cos\theta + b\sin\left[\left(\dfrac{a+b}{b}\right)\theta - \dfrac{\pi}{2}\right] = (a+b)\cos\theta - b\sin\left[\dfrac{\pi}{2} - \left(\dfrac{a+b}{b}\right)\theta\right]$$

$$= (a+b)\cos\theta - b\cos\left(\dfrac{a+b}{b}\right)\theta$$

and

$$y = (a+b)\sin\theta - b\cos\left[\left(\dfrac{a+b}{b}\right)\theta - \dfrac{\pi}{2}\right] = (a+b)\sin\theta - b\cos\left[\dfrac{\pi}{2} - \left(\dfrac{a+b}{b}\right)\theta\right]$$

$$= (a+b)\sin\theta - b\sin\left(\dfrac{a+b}{b}\right)\theta$$

Therefore, parametric equations for the epicycloid are

$x = (a+b)\cos\theta - b\cos\left(\dfrac{a+b}{b}\right)\theta$ and $y = (a+b)\sin\theta - b\sin\left(\dfrac{a+b}{b}\right)\theta$.

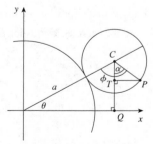

55. A polar equation for the circle is $r = 2a\sin\theta$. Thus the coordinates of Q are $x = r\cos\theta = 2a\sin\theta\cos\theta$ and $y = r\sin\theta = 2a\sin^2\theta$. The coordinates of R are $x = 2a\cot\theta$ and $y = 2a$. Since P is the midpoint of QR, we use the midpoint formula to get $x = a(\sin\theta\cos\theta + \cot\theta)$ and $y = a(1 + \sin^2\theta)$.

56. (a) It is apparent that $x = |OQ|$ and
$y = |QP| = |ST|$. From the diagram,
$x = |OQ| = a \cos \theta$ and $y = |ST| = b \sin \theta$.
Thus, parametric equations are $x = a \cos \theta$ and
$y = b \sin \theta$.

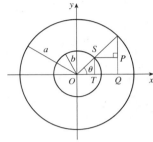

(b) The curve is graphed with $a = 5$ and $b = 2$.

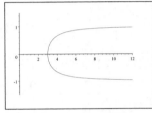

(c) To eliminate θ we rearrange: $\sin \theta = y/b \implies$
$\sin^2 \theta = (y/b)^2$ and $\cos \theta = x/a \implies$
$\cos^2 \theta = (x/a)^2$. Adding the two equations:
$\sin^2 \theta + \cos^2 \theta = 1 = x^2/a^2 + y^2/b^2$. As
indicated in part (b), the curve is an ellipse.

57. (a) A has coordinates $(a \cos \theta, a \sin \theta)$. Since OA is perpendicular to AB,
$\triangle OAB$ is a right triangle and B has coordinates $(a \sec \theta, 0)$. It follows
that P has coordinates $(a \sec \theta, b \sin \theta)$. Thus, the parametric equations
are $x = a \sec \theta$, $y = b \sin \theta$.

(b) The right half of the curve is graphed with $a = 3$ and $b = 1$.

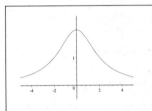

58. (a) $C = (2a \cot \theta, 2a)$, so the x-coordinate of P is $x = 2a \cot \theta$. Let
$B = (0, 2a)$. Then $\angle OAB$ is a right angle and $\angle OBA = \theta$, so
$|OA| = 2a \sin \theta$ and $A = (2a \sin \theta \cos \theta, 2a \sin^2 \theta)$. Thus, the
y-coordinate of P is $y = 2a \sin^2 \theta$.

(b) The curve is graphed with $a = 1$.

59. We use the equation for y from Example 6 and solve for θ. Thus for $0 \le \theta \le \pi$, $y = a(1 - \cos \theta) \Leftrightarrow \dfrac{a - y}{a} = \cos \theta$

$\Leftrightarrow \quad \theta = \cos^{-1}\left(\dfrac{a-y}{a}\right)$. Substituting into the equation for x, we get $x = a\left[\cos^{-1}\left(\dfrac{a-y}{a}\right) - \sin\left(\cos^{-1}\left(\dfrac{a-y}{a}\right)\right)\right]$.

However, $\sin\left(\cos^{-1}\left(\dfrac{a-y}{a}\right)\right) = \sqrt{1 - \left(\dfrac{a-y}{a}\right)^2} = \dfrac{\sqrt{2ay - y^2}}{a}$. Thus, $x = a\left[\cos^{-1}\left(\dfrac{a-y}{a}\right) - \dfrac{\sqrt{2ay - y^2}}{a}\right]$,

and we have $\dfrac{\sqrt{2ay - y^2} + x}{a} = \cos^{-1}\left(\dfrac{a-y}{a}\right) \implies 1 - \dfrac{y}{a} = \cos\left(\dfrac{\sqrt{2ay - y^2} + x}{a}\right) \implies$

$y = a\left[1 - \cos\left(\dfrac{\sqrt{2ay - y^2} + x}{a}\right)\right]$.

60. (a)

| $R = 0.5$ | $R = 1$ | $R = 3$ | $R = 5$ |

(b) The graph with $R = 5$ seems to most closely resemble the profile of the engine housing.

61. In the figure, since OQ and QT are perpendicular and OT and TP are perpendicular, the angles formed by their intersections are equal, that is, $\theta = \angle PTQ$. Now the coordinates of T are $(\cos\theta, \sin\theta)$. Since $|TP|$ is the length of the string that has been unwound from the circle, it must also have arc length θ, so $|TP| = \theta$. Thus 3the x-displacement from T to P is $\theta \cdot \sin\theta$ while the y-displacement from T to P is $\theta \cdot \cos\theta$. So the coordinates of P are $x = \cos\theta + \theta\sin\theta$ and $y = \sin\theta - \theta\cos\theta$.

62. (a) It takes 2π units of time. The parametric equations of the particle that moves twice as fast around the circle are $x = \sin 2t$, $y = \cos 2t$.

(b) From the first table, we see that the particle travels counterclockwise. If we want the particle to travel in a clockwise direction, then we want the second table to apply. Possible parametric equations for clockwise traversal of the unit circle are $x = -\sin t$, $y = \cos t$.

t	$x = \sin t$	$y = \cos t$
0	0	1
$\frac{\pi}{2}$	1	0
π	0	-1
$\frac{3\pi}{2}$	-1	0
2π	0	1

t	x	y
0	0	1
$\frac{\pi}{2}$	-1	0
π	0	-1
$\frac{3\pi}{2}$	1	0
2π	0	1

63. $C: x = t, y = t^2$; $D: x = \sqrt{t}, y = t, t \geq 0$ $E: x = \sin t, y = 1 - \cos^2 t$ $F: x = e^t, y = e^{2t}$

(a) For C, $x = t, y = t^2 \Rightarrow y = x^2$.
For D, $x = \sqrt{t}, y = t \Rightarrow y = x^2$.
For E, $x = \sin t \Rightarrow x^2 = \sin^2 t = 1 - \cos^2 t = y$ and so $y = x^2$.
For F, $x = e^t \Rightarrow x^2 = e^{2t} = y$ and so $y = x^2$. Therefore, the points on all four curves satisfy the same rectangular equation.

(b) Curve C is the entire parabola $y = x^2$. Curve D is the right half of the parabola because $t \geq 0$ and so $x \geq 0$. Curve E is the portion of the parabola for $-1 \leq x \leq 1$. Curve F is the portion of the parabola where $x > 0$, since $e^t > 0$ for all t.

C

D

E

F

Chapter 10 Review

1. $y^2 = 4x$. This is a parabola with $4p = 4 \iff p = 1$. The vertex is $(0,0)$, the focus is $(1,0)$, and the directrix is $x = -1$.

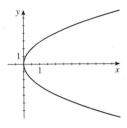

2. $x = \frac{1}{12}y^2 \iff y^2 = 12x$. This is a parabola with $4p = 12 \iff p = 3$. The vertex is $(0,0)$, the focus is $(3,0)$, and the directrix is $x = -3$.

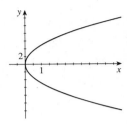

3. $x^2 + 8y = 0 \iff x^2 = -8y$. This is a parabola with $4p = -8 \iff p = -2$. The vertex is $(0,0)$, the focus is $(0,-2)$, and the directrix is $y = 2$.

4. $2x - y^2 = 0 \iff y^2 = 2x$. This is a parabola with $4p = 2 \iff p = \frac{1}{2}$. The vertex is $(0,0)$, the focus is $\left(\frac{1}{2}, 0\right)$, and the directrix is $x = -\frac{1}{2}$.

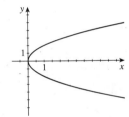

5. $x - y^2 + 4y - 2 = 0 \iff x - \left(y^2 - 4y + 4\right) - 2 = -4 \iff$
$x - (y-2)^2 = -2 \iff (y-2)^2 = x + 2$. This is a parabola with $4p = 1 \iff$
$p = \frac{1}{4}$. The vertex is $(-2, 2)$, the focus is $\left(-2 + \frac{1}{4}, 2\right) = \left(-\frac{7}{4}, 2\right)$, and the
directrix is $x = -2 - \frac{1}{4} = -\frac{9}{4}$.

6. $2x^2 + 6x + 5y + 10 = 0 \iff 2\left(x^2 + 3x + \frac{9}{4}\right) + 5y + 10 = \frac{9}{2} \iff$
$2\left(x + \frac{3}{2}\right)^2 = -5y - \frac{11}{2} \iff 2\left(x + \frac{3}{2}\right)^2 = -5\left(y + \frac{11}{10}\right) \iff$
$\left(x + \frac{3}{2}\right)^2 = -\frac{5}{2}\left(y + \frac{11}{10}\right)$. This is a parabola with $4p = -\frac{5}{2} \iff p = -\frac{5}{8}$. The
vertex is $\left(-\frac{3}{2}, -\frac{11}{10}\right)$, the focus is
$\left(-\frac{3}{2}, -\frac{11}{10} - \frac{5}{8}\right) = \left(-\frac{3}{2}, -\frac{44+25}{40}\right) = \left(-\frac{3}{2}, -\frac{69}{40}\right)$, and the directrix is
$y = -\frac{11}{10} + \frac{5}{8} = \frac{-44+25}{40} = -\frac{19}{40}$.

7. $\frac{1}{2}x^2 + 2x = 2y + 4$ $\Leftrightarrow$ $x^2 + 4x = 4y + 8$ $\Leftrightarrow$ $x^2 + 4x + 4 = 4y + 8$
$\Leftrightarrow$ $(x+2)^2 = 4(y+3)$. This is a parabola with $4p = 4$ $\Leftrightarrow$ $p = 1$. The
vertex is $(-2, -3)$, the focus is $(-2, -3+1) = (-2, -2)$, and the directrix is
$y = -3 - 1 = -4$.

8. $x^2 = 3(x+y)$ $\Leftrightarrow$ $x^2 - 3x = 3y$ $\Leftrightarrow$ $x^2 - 3x + \frac{9}{4} = 3y + \frac{9}{4}$ $\Leftrightarrow$
$\left(x - \frac{3}{2}\right)^2 = 3\left(y + \frac{3}{4}\right)$. This is a parabola with $4p = 3$ $\Leftrightarrow$ $p = \frac{3}{4}$. The vertex
is $\left(\frac{3}{2}, -\frac{3}{4}\right)$, the focus is $\left(\frac{3}{2}, -\frac{3}{4} + \frac{3}{4}\right) = \left(\frac{3}{2}, 0\right)$, and the directrix is
$y = -\frac{3}{4} - \frac{3}{4} = -\frac{3}{2}$.

9. $\dfrac{x^2}{9} + \dfrac{y^2}{25} = 1$. This is an ellipse with $a = 5$, $b = 3$, and $c = \sqrt{25 - 9} = 4$. The
center is $(0, 0)$, the vertices are $(0, \pm 5)$, the foci are $(0, \pm 4)$, the length of the
major axis is $2a = 10$, and the length of the minor axis is $2b = 6$.

10. $\dfrac{x^2}{49} + \dfrac{y^2}{9} = 1$. This is an ellipse with $a = 7$, $b = 3$, and $c = \sqrt{49 - 9} = 2\sqrt{10}$.
The center is $(0, 0)$, the vertices are $(\pm 7, 0)$, the foci are $(\pm 2\sqrt{10}, 0)$, the length
of the major axis is $2a = 14$, and the length of the minor axis is $2b = 6$.

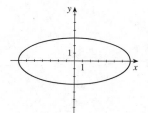

11. $x^2 + 4y^2 = 16$ $\Leftrightarrow$ $\dfrac{x^2}{16} + \dfrac{y^2}{4} = 1$. This is an ellipse with $a = 4$, $b = 2$, and
$c = \sqrt{16 - 4} = 2\sqrt{3}$. The center is $(0, 0)$, the vertices are $(\pm 4, 0)$, the foci are
$(\pm 2\sqrt{3}, 0)$, the length of the major axis is $2a = 8$, and the length of the minor axis
is $2b = 4$.

12. $9x^2 + 4y^2 = 1$ $\Leftrightarrow$ $\dfrac{x^2}{1/9} + \dfrac{y^2}{1/4} = 1$. This is an ellipse with $a = \frac{1}{2}$, $b = \frac{1}{3}$, and
$c = \sqrt{\frac{1}{4} - \frac{1}{9}} = \frac{1}{6}\sqrt{5}$. The center is $(0, 0)$, the vertices are $\left(0, \pm\frac{1}{2}\right)$, the foci are
$\left(0, \pm\frac{1}{6}\sqrt{5}\right)$, the length of the major axis is $2a = 1$, and the length of the minor
axis is $2b = \frac{2}{3}$.

13. $\dfrac{(x-3)^2}{9} + \dfrac{y^2}{16} = 1.$ This is an ellipse with $a = 4$, $b = 3$, and $c = \sqrt{16-9} = \sqrt{7}.$
The center is $(3,0)$, the vertices are $(3,\pm 4)$, the foci are $(3,\pm\sqrt{7})$, the length of
the major axis is $2a = 8$, and the length of the minor axis is $2b = 6$.

14. $\dfrac{(x-2)^2}{25} + \dfrac{(y+3)^2}{16} = 1.$ This is an ellipse with $a = 5$, $b = 4$, and
$c = \sqrt{25-16} = 3.$ The center is $(2,-3)$, the vertices are
$(2\pm 5, -3) = (-3,-3)$ and $(7,-3)$, the foci are $(2\pm 3, -3) = (-1,-3)$ and
$(5,-3)$, the length of the major axis is $2a = 10$, and the length of the minor axis is
$2b = 8$.

15. $4x^2 + 9y^2 = 36y \iff 4x^2 + 9\left(y^2 - 4y + 4\right) = 36 \iff$
$4x^2 + 9(y-2)^2 = 36 \iff \dfrac{x^2}{9} + \dfrac{(y-2)^2}{4} = 1.$ This is an ellipse with $a = 3$,
$b = 2$, and $c = \sqrt{9-4} = \sqrt{5}.$ The center is $(0,2)$, the vertices are $(\pm 3, 2)$, the
foci are $(\pm\sqrt{5}, 2)$, the length of the major axis is $2a = 6$, and the length of the
minor axis is $2b = 4$.

16. $2x^2 + y^2 = 2 + 4(x-y) \iff 2x^2 - 4x + y^2 + 4y = 2 \iff$
$2\left(x^2 - 2x + 1\right) + \left(y^2 + 4y + 4\right) = 2 + 2 + 4 \iff$
$2(x-1)^2 + (y+2)^2 = 8 \iff \dfrac{(x-1)^2}{4} + \dfrac{(y+2)^2}{8} = 1.$ This is an ellipse
with $a = 2\sqrt{2}$, $b = 2$, and $c = \sqrt{8-4} = 2.$ The center is $(1,-2)$, the vertices are
$\left(1, -2 \pm 2\sqrt{2}\right)$, the foci are $(1, -2 \pm 2)$, so the foci are $(1,0)$ and $(1,-4)$, the
length of the major axis is $2a = 4\sqrt{2}$, and the length of the minor axis is $2b = 4$.

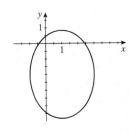

17. $-\dfrac{x^2}{9} + \dfrac{y^2}{16} = 1 \iff \dfrac{y^2}{16} - \dfrac{x^2}{9} = 0.$ This is a hyperbola with $a = 4$, $b = 3$, and
$c = \sqrt{16+9} = \sqrt{25} = 5.$ The center is $(0,0)$, the vertices are $(0,\pm 4)$, the foci
are $(0,\pm 5)$, and the asymptotes are $y = \pm\frac{4}{3}x$.

18. $\dfrac{x^2}{49} - \dfrac{y^2}{32} = 1.$ This is a hyperbola with $a = 7$, $b = 4\sqrt{2}$, and $c = \sqrt{49+32} = 9.$
The center is $(0,0)$, the vertices are $(\pm 7, 0)$, the foci are $(\pm 9, 0)$, and the
asymptotes are $y = \pm\frac{4\sqrt{2}}{7}x$.

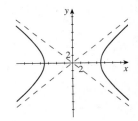

19. $x^2 - 2y^2 = 16$ $\Leftrightarrow$ $\dfrac{x^2}{16} - \dfrac{y^2}{8} = 1$. This is a hyperbola with $a = 4$, $b = 2\sqrt{2}$,

and $c = \sqrt{16 + 8} = \sqrt{24} = 2\sqrt{6}$. The center is $(0, 0)$, the vertices are $(\pm 4, 0)$,

the foci are $(\pm 2\sqrt{6}, 0)$, and the asymptotes are $y = \pm\dfrac{2\sqrt{2}}{4} x$ $\Leftrightarrow$ $y = \pm\dfrac{1}{\sqrt{2}} x$.

20. $x^2 - 4y^2 + 16 = 0$ $\Leftrightarrow$ $4y^2 - x^2 = 16$ $\Leftrightarrow$ $\dfrac{y^2}{4} - \dfrac{x^2}{16} = 1$. This is a

hyperbola with $a = 2$, $b = 4$, and $c = \sqrt{4 + 16} = 2\sqrt{5}$. The center is $(0, 0)$, the

vertices are $(0, \pm 2)$, the foci are $(0, \pm 2\sqrt{5})$, and the asymptotes are $y = \pm\dfrac{2}{4} x$

$\Leftrightarrow$ $y = \pm\dfrac{1}{2} x$.

21. $\dfrac{(x + 4)^2}{16} - \dfrac{y^2}{16} = 1$. This is a hyperbola with $a = 4$, $b = 4$ and

$c = \sqrt{16 + 16} = 4\sqrt{2}$. The center is $(-4, 0)$, the vertices are $(-4 \pm 4, 0)$ which

are $(-8, 0)$ and $(0, 0)$, the foci are $(-4 \pm 4\sqrt{2}, 0)$, and the asymptotes are

$y = \pm (x + 4)$.

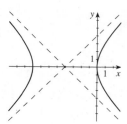

22. $\dfrac{(x - 2)^2}{8} - \dfrac{(y + 2)^2}{8} = 1$. This is a hyperbola with $a = 2\sqrt{2}$, $b = 2\sqrt{2}$ and

$c = \sqrt{8 + 8} = 4$. The center is $(2, -2)$, the vertices are $(2 \pm 2\sqrt{2}, -2)$, the foci

are $(2 \pm 4, -2) = (-2, -2)$ and $(6, -2)$, and the asymptotes are

$y + 2 = \pm (x - 2)$ $\Leftrightarrow$ $y = -x$ and $y = x - 4$.

23. $9y^2 + 18y = x^2 + 6x + 18$ $\Leftrightarrow$

$9\left(y^2 + 2y + 1\right) = \left(x^2 + 6x + 9\right) + 9 - 9 + 18$ $\Leftrightarrow$

$9\left(y + 1\right)^2 - \left(x + 3\right)^2 = 18$ $\Leftrightarrow$ $\dfrac{(y + 1)^2}{2} - \dfrac{(x + 3)^2}{18} = 1$. This is a

hyperbola with $a = \sqrt{2}$, $b = 3\sqrt{2}$, and $c = \sqrt{2 + 18} = 2\sqrt{5}$. The center is

$(-3, -1)$, the vertices are $(-3, -1 \pm \sqrt{2})$, the foci are $(-3, -1 \pm 2\sqrt{5})$, and the

asymptotes are $y + 1 = \pm\dfrac{1}{3}(x + 3)$ $\Leftrightarrow$ $y = \dfrac{1}{3} x$ and $y = -\dfrac{1}{3} x - 2$.

24. $y^2 = x^2 + 6y$ $\Leftrightarrow$ $\left(y^2 - 6y + 9\right) - x^2 = 9$ $\Leftrightarrow$ $(y - 3)^2 - x^2 = 9$ $\Leftrightarrow$

$\dfrac{(y - 3)^2}{9} - \dfrac{x^2}{9} = 1$. This is a hyperbola with $a = 3$, $b = 3$, and

$c = \sqrt{9 + 9} = 3\sqrt{2}$. The center is $(0, 3)$, the vertices are $(0, 3 \pm 3) = (0, 6)$ and

$(0, 0)$, the foci are $(0, 3 \pm 3\sqrt{2})$, and the asymptotes are $y - 3 = \pm x$ $\Leftrightarrow$

$y = x + 3$ and $y = -x + 3$.

25. This is a parabola that opens to the right with its vertex at $(0,0)$ and the focus at $(2,0)$. So $p = 2$, and the equation is $y^2 = 4\,(2)\,x \iff y^2 = 8x$.

26. This is an ellipse with the center at $(0,0)$, $a = 12$, and $b = 5$. The equation is then $\dfrac{x^2}{12^2} + \dfrac{y^2}{5^2} = 1 \iff \dfrac{x^2}{144} + \dfrac{y^2}{25} = 1$.

27. From the graph, the center is $(0,0)$, and the vertices are $(0,-4)$ and $(0,4)$. Since a is the distance from the center to a vertex, we have $a = 4$. Because one focus is $(0,5)$, we have $c = 5$, and since $c^2 = a^2 + b^2$, we have $25 = 16 + b^2 \iff b^2 = 9$. Thus an equation of the hyperbola is $\dfrac{y^2}{16} - \dfrac{x^2}{9} = 1$.

28. This is a parabola that opens to the left with its vertex at $(4,4)$, so its equation is of the form $(y-4)^2 = 4p\,(x-4)$ with $p < 0$. Since $(0,0)$ is a point on this hyperbola, we must have $(0-4)^2 = 4p\,(0-4) \iff 16 = -16p \iff p = -1$. Thus the equation is $(y-4)^2 = -4\,(x-4)$.

29. From the graph, the center of the ellipse is $(4,2)$, and so $a = 4$ and $b = 2$. The equation is $\dfrac{(x-4)^2}{4^2} + \dfrac{(y-2)^2}{2^2} = 1 \iff \dfrac{(x-4)^2}{16} + \dfrac{(y-2)^2}{4} = 1$.

30. From the graph, the center is at $(1,0)$, and the vertices are $(0,0)$ and $(2,0)$. Since a is the distance form the center to a vertex, $a = 1$. From the graph, the slope of one of the asymptotes is $\dfrac{b}{a} = 1 \iff b = 1$. Thus an equation of the hyperbola is $(x-1)^2 - y^2 = 1$.

31. $\dfrac{x^2}{12} + y = 1 \iff \dfrac{x^2}{12} = -(y-1) \iff x^2 = -12\,(y-1)$. This is a parabola with $4p = -12 \iff p = -3$. The vertex is $(0,1)$ and the focus is $(0, 1-3) = (0,-2)$.

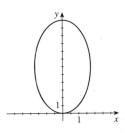

32. $\dfrac{x^2}{12} + \dfrac{y^2}{144} = \dfrac{y}{12} \iff 12x^2 + y^2 - 12y = 0 \iff$

$12x^2 + \left(y^2 - 12y + 36\right) = 36 \iff \dfrac{x^2}{3} + \dfrac{(y-6)^2}{36} = 1$. This is an ellipse with $a = 6$, $b = \sqrt{3}$, and $c = \sqrt{36-3} = \sqrt{33}$. The vertices are $(0, 6 \pm 6) = (0,0)$ and $(0,12)$, and the foci are $\left(0, 6 \pm \sqrt{33}\right)$.

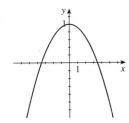

33. $x^2 - y^2 + 144 = 0 \iff \dfrac{y^2}{144} - \dfrac{x^2}{144} = 1$. This is a hyperbola with $a = 12$, $b = 12$, and $c = \sqrt{144 + 144} = 12\sqrt{2}$. The vertices are $(0, \pm 12)$ and the foci are $\left(0, \pm 12\sqrt{2}\right)$.

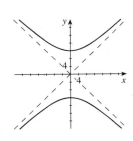

34. $x^2 + 6x = 9y^2$ $\Leftrightarrow$ $(x^2 + 6x + 9) - 9y^2 = 9$ $\Leftrightarrow$ $\dfrac{(x+3)^2}{9} - y^2 = 1$. This

is a hyperbola with $a = 3$, $b = 1$, and $c = \sqrt{9+1} = \sqrt{10}$. The vertices are

$(-3 \pm 3, 0) = (-6, 0)$ and $(0, 0)$, and the foci are $(-3 \pm \sqrt{10}, 0)$.

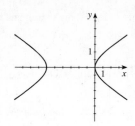

35. $4x^2 + y^2 = 8(x+y)$ $\Leftrightarrow$ $4(x^2 - 2x) + (y^2 - 8y) = 0$ $\Leftrightarrow$

$4(x^2 - 2x + 1) + (y^2 - 8y + 16) = 4 + 16$ $\Leftrightarrow$ $4(x-1)^2 + (y-4)^2 = 20$

$\Leftrightarrow$ $\dfrac{(x-1)^2}{5} + \dfrac{(y-4)^2}{20} = 1$. This is an ellipse with $a = 2\sqrt{5}$, $b = \sqrt{5}$, and

$c = \sqrt{20-5} = \sqrt{15}$. The vertices are $(1, 4 \pm 2\sqrt{5})$ and the foci are

$(1, 4 \pm \sqrt{15})$.

36. $3x^2 - 6(x+y) = 10$ $\Leftrightarrow$ $3x^2 - 6x = 6y + 10$ $\Leftrightarrow$

$3(x^2 - 2x + 1) = 6y + 10 + 3$ $\Leftrightarrow$ $3(x-1)^2 = 6y + 13$ $\Leftrightarrow$

$3(x-1)^2 = 6\left(y + \frac{13}{6}\right)$ $\Leftrightarrow$ $(x-1)^2 = 2\left(y + \frac{13}{6}\right)$. This is a parabola with

$4p = 2$ $\Leftrightarrow$ $p = \frac{1}{2}$. The vertex is $\left(1, -\frac{13}{6}\right)$ and the focus is

$\left(1, -\frac{13}{6} + \frac{1}{2}\right) = \left(1, -\frac{10}{6}\right) = \left(1, -\frac{5}{3}\right)$.

37. $x = y^2 - 16y$ $\Leftrightarrow$ $x + 64 = y^2 - 16y + 64$ $\Leftrightarrow$ $(y-8)^2 = x + 64$. This is

a parabola with $4p = 1$ $\Leftrightarrow$ $p = \frac{1}{4}$. The vertex is $(-64, 8)$ and the focus is

$\left(-64 + \frac{1}{4}, 8\right) = \left(-\frac{255}{4}, 8\right)$.

38. $2x^2 + 4 = 4x + y^2$ $\Leftrightarrow$ $y^2 - 2x^2 + 4x = 4$ $\Leftrightarrow$

$y^2 - 2(x^2 - 2x + 1) = 4 - 2$ $\Leftrightarrow$ $y^2 - 2(x-1)^2 = 2$ $\Leftrightarrow$

$\dfrac{y^2}{2} - (x-1)^2 = 1$. This is a hyperbola with $a = \sqrt{2}$, $b = 1$, and

$c = \sqrt{2+1} = \sqrt{3}$. The vertices are $(1, \pm\sqrt{2})$ and the foci are $(1, \pm\sqrt{3})$.

39. $2x^2 - 12x + y^2 + 6y + 26 = 0$ $\Leftrightarrow$ $2(x^2 - 6x) + (y^2 + 6y) = -26$ $\Leftrightarrow$

$2(x^2 - 6x + 9) + (y^2 + 6y + 9) = -26 + 18 + 9$ $\Leftrightarrow$

$2(x-3)^2 + (y+3)^2 = 1$ $\Leftrightarrow$ $\dfrac{(x-3)^2}{\frac{1}{2}} + (y+3)^2 = 1$. This is an ellipse

with $a = 1$, $b = \frac{\sqrt{2}}{2}$, and $c = \sqrt{1 - \frac{1}{2}} = \frac{\sqrt{2}}{2}$. The vertices are

$(3, -3 \pm 1) = (3, -4)$ and $(3, -2)$, and the foci are $\left(3, -3 \pm \frac{\sqrt{2}}{2}\right)$.

40. $36x^2 - 4y^2 - 36x - 8y = 31$ $\Leftrightarrow$ $36\left(x^2 - x\right) - 4\left(y^2 + 2y\right) = 31$ $\Leftrightarrow$

$36\left(x^2 - x + \frac{1}{4}\right) - 4\left(y^2 + 2y + 1\right) = 31 + 9 - 4$ $\Leftrightarrow$

$36\left(x - \frac{1}{2}\right)^2 - 4\left(y + 1\right)^2 = 36$ $\Leftrightarrow$ $\left(x - \frac{1}{2}\right)^2 - \dfrac{(y+1)^2}{9} = 1$. This is a

hyperbola with $a = 1$, $b = 3$, and $c = \sqrt{1 + 9} = \sqrt{10}$. The vertices are

$\left(\frac{1}{2} \pm 1, -1\right) = \left(-\frac{1}{2}, -1\right)$ and $\left(\frac{3}{2}, -1\right)$, and the foci are $\left(\frac{1}{2} \pm \sqrt{10}, -1\right)$.

41. $9x^2 + 8y^2 - 15x + 8y + 27 = 0$ $\Leftrightarrow$ $9\left(x^2 - \frac{5}{3}x + \frac{25}{36}\right) + 8\left(y^2 + y + \frac{1}{4}\right) = -27 + \frac{25}{4} + 2$ $\Leftrightarrow$

$9\left(x - \frac{5}{6}\right)^2 + 8\left(y + \frac{1}{2}\right)^2 = -\frac{75}{4}$. However, since the left-hand side of the equation is greater than or equal to 0, there is no

point that satisfies this equation. The graph is empty.

42. $x^2 + 4y^2 = 4x + 8$ $\Leftrightarrow$ $\left(x^2 - 4x + 4\right) + 4y^2 = 8 + 4$ $\Leftrightarrow$

$(x - 2)^2 + 4y^2 = 12$ $\Leftrightarrow$ $\dfrac{(x-2)^2}{12} + \dfrac{y^2}{3} = 1$. This is an ellipse with

$a = 2\sqrt{3}$, $b = \sqrt{3}$, and $c = \sqrt{12 - 3} = 3$. The vertices are $\left(2 \pm 2\sqrt{3}, 0\right)$ and the

foci are $(2 \pm 3, 0) = (-1, 0)$ and $(5, 0)$.

43. The parabola has focus $(0, 1)$ and directrix $y = -1$. Therefore, $p = 1$ and so $4p = 4$. Since the focus is on the y-axis and the vertex is $(0, 0)$, an equation of the parabola is $x^2 = 4y$.

44. The ellipse has center $C\left(0, 4\right)$, foci $F_1\left(0, 0\right)$ and $F_2\left(0, 8\right)$, and major axis of length 10. Then $2c = 8 - 0$ $\Leftrightarrow$ $c = 4$. Also, since the length of the major axis is 10, $2a = 10$ $\Leftrightarrow$ $a = 5$. Therefore, $b^2 = a^2 - c^2 = 25 - 16 = 9$. Since the foci are on the y-axis, the vertices are on the y-axis, and an equation of the ellipse is $\dfrac{x^2}{9} + \dfrac{(y-4)^2}{25} = 1$.

45. The hyperbola has vertices $(0, \pm 2)$ and asymptotes $y = \pm \frac{1}{2}x$. Therefore, $a = 2$, and the foci are on the y-axis. Since the slopes of the asymptotes are $\pm \frac{1}{2} = \pm \dfrac{a}{b}$ $\Leftrightarrow$ $b = 2a = 4$, an equation of the hyperbola is $\dfrac{y^2}{4} - \dfrac{x^2}{16} = 1$.

46. The hyperbola has center $C\left(2, 4\right)$, foci $F_1\left(2, 7\right)$ and $F_2\left(2, 1\right)$, and vertices $V_1\left(2, 6\right)$ and $V_2\left(2, 2\right)$. Thus, $2a = 6 - 2 = 4$ $\Leftrightarrow$ $a = 2$. Also, $2c = 7 - 1 = 6$ $\Leftrightarrow$ $c = 3$. So $b^2 = 9 - 4 = 5$. Since the hyperbola has center $C\left(2, 4\right)$, its equation is $\dfrac{(y-4)^2}{4} - \dfrac{(x-2)^2}{5} = 1$.

47. The ellipse has foci $F_1\left(1, 1\right)$ and $F_2\left(1, 3\right)$, and one vertex is on the x-axis. Thus, $2c = 3 - 1 = 2$ $\Leftrightarrow$ $c = 1$, and so the center of the ellipse is $C\left(1, 2\right)$. Also, since one vertex is on the x-axis, $a = 2 - 0 = 2$, and thus $b^2 = 4 - 1 = 3$. So an equation of the ellipse is $\dfrac{(x-1)^2}{3} + \dfrac{(y-2)^2}{4} = 1$.

48. The parabola has vertex $V\left(5, 5\right)$ and directrix the y-axis. Therefore, $-p = 0 - 5$ $\Leftrightarrow$ $p = 5$ $\Leftrightarrow$ $4p = 20$. Since the parabola opens to the right, its equation is $(y - 5)^2 = 20\left(x - 5\right)$.

49. The ellipse has vertices $V_1\left(7, 12\right)$ and $V_2\left(7, -8\right)$ and passes through the point $P\left(1, 8\right)$. Thus, $2a = 12 - (-8) = 20$ $\Leftrightarrow$

$a = 10$, and the center is $\left(7, \dfrac{-8 + 12}{2}\right) = (7, 2)$. Thus an equation of the ellipse has the form $\dfrac{(x-7)^2}{b^2} + \dfrac{(y-2)^2}{100} = 1$.

Since the point $P\left(1, 8\right)$ is on the ellipse, $\dfrac{(1-7)^2}{b^2} + \dfrac{(8-2)^2}{100} = 1$ $\Leftrightarrow$ $3600 + 36b^2 = 100b^2$ $\Leftrightarrow$ $64b^2 = 3600$ $\Leftrightarrow$

$b^2 = \frac{225}{4}$. Therefore, an equation of the ellipse is $\dfrac{(x-7)^2}{225/4} + \dfrac{(y-2)^2}{100} = 1$ $\Leftrightarrow$ $\dfrac{4(x-7)^2}{225} + \dfrac{(y-2)^2}{100} = 1$.

50. The parabola has vertex $V(-1, 0)$, horizontal axis of symmetry, and crosses the y-axis where $y = 2$. Since the parabola has a horizontal axis of symmetry and $V(-1, 0)$, its equation is of the form $y^2 = 4p(x + 1)$. Also, since the parabola crosses the y-axis where $y = 2$, it passes through the point $(0, 2)$. Substituting this point gives $(2)^2 = 4p(0 + 1)$ $\Leftrightarrow$ $4p = 4$. Therefore, an equation of the parabola is $y^2 = 4(x + 1)$.

51. The length of the major axis is $2a = 186,000,000$ $\Leftrightarrow$ $a = 93,000,000$. The eccentricity is $e = c/a = 0.017$, and so $c = 0.017(93,000,000) = 1,581,000$.

(a) The earth is closest to the sun when the distance is $a - c = 93,000,000 - 1,581,000 = 91,419,000$.

(b) The earth is furthest from the sun when the distance is $a + c = 93,000,000 + 1,581,000 = 94,581,000$.

52. We sketch the LORAN station on the y-axis and place the x-axis halfway between them as

suggested in the exercise. This gives us the general form $\dfrac{y^2}{a^2} - \dfrac{x^2}{b^2} = 1$. Since the ship is 80 miles

closer to A than to B we have $2a = 80$ $\Leftrightarrow$ $a = 40$. Since the foci are $(0, \pm 150)$, we have

$c = 150$. Thus $b^2 = c^2 - a^2 = 150^2 - 40^2 = 20900$. So this places the ship on the hyperbola

given by the equation $\dfrac{y^2}{1600} - \dfrac{x^2}{20,900} = 1$. When $x = 40$, we get $\dfrac{y^2}{1600} - \dfrac{1600}{20,900} = 1$ $\Leftrightarrow$

$\dfrac{y^2}{1600} = \dfrac{225}{209}$ $\Leftrightarrow$ $y \approx 41.5$. (Note that $y > 0$, since A is on the positive y-axis.) Thus, the ship's

position is approximately $(40, 41.5)$.

53. (a) The graphs of $\dfrac{x^2}{16 + k^2} + \dfrac{y^2}{k^2} = 1$ for $k = 1, 2, 4,$ and 8 are shown in

the figure.

(b) $c^2 = (16 + k^2) - k^2 = 16$ $\Rightarrow$ $c = \pm 4$. Since the center is

$(0, 0)$, the foci of each of the ellipses are $(\pm 4, 0)$.

54. (a) The graphs of $y = kx^2$ for $k = \frac{1}{2}, 1, 2,$ and 4 are shown in the figure.

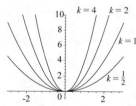

(b) $y = kx^2$ $\Leftrightarrow$ $x^2 = \frac{1}{k}y = 4\left(\frac{1}{4k}\right)y$. Thus the foci are $\left(0, \frac{1}{4k}\right)$.

(c) As k increases, the focus gets closer to the vertex.

55. (a) $x^2 + 4xy + y^2 = 1$. Then $A = 1$, $B = 4$, and $C = 1$, so the discriminant is $4^2 - 4(1)(1) = 12$. Since the discriminant is positive, the equation represents a hyperbola.

(b) $\cot 2\phi = \dfrac{A - C}{B} = \dfrac{1 - 1}{4} = 0 \Rightarrow 2\phi = 90° \Leftrightarrow \phi = 45°$. Therefore, $x = \frac{\sqrt{2}}{2}X - \frac{\sqrt{2}}{2}Y$ and $y = \frac{\sqrt{2}}{2}X + \frac{\sqrt{2}}{2}Y$.

Substituting into the original equation gives

$\left(\frac{\sqrt{2}}{2}X - \frac{\sqrt{2}}{2}Y\right)^2 + 4\left(\frac{\sqrt{2}}{2}X - \frac{\sqrt{2}}{2}Y\right)\left(\frac{\sqrt{2}}{2}X + \frac{\sqrt{2}}{2}Y\right) + \left(\frac{\sqrt{2}}{2}X + \frac{\sqrt{2}}{2}Y\right)^2 = 1$ $\Leftrightarrow$

$\frac{1}{2}\left(X^2 - 2XY + Y^2\right) + 2\left(X^2 + XY - XY - Y^2\right) + \frac{1}{2}\left(X^2 + 2XY + Y^2\right) = 1$ **(c)**

$\Leftrightarrow 3X^2 - Y^2 = 1 \Leftrightarrow 3X^2 - Y^2 = 1$. This is a hyperbola with $a = \frac{1}{\sqrt{3}}$, $b = 1$, and

$c = \sqrt{\frac{1}{3} + 1} = \frac{2}{\sqrt{3}}$. Therefore, the hyperbola has vertices $V\left(\pm\frac{1}{\sqrt{3}}, 0\right)$ and foci

$F\left(\pm\frac{2}{\sqrt{3}}, 0\right)$, in XY-coordinates.

56. (a) $5x^2 - 6xy + 5y^2 - 8x + 8y - 8 = 0$. Then $A = 5$, $B = -6$, and $C = 5$, so the discriminant is $(-6)^2 - 4(5)(5) = 64$.

Since the discriminant is negative, the equation represents an ellipse.

(b) $\cot 2\phi = \dfrac{A - C}{B} = 0 \;\Rightarrow\; 2\phi = 90° \;\Leftrightarrow\; \phi = 45°$. Therefore, $x = \frac{\sqrt{2}}{2}X - \frac{\sqrt{2}}{2}Y$ and $y = \frac{\sqrt{2}}{2}X + \frac{\sqrt{2}}{2}Y$.

Substituting into the original equation gives

$5\left(\frac{\sqrt{2}}{2}X - \frac{\sqrt{2}}{2}Y\right)^2 - 6\left(\frac{\sqrt{2}}{2}X - \frac{\sqrt{2}}{2}Y\right)\left(\frac{\sqrt{2}}{2}X + \frac{\sqrt{2}}{2}Y\right)$

$\qquad\qquad + 5\left(\frac{\sqrt{2}}{2}X + \frac{\sqrt{2}}{2}Y\right)^2 - 8\left(\frac{\sqrt{2}}{2}X - \frac{\sqrt{2}}{2}Y\right) + 8\left(\frac{\sqrt{2}}{2}X + \frac{\sqrt{2}}{2}Y\right) - 8 = 0 \;\Leftrightarrow$

$\frac{5}{2}\left(X^2 - 2XY + Y^2\right) - 3\left(X^2 - Y^2\right) + \frac{5}{2}\left(X^2 + 2XY + Y^2\right) - 4\sqrt{2}X + 4\sqrt{2}Y + 4\sqrt{2}X + 4\sqrt{2}Y - 8 = 0 \;\Leftrightarrow$

$5X^2 - 3X^2 + 3Y^2 + 5Y^2 + 8\sqrt{2}Y - 8 = 0 \;\Leftrightarrow$

(c)

$2X^2 + 8\left(Y^2 + \sqrt{2}Y + \frac{1}{2}\right) = 8 + 4 \;\Leftrightarrow\; \dfrac{X^2}{6} + \dfrac{(Y + 1)^2}{3/2} = 1$. This ellipse

has $a = \sqrt{6}$, $b = \sqrt{3/2}$, and $c = \sqrt{6 - \frac{3}{2}} = \frac{3\sqrt{2}}{2}$. Therefore, the vertices are

$V\left(\pm\sqrt{6}, -1\right)$ and the foci are $F\left(\pm\frac{3\sqrt{2}}{2}, -1\right)$.

57. (a) $7x^2 - 6\sqrt{3}xy + 13y^2 - 4\sqrt{3}x - 4y = 0$. Then $A = 7$, $B = -6\sqrt{3}$, and $C = 13$, so the discriminant is $\left(-6\sqrt{3}\right)^2 - 4(7)(13) = -256$. Since the discriminant is negative, the equation represents an ellipse.

(b) $\cot 2\phi = \dfrac{A - C}{B} = \dfrac{7 - 13}{-6\sqrt{3}} = \dfrac{1}{\sqrt{3}} \;\Rightarrow\; 2\phi = 60° \;\Leftrightarrow\; \phi = 30°$. Therefore, $x = \frac{\sqrt{3}}{2}X - \frac{1}{2}Y$ and

$y = \frac{1}{2}X + \frac{\sqrt{3}}{2}Y$. Substituting into the original equation gives

$7\left(\frac{\sqrt{3}}{2}X - \frac{1}{2}Y\right)^2 - 6\sqrt{3}\left(\frac{\sqrt{3}}{2}X - \frac{1}{2}Y\right)\left(\frac{1}{2}X + \frac{\sqrt{3}}{2}Y\right)$

$\qquad\qquad + 13\left(\frac{1}{2}X + \frac{\sqrt{3}}{2}Y\right)^2 - 4\sqrt{3}\left(\frac{\sqrt{3}}{2}X - \frac{1}{2}Y\right) - 4\left(\frac{1}{2}X + \frac{\sqrt{3}}{2}Y\right) = 0 \;\Leftrightarrow$

$\frac{7}{4}\left(3X^2 - 2\sqrt{3}XY + Y^2\right) - \frac{3\sqrt{3}}{2}\left(\sqrt{3}X^2 + 3XY - XY - \sqrt{3}Y^2\right)$

$\qquad\qquad + \frac{13}{4}\left(X^2 + 2\sqrt{3}XY + 3Y^2\right) - 6X + 2\sqrt{3}Y - 2X - 2\sqrt{3}Y = 0 \;\Leftrightarrow$

$X^2\left(\frac{21}{4} - \frac{9}{2} + \frac{13}{4}\right) - 8X + Y^2\left(\frac{7}{4} + \frac{9}{2} + \frac{39}{4}\right) = 0 \;\Leftrightarrow$

(c)

$4X^2 - 8X + 16Y^2 = 0 \;\Leftrightarrow\; 4\left(X^2 - 2X + 1\right) + 16Y^2 = 4 \;\Leftrightarrow$

$(X - 1)^2 + 4Y^2 = 1$. This ellipse has $a = 1$, $b = \frac{1}{2}$, and $c = \sqrt{1 - \frac{1}{4}} = \frac{1}{2}\sqrt{3}$.

Therefore, the vertices are $V(1 \pm 1, 0) = V_1(0, 0)$ and $V_2(2, 0)$ and the foci are

$F\left(1 \pm \frac{1}{2}\sqrt{3}, 0\right)$.

58. (a) $9x^2 + 24xy + 16y^2 = 25$. Then $A = 9$, $B = 24$, and $C = 16$, so the discriminant is $24^2 - 4(9)(16) = 0$. Since the discriminant is zero, the equation represents a parabola.

(b) $\cot 2\phi = \dfrac{A - C}{B} = \dfrac{9 - 16}{24} = -\dfrac{7}{24} \Rightarrow \cos 2\phi = -\dfrac{7}{25}$, so $\cos \phi = \sqrt{\dfrac{1 - (7/25)}{2}} = \dfrac{3}{5}$, $\sin \phi = \sqrt{\dfrac{1 + (7/25)}{2}} = \dfrac{4}{5}$,

and thus $x = \frac{3}{5}X - \frac{4}{5}Y$ and $y = \frac{4}{5}X + \frac{3}{5}Y$. Substituting,

(c)

$9x^2 + 24xy + 16y^2 = 25 \Leftrightarrow$

$9\left(\frac{3}{5}X - \frac{4}{5}Y\right)^2 + 24\left(\frac{3}{5}X - \frac{4}{5}Y\right)\left(\frac{4}{5}X + \frac{3}{5}Y\right) + 16\left(\frac{4}{5}X + \frac{3}{5}Y\right)^2 = 25 \Leftrightarrow$

$25X^2 = 25 \Leftrightarrow X^2 = 1 \Leftrightarrow X = \pm 1$. Thus the graph is a degenerate conic that consists of two lines. Converting back to xy-coordinates, we see that

$X = \frac{3}{5}x + \frac{4}{5}y$, so $\frac{3}{5}x + \frac{4}{5}y = \pm 1 \Leftrightarrow 3x + 4y = \pm 5$.

59. $5x^2 + 3y^2 = 60 \Leftrightarrow 3y^2 = 60 - 5x^2 \Leftrightarrow y^2 = 20 - \frac{5}{3}x^2$. This conic is an ellipse.

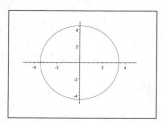

60. $9x^2 - 12y^2 + 36 = 0 \Leftrightarrow 12y^2 = 9x^2 + 36 \Leftrightarrow y^2 = \frac{3}{4}x^2 + 3 \Leftrightarrow$

$y = \pm\sqrt{\frac{3}{4}x^2 + 3}$. This conic is a hyperbola.

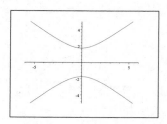

61. $6x + y^2 - 12y = 30 \Leftrightarrow y^2 - 12y = 30 - 6x \Leftrightarrow$

$y^2 - 12y + 36 = 66 - 6x \Leftrightarrow (y - 6)^2 = 66 - 6x \Leftrightarrow$

$y - 6 = \pm\sqrt{66 - 6x} \Leftrightarrow y = 6 \pm \sqrt{66 - 6x}$. This conic is a parabola.

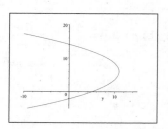

62. $52x^2 - 72xy + 73y^2 = 100 \Leftrightarrow 73y^2 - 72xy + 52x^2 - 100 = 0$. Using the quadratic formula,

$$y = \frac{72x \pm \sqrt{(-72x)^2 - 4(73)\left(52x^2 - 100\right)}}{146}$$

$$= \frac{72x \pm \sqrt{-10{,}000x^2 + 29{,}200}}{146} = \frac{72x \pm 20\sqrt{73 - 25x^2}}{146}$$

$$= \tfrac{36}{73}x + \tfrac{10}{73}\sqrt{73 - 25x^2}$$

This conic is an ellipse.

63. (a) $r = \dfrac{1}{1 - \cos\theta}$ $\Rightarrow$ $e = 1$. Therefore, this is a parabola.

(b)

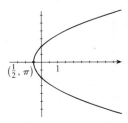

64. (a) $r = \dfrac{2}{1 + 2\sin\theta}$ $\Rightarrow$ $e = 2$. Therefore, this is a hyperbola.

(b)

65. (a) $r = \dfrac{4}{1 + 2\sin\theta}$ $\Rightarrow$ $e = 2$. Therefore this is a hyperbola.

(b)

66. (a) $r = \dfrac{12}{1 - 4\cos\theta}$ $\Rightarrow$ $e = 4$. Therefore, this is a hyperbola.

(b)

67. $x = 1 - t^2$, $y = 1 + t$ $\Leftrightarrow$ $t = y - 1$. Substituting for t gives $x = 1 - (y-1)^2$ $\Leftrightarrow$ $(y-1)^2 = 1 - x$ which is the rectangular coordinate equation.

68. $x = t^2 - 1$, $y = t^2 + 1$ $\Leftrightarrow$ $t^2 = y - 1$. Substituting for t^2 gives $x = (y-1) - 1$ $\Leftrightarrow$ $y = x + 2$ where $x \geq -1$ and $y \geq 1$.

69. $x = 1 + \cos t$ $\Leftrightarrow$ $\cos t = x - 1$, and $y = 1 - \sin t$ $\Leftrightarrow$ $\sin t = 1 - y$. Since $\cos^2 t + \sin^2 t = 1$, it follows that $(x-1)^2 + (1-y)^2 = 1$ $\Leftrightarrow$ $(x-1)^2 + (y-1)^2 = 1$. Since t is restricted by $0 \leq t \leq \frac{\pi}{2}$, $1 + \cos 0 \leq x \leq 1 + \cos\frac{\pi}{2}$ $\Leftrightarrow$ $1 \leq x \leq 2$, and similarly, $0 \leq y \leq 1$. (This is the lower right quarter of the circle.)

70. $x = \dfrac{1}{t} + 2$ $\Leftrightarrow$ $\dfrac{1}{t} = x - 2$, $y = \dfrac{2}{t^2}$. Substituting for $\dfrac{1}{t}$ gives $y = 2(x-2)^2$. Since t is restricted by $0 < t \leq 2$, we have $\dfrac{1}{t} \geq \dfrac{1}{2}$, so $x \geq \frac{5}{2}$ and $y \geq \frac{1}{2}$. The rectangular coordinate equation is $y = 2(x-2)^2$, $x \geq \frac{5}{2}$.

71. $x = \cos 2t; y = \sin 3t$

72. $x = \sin (t + \cos 2t), y = \cos (t + \sin 3t)$

73. The coordinates of Q are $x = \cos\theta$ and $y = \sin\theta$. The coordinates of R are $x = 1$ and $y = \tan\theta$. Hence, the midpoint P is $\left(\dfrac{1 + \cos\theta}{2}, \dfrac{\sin\theta + \tan\theta}{2} \right)$, so parametric equations for the curve are $x = \dfrac{1 + \cos\theta}{2}$ and $y = \dfrac{\sin\theta + \tan\theta}{2}$.

Chapter 10 Test

1. $x^2 = -12y$. This is a parabola with $4p = -12 \quad\Leftrightarrow\quad p = -3$. The focus is $(0, -3)$ and the directrix is $y = 3$.

2. $\dfrac{x^2}{16} + \dfrac{y^2}{4} = 1$. This is an ellipse with $a = 4$, $b = 2$, and $c = \sqrt{16 - 4} = 2\sqrt{3}$.

The vertices are $(\pm 4, 0)$, the foci are $\left(\pm 2\sqrt{3}, 0\right)$, the length of the major axis is $2a = 8$, and the length of the minor axis is $2b = 4$.

3. $\dfrac{y^2}{9} - \dfrac{x^2}{16} = 1$. This is a hyperbola with $a = 3$, $b = 4$, and $c = \sqrt{9 + 16} = 5$. The vertices are $(0, \pm 3)$, the foci are $(0, \pm 5)$, and the asymptotes are $y = \pm\frac{3}{4}x$.

4. This is a parabola that opens to the left with its vertex at $(0, 0)$. So its equation is of the form $y^2 = 4px$ with $p < 0$. Substituting the point $(-4, 2)$, we have $2^2 = 4p(-4) \quad\Leftrightarrow\quad 4 = -16p \quad\Leftrightarrow\quad p = -\frac{1}{4}$. So an equation is $y^2 = 4\left(-\frac{1}{4}\right) x \quad\Leftrightarrow\quad y^2 = -x$.

5. This is an ellipse tangent to the x-axis at $(0, 0)$ and with one vertex at the point $(4, 3)$. The center is $(0, 3)$, and $a = 4$ and $b = 3$. Thus the equation is $\dfrac{x^2}{16} + \dfrac{(y - 3)^2}{9} = 1$.

6. This a hyperbola with a horizontal transverse axis, vertices at $(1, 0)$ and $(3, 0)$, and foci at $(0, 0)$ and $(4, 0)$. Thus the center is $(2, 0)$, and $a = 3 - 2 = 1$ and $c = 4 - 2 = 2$. Thus $b^2 = 2^2 - 1^2 = 3$. So an equation is $\dfrac{(x-2)^2}{1^2} - \dfrac{y^2}{3} = 1$ $\Leftrightarrow$ $(x - 2)^2 - \dfrac{y^2}{3} = 1$.

7. $16x^2 + 36y^2 - 96x + 36y + 9 = 0$ $\Leftrightarrow$ $16\left(x^2 - 6x\right) + 36\left(y^2 + y\right) = -9$

$\Leftrightarrow$ $16\left(x^2 - 6x + 9\right) + 36\left(y^2 + y + \frac{1}{4}\right) = -9 + 144 + 9$ $\Leftrightarrow$

$16\left(x - 3\right)^2 + 36\left(y + \frac{1}{2}\right)^2 = 144$ $\Leftrightarrow$ $\dfrac{(x-3)^2}{9} + \dfrac{\left(y+\frac{1}{2}\right)^2}{4} = 1$. This is an

ellipse with $a = 3$, $b = 2$, and $c = \sqrt{9 - 4} = \sqrt{5}$. The center is $\left(3, -\frac{1}{2}\right)$, the

vertices are $\left(3 \pm 3, -\frac{1}{2}\right) = \left(0, -\frac{1}{2}\right)$ and $\left(6, -\frac{1}{2}\right)$, and the foci are

$(h \pm c, k) = \left(3 \pm \sqrt{5}, -\frac{1}{2}\right) = \left(3 + \sqrt{5}, -\frac{1}{2}\right)$ and $\left(3 - \sqrt{5}, -\frac{1}{2}\right)$.

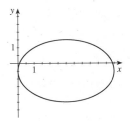

8. $9x^2 - 8y^2 + 36x + 64y = 164$ $\Leftrightarrow$ $9\left(x^2 + 4x\right) - 8\left(y^2 - 8y\right) = 164$ $\Leftrightarrow$

$9\left(x^2 + 4x + 4\right) - 8\left(y^2 - 8y + 16\right) = 164 + 36 - 128$ $\Leftrightarrow$

$9\left(x + 2\right)^2 - 8\left(y - 4\right)^2 = 72$ $\Leftrightarrow$ $\dfrac{(x+2)^2}{8} - \dfrac{(y-4)^2}{9} = 1$. This conic is a

hyperbola.

9. $2x + y^2 + 8y + 8 = 0$ $\Leftrightarrow$ $y^2 + 8y + 16 = -2x - 8 + 16$ $\Leftrightarrow$

$(y + 4)^2 = -2\left(x - 4\right)$. This is a parabola with $4p = -2$ $\Leftrightarrow$ $p = -\frac{1}{2}$. The

vertex is $(4, -4)$ and the focus is $\left(4 - \frac{1}{2}, -4\right) = \left(\frac{7}{2}, -4\right)$.

10. The hyperbola has foci $(0, \pm 5)$ and asymptotes $y = \pm\frac{3}{4}x$. Since the foci are $(0, \pm 5)$, $c = 5$, the foci are on the

y-axis, and the center is $(0, 0)$. Also, since $y = \pm\frac{3}{4}x = \pm\frac{a}{b}x$, it follows that $\dfrac{a}{b} = \dfrac{3}{4}$ $\Leftrightarrow$ $a = \frac{3}{4}b$. Then

$c^2 = 5^2 = 25 = a^2 + b^2 = \left(\frac{3}{4}b\right)^2 + b^2 = \frac{25}{16}b^2$ $\Leftrightarrow$ $b^2 = 16$, and by substitution, $a = \frac{3}{4}(4) = 3$. Therefore, an

equation of the hyperbola is $\dfrac{y^2}{9} - \dfrac{x^2}{16} = 1$.

11. The parabola has focus $(2, 4)$ and directrix the x-axis $(y = 0)$. Therefore, $2p = 4 - 0 = 4$ $\Leftrightarrow$ $p = 2$ $\Leftrightarrow$

$4p = 8$, and the vertex is $(2, 4 - p) = (2, 2)$. Hence, an equation of the parabola is $(x - 2)^2 = 8\left(y - 2\right)$ $\Leftrightarrow$

$x^2 - 4x + 4 = 8y - 16$ $\Leftrightarrow$ $x^2 - 4x - 8y + 20 = 0$.

12. We place the vertex of the parabola at the origin, so the parabola contains the points $(3, \pm 3)$, and the equation is of the form

$y^2 = 4px$. Substituting the point $(3, 3)$, we get $3^2 = 4p(3)$ $\Leftrightarrow$ $9 = 12p$ $\Leftrightarrow$ $p = \frac{3}{4}$. So the focus is $\left(\frac{3}{4}, 0\right)$, and

we should place the light bulb $\frac{3}{4}$ inch from the vertex.

13. (a) $5x^2 + 4xy + 2y^2 = 18$. Then $A = 5$, $B = 4$, and $C = 2$, so the discriminant is $(4)^2 - 4(5)(2) = -24$. Since the discriminant is negative, the equation represents an ellipse.

(b) $\cot 2\phi = \dfrac{A - C}{B} = \dfrac{5 - 2}{4} = \dfrac{3}{4}$. Thus, $\cos 2\phi = \frac{3}{5}$ and so $\cos \phi = \sqrt{\dfrac{1 + (3/5)}{2}} = \dfrac{2\sqrt{5}}{5}$,

$\sin \phi = \sqrt{\dfrac{1 - (3/5)}{2}} = \dfrac{\sqrt{5}}{5}$. It follows that $x = \dfrac{2\sqrt{5}}{5}X - \dfrac{\sqrt{5}}{5}Y$ and $y = \dfrac{\sqrt{5}}{5}X + \dfrac{2\sqrt{5}}{5}Y$. By

substitution, $5\left(\dfrac{2\sqrt{5}}{5}X - \dfrac{\sqrt{5}}{5}Y\right)^2 + 4\left(\dfrac{2\sqrt{5}}{5}X - \dfrac{\sqrt{5}}{5}Y\right)\left(\dfrac{\sqrt{5}}{5}X + \dfrac{2\sqrt{5}}{5}Y\right) + 2\left(\dfrac{\sqrt{5}}{5}X + \dfrac{2\sqrt{5}}{5}Y\right)^2 = 18$

$\Leftrightarrow \quad 4X^2 - 4XY + Y^2 + \dfrac{4}{5}\left(2X^2 + 4XY - XY - 2Y^2\right) + \dfrac{2}{5}\left(X^2 + 4XY + 4Y^2\right) = 18 \quad \Leftrightarrow$

$X^2\left(4 + \dfrac{8}{5} + \dfrac{2}{5}\right) + XY\left(-4 + \dfrac{12}{5} + \dfrac{8}{5}\right) + Y^2\left(1 - \dfrac{8}{5} + \dfrac{4}{5}\right) = 18 \quad \Leftrightarrow \quad 6X^2 + Y^2 = 18 \quad \Leftrightarrow \quad \dfrac{X^2}{3} + \dfrac{Y^2}{18} = 1$.

This is an ellipse with $a = 3\sqrt{2}$ and $b = \sqrt{3}$.

(c)

Since $\cos 2\phi = \frac{3}{5}$ we have

$2\phi = \cos^{-1} \frac{3}{5} \approx 53.13°$, so $\phi \approx 27°$.

(d) In XY-coordinates, the vertices are $V\left(0, \pm 3\sqrt{2}\right)$. Therefore, in

xy-coordinates, the vertices are $x = -\dfrac{3\sqrt{2}}{\sqrt{5}}$ and $y = \dfrac{6\sqrt{2}}{\sqrt{5}} \quad \Rightarrow$

$V_1\left(-\dfrac{3\sqrt{2}}{\sqrt{5}}, \dfrac{6\sqrt{2}}{\sqrt{5}}\right)$, and $x = \dfrac{3\sqrt{2}}{\sqrt{5}}$ and $y = -\dfrac{6\sqrt{2}}{\sqrt{5}} \quad \Rightarrow$

$V_2\left(\dfrac{3\sqrt{2}}{\sqrt{5}}, \dfrac{-6\sqrt{2}}{\sqrt{5}}\right)$.

14. (a) Since the focus of this conic is the origin and the directrix is $x = 2$, the equation has the form

$r = \dfrac{ed}{1 + e\cos\theta}$. Subsituting $e = \frac{1}{2}$ and $d = 2$ we

get $r = \dfrac{1}{1 + \frac{1}{2}\cos\theta} \quad \Leftrightarrow \quad r = \dfrac{2}{2 + \cos\theta}$.

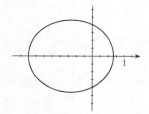

(b) $r = \dfrac{3}{2 - \sin\theta} \quad \Leftrightarrow \quad r = \dfrac{\frac{3}{2}}{1 - \frac{1}{2}\sin\theta}$. So $e = \frac{1}{2}$ and

the conic is an ellipse.

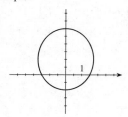

15. (a) $x = 3\sin\theta + 3$, $y = 2\cos\theta$, $0 \le \theta \le \pi$. From the work of part (b), we see that this is the half-ellipse shown.

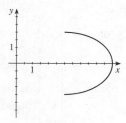

(b) $x = 3\sin\theta + 3 \Leftrightarrow x - 3 = 3\sin\theta \Leftrightarrow \dfrac{x - 3}{3} = \sin\theta$.

Squaring both sides gives $\dfrac{(x - 3)^2}{9} = \sin^2\theta$. Similarly,

$y = 2\cos\theta \Leftrightarrow \dfrac{y}{2} = \cos\theta$, and squaring both sides gives

$\dfrac{y^2}{4} = \cos^2\theta$. Since $\sin^2\theta + \cos^2\theta = 1$, it follows that

$\dfrac{(x - 3)^2}{9} + \dfrac{y^2}{4} = 1$. Since $0 \le \theta \le \pi$, $\sin\theta \ge 0$, so

$3\sin\theta \ge 0 \Rightarrow 3\sin\theta + 3 \ge 3$, and so $x \ge 3$. Thus the curve consists of only the right half of the ellipse.

Focus on Modeling: The Path of a Projectile

1. From $x = (v_0 \cos\theta)\,t$, we get $t = \dfrac{x}{v_0 \cos\theta}$. Substituting this value for t into the equation for y, we get

$$y = (v_0 \sin\theta)\,t - \tfrac{1}{2}gt^2 \quad \Leftrightarrow \quad y = (v_0 \sin\theta)\left(\frac{x}{v_0\cos\theta}\right) - \tfrac{1}{2}g\left(\frac{x}{v_0\cos\theta}\right)^2 \quad \Leftrightarrow \quad y = (\tan\theta)\,x - \frac{g}{2v_0^2\cos^2\theta}x^2.$$

This shows that y is a quadratic function of x, so its graph is a parabola as long as $\theta \neq 90°$. When $\theta = 90°$, the path of the projectile is a straight line up (then down).

2. Applying the given values, we get $x = (v_0 \cos\theta)\,t = 15t$ and

$y = 4 + (v_0 \sin\theta)\,t - \tfrac{1}{2}gt^2 = 4 + 25.98t - 16t^2$ as the parametric equations for

the path of the baseball. The baseball will hit the ground when

$y = 0 = 4 + 25.98t - 16t^2$. Using the quadratic formula,

$t = \dfrac{-25.98 \pm \sqrt{(25.98)^2 + 4(-16)(4)}}{-32} \approx 1.77$ seconds (since t must be positive). So the

baseball travels $x = 15 \cdot 1.77 = 26.5$ ft before hitting the ground after 1.77 s.

3. (a) We use the equation $t = \dfrac{2v_0 \sin\theta}{g}$. Substituting $g \approx 32$ ft/s^2, $\theta = 5°$, and $v_0 = 1000$, we get

$$t = \frac{2 \cdot 1000 \cdot \sin 5°}{32} \approx 5.447 \text{ seconds.}$$

(b) Substituting the given values into $y = (v_0 \sin\theta)\,t - \tfrac{1}{2}gt^2$, we get

$y = 87.2t - 16t^2$. The maximum value of y is attained at the vertex of the

parabola; thus $y = 87.2t - 16t^2 = -16\left(t^2 - 5.45t\right) \quad \Leftrightarrow$

$y = -16\left[t^2 - 2(2.725)\,t + 7.425625\right] + 118.7$. Thus the greatest height

is 118.7 ft.

(d)

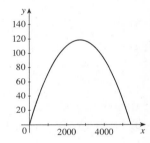

(c) The rocket hits the ground after 5.447 s, so substituting this into the

expression for the horizontal distance gives

$x = (1000 \cos 5°)\,5.447 = 5426$ ft.

4. The missile hits the ground when $t = \dfrac{2v_0 \sin\theta}{g}$, so the missile travels

$$x = (v_0 \cos\theta)\frac{2v_0 \sin\theta}{g} = \frac{v_0^2}{g}\sin 2\theta \text{ meters. Substituting } v_0 = 330 \text{ m/s,}$$

$x = 10$ km, and $g = 9.8$ m/s^2, we get $10000 = \dfrac{330^2}{9.8}\sin 2\theta \quad \Rightarrow$

$\sin 2\theta = 0.8999$. So $2\theta = 64.15° \quad \Leftrightarrow \quad \theta = 32.08°$ or $2\theta = 115.85° \quad \Leftrightarrow$

$\theta = 57.93°$. The missile fired at 32.08° will hit the target in 35.7 seconds, while

the missile fired at 57.93° reaches the target in 57.1 seconds.

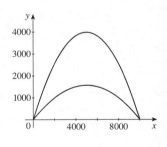

5. We use the equation of the parabola from Exercise 1 and find its vertex: $y = (\tan\theta)\,x - \dfrac{g}{2v_0^2\cos^2\theta}x^2 \quad \Leftrightarrow$

$$y = -\frac{g}{2v_0^2\cos^2\theta}\left[x^2 - \frac{2v_0^2\sin\theta\cos\theta x}{g}\right] \quad \Leftrightarrow \quad y = -\frac{g}{2v_0^2\cos^2\theta}\left[x^2 - \frac{2v_0^2\sin\theta\cos\theta x}{g} + \left(\frac{v_0^2\sin\theta\cos\theta}{g}\right)^2\right] +$$

$$\frac{g}{2v_0^2\cos^2\theta} \cdot \left(\frac{v_0^2\sin\theta\cos\theta}{g}\right)^2 \quad \Leftrightarrow \quad y = -\frac{g}{2v_0^2\cos^2\theta}\left[x - \frac{v_0^2\sin\theta\cos\theta}{g}\right]^2 + \frac{v_0^2\sin^2\theta}{2g}. \text{ Thus the vertex is at}$$

$\left(\dfrac{v_0^2\sin\theta\cos\theta}{g}, \dfrac{v_0^2\sin^2\theta}{2g}\right)$, so the maximum height is $\dfrac{v_0^2\sin^2\theta}{2g}$.

6. Since the horizontal component of the projectile's velocity has been reduced by w, the parametric equations become $x = (v_0 \cos \theta - w) t$, $y = (v_0 \sin \theta) t - \frac{1}{2} g t^2$.

7. In Exercise 6 we derived the equations $x = (v_0 \cos \theta - w) t$, $y = (v_0 \sin \theta) t - \frac{1}{2} g t^2$. We plot the graphs for the given values of v_0, w, and θ in the figure to the right. The projectile will be blown backwards if the horizontal component of its velocity is less than the speed of the wind, that is, $32 \cos \theta < 24 \quad \Leftrightarrow \quad \cos \theta < \frac{3}{4} \quad \Rightarrow \quad \theta > 41.4°$.

The optimal firing angle appears to be between $15°$ and $30°$. We graph the trajectory for $\theta = 20°$, $\theta = 23°$, and $\theta = 25°$. The solution appears to be close to $23°$.

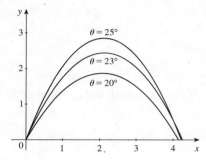

8. (a) Answers will vary.

(b) Both projectiles land at the same spot. The projectile fired with $\theta = 30°$ flies lower and lands first.

(c) When $\theta = 90°$, we have $y = v_0 t - 4.9t^2 = -4.9 \left(t^2 - \frac{v_o}{4.9} t \right) = -4.9 \left[t^2 - \frac{v_o}{4.9} t + \left(\frac{v_o}{9.8} \right)^2 \right] + \frac{v_0^2}{19.6}$. Thus, when v_0 is doubled the maximum height of the ball increases by a factor of 4.

11 Sequences and Series

11.1 Sequences and Summation Notation

1. $a_n = n + 1$. Then $a_1 = 1 + 1 = 2$, $a_2 = 2 + 1 = 3$, $a_3 = 3 + 1 = 4$, $a_4 = 4 + 1 = 5$, and $a_{100} = 100 + 1 = 101$.

2. $a_n = 2n + 3$. Then $a_1 = 2(1) + 3 = 5$, $a_2 = 2(2) + 3 = 7$, $a_3 = 2(3) + 3 = 9$, $a_4 = 2(4) + 3 = 11$, and $a_{100} = 2(100) + 3 = 203$.

3. $a_n = \dfrac{1}{n+1}$. Then $a_1 = \dfrac{1}{1+1} = \dfrac{1}{2}$, $a_2 = \dfrac{1}{2+1} = \dfrac{1}{3}$, $a_3 = \dfrac{1}{3+1} = \dfrac{1}{4}$, $a_4 = \dfrac{1}{4+1} = \dfrac{1}{5}$, and $a_{100} = \dfrac{1}{100+1} = \dfrac{1}{101}$.

4. $a_n = n^2 + 1$. Then $a_1 = (1)^2 + 1 = 2$, $a_2 = (2)^2 + 1 = 5$, $a_3 = (3)^2 + 1 = 10$, $a_4 = (4)^2 + 1 = 17$, and $a_{100} = (100)^2 + 1 = 10{,}001$.

5. $a_n = \dfrac{(-1)^n}{n^2}$. Then $a_1 = \dfrac{(-1)^1}{1^2} = -1$, $a_2 = \dfrac{(-1)^2}{2^2} = \dfrac{1}{4}$, $a_3 = \dfrac{(-1)^3}{3^2} = -\dfrac{1}{9}$, $a_4 = \dfrac{(-1)^4}{4^2} = \dfrac{1}{16}$, and $a_{100} = \dfrac{(-1)^{100}}{100^2} = \dfrac{1}{10{,}000}$.

6. $a_n = \dfrac{1}{n^2}$. Then $a_1 = \dfrac{1}{(1)^2} = 1$, $a_2 = \dfrac{1}{(2)^2} = \dfrac{1}{4}$, $a_3 = \dfrac{1}{(3)^2} = \dfrac{1}{9}$, $a_4 = \dfrac{1}{(4)^2} = \dfrac{1}{16}$, and $a_{100} = \dfrac{1}{(100)^2} = \dfrac{1}{10{,}000}$.

7. $a_n = 1 + (-1)^n$. Then $a_1 = 1 + (-1)^1 = 0$, $a_2 = 1 + (-1)^2 = 2$, $a_3 = 1 + (-1)^3 = 0$, $a_4 = 1 + (-1)^4 = 2$, and $a_{100} = 1 + (-1)^{100} = 2$.

8. $a_n = \dfrac{(-1)^{n+1}\, n}{n+1}$. Then $a_1 = \dfrac{(-1)^2 \cdot 1}{1+1} = \dfrac{1}{2}$, $a_2 = \dfrac{(-1)^3 \cdot 2}{2+1} = -\dfrac{2}{3}$, $a_3 = \dfrac{(-1)^4 \cdot 3}{3+1} = \dfrac{3}{4}$, $a_4 = \dfrac{(-1)^5 \cdot 4}{4+1} = -\dfrac{4}{5}$, and $a_{100} = \dfrac{(-1)^{101} \cdot 100}{101} = -\dfrac{100}{101}$.

9. $a_n = n^n$. Then $a_1 = 1^1 = 1$, $a_2 = 2^2 = 4$, $a_3 = 3^3 = 27$, $a_4 = 4^4 = 256$, and $a_{100} = 100^{100} = 10^{200}$.

10. $a_n = 3$. Then $a_1 = 3$, $a_2 = 3$, $a_3 = 3$, $a_4 = 3$, and $a_{100} = 3$.

11. $a_n = 2(a_{n-1} - 2)$ and $a_1 = 3$. Then $a_2 = 2[(3) - 2] = 2$, $a_3 = 2[(2) - 2] = 0$, $a_4 = 2[(0) - 2] = -4$, and $a_5 = 2[(-4) - 2] = -12$.

12. $a_n = \dfrac{a_{n-1}}{2}$ and $a_1 = -8$. Then $a_2 = \dfrac{-8}{2} = -4$, $a_3 = \dfrac{-4}{2} = -2$, $a_4 = \dfrac{-2}{2} = -1$, and $a_5 = \dfrac{-1}{2} = -\dfrac{1}{2}$.

13. $a_n = 2a_{n-1} + 1$ and $a_1 = 1$. Then $a_2 = 2(1) + 1 = 3$, $a_3 = 2(3) + 1 = 7$, $a_4 = 2(7) + 1 = 15$, and $a_5 = 2(15) + 1 = 31$.

14. $a_n = \dfrac{1}{1 + a_{n-1}}$ and $a_1 = 1$. Then $a_2 = \dfrac{1}{1+1} = \dfrac{1}{2}$, $a_3 = \dfrac{1}{1+\frac{1}{2}} = \dfrac{2}{3}$, $a_4 = \dfrac{1}{1+\frac{2}{3}} = \dfrac{3}{5}$, and $a_5 = \dfrac{1}{1+\frac{3}{5}} = \dfrac{5}{8}$.

15. $a_n = a_{n-1} + a_{n-2}$, $a_1 = 1$, and $a_2 = 2$. Then $a_3 = 2 + 1 = 3$, $a_4 = 3 + 2 = 5$, and $a_5 = 5 + 3 = 8$.

16. $a_n = a_{n-1} + a_{n-2} + a_{n-3}$ and $a_1 = 1$, $a_2 = 1$, and $a_3 = 1$. Then $a_4 = 1 + 1 + 1 = 3$ and $a_5 = 3 + 1 + 1 = 5$.

17. (a) $a_1 = 7$, $a_2 = 11$, $a_3 = 15$, $a_4 = 19$, $a_5 = 23$, $a_6 = 27$, $a_7 = 31$, $a_8 = 35$, $a_9 = 39$, $a_{10} = 43$

(b)

18. (a) $a_1 = 2$, $a_2 = 6$, $a_3 = 12$, $a_4 = 20$, $a_5 = 30$, $a_6 = 42$, $a_7 = 56$, $a_8 = 72$, $a_9 = 90$, $a_{10} = 110$

(b)

19. (a) $a_1 = \frac{12}{1} = 12$, $a_2 = \frac{12}{2} = 6$, $a_3 = \frac{12}{3} = 4$, $a_4 = \frac{12}{4} = 3$, $a_5 = \frac{12}{5}$, $a_6 = \frac{12}{6} = 2$, $a_7 = \frac{12}{7}$, $a_8 = \frac{12}{8} = \frac{3}{2}$, $a_9 = \frac{12}{9} = \frac{4}{3}$, $a_{10} = \frac{12}{10} = \frac{6}{5}$

(b)

18. (a) $a_1 = 6$, $a_2 = 2$, $a_3 = 6$, $a_4 = 2$, $a_5 = 6$, $a_6 = 2$, $a_7 = 6$, $a_8 = 2$, $a_9 = 6$, $a_{10} = 2$

(b)

21. (a) $a_1 = 2$, $a_2 = 0.5$, $a_3 = 2$, $a_4 = 0.5$, $a_5 = 2$, $a_6 = 0.5$, $a_7 = 2$, $a_8 = 0.5$, $a_9 = 2$, $a_{10} = 0.5$

(b)

18. (a) $a_1 = 1$, $a_2 = 3$, $a_3 = 2$, $a_4 = -1$, $a_5 = -3$, $a_6 = -2$, $a_7 = 1$, $a_8 = 3$, $a_9 = 2$, $a_{10} = -1$

(b)

23. $2, 4, 8, 16, \ldots$. All are powers of 2, so $a_1 = 2$, $a_2 = 2^2$, $a_3 = 2^3$, $a_4 = 2^4$, $\ldots$ Thus $a_n = 2^n$.

24. $-\frac{1}{3}, \frac{1}{9}, -\frac{1}{27}, \frac{1}{81}, \ldots$. The denominators are all powers of 3, and the terms alternate in sign. Thus $a_1 = \dfrac{(-1)^1}{3^1}$, $a_2 = \dfrac{(-1)^2}{3^2}$, $a_3 = \dfrac{(-1)^3}{3^3}$, $a_4 = \dfrac{(-1)^4}{3^4}$, $\ldots$. So $a_n = \dfrac{(-1)^n}{3^n}$.

25. $1, 4, 7, 10, \ldots$. The difference between any two consecutive terms is 3, so $a_1 = 3(1) - 2$, $a_2 = 3(2) - 2$, $a_3 = 3(3) - 2$, $a_4 = 3(4) - 2$, $\ldots$ Thus $a_n = 3n - 2$.

26. $5, -25, 125, -625, \ldots$. These terms are powers of 5, and the terms alternate in sign. So $a_1 = (-1)^2 \cdot 5^1$, $a_2 = (-1)^3 \cdot 5^2$, $a_3 = (-1)^4 \cdot 5^3$, $a_4 = (-1)^5 \cdot 5^4$, $\ldots$. Thus $a_n = (-1)^{n+1} \cdot 5^n$.

27. $1, \frac{3}{4}, \frac{5}{9}, \frac{7}{16}, \frac{9}{25}, \ldots$. We consider the numerator separately from the denominator. The numerators of the terms differ by 2, and the denominators are perfect squares. So $a_1 = \dfrac{2(1) - 1}{1^2}$, $a_2 = \dfrac{2(2) - 1}{2^2}$, $a_3 = \dfrac{2(3) - 1}{3^2}$, $a_4 = \dfrac{2(4) - 1}{4^2}$, $a_5 = \dfrac{2(5) - 1}{5^2}$, $\ldots$. Thus $a_n = \dfrac{2n - 1}{n^2}$.

28. $\frac{3}{4}, \frac{4}{5}, \frac{5}{6}, \frac{6}{7}, \ldots$. Both the numerator and the denominator increase by 1, so $a_1 = \dfrac{1+2}{1+3}$, $a_2 = \dfrac{2+2}{2+3}$, $a_3 = \dfrac{3+2}{3+3}$, $a_4 = \dfrac{4+2}{4+3}$, $\ldots$. Thus $a_n = \dfrac{n+2}{n+3}$.

29. $0, 2, 0, 2, 0, 2, \ldots$. These terms alternate between 0 and 2. So $a_1 = 1 - 1$, $a_2 = 1 + 1$, $a_3 = 1 - 1$, $a_4 = 1 + 1$, $a_5 = 1 - 1$, $a_6 = 1 + 1$, $\ldots$ Thus $a_n = 1 + (-1)^n$.

30. $1, \frac{1}{2}, 3, \frac{1}{4}, 5, \frac{1}{6}, \ldots$. So $a_1 = 1$, $a_2 = 2^{-1}$, $a_3 = 3^1$, $a_4 = 4^{-1}$, $\ldots$. Thus $a_n = n^{(-1)^{n+1}}$.

31. $a_1 = 1$, $a_2 = 3$, $a_3 = 5$, $a_4 = 7$, ... Therefore, $a_n = 2n - 1$. So $S_1 = 1$, $S_2 = 1 + 3 = 4$, $S_3 = 1 + 3 + 5+ = 9$, $S_4 = 1 + 3 + 5 + 7 = 16$, $S_5 = 1 + 3 + 5 + 7 + 9 = 25$, and $S_6 = 1 + 3 + 5 + 7 + 9 + 11 = 36$.

32. $a_1 = 1^2$, $a_2 = 2^2$, $a_3 = 3^2$, $a_4 = 4^2$, ... Therefore, $a_n = n^2$. So $S_1 = 1^2 = 1$, $S_2 = 1 + 2^2 = 5$, $S_3 = 5 + 3^2 = 5 + 9 = 14$, $S_4 = 14 + 4^2 = 14 + 16 = 30$, $S_5 = 30 + 5^2 = 30 + 25 = 55$, and $S_6 = 55 + 6^2 = 55 + 36 = 91$.

33. $a_1 = \frac{1}{3}$, $a_2 = \frac{1}{3^2}$, $a_3 = \frac{1}{3^3}$, $a_4 = \frac{1}{3^4}$, ... Therefore, $a_n = \frac{1}{3^n}$. So $S_1 = \frac{1}{3}$, $S_2 = \frac{1}{3} + \frac{1}{3^2} = \frac{4}{9}$, $S_3 = \frac{1}{3} + \frac{1}{3^2} + \frac{1}{3^3} = \frac{13}{27}$, $S_4 = \frac{1}{3} + \frac{1}{3^2} + \frac{1}{3^3} + \frac{1}{3^4} = \frac{40}{81}$, and $S_5 = \frac{1}{3} + \frac{1}{3^2} + \frac{1}{3^3} + \frac{1}{3^4} + \frac{1}{3^5} = \frac{121}{243}$, $S_6 = \frac{1}{3} + \frac{1}{3^2} + \frac{1}{3^3} + \frac{1}{3^4} + \frac{1}{3^5} + \frac{1}{3^6} = \frac{364}{729}$.

34. $a_1 = -1$, $a_2 = 1$, $a_3 = -1$, $a_4 = 1$, ... Therefore, $a_n = (-1)^n$. So $S_1 = -1$, $S_2 = -1 + 1 = 0$, $S_3 = 0 - 1 = -1$, $S_4 = -1 + 1 = 0$, $S_5 = 0 - 1 = -1$, and $S_6 = -1 + 1 = 0$.

35. $a_n = \dfrac{2}{3^n}$. So $S_1 = \frac{2}{3}$, $S_2 = \frac{2}{3} + \frac{2}{3^2} = \frac{8}{9}$, $S_3 = \frac{2}{3} + \frac{2}{3^2} + \frac{2}{3^3} = \frac{26}{27}$, and $S_4 = \frac{2}{3} + \frac{2}{3^2} + \frac{2}{3^3} + \frac{2}{3^4} = \frac{80}{81}$. Therefore, $S_n = \dfrac{3^n - 1}{3^n}$.

36. $a_n = \dfrac{1}{n+1} - \dfrac{1}{n+2}$. So $S_1 = \frac{1}{2} - \frac{1}{3}$, $S_2 = \left(\frac{1}{2} - \frac{1}{3}\right) + \left(\frac{1}{3} - \frac{1}{4}\right) = \frac{1}{2} + \left(-\frac{1}{3} + \frac{1}{3}\right) - \frac{1}{4} = \frac{1}{2} - \frac{1}{4}$, $S_3 = \left(\frac{1}{2} - \frac{1}{3}\right) + \left(\frac{1}{3} - \frac{1}{4}\right) + \left(\frac{1}{4} - \frac{1}{5}\right) = \frac{1}{2} + \left(-\frac{1}{3} + \frac{1}{3}\right) + \left(-\frac{1}{4} + \frac{1}{4}\right) - \frac{1}{5} = \frac{1}{2} - \frac{1}{5}$, and $S_4 = \left(\frac{1}{2} - \frac{1}{3}\right) + \left(\frac{1}{3} - \frac{1}{4}\right) + \left(\frac{1}{4} - \frac{1}{5}\right) + \left(\frac{1}{5} - \frac{1}{6}\right) = \frac{1}{2} + \left(-\frac{1}{3} + \frac{1}{3}\right) + \left(-\frac{1}{4} + \frac{1}{4}\right) + \left(-\frac{1}{5} + \frac{1}{5}\right) - \frac{1}{6} = \frac{1}{2} - \frac{1}{6}$. Therefore, $S_n = \left(\frac{1}{2} - \frac{1}{3}\right) + \left(\frac{1}{3} - \frac{1}{4}\right) + \cdots + \left(\frac{1}{n+1} - \frac{1}{n+2}\right) = \frac{1}{2} + \left(-\frac{1}{3} + \frac{1}{3}\right) + \cdots + \left(-\frac{1}{n+1} + \frac{1}{n+1}\right) - \frac{1}{n+2} = \frac{1}{2} - \frac{1}{n+2}$.

37. $a_n = \sqrt{n} - \sqrt{n+1}$. So $S_1 = \sqrt{1} - \sqrt{2} = 1 - \sqrt{2}$, $S_2 = \left(\sqrt{1} - \sqrt{2}\right) + \left(\sqrt{2} - \sqrt{3}\right) = 1 + \left(-\sqrt{2} + \sqrt{2}\right) - \sqrt{3} = 1 - \sqrt{3}$, $S_3 = \left(\sqrt{1} - \sqrt{2}\right) + \left(\sqrt{2} - \sqrt{3}\right) + \left(\sqrt{3} - \sqrt{4}\right) = 1 + \left(-\sqrt{2} + \sqrt{2}\right) + \left(-\sqrt{3} + \sqrt{3}\right) - \sqrt{4} = 1 - \sqrt{4}$,
$S_4 = \left(\sqrt{1} - \sqrt{2}\right) + \left(\sqrt{2} - \sqrt{3}\right) + \left(\sqrt{3} - \sqrt{4}\right) + \left(\sqrt{4} - \sqrt{5}\right)$
$\quad = 1 + \left(-\sqrt{2} + \sqrt{2}\right) + \left(-\sqrt{3} + \sqrt{3}\right) + \left(-\sqrt{4} + \sqrt{4}\right) - \sqrt{5} = 1 - \sqrt{5}$
Therefore,
$S_n = \left(\sqrt{1} - \sqrt{2}\right) + \left(\sqrt{2} - \sqrt{3}\right) + \cdots + \left(\sqrt{n} - \sqrt{n+1}\right)$
$\quad = 1 + \left(-\sqrt{2} + \sqrt{2}\right) + \left(-\sqrt{3} + \sqrt{3}\right) + \cdots + \left(-\sqrt{n} + \sqrt{n}\right) - \sqrt{n+1} = 1 - \sqrt{n+1}$

38. $a_n = \log\left(\dfrac{k}{k+1}\right) = \log k - \log(k+1)$. So $S_1 = \log 1 - \log 2 = -\log 2$, $S_2 = (-\log 2) + (\log 2 - \log 3) = -\log 3$, $S_3 = -\log 2 + (\log 2 - \log 3) + (\log 3 - \log 4) = (-\log 2 + \log 2) + (-\log 3 + \log 3) - \log 4 = -\log 4$, and $S_4 = -\log 2 + (\log 2 - \log 3) + (\log 3 - \log 4) + (\log 4 - \log 5)$
$\quad = (-\log 2 + \log 2) + (-\log 3 + \log 3) + (-\log 4 + \log 4) - \log 5 = -\log 5$
Therefore, $S_n = -\log(n+1)$.

39. $\sum_{k=1}^{4} k = 1 + 2 + 3 + 4 = 10$

40. $\sum_{k=1}^{4} k^2 = 1 + 2^2 + 3^2 + 4^2 = 1 + 4 + 9 + 16 = 30$

41. $\sum_{k=1}^{3} \dfrac{1}{k} = 1 + \frac{1}{2} + \frac{1}{3} = \frac{6}{6} + \frac{3}{6} + \frac{2}{6} = \frac{11}{6}$

42. $\sum_{j=1}^{100} (-1)^j = (-1)^1 + (-1)^2 + (-1)^3 + (-1)^4 + \cdots + (-1)^{99} + (-1)^{100} = -1 + 1 - 1 + 1 - 1 + \cdots - 1 + 1 = 0$

43. $\sum_{i=1}^{8} \left[1 + (-1)^i\right] = 0 + 2 + 0 + 2 + 0 + 2 + 0 + 2 = 8$

44. $\sum_{i=4}^{12} 10 = 10 + 10 + 10 + 10 + 10 + 10 + 10 + 10 + 10 = 90$

45. $\sum_{k=1}^{5} 2^{k-1} = 2^0 + 2^1 + 2^2 + 2^3 + 2^4 = 1 + 2 + 4 + 8 + 16 = 31$

46. $\sum_{i=1}^{3} i 2^i = 1 \cdot 2^1 + 2 \cdot 2^2 + 3 \cdot 2^3 = 2 + 8 + 24 = 34$

47. 385   **48.** 15,550   **49.** 46,438   **50.** 0.153146   **51.** 22   **52.** -0.688172

53. $\sum_{k=1}^{5} \sqrt{k} = \sqrt{1} + \sqrt{2} + \sqrt{3} + \sqrt{4} + \sqrt{5}$

54. $\sum_{i=0}^{4} \dfrac{2i-1}{2i+1} = \dfrac{2\cdot 0 - 1}{2\cdot 0 + 1} + \dfrac{2\cdot 1 - 1}{2\cdot 1 + 1} + \dfrac{2\cdot 2 - 1}{2\cdot 2 + 1} + \dfrac{2\cdot 3 - 1}{2\cdot 3 + 1} + \dfrac{2\cdot 4 - 1}{2\cdot 4 + 1} = -1 + \dfrac{1}{3} + \dfrac{3}{5} + \dfrac{5}{7} + \dfrac{7}{9}$

55. $\sum_{k=0}^{6} \sqrt{k+4} = \sqrt{4} + \sqrt{5} + \sqrt{6} + \sqrt{7} + \sqrt{8} + \sqrt{9} + \sqrt{10}$

56. $\sum_{k=6}^{9} k(k+3) = 6 \cdot 9 + 7 \cdot 10 + 8 \cdot 11 + 9 \cdot 12 = 54 + 70 + 88 + 108$

57. $\sum_{k=3}^{100} x^k = x^3 + x^4 + x^5 + \cdots + x^{100}$

58. $\sum_{j=1}^{n} (-1)^{j+1} x^j = (-1)^2 x + (-1)^3 x^2 + (-1)^4 x^3 + \cdots + (-1)^{n+1} x^n = x - x^2 + x^3 - \cdots + (-1)^{n+1} x^n$

59. $1 + 2 + 3 + 4 + \cdots + 100 = \sum_{k=1}^{100} k$

60. $2 + 4 + 6 + \cdots + 20 = \sum_{k=1}^{10} 2k$

61. $1^2 + 2^2 + 3^2 + \cdots + 10^2 = \sum_{k=1}^{10} k^2$

62. $\dfrac{1}{2\ln 2} - \dfrac{1}{3\ln 3} + \dfrac{1}{4\ln 4} - \dfrac{1}{5\ln 5} + \cdots + \dfrac{1}{100\ln 100} = \sum_{k=2}^{100} \dfrac{(-1)^k}{k \ln k}$

63. $\dfrac{1}{1\cdot 2} + \dfrac{1}{2\cdot 3} + \dfrac{1}{3\cdot 4} + \cdots + \dfrac{1}{999\cdot 1000} = \sum_{k=1}^{999} \dfrac{1}{k(k+1)}$

64. $\dfrac{\sqrt{1}}{1^2} + \dfrac{\sqrt{2}}{2^2} + \dfrac{\sqrt{3}}{3^2} + \cdots + \dfrac{\sqrt{n}}{n^2} = \sum_{k=1}^{n} \dfrac{\sqrt{k}}{k^2}$

65. $1 + x + x^2 + x^3 + \cdots + x^{100} = \sum_{k=0}^{100} x^k$

66. $1 - 2x + 3x^2 - 4x^3 + 5x^4 + \cdots - 100x^{99} = \sum_{k=1}^{100} (-1)^{k+1} \cdot k \cdot x^{k-1}$

67. $\sqrt{2},\ \sqrt{2\sqrt{2}},\ \sqrt{2\sqrt{2\sqrt{2}}},\ \sqrt{2\sqrt{2\sqrt{2\sqrt{2}}}},\ \ldots$. We simplify each term in an attempt to determine a formula for a_n. So
$a_1 = 2^{1/2}$, $a_2 = \sqrt{2 \cdot 2^{1/2}} = \sqrt{2^{3/2}} = 2^{3/4}$, $a_3 = \sqrt{2 \cdot 2^{3/4}} = \sqrt{2^{7/4}} = 2^{7/8}$, $a_4 = \sqrt{2 \cdot 2^{7/8}} = \sqrt{2^{15/8}} = 2^{15/16}$, $\ldots$.
Thus $a_n = 2^{(2^n - 1)/2^n}$.

68. $G_1 = 1$, $G_2 = 1$, $G_3 = 2$, $G_4 = 3$, $G_5 = 5$, $G_6 = 8$, $G_7 = 13$, $G_8 = 21$, $G_9 = 34$, $G_{10} = 55$

69. (a) $A_1 = \$2004$, $A_2 = \$2008.01$, $A_3 = \$2012.02$, $A_4 = \$2016.05$, $A_5 = \$2020.08$, $A_6 = \$2024.12$

(b) Since 3 years is 36 months, we get $A_{36} = \$2149.16$.

70. (a) $I_1 = 0$, $I_2 = \$0.50$, $I_3 = \$1.50$, $I_4 = \$3.01$, $I_5 = \$5.03$, $I_6 = \$7.55$

(b) Since 5 years is 60 months, we have $I_{60} = \$977.00$.

71. (a) $P_1 = 35{,}700$, $P_2 = 36{,}414$, $P_3 = 37{,}142$, $P_4 = 37{,}885$, $P_5 = 38{,}643$

(b) Since 2014 is 10 years after 2004, $P_{10} = 42{,}665$.

72. (a) The amount she owes at the end of the month, A_n, is the amount she owes at the beginning of the month, A_{n-1}, plus the interest, $0.005A_{n-1}$, minus the \$200 she repay her uncle. Thus $A_n = A_{n-1} + 0.005A_{n-1} - 200 \iff A_n = 1.005A_{n-1} - 200$.

(b) $A_1 = 9850$, $A_2 = 9699.25$, $A_3 = 9547.74$, $A_4 = 9395.48$, $A_5 = 9242.46$, $A_6 = 9088.67$. Thus she owes her uncle \$9088.67 after six months.

73. (a) The number of catfish at the end of the month, P_n, is the population at the start of the month, P_{n-1}, plus the increase in population, $0.08P_{n-1}$, minus the 300 catfish harvested. Thus $P_n = P_{n-1} + 0.08P_{n-1} - 300 \iff P_n = 1.08P_{n-1} - 300$.

(b) $P_1 = 5100$, $P_2 = 5208$, $P_3 = 5325$, $P_4 = 5451$, $P_5 = 5587$, $P_6 = 5734$, $P_7 = 5892$, $P_8 = 6064$, $P_9 = 6249$, $P_{10} = 6449$, $P_{11} = 6665$, $P_{12} = 6898$. Thus there should be 6898 catfish in the pond at the end of 12 months.

74. (a) Let n be the years since 2002. So $P_0 = \$240{,}000$. Each month the median price of a house in Orange County increases to 1.06 the previous months. Thus $P_n = 1.06^n P_0$.

(b) Since $2010 - 2002 = 8$. Thus $P_8 = 382{,}523.53$. Thus in 2010, the median price of a house in Orange County should be \$382,524.

75. (a) Let S_n be his salary in the nth year. Then $S_1 = \$30{,}000$. Since his salary increase by 2000 each year, $S_n = S_{n-1} + 2000$. Thus $S_1 = \$30{,}000$ and $S_n = S_{n-1} + 2000$.

(b) $S_5 = S_4 + 2000 = (S_3 + 2000) + 2000 = (S_2 + 2000) + 4000 = (S_1 + 2000) + 6000 = \$38{,}000$.

76. (a) Let n be the days after she starts, so $C_0 = 4$. And each day the concentration increases by 10%. Thus after n days the brine solution is $C_n = 1.10 C_{n-1}$ with $C_0 = 4$.

(b) $C_8 = 1.10 C_7 = 1.10 \left(1.10 C_6 \right) = \cdots = 1.10^8 \cdot C_0 = 1.10^8 \cdot 4 \approx 8.6$. Thus the brine solution is 8.6 g/L of salt.

77. Let F_n be the number of pairs of rabbits in the nth month. Clearly $F_1 = F_2 = 1$. In the nth month each pair that is two or more months old (that is, F_{n-2} pairs) will add a pair of offspring to the F_{n-1} pairs already present. Thus $F_n = F_{n-1} + F_{n-2}$. So F_n is the Fibonacci sequence.

78. (a) $a_n = n^2$. Then $a_1 = 1^2 = 1$, $a_2 = 2^2 = 4$, $a_3 = 3^2 = 9$, $a_4 = 4^2 = 16$.

(b) $a_n = n^2 + (n-1)(n-2)(n-3)(n-4)$, $a_1 = 1^2 + (1-1)(1-2)(1-3)(1-4) = 1 + 0(-1)(-2)(-3) = 1$,
$a_2 = 2^2 + (2-1)(2-2)(2-3)(2-4) = 4 + 1 \cdot 0(-1)(-2) = 4$,
$a_3 = 3^2 + (3-1)(3-2)(3-3)(3-4) = 9 + 2 \cdot 1 \cdot 0(-1) = 9$,
$a_4 = 4^2 + (4-1)(4-2)(4-3)(4-4) = 16 + 3 \cdot 2 \cdot 1 \cdot 0 = 16$.

Hence, the sequences agree in the first four terms. However, for the second sequence, $a_5 = 5^2 + (5-1)(5-2)(5-3)(5-4) = 25 + 4 \cdot 3 \cdot 2 \cdot 1 = 49$, and for the first sequence, $a_5 = 5^2 = 25$, and thus the sequences disagree from the fifth term on.

(c) $a_n = n^2 + (n-1)(n-2)(n-3)(n-4)(n-5)(n-6)$ agrees with $a_n = n^2$ in the first six terms only.

(d) $a_n = 2^n$ and $b_n = 2^n + (n-1)(n-2)(n-3)(n-4)$.

79. $a_{n+1} = \begin{cases} \dfrac{a_n}{2} & \text{if } a_n \text{ is even} \\ 3a_n + 1 & \text{if } a_n \text{ is odd} \end{cases}$ With $a_1 = 11$, we have $a_2 = 34$, $a_3 = 17$, $a_4 = 52$, $a_5 = 26$, $a_6 = 13$, $a_7 = 40$,

$a_8 = 20$, $a_9 = 10$, $a_{10} = 5$, $a_{11} = 16$, $a_{12} = 8$, $a_{13} = 4$, $a_{14} = 2$, $a_{15} = 1$, $a_{16} = 4$, $a_{17} = 2$, $a_{18} = 1$, $\ldots$ (with 4, 2, 1 repeating). So $a_{3n+1} = 4$, $a_{3n+2} = 2$, and $a_{3n} = 1$, for $n \geq 5$. With $a_1 = 25$, we have $a_2 = 76$, $a_3 = 38$, $a_4 = 19$, $a_5 = 58$, $a_6 = 29$, $a_7 = 88$, $a_8 = 44$, $a_9 = 22$, $a_{10} = 11$, $a_{11} = 34$, $a_{12} = 17$, $a_{13} = 52$, $a_{14} = 26$, $a_{15} = 13$, $a_{16} = 40$, $a_{17} = 20$, $a_{18} = 10$, $a_{19} = 5$, $a_{20} = 16$, $a_{21} = 8$, $a_{22} = 4$, $a_{23} = 2$, $a_{24} = 1$, $a_{25} = 4$, $a_{26} = 2$, $a_{27} = 1$, $\ldots$ (with 4, 2, 1 repeating). So $a_{3n+1} = 4$, $a_{3n+2} = 2$, and $a_{3n+3} = 1$ for $n \geq 7$.

We conjecture that the sequence will always return to the numbers 4, 2, 1 repeating.

80. $a_n = a_{n-a_{n-1}} + a_{n-a_{n-2}}$, $a_1 = 1$, and $a_2 = 1$. So $a_3 = a_{3-1} + a_{3-1} = a_2 + a_2 = 1 + 1 = 2$,
$a_4 = a_{4-2} + a_{4-1} = a_2 + a_3 = 1 + 2 = 3$, $a_5 = a_{5-3} + a_{5-2} = a_2 + a_3 = 1 + 2 = 3$,
$a_6 = a_{6-3} + a_{6-3} = a_3 + a_3 = 2 + 2 = 4$, $a_7 = a_{7-4} + a_{7-3} = a_3 + a_4 = 2 + 3 = 5$,
$a_8 = a_{8-5} + a_{8-4} = a_3 + a_4 = 2 + 3 = 5$, $a_9 = a_{9-5} + a_{9-5} = a_4 + a_4 = 3 + 3 = 6$, and
$a_{10} = a_{10-6} + a_{10-5} = a_4 + a_5 = 3 + 3 = 6$. The definition of a_n depends on the values of certain preceding terms. So a_n is the sum of two preceding terms whose choice depends on the *values* of a_{n-1} and a_{n-2} (not on $n-1$ and $n-2$).

11.2 **Arithmetic Sequences**

1. (a) $a_1 = 5 + 2(1-1) = 5$,

$a_2 = 5 + 2(2-1) = 5 + 2 = 7$,

$a_3 = 5 + 2(3-1) = 5 + 4 = 9$,

$a_4 = 5 + 2(4-1) = 5 + 6 = 11$,

$a_5 = 5 + 2(5-1) = 5 + 8 = 13$

(b) The common difference is 2.

(c)

2. (a) $a_1 = 3 - 4(1-1) = 3$, $a_2 = 3 - 4(2-1) = -1$,

$a_3 = 3 - 4(3-1) = -5$, $a_4 = 3 - 4(4-1) = -9$,

$a_5 = 3 - 4(5-1) = -13$

(b) The common difference is -4.

(c)

3. (a) $a_1 = \frac{5}{2} - (1-1) = \frac{5}{2}$, $a_2 = \frac{5}{2} - (2-1) = \frac{3}{2}$,

$a_3 = \frac{5}{2} - (3-1) = \frac{1}{2}$, $a_4 = \frac{5}{2} - (4-1) = -\frac{1}{2}$,

$a_5 = \frac{5}{2} - (5-1) = -\frac{3}{2}$

(b) The common difference is -1.

(c)

4. (a) $a_1 = \frac{1}{2}(1-1) = 0$, $a_2 = \frac{1}{2}(2-1) = \frac{1}{2}$,

$a_3 = \frac{1}{2}(3-1) = 1$, $a_4 = \frac{1}{2}(4-1) = \frac{3}{2}$,

$a_5 = \frac{1}{2}(5-1) = 2$

(b) The common difference is $\frac{1}{2}$.

(c)

5. $a = 3$, $d = 5$, $a_n = a + d(n-1) = 3 + 5(n-1)$. So $a_{10} = 3 + 5(10-1) = 48$.

6. $a = -6$, $d = 3$, $a_n = a + d(n-1) = -6 + 3(n-1)$. So $a_{10} = -6 + 3(10-1) = 21$.

7. $a = \frac{5}{2}$, $d = -\frac{1}{2}$, $a_n = a + d(n-1) = \frac{5}{2} - \frac{1}{2}(n-1)$. So $a_{10} = \frac{5}{2} - \frac{1}{2}(10-1) = -2$.

8. $a = \sqrt{3}$, $d = \sqrt{3}$, $a_n = a + d(n-1) = \sqrt{3} + \sqrt{3}(n-1)$. So $a_{10} = \sqrt{3} + \sqrt{3}(10-1) = 10\sqrt{3}$.

9. $a_4 - a_3 = 14 - 11 = 3$, $a_3 - a_2 = 11 - 8 = 3$, $a_2 - a_1 = 8 - 5 = 3$. This sequence is arithmetic with common difference 3.

10. Since $a_2 - a_1 = 6 - 3 = 3$ and $a_4 - a_3 = 13 - 9 = 4$, the terms of the sequence do not have a common difference. This sequence is not arithmetic.

11. Since $a_2 - a_1 = 4 - 2 = 2$ and $a_4 - a_3 = 16 - 8 = 8$, the terms of the sequence do not have a common difference. This sequence is not arithmetic.

12. $a_4 - a_3 = a_3 - a_2 = a_2 - a_1 = 2$. This sequence is arithmetic with common difference 2.

13. $a_4 - a_3 = -\frac{3}{2} - 0 = -\frac{3}{2}$, $a_3 - a_2 = 0 - \frac{3}{2} = -\frac{3}{2}$, $a_2 - a_1 = \frac{3}{2} - 3 = -\frac{3}{2}$. This sequence is arithmetic with common difference $-\frac{3}{2}$.

14. $a_4 - a_3 = \ln 16 - \ln 8 = \ln \frac{16}{8} = \ln 2$, $a_3 - a_2 = \ln 8 - \ln 4 = \ln \frac{8}{4} = \ln 2$, $a_2 - a_1 = \ln 4 - \ln 2 = \ln \frac{4}{2} = \ln 2$. This sequence is arithmetic with common difference $\ln 2$.

15. $a_4 - a_3 = 7.7 - 6.0 = 1.7$, $a_3 - a_2 = 6.0 - 4.3 = 1.7$, $4. - a_1 = 4.3 - 2.6 = 1.7$. This sequence is arithmetic with common difference 1.7.

16. Since $a_4 - a_3 = \frac{1}{5} - \frac{1}{4} = -\frac{1}{20}$ and $a_3 - a_2 = \frac{1}{4} - \frac{1}{3} = -\frac{1}{12}$, the terms of the sequence do not have a common difference. This sequence is not arithmetic.

17. $a_1 = 4 + 7\,(1) = 11$, $a_2 = 4 + 7\,(2) = 18$, $a_3 = 4 + 7\,(3) = 25$, $a_4 = 4 + 7\,(4) = 32$, $a_5 = 4 + 7\,(5) = 39$. This sequence is arithmetic, the common difference is $d = 7$ and $a_n = 4 + 7n = 4 + 7n - 7 + 7 = 11 + 7\,(n-1)$.

18. $a_1 = 4 + 2^1 = 6$, $a_2 = 4 + 2^2 = 8$, $a_3 = 4 + 2^3 = 12$, $a_4 = 4 + 2^4 = 20$, $a_5 = 4 + 2^5 = 36$. Since $a_4 - a_3 = 8$ and $a_3 - a_2 = 4$, the terms of the sequence do not have a common difference. This sequence is not arithmetic.

19. $a_1 = \dfrac{1}{1 + 2\,(1)} = \dfrac{1}{3}$, $a_2 = \dfrac{1}{1 + 2\,(2)} = \dfrac{1}{5}$, $a_3 = \dfrac{1}{1 + 2\,(3)} = \dfrac{1}{7}$, $a_4 = \dfrac{1}{1 + 2\,(4)} = \dfrac{1}{9}$, $a_5 = \dfrac{1}{1 + 2\,(5)} = \dfrac{1}{11}$. Since $a_4 - a_3 = \frac{1}{9} - \frac{1}{7} = -\frac{2}{63}$ and $a_3 - a_2 = \frac{1}{7} - \frac{1}{3} = -\frac{2}{21}$, the terms of the sequence do not have a common difference. This sequence is not arithmetic.

20. $a_1 = 1 + \frac{1}{2} = \frac{3}{2}$, $a_2 = 1 + \frac{2}{2} = 2$, $a_3 = 1 + \frac{3}{2} = \frac{5}{2}$, $a_4 = 1 + \frac{4}{2} = 3$, $a_5 = 1 + \frac{5}{2} = \frac{7}{2}$. This sequence is arithmetic, the common difference is $d = \frac{1}{2}$ and $a_n = 1 + \frac{n}{2} = 1 + \frac{1}{2}n - \frac{1}{2} + \frac{1}{2} = \frac{3}{2} + \frac{1}{2}\,(n-1)$.

21. $a_1 = 6\,(1) - 10 = -4$, $a_2 = 6\,(2) - 10 = 2$, $a_3 = 6\,(3) - 10 = 8$, $a_4 = 6\,(4) - 10 = 14$, $a_5 = 6\,(5) - 10 = 20$. This sequence is arithmetic, the common difference is $d = 6$ and $a_n = 6n - 10 = 6n - 6 + 6 - 10 = -4 + 6\,(n-1)$.

22. $a_1 = 3 + (-1)^1\,(1) = 2$, $a_2 = 3 + (-1)^2\,(2) = 5$, $a_3 = 3 + (-1)^3\,(3) = 0$, $a_4 = 3 + (-1)^4\,(4) = 7$, $a_5 = 3 + (-1)^5\,(5) = -2$. Since $a_4 - a_3 = 7$ and $a_3 - a_2 = -5$, the terms of the sequence do not have a common difference. This sequence is not arithmetic.

23. $2, 5, 8, 11, \ldots$. Then $d = a_2 - a_1 = 5 - 2 = 3$, $a_5 = a_4 + 3 = 11 + 3 = 14$, $a_n = 2 + 3\,(n-1)$, and $a_{100} = 2 + 3\,(99) = 299$.

24. $1, 5, 9, 13, \ldots$. Then $d = a_2 - a_1 = 5 - 1 = 4$, $a_5 = a_4 + 4 = 13 + 4 = 17$, $a_n = 1 + 4\,(n-1)$, $a_{100} = 1 + 4\,(99) = 397$.

25. $4, 9, 14, 19, \ldots$. Then $d = a_2 - a_1 = 9 - 4 = 5$, $a_5 = a_4 + 5 = 19 + 5 = 24$, $a_n = 4 + 5\,(n-1)$, and $a_{100} = 4 + 5\,(99) = 499$.

26. $11, 8, 5, 2, \ldots$. Then $d = a_2 - a_1 = 8 - 11 = -3$, $a_5 = a_4 - 3 = 2 - 3 = -1$, $a_n = 11 - 3\,(n-1)$, and $a_{100} = 11 - 3\,(99) = -286$.

27. $-12, -8, -4, 0, \ldots$. Then $d = a_2 - a_1 = -8 - (-12) = 4$, $a_5 = a_4 + 4 = 0 + 4 = 4$, $a_n = -12 + 4\,(n-1)$, and $a_{100} = -12 + 4\,(99) = 384$.

28. $\frac{7}{6}, \frac{5}{3}, \frac{13}{6}, \frac{8}{3}, \ldots$. Then $d = a_2 - a_1 = \frac{10}{6} - \frac{7}{6} = \frac{1}{2}$, $a_5 = a_4 + \frac{1}{2} = \frac{8}{3} + \frac{1}{2} = \frac{19}{6}$, $a_n = \frac{7}{6} + \frac{1}{2}\,(n-1)$, $a_{100} = \frac{7}{6} + \frac{1}{2}\,(99) = \frac{7+297}{6} = \frac{152}{3}$.

29. $25, 26.5, 28, 29.5, \ldots$. Then $d = a_2 - a_1 = 26.5 - 25 = 1.5$, $a_5 = a_4 + 1.5 = 29.5 + 1.5 = 31$, $a_n = 25 + 1.5\,(n-1)$, $a_{100} = 25 + 1.5\,(99) = 173.5$.

30. $15, 12.3, 9.6, 6.9, \ldots$. Then $d = a_2 - a_1 = 12.3 - 15 = -2.7$, $a_5 = a_4 - 2.7 = 6.9 - 2.7 = 4.2$, $a_n = 15 - 2.7\,(n-1)$, and $a_{100} = 15 - 2.7\,(99) = -252.3$.

31. $2, 2 + s, 2 + 2s, 2 + 3s, \ldots$. Then $d = a_2 - a_1 = 2 + s - 2 = s$, $a_5 = a_4 + s = 2 + 3s + s = 2 + 4s$, $a_n = 2 + (n-1)\,s$, and $a_{100} = 2 + 99s$.

32. $-t, -t + 3, -t + 6, -t + 9, \ldots$. Then $d = a_2 - a_1 = (-t + 3) - (-t) = 3$, $a_5 = a_4 + 3 = -t + 9 + 3 = -t + 12$, $a_n = -t + 3\,(n-1)$, and $a_{100} = -t + 3\,(99) = -t + 297$.

33. $a_{10} = \frac{55}{2}$, $a_2 = \frac{7}{2}$, and $a_n = a + d\,(n-1)$. Then $a_2 = a + d = \frac{7}{2} \;\Leftrightarrow\; d = \frac{7}{2} - a$. Substituting into $a_{10} = a + 9d = \frac{55}{2}$ gives $a + 9\left(\frac{7}{2} - a\right) = \frac{55}{2} \;\Leftrightarrow\; a = \frac{1}{2}$. Thus, the first term is $a_1 = \frac{1}{2}$.

34. $a_{12} = 32$, $a_5 = 18$, and $a_n = a + d\,(n-1)$. Then $a_5 = a + 4d = 18 \;\Leftrightarrow\; a = 18 - 4d$. Substituting for a, we have $a_{12} = a + 11d = 32 \;\Leftrightarrow\; (18 - 4d) + 11d = 32 \;\Leftrightarrow\; 7d = 14 \;\Leftrightarrow\; d = 2$. Then we have $a = 18 - 4 \cdot 2 = 10$, and hence, the 20th term is $a_{20} = 10 + 19\,(2) = 48$.

35. $a_{100} = 98$ and $d = 2$. Note that $a_{100} = a + 99d = a + 99\,(2) = a + 198$. Since $a_{100} = 98$, we have $a + 198 = a_{100} = 98 \;\Leftrightarrow\; a = -100$. Hence, $a_1 = -100$, $a_2 = -100 + 2 = -98$, and $a_3 = -100 + 4 = -96$.

36. $a_{20} = 101$, and $d = 3$. Note that $a_{20} = a + 19d = a + 19\,(3) = a + 57$. Since $a_{20} = 101$ we have $a + 57 = a_{20} = 101 \;\Leftrightarrow\; a = 44$. Hence the nth term is $a_n = 44 + 3\,(n-1) = 41 + 3n$.

37. The arithmetic sequence is 1, 4, 7, ... So $d = 4 - 1 = 3$ and $a_n = 1 + 3(n - 1)$. Then $a_n = 88 \iff 1 + 3(n - 1) = 88$
$\iff 3(n - 1) = 87 \iff n - 1 = 29 \iff n = 30$. So 88 is the 30th term.

38. If 11,937 is a term of an arithmetic sequence with $a_1 = 1$ and common difference 4, then $11937 = 1 + 4(n - 1)$ for some
integer n. Solving for n, we have $11937 = 1 + 4(n - 1) = -3 + 4n \iff 11940 = 4n \iff n = 2985$. Thus 11,937
is the 2985th term of this sequence.

39. $a = 1$, $d = 2$, $n = 10$. Then $S_{10} = \frac{10}{2}[2a + (10 - 1)d] = \frac{10}{2}[2 \cdot 1 + 9 \cdot 2] = 100$.

40. $a = 3$, $d = 2$, $n = 12$. Then $S_{12} = \frac{12}{2}[2a + (12 - 1)d] = \frac{12}{2}[2 \cdot 3 + 11 \cdot 2] = 168$.

41. $a = 4$, $d = 2$, $n = 20$. Then $S_{20} = \frac{20}{2}[2a + (20 - 1)d] = \frac{20}{2}[2 \cdot 4 + 19 \cdot 2] = 460$.

42. $a = 100$, $d = -5$, $n = 8$. Then $S_8 = \frac{8}{2}[2a + (8 - 1)d] = \frac{8}{2}[2 \cdot 100 - 7 \cdot 5] = 660$.

43. $a_1 = 55$, $d = 12$, $n = 10$. Then $S_{10} = \frac{10}{2}[2a + (10 - 1)d] = \frac{10}{2}[2 \cdot 55 + 9 \cdot 12] = 1090$.

44. $a_2 = 8$, $a_5 = 9.5$, $n = 15$. Thus $a_2 = a + d = 8$ and $a_5 = a + 4d = 9.5$. Subtracting the first equation from the
second gives $3d = 1.5 \iff d = 0.5$. Substituting for d in the first equation gives $a + 0.5 = 8 \iff a = 7.5$. Thus
$S_{15} = \frac{15}{2}[2 \cdot 7.5 + 14 \cdot 0.5] = 165$.

45. $1 + 5 + 9 + \cdots + 401$ is a partial sum of an arithmetic series, where $a = 1$ and $d = 5 - 1 = 4$.
The last term is $401 = a_n = 1 + 4(n - 1)$, so $n - 1 = 100 \iff n = 101$. So the partial sum is
$S_{101} = \frac{101}{2}(1 + 401) = 101 \cdot 201 = 20{,}301$.

46. $-3 + \left(-\frac{3}{2}\right) + 0 + \frac{3}{2} + 3 + \cdots + 30$ is a partial sum of an arithmetic sequence, where $a = -3$ and $d = \left(-\frac{3}{2}\right) - (-3) = \frac{3}{2}$.
The last term is $30 = a_n = -3 + \frac{3}{2}(n - 1)$, so $22 = n - 1 \iff n = 23$. So the partial sum is
$S_{23} = \frac{23}{2}(-3 + 30) = \frac{621}{2} = 310.5$.

47. $0.7 + 2.7 + 4.7 + \cdots + 56.7$ is a partial sum of an arithmetic series, where $a = 0.7$ and $d = 2.7 - 0.7 = 2$. The last term
is $56.7 = a_n = 0.7 + 2(n - 1) \iff 28 = n - 1 \iff n = 29$. So the partial sum is $S_{29} = \frac{29}{2}(0.7 + 56.7) = 832.3$.

48. $-10 + (-9.9) + (-9.8) + \cdots + (-0.1)$ is a partial sum of an arithmetic sequence, where $a = -10$ and $d = 0.1$.
The last term is $-0.1 = a_n = -10 + 0.1(n - 1)$, so $99 = n - 1 \iff n = 100$. So the partial sum is
$S_{100} = \frac{100}{2}(-10 - 0.1) = -505$.

49. $\sum_{k=0}^{10}(3 + 0.25k)$ is a partial sum of an arithmetic series where $a = 3 + 0.25 \cdot 0 = 3$ and $d = 0.25$. The last term is
$a_{11} = 3 + 0.25 \cdot 10 = 5.5$. So the partial sum is $S_{11} = \frac{11}{2}(3 + 5.5) = 46.75$.

50. $\sum_{n=0}^{20}(1 - 2n)$ is a partial sum of an arithmetic sequence where $a = 1 - 2 \cdot 0 = 1$, $d = -2$, and the last term is
$a_{21} = 1 - 2 \cdot 20 = -39$. So the partial sum is $S_{21} = \frac{21}{2}(1 - 39) = -399$.

51. Let x denote the length of the side between the length of the other two sides. Then the lengths of the three sides of the
triangle are $x - a$, x, and $x + a$, for some $a > 0$. Since $x + a$ is the longest side, it is the hypotenuse, and by the
Pythagorean Theorem, we know that $(x - a)^2 + x^2 = (x + a)^2 \iff x^2 - 2ax + a^2 + x^2 = x^2 + 2ax + a^2 \iff$
$x^2 - 4ax = 0 \iff x(x - 4a) = 0 \Rightarrow x = 4a$ ($x = 0$ is not a possible solution). Thus, the lengths of the three sides
are $x - a = 4a - a = 3a$, $x = 4a$, and $x + a = 4a + a = 5a$. The lengths $3a$, $4a$, $5a$ are proportional to 3, 4, 5, and so the
triangle is similar to a 3-4-5 triangle.

52. $P = 10^{1/10} \cdot 10^{2/10} \cdot 10^{3/10} \cdot \cdots \cdot 10^{19/10} = 10^{(1+2+3+\cdots+19)/10}$. Now, $1 + 2 + 3 + \cdots + 19$ is an arithmetic series with
$a = 1$, $d = 1$, and $n = 19$. Thus, $1 + 2 + 3 + \cdots + 19 = S_{19} = 19\dfrac{(1 + 19)}{2} = 190$, and so $P = 10^{190/10} = 10^{19}$.

53. The sequence $1, \frac{3}{5}, \frac{3}{7}, \frac{1}{3}, \ldots$ is harmonic if $1, \frac{5}{3}, \frac{7}{3}, 3, \ldots$ forms an arithmetic sequence. Since $\frac{5}{3} - 1 = \frac{7}{3} - \frac{5}{3} = 3 - \frac{7}{3} = \frac{2}{3}$,
the sequence of reciprocals is arithmetic and thus the original sequence is harmonic.

54. The two original numbers are 3 and 5. Thus, the reciprocals are $\frac{1}{3}$ and $\frac{1}{5}$, and their average is
$\frac{1}{2}\left(\frac{1}{3} + \frac{1}{5}\right) = \frac{1}{2}\left(\frac{5}{15} + \frac{3}{15}\right) = \frac{4}{15}$. Therefore, the harmonic mean is $\frac{15}{4}$.

55. We have an arithmetic sequence with $a = 5$ and $d = 2$. We seek n such that $2700 = S_n = \frac{n}{2}\left[2a + (n-1)d\right]$.

Solving for n, we have $2700 = \frac{n}{2}\left[10 + 2(n-1)\right]$ $\Leftrightarrow$ $5400 = 10n + 2n^2 - 2n$ $\Leftrightarrow$ $n^2 + 4n - 2700 = 0$ $\Leftrightarrow$ $(n-50)(n+54) = 0$ $\Leftrightarrow$ $n = 50$ or $n = -54$. Since n is a positive integer, 50 terms of the sequence must be added to get 2700.

56. Since the sequence is arithmetic, $a_4 - a_1 = 3d = 16 - 1 = 15$ $\Leftrightarrow$ $3d = 15$ $\Leftrightarrow$ $d = 5$. Now since $S_n = \frac{n}{2}\left[2a + (n-1)d\right]$ we have $2356 = \frac{n}{2}\left[2(1) + (n-1)5\right]$ $\Leftrightarrow$ $4712 = n(2 + 5n - 5) = 5n^2 - 3n$ $\Leftrightarrow$ $5n^2 - 3n - 4712 = 0$. Using the quadratic equation we have $n = \frac{3 \pm \sqrt{3^2 - 4(5)(4712)}}{2(5)} = \frac{3 \pm \sqrt{94249}}{10} = \frac{3 \pm 307}{10}$.

Since n is positive, we have $n = \frac{310}{10} = 31$. Thus 31 terms must be added.

57. The diminishing values of the computer form an arithmetic sequence with $a_1 = 12500$ and common difference $d = -1875$. Thus the value of the computer after 6 years is $a_7 = 12500 + (7-1)(-1875) = \$1250$.

58. The number of poles in a layer can be viewed as an arithmetic sequence, where $a_1 = 25$ and the common difference is -1. The number of poles in the first 12 layers is $S_{12} = \frac{12}{2}\left[2(25) + 11(-1)\right] = 6 \cdot 39 = 234$.

59. The increasing values of the man's salary form an arithmetic sequence with $a_1 = 30{,}000$ and common difference $d = 2300$. Then his total earnings for a ten-year period are $S_{10} = \frac{10}{2}\left[2(30{,}000) + 9(2300)\right] = 403{,}500$. Thus his total earnings for the 10 year period are \$403,500.

60. The number of cars that can park in a row can be viewed as an arithmetic sequence, where $a_1 = 20$ and the common difference is 2. Thus the number of cars that can park in the 21 rows is $S_{21} = \frac{21}{2}\left[2(20) + 20(2)\right] = 10.5 \cdot 80 = 840$.

61. The number of seats in the nth row is given by the nth term of an arithmetic sequence with $a_1 = 15$ and common difference $d = 3$. We need to find n such that $S_n = 870$. So we solve $870 = S_n = \frac{n}{2}\left[2(15) + (n-1)3\right]$ for n. We have $870 = \frac{n}{2}(27 + 3n)$ $\Leftrightarrow$ $1740 = 3n^2 + 27n$ $\Leftrightarrow$ $3n^2 + 27n - 1740 = 0$ $\Leftrightarrow$ $n^2 + 9n - 580 = 0$ $\Leftrightarrow$ $(x-20)(x+29) = 0$ $\Rightarrow$ $n = 20$ or $n = -29$. Since the number of rows is positive, the theater must have 20 rows.

62. The sequence is 16, 48, 80, ... This is an arithmetic sequence with $a = 16$ and $d = 48 - 16 = 32$.

(a) The total distance after 6 seconds is $S_6 = \frac{6}{2}(32 + 5 \cdot 32) = 3 \cdot 192 = 576$ ft.

(b) The total distance after n seconds is $S_n = \frac{n}{2}\left[32 + 32(n-1)\right] = 16n^2$ ft.

63. The number of gifts on the 12th day is $1 + 2 + 3 + 4 + \cdots + 12$. Since $a_2 - a_1 = a_3 - a_2 = a_4 - a_3 = \cdots = 1$, the number of gifts on the 12th day is the partial sum of an arithmetic sequence with $a = 1$ and $d = 1$. So the sum is $S_{12} = 12\left(\frac{1+12}{2}\right) = 6 \cdot 13 = 78$.

64. (a) We want an arithmetic sequence with 4 terms, so let $a_1 = 10$ and $a_4 = 18$. Since the sequence is arithmetic, $a_4 - a_1 = 3d = 18 - 10 = 8$ $\Leftrightarrow$ $3d = 8$ $\Leftrightarrow$ $d = \frac{8}{3}$. Therefore, $a_2 = 10 + \frac{8}{3} = \frac{38}{3}$ and $a_3 = 10 + 2\left(\frac{8}{3}\right) = \frac{46}{3}$ are the two arithmetic means between 10 and 18.

(b) We want an arithmetic sequence with 5 terms, so let $a_1 = 10$ and $a_5 = 18$. Since the sequence is arithmetic, $a_5 - a_1 = 4d = 18 - 10 = 8$ $\Leftrightarrow$ $4d = 8$ $\Leftrightarrow$ $d = 2$. Therefore, $a_2 = 10 + 2 = 12$, $a_3 = 10 + 2(2) = 14$, and $a_4 = 10 + 3(2) = 16$ are the three arithmetic means between 10 and 18.

(c) We want an arithmetic sequence with 6 terms, with the starting dosage $a_1 = 100$ and the final dosage $a_6 = 300$. Since the sequence is arithmetic, $a_6 - a_1 = 5d = 300 - 100 = 200$ $\Leftrightarrow$ $5d = 200$ $\Leftrightarrow$ $d = 40$. Therefore, $a_2 = 140$, $a_3 = 180$, $a_4 = 220$, $a_5 = 260$, and $a_6 = 300$. The patient should take 140 mg, then 180 mg, then 220 mg, then 260 mg, and finally arrive at 300 mg.

11.3 Geometric Sequences

1. (a) $a_1 = 5\,(2)^0 = 5$, $a_2 = 5\,(2)^1 = 10$,

$a_3 = 5\,(2)^2 = 20$, $a_4 = 5\,(2)^3 = 40$,

$a_5 = 5\,(2)^4 = 80$

(b) The common ratio is 2.

(c)

2. (a) $a_1 = 3\,(-4)^0 = 3$, $a_2 = 3\,(-4)^1 = -12$,

$a_3 = 3\,(-4)^2 = 48$, $a_4 = 3\,(-4)^3 = -192$,

$a_5 = 3\,(-4)^4 = 768$

(b) The common ratio is -4.

(c)

3. (a) $a_1 = \frac{5}{2}\left(-\frac{1}{2}\right)^0 = \frac{5}{2}$, $a_2 = \frac{5}{2}\left(-\frac{1}{2}\right)^1 = -\frac{5}{4}$,

$a_3 = \frac{5}{2}\left(-\frac{1}{2}\right)^2 = \frac{5}{8}$, $a_4 = \frac{5}{2}\left(-\frac{1}{2}\right)^3 = -\frac{5}{16}$,

$a_5 = \frac{5}{2}\left(-\frac{1}{2}\right)^4 = \frac{5}{32}$

(b) The common ratio is $-\frac{1}{2}$.

(c)

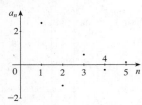

4. (a) $a_1 = 3^0 = 1$, $a_2 = 3^1 = 3$, $a_3 = 3^2 = 9$,

$a_4 = 3^3 = 27$, $a_5 = 3^4 = 81$

(b) The common ratio is 3.

(c)

5. $a = 3$, $r = 5$. So $a_n = ar^{n-1} = 3\,(5)^{n-1}$ and $a_4 = 3 \cdot 5^3 = 375$.

6. $a = -6$, $r = 3$. So $a_n = ar^{n-1} = -6\,(3)^{n-1}$ and $a_4 = -6 \cdot 3^3 = -162$.

7. $a = \frac{5}{2}$, $r = -\frac{1}{2}$. So $a_n = ar^{n-1} = \frac{5}{2}\left(-\frac{1}{2}\right)^{n-1}$ and $a_4 = \frac{5}{2} \cdot \left(-\frac{1}{2}\right)^3 = -\frac{5}{16}$.

8. $a = \sqrt{3}$, $r = \sqrt{3}$. So $a_n = ar^{n-1} = \sqrt{3}\left(\sqrt{3}\right)^{n-1} = \left(\sqrt{3}\right)^n$ and $a_4 = \sqrt{3} \cdot \left(\sqrt{3}\right)^3 = 9$.

9. $\frac{a_2}{a_1} = \frac{4}{2} = 2$, $\frac{a_3}{a_2} = \frac{8}{4} = 2$, $\frac{a_4}{a_3} = \frac{16}{8} = 2$. Since these ratios are the same, the sequence is geometric with the common ratio 2.

10. $\frac{a_2}{a_1} = \frac{6}{2} = 3$, $\frac{a_4}{a_3} = \frac{36}{18} = 2$. Since these ratios are not the same, this is not a geometric sequence.

11. $\frac{a_2}{a_1} = \frac{3/2}{3} = \frac{1}{2}$, $\frac{a_3}{a_2} = \frac{3/4}{3/2} = \frac{1}{2}$, $\frac{a_4}{a_3} = \frac{3/8}{3/4} = \frac{1}{2}$. Since these ratios are the same, the sequence is geometric with the common ratio $\frac{1}{2}$.

12. $\frac{a_2}{a_1} = \frac{-9}{27} = -\frac{1}{3}$, $\frac{a_3}{a_2} = \frac{3}{-9} = -\frac{1}{3}$, $\frac{a_4}{a_3} = -\frac{1}{3}$. Since these ratios are the same, the sequence is geometric with the common ratio $-\frac{1}{3}$.

13. $\frac{a_2}{a_1} = \frac{1/3}{1/2} = \frac{2}{3}$, $\frac{a_4}{a_3} = \frac{1/5}{1/4} = \frac{4}{5}$. Since these ratios are not the same, this is not a geometric sequence.

14. $\frac{a_2}{a_1} = \frac{e^4}{e^2} = e^2$, $\frac{a_3}{a_2} = \frac{e^6}{e^4} = e^2$, $\frac{a_4}{a_3} = \frac{e^8}{e^6} = e^2$. Since these ratios are the same, the sequence is geometric with the common ratio e^2.

15. $\dfrac{a_2}{a_1} = \dfrac{1.1}{1.0} = 1.1$, $\dfrac{a_3}{a_2} = \dfrac{1.21}{1.1} = 1.1$, $\dfrac{a_4}{a_3} = \dfrac{1.331}{1.21} = 1.1$. Since these ratios are the same, the sequence is geometric with the common ratio 1.1.

16. $\dfrac{a_2}{a_1} = \dfrac{\frac{1}{4}}{\frac{1}{2}} = \dfrac{1}{2}$, $\dfrac{a_4}{a_3} = \dfrac{\frac{1}{8}}{\frac{1}{6}} = \dfrac{3}{4}$. Since these ratios are not the same, this is not a geometric sequence.

17. $a_1 = 2\,(3)^1 = 6$, $a_2 = 2\,(3)^2 = 18$, $a_3 = 2\,(3)^3 = 54$, $a_4 = 2\,(3)^4 = 162$, $a_5 = 2\,(3)^5 = 486$. This sequence is geometric, the common ratio is $r = 3$ and $a_n = a_1 r^{n-1} = 6\,(3)^{n-1}$.

18. $a_1 = 4 + (3)^1 = 7$, $a_2 = 4 + (3)^2 = 13$, $a_3 = 4 + (3)^3 = 31$, $a_4 = 4 + (3)^4 = 85$, $a_5 = 4 + (3)^5 = 247$. Since $\dfrac{a_2}{a_1} = \dfrac{13}{7}$ and $\dfrac{a_3}{a_2} = \dfrac{31}{13}$ are different ratios, this is not a geometric sequence.

19. $a_1 = \dfrac{1}{4}$, $a_2 = \dfrac{1}{4^2} = \dfrac{1}{16}$, $a_3 = \dfrac{1}{4^3} = \dfrac{1}{64}$, $a_4 = \dfrac{1}{4^4} = \dfrac{1}{256}$, $a_5 = \dfrac{1}{4^5} = \dfrac{1}{1024}$. This sequence is geometric, the common ratio is $r = \frac{1}{4}$ and $a_n = a_1 r^{n-1} = \frac{1}{4}\left(\frac{1}{4}\right)^{n-1}$.

20. $a_1 = (-1)^1\,(2)^1 = -2$, $a_2 = (-1)^2\,(2)^2 = 4$, $a_3 = (-1)^3\,(2)^3 = -8$, $a_4 = (-1)^4\,(2)^4 = 16$, $a_5 = (-1)^5\,(2)^5 = -32$. This sequence is geometric, the common ratio is $r = -2$ and $a_n = a_1 r^{n-1} = -2\,(-2)^{n-1}$.

21. Since $\ln a^b = b \ln a$, we have $a_1 = \ln\left(5^0\right) = \ln 1 = 0$, $a_2 = \ln\left(5^1\right) = \ln 5$, $a_3 = \ln\left(5^2\right) = 2 \ln 5$, $a_4 = \ln\left(5^3\right) = 3 \ln 5$, $a_5 = \ln\left(5^4\right) = 4 \ln 5$. Since $a_1 = 0$ and $a_2 \neq 0$, this sequence is not geometric.

22. $a_1 = 1^1 = 1$, $a_2 = 2^2 = 4$, $a_3 = 3^3 = 54$, $a_4 = 4^4 = 256$, $a_5 = 5^5 = 3125$. Since $\dfrac{a_2}{a_1} = \dfrac{4}{1} = 4$ and $\dfrac{a_3}{a_2} = \dfrac{27}{4}$ are different, this is not a geometric sequence.

23. $2, 6, 18, 54, \ldots$. Then $r = \dfrac{a_2}{a_1} = \dfrac{6}{2} = 3$, $a_5 = a_4 \cdot 3 = 54\,(3) = 162$, and $a_n = 2 \cdot 3^{n-1}$.

24. $7, \dfrac{14}{3}, \dfrac{28}{9}, \dfrac{56}{27}, \ldots$. Then $r = \dfrac{a_2}{a_1} = \dfrac{\frac{14}{3}}{7} = \dfrac{2}{3}$, $a_5 = a_4 \cdot \dfrac{2}{3} = \dfrac{56}{27} \cdot \dfrac{2}{3} = \dfrac{112}{81}$, and $a_n = 7\left(\frac{2}{3}\right)^{n-1}$.

25. $0.3, -0.09, 0.027, -0.0081, \ldots$. Then $r = \dfrac{a_2}{a_1} = \dfrac{-0.09}{0.3} = -0.3$, $a_5 = a_4 \cdot (-0.3) = -0.0081\,(-0.3) = 0.00243$, and $a_n = 0.3\,(-0.3)^{n-1}$.

26. $1, \sqrt{2}, 2, 2\sqrt{2}, \ldots$. Then $r = \dfrac{a_2}{a_1} = \dfrac{\sqrt{2}}{1} = \sqrt{2}$, $a_5 = a_4 \cdot \sqrt{2} = 2\sqrt{2} \cdot \sqrt{2} = 4$, and $a_n = \left(\sqrt{2}\right)^{n-1}$.

27. $144, -12, 1, -\frac{1}{12}, \ldots$. Then $r = \dfrac{a_2}{a_1} = \dfrac{-12}{144} = -\dfrac{1}{12}$, $a_5 = a_4 \cdot \left(-\frac{1}{12}\right) = -\frac{1}{12}\left(-\frac{1}{12}\right) = \frac{1}{144}$, $a_n = 144\left(-\frac{1}{12}\right)^{n-1}$.

28. $-8, -2, -\frac{1}{2}, -\frac{1}{8}, \ldots$. Then $r = \dfrac{a_2}{a_1} = \dfrac{-2}{-8} = \dfrac{1}{4}$, $a_5 = a_4 \cdot \dfrac{1}{4} = -\frac{1}{8} \cdot \frac{1}{4} = -\frac{1}{32}$, and $a_n = -8\left(\frac{1}{4}\right)^{n-1}$.

29. $3, 3^{5/3}, 3^{7/3}, 27, \ldots$. Then $r = \dfrac{a_2}{a_1} = \dfrac{3^{5/3}}{3} = 3^{2/3}$, $a_5 = a_4 \cdot \left(3^{2/3}\right) = 27 \cdot 3^{2/3} = 3^{11/3}$, and $a_n = 3\left(3^{2/3}\right)^{n-1} = 3 \cdot 3^{(2n-2)/3} = 3^{(2n+1)/3}$.

30. $t, \dfrac{t^2}{2}, \dfrac{t^3}{4}, \dfrac{t^4}{8}, \ldots$. Then $r = \dfrac{a_2}{a_1} = \dfrac{\frac{t^2}{2}}{t} = \dfrac{t}{2}$, $a_5 = a_4 \cdot \dfrac{t}{2} = \dfrac{t^4}{8} \cdot \dfrac{t}{2} = \dfrac{t^5}{16}$, and $a_n = t\left(\dfrac{t}{2}\right)^{n-1}$.

31. $1, s^{2/7}, s^{4/7}, s^{6/7}, \ldots$. Then $r = \dfrac{a_2}{a_1} = \dfrac{s^{2/7}}{1} = s^{2/7}$, $a_5 = a_4 \cdot s^{2/7} = s^{6/7} \cdot s^{2/7} = s^{8/7}$, and $a_n = \left(s^{2/7}\right)^{n-1} = s^{(2n-2)/7}$.

32. $5, 5^{c+1}, 5^{2c+1}, 5^{3c+1}, \ldots$. Then $r = \dfrac{a_2}{a_1} = \dfrac{5^{c+1}}{5} = 5^c$, $a_5 = a_4 \cdot 5^c = 5^{3c+1} \cdot 5^c = 5^{4c+1}$, and $a_n = 5\,(5^c)^{n-1} = 5 \cdot 5^{cn-c} = 5^{cn-c+1}$.

33. $a_1 = 8$, $a_2 = 4$. Thus $r = \dfrac{a_2}{a_1} = \dfrac{4}{8} = \dfrac{1}{2}$ and $a_5 = a_1 r^{5-1} = 8\left(\frac{1}{2}\right)^4 = \dfrac{8}{16} = \dfrac{1}{2}$.

34. $a_1 = 3$, $a_3 = \frac{4}{3}$. Thus $r^2 = \frac{\frac{4}{3}}{3} = \frac{4}{9}$ $\Leftrightarrow$ $r = \pm\frac{2}{3}$. If $r = \frac{2}{3}$, then $a_5 = 3\left(\frac{2}{3}\right)^4 = \frac{16}{27}$, and if $r = -\frac{2}{3}$, then $a_5 = 3\left(-\frac{2}{3}\right)^4 = \frac{16}{27}$. Therefore, $a_5 = \frac{16}{27}$.

35. $r = \frac{2}{5}$, $a_4 = \frac{5}{2}$. Since $r = \frac{a_4}{a_3}$, we have $a_3 = \frac{a_4}{r} = \frac{5/2}{2/5} = \frac{25}{4}$.

36. $r = \frac{3}{2}$, $a_5 = 1$. Then $1 = a_5 = a \cdot r^4 = a\left(\frac{3}{2}\right)^4$ $\Leftrightarrow$ $1 = a\left(\frac{3}{2}\right)^4$ $\Leftrightarrow$ $a = \left(\frac{2}{3}\right)^4 = \frac{16}{81}$. Therefore, $a_1 = \frac{16}{81}$, $a_2 = \frac{16}{81}\left(\frac{3}{2}\right) = \frac{8}{27}$, and $a_3 = \frac{8}{27}\left(\frac{3}{2}\right) = \frac{4}{9}$.

37. The geometric sequence is $2, 6, 18, \ldots$. Thus $r = \frac{a_2}{a_1} = \frac{6}{2} = 3$. We need to find n so that $a_n = 2 \cdot 3^{n-1} = 118{,}098$ $\Leftrightarrow$ $3^{n-1} = 59{,}049$ $\Leftrightarrow$ $n - 1 = \log_3 59{,}049 = 10$ $\Leftrightarrow$ $n = 11$. Therefore, $118{,}098$ is the 11th term of the geometric sequence.

38. $a_2 = 10$, $a_5 = 1250$. Thus, $\frac{1250}{10} = \frac{a_5}{a_2} = \frac{ar^4}{ar} = r^3$ $\Leftrightarrow$ $r = 5$. Then $a_1 = \frac{a_2}{r} = \frac{10}{5} = 2$, so $a_n = 2 \cdot 5^{n-1}$. We seek n such that $a_n = 31{,}250$ $\Leftrightarrow$ $2 \cdot 5^{n-1} = 31{,}250$ $\Leftrightarrow$ $5^{n-1} = 15{,}625$ $\Leftrightarrow$ $n - 1 = \log_5 15{,}625 = 6$ $\Leftrightarrow$ $n = 7$. Therefore, $31{,}250$ is the 7th term of the sequence.

39. $a = 5$, $r = 2$, $n = 6$. Then $S_6 = 5\frac{1 - 2^6}{1 - 2} = (-5)(-63) = 315$.

40. $a = \frac{2}{3}$, $r = \frac{1}{3}$, $n = 4$. Then $S_4 = \left(\frac{2}{3}\right)\frac{1 - \left(\frac{1}{3}\right)^4}{1 - \frac{1}{3}} = \left(\frac{2}{3}\right)\frac{\frac{80}{81}}{\frac{2}{3}} = \frac{80}{81}$.

41. $a_3 = 28$, $a_6 = 224$, $n = 6$. So $\frac{a_6}{a_3} = \frac{ar^5}{ar^2} = r^3$. So we have $r^3 = \frac{a_6}{a_3} = \frac{224}{28} = 8$, and hence $r = 2$. Since $a_3 = a \cdot r^2$, we get $a = \frac{a_3}{r^2} = \frac{28}{2^2} = 7$. So $S_6 = 7\frac{1 - 2^6}{1 - 2} = (-7)(-63) = 441$.

42. $a_2 = 0.12$, $a_5 = 0.00096$, $n = 4$. So $r^3 = \frac{a_5}{a_2} = \frac{0.00096}{0.12} = 0.008$ $\Leftrightarrow$ $r = 0.2$, and thus $a_1 = \frac{a_2}{r} = \frac{0.12}{0.2} = 0.6$. Therefore, $S_4 = (0.6)\frac{1 - (0.2)^4}{1 - 0.2} = 0.7488$.

43. $1 + 3 + 9 + \cdots + 2187$ is a partial sum of a geometric sequence, where $a = 1$ and $r = \frac{a_2}{a_1} = \frac{3}{1} = 3$. Then the last term is $2187 = a_n = 1 \cdot 3^{n-1}$ $\Leftrightarrow$ $n - 1 = \log_3 2187 = 7$ $\Leftrightarrow$ $n = 8$. So the partial sum is $S_8 = (1)\frac{1 - 3^8}{1 - 3} = 3280$.

44. $1 - \frac{1}{2} + \frac{1}{4} - \frac{1}{8} + \cdots - \frac{1}{512}$ is a partial sum of a geometric sequence, where $a = 1$ and $r = \frac{a_2}{a_1} = \frac{-\frac{1}{2}}{1} = -\frac{1}{2}$. The last term is a_n, where $\frac{-1}{512} = a_n = 1\left(-\frac{1}{2}\right)^{n-1}$, so $n = 10$. So the partial sum is $S_{10} = (1)\frac{1 - \left(-\frac{1}{2}\right)^{10}}{1 - \left(-\frac{1}{2}\right)} = \frac{341}{512}$.

45. $\sum_{k=0}^{10} 3\left(\frac{1}{2}\right)^k$ is a partial sum of a geometric sequence, where $a = 3$, $r = \frac{1}{2}$, and $n = 11$. So the partial sum is $S_{11} = (3)\frac{1 - \left(\frac{1}{2}\right)^{11}}{1 - \left(\frac{1}{2}\right)} = 6\left[1 - \left(\frac{1}{2}\right)^{11}\right] \approx 5.997070313$.

46. $\sum_{j=0}^{5} 7\left(\frac{3}{2}\right)^j$ is a partial sum of a geometric sequence, where $a = 7$, $r = \frac{3}{2}$, and $n = 6$. So the partial sum is $S_6 = (7)\frac{1 - \left(\frac{3}{2}\right)^6}{1 - \frac{3}{2}} = (7)\frac{1 - \left(\frac{729}{64}\right)}{-\frac{1}{2}} = -14\left(1 - \frac{729}{64}\right) = \frac{4655}{32}$.

47. $1 + \frac{1}{3} + \frac{1}{9} + \frac{1}{27} + \cdots$ is an infinite geometric series with $a = 1$ and $r = \frac{1}{3}$. Therefore, the sum of the series is $S = \frac{a}{1 - r} = \frac{1}{1 - \left(\frac{1}{3}\right)} = \frac{3}{2}$.

48. $1 - \frac{1}{2} + \frac{1}{4} - \frac{1}{8} + \cdots$ is an infinite geometric series with $a = 1$ and $r = -\frac{1}{2}$. Therefore, the sum of the series is

$$S = \frac{1}{1 - \left(-\frac{1}{2}\right)} = \frac{1}{\frac{3}{2}} = \frac{2}{3}.$$

49. $1 - \frac{1}{3} + \frac{1}{9} - \frac{1}{27} + \cdots$ is an infinite geometric series with $a = 1$ and $r = -\frac{1}{3}$. Therefore, the sum of the series is

$$S = \frac{a}{1 - r} = \frac{1}{1 - \left(-\frac{1}{3}\right)} = \frac{3}{4}.$$

50. $\frac{2}{5} + \frac{4}{25} + \frac{8}{125} + \cdots$ is an infinite geometric series with $a = \frac{2}{5}$ and $r = \frac{2}{5}$. Therefore, the sum of the series is

$$S = \frac{\frac{2}{5}}{1 - \frac{2}{5}} = \frac{\frac{2}{5}}{\frac{3}{5}} = \frac{2}{3}.$$

51. $\frac{1}{3^6} + \frac{1}{3^8} + \frac{1}{3^{10}} + \frac{1}{3^{12}} + \cdots$ is an infinite geometric series with $a = \frac{1}{3^6}$ and $r = \frac{1}{3^2} = \frac{1}{9}$. Therefore, the sum of the series

is $S = \frac{a}{1 - r} = \frac{\frac{1}{3^6}}{1 - \left(\frac{1}{9}\right)} = \frac{1}{3^6} \cdot \frac{9}{8} = \frac{1}{648}.$

52. $3 - \frac{3}{2} + \frac{3}{4} - \frac{3}{8} + \cdots$ is an infinite geometric series with $a = 3$ and $r = -\frac{1}{2}$. Therefore, the sum of the series is

$$S = \frac{3}{1 - \left(-\frac{1}{2}\right)} = 2.$$

53. $-\frac{100}{9} + \frac{10}{3} - 1 + \frac{3}{10} - \cdots$ is an infinite geometric series with $a = -\frac{100}{9}$ and $r = \frac{\frac{10}{3}}{-\frac{100}{9}} = \frac{3}{10}$. Therefore, the sum of the

series is $S = \frac{a}{1 - r} = \frac{-\frac{100}{9}}{1 - \left(-\frac{3}{10}\right)} = \frac{-\frac{100}{9}}{\frac{13}{10}} = -\frac{100}{9} \cdot \frac{10}{13} = -\frac{1000}{117}.$

54. $\frac{1}{\sqrt{2}} + \frac{1}{2} + \frac{1}{2\sqrt{2}} + \frac{1}{4} + \cdots$ is an infinite geometric series with $a = \frac{1}{\sqrt{2}}$ and $r = \frac{1}{\sqrt{2}}$. Therefore, the sum of the series is

$$S = \frac{\frac{1}{\sqrt{2}}}{1 - \frac{1}{\sqrt{2}}} = \frac{1}{\sqrt{2} - 1} = \sqrt{2} + 1.$$

55. $0.777\ldots = \frac{7}{10} + \frac{7}{100} + \frac{7}{1000} + \cdots$ is an infinite geometric series with $a = \frac{7}{10}$ and $r = \frac{1}{10}$. Thus

$$0.777\ldots = \frac{a}{1 - r} = \frac{\frac{7}{10}}{1 - \frac{1}{10}} = \frac{7}{9}.$$

56. $0.2535353\ldots = 0.2 + \frac{53}{1000} + \frac{53}{100,000} + \frac{53}{10,000,000} + \cdots$ is an infinite geometric series (after the first term) with $a = \frac{53}{1000}$ and

$r = \frac{1}{100}$. Thus $0.05353\ldots = \frac{\frac{53}{1000}}{1 - \frac{1}{100}} = \frac{53}{1000} \cdot \frac{100}{99} = \frac{53}{990}$, and so $0.2535353\ldots = \frac{2}{10} + \frac{53}{990} = \frac{2 \cdot 99 + 53}{990} = \frac{251}{990}.$

57. $0.030303\ldots = \frac{3}{100} + \frac{3}{10,000} + \frac{3}{1,000,000} + \cdots$ is an infinite geometric series with $a = \frac{3}{100}$ and $r = \frac{1}{100}$. Thus

$$0.030303\ldots = \frac{a}{1 - r} = \frac{\frac{3}{100}}{1 - \frac{1}{100}} = \frac{3}{99} = \frac{1}{33}.$$

58. $2.11252525\ldots = 2.11 + \frac{25}{10,000} + \frac{25}{1,000,000} + \frac{25}{100,000,000} + \cdots$ is an infinite geometric series (after

the first term) with $a = \frac{25}{10,000}$ and $r = \frac{1}{100}$. Thus $0.00252525\ldots = \frac{\frac{25}{10,000}}{1 - \frac{1}{100}} = \frac{25}{9900}$, and so

$$2.11252525\ldots = \frac{211}{100} + \frac{25}{9900} = \frac{211 \cdot 99 + 25}{9900} = \frac{20,914}{9900} = \frac{10,457}{4950}.$$

59. $0.\overline{112} = 0.112112112\ldots = \frac{112}{1000} + \frac{112}{1,000,000} + \frac{112}{1,000,000,000} + \cdots$ is an infinite geometric series with $a = \frac{112}{1000}$ and

$r = \frac{1}{1000}$. Thus $0.112112112\ldots = \frac{a}{1 - r} = \frac{\frac{112}{1000}}{1 - \frac{1}{1000}} = \frac{112}{999}.$

60. $0.123123123\ldots = \frac{123}{1000} + \frac{123}{1,000,000} + \frac{123}{1,000,000,000} + \cdots$ is an infinite geometric series with $a = \frac{123}{1000}$ and $r = \frac{1}{1000}$. Thus

$$0.123123123\ldots = \frac{\frac{123}{1000}}{1 - \frac{1}{1000}} = \frac{123}{999}.$$

61. Since we have 5 terms, let us denote $a_1 = 5$ and $a_5 = 80$. Also, $\dfrac{a_5}{a_1} = r^4$ because the sequence is geometric, and so $r^4 = \frac{80}{5} = 16 \quad \Leftrightarrow \quad r = \pm 2$. If $r = 2$, the three geometric means are $a_2 = 10$, $a_3 = 20$, and $a_4 = 40$. (If $r = -2$, the three geometric means are $a_2 = -10$, $a_3 = 20$, and $a_4 = -40$, but these are not between 5 and 80.)

62. The sum is given by

$$\left(a + b\right) + \left(a^2 + 2b\right) + \left(a^3 + 3b\right) + \cdots + \left(a^{10} + 10b\right) = \left(a + a^2 + a^3 + \cdots + a^{10}\right) + \left(b + 2b + 3b + \cdots + 10b\right)$$

$$= a \cdot \frac{1 - a^9}{1 - a} + \frac{10}{2} \cdot (b + 10b) = a \cdot \frac{1 - a^9}{1 - a} + 55b$$

63. (a) The value at the end of the year is equal to the the value at beginning less the depreciation, so
$$V_n = V_{n-1} - 0.2V_{n-1} = 0.8V_{n-1} \text{ with } V_0 = 160{,}000. \text{ Thus } V_n = 160{,}000 \cdot 0.8^n.$$

(b) $V_n < 100{,}000 \quad \Leftrightarrow \quad 0.8^n \cdot 160{,}000 < 100{,}000 \quad \Leftrightarrow \quad 0.8^n < 0.625 \quad \Leftrightarrow \quad n \log 0.8 < \log 0.625 \quad \Leftrightarrow$
$n > \dfrac{\log 0.625}{\log 0.8} = 2.11$. Thus it will depreciate to below \$100,000 during the third year.

64. Let a_n denote the number of ancestors a person has n generations back. Then $a_1 = 2$, $a_2 = 4$, $a_3 = 8$, ... Since $\frac{4}{2} = \frac{8}{4} = \cdots = 2$, this is a geometric sequence with $r = 2$. Therefore, $a_{15} = 2 \cdot 2^{14} = 2^{15} = 32{,}768$.

65. Since the ball is dropped from a height of 80 feet, $a = 80$. Also since the ball rebounds three-fourths of the distance fallen, $r = \frac{3}{4}$. So on the nth bounce, the ball attains a height of $a_n = 80\left(\frac{3}{4}\right)^n$. Hence, on the fifth bounce, the ball goes $a_5 = 80\left(\frac{3}{4}\right)^5 = \frac{80 \cdot 243}{1024} \approx 19$ ft high.

66. $a = 5000$, $r = 1.08$. After 1 hour, there are $5000 \cdot 1.08 = 5400$, after 2 hours, $5400 \cdot 1.08 = 5832$, after 3 hours, $5832 \cdot 1.08 = 6298.56$, after 4 hours, $6298.56 \cdot 1.08 = 6802.4448$, and after 5 hours, $6802.4448 \cdot 1.08 \approx 7347$ bacteria. After n hours, the number of bacteria is $a_n = 5000 \cdot (1.08)^n$.

67. Let a_n be the amount of water remaining at the nth stage. We start with 5 gallons, so $a = 5$. When 1 gallon (that is, $\frac{1}{5}$ of the mixture) is removed, $\frac{4}{5}$ of the mixture (and hence $\frac{4}{5}$ of the water in the mixture) remains. Thus, $a_1 = 5 \cdot \frac{4}{5}, a_2 = 5 \cdot \frac{4}{5} \cdot \frac{4}{5}, \ldots,$ and in general, $a_n = 5\left(\frac{4}{5}\right)^n$. The amount of water remaining after 3 repetitions is $a_3 = 5\left(\frac{4}{5}\right)^3 = \frac{64}{25}$, and after 5 repetitions it is $a_5 = 5\left(\frac{4}{5}\right)^5 = \frac{1024}{625}$.

68. Let a_C denote the term of the geometric series that is the frequency of middle C. Then $a_C = 256$ and $a_{C+1} = 512$. Since this is a geometric sequence, $r = \frac{512}{256} = 2$, and so $a_{C-2} = \dfrac{a_C}{r^2} = \dfrac{256}{2^2} = 64$.

69. Let a_n be the height the ball reaches on the nth bounce. From the given information, a_n is the geometric sequence $a_n = 9 \cdot \left(\frac{1}{3}\right)^n$. (Notice that the ball hits the ground for the fifth time after the fourth bounce.)

(a) $a_0 = 9$, $a_1 = 9 \cdot \frac{1}{3} = 3$, $a_2 = 9 \cdot \left(\frac{1}{3}\right)^2 = 1$, $a_3 = 9 \cdot \left(\frac{1}{3}\right)^3 = \frac{1}{3}$, and $a_4 = 9 \cdot \left(\frac{1}{3}\right)^4 = \frac{1}{9}$. The total distance traveled is $a_0 + 2a_1 + 2a_2 + 2a_3 + 2a_4 = 9 + 2 \cdot 3 + 2 \cdot 1 + 2 \cdot \frac{1}{3} + 2 \cdot \frac{1}{9} = \frac{161}{9} = 17\frac{8}{9}$ ft.

(b) The total distance traveled at the instant the ball hits the ground for the nth time is

$$D_n = 9 + 2 \cdot 9 \cdot \frac{1}{3} + 2 \cdot 9 \cdot \left(\tfrac{1}{3}\right)^2 + 2 \cdot 9 \cdot \left(\tfrac{1}{3}\right)^3 + 2 \cdot 9 \cdot \left(\tfrac{1}{3}\right)^4 + \cdots + 2 \cdot 9 \cdot \left(\tfrac{1}{3}\right)^{n-1}$$

$$= 2\left[9 + 9 \cdot \tfrac{1}{3} + 9 \cdot \left(\tfrac{1}{3}\right)^2 + 9 \cdot \left(\tfrac{1}{3}\right)^3 + 9 \cdot \left(\tfrac{1}{3}\right)^4 + \cdots + 9 \cdot \left(\tfrac{1}{3}\right)^{n-1}\right] - 9$$

$$= 2\left[9 \cdot \frac{1 - \left(\frac{1}{3}\right)^n}{1 - \frac{1}{3}}\right] - 9 = 27\left[1 - \left(\tfrac{1}{3}\right)^n\right] - 9 = 18 - \left(\tfrac{1}{3}\right)^{n-3}$$

70. We have a geometric sequence with $a = 1$ and $r = 2$. Then $S_n = (1)\dfrac{1 - 2^n}{1 - 2} = 2^n - 1$. At the end of 30 days, she will have $S_{30} = 2^{30} - 1 = 1{,}073{,}741{,}823$ cents $= \$10{,}737{,}418.23$. To become a billionaire, we want $2^n - 1 = 10^{11}$ or approximately $2^n = 10^{11}$. So $\log 2^n = \log 10^{11} \quad \Leftrightarrow \quad n = \dfrac{11}{\log 2} \approx 36.5$. Thus it will take 37 days.

71. Let $a_1 = 1$ be the man with 7 wives. Also, let $a_2 = 7$ (the wives), $a_3 = 7a_2 = 7^2$ (the sacks), $a_4 = 7a_3 = 7^3$ (the cats), and $a_5 = 7a_4 = 7^4$ (the kits). The total is $a_1 + a_2 + a_3 + a_4 + a_5 = 1 + 7 + 7^2 + 7^3 + 7^4$, which is a partial sum of a geometric sequence with $a = 1$ and $r = 7$. Thus, the number in the party is $S_5 = 1 \cdot \dfrac{1 - 7^5}{1 - 7} = 2801$.

72. (a) $\sum_{k=1}^{10} 50 \left(\frac{1}{2}\right)^{k-1} = 50 \cdot \dfrac{1 - \left(\frac{1}{2}\right)^{10}}{1 - \frac{1}{2}} \approx 100 \left(1 - 0.0009765\right) = 99.9023$ mg

(b) $\sum_{k=1}^{\infty} 50 \left(\frac{1}{2}\right)^{k-1} = \dfrac{50}{1 - \frac{1}{2}} = 100$ mg

73. Let a_n be the height the ball reaches on the nth bounce. We have $a_0 = 1$ and $a_n = \frac{1}{2} a_{n-1}$. Since the total distance d traveled includes the bounce up as well and the distance down, we have

$$
\begin{aligned}
d &= a_0 + 2 \cdot a_1 + 2 \cdot a_2 + \cdots = 1 + 2\left(\frac{1}{2}\right) + 2\left(\frac{1}{2}\right)^2 + 2\left(\frac{1}{2}\right)^3 + 2\left(\frac{1}{2}\right)^4 + \cdots \\
&= 1 + 1 + \frac{1}{2} + \left(\frac{1}{2}\right)^2 + \left(\frac{1}{2}\right)^3 + \cdots = 1 + \sum_{i=0}^{\infty} \left(\frac{1}{2}\right)^i = 1 + \frac{1}{1 - \frac{1}{2}} = 3
\end{aligned}
$$

Thus the total distance traveled is about 3 m.

74. The time required for the ball to stop bouncing is $t = 1 + \frac{1}{\sqrt{2}} + \left(\frac{1}{\sqrt{2}}\right)^2 + \cdots$ which is an infinite geometric series with $a = 1$ and $r = \frac{1}{\sqrt{2}}$. The sum of this series is $t = \dfrac{1}{1 - \frac{1}{\sqrt{2}}} = \dfrac{\sqrt{2}}{\sqrt{2} - 1} = \dfrac{\sqrt{2}}{\sqrt{2} - 1} \cdot \dfrac{\sqrt{2} + 1}{\sqrt{2} + 1} = \dfrac{2 + \sqrt{2}}{2 - 1} = 2 + \sqrt{2}$. Thus the time required for the ball to stop is $2 + \sqrt{2} \approx 3.41$ s.

75. (a) If a square has side x, then by the Pythagorean Theorem the length of the side of the square formed by joining the midpoints is, $\sqrt{\left(\frac{x}{2}\right)^2 + \left(\frac{x}{2}\right)^2} = \sqrt{\frac{x^2}{4} + \frac{x^2}{4}} = \dfrac{x}{\sqrt{2}}$. In our case, $x = 1$ and the side of the first inscribed square is $\frac{1}{\sqrt{2}}$, the side of the second inscribed square is $\frac{1}{\sqrt{2}} \cdot \frac{1}{\sqrt{2}} = \left(\frac{1}{\sqrt{2}}\right)^2$, the side of the third inscribed square is $\left(\frac{1}{\sqrt{2}}\right)^3$, and so on. Since this pattern continues, the total area of all the squares is

$$
A = 1^2 + \left(\frac{1}{\sqrt{2}}\right)^2 + \left(\frac{1}{\sqrt{2}}\right)^4 + \left(\frac{1}{\sqrt{2}}\right)^6 + \cdots = 1 + \frac{1}{2} + \left(\frac{1}{2}\right)^2 + \left(\frac{1}{2}\right)^3 + \cdots = \frac{1}{1 - \frac{1}{2}} = 2.
$$

(b) As in part (a), the sides of the squares are $1, \frac{1}{\sqrt{2}}, \left(\frac{1}{\sqrt{2}}\right)^2, \left(\frac{1}{\sqrt{2}}\right)^3, \ldots$. Thus the sum of the perimeters is

$$
S = 4 \cdot 1 + 4 \cdot \frac{1}{\sqrt{2}} + 4 \cdot \left(\frac{1}{\sqrt{2}}\right)^2 + 4 \cdot \left(\frac{1}{\sqrt{2}}\right)^3 + \cdots,
$$

which is an infinite geometric series with $a = 4$ and $r = \frac{1}{\sqrt{2}}$. Thus the sum of the perimeters is $S = \dfrac{4}{1 - \frac{1}{\sqrt{2}}} = \dfrac{4\sqrt{2}}{\sqrt{2} - 1} = \dfrac{4\sqrt{2}}{\sqrt{2} - 1} \cdot \dfrac{\sqrt{2} + 1}{\sqrt{2} + 1} = \dfrac{4 \cdot 2 + 4\sqrt{2}}{2 - 1} = 8 + 4\sqrt{2}$.

76. Let A_n be the area of the disks of paper placed at the nth stage. Then $A_1 = \pi R^2$, $A_2 = 2 \cdot \pi \left(\frac{1}{2}R\right)^2 = \frac{\pi}{2} R^2$, $A_3 = 4 \cdot \pi \left(\frac{1}{4}R\right)^2 = \frac{\pi}{4} R^2, \ldots$. We see from this pattern that the total area is $A = \pi R^2 + \frac{1}{2}\pi R^2 + \frac{1}{4}\pi R^2 + \cdots$. Thus, the total area, A, is an infinite geometric series with $a_1 = \pi R^2$ and $r = \frac{1}{2}$. So $A = \dfrac{\pi R^2}{1 - \frac{1}{2}} = 2\pi R^2$.

77. Let a_n denote the area colored blue at nth stage. Since only the middle squares are colored blue, $a_n = \frac{1}{9} \times$ (area remaining yellow at the $(n-1)$th stage). Also, the area remaining yellow at the nth stage is $\frac{8}{9}$ of the area remaining yellow at the preceding stage. So $a_1 = \frac{1}{9}$, $a_2 = \frac{1}{9}\left(\frac{8}{9}\right)$, $a_3 = \frac{1}{9}\left(\frac{8}{9}\right)^2$, $a_4 = \frac{1}{9}\left(\frac{8}{9}\right)^3, \ldots$. Thus the total area colored blue $A = \frac{1}{9} + \frac{1}{9}\left(\frac{8}{9}\right) + \frac{1}{9}\left(\frac{8}{9}\right)^2 + \frac{1}{9}\left(\frac{8}{9}\right)^3 + \cdots$ is an infinite geometric series with $a = \frac{1}{9}$ and $r = \frac{8}{9}$. So the total area is $A = \dfrac{\frac{1}{9}}{1 - \frac{8}{9}} = 1$.

78. (a) $5, -3, 5, -3, \ldots$. Now $a_2 - a_1 = -3 - 5 = -8$, but $a_3 - a_2 = 5 - (-3) = 8$, and $\frac{a_2}{a_1} = -\frac{3}{5}$, but $\frac{a_3}{a_2} = -\frac{5}{3}$. Thus, the sequence is neither arithmetic nor geometric.

(b) $\frac{1}{3}, 1, \frac{5}{3}, \frac{7}{3}, \ldots$. Now $a_2 - a_1 = 1 - \frac{1}{3} = \frac{2}{3}$, $a_3 - a_2 = \frac{5}{3} - 1 = \frac{2}{3}$, and $a_4 - a_3 = \frac{7}{3} - \frac{5}{3} = \frac{2}{3}$. Therefore, the sequence is arithmetic with $d = \frac{2}{3}$ and $a_5 = \frac{7}{3} + \frac{2}{3} = 3$.

(c) $\sqrt{3}, 3, 3\sqrt{3}, 9, \ldots$. Now $\frac{a_2}{a_1} = \frac{3}{\sqrt{3}} = \sqrt{3}$, $\frac{a_3}{a_2} = \frac{3\sqrt{3}}{3} = \sqrt{3}$, and $\frac{a_4}{a_3} = \frac{9}{3\sqrt{3}} = \sqrt{3}$. Therefore, the sequence is geometric with $r = \sqrt{3}$ and $a_5 = 9\sqrt{3}$.

(d) $1, -1, 1, -1, \ldots$. Now $\frac{a_2}{a_1} = \frac{-1}{1} = -1$, $\frac{a_3}{a_2} = \frac{1}{-1} = -1$, and $\frac{a_4}{a_3} = \frac{-1}{1} = -1$. Therefore, the sequence is geometric with $r = -1$ and $a_5 = (-1)(-1) = 1$.

(e) $2, -1, \frac{1}{2}, 2, \ldots$. Now $a_2 - a_1 = -1 - 2 = -3$, but $a_3 - a_2 = \frac{1}{2} + 1 = \frac{3}{2}$, and so the sequence is not arithmetic. Also, $\frac{a_2}{a_1} = -\frac{1}{2}$, but $\frac{a_4}{a_3} = \frac{2}{\frac{1}{2}} = 4$, and so the sequence is not geometric. Thus, the sequence is neither arithmetic nor geometric.

(f) $x - 1, x, x + 1, x + 2, \ldots$. Now $a_2 - a_1 = x - (x - 1) = 1$, $a_3 - a_2 = (x + 1) - x = 1$, and $a_4 - a_3 = (x + 2) - (x + 1) = 1$. Therefore, the sequence is arithmetic with $d = 1$ and $a_5 = (x + 2) + 1 = x + 3$.

(g) $-3, -\frac{3}{2}, 0, \frac{3}{2}, \ldots$. Now $a_2 - a_1 = -\frac{3}{2} - (-3) = \frac{3}{2}$, $a_3 - a_2 = 0 - \left(-\frac{3}{2}\right) = \frac{3}{2}$, and $a_4 - a_3 = \frac{3}{2} - 0 = \frac{3}{2}$. Therefore, the sequence is arithmetic with $d = \frac{3}{2}$, and $a_5 = \frac{3}{2} + \frac{3}{2} = 3$.

(h) $\sqrt{5}, \sqrt[3]{5}, \sqrt[6]{5}, 1, \ldots$. Now $a_2 - a_1 = \sqrt[3]{5} - \sqrt{5}$, but $a_3 - a_2 = \sqrt[6]{5} - \sqrt[3]{5}$. Thus the sequence is not arithmetic. However, $\frac{a_2}{a_1} = \frac{\sqrt[3]{5}}{\sqrt{5}} = \frac{5^{1/3}}{5^{1/2}} = 5^{-1/6}$, $\frac{a_3}{a_2} = \frac{\sqrt[6]{5}}{\sqrt[3]{5}} = \frac{5^{1/6}}{5^{1/3}} = 5^{-1/6}$, and $\frac{a_4}{a_3} = \frac{1}{\sqrt[6]{5}} = \frac{1}{5^{1/6}} = 5^{-1/6}$. Therefore, the sequence is geometric with $r = 5^{-1/6}$ and $a_5 = 1 \cdot 5^{-1/6} = \frac{1}{\sqrt[6]{5}}$.

79. Let $a_1, a_2, a_3, \ldots$ be a geometric sequence with common ratio r. Thus $a_2 = a_1 r$, $a_3 = a_1 \cdot r^2, \ldots, a_n = a_1 \cdot r^{n-1}$. Hence, $\frac{1}{a_2} = \frac{1}{a_1 \cdot r} = \frac{1}{a_1} \cdot \frac{1}{r}$, $\frac{1}{a_3} = \frac{1}{a_1 \cdot r^2} = \frac{1}{a_1} \cdot \frac{1}{r^2} = \frac{1}{a_1} \left(\frac{1}{r}\right)^2, \ldots \frac{1}{a_n} = \frac{1}{a_1 \cdot r^{n-1}} = \frac{1}{a_1} \cdot \frac{1}{r^{n-1}} = \frac{1}{a_1} \left(\frac{1}{r}\right)^{n-1}$, and so $\frac{1}{a_1}, \frac{1}{a_2}, \frac{1}{a_3}, \ldots$ is a geometric sequence with common ratio $\frac{1}{r}$.

80. $a_1, a_2, a_3, \ldots$ is a geometric sequence with common ratio r. Thus $a_2 = a_1 r$, $a_3 = a_1 \cdot r^2, \ldots, a_n = a_1 \cdot r^{n-1}$. Hence $\log a_2 = \log(a_1 r) = \log a_1 + \log r$, $\log a_3 = \log(a_1 \cdot r^2) = \log a_1 + \log(r^2) = \log a_1 + 2\log r, \ldots$, $\log a_n = \log(a_1 \cdot r^{n-1}) = \log a_1 + \log(r^{n-1}) = \log a_1 + (n - 1)\log r$, and so $\log a_1, \log a_2, \log a_3, \ldots$ is an arithmetic sequence with common difference $\log r$.

81. Since $a_1, a_2, a_3, \ldots$ is an arithmetic sequence with common difference d, the terms can be expressed as $a_2 = a_1 + d$, $a_3 = a_1 + 2d, \ldots, a_n = a_1 + (n - 1)d$. So $10^{a_2} = 10^{a_1 + d} = 10^{a_1} \cdot 10^d$, $10^{a_3} = 10^{a_1 + 2d} = 10^{a_1} \cdot (10^d)^2, \ldots$, $10^{a_n} = 10^{a_1 + (n-1)d} = 10^{a_1} \cdot (10^d)^{n-1}$, and so $10^{a_1}, 10^{a_2}, 10^{a_3}, \ldots$ is a geometric sequence with common ratio $r = 10^d$.

11.4   Mathematics of Finance

1. $n = 10$, $R = \$1000$, $i = 0.06$. So $A_f = R\dfrac{(1+i)^n - 1}{i} = 1000\dfrac{(1+0.06)^{10} - 1}{0.06} = \$13{,}180.79$.

2. $R = 500$, $n = 24$, $i = \dfrac{0.08}{12} \approx 0.0066667$. So $A_f = R\dfrac{(1+i)^n - 1}{i} = 500\dfrac{(1.0066667)^{24} - 1}{0.0066667} = \$12{,}966.59$.

3. $n = 20$, $R = \$5000$, $i = 0.12$. So $A_f = R\dfrac{(1+i)^n - 1}{i} = 5000\dfrac{(1+0.12)^{20} - 1}{0.12} = \$360{,}262.21$.

4. $R = 500$, $n = 20$, $i = \dfrac{0.06}{2} = 0.03$. So $A_f = R\dfrac{(1+i)^n - 1}{i} = 500\dfrac{(1.03)^{20} - 1}{0.03} = \$13{,}435.19$.

5. $n = 16$, $R = \$300$, $i = \dfrac{0.08}{4} = 0.02$. So $A_f = R\dfrac{(1+i)^n - 1}{i} = 300\dfrac{(1+0.02)^{16} - 1}{0.02} = \$5{,}591.79$.

6. $A_f = 5000$, $n = 4 \cdot 2 = 8$, $i = \dfrac{0.10}{4} = 0.025$. So $R = \dfrac{iA_f}{(1+i)^n - 1} = \dfrac{(0.025)(5000)}{(1.025)^8 - 1} = \$572.34$.

7. $A_f = \$2000$, $i = \dfrac{0.06}{12} = 0.005$, $n = 8$. Then $R = \dfrac{iA_f}{(1+i)^n - 1} = \dfrac{(0.005)(2000)}{(1+0.005)^8 - 1} = \$245.66$.

8. $R = 1000$, $n = 20$, $i = \dfrac{0.09}{2} = 0.045$. So $A_p = R\dfrac{1-(1+i)^{-n}}{i} = 1000\dfrac{1-(1.045)^{-20}}{0.045} = \$13{,}007.94$.

9. $R = \$200$, $n = 20$, $i = \dfrac{0.09}{2} = 0.045$. So $A_p = R\dfrac{1-(1+i)^{-n}}{i} = (200)\dfrac{1-(1+0.045)^{-20}}{0.045} = \$2601.59$.

10. $A_p = 50{,}000$, $n = 10(2) = 20$, $i = \dfrac{0.08}{2} = 0.04$. So $R = \dfrac{iA_p}{1-(1+i)^{-n}} = \dfrac{(0.04)(50{,}000)}{1-(1.04)^{-20}} = \$3679.09$.

11. $A_p = \$12{,}000$, $i = \dfrac{0.105}{12} = 0.00875$, $n = 48$. Then $R = \dfrac{iA_p}{1-(1+i)^{-n}} = \dfrac{(0.00875)(12000)}{1-(1+0.00875)^{-48}} = \$307.24$.

12. $A_p = 80{,}000$, $i = \dfrac{0.09}{12} = 0.0075$. Over a 30 year period, $n = 30(12) = 360$, and the monthly payment is

$R = \dfrac{iA_p}{1-(1+i)^{-n}} = \dfrac{(0.0075)(80{,}000)}{1-(1.0075)^{-360}} = \$643.70$. Over a 15 year period, $n = 15 \cdot 12 = 180$, and so the monthly

payment is $R = \dfrac{80{,}000 \cdot 0.0075}{1-(1.0075)^{-180}} = \$811.41$.

13. $A_p = \$100{,}000$, $i = \dfrac{0.08}{12} \approx 0.006667$, $n = 360$. Then $R = \dfrac{iA_p}{1-(1+i)^{-n}} = \dfrac{(0.006667)(100{,}000)}{1-(1+0.006667)^{-360}} = \$733.76$.

Therefore, the total amount paid on this loan over the 30 year period is $(360)(733.76) = \$264{,}153.60$.

14. $R = 650$, $n = 12(30) = 360$, $i = \dfrac{0.09}{12} = 0.0075$. So $A_p = R\dfrac{1-(1+i)^{-n}}{i} = 650\dfrac{1-(1.0075)^{-360}}{0.0075} = \$80{,}783.21$.

Therefore, the couple can afford a loan of $\$80{,}783.21$.

15. $A_p = 100{,}000$, $n = 360$, $i = \dfrac{0.0975}{12} = 0.008125$.

(a) $R = \dfrac{iA_p}{1-(1+i)^{-n}} = \dfrac{(0.008125)(100{,}000)}{1-(1+0.008125)^{-360}} = \$859.15$.

(b) The total amount that will be paid over the 30 year period is $(360)(859.15) = \$309{,}294.00$.

(c) $R = \$859.15$, $i = \dfrac{0.0975}{12} = 0.008125$, $n = 360$. So $A_f = 859.15\dfrac{(1+0.008125)^{360} - 1}{0.008125} = \$1{,}841{,}519.29$.

16. $R = 220$, $n = 12(3) = 36$, $i = \dfrac{0.08}{12} \approx 0.00667$. The amount borrowed is

$A_p = R\dfrac{1-(1+i)^{-n}}{i} = 220\dfrac{1-(1.00667)^{-36}}{0.00667} = \$7{,}020.60$. So she purchased the car for

$\$7{,}020.60 + \$2000 = \$9020.60$.

17. $R = \$30$, $i = \dfrac{0.10}{12} \approx 0.008333$, $n = 12$. Then $A_p = R\dfrac{1-(1+i)^{-n}}{i} = 30\dfrac{1-(1+0.008333)^{-12}}{0.008333} = \$341.24$.

18. $A_p = \$12{,}500$, $R = \$420$, $n = 36$. We want to solve for the interest rate using the

equation $R = \dfrac{iA_P}{1-(1+i)^{-n}}$. Let x be the interest rate, then $i = \dfrac{x}{12}$. So we can

express R as a function of x as follows: $R\left(x\right) = \dfrac{\dfrac{x}{12} \cdot 12{,}500}{1-\left(1+\dfrac{x}{12}\right)^{-36}}$. We graph

$R\left(x\right)$ and $y = 420$ in the rectangle $[0.12, 0.13]$ by $[415, 425]$. The x-coordinate of
the intersection is about 0.1280, which corresponds to an interest rate of 12.80%.

19. $A_p = \$640$, $R = \$32$, $n = 24$. We want to solve the equation $R = \dfrac{iA_P}{1-(1+i)^{n}}$

for the interest rate i. Let x be the interest rate, then $i = \dfrac{x}{12}$. So we can express R

as a function of x by $R\left(x\right) = \dfrac{\dfrac{x}{12} \cdot 640}{1-\left(1+\dfrac{x}{12}\right)^{-24}}$. We graph $R\left(x\right)$ and $y = 32$ in

the rectangle $[0.12, 0.22] \times [30, 34]$. The x-coordinate of the intersection is about
0.1816, which corresponds to an interest rate of 18.16%.

20. $A_p = \$2000 - \$200 = \$1800$, $R = \$88$, $n = 24$. We want to solve for the

interest rate using the equation $R = \dfrac{iA_P}{1-(1+i)^{-n}}$. Let x be the interest rate, then

$i = \dfrac{x}{12}$. So we can express R as a function of x as follows:

$R\left(x\right) = \dfrac{\dfrac{x}{12} \cdot 1800}{1-\left(1+\dfrac{x}{12}\right)^{-24}}$. We graph $R\left(x\right)$ and $y = 88$ in theviewing rectangle

$[0.14, 0.16]$ by $[87, 89]$. The x-coordinate of the intersection is about 0.1584,
which corresponds to an interest rate of 15.84%.

21. $A_p = \$189.99$, $R = \$10.50$, $n = 20$. We want to solve the equation

$R = \dfrac{iA_P}{1-(1+i)^{n}}$ for the interest rate i. Let x be the interest rate, then $i = \dfrac{x}{12}$.

So we can express R as a function of x by $R\left(x\right) = \dfrac{\dfrac{x}{12} \cdot 189.99}{1-\left(1+\dfrac{x}{12}\right)^{-20}}$. We graph

$R\left(x\right)$ and $y = 10.50$ in the rectangle $[0.10, 0.18] \times [10, 11]$. The x-coordinate of
the intersection is about 0.1168, which corresponds to an interest rate of 11.68%.

22. (a) The present value of the kth payment is $PV = R(1+i)^{-k} = \dfrac{R}{(1+i)^k}$. The present value of an annuity is the sum of

the present values of each of the payments of R dollars, as shown in the time line.

(b) $A_p = \dfrac{R}{1+i} + \dfrac{R}{(1+i)^2} + \dfrac{R}{(1+i)^3} + \cdots + \dfrac{R}{(1+i)^n}$

$\qquad = \dfrac{R}{1+i} + \left(\dfrac{R}{1+i}\right)\left(\dfrac{1}{1+i}\right) + \left(\dfrac{R}{1+i}\right)\left(\dfrac{1}{1+i}\right)^2 + \cdots + \left(\dfrac{R}{1+i}\right)\left(\dfrac{1}{1+i}\right)^{n-1}$

This is a geometric series with $a = \dfrac{R}{1+i}$ and $r = \dfrac{1}{1+i}$. Since $S_n = a\dfrac{1-r^n}{1-r}$, we have

$A_p = \left(\dfrac{R}{1+i}\right)\dfrac{1 - \left[\dfrac{1}{(1+i)}\right]^n}{1 - \left(\dfrac{1}{1+i}\right)} = R\dfrac{1-(1+i)^{-n}}{(1+i)\left[1 - \left(\dfrac{1}{1+i}\right)\right]} = R\dfrac{1-(1+i)^{-n}}{(1+i)-1} = R\dfrac{1-(1+i)^{-n}}{i}.$

23. (a) The present value of the kth payment is $PV = \dfrac{R}{(1+i)^k}$. The amount of money to be invested now (A_p) to ensure an

annuity in perpetuity is the (infinite) sum of the present values of each of the payments, as shown in the time line.

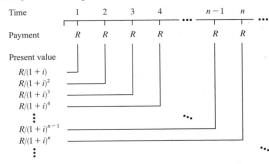

(b) $A_p = \dfrac{R}{1+i} + \dfrac{R}{(1+i)^2} + \dfrac{R}{(1+i)^3} + \cdots + \dfrac{R}{(1+i)^n} + \cdots$. This is an infinite geometric series with $a = \dfrac{R}{1+i}$ and

$r = \dfrac{1}{1+i}$. Therefore, $A_p = \dfrac{\dfrac{R}{1+i}}{1 - \dfrac{1}{1+i}} = \dfrac{R}{1+i} \cdot \dfrac{1+i}{i} = \dfrac{R}{i}.$

(c) Using the result from part (b), we have $R = 5000$ and $i = 0.10$. Then $A_p = \dfrac{R}{i} = \dfrac{5000}{0.10} = \$50{,}000$.

(d) We are given two different time periods: the interest is compounded quarterly, while the annuity is paid yearly. In order to use the formula in part (b), we need to find the effective annual interest rate produced by 8% interest compounded quarterly, which is $(1+i/n)^n - 1$. Now $i = 8\%$ and it is compounded quarterly, $n = 4$, so the effective annual yield is $(1+0.02)^4 - 1 \approx 0.08243216$. Thus by the formula in part (b), the amount that must be invested is
$A_p = \dfrac{3000}{0.08243216} = \$36{,}393.56$.

24. (a) Using the hint, we calculate the present value of the remaining 240 payments with $R = 724.17$, $i = 0.0075$, and
$n = 240$. Since $A_p = R\dfrac{1 - (1+i)^{-n}}{i} = (724.17)\dfrac{1 - (1.0075)^{-240}}{0.0075} = 80{,}487.84$, they still owe $80,487.84 on their mortgage.

(b) On their next payment, $0.0075\,(80{,}487.84) = \$603.66$ is interest and $\$724.17 - 603.66 = \$120.51$ goes toward the principal.

11.5   Mathematical Induction

1. Let $P(n)$ denote the statement $2 + 4 + 6 + \cdots + 2n = n(n+1)$.

Step 1: $P(1)$ is the statement that $2 = 1(1+1)$, which is true.

Step 2: Assume that $P(k)$ is true; that is, $2 + 4 + 6 + \cdots + 2k = k(k+1)$. We want to use this to show that $P(k+1)$ is true. Now

$$
\begin{aligned}
2 + 4 + 6 + \cdots + 2k + 2(k+1) &= k(k+1) + 2(k+1) &&\text{induction hypothesis}\\
&= (k+1)(k+2) = (k+1)[(k+1)+1]
\end{aligned}
$$

Thus, $P(k+1)$ follows from $P(k)$. So by the Principle of Mathematical Induction, $P(n)$ is true for all n.

2. Let $P(n)$ denote the statement $1 + 4 + 7 + 10 + \cdots + (3n-2) = \dfrac{n(3n-1)}{2}$.

Step 1: $P(1)$ is the statement that $1 = \dfrac{1[3(1)-1]}{2} = \dfrac{1 \cdot 2}{2}$, which is true.

Step 2: Assume that $P(k)$ is true; that is. $1 + 4 + 7 + \cdots + (3k-2) = \dfrac{k(3k-1)}{2}$. We want to use this to show that $P(k+1)$ is true. Now

$$
\begin{aligned}
1 + 4 + 7 + 10 + \cdots + (3k-2) + [3(k+1)-2] &= \dfrac{k(3k-1)}{2} + 3k + 1 &&\text{induction hypothesis}\\
&= \dfrac{k(3k-1)}{2} + \dfrac{6k+2}{2} = \dfrac{3k^2 - k + 6k + 2}{2} = \dfrac{3k^2 + 5k + 2}{2}\\
&= \dfrac{(k+1)(3k+2)}{2} = \dfrac{(k+1)[3(k+1)-1]}{2}
\end{aligned}
$$

Thus, $P(k+1)$ follows from $P(k)$. So by the Principle of Mathematical Induction, $P(n)$ is true for all n.

3. Let $P(n)$ denote the statement $5 + 8 + 11 + \cdots + (3n+2) = \dfrac{n(3n+7)}{2}$.

Step 1: We need to show that $P(1)$ is true. But $P(1)$ says that $5 = \dfrac{1 \cdot (3 \cdot 1 + 7)}{2}$, which is true.

Step 2: Assume that $P(k)$ is true; that is, $5 + 8 + 11 + \cdots + (3k+2) = \dfrac{k(3k+7)}{2}$. We want to use this to show that $P(k+1)$ is true. Now

$$
\begin{aligned}
5 + 8 + 11 + \cdots + (3k+2) + [3(k+1)+2] &= \dfrac{k(3k+7)}{2} + (3k+5) &&\text{induction hypothesis}\\
&= \dfrac{3k^2 + 7k}{2} + \dfrac{6k+10}{2} = \dfrac{3k^2 + 13k + 10}{2}\\
&= \dfrac{(3k+10)(k+1)}{2} = \dfrac{(k+1)[3(k+1)+7]}{2}
\end{aligned}
$$

Thus, $P(k+1)$ follows from $P(k)$. So by the Principle of Mathematical Induction, $P(n)$ is true for all n.

4. Let $P(n)$ denote the statement $1^2 + 2^2 + 3^2 + \cdots + n^2 = \dfrac{n(n+1)(2n+1)}{6}$.

Step 1: $P(1)$ is the statement that $1^2 = \dfrac{1 \cdot 2 \cdot 3}{6}$, which is true.

Step 2: Assume that $P(k)$ is true; that is, $1^2 + 2^2 + 3^2 + \cdots + k^2 = \dfrac{k(k+1)(2k+1)}{6}$. We want to use this to show that $P(k+1)$ is true. Now,

$$
\begin{aligned}
1^2 + 2^2 + 3^2 + \cdots + k^2 + (k+1)^2 &= \dfrac{k(k+1)(2k+1)}{6} + (k+1)^2 \qquad \text{induction hypothesis}\\
&= (k+1)\left[\dfrac{k(2k+1)+6(k+1)}{6}\right] = (k+1)\left[\dfrac{2k^2+k+6k+6}{6}\right]\\
&= (k+1)\left[\dfrac{2k^2+7k+6}{6}\right] = \dfrac{(k+1)(k+2)(2k+3)}{6}\\
&= \dfrac{(k+1)[(k+1)+1][2(k+1)+1]}{6}.
\end{aligned}
$$

Thus $P(k+1)$ follows from $P(k)$. So by the Principle of Mathematical Induction, $P(n)$ is true for all n.

5. Let $P(n)$ denote the statement $1 \cdot 2 + 2 \cdot 3 + 3 \cdot 4 + \cdots + n(n+1) = \dfrac{n(n+1)(n+2)}{3}$.

Step 1: $P(1)$ is the statement that $1 \cdot 2 = \dfrac{1 \cdot (1+1) \cdot (1+2)}{3}$, which is true.

Step 2: Assume that $P(k)$ is true; that is, $1 \cdot 2 + 2 \cdot 3 + 3 \cdot 4 + \cdots + k(k+1) = \dfrac{k(k+1)(k+2)}{3}$. We want to use this to show that $P(k+1)$ is true. Now
$$
\begin{aligned}
1 \cdot 2 + 2 \cdot 3 + 3 \cdot 4 + \cdots + k(k+1) &+ (k+1)[(k+1)+1]\\
&= \dfrac{k(k+1)(k+2)}{3} + (k+1)(k+2) \qquad \text{induction hypothesis}\\
&= \dfrac{k(k+1)(k+2)}{3} + \dfrac{3(k+1)(k+2)}{3} = \dfrac{(k+1)(k+2)(k+3)}{3}
\end{aligned}
$$

Thus, $P(k+1)$ follows from $P(k)$. So by the Principle of Mathematical Induction, $P(n)$ is true for all n.

6. Let $P(n)$ denote the statement $1 \cdot 3 + 2 \cdot 4 + 3 \cdot 5 + \cdots + n(n+2) = \dfrac{n(n+1)(2n+7)}{6}$.

Step 1: $P(1)$ is the statement that $1 \cdot 3 = \dfrac{1 \cdot 2 \cdot 9}{6}$, which is true.

Step 2: Assume that $P(k)$ is true; that is, $1 \cdot 3 + 2 \cdot 4 + 3 \cdot 5 + \cdots + k(k+2) = \dfrac{k(k+1)(2k+7)}{6}$. We want to use this to show that $P(k+1)$ is true. Now
$$
\begin{aligned}
1 \cdot 3 + 2 \cdot 4 + 3 \cdot 5 + \cdots + k(k+2) &+ (k+1)[(k+1)+2]\\
&= \dfrac{k(k+1)(2k+7)}{6} + (k+1)(k+3) \qquad \text{induction hypothesis}\\
&= (k+1)\left[\dfrac{k(2k+7)}{6} + \dfrac{6(k+3)}{6}\right] = (k+1)\left(\dfrac{2k^2+7k+6k+18}{6}\right)\\
&= \dfrac{(k+1)[(k+1)+1][2(k+1)+7]}{6}
\end{aligned}
$$

Thus $P(k+1)$ follows from $P(k)$. So by the Principle of Mathematical Induction, $P(n)$ is true for all n.

7. Let $P(n)$ denote the statement $1^3 + 2^3 + 3^3 + \cdots + n^3 = \dfrac{n^2(n+1)^2}{4}$.

Step 1: $P(1)$ is the statement that $1^3 = \dfrac{1^2 \cdot (1+1)^2}{4}$, which is clearly true.

Step 2: Assume that $P(k)$ is true; that is, $1^3 + 2^3 + 3^3 + \cdots + k^3 = \dfrac{k^2(k+1)^2}{4}$. We want to use this to show that $P(k+1)$ is true. Now

$$
\begin{aligned}
1^3 + 2^3 + 3^3 + \cdots + k^3 + (k+1)^3 &= \frac{k^2(k+1)^2}{4} + (k+1)^3 \qquad \text{induction hypothesis}\\
&= \frac{(k+1)^2\left[k^2 + 4(k+1)\right]}{4} = \frac{(k+1)^2\left[k^2 + 4k + 4\right]}{4}\\
&= \frac{(k+1)^2(k+2)^2}{4} = \frac{(k+1)^2\left[(k+1)+1\right]^2}{4}
\end{aligned}
$$

Thus, $P(k+1)$ follows from $P(k)$. So by the Principle of Mathematical Induction, $P(n)$ is true for all n.

8. Let $P(n)$ denote the statement $1^3 + 3^3 + 5^3 + \cdots + (2n-1)^3 = n^2(2n^2 - 1)$.

Step 1: $P(1)$ is the statement that $1^3 = 1^2(2 \cdot 1^2 - 1)$, which is clearly true.

Step 2: Assume that $P(k)$ is true; that is, $1^3 + 3^3 + 5^3 + \cdots + (2k-1)^3 = k^2(2k^2 - 1)$. We want to use this to show that $P(k+1)$ is true. Now

$$
\begin{aligned}
1^3 + 3^3 + 5^3 + \cdots + (2k-1)^3 + (2k+1)^3 &= k^2(2k^2 - 1) + (2k+1)^3 \qquad \text{induction hypothesis}\\
&= 2k^4 - k^2 + 8k^3 + 12k^2 + 6k + 1 = 2k^4 + 8k^3 + 11k^2 + 6k + 1\\
&= (k^2 + 2k + 1)(2k^2 + 4k + 1) = (k+1)^2\left[2(k+1)^2 - 1\right]
\end{aligned}
$$

Thus $P(k+1)$ follows from $P(k)$. So by the Principle of Mathematical Induction, $P(n)$ is true for all n.

9. Let $P(n)$ denote the statement $2^3 + 4^3 + 6^3 + \cdots + (2n)^3 = 2n^2(n+1)^2$.

Step 1: $P(1)$ is true since $2^3 = 2(1)^2(1+1)^2 = 2 \cdot 4 = 8$.

Step 2: Assume that $P(k)$ is true; that is, $2^3 + 4^3 + 6^3 + \cdots + (2k)^3 = 2k^2(k+1)^2$. We want to use this to show that $P(k+1)$ is true. Now

$$
\begin{aligned}
2^3 + 4^3 + 6^3 + \cdots + (2k)^3 + [2(k+1)]^3 &= 2k^2(k+1)^2 + [2(k+1)]^3 \qquad \text{induction hypothesis}\\
&= 2k^2(k+1)^2 + 8(k+1)(k+1)^2 = (k+1)^2(2k^2 + 8k + 8)\\
&= 2(k+1)^2(k+2)^2 = 2(k+1)^2\left[(k+1)+1\right]^2
\end{aligned}
$$

Thus, $P(k+1)$ follows from $P(k)$. So by the Principle of Mathematical Induction, $P(n)$ is true for all n.

10. Let $P(n)$ denote the statement $\dfrac{1}{1 \cdot 2} + \dfrac{1}{2 \cdot 3} + \dfrac{1}{3 \cdot 4} + \cdots + \dfrac{1}{n(n+1)} = \dfrac{n}{n+1}$.

Step 1: $P(1)$ is the statement that $\dfrac{1}{1 \cdot 2} = \frac{1}{2}$, which is clearly true.

Step 2: Assume that $P(k)$ is true; that is $\dfrac{1}{1 \cdot 2} + \dfrac{1}{2 \cdot 3} + \dfrac{1}{3 \cdot 4} + \cdots + \dfrac{1}{k(k+1)} = \dfrac{k}{k+1}$. We want to use this to show that $P(k+1)$ is true. Now

$$
\begin{aligned}
\frac{1}{1 \cdot 2} + \frac{1}{2 \cdot 3} + \cdots + \frac{1}{k(k+1)} + \frac{1}{(k+1)(k+2)} &= \frac{k}{k+1} + \frac{1}{(k+1)(k+2)} \qquad \text{induction hypothesis}\\
&= \frac{k(k+2) + 1}{(k+1)(k+2)} = \frac{k^2 + 2k + 1}{(k+1)(k+2)} = \frac{(k+1)^2}{(k+1)(k+2)}\\
&= \frac{k+1}{k+2} = \frac{k+1}{(k+1)+1}
\end{aligned}
$$

Thus $P(k+1)$ follows from $P(k)$. So by the Principle of Mathematical Induction, $P(n)$ is true for all n.

11. Let $P(n)$ denote the statement $1 \cdot 2 + 2 \cdot 2^2 + 3 \cdot 2^3 + 4 \cdot 2^4 + \cdots + n \cdot 2^n = 2[1 + (n-1) 2^n]$.

Step 1: $P(1)$ is the statement that $1 \cdot 2 = 2[1 + 0]$, which is clearly true.

Step 2: Assume that $P(k)$ is true; that is, $1 \cdot 2 + 2 \cdot 2^2 + 3 \cdot 2^3 + 4 \cdot 2^4 + \cdots + k \cdot 2^k = 2\left[1 + (k-1) 2^k\right]$. We want to use this to show that $P(k+1)$ is true. Now

$1 \cdot 2 + 2 \cdot 2^2 + 3 \cdot 2^3 + 4 \cdot 2^4 + \cdots + k \cdot 2^k + (k+1) \cdot 2^{(k+1)}$

$$= 2\left[1 + (k-1) 2^k\right] + (k+1) \cdot 2^{k+1} \qquad \text{induction hypothesis}$$

$$= 2\left[1 + (k-1) \cdot 2^k + (k+1) \cdot 2^k\right] = 2\left[1 + 2k \cdot 2^k\right]$$

$$= 2\left[1 + k \cdot 2^{k+1}\right] = 2\left\{1 + [(k+1) - 1] 2^{k+1}\right\}$$

Thus $P(k+1)$ follows from $P(k)$. So by the Principle of Mathematical Induction, $P(n)$ is true for all n.

12. Let $P(n)$ denote the statement $1 + 2 + 2^2 + \cdots + 2^{n-1} = 2^n - 1$.

Step 1: $P(1)$ is the statement that $1 = 2^1 - 1$, which is clearly true.

Step 2: Assume that $P(k)$ is true; that is, $1 + 2 + 2^2 + \cdots + 2^{k-1} = 2^k - 1$. We want to use this to show that $P(k+1)$ is true. Now

$$1 + 2 + 2^2 + \cdots + 2^{k-1} + 2^k = 2^k - 1 + 2^k \qquad \text{induction hypothesis}$$

$$= 2 \cdot 2^k - 1 = 2^{k+1} - 1$$

Thus $P(k+1)$ follows from $P(k)$. So by the Principle of Mathematical Induction, $P(n)$ is true for all n.

13. Let $P(n)$ denote the statement $n^2 + n$ is divisible by 2.

Step 1: $P(1)$ is the statement that $1^2 + 1 = 2$ is divisible by 2, which is clearly true.

Step 2: Assume that $P(k)$ is true; that is, $k^2 + k$ is divisible by 2. Now

$(k+1)^2 + (k+1) = k^2 + 2k + 1 + k + 1 = (k^2 + k) + 2k + 2 = (k^2 + k) + 2(k+1)$. By the induction hypothesis, $k^2 + k$ is divisible by 2, and clearly $2(k+1)$ is divisible by 2. Thus, the sum is divisible by 2, so $P(k+1)$ is true. Therefore, $P(k+1)$ follows from $P(k)$. So by the Principle of Mathematical Induction, $P(n)$ is true for all n.

14. Let $P(n)$ denote the statement that $5^n - 1$ is divisible by 4.

Step 1: $P(1)$ is the statement that $5^1 - 1 = 4$ is divisible by 4, which is clearly true.

Step 2: Assume that $P(k)$ is true; that is, $5^k - 1$ is divisible by 4. We want to use this to show that $P(k+1)$ is true. Now, $5^{(k+1)} - 1 = 5 \cdot 5^k - 1 = 5 \cdot 5^k - 5 + 4 = 5(5^k - 1) + 4$ which is divisible by 4 since $5(5^k - 1)$ is divisible by 4 by the induction hypothesis. Thus $P(k+1)$ follows from $P(k)$. So by the Principle of Mathematical Induction, $P(n)$ is true for all n.

15. Let $P(n)$ denote the statement that $n^2 - n + 41$ is odd.

Step 1: $P(1)$ is the statement that $1^2 - 1 + 41 = 41$ is odd, which is clearly true.

Step 2: Assume that $P(k)$ is true; that is, $k^2 - k + 41$ is odd. We want to use this to show that $P(k+1)$ is true. Now, $(k+1)^2 - (k+1) + 41 = k^2 + 2k + 1 - k - 1 + 41 = (k^2 - k + 41) + 2k$, which is also odd because $k^2 - k + 41$ is odd by the induction hypothesis, $2k$ is always even, and an odd number plus an even number is always odd. Therefore, $P(k+1)$ follows from $P(k)$. So by the Principle of Mathematical Induction, $P(n)$ is true for all n.

16. Let $P(n)$ denote the statement that $n^3 - n + 3$ is divisible by 3.

Step 1: $P(1)$ is the statement that $1^3 - 1 + 3 = 3$ is divisible by 3, which is true.

Step 2: Assume that $P(k)$ is true; that is, $k^3 - k + 3$ is divisible by 3. We want to use this to show that $P(k+1)$ is true. Now, $(k+1)^3 - (k+1) + 3 = k^3 + 3k^2 + 3k + 1 - k - 1 + 3 = k^3 - k + 3 + 3k^2 + 3k = (k^3 - k + 3) + 3(k^2 + k)$, which is divisible by 3, since $k^3 - k + 3$ is divisible by 3 by the induction hypothesis, and $3(k^2 + k)$ is divisible by 3. Thus $P(k+1)$ follows from $P(k)$. So by the Principle of Mathematical Induction, $P(n)$ is true for all n.

17. Let $P(n)$ denote the statement that $8^n - 3^n$ is divisible by 5.

Step 1: $P(1)$ is the statement that $8^1 - 3^1 = 5$ is divisible by 5, which is clearly true.

Step 2: Assume that $P(k)$ is true; that is, $8^k - 3^k$ is divisible by 5. We want to use this to show that $P(k+1)$ is true. Now, $8^{k+1} - 3^{k+1} = 8 \cdot 8^k - 3 \cdot 3^k = 8 \cdot 8^k - (8 - 5) \cdot 3^k = 8 \cdot (8^k - 3^k) + 5 \cdot 3^k$, which is divisible by 5 because $8^k - 3^k$ is divisible by 5 by our induction hypothesis, and $5 \cdot 3^k$ is divisible by 5. Thus $P(k+1)$ follows from $P(k)$. So by the Principle of Mathematical Induction, $P(n)$ is true for all n.

18. Let $P(n)$ denote the statement that $3^{2n} - 1$ is divisible by 8.

Step 1: $P(1)$ is the statement that $3^2 - 1 = 8$ is divisible by 8, which is clearly true.

Step 2: Assume that $P(k)$ is true; that is, $3^{2k} - 1$ is divisible by 8. We want to use this to show that $P(k+1)$ is true. Now, $3^{2(k+1)} - 1 = 9 \cdot 3^{2k} - 1 = 9 \cdot 3^{2k} - 9 + 8 = 9(3^{2k} - 1) + 8$, which is divisible by 8, since $3^{2k} - 1$ is divisible by 8 by the induction hypothesis. Thus $P(k+1)$ follows from $P(k)$. So by the Principle of Mathematical Induction, $P(n)$ is true for all n.

19. Let $P(n)$ denote the statement $n < 2^n$.

Step 1: $P(1)$ is the statement that $1 < 2^1 = 2$, which is clearly true.

Step 2: Assume that $P(k)$ is true; that is, $k < 2^k$. We want to use this to show that $P(k+1)$ is true. Adding 1 to both sides of $P(k)$ we have $k + 1 < 2^k + 1$. Since $1 < 2^k$ for $k \geq 1$, we have $2^k + 1 < 2^k + 2^k = 2 \cdot 2^k = 2^{k+1}$. Thus $k + 1 < 2^{k+1}$, which is exactly $P(k+1)$. Therefore, $P(k+1)$ follows from $P(k)$. So by the Principle of Mathematical Induction, $P(n)$ is true for all n.

20. Let $P(n)$ denote the statement $(n+1)^2 < 2n^2$, for all $n \geq 3$.

Step 1: $P(3)$ is the statement that $(3+1)^2 < 2 \cdot 3^2$ or $16 < 18$, which is true.

Step 2: Assume that $P(k)$ is true; that is, $(k+1)^2 < 2k^2$, $k \geq 3$. We want to use this to show that $P(k+1)$ is true. Now

$$
\begin{aligned}
(k+2)^2 &= k^2 + 4k + 4 = (k^2 + 2k + 1) + (2k + 3) = (k+1)^2 + (2k+1) \\
&< 2k^2 + (2k + 3) \qquad\qquad\qquad\qquad\qquad \text{induction hypothesis} \\
&< 2k^2 + (2k + 3) + (2k - 1) \qquad\qquad\qquad \text{because } 2k - 1 > 0 \text{ for } k \geq 3 \\
&= 2k^2 + 4k + 2 = 2(k+1)^2
\end{aligned}
$$

Thus $P(k+1)$ follows from $P(k)$. So by the Principle of Mathematical Induction, $P(n)$ is true for all $n \geq 3$.

21. Let $P(n)$ denote the statement $(1+x)^n \geq 1 + nx$, if $x > -1$.

Step 1: $P(1)$ is the statement that $(1+x)^1 \geq 1 + 1x$, which is clearly true.

Step 2: Assume that $P(k)$ is true; that is, $(1+x)^k \geq 1 + kx$. Now, $(1+x)^{k+1} = (1+x)(1+x)^k \geq (1+x)(1+kx)$, by the induction hypothesis. Since $(1+x)(1+kx) = 1 + (k+1)x + kx^2 \geq 1 + (k+1)x$ (since $kx^2 \geq 0$), we have $(1+x)^{k+1} \geq 1 + (k+1)x$, which is $P(k+1)$. Thus $P(k+1)$ follows from $P(k)$. So the Principle of Mathematical Induction, $P(n)$ is true for all n.

22. Let $P(n)$ denote the statement $100n \leq n^2$, for all $n \geq 100$.

Step 1: $P(100)$ is the statement that $100(100) \leq (100)^2$, which is true.

Step 2: Assume that $P(k)$ is true; that is, $100k \leq k^2$. We want to use this to show that $P(k+1)$ is true. Now

$$
\begin{aligned}
100(k+1) &= 100k + 100 \leq k^2 + 100 && \text{induction hypothesis} \\
&\leq k^2 + 2k + 1 = (k+1)^2 && \text{because } 2k+1 \geq 100 \text{ for } k \geq 100
\end{aligned}
$$

Thus $P(k+1)$ follows from $P(k)$. So by the Principle of Mathematical Induction, $P(n)$ is true for all $n \geq 100$.

23. Let $P(n)$ be the statement that $a_n = 5 \cdot 3^{n-1}$.

Step 1: $P(1)$ is the statement that $a_1 = 5 \cdot 3^0 = 5$, which is true.

Step 2: Assume that $P(k)$ is true; that is, $a_k = 5 \cdot 3^{k-1}$. We want to use this to show that $P(k+1)$ is true. Now, $a_{k+1} = 3a_k = 3 \cdot (5 \cdot 3^{k-1})$, by the induction hypothesis. Therefore, $a_{k+1} = 3 \cdot (5 \cdot 3^{k-1}) = 5 \cdot 3^k$, which is exactly $P(k+1)$. Thus, $P(k+1)$ follows from $P(k)$. So by the Principle of Mathematical Induction, $P(n)$ is true for all n.

24. $a_{n+1} = 3a_n - 8$ and $a_1 = 4$. Then $a_2 = 3 \cdot 4 - 8 = 4$, $a_3 = 3 \cdot 4 - 8 = 4$, $a_4 = 3 \cdot 4 - 8 = 4$, $\ldots$, and the conjecture is that $a_n = 4$. Let $P(n)$ denote the statement that $a_n = 4$.

Step 1: $P(1)$ is the statement that $a_1 = 4$, which is true.

Step 2: Assume that $P(k)$ is true; that is, $a_k = 4$. We want to use this to show that $P(k+1)$ is true. Now, $a_{k+1} = 3 \cdot a_k - 8 = 3 \cdot 4 - 8 = 4$, by the induction hypothesis. This is exactly $P(k+1)$, so by the Principle of Mathematical Induction, $P(n)$ is true for all n.

25. Let $P(n)$ be the statement that $x - y$ is a factor of $x^n - y^n$ for all natural numbers n.

Step 1: $P(1)$ is the statement that $x - y$ is a factor of $x^1 - y^1$, which is clearly true.

Step 2: Assume that $P(k)$ is true; that is, $x - y$ is a factor of $x^k - y^k$. We want to use this to show that $P(k+1)$ is true. Now, $x^{k+1} - y^{k+1} = x^{k+1} - x^k y + x^k y - y^{k+1} = x^k(x-y) + (x^k - y^k)y$, for which $x - y$ is a factor because $x - y$ is a factor of $x^k(x-y)$, and $x - y$ is a factor of $(x^k - y^k)y$, by the induction hypothesis. Thus $P(k+1)$ follows from $P(k)$. So by the Principle of Mathematical Induction, $P(n)$ is true for all n.

26. Let $P(n)$ be the statement that $x + y$ is a factor of $x^{2n-1} + y^{2n-1}$.

Step 1: $P(1)$ is the statement that $x + y$ is a factor of $x^1 + y^1$, which is clearly true.

Step 2: Assume that $P(k)$ is true; that is, $x + y$ is a factor of $x^{2k-1} + y^{2k-1}$. We want to use this to show that $P(k+1)$ is true. Now

$$
\begin{aligned}
x^{2(k+1)-1} + y^{2(k+1)-1} &= x^{2k+1} + y^{2k+1} = x^{2k+1} - x^{2k-1}y^2 + x^{2k-1}y^2 + y^{2k+1} \\
&= x^{2k-1}(x^2 - y^2) + (x^{2k-1} + y^{2k-1})y^2
\end{aligned}
$$

for which $x + y$ is a factor. This is because $x + y$ is a factor of $x^2 - y^2 = (x+y)(x-y)$ and $(x+y)$ is a factor of $x^{2k-1} + y^{2k-1}$ by our induction hypothesis. Thus $P(k+1)$ follows from $P(k)$. So by the Principle of Mathematical Induction, $P(n)$ is true for all n.

27. Let $P(n)$ denote the statement that F_{3n} is even for all natural numbers n.

Step 1: $P(1)$ is the statement that F_3 is even. Since $F_3 = F_2 + F_1 = 1 + 1 = 2$, this statement is true.

Step 2: Assume that $P(k)$ is true; that is, F_{3k} is even. We want to use this to show that $P(k+1)$ is true. Now,

$F_{3(k+1)} = F_{3k+3} = F_{3k+2} + F_{3k+1} = F_{3k+1} + F_{3k} + F_{3k+1} = F_{3k} + 2 \cdot F_{3k+1}$, which is even because F_{3k} is even by

the induction hypothesis, and $2 \cdot F_{3k+1}$ is even. Thus $P(k+1)$ follows from $P(k)$. So by the Principle of Mathematical

Induction, $P(n)$ is true for all n.

28. Let $P(n)$ denote the statement that $F_1 + F_2 + F_3 + \cdots + F_n = F_{n+2} - 1$.

Step 1: $P(1)$ is the statement that $F_1 = F_3 - 1$. But $F_1 = 1 = 2 - 1 = F_3 - 1$, which is true.

Step 2: Assume that $P(k)$ is true; that is, $F_1 + F_2 + F_3 + \cdots + F_k = F_{k+2} - 1$. We want to use this to show that $P(k+1)$

is true. Now $F_{(k+1)+2} - 1 = F_{k+3} - 1 = F_{k+2} + F_{k+1} - 1 = (F_{k+2} - 1) + F_{k+1} = F_1 + F_2 + F_3 + \cdots + F_k + F_{k+1}$

by the induction hypothesis. Thus $P(k+1)$ follows from $P(k)$. So by the Principle of Mathematical Induction, $P(n)$ is

true for all n.

29. Let $P(n)$ denote the statement that $F_1^2 + F_2^2 + F_3^2 + \cdots + F_n^2 = F_n \cdot F_{n+1}$.

Step 1: $P(1)$ is the statement that $F_1^2 = F_1 \cdot F_2$ or $1^2 = 1 \cdot 1$, which is true.

Step 2: Assume that $P(k)$ is true, that is, $F_1^2 + F_2^2 + F_3^2 + \cdots + F_k^2 = F_k \cdot F_{k+1}$. We want to use this to show that

$P(k+1)$ is true. Now

$$
\begin{aligned}
F_1^2 + F_2^2 + F_3^2 + \cdots + F_k^2 + F_{k+1}^2 &= F_k \cdot F_{k+1} + F_{k+1}^2 && \text{induction hypothesis} \\
&= F_{k+1}(F_k + F_{k+1}) \\
&= F_{k+1} \cdot F_{k+2} && \text{by definition of the Fibonacci sequence}
\end{aligned}
$$

Thus $P(k+1)$ follows from $P(k)$. So by the Principle of Mathematical Induction, $P(n)$ is true for all n.

30. Let $P(n)$ denote the statement that $F_1 + F_3 + \cdots + F_{2n-1} = F_{2n}$.

Step 1: $P(1)$ is the statement that $F_1 = F_2$, which is true since $F_1 = 1$ and $F_2 = 1$.

Step 2: Assume that $P(k)$ is true; that is, $F_1 + F_3 + \cdots + F_{2k-1} = F_{2k}$, for some $k \geq 1$. We want to use this to show that

$P(k+1)$ is true; that is, $F_1 + F_3 + \cdots + F_{2(k+1)-1} = F_{2(k+1)}$. Now

$$
\begin{aligned}
F_1 + F_3 + \cdots + F_{2k-1} + F_{2k+1} &= F_{2k} + F_{2k+1} && \text{induction hypothesis} \\
&= F_{2k+2} && \text{definition of } F_{2k+2} \\
&= F_{2(k+1)}
\end{aligned}
$$

Therefore, $P(k+1)$ is true. So by the Principle of Mathematical Induction, $P(n)$ is true for all n.

31. Let $P(n)$ denote the statement $\begin{bmatrix} 1 & 1 \\ 1 & 0 \end{bmatrix}^n = \begin{bmatrix} F_{n+1} & F_n \\ F_n & F_{n-1} \end{bmatrix}$.

Step 1: Since $\begin{bmatrix} 1 & 1 \\ 1 & 0 \end{bmatrix}^2 = \begin{bmatrix} 1 & 1 \\ 1 & 0 \end{bmatrix}\begin{bmatrix} 1 & 1 \\ 1 & 0 \end{bmatrix} = \begin{bmatrix} 2 & 1 \\ 1 & 1 \end{bmatrix} = \begin{bmatrix} F_3 & F_2 \\ F_2 & F_1 \end{bmatrix}$, it follows that $P(2)$ is true.

Step 2: Assume that $P(k)$ is true; that is, $\begin{bmatrix} 1 & 1 \\ 1 & 0 \end{bmatrix}^k = \begin{bmatrix} F_{k+1} & F_k \\ F_k & F_{k-1} \end{bmatrix}$. We show that $P(k+1)$ follows from this. Now,

$$\begin{bmatrix} 1 & 1 \\ 1 & 0 \end{bmatrix}^{k+1} = \begin{bmatrix} 1 & 1 \\ 1 & 0 \end{bmatrix}^k \begin{bmatrix} 1 & 1 \\ 1 & 0 \end{bmatrix} = \begin{bmatrix} F_{k+1} & F_k \\ F_k & F_{k-1} \end{bmatrix}\begin{bmatrix} 1 & 1 \\ 1 & 0 \end{bmatrix} \qquad \text{induction hypothesis}$$

$$= \begin{bmatrix} F_{k+1}+F_k & F_{k+1} \\ F_k+F_{k-1} & F_k \end{bmatrix} = \begin{bmatrix} F_{k+2} & F_{k+1} \\ F_{k+1} & F_k \end{bmatrix} \qquad \text{by definition of the Fibonacci sequence}$$

Thus $P(k+1)$ follows from $P(k)$. So by the Principle of Mathematical Induction, $P(n)$ is true for all $n \geq 2$.

32. Let $a_1 = 1$ and $a_{n+1} = \dfrac{1}{1+a_n}$, for $n \geq 1$. Let $P(n)$ be the statement that $a_n = \dfrac{F_n}{F_{n+1}}$, for all $n \geq 1$.

Step 1: $P(1)$ is the statement that $a_1 = \dfrac{F_1}{F_2}$, which is true since $a_1 = 1$ and $\dfrac{F_1}{F_2} = \frac{1}{1} = 1$.

Step 2: Assume that $P(k)$ is true; that is, $a_k = \dfrac{F_k}{F_{k+1}}$. We want to use this to show that $P(k+1)$ is true. Now

$$a_{k+1} = \frac{1}{1+a_k}\ \text{(definition of } a_{k+1}) = \frac{1}{1+\dfrac{F_k}{F_{k+1}}}\ \text{(induction hypothesis)} = \frac{F_{k+1}}{F_k+F_{k+1}} = \frac{F_{k+1}}{F_{k+2}}\ \text{(definition of } F_{k+2}).$$

Thus $P(k+1)$ follows from $P(k)$. So by the Principle of Mathematical Induction, $P(n)$ is true for all $n \geq 100$.

33. Since $F_1 = 1$, $F_2 = 1$, $F_3 = 2$, $F_4 = 3$, $F_5 = 5$, $F_6 = 8$, $F_7 = 13$, ... our conjecture is that $F_n \geq n$, for all $n \geq 5$. Let $P(n)$ denote the statement that $F_n \geq n$.

Step 1: $P(5)$ is the statement that $F_5 = 5 \geq 5$, which is clearly true.

Step 2: Assume that $P(k)$ is true; that is, $F_k \geq k$, for some $k \geq 5$. We want to use this to show that $P(k+1)$ is true. Now, $F_{k+1} = F_k + F_{k-1} \geq k + F_{k-1}$ (by the induction hypothesis)$\geq k+1$ (because $F_{k-1} \geq 1$). Thus $P(k+1)$ follows from $P(k)$. So by the Principle of Mathematical Induction, $P(n)$ is true for all $n \geq 5$.

34. Since $100 \cdot 10 = 10^3$, $100 \cdot 11 < 11^3$, $100 \cdot 12 < 12^3$, ..., our conjecture is that $100n \leq n^3$, for all natural numbers $n \geq 10$. Let $P(n)$ denote the statement that $100n \leq n^3$, for $n \geq 10$.

Step 1: $P(10)$ is the statement that $100 \cdot 10 = 1{,}000 \leq 10^3 = 1{,}000$, which is true.

Step 2: Assume that $P(k)$ is true; that is, $100k \leq k^3$. We want to use this to show that $P(k+1)$ is true. Now

$$\begin{aligned}
100(k+1) &= 100k+100 \leq k^2+100 & \text{induction hypothesis} \\
&\leq k^3+k^2 & \text{because } k \geq 10 \\
&\leq k^3+3k^2+3k+1 = (k+1)^3 &
\end{aligned}$$

Thus $P(k+1)$ follows from $P(k)$. So by the Principle of Mathematical Induction, $P(n)$ is true for all $n \geq 10$.

35. (a) $P(n) = n^2 - n + 11$ is prime for all n. This is false as the case for $n = 11$ demonstrates: $P(11) = 11^2 - 11 + 11 = 121$, which is not prime since $11^2 = 121$.

(b) $n^2 > n$, for all $n \geq 2$. This is true. Let $P(n)$ denote the statement that $n^2 > n$.

Step 1: $P(2)$ is the statement that $2^2 = 4 > 2$, which is clearly true.

Step 2: Assume that $P(k)$ is true; that is, $k^2 > k$. We want to use this to show that $P(k+1)$ is true. Now $(k+1)^2 = k^2 + 2k + 1$. Using the induction hypothesis (to replace k^2), we have $k^2 + 2k + 1 > k + 2k + 1 = 3k + 1 > k + 1$, since $k \geq 2$. Therefore, $(k+1)^2 > k + 1$, which is exactly $P(k+1)$. Thus $P(k+1)$ follows from $P(k)$. So by the Principle of Mathematical Induction, $P(n)$ is true for all n.

(c) $2^{2n+1} + 1$ is divisible by 3, for all $n \geq 1$. This is true. Let $P(n)$ denote the statement that $2^{2n+1} + 1$ is divisible by 3.

Step 1: $P(1)$ is the statement that $2^3 + 1 = 9$ is divisible by 3, which is clearly true.

Step 2: Assume that $P(k)$ is true; that is, $2^{2k+1} + 1$ is divisible by 3. We want to use this to show that $P(k+1)$ is true. Now, $2^{2(k+1)+1} + 1 = 2^{2k+3} + 1 = 4 \cdot 2^{2k+1} + 1 = (3+1) 2^{2k+1} + 1 = 3 \cdot 2^{2k+1} + (2^{2k+1} + 1)$, which is divisible by 3 since $2^{2k+1} + 1$ is divisible by 3 by the induction hypothesis, and $3 \cdot 2^{2k+1}$ is clearly divisible by 3. Thus $P(k+1)$ follows from $P(k)$. So by the Principle of Mathematical Induction, $P(n)$ is true for all n.

(d) The statement $n^3 \geq (n+1)^2$ for all $n \geq 2$ is false. The statement fails when $n = 2$: $2^3 = 8 < (2+1)^2 = 9$.

(e) $n^3 - n$ is divisible by 3, for all $n \geq 2$. This is true. Let $P(n)$ denote the statement that $n^3 - n$ is divisible by 3.

Step 1: $P(2)$ is the statement that $2^3 - 2 = 6$ is divisible by 3, which is clearly true.

Step 2: Assume that $P(k)$ is true; that is, $k^3 - k$ is divisible by 3. We want to use this to show that $P(k+1)$ is true. Now $(k+1)^3 - (k+1) = k^3 + 3k^2 + 3k + 1 - (k+1) = k^3 + 3k^2 + 2k = k^3 - k + 3k^2 + 2k + k = (k^3 - k) + 3(k^2 + k)$. The term $k^3 - k$ is divisible by 3 by our induction hypothesis, and the term $3(k^2 + k)$ is clearly divisible by 3. Thus $(k+1)^3 - (k+1)$ is divisible by 3, which is exactly $P(k+1)$. So by the Principle of Mathematical Induction, $P(n)$ is true for all n.

(f) $n^3 - 6n^2 + 11n$ is divisible by 6, for all $n \geq 1$. This is true. Let $P(n)$ denote the statement that $n^3 - 6n^2 + 11n$ is divisible by 6.

Step 1: $P(1)$ is the statement that $(1)^3 - 6(1)^2 + 11(1) = 6$ is divisible by 6, which is clearly true.

Step 2: Assume that $P(k)$ is true; that is, $k^3 - 6k^2 + 11k$ is divisible by 6. We show that $P(k+1)$ is then also true. Now

$$
\begin{aligned}
(k+1)^3 - 6(k+1)^2 + 11(k+1) &= k^3 + 3k^2 + 3k + 1 - 6k^2 - 12k - 6 + 11k + 11 \\
&= k^3 - 3k^2 + 2k + 6 = k^3 - 6k^2 + 11k + (3k^2 - 9k + 6) \\
&= (k^3 - 6k^2 + 11k) + 3(k^2 - 3k + 2) = (k^3 - 6k^2 + 11k) + 3(k-1)(k-2)
\end{aligned}
$$

In this last expression, the first term is divisible by 6 by our induction hypothesis. The second term is also divisible by 6. To see this, notice that $k - 1$ and $k - 2$ are consecutive natural numbers, and so one of them must be even (divisible by 2). Since 3 also appears in this second term, it follows that this term is divisible by 2 and 3 and so is divisible by 6. Thus $P(k+1)$ follows from $P(k)$. So by the Principle of Mathematical Induction, $P(n)$ is true for all n.

36. The induction step fails when $k = 2$, that is, $P(2)$ does not follow from $P(1)$. If there are only two cats, Midnight and Sparky, and we remove Sparky, then only Midnight remains. So at this point, we still know only that Midnight is black. Now removing Midnight and putting Sparky back leaves Midnight alone. So the induction hypothesis does not allow us to conclude that Sparky is black.

11.6 The Binomial Theorem

1. $(x + y)^6 = x^6 + 6x^5y + 15x^4y^2 + 20x^3y^3 + 15x^2y^4 + 6xy^5 + y^6$

2. $(2x + 1)^4 = (2x)^4 + 4(2x)^3 + 6(2x)^2 + 4 \cdot 2x + 1 = 16x^4 + 32x^3 + 24x^2 + 8x + 1$

3. $\left(x + \dfrac{1}{x}\right)^4 = x^4 + 4x^3 \cdot \dfrac{1}{x} + 6x^2 \left(\dfrac{1}{x}\right)^2 + 4x \left(\dfrac{1}{x}\right)^3 + \left(\dfrac{1}{x}\right)^4 = x^4 + 4x^2 + 6 + \dfrac{4}{x^2} + \dfrac{1}{x^4}$

4. $(x - y)^5 = x^5 - 5x^4y + 10x^3y^2 - 10x^2y^3 + 5xy^4 - y^5$

5. $(x - 1)^5 = x^5 - 5x^4 + 10x^3 - 10x^2 + 5x - 1$

6. $\left(\sqrt{a} + \sqrt{b}\right)^6 = a^3 + 6a^2\sqrt{a}\sqrt{b} + 15a^2b + 20a\sqrt{ab}\sqrt{b} + 15ab^2 + 6\sqrt{a}b^2\sqrt{b} + b^3$

$\qquad = a^3 + 6a^2\sqrt{ab} + 15a^2b + 20ab\sqrt{ab} + 15ab^2 + 6b^2\sqrt{ab} + b^3$

or $a^3 + 6a^{5/2}b^{1/2} + 15a^2b + 20a^{3/2}b^{3/2} + 15ab^2 + 6a^{1/2}b^{5/2} + b^3$.

7. $(x^2y - 1)^5 = (x^2y)^5 - 5(x^2y)^4 + 10(x^2y)^3 - 10(x^2y)^2 + 5x^2y - 1 = x^{10}y^5 - 5x^8y^4 + 10x^6y^3 - 10x^4y^2 + 5x^2y - 1$

8. $(1 + \sqrt{2})^6 = 1^6 + 6 \cdot 1^5 \cdot \sqrt{2} + 15 \cdot 1^4 \cdot 2 + 20 \cdot 1^3 \cdot 2\sqrt{2} + 15 \cdot 1^2 \cdot 4 + 6 \cdot 1 \cdot 4\sqrt{2} + 2^3$

$\qquad = 1 + 6\sqrt{2} + 30 + 40\sqrt{2} + 60 + 24\sqrt{2} + 8 = 99 + 70\sqrt{2}$

9. $(2x - 3y)^3 = (2x)^3 - 3(2x)^2 3y + 3 \cdot 2x(3y)^2 - (3y)^3 = 8x^3 - 36x^2y + 54xy^2 - 27y^3$

10. $(1 + x^3)^3 = 1^3 + 3 \cdot 1^2 \cdot x^3 + 3 \cdot 1(x^3)^2 + (x^3)^3 = 1 + 3x^3 + 3x^6 + x^9$

11. $\left(\dfrac{1}{x} - \sqrt{x}\right)^5 = \left(\dfrac{1}{x}\right)^5 - 5\left(\dfrac{1}{x}\right)^4\sqrt{x} + 10\left(\dfrac{1}{x}\right)^3 x - 10\left(\dfrac{1}{x}\right)^2 x\sqrt{x} + 5\left(\dfrac{1}{x}\right)x^2 - x^2\sqrt{x}$

$\qquad = \dfrac{1}{x^5} - \dfrac{5}{x^{7/2}} + \dfrac{10}{x^2} - \dfrac{10}{x^{1/2}} + 5x - x^{5/2}$

12. $\left(2 + \dfrac{x}{2}\right)^5 = (2)^5 + 5(2)^4\dfrac{x}{2} + 10(2)^3\left(\dfrac{x}{2}\right)^2 + 10(2)^2\left(\dfrac{x}{2}\right)^3 + 5(2)\left(\dfrac{x}{2}\right)^4 + \left(\dfrac{x}{2}\right)^5 = 32 + 40x + 20x^2 + 5x^3 + \dfrac{5}{8}x^4 + \dfrac{1}{32}x^5$

13. $\dbinom{6}{4} = \dfrac{6!}{4!\,2!} = \dfrac{6 \cdot 5 \cdot 4!}{2 \cdot 1 \cdot 4!} = 15$

14. $\dbinom{8}{3} = \dfrac{8!}{3!\,5!} = \dfrac{8 \cdot 7 \cdot 6 \cdot 5!}{3 \cdot 2 \cdot 1 \cdot 5!} = 8 \cdot 7 = 56$

15. $\dbinom{100}{98} = \dfrac{100!}{98!\,2!} = \dfrac{100 \cdot 99 \cdot 98!}{98! \cdot 2 \cdot 1} = 4950$

16. $\dbinom{10}{5} = \dfrac{10!}{5!\,5!} = \dfrac{10 \cdot 9 \cdot 8 \cdot 7 \cdot 6 \cdot 5!}{5 \cdot 4 \cdot 3 \cdot 2 \cdot 1 \cdot 5!} = 3 \cdot 2 \cdot 7 \cdot 6 = 252$

17. $\dbinom{3}{1}\dbinom{4}{2} = \dfrac{3!}{1!\,2!}\dfrac{4!}{2!\,2!} = \dfrac{3 \cdot 2! \cdot 4 \cdot 3 \cdot 2!}{1 \cdot 2! \cdot 2 \cdot 1 \cdot 2!} = 18$

18. $\dbinom{5}{2}\dbinom{5}{3} = \dfrac{5!}{2!\,3!} \cdot \dfrac{5!}{3!\,2!} = \dfrac{5 \cdot 4 \cdot 3!}{2 \cdot 1 \cdot 3!} \cdot \dfrac{5 \cdot 4 \cdot 3!}{3! \cdot 2 \cdot 1} = 10 \cdot 10 = 100$

19. $\binom{5}{0} + \binom{5}{1} + \binom{5}{2} + \binom{5}{3} + \binom{5}{4} + \binom{5}{5} = (1 + 1)^5 = 2^5 = 32$

20. $\dbinom{5}{0} - \dbinom{5}{1} + \dbinom{5}{2} - \dbinom{5}{3} + \dbinom{5}{4} - \dbinom{5}{5} = 1 - \dfrac{5!}{1!\,4!} + \dfrac{5!}{2!\,3!} - \dfrac{5!}{3!\,2!} + \dfrac{5!}{4!\,1!} - 1 = 0$. Notice that the first and sixth

terms cancel, as do the second and fifth terms and the third and fourth terms.

21. $(x + 2y)^4 = \binom{4}{0}x^4 + \binom{4}{1}x^3 \cdot 2y + \binom{4}{2}x^2 \cdot 4y^2 + \binom{4}{3}x \cdot 8y^3 + \binom{4}{4}16y^4 = x^4 + 8x^3y + 24x^2y^2 + 32xy^3 + 16y^4$

22. $(1 - x)^5 = \binom{5}{0}(1)^5 - \binom{5}{1}(1)^4 x + \binom{5}{2}(1)^3 x^2 - \binom{5}{3}(1)^2 x^3 + \binom{5}{4}(1)x^4 - \binom{5}{5}x^5 = 1 - 5x + 10x^2 - 10x^3 + 5x^4 - x^5$

23. $\left(1+\dfrac{1}{x}\right)^6 = \binom{6}{0}1^6 + \binom{6}{1}1^5\left(\dfrac{1}{x}\right) + \binom{6}{2}1^4\left(\dfrac{1}{x}\right)^2 + \binom{6}{3}1^3\left(\dfrac{1}{x}\right)^3 + \binom{6}{4}1^2\left(\dfrac{1}{x}\right)^4 + \binom{6}{5}1\left(\dfrac{1}{x}\right)^5 + \binom{6}{6}\left(\dfrac{1}{x}\right)^6$

$= 1 + \dfrac{6}{x} + \dfrac{15}{x^2} + \dfrac{20}{x^3} + \dfrac{15}{x^4} + \dfrac{6}{x^5} + \dfrac{1}{x^6}$

24. $(2A + B^2)^4 = \binom{4}{0}(2A)^4 + \binom{4}{1}(2A)^3(B^2) + \binom{4}{2}(2A)^2(B^2)^2 + \binom{4}{3}(2A)(B^2)^3 + \binom{4}{4}(B^2)^4$

$= 16A^4 + 32A^3B^2 + 24A^2B^4 + 8AB^6 + B^8$

25. The first three terms in the expansion of $(x + 2y)^{20}$ are $\binom{20}{0}x^{20} = x^{20}$, $\binom{20}{1}x^{19} \cdot 2y = 40x^{19}y$, and $\binom{20}{2}x^{18} \cdot (2y)^2 = 760x^{18}y^2$.

26. The first four terms in the expansion of $\left(x^{1/2} + 1\right)^{30}$ are $\binom{30}{0}\left(x^{1/2}\right)^{30} = x^{15}$, $\binom{30}{1}\left(x^{1/2}\right)^{29}(1) = 30x^{29/2}$, $\binom{30}{2}\left(x^{1/2}\right)^{28}(1)^2 = 435x^{14}$, and $\binom{30}{3}\left(x^{1/2}\right)^{27}(1)^3 = 4060x^{27/2}$.

27. The last two terms in the expansion of $\left(a^{2/3} + a^{1/3}\right)^{25}$ are $\binom{25}{24}a^{2/3} \cdot \left(a^{1/3}\right)^{24} = 25a^{26/3}$, and $\binom{25}{25}a^{25/3} = a^{25/3}$.

28. The first three terms in the expansion of $\left(x + \dfrac{1}{x}\right)^{40}$ are $\binom{40}{0}x^{40} = x^{40}$, $\binom{40}{1}x^{39}\left(\dfrac{1}{x}\right) = 40x^{38}$, and

$\binom{40}{2}x^{38}\left(\dfrac{1}{x}\right)^2 = 780x^{36}$.

29. The middle term in the expansion of $(x^2 + 1)^{18}$ occurs when both terms are raised to the 9th power. So this term is $\binom{18}{9}\left(x^2\right)^9 1^9 = 48{,}620x^{18}$.

30. The fifth term in the expansion of $(ab - 1)^{20}$ is $\binom{20}{4}(ab)^{16}(-1)^4 = 4845a^{16}b^{16}$.

31. The 24th term in the expansion of $(a + b)^{25}$ is $\binom{25}{23}a^2b^{23} = 300a^2b^{23}$.

32. The 28th term in the expansion of $(A - B)^{30}$ is $\binom{30}{27}A^3(-B)^{27} = -4060A^3B^{27}$.

33. The 100th term in the expansion of $(1 + y)^{100}$ is $\binom{100}{99}1^1 \cdot y^{99} = 100y^{99}$.

34. The second term in the expansion of $\left(x^2 - \dfrac{1}{x}\right)^{25}$ is $\binom{25}{1}\left(x^2\right)^{24}\left(-\dfrac{1}{x}\right) = -25x^{47}$.

35. The term that contains x^4 in the expansion of $(x + 2y)^{10}$ has exponent $r = 4$. So this term is $\binom{10}{4}x^4 \cdot (2y)^{10-4} = 13{,}440x^4y^6$.

36. The rth term in the expansion of $(\sqrt{2} + y)^{12}$ is $\binom{12}{r}(\sqrt{2})^r y^{12-r}$. The term that contains y^3 occurs when $12 - r = 3 \Leftrightarrow r = 9$. Therefore, the term is $\binom{12}{9}(\sqrt{2})^9 y^3 = 3520\sqrt{2}y^3$.

37. The rth term is $\binom{12}{r}a^r(b^2)^{12-r} = \binom{12}{r}a^r b^{24-2r}$. Thus the term that contains b^8 occurs where $24 - 2r = 8 \Leftrightarrow r = 8$. So the term is $\binom{12}{8}a^8 b^8 = 495a^8 b^8$.

38. The rth term is $\binom{8}{r}(8x)^r\left(\dfrac{1}{2x}\right)^{8-r} = \binom{8}{r}\dfrac{8^r}{2^{8-r}} \cdot \dfrac{x^r}{x^{8-r}} = \binom{8}{r}\dfrac{8^r}{2^{8-r}} \cdot x^{2r-8}$. So the term that does not contain x occurs

when $2r - 8 = 0 \Leftrightarrow r = 4$. Thus, the term is $\binom{8}{4}(8x)^4\left(\dfrac{1}{2x}\right)^4 = 17{,}920$.

39. $x^4 + 4x^3y + 6x^2y^2 + 4xy^3 + y^4 = (x + y)^4$

40. $(x - 1)^5 + 5(x - 1)^4 + 10(x - 1)^3 + 10(x - 1)^2 + 5(x - 1) + 1 = [(x - 1) + 1]^5 = x^5$

41. $8a^3 + 12a^2b + 6ab^2 + b^3 = \binom{3}{0}(2a)^3 + \binom{3}{1}(2a)^2 b + \binom{3}{2}2ab^2 + \binom{3}{3}b^3 = (2a + b)^3$

42. $x^8 + 4x^6y + 6x^4y^2 + 4x^2y^3 + y^4 = \binom{4}{0}\left(x^2\right)^4 + \binom{4}{1}\left(x^2\right)^3 y + \binom{4}{2}\left(x^2\right)^2 y^2 + \binom{4}{3}x^2y^3 + \binom{4}{4}y^4 = (x^2 + y)^4$

43. $\dfrac{(x + h)^3 - x^3}{h} = \dfrac{x^3 + 3x^2h + 3xh^2 + h^3 - x^3}{h} = \dfrac{3x^2h + 3xh^2 + h^3}{h} = \dfrac{h\left(3x^2 + 3xh + h^2\right)}{h} = 3x^2 + 3xh + h^2$

44. $\dfrac{(x+h)^4 - x^4}{h} = \dfrac{\binom{4}{0}x^4 + \binom{4}{1}x^3h + \binom{4}{2}x^2h^2 + \binom{4}{3}xh^3 + \binom{4}{4}h^4 - x^4}{h} = \dfrac{x^4 + 4x^3h + 6x^2h^2 + 4xh^3 + h^4 - x^4}{h}$

$= \dfrac{4x^3h + 6x^2h^2 + 4xh^3 + h^4}{h} = \dfrac{h\left(4x^3 + 6x^2h + 4xh^2 + h^3\right)}{h} = 4x^3 + 6x^2h + 4xh^2 + h^3$

45. $(1.01)^{100} = (1 + 0.01)^{100}$. Now the first term in the expansion is $\binom{100}{0}1^{100} = 1$, the second term is

$\binom{100}{1}1^{99}(0.01) = 1$, and the third term is $\binom{100}{2}1^{98}(0.01)^2 = 0.495$. Now each term is nonnegative, so

$(1.01)^{100} = (1 + 0.01)^{100} > 1 + 1 + .0.495 > 2$. Thus $(1.01)^{100} > 2$.

46. $\binom{n}{0} = \dfrac{n!}{0!n!} = \dfrac{n!}{1 \cdot n!} = 1$. $\binom{n}{n} = \dfrac{n!}{n!0!} = \dfrac{n!}{n! \cdot 1} = 1$. Therefore, $\binom{n}{0} = \binom{n}{n}$.

47. $\binom{n}{1} = \dfrac{n!}{1!\,(n-1)!} = \dfrac{n\,(n-1)!}{1\,(n-1)!} = \dfrac{n}{1} = n$. $\binom{n}{n-1} = \dfrac{n!}{(n-1)!\,1!} = \dfrac{n\,(n-1)!}{(n-1)!\,1} = n$. Therefore,

$\binom{n}{1} = \binom{n}{n-1} = n$.

48. $\binom{n}{r} = \dfrac{n!}{r!\,(n-r)!} = \dfrac{n!}{(n-r)!\,r!} = \binom{n}{n-r}$ for $0 \le r \le n$.

49. (a) $\binom{n}{r-1} + \binom{n}{r} = \dfrac{n!}{(r-1)!\,[n-(r-1)]!} + \dfrac{n!}{r!\,(n-r)!}$.

(b) $\dfrac{n!}{(r-1)!\,[n-(r-1)]!} + \dfrac{n!}{r!\,(n-r)!} = \dfrac{r \cdot n!}{r \cdot (r-1)!\,(n-r+1)!} + \dfrac{(n-r+1) \cdot n!}{r!\,(n-r+1)\,(n-r)!}$

$= \dfrac{r \cdot n!}{r!\,(n-r+1)!} + \dfrac{(n-r+1) \cdot n!}{r!\,(n-r+1)!}$

Thus a common denominator is $r!\,(n-r+1)!$.

(c) Therefore, using the results of parts (a) and (b),

$\binom{n}{r-1} + \binom{n}{r} = \dfrac{n!}{(r-1)!\,[n-(r-1)]!} + \dfrac{n!}{r!\,(n-r)!} = \dfrac{r \cdot n!}{r!\,(n-r+1)!} + \dfrac{(n-r+1) \cdot n!}{r!\,(n-r+1)!}$

$= \dfrac{r \cdot n! + (n-r+1) \cdot n!}{r!\,(n-r+1)!} = \dfrac{n!\,(r+n-r+1)}{r!\,(n-r+1)!} = \dfrac{n!\,(n+1)}{r!\,(n+1-r)!} = \dfrac{(n+1)!}{r!\,(n+1-r)!} = \binom{n+1}{r}$

50. Let $P(n)$ be the proposition that $\binom{n}{r}$ is an integer for the number n, $0 \le r \le n$.

Step 1: Suppose $n = 0$. If $0 \le r \le n$, then $r = 0$, and so $\binom{n}{r} = \binom{0}{0} = 1$, which is obviously an integer. Therefore,

$P(0)$ is true.

Step 2: Suppose that $P(k)$ is true. We want to use this to show that $P(k+1)$ must also be true; that is, $\binom{k+1}{r}$ is an

integer for $0 \le r \le k+1$. But we know that $\binom{k+1}{r} = \binom{k}{r-1} + \binom{k}{r}$ by the key property of binomial coefficients

(see Exercise 49). Furthermore, $\binom{k}{r-1}$ and $\binom{k}{r}$ are both integers by the induction hypothesis. Since the sum of two

integers is always an integer, $\binom{k+1}{r}$ must be an integer. Thus, $P(k+1)$ is true if $P(k)$ is true. So by the Principal of

Mathematical induction, $\binom{n}{r}$ is an integer for all $n \ge 0$, $0 \le r \le n$.

51. Notice that $(100!)^{101} = (100!)^{100} \cdot 100!$ and $(101!)^{100} = (101 \cdot 100!)^{100} = 101^{100} \cdot (100!)^{100}$. Now

$100! = 1 \cdot 2 \cdot 3 \cdot 4 \cdots 99 \cdot 100$ and $101^{100} = 101 \cdot 101 \cdot 101 \cdots 101$. Thus each of these last two expressions consists

of 100 factors multiplied together, and since each factor in the product for 101^{100} is larger than each factor in the product

for $100!$, it follows that $100! < 101^{100}$. Thus $(100!)^{100} \cdot 100! < (100!)^{100} \cdot 101^{100}$. So $(100!)^{101} < (101!)^{100}$.

52.

$$1 + 1 = 2$$
$$1 + 2 + 1 = 4$$
$$1 + 3 + 3 + 1 = 8$$
$$1 + 4 + 6 + 4 + 1 = 16$$
$$1 + 5 + 10 + 10 + 5 + 1 = 32$$

Conjecture: The sum is 2^n.

Proof:

$$2^n = (1 + 1)^n = \binom{n}{0} 1^0 \cdot 1^n + \binom{n}{1} 1^1 \cdot 1^{n-1} + \binom{n}{2} 1^2 \cdot 1^{n-2} + \cdots + \binom{n}{n} 1^n \cdot 1^0$$

$$= \binom{n}{0} + \binom{n}{1} + \binom{n}{2} + \cdots + \binom{n}{n}$$

53. $0 = 0^n = (-1 + 1)^n = \binom{n}{0} (-1)^0 (1)^n + \binom{n}{1} (-1)^1 (1)^{n-1} + \binom{n}{2} (-1)^2 (1)^{n-2} + \cdots + \binom{n}{n} (-1)^n (1)^0$

$$= \binom{n}{0} - \binom{n}{1} + \binom{n}{2} - \cdots + (-1)^k \binom{n}{k} + \cdots + (-1)^n \binom{n}{n}$$

Chapter 11 Review

1. $a_n = \dfrac{n^2}{n+1}$. Then $a_1 = \dfrac{1^2}{1+1} = \dfrac{1}{2}$, $a_2 = \dfrac{2^2}{2+1} = \dfrac{4}{3}$, $a_3 = \dfrac{3^2}{3+1} = \dfrac{9}{4}$, $a_4 = \dfrac{4^2}{4+1} = \dfrac{16}{5}$, and

$a_{10} = \dfrac{10^2}{10+1} = \dfrac{100}{11}$.

2. $a_n = (-1)^n \dfrac{2^n}{n}$. Then $a_1 = (-1)^1 \dfrac{2^1}{1} = -2$, $a_2 = (-1)^2 \dfrac{2^2}{2} = 2$, $a_3 = (-1)^3 \dfrac{2^3}{3} = -\dfrac{8}{3}$, $a_4 = (-1)^4 \dfrac{2^4}{4} = 4$, and

$a_{10} = (-1)^{10} \dfrac{2^{10}}{10} = \dfrac{1024}{10} = \dfrac{512}{5}$.

3. $a_n = \dfrac{(-1)^n + 1}{n^3}$. Then $a_1 = \dfrac{(-1)^1 + 1}{1^3} = 0$, $a_2 = \dfrac{(-1)^2 + 1}{2^3} = \dfrac{2}{8} = \dfrac{1}{4}$, $a_3 = \dfrac{(-1)^3 + 1}{3^3} = 0$,

$a_4 = \dfrac{(-1)^4 + 1}{4^3} = \dfrac{2}{64} = \dfrac{1}{32}$, and $a_{10} = \dfrac{(-1)^{10} + 1}{10^3} = \dfrac{1}{500}$.

4. $a_n = \dfrac{n(n+1)}{2}$. Then $a_1 = \dfrac{1(1+1)}{2} = 1$, $a_2 = \dfrac{2(2+1)}{2} = 3$, $a_3 = \dfrac{3(3+1)}{2} = 6$, $a_4 = \dfrac{4(4+1)}{2} = 10$, and

$a_{10} = \dfrac{10(10+1)}{2} = 55$.

5. $a_n = \dfrac{(2n)!}{2^n n!}$. Then $a_1 = \dfrac{(2 \cdot 1)!}{2^1 \cdot 1!} = 1$, $a_2 = \dfrac{(2 \cdot 2)!}{2^2 \cdot 2!} = 3$, $a_3 = \dfrac{(2 \cdot 3)!}{2^3 \cdot 3!} = \dfrac{6 \cdot 5 \cdot 4}{8} = 15$,

$a_4 = \dfrac{(2 \cdot 4)!}{2^4 \cdot 4!} = \dfrac{8 \cdot 7 \cdot 6 \cdot 5}{16} = 105$, and $a_{10} = \dfrac{(2 \cdot 10)!}{2^{10} \cdot 10!} = 654{,}729{,}075$.

6. $a_n = \binom{n+1}{2}$. Then $a_1 = \binom{1+1}{2} = 1$, $a_2 = \binom{2+1}{2} = \dfrac{3!}{2! \, 1!} = 3$, $a_3 = \binom{3+1}{2} = \dfrac{4!}{2! \, 2!} = 6$,

$a_4 = \binom{4+1}{2} = \dfrac{5!}{2! \, 3!} = 10$, and $a_{10} = \binom{10+1}{2} = \dfrac{11!}{2! \, 9!} = 55$.

7. $a_n = a_{n-1} + 2n - 1$ and $a_1 = 1$. Then $a_2 = a_1 + 4 - 1 = 4$, $a_3 = a_2 + 6 - 1 = 9$, $a_4 = a_3 + 8 - 1 = 16$,

$a_5 = a_4 + 10 - 1 = 25$, $a_6 = a_5 + 12 - 1 = 36$, and $a_7 = a_6 + 14 - 1 = 49$.

8. $a_n = \dfrac{a_{n-1}}{n}$ and $a_1 = 1$. Then $a_2 = \dfrac{a_1}{2} = \dfrac{1}{2}$, $a_3 = \dfrac{a_2}{3} = \dfrac{1}{6}$, $a_4 = \dfrac{a_3}{4} = \dfrac{1}{24}$, $a_5 = \dfrac{a_4}{5} = \dfrac{1}{120}$, $a_6 = \dfrac{a_5}{6} = \dfrac{1}{720}$, and

$a_7 = \dfrac{a_6}{7} = \dfrac{1}{5040}$.

9. $a_n = a_{n-1} + 2a_{n-2}$, $a_1 = 1$ and $a_2 = 3$. Then $a_3 = a_2 + 2a_1 = 5$, $a_4 = a_3 + 2a_2 = 11$, $a_5 = a_4 + 2a_3 = 21$, $a_6 = a_5 + 2a_4 = 43$, and $a_7 = a_6 + 2a_5 = 85$.

10. $a_n = \sqrt{3a_{n-1}}$ and $a_1 = \sqrt{3} = 3^{1/2}$. Then $a_2 = \sqrt{3a_1} = \sqrt{3\sqrt{3}} = \left(3 \cdot 3^{1/2}\right)^{1/2} = 3^{3/4}$,

$a_3 = \sqrt{3a_2} = \sqrt{3 \cdot 3^{3/4}} = \sqrt{3^{7/4}} = 3^{7/8}$, $a_4 = \sqrt{3a_3} = \sqrt{3 \cdot 3^{7/8}} = \sqrt{3^{15/8}} = 3^{15/16}$,

$a_5 = \sqrt{3a_4} = \sqrt{3 \cdot 3^{15/16}} = \sqrt{3^{31/16}} = 3^{31/32}$, $a_6 = \sqrt{3a_5} = \sqrt{3 \cdot 3^{31/32}} = \sqrt{3^{63/32}} = 3^{63/64}$,

$a_7 = \sqrt{3a_6} = \sqrt{3 \cdot 3^{63/64}} = \sqrt{3^{127/64}} = 3^{127/128}$.

11. (a) $a_1 = 2(1) + 5 = 7$, $a_2 = 2(2) + 5 = 9$,

$a_3 = 2(3) + 5 = 11$, $a_4 = 2(4) + 5 = 13$,

$a_5 = 2(5) + 5 = 15$

(b)

(c) This sequence is arithmetic with common difference 2.

12. (a) $a_1 = \dfrac{5}{2^1} = \dfrac{5}{2}$, $a_2 = \dfrac{5}{2^2} = \dfrac{5}{4}$, $a_3 = \dfrac{5}{2^3} = \dfrac{5}{8}$,

$a_4 = \dfrac{5}{2^4} = \dfrac{5}{16}$, $a_5 = \dfrac{5}{2^5} = \dfrac{5}{32}$

(b)

(c) This sequence is geometric with common ratio $\frac{1}{2}$.

13. (a) $a_1 = \dfrac{3^1}{2^2} = \dfrac{3}{4}$, $a_2 = \dfrac{3^2}{2^3} = \dfrac{9}{8}$, $a_3 = \dfrac{3^3}{2^4} = \dfrac{27}{16}$,

$a_4 = \dfrac{3^4}{2^5} = \dfrac{81}{32}$, $a_5 = \dfrac{3^5}{2^6} = \dfrac{243}{64}$

(b)

(c) This sequence is geometric with common ratio $\frac{3}{2}$.

14. (a) $a_1 = 4 - \dfrac{1}{2} = \dfrac{7}{2}$, $a_2 = 4 - \dfrac{2}{2} = 3$, $a_3 = 4 - \dfrac{3}{2} = \dfrac{5}{2}$,

$a_4 = 4 - \dfrac{4}{2} = 2$, $a_5 = 4 - \dfrac{5}{2} = \dfrac{3}{2}$

(b)

(c) This sequence is arithmetic with common difference $-\frac{1}{2}$.

15. $5, 5.5, 6, 6.5, \ldots$. Since $5.5 - 5 = 6 - 5.5 = 6.5 - 6 = 0.5$, this is an arithmetic sequence with $a_1 = 5$ and $d = 0.5$. Then $a_5 = a_4 + 0.5 = 7$.

16. $1, -\frac{3}{2}, 2, -\frac{5}{2}, \ldots$. Since $-\frac{3}{2} - 1 \neq 2 + \frac{3}{2}$, and $\dfrac{-\frac{3}{2}}{1} \neq \dfrac{2}{-\frac{3}{2}}$, the series is neither arithmetic nor geometric.

17. $\sqrt{2}, 2\sqrt{2}, 3\sqrt{2}, 4\sqrt{2}, \ldots$. Since $2\sqrt{2} - \sqrt{2} = 3\sqrt{2} - 2\sqrt{2} = 4\sqrt{2} - 3\sqrt{2} = \sqrt{2}$, this is an arithmetic sequence with $a_1 = \sqrt{2}$ and $d = \sqrt{2}$. Then $a_5 = a_4 + \sqrt{2} = 4\sqrt{2} + \sqrt{2} = 5\sqrt{2}$.

18. $\sqrt{2}, 2, 2\sqrt{2}, 4, \ldots$. Since $\dfrac{2}{\sqrt{2}} = \dfrac{2\sqrt{2}}{2} = \dfrac{4}{2\sqrt{2}} = \sqrt{2}$, this is a geometric sequence with $a_1 = \sqrt{2}$ and $r = \sqrt{2}$. Then $a_5 = a_4 \cdot r = 4 \cdot \sqrt{2} = 4\sqrt{2}$.

19. $t - 3, t - 2, t - 1, t, \ldots$. Since $(t - 2) - (t - 3) = (t - 1) - (t - 2) = t - (t - 1) = 1$, this is an arithmetic sequence with $a_1 = t - 3$ and $d = 1$. Then $a_5 = a_4 + 1 = t + 1$.

20. $t^3, t^2, t, 1, \ldots$. Since $\dfrac{t^2}{t^3} = \dfrac{t}{t^2} = \dfrac{1}{t}$, this is a geometric sequence with $a_1 = t^3$ and $r = \dfrac{1}{t}$. Then $a_5 = a_4 \cdot r = 1 \cdot \dfrac{1}{t} = \dfrac{1}{t}$.

21. $\frac{3}{4}, \frac{1}{2}, \frac{1}{3}, \frac{2}{9}, \ldots$. Since $\dfrac{\frac{1}{2}}{\frac{3}{4}} = \dfrac{\frac{1}{3}}{\frac{1}{2}} = \dfrac{\frac{2}{9}}{\frac{1}{3}} = \dfrac{2}{3}$, this is a geometric sequence with $a_1 = \dfrac{3}{4}$ and $r = \dfrac{2}{3}$. Then

$a_5 = a_4 \cdot r = \dfrac{2}{9} \cdot \dfrac{2}{3} = \dfrac{4}{27}$.

22. $a, 1, \dfrac{1}{a}, \dfrac{1}{a^2}, \ldots$. Since $\dfrac{1}{a} = \dfrac{\frac{1}{a}}{1}$ and $\dfrac{\frac{1}{a^2}}{\frac{1}{a}} = \dfrac{1}{a}$, this is a geometric sequence with $a_1 = a$ and $r = \dfrac{1}{a}$. Then

$$a_5 = a_4 \cdot r = \dfrac{1}{a^2} \cdot \dfrac{1}{a} = \dfrac{1}{a^3}.$$

23. $3, 6i, -12, -24i, \ldots$. Since $\dfrac{6i}{3} = 2i$, $\dfrac{-12}{6i} = \dfrac{-2}{i} = \dfrac{-2i}{i^2} = 2i$, $\dfrac{-24i}{-12} = 2i$, this is a geometric sequence with common ratio $r = 2i$.

24. The sequence $2, 2 + 2i, 4i, -4 + 4i, -8, \ldots$ is geometric (where $i^2 = -1$), since $\dfrac{a_2}{a_1} = \dfrac{2 + 2i}{2} = 1 + i$,

$\dfrac{a_3}{a_2} = \dfrac{4i}{2 + 2i} = \dfrac{4i}{2 + 2i} \cdot \dfrac{2 - 2i}{2 - 2i} = \dfrac{8 + 8i}{8} = 1 + i$, $\dfrac{a_4}{a_3} = \dfrac{-4 + 4i}{4i} = -\dfrac{1}{i} + 1 = -\dfrac{1}{i} \cdot \dfrac{i}{i} + 1 = \dfrac{-i}{i^2} + 1 = 1 + i$,

$\dfrac{a_5}{a_4} = \dfrac{-8}{-4 + 4i} = \dfrac{-8}{-4 + 4i} \cdot \dfrac{-4 - 4i}{-4 - 4i} = \dfrac{32 + 32i}{32} = 1 + i$. Thus the common ratio is $i + 1$ and the first term is 2. So the

nth term is $a_n = a_1 r^{n-1} = 2 (1 + i)^{n-1}$.

25. $a_6 = 17 = a + 5d$ and $a_4 = 11 = a + 3d$. Then, $a_6 - a_4 = 17 - 11 \Leftrightarrow (a + 5d) - (a + 3d) = 6 \Leftrightarrow 6 = 2d \Leftrightarrow d = 3$. Substituting into $11 = a + 3d$ gives $11 = a + 3 \cdot 3$, and so $a = 2$. Thus $a_2 = a + (2 - 1) d = 2 + 3 = 5$.

26. $a_{20} = 96$ and $d = 5$. Then $96 = a_{20} = a + 19 \cdot 5 = a + 95 \Leftrightarrow a = 96 - 95 = 1$. Therefore, $a_n = 1 + 5 (n - 1)$.

27. $a_3 = 9$ and $r = \dfrac{3}{2}$. Then $a_5 = a_3 \cdot r^2 = 9 \cdot \left(\dfrac{3}{2}\right)^2 = \dfrac{81}{4}$.

28. $a_2 = 10$ and $a_5 = \dfrac{1250}{27}$. Then $r^3 = \dfrac{a_5}{a_2} = \dfrac{\frac{1250}{27}}{10} = \dfrac{125}{27} \Leftrightarrow r = \dfrac{5}{3}$ and $a = a_1 = \dfrac{a_2}{r} = \dfrac{10}{\frac{5}{3}} = 6$. Therefore,

$a_n = ar^{n-1} = 6 \left(\dfrac{5}{3}\right)^{n-1}$.

29. (a) $A_n = 32{,}000 \cdot 1.05^{n-1}$

(b) $A_1 = \$32{,}000$, $A_2 = 32{,}000 \cdot 1.05^1 = \$33{,}600$, $A_3 = 32{,}000 \cdot 1.05^2 = \$35{,}280$, $A_4 = 32{,}000 \cdot 1.05^3 = \$37{,}044$, $A_5 = 32{,}000 \cdot 1.05^4 = \$38{,}896.20$, $A_6 = 32{,}000 \cdot 1.05^5 = \$40{,}841.01$, $A_7 = 32{,}000 \cdot 1.05^6 = \$42{,}883.06$, $A_8 = 32{,}000 \cdot 1.05^7 = \$45{,}027.21$

30. (a) $A_n = 35{,}000 + 1{,}200 (n - 1)$

(b) $A_8 = 35{,}000 + 1{,}200 (7) = \$43{,}400$. The salary for this teacher is higher for the first 6 years is higher, but from the 7th year on, the salary of the teacher in Exercise 29 is higher.

31. Let a_n be the number of bacteria in the dish at the end of $5n$ seconds. So $a_0 = 3$, $a_1 = 3 \cdot 2$, $a_2 = 3 \cdot 2^2$, $a_3 = 3 \cdot 2^3, \ldots$. Then, clearly, a_n is a geometric sequence with $r = 2$ and $a = 3$. Thus at the end of $60 = 5 (12)$ seconds, the number of bacteria is $a_{12} = 3 \cdot 2^{12} = 12{,}288$.

32. Let d be the common difference in the arithmetic sequence $a_1, a_2, a_3, \ldots$, so that $a_n = a_1 + (n - 1) d$, $n = 1, 2, 3, \ldots$, and let e be the common difference for $b_1, b_2, b_3, \ldots$, so that $b_n = b_1 + (n - 1) e$. Then $a_n + b_n = [a_1 + (n - 1) a] + [b_1 + (n - 1) e] = (a_1 + b_1) + (n - 1) (d + e)$, $n = 1, 2, 3, \ldots$. Thus $a_1 + b_1, a_2 + b_2, \ldots$ is an arithmetic sequence with first term $a_1 + b_1$ and common difference $d + e$.

33. Suppose that the common ratio in the sequence $a_1, a_2, a_3, \ldots$ is r. Also, suppose that the common ratio in the sequence $b_1, b_2, b_3, \ldots$ is s. Then $a_n = a_1 r^{n-1}$ and $b_n = b_1 s^{n-1}$, $n = 1, 2, 3, \ldots$. Thus $a_n b_n = a_1 r^{n-1} \cdot b_1 s^{n-1} = (a_1 b_1) (rs)^{n-1}$. So the sequence $a_1 b_1, a_2 b_2, a_3 b_3, \ldots$ is geometric with first term $a_1 b_1$ and common ratio rs.

34. (a) Yes. If the common difference is d, then $a_n = a_1 + (n - 1) d$. So $a_n + 2 = a_1 + 2 + (n - 1) d$, and thus the sequence $a_1 + 2, a_2 + 2, a_3 + 2, \ldots$ is an arithmetic sequence with the common difference d, but with the first term $a_1 + 2$.

(b) Yes. If the common ratio is r, then $a_n = a_1 \cdot r^{n-1}$. So $5a_n = (5a_1) \cdot r^{n-1}$, and the sequence $5a_1, 5a_2, 5a_3, \ldots$ is also geometric, with common ratio r, but with the first term $5a_1$.

35. (a) $6, x, 12, \ldots$ is arithmetic if $x - 6 = 12 - x \Leftrightarrow 2x = 18 \Leftrightarrow x = 9$.

(b) $6, x, 12, \ldots$ is geometric if $\dfrac{x}{6} = \dfrac{12}{x} \Leftrightarrow x^2 = 72 \Leftrightarrow x = \pm 6\sqrt{2}$.

36. (a) $2, x, y, 17, \ldots$ is arithmetic. Therefore, $15 = 17 - 2 = a_4 - a_1 = a + 3d - a = 3d$. So $d = 5$, and hence, $x = a + d = 2 + 5 = 7$ and $y = a + 2d = 2 + 2 \cdot 5 = 12$.

(b) $2, x, y, 17, \ldots$ is geometric. Therefore, $\frac{17}{2} = \frac{a_4}{a_1} = \frac{ar^3}{a} = r^3 \iff r = \left(\frac{17}{2}\right)^{1/3}$. So

$x = a_2 = ar = 2\left(\frac{17}{2}\right)^{1/3} = 2^{2/3}17^{1/3}$ and $y = a_3 = ar^2 = 2\left[\left(\frac{17}{2}\right)^{1/3}\right]^2 = 2\left(\frac{17}{2}\right)^{2/3} = 2^{1/3}17^{2/3}$.

37. $\sum_{k=3}^{6} (k+1)^2 = (3+1)^2 + (4+1)^2 + (5+1)^2 + (6+1)^2 = 16 + 25 + 36 + 49 = 126$

38. $\sum_{i=1}^{4} \frac{2i}{2i-1} = \frac{2 \cdot 1}{2 \cdot 1 - 1} + \frac{2 \cdot 2}{2 \cdot 2 - 1} + \frac{2 \cdot 3}{2 \cdot 3 - 1} + \frac{2 \cdot 4}{2 \cdot 4 - 1} = 2 + \frac{4}{3} + \frac{6}{5} + \frac{8}{7} = \frac{210 + 140 + 126 + 120}{105} = \frac{596}{105}$

39. $\sum_{k=1}^{6} (k+1)\,2^{k-1} = 2 \cdot 2^0 + 3 \cdot 2^1 + 4 \cdot 2^2 + 5 \cdot 2^3 + 6 \cdot 2^4 + 7 \cdot 2^5 = 2 + 6 + 16 + 40 + 96 + 224 = 384$

40. $\sum_{m=1}^{5} 3^{m-2} = 3^{-1} + 3^0 + 3^1 + 3^2 + 3^3 = \frac{1}{3} + 1 + 3 + 9 + 27 = \frac{121}{3}$

41. $\sum_{k=1}^{10} (k-1)^2 = 0^2 + 1^2 + 2^2 + 3^2 + 4^2 + 5^2 + 6^2 + 7^2 + 8^2 + 9^2$

42. $\sum_{j=2}^{100} \frac{1}{j-1} = \frac{1}{1} + \frac{1}{2} + \frac{1}{3} + \frac{1}{4} + \frac{1}{5} + \cdots + \frac{1}{98} + \frac{1}{99}$

43. $\sum_{k=1}^{50} \frac{3^k}{2^{k+1}} = \frac{3}{2^2} + \frac{3^2}{2^3} + \frac{3^3}{2^4} + \frac{3^4}{2^5} + \cdots + \frac{3^{49}}{2^{50}} + \frac{3^{50}}{2^{51}}$

44. $\sum_{n=1}^{10} n^2 2^n = 1^2 \cdot 2^1 + 2^2 \cdot 2^2 + 3^2 \cdot 2^3 + \cdots + 9^2 \cdot 2^9 + 10^2 \cdot 2^{10}$

45. $3 + 6 + 9 + 12 + \cdots + 99 = 3\,(1) + 3\,(2) + 3\,(3) + \cdots + 3\,(33) = \sum_{k=1}^{33} 3k$

46. $1^2 + 2^2 + 3^3 + \cdots + 100^2 = \sum_{k=1}^{100} k^2$

47. $1 \cdot 2^3 + 2 \cdot 2^4 + 3 \cdot 2^5 + 4 \cdot 2^6 + \cdots + 100 \cdot 2^{102}$

$$= (1)\,2^{(1)+2} + (2)\,2^{(2)+2} + (3)\,2^{(3)+2} + (4)\,2^{(4)+2} + \cdots + (100)\,2^{(100)+2}$$
$$= \sum_{k=1}^{100} k \cdot 2^{k+2}$$

48. $\dfrac{1}{1 \cdot 2} + \dfrac{1}{2 \cdot 3} + \dfrac{1}{3 \cdot 4} + \cdots + \dfrac{1}{999 \cdot 1000} = \sum_{k=1}^{999} \dfrac{1}{k\,(k+1)}$

49. $1 + 0.9 + (0.9)^2 + \cdots + (0.9)^5$ is a geometric series with $a = 1$ and $r = \dfrac{0.9}{1} = 0.9$. Thus, the sum of the series is

$S_6 = \dfrac{1 - (0.9)^6}{1 - 0.9} = \dfrac{1 - 0.531441}{0.1} = 4.68559.$

50. $3 + 3.7 + 4.4 + \cdots + 10$ is an arithmetic series with $a = 3$ and $d = 0.7$. Then $10 = a_n = 3 + 0.7\,(n-1) \iff 0.7\,(n-1) = 7 \iff n = 11$. So the sum of the series is $S_{11} = \frac{11}{2}\,(3 + 10) = \frac{143}{2} = 71.5$.

51. $\sqrt{5} + 2\sqrt{5} + 3\sqrt{5} + \cdots + 100\sqrt{5}$ is an arithmetic series with $a = \sqrt{5}$ and $d = \sqrt{5}$. Then $100\sqrt{5} = a_n = \sqrt{5} + \sqrt{5}\,(n-1)$ $\iff n = 100$. So the sum is $S_{100} = \frac{100}{2}\,(\sqrt{5} + 100\sqrt{5}) = 50\,(101\sqrt{5}) = 5050\sqrt{5}$.

52. $\frac{1}{3} + \frac{2}{3} + 1 + \frac{4}{3} + \cdots + 33$ is an arithmetic series with $a = \frac{1}{3}$ and $d = \frac{1}{3}$. Then $a_n = 33 = \frac{1}{3} + \frac{1}{3}\,(n-1) \iff n = 99$. So the sum is $S_{99} = \frac{99}{2}\left(\frac{2}{3} + \dfrac{99 - 1}{3}\right) = \frac{99}{2} \cdot \frac{100}{3} = 1650$.

53. $\sum_{n=0}^{6} 3 \cdot (-4)^n$ is a geometric series with $a = 3$, $r = -4$, and $n = 7$. Therefore, the sum of the series is

$S_7 = 3 \cdot \dfrac{1 - (-4)^7}{1 - (-4)} = \frac{3}{5}\,(1 + 4^7) = 9831.$

54. $\sum_{k=0}^{8} 7 \cdot 5^{k/2}$ is a geometric series with $a = 7$, $r = 5^{1/2}$, and $n = 9$. Thus, the sum of the series is

$S_9 = 7 \cdot \dfrac{1 - 5^{9/2}}{1 - 5} = \frac{7}{4}\left(5^{9/2} - 1\right) = \frac{7}{4}\left(625\sqrt{5} - 1\right).$

55. We have an arithmetic sequence with $a = 7$ and $d = 3$. Then $S_n = 325 = \dfrac{n}{2}\,[2a + (n-1)\,d] = \dfrac{n}{2}\,[14 + 3\,(n-1)] = \dfrac{n}{2}\,(11 + 3n) \iff 650 = 3n^2 + 11n \iff (3n + 50)\,(n - 13) = 0 \iff n = 13$ (because $n = -\frac{50}{3}$ is inadmissible). Thus, 13 terms must be added.

56. We have a geometric series with $S_3 = 52$ and $r = 3$. Then $52 = S_3 = a + 3a + 9a = 13a \Leftrightarrow a = 4$, and so the first term is 4.

57. This is a geometric sequence with $a = 2$ and $r = 2$. Then $S_{15} = 2 \cdot \dfrac{1 - 2^{15}}{1 - 2} = 2\left(2^{15} - 1\right) = 65{,}534$, and so the total number of ancestors is 65,534.

58. $R = 1000$, $i = 0.08$, and $n = 16$. Thus, $A = 1000\dfrac{1.08^{16} - 1}{1.08 - 1} = 12{,}500\left[1.08^{16} - 1\right] = \$30{,}324.28$.

59. $A = 10{,}000$, $i = 0.03$, and $n = 4$. Thus, $10{,}000 = R\dfrac{(1.03)^4 - 1}{0.03} \Leftrightarrow R = \dfrac{10{,}000 \cdot 0.03}{(1.03)^4 - 1} = \$2390.27$.

60. $A = 60{,}000$ and $i = \dfrac{0.09}{12} = 0.0075$.

   (a) If the period is 30 years, $n = 360$ and $R = \dfrac{60{,}000 \cdot 0.0075}{1 - 1.0075^{-360}} = \$482.77$.

   (b) If the period is 15 years, $n = 180$ and $R = \dfrac{60{,}000 \cdot 0.0075}{1 - 1.0075^{-180}} = \$608.56$.

61. $1 - \frac{2}{5} + \frac{4}{25} - \frac{8}{125} + \cdots$ is a geometric series with $a = 1$ and $r = -\frac{2}{5}$. Therefore, the sum is $S = \dfrac{a}{1 - r} = \dfrac{1}{1 - \left(-\frac{2}{5}\right)} = \dfrac{5}{7}$.

62. $0.1 + 0.01 + 0.001 + 0.0001 + \cdots$ is an infinite geometric series with $a = 0.1$ and $r = 0.1$. Therefore, the sum is $S = \dfrac{0.1}{1 - 0.1} = \dfrac{1}{9}$.

63. $1 + \dfrac{1}{3^{1/2}} + \dfrac{1}{3} + \dfrac{1}{3^{3/2}} + \cdots$ is an infinite geometric series with $a = 1$ and $r = \dfrac{1}{\sqrt{3}}$. Thus, the sum is

$S = \dfrac{1}{1 - \frac{1}{\sqrt{3}}} = \dfrac{\sqrt{3}}{\sqrt{3} - 1} = \frac{1}{2}\left(3 + \sqrt{3}\right)$.

64. $a + ab^2 + ab^4 + ab^6 + \cdots$ is an infinite geometric series with first term a and common ratio b^2. Thus, the sum is $S = \dfrac{a}{1 - b^2}$.

65. Let $P(n)$ denote the statement that $1 + 4 + 7 + \cdots + (3n - 2) = \dfrac{n(3n - 1)}{2}$.

   Step 1: $P(1)$ is the statement that $1 = \dfrac{1\left[3(1) - 1\right]}{2} = \dfrac{1 \cdot 2}{2}$, which is true.

   Step 2: Assume that $P(k)$ is true; that is, $1 + 4 + 7 + \cdots + (3k - 2) = \dfrac{k(3k - 1)}{2}$. We want to use this to show that $P(k + 1)$ is true. Now

$$
\begin{aligned}
1 + 4 + 7 + 10 + \cdots + (3k - 2) + [3(k + 1) - 2] &= \frac{k(3k - 1)}{2} + 3k + 1 \qquad \text{induction hypothesis} \\
&= \frac{k(3k - 1)}{2} + \frac{6k + 2}{2} = \frac{3k^2 - k + 6k + 2}{2} \\
&= \frac{3k^2 + 5k + 2}{2} = \frac{(k + 1)(3k + 2)}{2} \\
&= \frac{(k + 1)[3(k + 1) - 1]}{2}
\end{aligned}
$$

Thus, $P(k + 1)$ follows from $P(k)$. So by the Principle of Mathematical Induction, $P(n)$ is true for all n.

66. Let $P(n)$ denote the statement that $\dfrac{1}{1\cdot 3} + \dfrac{1}{3\cdot 5} + \dfrac{1}{5\cdot 7} + \cdots + \dfrac{1}{(2n-1)(2n+1)} = \dfrac{n}{2n+1}$.

Step 1: $P(1)$ is the statement that $\dfrac{1}{1\cdot 3} = \dfrac{1}{2\cdot 1 + 1}$, which is true.

Step 2: Assume that $P(k)$ is true; that is, $\dfrac{1}{1\cdot 3} + \dfrac{1}{3\cdot 5} + \dfrac{1}{5\cdot 7} + \cdots + \dfrac{1}{(2k-1)(2k+1)} = \dfrac{k}{2k+1}$. We want to use this

to show that $P(k+1)$ is true. Now

$$\dfrac{1}{1\cdot 3} + \dfrac{1}{3\cdot 5} + \dfrac{1}{5\cdot 7} + \cdots + \dfrac{1}{(2k-1)(2k+1)} + \dfrac{1}{(2k+1)(2k+3)}$$

$$= \dfrac{k}{2k+1} + \dfrac{1}{(2k+1)(2k+3)} \qquad\qquad\qquad \text{induction hypothesis}$$

$$= \dfrac{k(2k+3)+1}{(2k+1)(2k+3)} = \dfrac{2k^2+3k+1}{(2k+1)(2k+3)}$$

$$= \dfrac{(k+1)(2k+1)}{(2k+1)(2k+3)} = \dfrac{k+1}{2k+3} = \dfrac{k+1}{2(k+1)+1}$$

Thus $P(k+1)$ follows from $P(k)$. So by the Principle of Mathematical Induction, $P(n)$ is true for all n.

67. Let $P(n)$ denote the statement that $\left(1+\dfrac{1}{1}\right)\left(1+\dfrac{1}{2}\right)\left(1+\dfrac{1}{3}\right)\cdots\cdots\left(1+\dfrac{1}{n}\right) = n+1$.

Step 1: $P(1)$ is the statement that $1 + \frac{1}{1} = 1 + 1$, which is clearly true.

Step 2: Assume that $P(k)$ is true; that is, $\left(1+\dfrac{1}{1}\right)\left(1+\dfrac{1}{2}\right)\left(1+\dfrac{1}{3}\right)\cdots\cdots\left(1+\dfrac{1}{k}\right) = k+1$. We want to use this to

show that $P(k+1)$ is true. Now

$$\left(1+\dfrac{1}{1}\right)\left(1+\dfrac{1}{2}\right)\left(1+\dfrac{1}{3}\right)\cdots\cdots\left(1+\dfrac{1}{k}\right)\left(1+\dfrac{1}{k+1}\right)$$

$$= \left[\left(1+\dfrac{1}{1}\right)\left(1+\dfrac{1}{2}\right)\left(1+\dfrac{1}{3}\right)\cdots\cdots\left(1+\dfrac{1}{k}\right)\right]\left(1+\dfrac{1}{k+1}\right)$$

$$= (k+1)\left(1+\dfrac{1}{k+1}\right) \qquad\qquad\qquad \text{induction hypothesis}$$

$$= (k+1)+1$$

Thus, $P(k+1)$ follows from $P(k)$. So by the Principle of Mathematical Induction, $P(n)$ is true for all n.

68. Let $P(n)$ denote the statement that $7^n - 1$ is divisible by 6.

Step 1: $P(1)$ is the statement that $7^1 - 1 = 6$ is divisible by 6, which is clearly true.

Step 2: Assume that $P(k)$ is true; that is, $7^k - 1$ is divisible by 6. We want to use this to show that $P(k+1)$ is true. Now $7^{k+1} - 1 = 7\cdot 7^k - 1 = 7\cdot 7^k - 7 + 6 = 7\left(7^k - 1\right) + 6$, which is divisible by 6. This is because $7^k - 1$ is divisible by 6 by the induction hypothesis, and clearly 6 is divisible by 6. Thus $P(k+1)$ follows from $P(k)$. So by the Principle of Mathematical Induction, $P(n)$ is true for all n.

69. $a_{n+1} = 3a_n + 4$ and $a_1 = 4$. Let $P(n)$ denote the statement that $a_n = 2\cdot 3^n - 2$.

Step 1: $P(1)$ is the statement that $a_1 = 2\cdot 3^1 - 2 = 4$, which is clearly true.

Step 2: Assume that $P(k)$ is true; that is, $a_k = 2\cdot 3^k - 2$. We want to use this to show that $P(k+1)$ is true. Now

$$\begin{aligned}
a_{k+1} &= 3a_k + 4 \qquad\qquad\qquad &\text{definition of } a_{k+1}\\
&= 3\left(2\cdot 3^k - 2\right) + 4 \qquad\qquad\qquad &\text{induction hypothesis}\\
&= 2\cdot 3^{k+1} - 6 + 4 = 2\cdot 3^{k+1} - 2
\end{aligned}$$

Thus $P(k+1)$ follows from $P(k)$. So by the Principle of Mathematical Induction, $P(n)$ is true for all n.

70. Let $P(n)$ denote the statement that F_{4n} is divisible by 3.

Step 1: Show that $P(1)$ is true, but $P(1)$ is true since $F_4 = 3$ is divisible by 3.

Step 2: Assume that $P(k)$ is true; that is, F_{4k} is divisible by 3. We want to use this to show that $P(k+1)$ is true. Now, $F_{4(k+1)} = F_{4k+4} = F_{4k+2} + F_{4k+3} = (F_{4k} + F_{4k+1}) + (F_{4k+1} + F_{4k+2}) = F_{4k} + F_{4k+1} + F_{4k+1} + (F_{4k} + F_{4k+1}) = 2 \cdot F_{4k} + 3 \cdot F_{4k+1}$, which is divisible by 3 because F_{4k} is divisible by 3 by our induction hypothesis, and $3 \cdot F_{4k+1}$ is clearly divisible by 3. Thus, $P(k+1)$ follows from $P(k)$. So by the Principle of Mathematical Induction, $P(n)$ is true for all n.

71. Let $P(n)$ denote the statement that $n! > 2^n$, for all natural numbers $n \geq 4$.

Step 1: $P(4)$ is the statement that $4! = 24 > 2^4 = 16$, which is true.

Step 2: Assume that $P(k)$ is true; that is, $k! > 2^k$. We want to use this to show that $P(k+1)$ is true. Now

$$
\begin{aligned}
(k+1)! &= (k+1)\,k! > (k+1) \cdot 2^k & \text{induction hypothesis} \\
&> 2 \cdot 2^k & \text{because } k+1 > 2 \text{ for } k \geq 4 \\
&= 2^{k+1}
\end{aligned}
$$

Thus $P(k+1)$ follows from $P(k)$. So by the Principle of Mathematical Induction, $P(n)$ is true for all $n \geq 4$.

72. $\dbinom{5}{2}\dbinom{5}{3} = \dfrac{5!}{2!\,3!} \cdot \dfrac{5!}{3!\,2!} = \dfrac{5 \cdot 4}{2} \cdot \dfrac{5 \cdot 4}{2} = 10 \cdot 10 = 100$

73. $\dbinom{10}{2} + \dbinom{10}{6} = \dfrac{10!}{2!\,8!} + \dfrac{10!}{6!\,4!} = \dfrac{10 \cdot 9}{2} + \dfrac{10 \cdot 9 \cdot 8 \cdot 7}{4 \cdot 3 \cdot 2} = 45 + 210 = 255.$

74. $\sum_{k=0}^{5} \binom{5}{k} = \binom{5}{0} + \binom{5}{1} + \binom{5}{2} + \binom{5}{3} + \binom{5}{4} + \binom{5}{5} = 2\left(\frac{5!}{0!\,5!} + \frac{5!}{1!\,4!} + \frac{5!}{2!\,3!}\right) = 2(1 + 5 + 10) = 32$

75. $\sum_{k=0}^{8} \binom{8}{k}\binom{8}{8-k} = 2\binom{8}{0}\binom{8}{8} + 2\binom{8}{1}\binom{8}{7} + 2\binom{8}{2}\binom{8}{6} + 2\binom{8}{3}\binom{8}{5} + \binom{8}{4}\binom{8}{4} = 2 + 2 \cdot 8^2 + 2 \cdot (28)^2 + 2 \cdot (56)^2 + (70)^2 = 12{,}870.$

76. $\left(1 - x^2\right)^6 = \binom{6}{0}1^6 - \binom{6}{1}1^5 x^2 + \binom{6}{2}1^4 x^4 - \binom{6}{3}1^3 x^6 + \binom{6}{4}1^2 x^8 - \binom{6}{5}x^{10} + \binom{6}{6}x^{12}$
$= 1 - 6x^2 + 15x^4 - 20x^6 + 15x^8 - 6x^{10} + x^{12}$

77. $(2x + y)^4 = \binom{4}{0}(2x)^4 + \binom{4}{1}(2x)^3 y + \binom{4}{2}(2x)^2 y^2 + \binom{4}{3} \cdot 2xy^3 + \binom{4}{4}y^4 = 16x^4 + 32x^3 y + 24x^2 y^2 + 8xy^3 + y^4$

78. The 20th term is $\binom{22}{19}a^3 b^{19} = 1540 a^3 b^{19}.$

79. The first three terms in the expansion of $\left(b^{-2/3} + b^{1/3}\right)^{20}$ are $\binom{20}{0}\left(b^{-2/3}\right)^{20} = b^{-40/3}$, $\binom{20}{1}\left(b^{-2/3}\right)^{19}$

$\left(b^{1/3}\right) = 20b^{-37/3}$, and $\binom{20}{2}\left(b^{-2/3}\right)^{18}\left(b^{1/3}\right)^2 = 190 b^{-34/3}.$

80. The rth term in the expansion of $(A + 3B)^{10}$ is $\binom{10}{r}A^r (3B)^{10-r}$. The term that contains A^6 occurs when $r = 6$. Thus, the term is $\binom{10}{6}A^6 (3B)^4 = 210 A^6 81 B^4 = 17{,}010 A^6 B^4.$

Chapter 11 Test

1. $a_1 = 1^2 - 1 = 0$, $a_2 = 2^2 - 1 = 3$, $a_3 = 3^2 - 1 = 8$, $a_4 = 4^2 - 1 = 15$, and $a_{10} = 10^2 - 1 = 99.$

2. $a_{n+2} = (a_n)^2 - a_{n+1}$, $a_1 = 1$ and $a_2 = 1$. Then $a_3 = a_1^2 - a_2 = 1^2 - 1 = 0$, $a_4 = a_2^2 - a_3 = 1^2 - 0 = 1$, and $a_5 = a_3^2 - a_4 = 0^2 - 1 = -1.$

3. $d = 76 - 80 = -4$. So $a_4 = a_3 + (-4) = 72 + (-4) = 68$ and $a_n = a_1 + (n-1)\,d = 80 + (n-1)(-4) = 84 - 4n.$

4. Since $a_n = a_1 r^{n-1}$, we substitute $a_1 = 25$, $a_4 = \frac{1}{5}$, and $n = 4$ and solve for r. This gives $\frac{1}{5} = 25r^3 \Leftrightarrow r^3 = \frac{1}{125} = \frac{1}{5^3} \Leftrightarrow r = \frac{1}{5}$. So the common ratio is $\frac{1}{5}$ and $a_5 = a_1 r^4 = 25\left(\frac{1}{5}\right)^4 = \frac{1}{25}.$

5. (a) If $a_1, a_2, a_3, \ldots$ is an arithmetic sequence, then the sequence $a_1^2, a_2^2, a_3^2, \ldots$ is also arithmetic. This statement is false. For a counterexample, consider $a_1 = 1$, $a_2 = 2$, $a_3 = 3 \ldots$. Then $a_1, a_2, a_3, \ldots$ is an arithmetic sequence with $a = 1$ and $d = 1$. However, the sequence $a_1^2, a_2^2, a_3^2, \ldots$ becomes 1, 4, 9, $\ldots$, which is not arithmetic because there is no common difference.

(b) If $a_1, a_2, a_3, \ldots$ is a geometric sequence, then the sequence $a_1^2, a_2^2, a_3^2, \ldots$ is also geometric. This statement is true. Let the common ratio for the geometric series $a_1, a_2, a_3, \ldots$ be r, so that $a_n = a_1 r^{n-1}$, $n = 1, 2, 3, \ldots$. Then $a_n^2 = \left(a_1 r^{n-1}\right)^2 = \left(a_1^2\right)\left(r^2\right)^{n-1}$. Therefore, the sequence $a_1^2, a_2^2, a_3^2, \ldots$ is geometric with common ratio r^2.

6. (a) The nth partial sum an arithmetic sequence is $S_n = \dfrac{n}{2}\left(a + a_n\right)$ or $S_n = \dfrac{n}{2}\left[2a + (n-1)d\right]$.

(b) $a_1 = 10$ and $a_{10} = 2$. Then $S_{10} = \frac{10}{2}\left(10 + 2\right) = 60$.

(c) Since $S_{10} = \frac{10}{2}\left(2 \cdot 10 + 9d\right) = 60$, then $5\left(20 + 9d\right) = 60 \quad \Leftrightarrow \quad d = -\frac{8}{9}$, and so the common difference is $-\frac{8}{9}$. Then $a_{100} = a + 99d = 10 - \frac{8}{9} \cdot 99 = -78$.

7. (a) The nth partial sum a geometric sequence is $S_n = a\dfrac{1 - r^n}{1 - r}$, where $r \neq 1$.

(b) The geometric series $\frac{1}{3} + \frac{2}{3^2} + \frac{2^2}{3^3} + \frac{2^3}{3^4} + \cdots + \frac{2^9}{3^{10}}$ has $a = \frac{1}{3}$, $r = \frac{2}{3}$, and $n = 10$. So
$$S_{10} = \frac{1}{3} \cdot \frac{1 - (2/3)^{10}}{1 - (2/3)} = \frac{1}{3} \cdot 3\left(1 - \frac{1024}{59{,}049}\right) = \frac{58{,}025}{59{,}049}.$$

8. The infinite geometric series $1 + \frac{1}{2^{1/2}} + \frac{1}{2} + \frac{1}{2^{3/2}} + \cdots$ has $a = 1$ and $r = 2^{-1/2} = \frac{1}{\sqrt{2}}$. Thus,
$$S = \frac{1}{1 - 1/\sqrt{2}} = \frac{\sqrt{2}}{\sqrt{2} - 1} = \frac{\sqrt{2}}{\sqrt{2} - 1} \cdot \frac{\sqrt{2} + 1}{\sqrt{2} + 1} = 2 + \sqrt{2}.$$

9. Let $P(n)$ denote the statement that $1^2 + 2^2 + 3^2 + \cdots + n^2 = \dfrac{n(n+1)(2n+1)}{6}$.

Step 1: Show that $P(1)$ is true. But $P(1)$ says that $1^2 = \dfrac{1 \cdot 2 \cdot 3}{6}$, which is true.

Step 2: Assume that $P(k)$ is true; that is, $1^2 + 2^2 + 3^2 + \cdots + k^2 = \dfrac{k(k+1)(2k+1)}{6}$. We want to use this to show that $P(k+1)$ is true. Now

$$
\begin{aligned}
1^2 + 2^2 + 3^2 + \cdots + k^2 + (k+1)^2 &= \frac{k(k+1)(2k+1)}{6} + (k+1)^2 \qquad \text{induction hypothesis}\\
&= \frac{k(k+1)(2k+1) + 6(k+1)^2}{6} = \frac{(k+1)(2k^2 + k) + (6k+6)(k+1)}{6}\\
&= \frac{(k+1)(2k^2 + k + 6k + 6)}{6} = \frac{(k+1)(2k^2 + 7k + 6)}{6}\\
&= \frac{(k+1)(k+2)(2k+3)}{6} = \frac{(k+1)\left[(k+1) + 1\right]\left[2(k+1) + 1\right]}{6}
\end{aligned}
$$

Thus $P(k+1)$ follows from $P(k)$. So by the Principle of Mathematical Induction, $P(n)$ is true for all n.

10. (a) $\sum_{n=1}^{5}\left(1 - n^2\right) = \left(1 - 1^2\right) + \left(1 - 2^2\right) + \left(1 - 3^2\right) + \left(1 - 4^2\right) + \left(1 - 5^2\right) = 0 - 3 - 8 - 15 - 24 = -50$

(b) $\sum_{n=3}^{6}(-1)^n\, 2^{n-2} = (-1)^3\, 2^{3-2} + (-1)^4\, 2^{4-2} + (-1)^5\, 2^{5-2} + (-1)^6\, 2^{6-2} = -2 + 4 - 8 + 16 = 10$

11. $\left(2x + y^2\right)^5 = \binom{5}{0}(2x)^5 + \binom{5}{1}(2x)^4\, y^2 + \binom{5}{2}(2x)^3\left(y^2\right)^2 + \binom{5}{3}(2x)^2\left(y^2\right)^3 + \binom{5}{4}(2x)\left(y^2\right)^4 + \binom{5}{5}\left(y^2\right)^5$
$= 32x^5 + 80x^4 y^2 + 80x^3 y^4 + 40x^2 y^6 + 10xy^8 + y^{10}$

12. $\binom{10}{3}(3x)^3(-2)^7 = 120 \cdot 27x^3 (-128) = -414{,}720x^3$

13. (a) Each week he gains 24% in weight, that is, $0.24a_n$. Thus, $a_{n+1} = a_n + 0.24a_n = 1.24a_n$ for $n \geq 1$. a_0 is given to be 0.85 lb.

(b) $a_6 = 1.24a_5 = 1.24\left(1.24a_4\right) = \cdots = 1.24^6 a_0 = 1.24^6\,(0.85) \approx 3.1$ lb

(c) The sequence $a_1, a_2, a_3, \ldots$ is geometric with common ratio 1.24.

Focus on Modeling: Modeling with Recursive Sequences

1. (a) Since there are 365 days in a year, the interest earned per day is $\dfrac{0.0365}{365} = 0.0001$. Thus the amount in the account at the end of the nth day is $A_n = 1.0001A_{n-1}$ with $A_0 = \$275{,}000$.

(b) $A_0 = \$275{,}000$, $A_1 = 1.0001A_0 = 1.0001 \cdot 275{,}000 = \$275{,}027.50$,
$A_2 = 1.0001A_1 = 1.0001\left(1.0001A_0\right) = 1.0001^2 A_0 = \$275{,}055.00$,
$A_3 = 1.0001A_2 = 1.0001\left(1.0001^2 A_0\right) = 1.0001^3 A_0 = \$275{,}082.51$,
$A_4 = 1.0001A_3 = 1.0001\left(1.0001^3 A_0\right) = 1.0001^4 A_0 = \$275{,}110.02$,
$A_5 = 1.0001A_4 = 1.0001\left(1.0001^4 A_0\right) = 1.0001^5 A_0 = \$275{,}137.53$,
$A_6 = 1.0001A_5 = 1.0001\left(1.0001^5 A_0\right) = 1.0001^6 A_0 = \$275{,}165.04$,
$A_7 = 1.0001A_6 = 1.0001\left(1.0001^6 A_0\right) = 1.0001^7 A_0 = \$275{,}192.56$

(c) $A_n = 1.0001^n \cdot 275{,}000$

2. (a) $T_n = T_{n-1} + 1.5$ with $T_1 = 5$.

(b) $T_1 = 5$, $T_2 = T_1 + 1.5 = 5 + 1.5 = 6.5$, $T_3 = T_2 + 1.5 = (5 + 1.5) + 1.5 = 5 + 2 \cdot 1.5 = 8.0$,
$T_4 = T_3 + 1.5 = (5 + 2 \cdot 1.5) + 1.5 = 5 + 3 \cdot 1.5 = 9.5$, $T_5 = T_4 + 1.5 = (5 + 3 \cdot 1.5) + 1.5 = 5 + 4 \cdot 1.5 = 11.0$,
$T_6 = T_5 + 1.5 = (5 + 4 \cdot 1.5) + 1.5 = 5 + 5 \cdot 1.5 = 12.5$

(c) This is an arithmetic sequence with $T_n = 5 + 1.5\,(n - 1)$.

(d) $T_n = 65 = 5 + 1.5n - 1.5 \iff 61.5 = 1.5n \iff n = 41.$ So Sheila swims 65 minutes on the 41st day.

(e) Using the partial sum of an arithmetic sequence, she swims for $\frac{30}{2}\left[2\,(5) + (30 - 1)\,1.5\right] = 15 \cdot 53.5 = 802.5$ minutes $= 13$ hours 22.5 minutes.

3. (a) Since there are 12 months in a year, the interest earned per day is $\dfrac{0.03}{12} = 0.0025$. Thus the amount in the account at the end of the nth month is $A_n = 1.0025A_{n-1} + 100$ with $A_0 = \$100$.

(b) $A_0 = \$100$, $A_1 = 1.0025A_0 + 100 = 1.0025 \cdot 100 + 100 = \$200.25$, $A_2 = 1.0025A_1 + 100 = 1.0025\left(1.0025 \cdot 100 + 100\right) + 100 = 1.0025^2 \cdot 100 + 1.0025 \cdot 100 + 100 = \$300.75$, $A_3 = 1.0025A_2 + 100 = 1.0025\left(1.0025^2 \cdot 100 + 1.0025 \cdot 100 + 100\right) + 100 = 1.0025^3 \cdot 100 + 1.0025^2 \cdot 100 + 1.0025 \cdot 100 + 100 = \$401.50$, $A_4 = 1.0025A_3 + 100 = 1.0025\left(1.0025^3 \cdot 100 + 1.0025^2 \cdot 100 + 1.0025 \cdot 100 + 100\right) + 100 = 1.0025^4 \cdot 100 + 1.0025^3 \cdot 100 + 1.0025^2 \cdot 100 + 1.0025 \cdot 100 + 100 = \$502.51$

(c) $A_n = 1.0025^n \cdot 100 + \cdots + 1.0025^2 \cdot 100 + 1.0025 \cdot 100 + 100$, the partial sum of a geometric series, so
$$A_n = 100 \cdot \frac{1 - 1.0025^{n+1}}{1 - 1.0025} = 100 \cdot \frac{1.0025^{n+1} - 1}{0.0025}.$$

(d) Since 5 years is 60 months, we have $A_{60} = 100 \cdot \dfrac{1.0025^{61} - 1}{0.0025} \approx \$6{,}580.83$.

4. In each case, $P_0 = 4000$.

(a) $P_n = 1.2P_{n-1}.$ $P_5 = 1.2^5\,(4000) \approx 9953$.

(b) $P_n = 1.2P_{n-1} - 600$. $P_1 = 1.2\,(4000) - 600 = 4200$, $P_2 = 1.2\,(4200) - 600 = 4440$, $P_3 = 1.2\,(4440) - 600 = 4728$, $P_4 = 1.2\,(4728) - 600 = 5073$, $P_5 = 1.2\,(5073) - 600 = 5488$.

(c) $P_n = 1.2P_{n-1} + 250$. $P_1 = 1.2\,(4000) + 250 = 5050$, $P_2 = 1.2\,(5050) + 250 = 6310$, $P_3 = 1.2\,(6310) + 250 = 7822$, $P_4 = 1.2\,(7822) + 250 = 9636$, $P_5 = 1.2\,(9636) + 250 = 11{,}814$.

(d) Since 10% is have $P_n = 1.2P_{n-1} - 0.1P_{n-1} + 300 = 1.1P_{n-1} + 300$. $P_1 = 1.1\,(4000) + 300 = 4700$, $P_2 = 1.1\,(4700) + 300 = 5470$, $P_3 = 1.1\,(5470) + 300 = 6317$, $P_4 = 1.1\,(6317) + 300 = 7249$, $P_5 = 1.1\,(7249) + 300 = 8{,}274$.

5. (a) The amount A_n of pollutants in the lake in the nth year is 30% of the amount from the preceding year $(0.30A_{n-1})$ plus the amount discharged that year (2400 tons). Thus $A_n = 0.30A_{n-1} + 2400$.

(b) $A_0 = 2400$, $A_1 = 0.30\,(2400) + 2400 = 3120$,

$A_2 = 0.30\,[0.30\,(2400) + 2400] + 2400 = 0.30^2\,(2400) + 2400\,(2400) + 2400 = 3336$,

$A_3 = 0.30\,[0.30^2\,(2400) + 2400\,(2400) + 2400] + 2400$

$\quad = 0.03^3\,(2400) + 0.30^2\,(2400) + 2400\,(2400) + 2400 = 3400.8$,

$A_4 = 0.30\,[0.03^3\,(2400) + 0.30^2\,(2400) + 2400\,(2400) + 2400] + 2400$

$\quad = 0.03^4\,(2400) + 0.03^3\,(2400) + 0.30^2\,(2400) + 2400\,(2400) + 2400 = 3420.2$

(c) A_n is the partial sum of a geometric series, so

$A_n = 2400 \cdot \dfrac{1 - 0.30^{n+1}}{1 - 0.30} = 2400 \cdot \dfrac{1 - 0.30^{n+1}}{0.70}$

$\quad \approx 3428.6\,\left(1 - 0.30^{n+1}\right)$

(d) $A_6 = 2400 \cdot \dfrac{1 - 0.30^7}{0.70} = 3427.8$ tons. The sum of a geometric

series, is $A = 2400 \cdot \dfrac{1}{0.70} = 3428.6$ tons.

(e)

6. (a) $U_n = 1.05U_{n-1} + 0.10\,(1.05U_{n-1}) = 1.10\,(1.05)\,U_{n-1} = 1.155U_{n-1}$ with $U_0 = 5000$.

(b) $U_0 = \$5000$, $U_1 = 1.155U_0 = \$5775$, $U_2 = 1.155U_1 = 1.155\,(1.155 \cdot 5000) = 1.155^2 \cdot 5000 = \$6670.13$, $U_3 = 1.155U_2 = 1.155\,(1.155^2 \cdot 5000) = 1.155^3 \cdot 5000 = \$7703.99$, $U_4 = 1.155U_3 = 1.155\,(1.155^3 \cdot 5000) = 1.155^4 \cdot 5000 = \$8898.11$.

(c) Using the pattern we found in part (b), we have $U_n = 1.155^n \cdot 5000$.

(d) $U_{10} = 1.155^{10} \cdot 5000 = \$21,124.67$.

7. (a) In the nth year since Victoria's initial deposit the amount V_n in her CD is the amount from the preceding year (V_{n-1}), plus the 5% interest earned on that amount $(0.05V_{n-1})$, plus $500 times the number of years since her initial deposit $(500n)$. Thus $V_n = 1.05V_{n-1} + 500n$.

(b) Ursula's savings surpass Victoria's savings in the 35th year.

8. (a) $T_n = T_{n-1} - 0.03\,(T_{n-1} - 70) = 0.97T_{n-1} + 2.1$, with $T_0 = 170$.

(c)

(b) $T_0 = 170\,°F$; $T_{10} = 143.7\,°F$; $T_{20} = 124.4\,°F$; $T_{30} = 110.1\,°F$; $T_{40} = 99.6\,°F$; $T_{50} = 91.8\,°F$; $T_{60} = 86.1\,°F$.

The temperature of the soup approaches $70\,°F$.

9. (a) $R_1 = 104$, $R_2 = 108.0$, $R_3 = 112.0$, $R_4 = 115.9$, $R_5 = 119.8$, $R_6 = 123.7$, $R_7 = 127.4$

(b)

As n becomes large the raccoon population approaches 200.

12.1   Finding Limits Numerically and Graphically

1.

x	3.9	3.99	3.999	4.001	4.01	4.1
$f(x)$	0.25158	0.25016	0.25002	0.24998	0.24984	0.24845

$$\lim_{x \to 4} \frac{\sqrt{x} - 2}{x - 4} = 0.25$$

2.

x	1.9	1.99	1.999	2.001	2.01	2.1
$f(x)$	0.20408	0.20040	0.20004	0.19996	0.19960	0.19608

$$\lim_{x \to 2} \frac{x - 2}{x^2 + x - 6} = 0.2$$

3.

x	0.9	0.99	0.999	1.001	1.01	1.1
$f(x)$	0.36900	0.33669	0.33367	0.3330	0.33002	0.30211

$$\lim_{x \to 1} \frac{x - 1}{x^3 - 1} = 0.33333$$

4.

x	-0.1	-0.01	-0.001	0.001	0.01	0.1
$f(x)$	0.95163	0.99502	0.99950	1.00050	1.00502	1.05171

$$\lim_{x \to 0} \frac{e^x - 1}{x} = 1$$

5.

x	± 1	± 0.5	± 0.1	± 0.05	± 0.01
$f(x)$	0.84147	0.95885	0.99833	0.99958	0.99998

$$\lim_{x \to 0} \frac{\sin x}{x} = 1$$

6.

x	0.1	0.01	0.001	0.0001	0.00001
$f(x)$	-0.23026	-0.04605	-0.00690	-0.00092	-0.00012

$$\lim_{x \to 0^+} x \ln x = 0$$

7.

x	$f(x)$
-3.9	-1.11111
-3.99	-1.01010
-3.99	-1.00100
-4.001	-0.99900
-4.01	-0.99010
-4.1	-0.90909

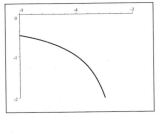

$$\lim_{x \to -4} \frac{x + 4}{x^2 + 7x + 12} = -1$$

8.

x	$f(x)$
0.9	1.42632
0.99	1.49251
0.999	1.49925
1.001	1.50075
1.01	1.50751
1.1	1.57619

$$\lim_{x \to 1} \frac{x^3 - 1}{x^2 - 1} = 1.5$$

9.

x	$f(x)$
-0.1	0.44619
-0.01	0.50396
$-0.0.01$	0.51013
0.001	0.51152
0.01	0.51779
0.1	0.58496

$$\lim_{x \to 0} \frac{5^x - 3^x}{x} = 0.5108$$

10.

x	$f(x)$
-0.1	0.16713
-0.01	0.16671
$-0.0.01$	0.16667
0.001	0.16666
0.01	0.16662
0.1	0.16621

$$\lim_{x \to 0} \frac{\sqrt{x + 9} - 3}{x} = 0.16667$$

11.

x	$f(x)$
0.9	0.50878
0.99	0.50084
0.999	0.50008
1.001	0.49992
1.01	0.49917
1.1	0.49206

$$\lim_{x \to 1} \left(\frac{1}{\ln x} - \frac{1}{x-1} \right) = 0.5000$$

12.

x	$f(x)$
± 0.5	0.11044
± 0.1	0.30934
± 0.05	0.66387
± 0.01	0.66656
± 0.001	0.66667

$$\lim_{x \to 0} \frac{\tan 2x}{\tan 3x} = 0.66667$$

13. (a) $\displaystyle \lim_{x \to 1^-} f(x) = 2$

(b) $\displaystyle \lim_{x \to 1^+} f(x) = 3$

(c) $\displaystyle \lim_{x \to 1} f(x)$ does not exist; $\displaystyle \lim_{x \to 1^-} f(x) \neq \lim_{x \to 1^+} f(x)$.

(d) $\displaystyle \lim_{x \to 5} f(x) = 4$

(e) $f(5)$ is not defined.

14. (a) $\displaystyle \lim_{x \to 0} f(x) = 3$

(b) $\displaystyle \lim_{x \to 3^-} f(x) = 4$

(c) $\displaystyle \lim_{x \to 3^+} f(x) = 2$

(d) $\displaystyle \lim_{x \to 3} f(x)$ does not exist; $\displaystyle \lim_{x \to 3^-} f(x) \neq \lim_{x \to 3^+} f(x)$.

(e) $f(3) = 3$

15. (a) $\displaystyle \lim_{t \to 0^-} g(t) = -1$

(b) $\displaystyle \lim_{t \to 0^+} g(t) = -2$

(c) $\displaystyle \lim_{t \to 0} g(t)$ does not exist; $\displaystyle \lim_{t \to 0^-} g(t) \neq \lim_{t \to 0^+} g(t)$.

(d) $\displaystyle \lim_{t \to 2^-} g(t) = 2$

(e) $\displaystyle \lim_{t \to 2^+} g(t) = 0$

(f) $\displaystyle \lim_{t \to 2} g(t)$ does not exist; $\displaystyle \lim_{t \to 2^-} g(t) \neq \lim_{t \to 2^+} g(t)$.

(g) $g(2) = 1$

(h) $\displaystyle \lim_{t \to 4} g(t) = 3$

16. (a) $\displaystyle \lim_{x \to 3} f(x) = 2$

(b) $\displaystyle \lim_{x \to 1} f(x) = -1$

(c) $\displaystyle \lim_{x \to -3} f(x) = 1$

(d) $\displaystyle \lim_{x \to 2^-} f(x) = 1$

(e) $\displaystyle \lim_{x \to 2^+} f(x) = 2$

(f) $\displaystyle \lim_{x \to 2} f(x)$ does not exist; $\displaystyle \lim_{x \to 2^-} f(x) \neq \lim_{x \to 2^+} f(x)$.

17. $\displaystyle \lim_{x \to 1} \frac{x^3 + x^2 + 3x - 5}{2x^2 - 5x + 3} = -8.00$

18. $\displaystyle \lim_{x \to 2} \frac{x^3 + 6x^2 - 5x + 1}{x^3 - x^2 - 8x + 12}$ does not exist.

19. $\displaystyle \lim_{x \to 0} \ln(\sin^2 x)$ does not exist.

20. $\displaystyle \lim_{x \to 0} \frac{x^2}{\cos 5x - \cos 4x} = -0.22$

21. $\lim\limits_{x \to 0} \cos \dfrac{1}{x}$ does not exist.

22. $\lim\limits_{x \to 0} \dfrac{1}{1 + e^{1/x}}$ does not exist.

23. $f(x) = \begin{cases} x^2 & \text{if } x \le 2 \\ 6 - x & \text{if } x > 2 \end{cases}$

(a) $\lim\limits_{x \to 2^-} f(x) = 4$

(b) $\lim\limits_{x \to 2^+} f(x) = 4$

(c) $\lim\limits_{x \to 2} f(x) = 4$

24. $f(x) = \begin{cases} 2 & \text{if } x < 0 \\ x + 1 & \text{if } x \ge 0 \end{cases}$

(a) $\lim\limits_{x \to 0^-} f(x) = 2$

(b) $\lim\limits_{x \to 0^+} f(x) = 1$

(c) $\lim\limits_{x \to 0} f(x)$ does not exist.

25. $f(x) = \begin{cases} -x + 3 & \text{if } x < -1 \\ 3 & \text{if } x \ge -1 \end{cases}$

(a) $\lim\limits_{x \to -1^-} f(x) = 4$

(b) $\lim\limits_{x \to -1^+} f(x) = 3$

(c) $\lim\limits_{x \to -1} f(x)$ does not exist.

26. $f(x) = \begin{cases} 2x + 10 & \text{if } x \le -2 \\ -x + 4 & \text{if } x > -2 \end{cases}$

(a) $\lim\limits_{x \to -2^-} f(x) = 6$

(b) $\lim\limits_{x \to -2^+} f(x) = 6$

(c) $\lim\limits_{x \to -2} f(x) = 6$

27. There are an infinite number of functions satisfying the given conditions. The graph of one such function is shown.

28. (a)

x	1	0.5	0.1	0.05	0.01	0.005
$f(x)$	0.55741	0.37042	0.33467	0.333366	0.33335	0.33333

(b) From the table, $\lim\limits_{x \to 0} \dfrac{\tan x - x}{x^3}$ appears to be 0.33333 or $\frac{1}{3}$.

(c) In calculus, you will find that $\tan x > x$ for $x > 0$, so $\tan x - x > 0$. However, to evaluate $\tan x$, most calculators use a polynomial that starts with the terms $x + \dfrac{x^3}{3} + \dfrac{2x^5}{15} + \dfrac{17x^7}{315}$. For very small x (say $x = 0.00001$), the sum of the first two terms is 0.000010000000000333. But the calculator can't keep track of this many digits, so it will consider this number to be equal to 0.00001. Therefore, according to the calculator, $\tan 0.00001 - 0.00001 = 0$.

(d) In the first viewing rectangle, $[-1, 1]$ by $[0, 1]$, it appears that the limit is $\frac{1}{3}$. In the second viewing rectangle, $[-0.000001, 0.000001]$ by $[0.32, 0.35]$, we can see the erratic behavior.

12.2   Finding Limits Algebraically

1. (a) $\lim\limits_{x \to a} [f(x) + h(x)] = \lim\limits_{x \to a} f(x) + \lim\limits_{x \to a} h(x) = -3 + 8 = 5$

(b) $\lim\limits_{x \to a} [f(x)]^2 = \left[\lim\limits_{x \to a} f(x)\right]^2 = (-3)^2 = 9$

(c) $\lim\limits_{x \to a} \sqrt[3]{h(x)} = \sqrt[3]{\lim\limits_{x \to a} h(x)} = \sqrt[3]{8} = 2$

(d) $\lim\limits_{x \to a} \dfrac{1}{f(x)} = \dfrac{1}{\lim\limits_{x \to a} f(x)} = -\dfrac{1}{3}$

(e) $\lim\limits_{x \to a} \dfrac{f(x)}{h(x)} = \dfrac{\lim\limits_{x \to a} f(x)}{\lim\limits_{x \to a} h(x)} = -\dfrac{3}{8}$

(f) $\lim\limits_{x \to a} \dfrac{g(x)}{f(x)} = \dfrac{\lim\limits_{x \to a} g(x)}{\lim\limits_{x \to a} f(x)} = \dfrac{0}{-3} = 0$

(g) $\lim\limits_{x \to a} \dfrac{f(x)}{g(x)}$ does not exist since $\lim\limits_{x \to a} g(x) = 0$.

(h) $\lim\limits_{x \to a} \dfrac{2f(x)}{h(x) - f(x)} = \dfrac{\lim\limits_{x \to a} [2f(x)]}{\lim\limits_{x \to a} [h(x) - f(x)]} = \dfrac{2 \cdot \left[\lim\limits_{x \to a} f(x)\right]}{\left[\lim\limits_{x \to a} h(x)\right] - \left[\lim\limits_{x \to a} f(x)\right]} = \dfrac{2(-3)}{8 - (-3)} = -\dfrac{6}{11}$

2. (a) $\lim\limits_{x \to 2} [f(x) + g(x)] = \left[\lim\limits_{x \to 2} f(x)\right] + \left[\lim\limits_{x \to 2} g(x)\right] = 2 + 0 = 2$

(b) $\lim\limits_{x \to 1} [f(x) + g(x)] = \left[\lim\limits_{x \to 1} f(x)\right] + \left[\lim\limits_{x \to 1} g(x)\right]$. However, since $\lim\limits_{x \to 1} g(x)$ does not exist, $\lim\limits_{x \to 1} [f(x) + g(x)]$ does not exist.

(c) $\lim\limits_{x \to 0} [f(x) g(x)] = \left[\lim\limits_{x \to 0} f(x)\right] \left[\lim\limits_{x \to 0} g(x)\right] = (0)(1.5) = 0$

(d) $\lim\limits_{x \to -1} \dfrac{f(x)}{g(x)} = \dfrac{\lim\limits_{x \to -1} f(x)}{\lim\limits_{x \to -1} g(x)}$. However, since $\lim\limits_{x \to -1} g(x) = 0$, $\lim\limits_{x \to -1} \dfrac{f(x)}{g(x)}$ does not exist.

(e) $\lim\limits_{x \to 2} x^3 f(x) = \left[\lim\limits_{x \to 2} x^3\right] \left[\lim\limits_{x \to 2} f(x)\right] = (2)^3 (2) = 16$

(f) $\lim\limits_{x \to 1} \sqrt{3 + f(x)} = \sqrt{\lim\limits_{x \to 1} [3 + f(x)]} = \sqrt{3 + \left[\lim\limits_{x \to 1} (f) x\right]} = \sqrt{3 + 1} = 2$

3. $\lim\limits_{x \to 4} \left(5x^2 - 2x + 3\right) = 5 \lim\limits_{x \to 4} x^2 - 2 \lim\limits_{x \to 4} x + \lim\limits_{x \to 4} 3$ Laws 1, 2, and 3

$$= 5(4)^2 - 2(4) + 3 \qquad \text{Special Limits 1, 2, and 3}$$

$$= 80 - 8 + 3 = 75$$

4. $\lim\limits_{x \to 3} \left(x^3 + 2\right)\left(x^2 - 5x\right) = \left[\lim\limits_{x \to 3}\left(x^3 + 2\right)\right]\left[\lim\limits_{x \to 3}\left(x^2 - 5x\right)\right]$ Law 4

$$= \left[\lim\limits_{x \to 3} x^3 + \lim\limits_{x \to 3} 2\right]\left[\lim\limits_{x \to 3} x^2 - 5 \lim\limits_{x \to 3} x\right] \qquad \text{Laws 1 and 2}$$

$$= \left[(3)^3 + 2\right]\left[(3)^2 - 5(3)\right] \qquad \text{Special Limits 1, 2, and 3}$$

$$= (29)(-6) = -174$$

5. $\lim\limits_{x \to -1} \dfrac{x - 2}{x^2 + 4x - 3} = \dfrac{\lim\limits_{x \to -1} x - 2}{\lim\limits_{x \to -1} x^2 + 4x - 3}$ Law 5

$$= \dfrac{\lim\limits_{x \to -1} x - \lim\limits_{x \to -1} 2}{\lim\limits_{x \to -1} x^2 + 4 \lim\limits_{x \to -1} x - \lim\limits_{x \to -1} 3} \qquad \text{Laws 1, 2, and 3}$$

$$= \dfrac{(-1) - 2}{(-1)^2 + 4(-1) - 3} \qquad \text{Special Limits 1, 2, and 3}$$

$$= \dfrac{-3}{-6} = \dfrac{1}{2}$$

6. $\lim\limits_{x \to 1} \left(\dfrac{x^4 + x^2 - 6}{x^4 + 2x + 3} \right)^2 = \left(\lim\limits_{x \to 1} \dfrac{x^4 + x^2 - 6}{x^4 + 2x + 3} \right)^2$ Law 6

$\qquad = \left[\dfrac{\lim\limits_{x \to 1} \left(x^4 + x^2 - 6 \right)}{\lim\limits_{x \to 1} \left(x^4 + 2x + 3 \right)} \right]^2$ Law 5

$\qquad = \left(\dfrac{\lim\limits_{x \to 1} x^4 + \lim\limits_{x \to 1} x^2 - \lim\limits_{x \to 1} 6}{\lim\limits_{x \to 1} x^4 + 2 \lim\limits_{x \to 1} x + \lim\limits_{x \to 1} 3} \right)^2$ Laws 1, 2, and 3

$\qquad = \left[\dfrac{(1)^4 + (1)^2 - 6}{(1)^4 + 2\,(1) + 3} \right]^2$ Special Limits 1, 2, and 3

$\qquad = \left(\dfrac{-4}{6} \right)^2 = \dfrac{4}{9}$

7. $\lim\limits_{t \to -2} (t+1)^9 \left(t^2 - 1 \right) = \left[\lim\limits_{t \to -2} (t+1)^9 \right] \left[\lim\limits_{t \to -2} t^2 - 1 \right]$ Law 4

$\qquad = \left[\lim\limits_{t \to -2} t + 1 \right]^9 \left[\lim\limits_{t \to -2} t^2 - 1 \right]$ Law 6

$\qquad = \left[\lim\limits_{t \to -2} t + \lim\limits_{t \to -2} 1 \right]^9 \left[\lim\limits_{t \to -2} t^2 - \lim\limits_{t \to -2} 1 \right]$ Laws 1, 2, and 3

$\qquad = [(-2) + 1]^9 \left[(-2)^2 - 1 \right]$ Special Limits 1, 2, and 3

$\qquad = (-1)^9 \,(4 - 1) = (-1)\,(3) = -3$

8. $\lim\limits_{u \to -2} \sqrt{u^4 + 3u + 6} = \sqrt{\lim\limits_{u \to -2} \left[u^4 + 3u + 6 \right]}$ Law 7

$\qquad = \sqrt{\lim\limits_{u \to -2} u^4 + 3 \lim\limits_{u \to -2} u + \lim\limits_{u \to -2} 6}$ Laws 1 and 3

$\qquad = \sqrt{(-2)^4 + 3\,(-2) + 6}$ Special Limits 1, 2, and 3

$\qquad = \sqrt{16} = 4$

9. $\lim\limits_{x \to 2} \dfrac{x^2 + x - 6}{x - 2} = \lim\limits_{x \to 2} \dfrac{(x - 2)\,(x + 3)}{x - 2} = \lim\limits_{x \to 2} x + 3 = 5$

10. $\lim\limits_{x \to -4} \dfrac{x^2 + 5x + 4}{x^2 + 3x - 4} = \lim\limits_{x \to -4} \dfrac{(x + 1)\,(x + 4)}{(x - 1)\,(x + 4)} = \lim\limits_{x \to -4} \dfrac{x + 1}{x - 1} = \dfrac{(-4) + 1}{(-4) - 1} = \dfrac{3}{5}$

11. $\lim\limits_{x \to 2} \dfrac{x^2 - x + 6}{x + 2} = \dfrac{(2)^2 - (2) + 6}{(2) + 2} = \dfrac{8}{4} = 2$

12. $\lim\limits_{x \to 1} \dfrac{x^3 - 1}{x^2 - 1} = \lim\limits_{x \to 1} \dfrac{(x - 1)\,\left(x^2 + x + 1 \right)}{(x - 1)\,(x + 1)} = \lim\limits_{x \to 1} \dfrac{x^2 + x + 1}{x + 1} = \dfrac{1^2 + 1 + 1}{1 = 1} = \dfrac{3}{2}$

13. $\lim\limits_{t \to -3} \dfrac{t^2 - 9}{2t^2 + 7t + 3} = \lim\limits_{t \to -3} \dfrac{(t - 3)\,(t + 3)}{(t + 3)\,(2t + 1)} = \lim\limits_{t \to -3} \dfrac{t - 3}{2t + 1} = \dfrac{(-3) - 3}{2\,(-3) + 1} = \dfrac{-6}{-5} = \dfrac{6}{5}$

14. $\lim\limits_{h \to 0} \dfrac{\sqrt{1 + h} - 1}{h} = \lim\limits_{h \to 0} \dfrac{\left(\sqrt{1 + h} - 1 \right)\left(\sqrt{1 + h} + 1 \right)}{h \left(\sqrt{1 + h} + 1 \right)} = \lim\limits_{h \to 0} \dfrac{1 + h - 1}{h \left(\sqrt{1 + h} + 1 \right)}$

$\qquad = \lim\limits_{h \to 0} \dfrac{h}{h \left(\sqrt{1 + h} + 1 \right)} = \lim\limits_{h \to 0} \dfrac{1}{\sqrt{1 + h} + 1} = \dfrac{1}{\sqrt{1 + (0)} + 1} = \dfrac{1}{2}$

15. $\lim\limits_{h \to 0} \dfrac{(2 + h)^3 - 8}{h} = \lim\limits_{h \to 0} \dfrac{8 + 12h + 6h^2 + h^3 - 8}{h} = \lim\limits_{h \to 0} \dfrac{12h + 6h^2 + h^3}{h}$

$\qquad = \lim\limits_{h \to 0} \dfrac{h \left(12 + 6h + h^2 \right)}{h} = \lim\limits_{h \to 0} 12 + 6h + h^2 = 12$

16. $\lim\limits_{x\to 2}\dfrac{x^4-16}{x-2}=\lim\limits_{x\to 2}\dfrac{(x-2)(x+2)(x^2+4)}{x-2}=\lim\limits_{x\to 2}(x+2)(x^2+4)$

$\qquad = [2+(2)]\left[(2)^2+4\right]=4\,(8)=32$

17. $\lim\limits_{x\to 7}\dfrac{\sqrt{x+2}-3}{x-7}=\lim\limits_{x\to 7}\dfrac{\left(\sqrt{x+2}-3\right)\left(\sqrt{x+2}+3\right)}{(x-7)\left(\sqrt{x+2}+3\right)}=\lim\limits_{x\to 7}\dfrac{x+2-9}{(x-7)\left(\sqrt{x+2}+3\right)}$

$\qquad =\lim\limits_{x\to 7}\dfrac{x-7}{(x-7)\sqrt{x+2}+3}=\lim\limits_{x\to 7}\dfrac{1}{\sqrt{x+2}+3}=\dfrac{1}{\sqrt{7+2}+3}=\dfrac{1}{6}$

18. $\lim\limits_{h\to 0}\dfrac{(3+h)^{-1}-3^{-1}}{h}=\lim\limits_{h\to 0}\dfrac{\left[(3+h)^{-1}-3^{-1}\right]\cdot 3\,(3+h)}{h\cdot 3\,(3+h)}=\lim\limits_{h\to 0}\dfrac{3-(3+h)}{3h\,(3+h)}$

$\qquad =\lim\limits_{h\to 0}\dfrac{h}{3h\,(3+h)}=\lim\limits_{h\to 0}\dfrac{1}{3\,(3+h)}=\dfrac{1}{3\,[3+(0)]}=\dfrac{1}{9}$

19. $\lim\limits_{x\to -4}\dfrac{\frac{1}{4}+\frac{1}{x}}{4+x}=\lim\limits_{x\to -4}\dfrac{\left(\frac{1}{4}+\frac{1}{x}\right)4x}{(4+x)\,4x}=\lim\limits_{x\to -4}\dfrac{x+4}{(4+x)\,4x}=\lim\limits_{x\to -4}\dfrac{1}{4x}=\dfrac{1}{4\,(-4)}=-\dfrac{1}{16}$

20. $\lim\limits_{t\to 0}\left(\dfrac{1}{t}-\dfrac{1}{t^2+t}\right)=\lim\limits_{t\to 0}\dfrac{t+1-1}{t\,(t+1)}=\lim\limits_{t\to 0}\dfrac{t}{t\,(t+1)}=\lim\limits_{t\to 0}\dfrac{1}{t+1}=\dfrac{1}{1+0}=1$

21. $\lim\limits_{x\to 1}\dfrac{x^2-1}{\sqrt{x}-1}=\lim\limits_{x\to 1}\dfrac{(x-1)(x+1)\left(\sqrt{x}+1\right)}{\left(\sqrt{x}-1\right)\left(\sqrt{x}+1\right)}=\lim\limits_{x\to 1}\dfrac{(x-1)(x+1)\left(\sqrt{x}+1\right)}{x-1}$

$\qquad =\lim\limits_{x\to 1}(x+1)\left(\sqrt{x}+1\right)=[(1)+1]\left[\sqrt{1}+1\right]=2\cdot 2=4$

22. $\lim\limits_{x\to 0}\dfrac{(4+x)^3-64}{x}=\lim\limits_{x\to 0}\dfrac{64+48x+12x^2+x^3-64}{x}=\lim\limits_{x\to 0}\dfrac{48x+12x^2+x^3}{x}$

$\qquad =\lim\limits_{x\to 0}\dfrac{x\left(48+12x+x^2\right)}{x}=\lim\limits_{x\to 0}48+12x+x^2$

$\qquad =48+12\,(0)+(0)^2=48$

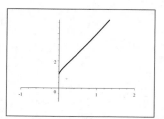

23. $\lim\limits_{x\to -1}\dfrac{x^2-x-2}{x^3-x}=\lim\limits_{x\to -1}\dfrac{(x-2)(x+1)}{x\,(x-1)(x+1)}=\lim\limits_{x\to -1}\dfrac{x-2}{x\,(x-1)}$

$\qquad =\dfrac{(-1)-2}{(-1)\,[(-1)-1]}=-\dfrac{3}{2}$

24. $\lim\limits_{x\to 1}\dfrac{x^8-1}{x^5-1}=\lim\limits_{x\to 1}\dfrac{\left(x^4-1\right)\left(x^4+1\right)}{(x-1)\left(x^4+x^3+x^2+x+1\right)}$

$\qquad =\lim\limits_{x\to 0}\dfrac{\left(x^2-1\right)\left(x^2+1\right)\left(x^4+1\right)}{(x-1)\left(x^4+x^3+x^2+x+1\right)}$

$\qquad =\lim\limits_{x\to 0}\dfrac{(x-1)(x+1)\left(x^2+1\right)\left(x^4+1\right)}{(x-1)\left(x^4+x^3+x^2+x+1\right)}$

$\qquad =\lim\limits_{x\to 0}\dfrac{(x+1)\left(x^2+1\right)\left(x^4+1\right)}{x^4+x^3+x^2+x+1}$

$\qquad =\dfrac{(1+1)\left(1^2+1\right)\left(1^4+1\right)}{1^4+1^3+1^2+1+1}=\dfrac{(2)(2)(2)}{5}=\dfrac{8}{5}$

25. (a)

From the graph,

$$\lim_{x \to 0} \frac{x}{\sqrt{1+3x}-1} \approx 0.67$$

(b)

x	-0.1	-0.01	-0.001	0.001	0.01	0.1
$f(x)$	0.61222	0.66163	0.66617	0.66717	0.67183	0.71339

(c) $\displaystyle \lim_{x \to 0} \frac{x}{\sqrt{1+3x}-1} = \lim_{x \to 0} \frac{x\left(\sqrt{1+3x}+1\right)}{\left(\sqrt{1+3x}-1\right)\left(\sqrt{1+3x}+1\right)}$

$\displaystyle = \lim_{x \to 0} \frac{x\left(\sqrt{1+3x}+1\right)}{(1+3x)-1} = \lim_{x \to 0} \frac{x\left(\sqrt{1+3x}+1\right)}{3x}$

$\displaystyle = \lim_{x \to 0} \frac{\sqrt{1+3x}+1}{3} = \frac{\sqrt{1+3(0)}+1}{3} = \frac{2}{3}$

26. (a)

From the graph,

$$\lim_{x \to 0} \frac{\sqrt{3+x}-\sqrt{3}}{x} = 0.29$$

(b)

x	-0.1	-0.01	-0.001	0.001	0.01	0.1
$f(x)$	0.28892	0.28892	0.28870	0.28865	0.28843	0.28631

(c) $\displaystyle \lim_{x \to 0} \frac{\sqrt{3+x}-\sqrt{3}}{x} = \lim_{x \to 0} \frac{\left(\sqrt{3+x}-\sqrt{3}\right)\left(\sqrt{3+x}+\sqrt{3}\right)}{x\left(\sqrt{3+x}+\sqrt{3}\right)}$

$\displaystyle = \lim_{x \to 0} \frac{(3+x)-3}{x\left(\sqrt{3+x}+\sqrt{3}\right)} = \lim_{x \to 0} \frac{x}{x\left(\sqrt{3+x}+\sqrt{3}\right)}$

$\displaystyle = \lim_{x \to 0} \frac{1}{\sqrt{3+x}+\sqrt{3}} = \frac{1}{\sqrt{3+0}+\sqrt{3}} = \frac{1}{2\sqrt{3}}$

27. $\displaystyle \lim_{x \to -4^-} |x+4| = \lim_{x \to -4^-} -(x+4) = 0$ and $\displaystyle \lim_{x \to -4^+} |x+4| = \lim_{x \to -4^+} x+4 = 0$. Therefore $\displaystyle \lim_{x \to -4^+} |x+4| = 0$.

28. $\displaystyle \lim_{x \to -4^-} \frac{|x+4|}{x+4} = \lim_{x \to -4^-} \frac{-(x+4)}{x+4} = -1$ and $\displaystyle \lim_{x \to -4^+} \frac{|x+4|}{x+4} = \lim_{x \to -4^+} \frac{x+4}{x+4} = 1$. So $\displaystyle \lim_{x \to -4} \frac{|x+4|}{x+4}$ does not exist.

29. $\displaystyle \lim_{x \to 2^-} \frac{|x-2|}{x-2} = \lim_{x \to 2^-} \frac{-(x-2)}{x-2} = -1$ and $\displaystyle \lim_{x \to 2^+} \frac{|x-2|}{x-2} = \lim_{x \to 2^+} \frac{x-2}{x-2} = 1$. So $\displaystyle \lim_{x \to 2} \frac{|x-2|}{x-2}$ does not exist.

30. $\displaystyle \lim_{x \to -1.5^-} \frac{2x^2-3x}{|2x-3|} = \lim_{x \to -1.5^-} \frac{x(2x-3)}{-(2x-3)} = \lim_{x \to -1.5^-} -x = 1.5$ and

$\displaystyle \lim_{x \to -1.5^+} \frac{2x^2-3x}{|2x-3|} = \lim_{x \to -1.5^+} \frac{x(2x-3)}{2x-3} = \lim_{x \to -1.5^+} x = -1.5$. So $\displaystyle \lim_{x \to -1.5} \frac{2x^2-3x}{|2x-3|}$ does not exist.

31. $\displaystyle \lim_{x \to 0^-} \left(\frac{1}{x} - \frac{1}{|x|}\right) = \lim_{x \to 0^-} \left(\frac{1}{x} - \frac{1}{-x}\right) = \lim_{x \to 0^-} \frac{2}{x}$ which does not exist.

32. $\displaystyle \lim_{x \to 0^+} \left(\frac{1}{x} - \frac{1}{|x|}\right) = \lim_{x \to 0^+} \left(\frac{1}{x} - \frac{1}{x}\right) = \lim_{x \to 0^+} 0 = 0$

33. (a) $\displaystyle \lim_{x \to 2^-} f(x) = \lim_{x \to 2^-} (x-1) = 1$ and

$\displaystyle \lim_{x \to 2^+} f(x) = \lim_{x \to 2^+} (x^2 - 4x + 6) = 2$.

(b) Since $\displaystyle \lim_{x \to 2^-} f(x) \neq \lim_{x \to 2^+} f(x)$, $\displaystyle \lim_{x \to 2} f(x)$ does not exist.

(c)

34. (a) (i) $\lim\limits_{x\to 0^+} h(x) = \lim\limits_{x\to 0^+} x^2 = 0$

(b)

(ii) $\lim\limits_{x\to 0} h(x) = 0$ since $\lim\limits_{x\to 0^-} h(x) = \lim\limits_{x\to 0^-} x = 0$ and

$\lim\limits_{x\to 0^+} h(x) = \lim\limits_{x\to 0^+} x^2 = 0.$

(iii) $\lim\limits_{x\to 1} h(x) = \lim\limits_{x\to 1} x^2 = 1$

(iv) $\lim\limits_{x\to 2^-} h(x) = \lim\limits_{x\to 2^-} x^2 = 4$

(v) $\lim\limits_{x\to 2^+} h(x) = \lim\limits_{x\to 2^+} (8-x) = 6$

(vi) $\lim\limits_{x\to 2} f(x)$ does not exist since $\lim\limits_{x\to 2^-} h(x) \neq \lim\limits_{x\to 2^+} h(x).$

35. (a) The equation is true only for $x \neq 2$. That is, $x = 2$ is in the domain of $f(x) = x + 3$ but not in the domain of

$g(x) = \dfrac{x^2 + x - 6}{x - 2}.$

(b) When we take the limit we have $x \neq 2$.

36. $\lim\limits_{v\to c^-} L = \lim\limits_{v\to c^-} L_0 \sqrt{1 - \dfrac{v^2}{c^2}} = L_0 \lim\limits_{v\to c^-} \sqrt{1 - \dfrac{v^2}{c^2}} = L_0 \sqrt{\lim\limits_{v\to c^-} \left(1 - \dfrac{v^2}{c^2}\right)} = L_0(0) = 0.$ The left-hand limit is

necessary because $\sqrt{1 - \dfrac{v^2}{c^2}}$ is not defined for $v > c$.

37. (a) Many answers are possible, for example let $f(x) = \dfrac{x+4}{x-2}$ and $g(x) = \dfrac{x-8}{x-2}$. Then neither $\lim\limits_{x\to 2} f(x)$ nor $\lim\limits_{x\to 2} g(x)$

exist, but $\lim\limits_{x\to 2} f(x) + g(x) = \lim\limits_{x\to 2} \left(\dfrac{x+4}{x-2} + \dfrac{x-8}{x-2}\right) = \lim\limits_{x\to 2} \dfrac{2x-4}{x-2} = \lim\limits_{x\to 2} \dfrac{2(x-2)}{x-2} = \lim\limits_{x\to 2} 2 = 2.$

(b) Many answers are possible, for example let $f(x) = \dfrac{|x-2|}{x-2}$ and $g(x) = \dfrac{x-2}{|x-2|}$. Then neither $\lim\limits_{x\to 2} f(x)$ nor

$\lim\limits_{x\to 2} g(x)$ exist, but $\lim\limits_{x\to 2} [f(x)g(x)] = \lim\limits_{x\to 2} \left(\dfrac{|x-2|}{x-2} \cdot \dfrac{x-2}{|x-2|}\right) = \lim\limits_{x\to 2} 1 = 1.$

12.3   Tangent Lines and Derivatives

1. $m = \lim\limits_{h\to 0} \dfrac{f(1+h) - f(1)}{h} = \lim\limits_{h\to 0} \dfrac{[3(1+h)+4] - [3(1)+4]}{h} = \lim\limits_{h\to 0} \dfrac{7+3h-7}{h} = \lim\limits_{h\to 0} \dfrac{3h}{h} = \lim\limits_{h\to 0} 3 = 3$

2. $m = \lim\limits_{h\to 0} \dfrac{f(-3+h) - f(-3)}{h} = \lim\limits_{h\to 0} \dfrac{[5-2(-3+h)] - [5-2(-3)]}{h} = \lim\limits_{h\to 0} \dfrac{11-2h-11}{h} = \lim\limits_{h\to 0} \dfrac{-2h}{h}$

$= \lim\limits_{h\to 0} (-2) = -2$

3. $m = \lim\limits_{h\to 0} \dfrac{f(-1+h) - f(-1)}{h} = \lim\limits_{h\to 0} \dfrac{[4(-1+h)^2 - 3(-1+h)] - [4(-1)^2 - 3(-1)]}{h}$

$= \lim\limits_{h\to 0} \dfrac{4-8h+4h^2+3-3h-7}{h} = \lim\limits_{h\to 0} \dfrac{-11h+4h^2}{h} = \lim\limits_{h\to 0} \dfrac{h(-11+4h)}{h}$

$= \lim\limits_{h\to 0} (-11+4h) = -11$

4. $m = \lim\limits_{h\to 0} \dfrac{f(1+h) - f(1)}{h} = \lim\limits_{h\to 0} \dfrac{[1+2(1+h)-3(1+h)^2] - [1+2(1)-3(1)^2]}{h}$

$= \lim\limits_{h\to 0} \dfrac{1+2+2h-3-6h-3h^2}{h} = \lim\limits_{h\to 0} \dfrac{-4h-3h^2}{h} = \lim\limits_{h\to 0} \dfrac{h(-4-3h)}{h}$

$= \lim\limits_{h\to 0} (-4-3h) = -4$

5. $m = \lim\limits_{h \to 0} \dfrac{f(2+h) - f(2)}{h} = \lim\limits_{h \to 0} \dfrac{\left[2(2+h)^3\right] - \left[2(2)^3\right]}{h} = \lim\limits_{h \to 0} \dfrac{16 + 24h + 12h^2 + 2h^3 - 16}{h}$

$= \lim\limits_{h \to 0} \dfrac{24h + 12h^2 + 2h^3}{h} = \lim\limits_{h \to 0} \dfrac{h\left(24 + 12h + 2h^2\right)}{h} = \lim\limits_{h \to 0} \left(24 + 12h + 2h^2\right) = 24$

6. $m = \lim\limits_{h \to 0} \dfrac{f(2+h) - f(2)}{h} = \lim\limits_{h \to 0} \dfrac{\left[\dfrac{6}{2+h+1}\right] - \left[\dfrac{6}{2+1}\right]}{h} = \lim\limits_{h \to 0} \dfrac{\dfrac{6}{3+h} - 2}{h} = \lim\limits_{h \to 0} \dfrac{6 - 2(3+h)}{h(3+h)}$

$= \lim\limits_{h \to 0} \dfrac{-2h}{h(3+h)} = \lim\limits_{h \to 0} \dfrac{-2}{3+h} = -\tfrac{2}{3}$

7. $m = \lim\limits_{h \to 0} \dfrac{\left[(-1+h) + (-1+h)^2\right] - \left[(-1) + (-1)^2\right]}{h} = \lim\limits_{h \to 0} \dfrac{-1 + h + 1 - 2h + h^2}{h}$

$= \lim\limits_{h \to 0} \dfrac{-h + h^2}{h} = \lim\limits_{h \to 0} \dfrac{h(-1+h)}{h} = \lim\limits_{h \to 0} (-1+h) = -1$

Thus an equation of the tangent line at $(-1, 0)$ is $y - 0 = -1(x+1)$ $\Leftrightarrow$
$y = -x - 1$.

8. $m = \lim\limits_{h \to 0} \dfrac{\left[2(1+h) - (1+h)^3\right] - \left[2(1) - 1^3\right]}{h} = \lim\limits_{h \to 0} \dfrac{2 + 2h - 1 - 3h - 3h^2 - h^3 - 1}{h}$

$= \lim\limits_{h \to 0} \dfrac{-h - 2h^2 - h^3}{h} = \lim\limits_{h \to 0} \dfrac{h(-1 - 2h - h^2)}{h} = \lim\limits_{h \to 0} (-1 - 2h - h^2) = -1$

Thus an equation of the tangent line at $(1, 1)$ is $y - 1 = -1(x-1)$ $\Leftrightarrow$
$y = -x + 2$.

9. $m = \lim\limits_{h \to 0} \dfrac{\dfrac{2+h}{2+h-1} - \dfrac{2}{2-1}}{h} = \lim\limits_{h \to 0} \dfrac{\left(\dfrac{2+h}{1+h} - 2\right)}{h} \cdot \dfrac{(1+h)}{(1+h)}$

$= \lim\limits_{h \to 0} \dfrac{2 + h - 2 - 2h}{h(1+h)} = \lim\limits_{h \to 0} \dfrac{-h}{h(1+h)} = \lim\limits_{h \to 0} \dfrac{-1}{1+h} = -1$

Thus an equation of the tangent line at $(2, 2)$ is $y - 2 = -1(x-2)$ $\Leftrightarrow$
$y = -x + 4$.

10. $m = \lim\limits_{h \to 0} \dfrac{\left[\dfrac{1}{(-1+h)^2}\right] - \left[\dfrac{1}{(-1)^2}\right]}{h} = \lim\limits_{h \to 0} \dfrac{\left[\dfrac{1}{(-1+h)^2}\right] - 1}{h}$

$= \lim\limits_{h \to 0} \dfrac{\left(\left[\dfrac{1}{(-1+h)^2}\right] - 1\right)(-1+h)^2}{h(-1+h)^2} = \lim\limits_{h \to 0} \dfrac{1 - (-1+h)^2}{h(-1+h)^2}$

$= \lim\limits_{h \to 0} \dfrac{1 - 1 + 2h - h^2}{h} = \lim\limits_{h \to 0} \dfrac{2h - h^2}{h} = \lim\limits_{h \to 0} \dfrac{h(2-h)}{h} = \lim\limits_{h \to 0} (2 - h) = 2$

Thus an equation of the tangent line at $(-1, 1)$ is $y - 1 = 2(x+1)$ $\Leftrightarrow$
$y = 2x + 3$.

11. $m = \lim\limits_{h \to 0} \dfrac{\sqrt{(1+h)+3} - \sqrt{1+3}}{h} = \lim\limits_{h \to 0} \dfrac{\sqrt{h+4} - 2}{h} = \lim\limits_{h \to 0} \dfrac{\left(\sqrt{h+4} - 2\right)\left(\sqrt{h+4} + 2\right)}{h\left(\sqrt{h+4} + 2\right)}$

$= \lim\limits_{h \to 0} \dfrac{h+4-4}{h\left(\sqrt{h+4} + 2\right)} = \lim\limits_{h \to 0} \dfrac{h}{h\left(\sqrt{h+4} + 2\right)} = \lim\limits_{h \to 0} \dfrac{1}{\sqrt{h+4} + 2} = \frac{1}{4}$

$y = \frac{1}{4}x + \frac{7}{4}$

$y = \sqrt{x+3}$

Thus an equation of the tangent line at $(1, 2)$ is $y - 2 = \frac{1}{4}(x - 1) \quad \Leftrightarrow$

$y = \frac{1}{4}x + \frac{7}{4}$.

12. $m = \lim\limits_{h \to 0} \dfrac{\sqrt{1 + 2(4+h)} - \sqrt{1 + 2(4)}}{h} = \lim\limits_{h \to 0} \dfrac{\sqrt{2h + 9} - 3}{h}$

$= \lim\limits_{h \to 0} \dfrac{\left(\sqrt{2h+9} - 3\right)\left(\sqrt{2h+9} + 3\right)}{h\left(\sqrt{2h+9} + 3\right)} = \lim\limits_{h \to 0} \dfrac{2h + 9 - 9}{h\left(\sqrt{2h+9} + 3\right)}$

$= \lim\limits_{h \to 0} \dfrac{2h}{h\left(\sqrt{2h+9} + 3\right)} = \lim\limits_{h \to 0} \dfrac{2}{\sqrt{2h+9} + 3} = \dfrac{2}{3+3} = \frac{1}{3}$

$y = \frac{1}{3}x + \frac{5}{3}$

$y = \sqrt{1 + 2x}$

Thus an equation of the tangent line at $(4, 3)$ is $y - 3 = \frac{1}{3}(x - 4) \quad \Leftrightarrow$

$y = \frac{1}{3}x + \frac{5}{3}$.

13. $f'(2) = \lim\limits_{h \to 0} \dfrac{f(2+h) - f(2)}{h} = \lim\limits_{h \to 0} \dfrac{\left[1 - 3(2+h)^2\right] - \left[1 - 3(2)^2\right]}{h} = \lim\limits_{h \to 0} \dfrac{1 - 12 - 12h - 3h^2 + 11}{h}$

$= \lim\limits_{h \to 0} \dfrac{-12h - 3h^2}{h} = \lim\limits_{h \to 0} \dfrac{h(-12 - 3h)}{h} = \lim\limits_{h \to 0} (-12 - 3h) = -12$

14. $f'(-1) = \lim\limits_{h \to 0} \dfrac{f(-1+h) - f(-1)}{h} = \lim\limits_{h \to 0} \dfrac{\left[2 - 3(-1+h) + (-1+h)^2\right] - \left[2 - 3(-1) + (-1)^2\right]}{h}$

$= \lim\limits_{h \to 0} \dfrac{2 + 3 - 3h + 1 - 2h + h^2 - 2 - 3 - 1}{h} = \lim\limits_{h \to 0} \dfrac{-5h + h^2}{h} = \lim\limits_{h \to 0} \dfrac{h(-5 + h)}{h} = \lim\limits_{h \to 0} (-5 + h) = -5$

15. $g'(1) = \lim\limits_{h \to 0} \dfrac{g(1+h) - g(1)}{h} = \lim\limits_{h \to 0} \dfrac{(1+h)^4 - (1)^4}{h} = \lim\limits_{h \to 0} \dfrac{4h + 6h^2 + 4h^3 + h^4}{h} = \lim\limits_{h \to 0} \dfrac{h\left(4 + 6h + 4h^2 + h^3\right)}{h}$

$= \lim\limits_{h \to 0} \left(4 + 6h + 4h^2 + h^3\right) = 4$

16. $g'(1) = \lim\limits_{h \to 0} \dfrac{g(1+h) - g(1)}{h} = \lim\limits_{h \to 0} \dfrac{\left[2(1+h)^2 + (1+h)^3\right] - \left[2(1)^2 + (1)^3\right]}{h}$

$= \lim\limits_{h \to 0} \dfrac{2 + 4h + 2h^2 + 1 + 3h + 3h^2 + h^3 - 2 - 1}{h} = \lim\limits_{h \to 0} \dfrac{7h + 5h^2 + h^3}{h} = \lim\limits_{h \to 0} \dfrac{h\left(7 + 5h + h^2\right)}{h}$

$= \lim\limits_{h \to 0} \left(7 + 5h + h^2\right) = 7$

17. $F'(4) = \lim\limits_{h \to 0} \dfrac{F(4+h) - F(4)}{h} = \lim\limits_{h \to 0} \dfrac{\left[\dfrac{1}{\sqrt{4+h}}\right] - \left[\dfrac{1}{\sqrt{4}}\right]}{h} = \lim\limits_{h \to 0} \dfrac{\dfrac{1}{\sqrt{4+h}} - \dfrac{1}{2}}{h}$

$= \lim\limits_{h \to 0} \dfrac{\left(\dfrac{1}{\sqrt{4+h}} - \dfrac{1}{2}\right)2\sqrt{4+h}}{h \cdot 2\sqrt{4+h}} = \lim\limits_{h \to 0} \dfrac{2 - \sqrt{4+h}}{2h\sqrt{4+h}} = \lim\limits_{h \to 0} \dfrac{\left(2 - \sqrt{4+h}\right)\left(2 + \sqrt{4+h}\right)}{2h\sqrt{4+h}\left(2 + \sqrt{4+h}\right)}$

$= \lim\limits_{h \to 0} \dfrac{4 - (4+h)}{2h\sqrt{4+h}\left(2 + \sqrt{4+h}\right)} = \lim\limits_{h \to 0} \dfrac{-h}{2h\sqrt{4+h}\left(2 + \sqrt{4+h}\right)} = \lim\limits_{h \to 0} \dfrac{-1}{2\sqrt{4+h}\left(2 + \sqrt{4+h}\right)} = -\dfrac{1}{16}$

18. $G'(4) = \lim\limits_{h \to 0} \dfrac{G(4+h) - G(4)}{h} = \lim\limits_{h \to 0} \dfrac{\left[1 + 2\sqrt{4+h}\right] - \left[1 + 2\sqrt{4}\right]}{h} = \lim\limits_{h \to 0} \dfrac{1 + 2\sqrt{4+h} - 1 - 4}{h}$

$= \lim\limits_{h \to 0} \dfrac{2\sqrt{4+h} - 4}{h} = \lim\limits_{h \to 0} \dfrac{2\left(\sqrt{4+h} - 2\right)\left(\sqrt{4+h} + 2\right)}{h\left(\sqrt{4+h} + 2\right)} = \lim\limits_{h \to 0} \dfrac{2(4 + h - 4)}{h\left(\sqrt{4+h} + 2\right)}$

$= \lim\limits_{h \to 0} \dfrac{2h}{h\left(\sqrt{4+h} + 2\right)} = \lim\limits_{h \to 0} \dfrac{2}{\sqrt{4+h} + 2} = \frac{1}{2}$

19. $f'(a) = \lim\limits_{x \to a} \dfrac{f(x) - f(a)}{x - a} = \lim\limits_{x \to a} \dfrac{[x^2 + 2x] - [a^2 + 2a]}{x - a} = \lim\limits_{x \to a} \dfrac{x^2 + 2x - a^2 - 2a}{x - a} = \lim\limits_{x \to a} \dfrac{x^2 - a^2 + 2x - 2a}{x - a}$

$= \lim\limits_{x \to a} \dfrac{(x - a)(x + a) + 2(x - a)}{x - a} = \lim\limits_{x \to a} \dfrac{(x - a)[(x + a) + 2]}{x - a} = \lim\limits_{x \to a} (x + a + 2) = 2a + 2$

20. $f'(a) = \lim\limits_{x \to a} \dfrac{f(x) - f(a)}{x - a} = \lim\limits_{x \to a} \dfrac{\left[-\dfrac{1}{x^2}\right] - \left[-\dfrac{1}{a^2}\right]}{x - a} = \lim\limits_{x \to a} \dfrac{\dfrac{1}{a^2} - \dfrac{1}{x^2}}{x - a} = \lim\limits_{x \to a} \dfrac{\left(\dfrac{1}{a^2} - \dfrac{1}{x^2}\right) a^2 x^2}{(x - a) a^2 x^2}$

$= \lim\limits_{x \to a} \dfrac{x^2 - a^2}{(x - a) a^2 x^2} = \lim\limits_{x \to a} \dfrac{(x - a)(x + a)}{(x - a) a^2 x^2} = \lim\limits_{x \to a} \dfrac{x + a}{a^2 x^2} = \dfrac{2a}{a^4} = \dfrac{2}{a^3}$

21. $f'(a) = \lim\limits_{x \to a} \dfrac{f(x) - f(a)}{x - a} = \lim\limits_{x \to a} \dfrac{\left[\dfrac{x}{x + 1}\right] - \left[\dfrac{a}{a + 1}\right]}{x - a} = \lim\limits_{x \to a} \dfrac{\left(\left[\dfrac{x}{x + 1}\right] - \left[\dfrac{a}{a + 1}\right]\right)(a + 1)(x + 1)}{(x - a)(a + 1)(x + 1)}$

$= \lim\limits_{x \to a} \dfrac{x(a + 1) - a(x + 1)}{(x - a)(a + 1)(x + 1)} = \lim\limits_{x \to a} \dfrac{ax + x - ax - a}{(x - a)(a + 1)(x + 1)} = \lim\limits_{x \to a} \dfrac{x - a}{(x - a)(a + 1)(x + 1)}$

$= \lim\limits_{x \to a} \dfrac{1}{(a + 1)(x + 1)} = \dfrac{1}{(a + 1)^2}$

22. $f'(a) = \lim\limits_{x \to a} \dfrac{f(x) - f(a)}{x - a} = \lim\limits_{x \to a} \dfrac{\sqrt{x - 2} - \sqrt{a - 2}}{x - a} = \lim\limits_{x \to a} \dfrac{\left(\sqrt{x - 2} - \sqrt{a - 2}\right)\left(\sqrt{x - 2} + \sqrt{a - 2}\right)}{(x - a)\left(\sqrt{x - 2} + \sqrt{a - 2}\right)}$

$= \lim\limits_{x \to a} \dfrac{(x - 2) - (a - 2)}{(x - a)\left(\sqrt{x - 2} + \sqrt{a - 2}\right)} = \lim\limits_{x \to a} \dfrac{x - a}{(x - a)\left(\sqrt{x - 2} + \sqrt{a - 2}\right)} = \lim\limits_{x \to a} \dfrac{1}{\sqrt{x - 2} + \sqrt{a - 2}} = \dfrac{1}{2\sqrt{a - 2}}$

23. (a) $f'(a) = \lim\limits_{x \to a} \dfrac{f(x) - f(a)}{x - a} = \lim\limits_{x \to a} \dfrac{[x^3 - 2x + 4] - [a^3 - 2a + 4]}{x - a} = \lim\limits_{x \to a} \dfrac{x^3 - 2x + 4 - a^3 + 2a - 4}{x - a}$

$= \lim\limits_{x \to a} \dfrac{x^3 - a^3 - 2x + 2a}{x - a} = \lim\limits_{x \to a} \dfrac{(x - a)(x^2 + ax + a^2) - 2(x - a)}{x - a}$

$= \lim\limits_{x \to a} \dfrac{(x - a)(x^2 + ax + a^2 - 2)}{x - a} = \lim\limits_{x \to a} (x^2 + ax + a^2 - 2) = 3a^2 - 2$

(b) $f(0) = 0^3 - 2(0) + 4 = 4$ and $f'(0) = 3(0)^2 - 2 = -2$. So the equation of line tangent to $f(x)$ at $x = 0$ is
$y - 4 = -2(x - 0) \Leftrightarrow y = -2x + 4$. $f(1) = 1^3 - 2(1) + 4 = 3$ and $f'(1) = 3(1)^2 - 2 = 1$. So an
equation of the line tangent to $f(x)$ at $x = 1$ is $y - 3 = 1(x - 1)$ $\Leftrightarrow$ $y = x + 2$. $f(2) = 2^3 - 2(2) + 4 = 8$
and $f'(2) = 3(2)^2 - 2 = 10$, so an equation of the line tangent to $f(x)$ at $x = 2$ is $y - 8 = 10(x - 2)$ $\Leftrightarrow$
$y = 10x - 12$.

(c)

24. (a) $g'(a) = \lim\limits_{x \to a} \dfrac{g(x) - g(a)}{x - a} = \lim\limits_{x \to a} \dfrac{\dfrac{1}{2x - 1} - \dfrac{1}{2a - 1}}{x - a} = \lim\limits_{x \to a} \dfrac{\dfrac{1}{2a + 2h - 1} - \dfrac{1}{2a - 1}}{h}$

$= \lim\limits_{x \to a} \dfrac{\left(\dfrac{1}{2x - 1} - \dfrac{1}{2a - 1}\right)(2a - 1)(2x - 1)}{(x - a)(2a - 1)(2x - 1)} = \lim\limits_{x \to a} \dfrac{(2a - 1) - (2x - 1)}{h(x - a)(2a - 1)(2x - 1)}$

$= \lim\limits_{x \to a} \dfrac{-2x + 2a}{(x - a)(2a - 1)(2x - 1)} = \lim\limits_{x \to a} \dfrac{-2(x - a)}{(x - a)(2a - 1)(2x - 1)} = \lim\limits_{x \to a} \dfrac{-2}{(2a - 1)(2x - 1)} = \dfrac{-2}{(2a - 1)^2}$

(b) $g(-1) = \dfrac{1}{2(-1) - 1} = -\dfrac{1}{3}$ and $g'(-1) = \dfrac{-2}{[2(-1) - 1]^2} = -\dfrac{2}{9}$, so an equation of the line tangent to $g(x)$ at

$x = -1$ is $y + \frac{1}{3} = -\frac{2}{9}(x + 1) \quad \Leftrightarrow \quad y = -\frac{2}{9}x - \frac{5}{9}$. $g(0) = \dfrac{1}{2(0) - 1} = -1$ and $g'(0) = \dfrac{-2}{[2(0) - 1]^2} = -2$, so

an equation of the line tangent to $g(x)$ at $x = 0$ is $y + 1 = -2(x - 0)$ **(c)**

$\Leftrightarrow \quad y = -2x - 1.$ $g(1) = \dfrac{1}{2(1) - 1} = 1$ and

$g'(1) = \dfrac{-2}{[2(1) - 1]^2} = -2$, so an equation of the line tangent to $g(x)$ at

$x = 1$ is $y - 1 = -2(x - 1) \quad \Leftrightarrow \quad y = -2x + 3.$

25. Let $s(t) = 40t - 16t^2$. Then

$$v(2) = \lim\limits_{t \to 2} \dfrac{(40t - 16t^2) - 16}{t - 2} = \lim\limits_{t \to 2} \dfrac{-16t^2 + 40t - 16}{t - 2} = \lim\limits_{t \to 2} \dfrac{-8(2t^2 - 5t + 2)}{t - 2}$$

$$= \lim\limits_{t \to 2} \dfrac{-8(t - 2)(2t - 1)}{t - 2} = -8\lim\limits_{t \to 2}(2t - 1) = -8(3) = -24$$

Thus, the instantaneous velocity when $t = 2$ is -24 ft/s.

26. (a) $v'(1) = \lim\limits_{h \to 0} \dfrac{H(1 + h) - H(1)}{h} = \lim\limits_{h \to 0} \dfrac{[58(1 + h) - 0.83(1 + h)^2] - [58(1) - 0.83(1)^2]}{h}$

$= \lim\limits_{h \to 0} \dfrac{58 + 58h - 0.83 - 1.66h - 0.83h^2 - 58 + 0.83}{h} = \lim\limits_{h \to 0} \dfrac{56.34h - 0.83h^2}{h}$

$= \lim\limits_{h \to 0} \dfrac{h(56.34 - 0.83h)}{h} = \lim\limits_{h \to 0}(56.34 - 0.83h) = 56.34$ m/s

(b) $v'(a) = \lim\limits_{h \to 0} \dfrac{H(a + h) - H(a)}{h} = \lim\limits_{h \to 0} \dfrac{[58(a + h) - 0.83(a + h)^2] - [58(a) - 0.83(a)^2]}{h}$

$= \lim\limits_{h \to 0} \dfrac{58a + 58h - 0.83a^2 - 1.66ah - 0.83h^2 - 58a + 0.83a^2}{h}$

$= \lim\limits_{h \to 0} \dfrac{58h - 1.66ah - 0.83h^2}{h} = \lim\limits_{h \to 0} \dfrac{h(58 - 1.66a - 0.83h)}{h}$

$= \lim\limits_{h \to 0}(58 - 1.66a - 0.83h) = 58 - 1.66a$ m/s

(c) $H(t) = 0$ when $58t - 0.83t^2 = 0 \Leftrightarrow t(58 - 0.83t) = 0 \quad \Leftrightarrow \quad t = \frac{58}{0.83} \approx 69.88$ s (since t cannot be 0).

(d) $H'(69.88) = 58 - 1.66(69.88) = -58$ m/s

27. $v(a) = \lim\limits_{h \to 0} \dfrac{s(a+h) - s(a)}{h} = \lim\limits_{h \to 0} \dfrac{\left[4(a+h)^3 + 6(a+h) + 2\right] - \left[4a^3 + 6a + 2\right]}{h}$

$= \lim\limits_{h \to 0} \dfrac{4a^3 + 12a^2 h + 12ah^2 + 4h^3 + 6a + 6h + 2 - 4a^3 - 6a - 2}{h}$

$= \lim\limits_{h \to 0} \dfrac{12a^2 h + 12ah^2 + 4h^3 + 6h}{h} = \lim\limits_{h \to 0} \dfrac{h\left(12a^2 + 12ah + 4h^2 + 6\right)}{h}$

$= \lim\limits_{h \to 0} \left(12a^2 + 12ah + 4h^2 + 6\right) = 12a^2 + 6$ m/s

So $v(1) = 12(1)^2 + 6 = 18$ m/s, $v(2) = 12(2)^2 + 6 = 54$ m/s, and $v(3) = 12(3)^2 + 6 = 114$ m/s.

28. $S'(2) = \lim\limits_{h \to 0} \dfrac{S(2+h) - S(2)}{h} = \lim\limits_{h \to 0} \dfrac{\left[4\pi(2+h)^2\right] - \left[4\pi(2)^2\right]}{h} = \lim\limits_{h \to 0} \dfrac{16\pi + 16\pi h + 4\pi h^2 - 16\pi}{h}$

$= \lim\limits_{h \to 0} \dfrac{16\pi h + 4\pi h^2}{h} = \lim\limits_{h \to 0} \dfrac{h(16\pi + 4\pi h)}{h} = \lim\limits_{h \to 0} (16\pi + 4\pi h) = 16\pi$ ft/s

29. The slope of the tangent (that is, the rate of change in temperature with respect to time) at $t = 1$ h seems to be about

$\dfrac{147 - 106}{90 - 30} \approx 0.7°$ F/min.

30. (a) For the time interval $[40, 42]$ the average rate is $\dfrac{2948 - 2806}{42 - 40} = 71$ heartbeats/min. For the time interval $[42, 44]$ the

average rate is $\dfrac{3080 - 2948}{44 - 42} = 66$ heartbeats/min.

(b) The patient's heart rate is about $\dfrac{71 + 66}{2} = 68.5$ heartbeats/min.

31. (a) For the time interval $[10, 15]$ the average rate is $\dfrac{250 - 444}{15 - 10} = -38.8$ gal/min. For the time interval $[15, 20]$ the

average rate is $\dfrac{111 - 250}{20 - 15} = -27.8$ gal/min.

(b) $V'(15) \approx \dfrac{-38.8 - 27.8}{2} = -33.3$ gal/min.

32. For 1920, we average the difference quotients obtained using the years 1910 and

1930. Let $A = \dfrac{P(1910) - P(1920)}{1910 - 1920} = \dfrac{1750 - 1860}{-10} = 11$ million/year

and $B = \dfrac{P(1930) - P(1920)}{1930 - 1920} = \dfrac{2070 - 1860}{10} = 21$ million/year. Then

$P'(1920) \approx \dfrac{A + B}{2} = \dfrac{11 + 21}{2} = 16$ million/year.

33. $g'(0)$ is the only negative value. The slope at $x = 4$ is smaller than the slope at $x = 2$ and both are smaller than the slope at $x = -2$. Thus, $g'(0) < 0 < g'(4) < g'(2) < g'(-2)$.

34. (a) Since the slope of the tangent at $t = 0$ is 0, the car's initial velocity was 0.

(b) The slope of the tangent is greater at C than at B, so the car is going faster at C.

(c) Near A, the tangent lines are becoming steeper as x increases, so the velocity was increasing, so the car was speeding up. Near B, the tangent lines are becoming less steep, so the car was slowing down. The steepest tangent near C is the one at C, so at C the car had just finished speeding up, and was about to start slowing down.

(d) Between D and E, the slope of the tangent is 0, so the car did not move during that time.

12.4 Limits at Infinity; Limits of Sequences

1. (a) $\lim\limits_{x \to \infty} f(x) = -1$ and $\lim\limits_{x \to -\infty} f(x) = 2$.

(b) Horizontal asymptotes: $y = -1$ and $y = 2$.

2. (a) $\lim\limits_{x \to \infty} f(x) = 3$ and $\lim\limits_{x \to -\infty} f(x) = -2$.

(b) Horizontal asymptotes: $y = 3$ and $y = -2$.

3. $\lim\limits_{x \to \infty} \dfrac{6}{x} = 0$

4. $\lim\limits_{x \to \infty} \dfrac{3}{x^4} = 0$

5. $\lim\limits_{x \to \infty} \dfrac{2x+1}{5x-1} = \lim\limits_{x \to \infty} \dfrac{2 + \dfrac{1}{x}}{5 - \dfrac{1}{x}} = \dfrac{\lim\limits_{x \to \infty} 2 + \lim\limits_{x \to \infty} \dfrac{1}{x}}{\lim\limits_{x \to \infty} 5 - \lim\limits_{x \to \infty} \dfrac{1}{x}} = \dfrac{2+0}{5-0} = \dfrac{2}{5}$

6. $\lim\limits_{x \to \infty} \dfrac{2-3x}{4x+5} = \lim\limits_{x \to \infty} \dfrac{\dfrac{2}{x} - 3}{4 + \dfrac{5}{x}} = \dfrac{\lim\limits_{x \to \infty} \dfrac{2}{x} - \lim\limits_{x \to \infty} 3}{\lim\limits_{x \to \infty} 4 + \lim\limits_{x \to \infty} \dfrac{5}{x}} = \dfrac{0-3}{4+0} = -\dfrac{3}{4}$

7. $\lim\limits_{x \to \infty} \dfrac{4x^2+1}{2+3x^2} = \lim\limits_{x \to \infty} \dfrac{4 + \dfrac{1}{x^2}}{\dfrac{2}{x^2} + 3} = \dfrac{\lim\limits_{x \to \infty} 4 + \lim\limits_{x \to \infty} \dfrac{1}{x^2}}{\lim\limits_{x \to \infty} \dfrac{2}{x^2} + \lim\limits_{x \to \infty} 3} = \dfrac{4+0}{0+3} = \dfrac{4}{3}$

8. $\lim\limits_{x \to -\infty} \dfrac{x^2+2}{x^3+x+1} = \lim\limits_{x \to -\infty} \dfrac{\dfrac{1}{x} + \dfrac{2}{x^3}}{1 + \dfrac{1}{x^2} + \dfrac{1}{x^3}} = \dfrac{\lim\limits_{x \to -\infty} \dfrac{1}{x} + \lim\limits_{x \to -\infty} \dfrac{2}{x^3}}{\lim\limits_{x \to -\infty} 1 + \lim\limits_{x \to -\infty} \dfrac{1}{x^2} + \lim\limits_{x \to -\infty} \dfrac{1}{x^3}} = \dfrac{0+0}{1+0+0} = 0$

9. $\lim\limits_{t \to \infty} \dfrac{8t^3+t}{(2t-1)(2t^2+1)} = \lim\limits_{t \to \infty} \dfrac{8 + \dfrac{1}{t^2}}{\left(\dfrac{2t-1}{t}\right)\left(\dfrac{2t^2+1}{t^2}\right)} = \lim\limits_{t \to \infty} \dfrac{8 + \dfrac{1}{t^2}}{\left(2 - \dfrac{1}{t}\right)\left(2 + \dfrac{1}{t^2}\right)}$

$$= \dfrac{\lim\limits_{t \to \infty} 8 + \lim\limits_{t \to \infty} \dfrac{1}{t^2}}{\left[\lim\limits_{t \to \infty}\left(2 - \dfrac{1}{t}\right)\right]\left[\lim\limits_{t \to \infty}\left(2 + \dfrac{1}{t^2}\right)\right]} = \dfrac{\lim\limits_{t \to \infty} 8 + \lim\limits_{t \to \infty} \dfrac{1}{t^2}}{\left[\lim\limits_{t \to \infty} 2 - \lim\limits_{t \to \infty} \dfrac{1}{t}\right]\left[\lim\limits_{t \to \infty} 2 + \lim\limits_{t \to \infty} \dfrac{1}{t^2}\right]}$$

$$= \dfrac{8+0}{(2-0)(2+0)} = 2$$

10. $\lim\limits_{r \to \infty} \dfrac{4r^3-r^2}{(r+1)^3} = \lim\limits_{r \to \infty} \dfrac{4 - \dfrac{1}{r}}{\dfrac{(r+1)^3}{r^3}} = \lim\limits_{r \to \infty} \dfrac{4 - \dfrac{1}{r}}{\left(1 + \dfrac{1}{r}\right)^3} = \dfrac{\lim\limits_{r \to \infty} 4 - \lim\limits_{r \to \infty} \dfrac{1}{r}}{\lim\limits_{r \to \infty}\left(1 + \dfrac{1}{r}\right)^3} = \dfrac{\lim\limits_{r \to \infty} 4 - \lim\limits_{r \to \infty} \dfrac{1}{r}}{\left(\lim\limits_{r \to \infty} 1 + \lim\limits_{r \to \infty} \dfrac{1}{r}\right)^3} = \dfrac{4-0}{(1+0)^3} = 4$

11. $\lim\limits_{x \to \infty} \dfrac{x^4}{1-x^2+x^3} = \lim\limits_{x \to \infty} \dfrac{1}{\dfrac{1}{x^4} - \dfrac{1}{x^2} + \dfrac{1}{x}} = \dfrac{\lim\limits_{x \to \infty} 1}{\lim\limits_{x \to \infty} \dfrac{1}{x^4} - \lim\limits_{x \to \infty} \dfrac{1}{x^2} + \lim\limits_{x \to \infty} \dfrac{1}{x}} = \dfrac{1}{0}$, so the limit does not exist.

12. $\lim\limits_{t \to \infty} \left(\dfrac{1}{t} - \dfrac{2t}{t-1}\right) = \lim\limits_{t \to \infty} \left(\dfrac{1}{t} - \dfrac{2}{1 - \dfrac{1}{t}}\right) = \lim\limits_{t \to \infty} \dfrac{1}{t} - \lim\limits_{t \to \infty} \dfrac{2}{1 - \dfrac{1}{t}} = \lim\limits_{t \to \infty} \dfrac{1}{t} - \dfrac{\lim\limits_{t \to \infty} 2}{\lim\limits_{t \to \infty} 1 - \lim\limits_{t \to \infty} \dfrac{1}{t}} = 0 - \dfrac{2}{1-0} = -2$

13. $\lim\limits_{x \to -\infty} \left(\dfrac{x-1}{x+1} + 6\right) = \lim\limits_{x \to -\infty} \left(\dfrac{1 - \dfrac{1}{x}}{1 + \dfrac{1}{x}} + 6\right) = \lim\limits_{x \to -\infty} \dfrac{1 - \dfrac{1}{x}}{1 + \dfrac{1}{x}} + \lim\limits_{x \to -\infty} 6 = \dfrac{\lim\limits_{x \to -\infty} 1 - \lim\limits_{x \to -\infty} \dfrac{1}{x}}{\lim\limits_{x \to -\infty} 1 + \lim\limits_{x \to -\infty} \dfrac{1}{x}} + \lim\limits_{x \to -\infty} 6$

$$= \dfrac{1-0}{1+0} + 6 = 7$$

14. From the periodic nature of the cosine function, the values of $\cos x$ oscillates between -1 and 1 infinitely often and so they don't approach any definite number. Therefore, $\lim\limits_{x \to \infty} \cos x$ does not exist.

15.

x	$\dfrac{\sqrt{x^2 + 4x}}{4x + 1}$
-10	-0.1986
-100	-0.2456
-1000	-0.2496

From the table it appears that $\displaystyle\lim_{x \to -\infty} \dfrac{\sqrt{x^2 + 4x}}{4x + 1} = -0.25$.

16.

x	$\sqrt{9x^2 + x} - 3x$
10	0.16620
100	0.16662
1000	0.16666

From the table it appears that $\displaystyle\lim_{x \to \infty} \left(\sqrt{9x^2 + x} - 3x\right) = 0.16666$.

17.

x	x^5/e^x
10	4.5399
100	3.720×10^{-34}
1000	0

From the table it appears that $\displaystyle\lim_{x \to \infty} \dfrac{x^5}{e^x} = 0$.

18.

x	$(1 + 2/x)^{3x}$
10	237.37
100	380.23
1000	401.02
$10,000$	403.19
$100,000$	403.41

From the table it appears that $\displaystyle\lim_{x \to \infty} (1 + 2/x)^{3x} = 403.4288$. (In Calculus you will see that the limit is e^6.)

19. $\displaystyle\lim_{n \to \infty} a_n = \lim_{n \to \infty} \dfrac{1 + n}{n + n^2} = \lim_{n \to \infty} \dfrac{\dfrac{1}{n^2} + \dfrac{1}{n}}{\dfrac{1}{n} + 1} = \dfrac{\displaystyle\lim_{n \to \infty} \dfrac{1}{n^2} + \lim_{n \to \infty} \dfrac{1}{n}}{\displaystyle\lim_{n \to \infty} \dfrac{1}{n} + \lim_{n \to \infty} 1} = \dfrac{0 + 0}{0 + 1} = 0$

20. $\displaystyle\lim_{n \to \infty} a_n = \lim_{n \to \infty} \dfrac{5n}{n + 5} = \lim_{n \to \infty} \dfrac{5}{1 + \dfrac{5}{n}} = \dfrac{\displaystyle\lim_{n \to \infty} 5}{\displaystyle\lim_{n \to \infty} 1 + \lim_{n \to \infty} \dfrac{5}{n}} = \dfrac{5}{1 + 0} = 5$

21. $a_n = \dfrac{n^2}{n + 1}$ is divergent since $\displaystyle\lim_{n \to \infty} a_n = \lim_{n \to \infty} \dfrac{n^2}{n + 1} = \lim_{n \to \infty} \dfrac{1}{\dfrac{1}{n} + \dfrac{1}{n^2}} = \dfrac{\displaystyle\lim_{n \to \infty} 1}{\displaystyle\lim_{n \to \infty} \dfrac{1}{n} + \lim_{n \to \infty} \dfrac{1}{n^2}} = \dfrac{1}{0 + 0}$ which is not

defined.

22. $\displaystyle\lim_{n \to \infty} a_n = \lim_{n \to \infty} \dfrac{n - 1}{n^3 + 1} = \lim_{n \to \infty} \dfrac{\dfrac{1}{n^2} - \dfrac{1}{n^3}}{1 + \dfrac{1}{n^3}} = \dfrac{\displaystyle\lim_{n \to \infty} \dfrac{1}{n^2} - \lim_{n \to \infty} \dfrac{1}{n^3}}{\displaystyle\lim_{n \to \infty} 1 + \lim_{n \to \infty} \dfrac{1}{n^3}} = \dfrac{0 - 0}{1 + 0} = 0$

23. $\lim\limits_{n\to\infty} a_n = \lim\limits_{n\to\infty} \dfrac{1}{3^n} = 0$

24. $\lim\limits_{n\to\infty} a_n = 0$ since both $\lim\limits_{n\to\infty} a_{2n} = \lim\limits_{n\to\infty} \dfrac{1}{2n} = 0$ and $\lim\limits_{n\to\infty} a_{2n+1} = \lim\limits_{n\to\infty} \dfrac{-1}{2n+1} = 0.$

25. $a_n = \sin(n\pi/2)$, because of the periodic nature of the sine function, the terms of this sequence repeat the sequence $1, 0,$ $-1, 0$ infinitely often and so they don't approach any definite number. Therefore, $\lim\limits_{n\to\infty} a_n$ does not exist, and the sequence is divergent.

26. From the periodic nature of the cosine function, the values of $\cos n\pi$ oscillates between -1 and 1 infinitely often and so they don't approach any definite number. Therefore, $\lim\limits_{n\to\infty} \cos n\pi$ does not exist.

27. $\lim\limits_{n\to\infty} a_n = \lim\limits_{n\to\infty} \dfrac{3}{n^2}\left[\dfrac{n(n+1)}{2}\right] = \lim\limits_{n\to\infty} \dfrac{3}{2}\left(\dfrac{n}{n}\right)\left(\dfrac{n+1}{n}\right) = \lim\limits_{n\to\infty} \dfrac{3}{2}\,(1)\left(1+\dfrac{1}{n}\right)$

$= \lim\limits_{n\to\infty} \dfrac{3}{2}\cdot \lim\limits_{n\to\infty} 1\cdot \lim\limits_{n\to\infty}\left(1+\dfrac{1}{n}\right) = \dfrac{3}{2}\cdot 1\cdot 1 = \dfrac{3}{2}$

28. $\lim\limits_{n\to\infty} a_n = \lim\limits_{n\to\infty} \dfrac{5}{n}\left(n+\dfrac{4}{n}\left[\dfrac{n(n+1)}{2}\right]\right) = \lim\limits_{n\to\infty}\left(5+\dfrac{20}{n^2}\cdot\dfrac{n(n+1)}{2}\right) = \lim\limits_{n\to\infty}\left(5+10\cdot\dfrac{n+1}{n}\right)$

$= \lim\limits_{n\to\infty}\left(5+10\cdot\left[1+\dfrac{1}{n}\right]\right) = \lim\limits_{n\to\infty} 5 + 10\cdot \lim\limits_{n\to\infty}\left(1+\dfrac{1}{n}\right) = 5+10\cdot 1 = 15$

29. $\lim\limits_{n\to\infty} a_n = \lim\limits_{n\to\infty} \dfrac{24}{n^3}\left[\dfrac{n(n+1)(2n+1)}{6}\right] = \lim\limits_{n\to\infty} 4\left(\dfrac{n}{n}\right)\left(\dfrac{n+1}{n}\right)\left(\dfrac{2n+1}{n}\right)$

$= \lim\limits_{n\to\infty} 4\,(1)\left(1+\dfrac{1}{n}\right)\left(2+\dfrac{1}{n}\right) = 4 \lim\limits_{n\to\infty}\left(1+\dfrac{1}{n}\right)\cdot \lim\limits_{n\to\infty}\left(2+\dfrac{1}{n}\right) = 4\cdot 1\cdot 2 = 8$

30. $\lim\limits_{n\to\infty} a_n = \lim\limits_{n\to\infty} \dfrac{12}{n^4}\left[\dfrac{n(n+1)}{2}\right]^2 = \lim\limits_{n\to\infty} \dfrac{12}{4}\left[\dfrac{n(n+1)}{n^2}\right]^2 = 3 \lim\limits_{n\to\infty}\left(\dfrac{n+1}{n}\right)^2$

$= 3 \lim\limits_{n\to\infty}\left(1+\dfrac{1}{n}\right)^2 = 3\left(\lim\limits_{n\to\infty}\left[1+\dfrac{1}{n}\right]\right)^2 = 3\,(1)^2 = 3$

31. (a) $C(t) = \dfrac{\text{amount of salt}}{\text{volume of water}} = \dfrac{30\cdot 25t}{5000+25t} = \dfrac{30t}{200+t}.$

(b) $\lim\limits_{t\to\infty} \dfrac{30t}{200+t} = \lim\limits_{t\to\infty} \dfrac{30}{\dfrac{200}{t}+1} = \dfrac{\lim\limits_{t\to\infty} 30}{\lim\limits_{t\to\infty}\dfrac{200}{t}+\lim\limits_{t\to\infty} 1} = \dfrac{30}{0+1} = 30 \text{ g/L.}$

32. (a) $\lim\limits_{t\to\infty} v(t) = \lim\limits_{t\to\infty} 1.2\left(1-e^{-8.2t}\right) = 1.2 \lim\limits_{t\to\infty}\left(1-\dfrac{1}{e^{8.2t}}\right)$

$= 1.2\left(\lim\limits_{t\to\infty} 1 - \lim\limits_{t\to\infty}\dfrac{1}{e^{8.2t}}\right) = 1.2$

(b) From the graph we see that the raindrop reaches 99% of its terminal velocity in 0.56 s.

33. (a) $a_1 = 0$

$$a_2 = \sqrt{2 + a_1} = \sqrt{2 + 0} = 1.41421356$$

$$a_3 = \sqrt{2 + a_2} = \sqrt{3.41421356} = 1.84775907$$

$$a_4 = \sqrt{2 + a_3} = \sqrt{3.84775907} = 1.96157056$$

$$a_5 = \sqrt{2 + a_4} = \sqrt{3.96157056} = 1.99036945$$

$$a_6 = \sqrt{2 + a_5} = \sqrt{3.99036945} = 1.99759091$$

$$a_7 = \sqrt{2 + a_6} = \sqrt{3.99759091} = 1.99939764$$

$$a_8 = \sqrt{2 + a_7} = \sqrt{3.99939764} = 1.99984940$$

$$a_9 = \sqrt{2 + a_8} = \sqrt{3.99984940} = 1.99996235$$

$$a_{10} = \sqrt{2 + a_9} = \sqrt{3.99996235} = 1.99999059$$

From the table, it appears that $\lim\limits_{n \to \infty} a_n = 2$.

(b) Let $\lim\limits_{n \to \infty} a_n = L$. Then we can also have

$\lim\limits_{n \to \infty} a_{n=1} = L$. Thus, we have

$$L = \lim_{n \to \infty} a_{n+1} = \lim_{n \to \infty} \sqrt{2 + a_n}$$

$$= \sqrt{\lim_{n \to \infty} (2 + a_n)} = \sqrt{\lim_{n \to \infty} 2 + \lim_{n \to \infty} a_n}$$

$$= \sqrt{2 + L}$$

So $L = \sqrt{2 + L} \;\Rightarrow\; L^2 = 2 + L \;\Leftrightarrow$

$L^2 - L - 2 = 0 \;\Leftrightarrow\; (L - 2)(L + 1) = 0 \;\Leftrightarrow$

$L = 2$ or $L = -1$. But $L \geq 0$, so $L \neq -1$. Therefore,

$\lim\limits_{n \to \infty} a_n = 2$.

12.5   Areas

1. (a) Since f is *increasing*, we can obtain a *lower* estimate by using *left* endpoints. We are instructed to use five rectangles, so $n = 5$.

$$L_5 = \sum_{i=1}^{5} f(x_{i-1}) \,\Delta x \quad [\Delta x = \tfrac{10 - 0}{5} = 2]$$

$$= f(x_0) \cdot 2 + f(x_1) \cdot 2 + f(x_2) \cdot 2 + f(x_3) \cdot 2 + f(x_4) \cdot 2$$

$$= 2\,[f(0) + f(2) + f(4) + f(6) + f(8)]$$

$$\approx 2\,(1 + 3 + 4.3 + 5.4 + 6.3) = 2\,(20) = 40$$

Since f is *increasing*, we can obtain an *upper* estimate by using *right* endpoints.

$$R_5 = \sum_{i=1}^{5} f(x_i) \,\Delta x$$

$$= 2\,[f(x_1) + f(x_2) + f(x_3) + f(x_4) + f(x_5)]$$

$$= 2\,[f(2) + f(4) + f(6) + f(8) + f(10)]$$

$$\approx 2\,(3 + 4.3 + 5.4 + 6.3 + 7) = 2\,(26) = 52$$

(b) $L_{10} = \sum\limits_{i=1}^{10} f(x_{i-1}) \,\Delta x \quad [\Delta x = \tfrac{10 - 0}{10} = 1]$

$$= 1\,[f(x_0) + f(x_1) + \cdots + f(x_9)]$$

$$= f(0) + f(1) + \cdots + f(9)$$

$$\approx 1 + 2.1 + 3 + 3.7 + 4.3 + 4.9 + 5.4 + 5.8 + 6.3 + 6.7$$

$$= 43.2$$

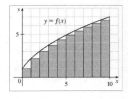

$$R_{10} = \sum_{i=1}^{10} f(x_i) \,\Delta x = f(1) + f(2) + \cdots + f(10)$$

$$= L_{10} + 1 \cdot f(10) - 1 \cdot f(0) \quad \left[\begin{array}{c}\text{add rightmost rectangle,}\\ \text{subtract leftmost}\end{array}\right]$$

$$= 43.2 + 7 - 1 = 49.2$$

2. (a) (i) $L_6 = \sum\limits_{i=1}^{6} f(x_{i-1}) \, \Delta x$ $[\Delta x = \frac{12-0}{6} = 2]$

$\qquad = 2\,[f(x_0) + f(x_1) + f(x_2) + f(x_3) + f(x_4) + f(x_5)]$

$\qquad = 2\,[f(0) + f(2) + f(4) + f(6) + f(8) + f(10)]$

$\qquad \approx 2\,(9 + 8.8 + 8.2 + 7.3 + 5.9 + 4.1)$

$\qquad = 2\,(43.3) = 86.6$

(ii) $R_6 = L_6 + 2 \cdot f(12) - 2 \cdot f(0)$

$\qquad \approx 86.6 + 2\,(1) - 2\,(9) = 70.6$

(b) Since f is *decreasing*, we obtain an *overestimate* by using *left* endpoints, that is, L_6.

(c) R_6 gives us an underestimate.

3. $\Delta x = \frac{2-0}{4} = \frac{1}{2}$, so $R_4 = \sum\limits_{i=1}^{4} f(x_i) \, \Delta x = f\left(\frac{1}{2}\right) \cdot \frac{1}{2} + f(1) \cdot \frac{1}{2} + f\left(\frac{3}{2}\right) \cdot \frac{1}{2} + f(2) \cdot \frac{1}{2} = \frac{1}{2}\left(\frac{9}{4} + \frac{10}{4} + \frac{11}{4} + \frac{12}{4}\right) = \frac{42}{8} = \frac{21}{4}$

4. $\Delta x = \frac{1+1}{4} = \frac{1}{2}$, so

$R_4 = \sum\limits_{i=1}^{4} f(x_i) \, \Delta x = \frac{1}{2} \cdot f\left(-\frac{1}{2}\right) + \frac{1}{2} \cdot f(0) + \frac{1}{2} \cdot f\left(\frac{1}{2}\right) + \frac{1}{2} \cdot f(1) = \frac{1}{2} \cdot \frac{15}{4} + \frac{1}{2} \cdot \frac{16}{4} + \frac{1}{2} \cdot \frac{15}{4} + \frac{1}{2} \cdot \frac{12}{4} = \frac{58}{8} = \frac{29}{4}$

5. $\Delta x = \frac{7-1}{6} = 1$, so

$R_6 = \sum\limits_{i=1}^{6} f(x_i) \, \Delta x = f(2) \cdot 1 + f(3) \cdot 1 + f(4) \cdot 1 + f(5) \cdot 1 + f(6) \cdot 1 + f(7) \cdot 1 = 2 + \frac{4}{3} + 1 + \frac{4}{5} + \frac{4}{6} + \frac{4}{7} = \frac{223}{35} \approx 6.37$

6. $\Delta x = \frac{2-0}{8} = \frac{1}{4}$, so

$R_8 = \sum\limits_{i=1}^{8} f(x_i) \, \Delta x = \frac{1}{4} \cdot f\left(\frac{1}{4}\right) + \frac{1}{4} \cdot f\left(\frac{2}{4}\right) + \frac{1}{4} \cdot f\left(\frac{3}{4}\right) + \frac{1}{4} \cdot f\left(\frac{4}{4}\right) + \frac{1}{4} \cdot f\left(\frac{5}{4}\right) + \frac{1}{4} \cdot f\left(\frac{6}{4}\right) + \frac{1}{4} \cdot f\left(\frac{7}{4}\right) + \frac{1}{4} \cdot f\left(\frac{8}{4}\right)$

$\qquad = \frac{1}{4}\,[2.234375 + 4.375 + 6.328125 + 8 + 9.296875 + 10.125 + 10.390625 + 10] = \frac{1}{4}\,(60.75) = 15.1875$

7. (a) $R_4 = \sum\limits_{i=1}^{4} f(x_i) \, \Delta x$ $\left(\Delta x = \dfrac{5-1}{4} = 1\right)$

$\qquad = f(x_1) \cdot 1 + f(x_2) \cdot 1 + f(x_3) \cdot 1 + f(x_4) \cdot 1$

$\qquad = f(2) + f(3) + f(4) + f(5)$

$\qquad = \frac{1}{2} + \frac{1}{3} + \frac{1}{4} + \frac{1}{5} = \frac{77}{60} = 1.28\overline{3}$

Since f is decreasing on $[1, 5]$, an underestimate is obtained by the right endpoint approximation, R_4.

(b) $L_4 = \sum\limits_{i=1}^{4} f(x_{i-1}) \, \Delta x$

$\qquad = f(1) + f(2) + f(3) + f(4)$

$\qquad = 1 + \frac{1}{2} + \frac{1}{3} + \frac{1}{4} = \frac{25}{12} = 2.08\overline{3}$

L_4 is an overestimate. Alternatively, we could just add the area of the leftmost rectangle and subtract the area of the rightmost; that is,

$L_4 = R_4 + f(1) \cdot 1 - f(5) \cdot 1.$

8. (a) $R_5 = \sum\limits_{i=1}^{5} f(x_i)\,\Delta x \quad \left(\Delta x = \dfrac{5-0}{5} = 1\right)$

$= f(x_1)\cdot 1 + f(x_2)\cdot 1 + f(x_3)\cdot 1 + f(x_4)\cdot 1 + f(x_5)\cdot 1$

$= f(1) + f(2) + f(3) + f(4) + f(5)$

$= 24 + 21 + 16 + 9 + 0 = 70$

Since f is decreasing on $[0, 5]$, R_5 is an underestimate.

(b) $L_5 = \sum\limits_{i=1}^{5} f(x_{i-1})\,\Delta x$

$= f(0) + f(1) + f(2) + f(3) + f(4)$

$= 25 + 24 + 21 + 16 + 9 = 95$

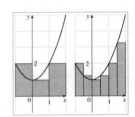

L_5 is an overestimate.

9. (a) $f(x) = 1 + x^2$ and $\Delta x = \dfrac{2 - (-1)}{3} = 1$, so

$R_3 = f(0)\cdot 1 + f(1)\cdot 1 + f(2)\cdot 1 = 1\,[1 + 2 + 5] = 8.$

If $\Delta x = \dfrac{2 - (-1)}{6} = 0.5$ then

$R_6 = 0.5\,[f(-0.5) + f(0) + f(0.5) + f(1) + f(1.5) + f(2)]$

$= 0.5\,(1.25 + 1 + 1.25 + 2 + 3.25 + 5) = 0.5\,(13.75) = 6.875$

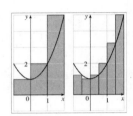

(b) $L_3 = f(-1)\cdot 1 + f(0)\cdot 1 + f(1)\cdot 1 = 1\,[2 + 1 + 2] = 5$

$L_6 = 0.5\,[f(-1) + f(-0.5) + f(0) + f(0.5) + f(1) + f(1.5)]$

$= 0.5\,(2 + 1.25 + 1 + 1.25 + 2 + 3.25)$

$= 0.5\,(10.75) = 5.375$

10. (a) (i) $f(x) = e^{-x}$ and $\Delta x = \dfrac{4 - 0}{4} = 1$, so

$R_4 = \sum\limits_{i=1}^{4} f(x_i)\,\Delta x = f(x_1)\cdot 1 + f(x_2)\cdot 1 + f(x_3)\cdot 1 + f(x_4)\cdot 1$

$= f(1) + f(2) + f(3) + f(4)$

$= 0.3678 + 0.1353 + 0.0498 + 0.0183 = 0.5712$

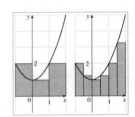

(ii) $L_4 = \sum\limits_{i=1}^{4} f(x_{i-1})\,\Delta x$

$= f(0) + f(1) + f(2) + f(3)$

$= 1 + 0.3678 + 0.1353 + 0.0498 = 1.5529$

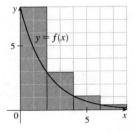

(b) (i) $\Delta x = \dfrac{4-0}{8} = 0.5$, so

$$R_8 = \sum_{i=1}^{8} f\left(x_i\right)\Delta x$$
$$= 0.5\left[f\left(0.5\right) + f\left(1\right) + f\left(1.5\right) + f\left(2\right)\right.$$
$$\left. + f\left(2.5\right) + f\left(3\right) + f\left(3.5\right) + f\left(4\right)\right]$$
$$= 0.5\left[0.6065 + 0.3678 + 0.2231 + 0.1353\right.$$
$$\left. + 0.0821 + 0.0498 + 0.0302 + 0.0183\right]$$
$$= 0.5\left(1.5131\right) = 0.75655$$

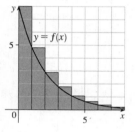

(ii) $L_8 = 0.5\left[f\left(0\right) + f\left(0.5\right) + f\left(1\right) + f\left(1.5\right)\right.$
$$\left. + f\left(2\right) + f\left(2.5\right) + f\left(3\right) + f\left(3.5\right)\right]$$
$$= 0.5\left[1 + 0.6065 + 0.3678 + 0.2231\right.$$
$$\left. + 0.1353 + 0.0821 + 0.0498 + 0.0302\right]$$
$$= 0.5\left(2.5131\right) = 1.25655$$

11. $f\left(x\right) = 3x$ and $\Delta x = \dfrac{5-0}{n} = \dfrac{5}{n}$ and $x_k = \dfrac{5k}{n}$, so

$$A = \lim_{n\to\infty} \sum_{k=1}^{n} f\left(x_k\right)\Delta x = \lim_{n\to\infty} \sum_{k=1}^{n} 3\left(\dfrac{5k}{n}\right)\cdot\dfrac{5}{n}$$
$$= \lim_{n\to\infty} \sum_{k=1}^{n} \dfrac{75k}{n^2} = \lim_{n\to\infty} \dfrac{75}{n^2} \sum_{k=1}^{n} k = \lim_{n\to\infty} \dfrac{75}{n^2}\cdot\dfrac{n\left(n+1\right)}{2}$$
$$= \lim_{n\to\infty} \dfrac{75\left(n+1\right)}{2n} = \lim_{n\to\infty} \dfrac{75}{2}\left(1 + \dfrac{1}{n}\right) = \dfrac{75}{2}\left(1+0\right) = \dfrac{75}{2}$$

Using geometry, the area of the triangle is $\dfrac{1}{2}\left(5\right)\left(15\right) = \dfrac{75}{2}$.

12. $f\left(x\right) = 2x + 1$, $\Delta x = \dfrac{3-1}{n} = \dfrac{2}{n}$ and $x_k = 1 + \dfrac{2k}{n}$, so

$$A = \lim_{n\to\infty} \sum_{k=1}^{n} f\left(x_k\right)\Delta x = \lim_{n\to\infty} \sum_{k=1}^{n} \left[2\left(1 + \dfrac{2k}{n}\right) + 1\right]\cdot\dfrac{2}{n}$$
$$= \lim_{n\to\infty} \sum_{k=1}^{n} \left(\dfrac{6}{n} + \dfrac{8k}{n^2}\right) = \lim_{n\to\infty} \left[\left(\sum_{k=1}^{n} \dfrac{6}{n}\right) + \left(\sum_{k=1}^{n} \dfrac{8k}{n^2}\right)\right]$$
$$= \lim_{n\to\infty} \left[\left(\dfrac{6}{n}\cdot\sum_{k=1}^{n} 1\right) + \left(\dfrac{8}{n^2}\cdot\sum_{k=1}^{n} k\right)\right]$$
$$= \lim_{n\to\infty} \left[\left(\dfrac{6}{n}\cdot n\right) + \left(\dfrac{8}{n^2}\cdot\dfrac{n\left(n+1\right)}{2}\right)\right]$$
$$= \lim_{n\to\infty} \left(6 + \dfrac{4\left(n+1\right)}{n}\right) = \lim_{n\to\infty} \left[6 + 4\left(1 + \dfrac{1}{n}\right)\right]$$
$$= 6 + 4\left(1+0\right) = 10$$

Using geometry, the area of the trapezoid is $2\left(\dfrac{3+7}{2}\right) = 10$.

13. $f(x) = 3x^2$, $a = 0$, $b = 2$, $\Delta x = \dfrac{2-0}{n} = \dfrac{2}{n}$, and $x_k = \dfrac{2k}{n}$, so

$$A = \lim_{n \to \infty} \sum_{k=1}^{n} f(x_k)\,\Delta x = \lim_{n \to \infty} \sum_{k=1}^{n} 3\left(\frac{2k}{n}\right)^2 \cdot \frac{2}{n} = \lim_{n \to \infty} \sum_{k=1}^{n} \frac{24k^2}{n^3} = \lim_{n \to \infty} \frac{24}{n^3} \cdot \sum_{k=1}^{n} k^2$$

$$= \lim_{n \to \infty} \frac{24}{n^3} \cdot \frac{n(n+1)(2n+1)}{6} = \lim_{n \to \infty} \frac{4(2n^2+3n+1)}{n^2} = \lim_{n \to \infty} 4\left(2 + \frac{3}{n} + \frac{1}{n^2}\right)$$

$$= 4(2 + 0 + 0) = 8$$

14. $f(x) = x + x^2$, $a = 0$, $b = 1$, $\Delta x = \dfrac{1-0}{n} = \dfrac{1}{n}$, and $x_k = \dfrac{k}{n}$, so

$$A = \lim_{n \to \infty} \sum_{k=1}^{n} f(x_k)\,\Delta x = \lim_{n \to \infty} \sum_{k=1}^{n} \left[\left(\frac{k}{n}\right) + \left(\frac{k}{n}\right)^2\right] \cdot \frac{1}{n} = \lim_{n \to \infty} \sum_{k=1}^{n} \left[\frac{k}{n^2} + \frac{k^2}{n^3}\right]$$

$$= \lim_{n \to \infty} \left(\frac{1}{n^2} \sum_{k=1}^{n} k + \frac{1}{n^3} \sum_{k=1}^{n} k^2\right) = \lim_{n \to \infty} \left(\frac{1}{n^2} \cdot \frac{n(n+1)}{2} + \frac{1}{n^3} \cdot \frac{n(n+1)(2n+1)}{6}\right)$$

$$= \lim_{n \to \infty} \frac{n+1}{2n} + \frac{2n^2+3n+1}{6n^2} = \lim_{n \to \infty} \left[\frac{1}{2}\left(1 + \frac{1}{n}\right) + \frac{1}{6}\left(2 + \frac{3}{n} + \frac{1}{n^2}\right)\right]$$

$$= \tfrac{1}{2}(1+0) + \tfrac{1}{6}(2+0+0) = \tfrac{5}{6}$$

15. $f(x) = x^3 + 2$, $a = 0$, $b = 5$, $\Delta x = \dfrac{5-0}{n} = \dfrac{5}{n}$, and $x_k = \dfrac{5k}{n}$, so

$$A = \lim_{n \to \infty} \sum_{k=1}^{n} f(x_k)\,\Delta x = \lim_{n \to \infty} \sum_{k=1}^{n} \left[\left(\frac{5k}{n}\right)^3 + 2\right] \cdot \frac{5}{n} = \lim_{n \to \infty} \sum_{k=1}^{n} \left[\frac{625k^3}{n^4} + \frac{10}{n}\right]$$

$$= \lim_{n \to \infty} \left[\frac{625}{n^4} \cdot \sum_{k=1}^{n} k^3 + \frac{10}{n} \cdot \sum_{k=1}^{n} 1\right] = \lim_{n \to \infty} \left(\frac{625}{n^4} \cdot \frac{n^2(n+1)^2}{4} + \frac{10}{n} \cdot n\right)$$

$$= \lim_{n \to \infty} \left[\frac{625(n^2+2n+1)}{4n^2} + 10\right] = \lim_{n \to \infty} \left[\frac{625}{4}\left(1 + \frac{2}{n} + \frac{1}{n^2}\right) + 10\right]$$

$$= \tfrac{625}{4}(1+0+0) + 10 = \tfrac{665}{4} = 166.25$$

16. $f(x) = 4x^3$, $a = 2$, $b = 5$, $\Delta x = \dfrac{5-2}{n} = \dfrac{3}{n}$, and $x_k = 2 + \dfrac{3k}{n}$, so

$$A = \lim_{n \to \infty} \sum_{k=1}^{n} f(x_k)\,\Delta x = \lim_{n \to \infty} \sum_{k=1}^{n} 4\left(2 + \frac{3k}{n}\right)^3 \cdot \frac{3}{n}$$

$$= \lim_{n \to \infty} \sum_{k=1}^{n} \frac{12}{n} \cdot \left(8 + \frac{36k}{n} + \frac{54k^2}{n^2} + \frac{27k^3}{n^3}\right) = \lim_{n \to \infty} \sum_{k=1}^{n} \left(\frac{96}{n} + \frac{432k}{n^2} + \frac{648k^2}{n^3} + \frac{324k^3}{n^4}\right)$$

$$= \lim_{n \to \infty} \left(\sum_{k=1}^{n} \frac{96}{n} + \sum_{k=1}^{n} \frac{432k}{n^2} + \sum_{k=1}^{n} \frac{648k^2}{n^3} + \sum_{k=1}^{n} \frac{324k^3}{n^4}\right)$$

$$= \lim_{n \to \infty} \left(\frac{96}{n} \sum_{k=1}^{n} 1 + \frac{432}{n^2} \sum_{k=1}^{n} k + \frac{648}{n^3} \sum_{k=1}^{n} k^2 + \frac{324}{n^4} \sum_{k=1}^{n} k^3\right)$$

$$= \lim_{n \to \infty} \left(\frac{96}{n} \cdot n + \frac{432}{n^2} \cdot \frac{n(n+1)}{2} + \frac{648}{n^3} \cdot \frac{n(n+1)(2n+1)}{6} + \frac{324}{n^4} \cdot \frac{n^2(n+1)^2}{4}\right)$$

$$= \lim_{n \to \infty} \left(96 + 216 \cdot \frac{(n+1)}{n} + 108 \cdot \frac{2n^2+3n+1}{n^2} + 81 \cdot \frac{n^2+2n+1}{n^2}\right)$$

$$= \lim_{n \to \infty} \left[96 + 216\left(1 + \frac{1}{n}\right) + 108\left(2 + \frac{3}{n} + \frac{1}{n^2}\right) + 81\left(1 + \frac{2}{n} + \frac{1}{n^2}\right)\right]$$

$$= 96 + 216 + 216 + 81 = 609$$

17. $f(x) = x + 6x^2$, $a = 1$, $b = 4$, $\Delta x = \dfrac{4-1}{n} = \dfrac{3}{n}$, and $x_k = 1 + \dfrac{3k}{n}$, so

$$A = \lim_{n\to\infty} \sum_{k=1}^{n} f(x_k)\,\Delta x = \lim_{n\to\infty} \sum_{k=1}^{n} \left[\left(1 + \frac{3k}{n}\right) + 6\left(1 + \frac{3k}{n}\right)^2\right] \cdot \frac{3}{n}$$

$$= \lim_{n\to\infty} \sum_{k=1}^{n} \left[\frac{3}{n} + \frac{9k}{n^2} + \frac{18}{n} + \frac{108k}{n^2} + \frac{162k^2}{n^3}\right]$$

$$= \lim_{n\to\infty} \left[\frac{21}{n} \sum_{k=1}^{n} 1 + \frac{117}{n^2} \sum_{k=1}^{n} k + \frac{162}{n^3} \sum_{k=1}^{n} k^2\right]$$

$$= \lim_{n\to\infty} \left(\frac{21}{n} \cdot n + \frac{117}{n^2} \cdot \frac{n(n+1)}{2} + \frac{162}{n^3} \cdot \frac{n(n+1)(2n+1)}{6}\right)$$

$$= \lim_{n\to\infty} \left(21 + \tfrac{117}{2} \cdot \frac{(n+1)}{n} + 27 \cdot \frac{2n^2 + 3n + 1}{n^2}\right)$$

$$= \lim_{n\to\infty} \left[21 + \tfrac{117}{2}\left(1 + \frac{1}{n}\right) + 27\left(2 + \frac{3}{n} + \frac{1}{n^2}\right)\right] = 21 + \tfrac{117}{2} + 54 = 133.5$$

18. $f(x) = 20 - 2x^2$, $a = 2$, $b = 3$, $\Delta x = \dfrac{3-2}{n} = \dfrac{1}{n}$, and $x_k = 2 + \dfrac{k}{n}$, so

$$A = \lim_{n\to\infty} \sum_{k=1}^{n} f(x_k)\,\Delta x = \lim_{n\to\infty} \sum_{k=1}^{n} \left[20 - 2\left(2 + \frac{k}{n}\right)^2\right] \cdot \frac{1}{n}$$

$$= \lim_{n\to\infty} \sum_{k=1}^{n} \left[\frac{20}{n} - \frac{2}{n}\left(4 + \frac{4k}{n} + \frac{k^2}{n^2}\right)\right] = \lim_{n\to\infty} \sum_{k=1}^{n} \left[\frac{20}{n} - \frac{8}{n} - \frac{8k}{n^2} - \frac{2k^2}{n^3}\right]$$

$$= \lim_{n\to\infty} \left(\frac{12}{n} \sum_{k=1}^{n} 1 - \frac{8}{n^2} \sum_{k=1}^{n} k - \frac{2}{n^3} \sum_{k=1}^{n} k^2\right)$$

$$= \lim_{n\to\infty} \left(\frac{12}{n} \cdot n - \frac{8}{n^2} \cdot \frac{n(n+1)}{2} + \frac{2}{n^3} \cdot \frac{n(n+1)(2n+1)}{6}\right)$$

$$= \lim_{n\to\infty} \left(12 - 4 \cdot \frac{n+1}{n} - \tfrac{1}{3} \cdot \frac{n+1}{n} \cdot \frac{2n+1}{n}\right)$$

$$= \lim_{n\to\infty} \left[12 - 4 \cdot \left(1 + \frac{1}{n}\right) - \tfrac{1}{3} \cdot \left(1 + \frac{1}{n}\right) \cdot \left(2 + \frac{1}{n}\right)\right] = 12 - 4 - \tfrac{2}{3} = \tfrac{22}{3}$$

19. (a) $R_{10} \approx 161.2656$, $R_{20} \approx 147.9666$, and $R_{100} \approx 137.8067$.

    (b) (i) For $f(x) = \sin x$ on $[0, \pi]$, $R_{100} \approx 1.99984$.

       (ii) For $f(x) = e^{-x^2}$ on $[-1, 1]$, $R_{100} \approx 1.49360$.

20. For regions with straight boundaries we draw a vertical line through each vertex. This creates triangles and trapezoids whose area is easily found. For regions with curved boundaries, we must use the limit process to determine the area.

Chapter 12 Review

1.

x	$f(x)$
1.9	1.11111
1.99	1.01010
1.999	1.00100
2.001	0.99990
2.01	0.99100
2.1	0.90909

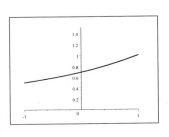

$$\lim_{x\to 2} \frac{x-2}{x^2-3x+2} = 1$$

2.

t	$f(t)$
−1.1	0.43290
−1.01	0.49259
−1.001	0.49925
−0.999	0.50075
−0.99	0.50759
−0.9	0.58480

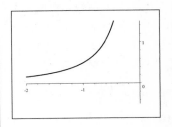

$$\lim_{t\to -1} \frac{t+1}{t^3-t} = 0.5$$

3.

t	$f(t)$
−0.1	0.66967
−0.01	0.69075
−0.001	0.69291
0.001	0.69339
0.01	0.69556
0.1	0.71773

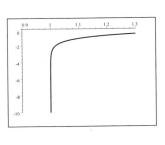

$$\lim_{x\to 0} \frac{2^x-1}{x} = 0.693$$

4.

x	$f(x)$
±0.5	1.68294
±0.1	1.98669
±0.05	1.99667
±0.01	1.99987
±0.001	1.99999

$$\lim_{x\to 0} \frac{\sin 2x}{x} = 2$$

5.

x	$f(x)$
1.5	−0.34657
1.1	−1.15129
1.05	−1.49787
1.01	−2.30258
1.001	−3.45388
1.0001	−4.60517

$$\lim_{x\to 1^+} \ln\sqrt{x-1} \text{ does not exist.}$$

6.

x	$f(x)$
−0.1	−1.00335
−0.05	−1.00083
−0.01	−1.00003
−0.001	−1.00000
−0.0001	−1.00000

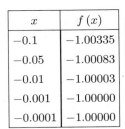

$$\lim_{x\to 0^-} \frac{\tan x}{|x|} = -1$$

7. (a) $\lim_{x\to 2^+} f(x)$ does not exist; f does not approach a finite value.

(b) $\lim_{x\to -3^+} f(x) = 2.4$

(c) $\lim_{x\to -3^-} f(x) = 2.4$

(d) $\lim_{x\to -3} f(x) = 2.4$

(e) $\lim_{x\to 4} f(x) = 0.5$

(f) $\lim_{x\to \infty} f(x) = 1$

(g) $\lim_{x\to -\infty} f(x) = 2$

(h) $\lim_{x\to 0} f(x)\, f(x) = \left(\lim_{x\to 0} f(x)\right)\left(\lim_{x\to 0} f(x)\right)$
$$= 0 \cdot 0 = 0$$

8. (a) $\lim\limits_{x \to -1^-} f(x) = \lim\limits_{x \to -1^-} 2 = 2$

(b) $\lim\limits_{x \to -1^+} f(x) = \lim\limits_{x \to -1^+} x^2 = (-1)^2 = 1$

(c) $\lim\limits_{x \to -1} f(x)$ does not exist;

$\qquad \lim\limits_{x \to -1^-} f(x) \neq \lim\limits_{x \to -1^+} f(x).$

(d) $\lim\limits_{x \to 2^-} f(x) = \lim\limits_{x \to 2^-} x^2 = (2)^2 = 4$

(e) $\lim\limits_{x \to 2^+} f(x) = \lim\limits_{x \to 2^+} (x+2) = (2) + 2 = 4$

(f) $\lim\limits_{x \to 2} f(x) = 4$

(g) $\lim\limits_{x \to 0} f(x) = \lim\limits_{x \to 0} x^2 = 0^2 = 0$

(h) $\lim\limits_{x \to 3} (f(x))^2 = \left(\lim\limits_{x \to 3} f(x)\right)^2 = \left(\lim\limits_{x \to 3} (x+2)\right)^2$

$\qquad\qquad = (3+2)^2 = 25$

9. $\lim\limits_{x \to 2} \dfrac{x+1}{x-3} = \dfrac{2+1}{2-3} = -3$

10. $\lim\limits_{t \to 1} \left(t^3 - 3t + 6\right) = 1^3 - 3(1) + 6 = 4$

11. $\lim\limits_{x \to 3} \dfrac{x^2 + x - 12}{x-3} = \lim\limits_{x \to 3} \dfrac{(x-3)(x+4)}{x-3} = \lim\limits_{x \to 3} (x+4) = 3+4 = 7$

12. $\lim\limits_{x \to -2} \dfrac{x^2 - 4}{x^2 + x - 2} = \lim\limits_{x \to -2} \dfrac{(x+2)(x-2)}{(x+2)(x-1)} = \lim\limits_{x \to -2} \dfrac{x-2}{x-1} = \dfrac{-2-2}{-2-1} = \dfrac{4}{3}$

13. $\lim\limits_{u \to 0} \dfrac{(u+1)^2 - 1}{u} = \lim\limits_{u \to 0} \dfrac{u^2 + 2u + 1 - 1}{u} = \lim\limits_{u \to 0} \dfrac{u^2 + 2u}{u} = \lim\limits_{u \to 0} (u+2) = 0 + 2 = 2$

14. $\lim\limits_{z \to 9} \dfrac{\sqrt{z} - 3}{z - 9} = \lim\limits_{z \to 9} \dfrac{\sqrt{z} - 3}{(\sqrt{x} + 3)(\sqrt{z} - 3)} = \lim\limits_{z \to 9} \dfrac{1}{\sqrt{z} + 3} = \dfrac{1}{\sqrt{9} + 3} = \dfrac{1}{6}$

15. $\lim\limits_{x \to 3^-} \dfrac{x-3}{|x-3|} = \lim\limits_{x \to 3^-} \dfrac{x-3}{-(x-3)} = \lim\limits_{x \to 3^-} -1 = -1$

16. $\lim\limits_{x \to 0} \left(\dfrac{1}{x} + \dfrac{2}{x^2 - 2x}\right) = \lim\limits_{x \to 0} \left(\dfrac{x-2}{x(x-2)} + \dfrac{2}{x(x-2)}\right) = \lim\limits_{x \to 0} \left(\dfrac{x}{x(x-2)}\right) = \lim\limits_{x \to 0} \left(\dfrac{2}{x-2}\right) = \dfrac{1}{0-2} = -\dfrac{1}{2}$

17. $\lim\limits_{x \to \infty} \dfrac{2x}{x-4} = \lim\limits_{x \to \infty} \dfrac{2}{1 - \dfrac{4}{x}} = \dfrac{2}{1-0} = 2$

18. $\lim\limits_{x \to \infty} \dfrac{x^2 + 1}{x^4 - 3x + 6} = \lim\limits_{x \to \infty} \dfrac{\dfrac{1}{x^2} + \dfrac{1}{x^4}}{1 - \dfrac{3}{x^3} + \dfrac{6}{x^4}} == \dfrac{0+0}{1-0+0} = 0$

19. $\lim\limits_{x \to \infty} \cos^2 x$ does not exist since cosine squared alternates between 0 and 1.

20. $\lim\limits_{x \to -\infty} \dfrac{x^4}{x^3 - 1} = \lim\limits_{x \to -\infty} \dfrac{1}{\dfrac{1}{x} - \dfrac{1}{x^4}} = \dfrac{1}{0}$ which is not defined, hence this limit does not exist.

21. $f'(4) = \lim\limits_{h \to 0} \dfrac{f(4+h) - f(4)}{h} = \lim\limits_{h \to 0} \dfrac{[3(4+h) - 5] - [3(4) - 5]}{h} = \lim\limits_{h \to 0} \dfrac{12 + 3h - 5 - 12 + 5}{h}$

$\qquad = \lim\limits_{h \to 0} \dfrac{3h}{h} = \lim\limits_{h \to 0} 3 = 3$

22. $g'(-1) = \lim\limits_{h \to 0} \dfrac{g(-1+h) - g(-1)}{h} = \lim\limits_{h \to 0} \dfrac{[2(-1+h)^2 - 1] - [2(-1)^2 - 1]}{h} = \lim\limits_{h \to 0} \dfrac{2 - 4h + 2h^2 - 1 - 2 + 11}{h}$

$\qquad = \lim\limits_{h \to 0} \dfrac{-4h + h^2}{h} = \lim\limits_{h \to 0} \dfrac{h(-4+h)}{h} = \lim\limits_{h \to 0} (-4+h) = -4$

23. $f'(16) = \lim\limits_{h \to 0} \dfrac{f(16+h) - f(16)}{h} = \lim\limits_{h \to 0} \dfrac{\sqrt{16+h} - \sqrt{16}}{h} = \lim\limits_{h \to 0} \dfrac{(\sqrt{16+h} - 4)}{h} \cdot \dfrac{(\sqrt{16+h} + 4)}{(\sqrt{16+h} + 4)}$

$\qquad = \lim\limits_{h \to 0} \dfrac{16 + h - 16}{h(\sqrt{16+h} + 4)} = \lim\limits_{h \to 0} \dfrac{h}{h(\sqrt{16+h} + 4)} = \lim\limits_{h \to 0} \dfrac{1}{\sqrt{16+h} + 4} = \dfrac{1}{8}$

24. $f'(1) = \lim\limits_{h \to 0} \dfrac{f(1+h) - f(1)}{h} = \lim\limits_{h \to 0} \dfrac{\left[\frac{1+h}{(1+h)+1}\right] - \left[\frac{1}{1+1}\right]}{h} = \lim\limits_{h \to 0} \dfrac{\frac{1+h}{2+h} - \frac{1}{2}}{h} = \lim\limits_{h \to 0} \dfrac{2(1+h) - (2+h)}{h \cdot 2(2+h)}$

$\qquad = \lim\limits_{h \to 0} \dfrac{2 + 2h - 2 - h}{2h(2+h)} = \lim\limits_{h \to 0} \dfrac{h}{2h(2+h)} = \lim\limits_{h \to 0} \dfrac{1}{2(2+h)} = \frac{1}{4}$

25. (a) $f'(a) = \lim\limits_{x \to a} \dfrac{f(x) - f(a)}{x - a} = \lim\limits_{x \to a} \dfrac{[6 - 2x] - [6 - 2a]}{x - a} = \lim\limits_{x \to a} \dfrac{6 - 2x - 6 + 2a}{x - a} = \lim\limits_{x \to a} \dfrac{-2x + 2a}{x - a}$

$\qquad = \lim\limits_{x \to a} \dfrac{-2(x - a)}{x - a} = \lim\limits_{x \to a} -2 = -2$

(b) $f'(2) = -2$ and $f'(-2) = -2$.

26. (a) $f'(a) = \lim\limits_{x \to a} \dfrac{f(x) - f(a)}{x - a} = \lim\limits_{x \to a} \dfrac{[x^2 - 3x] - [a^2 - 3a]}{x - a} = \lim\limits_{x \to a} \dfrac{x^2 - a^2 - 3x + 3a}{x - a}$

$\qquad = \lim\limits_{x \to a} \dfrac{(x - a)(x + a) - 3(x - a)}{x - a} = \lim\limits_{x \to a} \dfrac{(x - a)[(x + a) - 3]}{x - a}$

$\qquad = \lim\limits_{x \to a} (x + a - 3) = 2a - 3$

(b) $f'(2) = 2(2) - 3 = 1$ and $f'(-2) = 2(-2) - 3 = -7$.

27. (a) $f'(a) = \lim\limits_{x \to a} \dfrac{f(x) - f(a)}{x - a} = \lim\limits_{x \to a} \dfrac{\sqrt{x+6} - \sqrt{a+6}}{x - a} = \lim\limits_{x \to a} \dfrac{\left(\sqrt{x+6} - \sqrt{a+6}\right)\left(\sqrt{x+6} + \sqrt{a+6}\right)}{(x - a)\left(\sqrt{x+6} + \sqrt{a+6}\right)}$

$\qquad = \lim\limits_{x \to a} \dfrac{x + 6 - a - 6}{(x - a)\left(\sqrt{x+6} + \sqrt{a+6}\right)} = \lim\limits_{x \to a} \dfrac{x - a}{(x - a)\left(\sqrt{x+6} + \sqrt{a+6}\right)}$

$\qquad = \lim\limits_{x \to a} \dfrac{1}{\sqrt{x+6} + \sqrt{a+6}} = \dfrac{1}{2\sqrt{a+6}}$

(b) $f'(2) = \dfrac{1}{2\sqrt{2+6}} = \dfrac{1}{4\sqrt{2}} = \dfrac{\sqrt{2}}{8}$ and $f'(-2) = \dfrac{1}{2\sqrt{-2+6}} = \frac{1}{4}$.

28. (a) $f'(a) = \lim\limits_{x \to a} \dfrac{f(x) - f(a)}{x - a} = \lim\limits_{x \to a} \dfrac{\frac{4}{x} - \frac{4}{a}}{x - a} = \lim\limits_{x \to a} \dfrac{\left(\frac{4}{x} - \frac{4}{a}\right)ax}{(x - a)ax}$

$\qquad = \lim\limits_{x \to a} \dfrac{4a - 4x}{(x - a)ax} = \lim\limits_{x \to a} \dfrac{-4(x - a)}{(x - a)ax} = \lim\limits_{x \to a} \dfrac{-4}{ax} = -\dfrac{4}{a^2}$

(b) $f'(2) = \dfrac{-4}{(2)^2} = -1$ and $f'(-2) = \dfrac{-4}{(-2)^2} = -1$.

29. $m = \lim\limits_{h \to 0} \dfrac{f(1+h) - f(1)}{h} = \lim\limits_{h \to 0} \dfrac{\left[4(1+h) - (1+h)^2\right] - \left[4(1) - (1)^2\right]}{h}$

$\qquad = \lim\limits_{h \to 0} \dfrac{4 + 4h - 1 - 2h - h^2 - 3}{h} = \lim\limits_{h \to 0} \dfrac{2h - h^2}{h} = \lim\limits_{h \to 0} \dfrac{h(2 - h)}{h} = \lim\limits_{h \to 0} (2 - h) = 2$

$\qquad$ So an equation of the line tangent to $y = 4x - x^2$ at $(1, 3)$ is $y - 3 = 2(x - 1) \quad \Leftrightarrow \quad y = 2x + 1$.

30. $m = \lim\limits_{h \to 0} \dfrac{f(1+h) - f(1)}{h} = \lim\limits_{h \to 0} \dfrac{\sqrt{1+h} - \sqrt{1}}{h} = \lim\limits_{h \to 0} \dfrac{\left(\sqrt{1+h} - 1\right)}{h} \cdot \dfrac{\left(\sqrt{1+h} + 1\right)}{\left(\sqrt{1+h} + 1\right)}$

$\qquad = \lim\limits_{h \to 0} \dfrac{1 + h - 1}{h\left(\sqrt{1+h} + 1\right)} = \lim\limits_{h \to 0} \dfrac{h}{h\left(\sqrt{1+h} + 1\right)} = \lim\limits_{h \to 0} \dfrac{1}{\sqrt{1+h} + 1} = \dfrac{1}{1+1} = \frac{1}{2}$

$\qquad$ So an equation of the line tangent to $y = \sqrt{x}$ at $(1, 1)$ is $y - 1 = \frac{1}{2}(x - 1) \quad \Leftrightarrow \quad y = \frac{1}{2}x + \frac{1}{2}$.

31. $m = \lim\limits_{h \to 0} \dfrac{f(3+h) - f(3)}{h} = \lim\limits_{h \to 0} \dfrac{[2(3+h)] - [2(3)]}{h} = \lim\limits_{h \to 0} \dfrac{6 + 2h - 6}{h} = \lim\limits_{h \to 0} \dfrac{2h}{h} = \lim\limits_{h \to 0} 2 = 2$.

$\qquad$ So an equation of the line tangent to $y = 2x$ at $(3, 6)$ is $y - 6 = 2(x - 3) \quad \Leftrightarrow \quad y = 2x$.

32. $m = \lim\limits_{h \to 0} \dfrac{f(2+h) - f(2)}{h} = \lim\limits_{h \to 0} \dfrac{[(2+h)^2 - 3] - [2^2 - 3]}{h} = \lim\limits_{h \to 0} \dfrac{4 + 4h + h^2 - 3 - 4 + 1}{h}$

$= \lim\limits_{h \to 0} \dfrac{4h + h^2}{h} = \lim\limits_{h \to 0} \dfrac{h(4+h)}{h} = \lim\limits_{h \to 0} (4+h) = 4$

So an equation of the line tangent to $y = x^2 - 3$ at $(2, 1)$ is $y - 1 = 4(x - 2) \quad \Leftrightarrow \quad y = 4x - 7$.

33. $m = \lim\limits_{h \to 0} \dfrac{f(2+h) - f(2)}{h} = \lim\limits_{h \to 0} \dfrac{\dfrac{1}{2+h} - \dfrac{1}{2}}{h} = \lim\limits_{h \to 0} \dfrac{\left(\dfrac{1}{2+h} - \dfrac{1}{2}\right)}{h} \cdot \dfrac{2(2+h)}{2(2+h)}$

$= \lim\limits_{h \to 0} \dfrac{2 - (2+h)}{2h(2+h)} = \lim\limits_{h \to 0} \dfrac{-h}{2h(2+h)} = \lim\limits_{h \to 0} \dfrac{-1}{2(2+h)} = -\dfrac{1}{4}$

So an equation of the line tangent to $y = \dfrac{1}{x}$ at $\left(2, \dfrac{1}{2}\right)$ is $y - \dfrac{1}{2} = -\dfrac{1}{4}(x - 2) \Leftrightarrow y = -\dfrac{1}{4}x + 1$.

34. $m = \lim\limits_{h \to 0} \dfrac{f(3+h) - f(3)}{h} = \lim\limits_{h \to 0} \dfrac{\sqrt{(3+h) + 1} - \sqrt{3+1}}{h} = \lim\limits_{h \to 0} \dfrac{\sqrt{4+h} - 2}{h}$

$= \lim\limits_{h \to 0} \dfrac{(\sqrt{4+h} - 2)}{h} \cdot \dfrac{(\sqrt{4+h} + 2)}{(\sqrt{4+h} + 2)} = \lim\limits_{h \to 0} \dfrac{4 + h - 4}{h(\sqrt{4+h} + 2)} = \lim\limits_{h \to 0} \dfrac{h}{h(\sqrt{4+h} + 2)}$

$= \lim\limits_{h \to 0} \dfrac{1}{\sqrt{4+h} + 2} = \dfrac{1}{\sqrt{4} + 2} = \dfrac{1}{4}$

So an equation of the line tangent to $y = \sqrt{x+1}$ at $(3, 2)$ is $y - 2 = \dfrac{1}{4}(x - 3) \quad \Leftrightarrow \quad y = \dfrac{1}{4}x + \dfrac{5}{4}$.

35. (a) $v(2) = \lim\limits_{t \to 2} \dfrac{h(t) - h(2)}{t - 2} = \lim\limits_{t \to 2} \dfrac{[640 - 16t^2] - [640 - 16(2)^2]}{t - 2} = \lim\limits_{t \to 2} \dfrac{640 - 16t^2 - 640 + 64}{t - 2}$

$= \lim\limits_{t \to 2} \dfrac{-16t^2 + 64}{t - 2} = \lim\limits_{t \to 2} \dfrac{-16(t+2)(t-2)}{t - 2} = \lim\limits_{t \to 2} -16(t+2) = 64 \text{ ft/s}$

(b) $v(a) = \lim\limits_{t \to a} \dfrac{h(t) - h(a)}{t - a} = \lim\limits_{t \to a} \dfrac{[640 - 16t^2] - [640 - 16a^2]}{t - a} = \lim\limits_{t \to a} \dfrac{640 - 16t^2 - 640 + 16a^2}{t - a}$

$= \lim\limits_{t \to a} \dfrac{-16t^2 + 16a^2}{t - a} = \lim\limits_{t \to a} \dfrac{-16(t+a)(t-a)}{t - a} = \lim\limits_{t \to a} \dfrac{58h - 1.66ah - 0.83h^2}{h}$

$= \lim\limits_{t \to a} \dfrac{h(58 - 1.66a - 0.83h)}{h} = \lim\limits_{t \to a} -16(t+a) = -32a \text{ ft/s}$

(c) $h(t) = 0$ when $640 - 16t^2 = 0 \Leftrightarrow -16(t^2 - 40) = 0 \quad \Leftrightarrow \quad t^2 = 40 \quad \Rightarrow \quad t = \sqrt{40} \approx 6.32 \text{ s (since } t \geq 0\text{)}.$

(d) $v(6.32) = -32(6.32) = -202.4 \text{ ft/s}.$

36. (a) $PT = 100 \quad \Leftrightarrow \quad P = \dfrac{100}{T}$

(b) $P'(300) = \lim\limits_{h \to 0} \dfrac{P(300+h) - P(300)}{h} = \lim\limits_{h \to 0} \dfrac{\dfrac{100}{300+h} - \dfrac{100}{300}}{h} = \lim\limits_{h \to 0} \dfrac{\left(\dfrac{100}{300+h} - \dfrac{1}{3}\right) 3(300+h)}{h \cdot 3(300+h)}$

$= \lim\limits_{h \to 0} \dfrac{300 - 300 - h}{3h(300+h)} = \lim\limits_{h \to 0} \dfrac{-h}{3h(300+h)} = \lim\limits_{h \to 0} \dfrac{-1}{3(300+h)} = -\dfrac{1}{900}$

37. $\lim\limits_{n \to \infty} a_n = \lim\limits_{n \to \infty} \dfrac{n}{5n + 1} = \lim\limits_{n \to \infty} \dfrac{1}{5 + \dfrac{1}{n}} = \dfrac{1}{5 + 0} = \dfrac{1}{5}$

38. $\lim\limits_{n \to \infty} a_n = \lim\limits_{n \to \infty} \dfrac{n^3}{n^3 + 1} = \lim\limits_{n \to \infty} \dfrac{1}{1 + \dfrac{1}{n^3}} = \dfrac{1}{1 + 0} = 1$

39. $\lim\limits_{n \to \infty} a_n = \lim\limits_{n \to \infty} \left(\dfrac{n(n+1)}{2n^2}\right) = \lim\limits_{n \to \infty} \dfrac{1}{2} \left(\dfrac{n}{n}\right)\left(\dfrac{n+1}{n}\right) = \lim\limits_{n \to \infty} \dfrac{1}{2}(1)\left(1 + \dfrac{1}{n}\right)$

$= \lim\limits_{n \to \infty} \dfrac{1}{2} \cdot \lim\limits_{n \to \infty} 1 \cdot \lim\limits_{n \to \infty} \left(1 + \dfrac{1}{n}\right) = \dfrac{1}{2} \cdot 1 \cdot 1 = \dfrac{1}{2}$

40. $\lim\limits_{n\to\infty} a_n = \lim\limits_{n\to\infty} \dfrac{n^3}{2n+6} = \dfrac{\lim\limits_{n\to\infty} \dfrac{n^3}{n^3}}{\lim\limits_{n\to\infty} \dfrac{2n}{n^3} + \lim\limits_{n\to\infty} \dfrac{8}{n^3}} = \dfrac{1}{0+0}$, which is undefined so the limit does not exist.

41. The sequence $a_n = \cos\left(\dfrac{n\pi}{2}\right)$ is the sequence $0, -1, 0, 1, 0, -1, 0, 1, 0, -1, 0, 1, \ldots$ which does not go to any one value.

Thus this sequence does not converge.

42. $\lim\limits_{n\to\infty} a_n = \lim\limits_{n\to\infty} \dfrac{10}{3^n} = 0$ since the numerator is constant and the denominator grows without bounds.

43. $f(x) = \sqrt{x}$ and $\Delta x = 0.5$, so

$$R_6 = \sum_{i=1}^{6} f(x_i)\,\Delta x = f(x_1)\cdot 0.5 + f(x_2)\cdot 0.5 + f(x_3)\cdot 0.5 + f(x_4)\cdot 0.5 + f(x_5)\cdot 0.5 + f(x_6)\cdot 0.5$$

$$= 0.5\left[f(0.5) + f(1) + f(1.5) + f(2) + f(2.5) + f(3)\right]$$

$$\approx 0.5\,(0.7071 + 1 + 1.2247 + 1.4142 + 1.5811 + 1.7320) = 0.5\,(7.6591) = 3.8296$$

44. $f(x) = 4x - x^2$ and $\Delta x = 0.5$, so

$$R_4 = \sum_{i=1}^{4} f(x_i)\,\Delta x = f(x_1)\cdot 0.5 + f(x_2)\cdot 0.5 + f(x_3)\cdot 0.5 + f(x_4)\cdot 0.5$$

$$= 0.5\left[f(1.5) + f(2) + f(2.5) + f(3)\right] = 0.5\,(3.75 + 4 + 3.75 + 3) = 0.5\,(14.5) = 7.25$$

45. $f(x) = 2x + 3$, $a = 0$, $b = 2$, $\Delta x = \dfrac{2-0}{n} = \dfrac{2}{n}$, and $x_k = \dfrac{2k}{n}$, so

$$A = \lim_{n\to\infty}\sum_{k=1}^{n} f(x_k)\,\Delta x = \lim_{n\to\infty}\sum_{k=1}^{n}\left[2\left(\dfrac{2k}{n}\right)+3\right]\cdot\dfrac{2}{n} = \lim_{n\to\infty}\sum_{k=1}^{n}\left[\dfrac{8k}{n^2}+\dfrac{6}{n}\right] = \lim_{n\to\infty}\left[\dfrac{8}{n^2}\cdot\sum_{k=1}^{n} k + \dfrac{6}{n}\cdot\sum_{k=1}^{n} 1\right]$$

$$= \lim_{n\to\infty}\left(\dfrac{8}{n^2}\cdot\dfrac{n(n+1)}{2}+\dfrac{6}{n}\cdot n\right) = \lim_{n\to\infty}\left[\dfrac{4(n+1)}{n}+6\right] = \lim_{n\to\infty}\left[4\left(1+\dfrac{1}{n}\right)+6\right] = 4(1+0)+6 = 10$$

46. $f(x) = x^2 + 1$, $a = 0$, $b = 3$, $\Delta x = \dfrac{3-0}{n} = \dfrac{3}{n}$, and $x_k = \dfrac{3k}{n}$, so

$$A = \lim_{n\to\infty}\sum_{k=1}^{n} f(x_k)\,\Delta x = \lim_{n\to\infty}\sum_{k=1}^{n}\left[\left(\dfrac{3k}{n}\right)^2+1\right]\cdot\dfrac{3}{n} = \lim_{n\to\infty}\sum_{k=1}^{n}\left[\dfrac{27k^2}{n^3}+\dfrac{3}{n}\right] = \lim_{n\to\infty}\left[\dfrac{27}{n^3}\sum_{k=1}^{n} k^2 + \dfrac{3}{n}\sum_{k=1}^{n} 1\right]$$

$$= \lim_{n\to\infty}\left(\dfrac{27}{n^3}\cdot\dfrac{n(n+1)(2n+1)}{6}+\dfrac{3}{n}\cdot n\right) = \lim_{n\to\infty}\left(\dfrac{9}{2}\cdot\dfrac{2n^2+3n+1}{n^2}\right)$$

$$= \lim_{n\to\infty}\left[\dfrac{9}{2}\left(2+\dfrac{3}{n}+\dfrac{1}{n^2}\right)+3\right] = \tfrac{9}{2}(2+0+0)+3 = 12$$

47. $f(x) = x^2 - x$, $a = 1$, $b = 2$, $\Delta x = \dfrac{2-1}{n} = \dfrac{1}{n}$, and $x_k = 1 + \dfrac{k}{n}$, so

$$A = \lim_{n\to\infty}\sum_{k=1}^{n} f(x_k)\,\Delta x = \lim_{n\to\infty}\sum_{k=1}^{n}\left[\left(1+\dfrac{k}{n}\right)^2 - \left(1+\dfrac{k}{n}\right)\right]\cdot\dfrac{1}{n}$$

$$= \lim_{n\to\infty}\sum_{k=1}^{n}\left[1+\dfrac{2k}{n}+\dfrac{k^2}{n^2}-1-\dfrac{k}{n}\right]\cdot\dfrac{1}{n} = \lim_{n\to\infty}\sum_{k=1}^{n}\left[\dfrac{k}{n^2}+\dfrac{k^2}{n^3}\right] = \lim_{n\to\infty}\left[\sum_{k=1}^{n}\dfrac{k}{n^2}+\sum_{k=1}^{n}\dfrac{k^2}{n^3}\right]$$

$$= \lim_{n\to\infty}\left[\dfrac{1}{n^2}\sum_{k=1}^{n} k + \dfrac{1}{n^3}\sum_{k=1}^{n} k^2\right] = \lim_{n\to\infty}\left[\dfrac{1}{n^2}\cdot\dfrac{n(n+1)}{2}+\dfrac{1}{n^3}\cdot\dfrac{n(n+1)(2n+1)}{6}\right]$$

$$= \lim_{n\to\infty}\left(\tfrac{1}{2}\cdot\dfrac{(n+1)}{n}+\tfrac{1}{6}\cdot\dfrac{2n^2+3n+1}{n^2}\right) = \lim_{n\to\infty}\left[\tfrac{1}{2}\left(1+\dfrac{1}{n}\right)+\tfrac{1}{6}\left(2+\dfrac{3}{n}+\dfrac{1}{n^2}\right)\right]$$

$$= \tfrac{1}{2}(1+0)+\tfrac{1}{6}(2+0+0) = \tfrac{5}{6} = 0.8\overline{3}$$

48. $f(x) = x^3$, $a = 1$, $b = 2$, $\Delta x = \dfrac{2-1}{n} = \dfrac{1}{n}$, and $x_k = 1 + \dfrac{k}{n}$, so

$$A = \lim_{n\to\infty} \sum_{k=1}^{n} f(x_k)\,\Delta x = \lim_{n\to\infty} \sum_{k=1}^{n} \left(1 + \frac{k}{n}\right)^3 \cdot \frac{1}{n} = \lim_{n\to\infty} \sum_{k=1}^{n} \frac{1}{n} \cdot \left(1 + \frac{3k}{n} + \frac{3k^2}{n^2} + \frac{k^3}{n^3}\right)$$

$$= \lim_{n\to\infty} \sum_{k=1}^{n} \left(\frac{1}{n} + \frac{3k}{n^2} + \frac{3k^2}{n^3} + \frac{k^3}{n^4}\right) = \lim_{n\to\infty} \left(\sum_{k=1}^{n} \frac{1}{n} + \sum_{k=1}^{n} \frac{3k}{n^2} + \sum_{k=1}^{n} \frac{3k^2}{n^3} + \sum_{k=1}^{n} \frac{k^3}{n^4}\right)$$

$$= \lim_{n\to\infty} \left(\frac{1}{n} \sum_{k=1}^{n} 1 + \frac{3}{n^2} \sum_{k=1}^{n} k + \frac{3}{n^3} \sum_{k=1}^{n} k^2 + \frac{1}{n^4} \sum_{k=1}^{n} k^3\right)$$

$$= \lim_{n\to\infty} \left(\frac{1}{n} \cdot n + \frac{3}{n^2} \cdot \frac{n(n+1)}{2} + \frac{3}{n^3} \cdot \frac{n(n+1)(2n+1)}{6} + \frac{1}{n^4} \cdot \frac{n^2(n+1)^2}{4}\right)$$

$$= \lim_{n\to\infty} \left(1 + \frac{3}{2} \cdot \frac{(n+1)}{n} + \frac{1}{2} \cdot \frac{2n^2 + 3n + 1}{n^2} + \frac{1}{4} \cdot \frac{n^2 + 2n + 1}{n^2}\right)$$

$$= \lim_{n\to\infty} \left[1 + \frac{3}{2}\left(1 + \frac{1}{n}\right) + \frac{1}{2}\left(2 + \frac{3}{n} + \frac{1}{n^2}\right) + \frac{1}{4}\left(1 + \frac{2}{n} + \frac{1}{n^2}\right)\right]$$

$$= 1 + \tfrac{3}{2} + 1 + \tfrac{1}{4} = \tfrac{15}{4} = 3.75$$

Chapter 12 Test

1. (a)

x	$f(x)$
-0.1	0.50335
-0.01	0.50003
-0.001	0.50000

x	$f(x)$
0.001	0.50000
0.01	0.50003
0.1	0.50335

$$\lim_{x\to0} \frac{x}{\sin 2x} = 0.5$$

(b)

2. (a) $\displaystyle\lim_{x\to-1^-} f(x) = \lim_{x\to-1^-} 1 = 1$

(b) $\displaystyle\lim_{x\to-1^+} f(x) = \lim_{x\to-1^+} x^2 = (-1)^2 = 1$

(c) $\displaystyle\lim_{x\to-1} f(x) = 1$

(d) $\displaystyle\lim_{x\to0^-} f(x) = \lim_{x\to0^-} x^2 = (0)^2 = 0$

(e) $\displaystyle\lim_{x\to0^+} f(x) = \lim_{x\to0^+} x^2 = (0)^2 = 0$

(f) $\displaystyle\lim_{x\to0} f(x) = 0$

(g) $\displaystyle\lim_{x\to2^-} f(x) = \lim_{x\to2^-} x^2 = (2)^2 = 4$

(h) $\displaystyle\lim_{x\to2^+} f(x) = \lim_{x\to2^+} (4-x) = 4 - (2) = 2$

(i) $\displaystyle\lim_{x\to2} f(x)$ does not exist; $\displaystyle\lim_{x\to2^-} f(x) \neq \lim_{x\to2^+} f(x)$.

3. (a) $\displaystyle\lim_{x\to2} \frac{x^2 + 2x - 8}{x-2} = \lim_{x\to2} \frac{(x-2)(x+4)}{x-2} = \lim_{x\to2} (x+4) = 2 + 4 = 6$

(b) $\displaystyle\lim_{x\to2} \frac{x^2 - 2x - 8}{x+2} = \frac{2^2 - 2(2) - 8}{2+2} = -2$

(c) $\displaystyle\lim_{x\to2} \frac{1}{x-2}$ does not exist because $\left|\dfrac{1}{x-2}\right|$ grows without bound as $x \to 2$.

(d) $\displaystyle\lim_{x\to2^-} \frac{x-2}{|x-2|} = \lim_{x\to2^-} \frac{x-2}{-(x-2)} = \lim_{x\to2^-} -1 = -1$ and $\displaystyle\lim_{x\to2^+} \frac{x-2}{|x-2|} = \lim_{x\to2^+} \frac{x-2}{x-2} = \lim_{x\to2^+} 1 = 1$. Since $\displaystyle\lim_{x\to2^-} \frac{x-2}{|x-2|} \neq \lim_{x\to2^+} \frac{x-2}{|x-2|}$, $\displaystyle\lim_{x\to2} \frac{x-2}{|x-2|}$ does not exist.

(e) $\displaystyle\lim_{z\to4} \frac{\sqrt{z}-2}{z-4} = \lim_{z\to4} \frac{\sqrt{x}-2}{(\sqrt{x}+2)(\sqrt{x}-2)} = \lim_{z\to4} \frac{1}{\sqrt{x}+2} = \frac{1}{\sqrt{4}+2} = \frac{1}{4}$

(f) $\displaystyle\lim_{x\to\infty} \frac{2x^2 - 4}{x^2 + x} = \lim_{x\to\infty} \frac{2 - 4/x^2}{1 - 1/x} = \frac{2-0}{1-0} = 2$

4. (a) $f(x) = x^2 - 2x$, so

$$
\begin{aligned}
f'(x) &= \lim_{h \to 0} \frac{f(x+h) - f(x)}{h} = \lim_{h \to 0} \frac{\left[(x+h)^2 - 2(x+h)\right] - \left[x^2 - 2x\right]}{h} \\
&= \lim_{h \to 0} \frac{x^2 + 2hx + h^2 - 2x - 2h - x^2 + 2x}{h} = \lim_{h \to 0} \frac{2hx + h^2 - 2h}{h} \\
&= \lim_{h \to 0} \frac{h(2x + h - 2)}{h} = \lim_{h \to 0} (2x + h - 2) = 2x - 2
\end{aligned}
$$

(b) $f'(-1) = 2(-1) - 2 = -4 \qquad f'(1) = 2(1) - 2 = 0 \qquad f'(2) = 2(2) - 2 = 2$

5. $m = \lim_{h \to 0} \dfrac{f(9+h) - f(9)}{h} = \lim_{h \to 0} \dfrac{\sqrt{9+h} - \sqrt{9}}{h} = \lim_{h \to 0} \dfrac{\sqrt{9+h} - 3}{h}$

$$
\begin{aligned}
&= \lim_{h \to 0} \frac{\left(\sqrt{9+h} - 3\right)}{h} \cdot \frac{\left(\sqrt{9+h} + 3\right)}{\left(\sqrt{9+h} + 3\right)} = \lim_{h \to 0} \frac{(9+h) - 9}{h\left(\sqrt{9+h} + 3\right)} = \lim_{h \to 0} \frac{h}{h\left(\sqrt{9+h} + 3\right)} \\
&= \lim_{h \to 0} \frac{1}{\sqrt{9+h} + 3} = \frac{1}{3+3} = \tfrac{1}{6}
\end{aligned}
$$

So an equation of the line tangent to $f(x) = \sqrt{x}$ at $(9, 3)$ is $y - 3 = \tfrac{1}{6}(x - 9) \Leftrightarrow y = \tfrac{1}{6}x + \tfrac{3}{2}$.

6. (a) $\displaystyle \lim_{n \to \infty} a_n = \lim_{n \to \infty} \frac{n}{n^2 + 4} = \lim_{n \to \infty} \frac{\dfrac{1}{n}}{1 + \dfrac{4}{n^2}} = \lim_{n \to \infty} \frac{0}{1 + 0} = 0$

(b) The sequence $a_n = \sec n\pi$ is the sequence $-1, 1, -1, 1, -1, 1, \ldots$ which does not go to any one value. Thus this sequence does not converge.

7. (a) $f(x) = 4 - x^2$ and $\Delta x = \dfrac{1 - 0}{5} = 0.2$, so

$$
\begin{aligned}
R_5 &= \sum_{k=1}^{5} f(x_k)\, \Delta x = f(0.2) \cdot 0.2 + f(0.4) \cdot 0.2 + f(0.6) \cdot 0.2 + f(0.8) \cdot 0.2 + f(1) \cdot 0.2 \\
&= 0.2\,(3.96 + 3.84 + 3.64 + 3.36 + 3) = 0.2\,(17.8) = 3.56
\end{aligned}
$$

(b) $f(x) = 4 - x^2$, $a = 0$, $b = 1$, $\Delta x = \dfrac{1 - 0}{n} = \dfrac{1}{n}$, and $x_k = \dfrac{k}{n}$, so

$$
\begin{aligned}
A &= \lim_{n \to \infty} \sum_{k=1}^{n} f(x_k)\, \Delta x = \lim_{n \to \infty} \sum_{k=1}^{n} \left[4 - \left(\frac{k}{n}\right)^2 \right] \cdot \frac{1}{n} = \lim_{n \to \infty} \sum_{k=1}^{n} \left[\frac{1}{n} - \frac{k^2}{n^3} \right] \\
&= \lim_{n \to \infty} \left[\frac{4}{n} \cdot \sum_{k=1}^{n} 1 - \frac{1}{n^3} \cdot \sum_{k=1}^{n} k^2 \right] = \lim_{n \to \infty} \left(\frac{4}{n} \cdot n - \frac{1}{n^3} \cdot \frac{n(n+1)(2n+1)}{6} \right) \\
&= \lim_{n \to \infty} \left[4 - \frac{1}{6} \left(\frac{n+1}{n}\right) \left(\frac{2n+1}{n}\right) \right] = \lim_{n \to \infty} \left[4 - \frac{1}{6} \left(1 + \frac{1}{n}\right) \left(2 + \frac{1}{n}\right) \right] \\
&= 4 - \tfrac{1}{6}(1 + 0)(2 + 0) = \tfrac{11}{3}
\end{aligned}
$$

Focus on Modeling: Interpretations of Area

1. Work $=$ force $\times$ distance, so the work done in moving the tree the kth interval is $w_k = f(x_k)\,\Delta x$, where

$f(x) = 1500 + 10x - \frac{1}{2}x^2$, $a = 0$, $b = 40$, $\Delta x = \dfrac{40 - 0}{n} = \dfrac{40}{n}$, and $x_k = \dfrac{40k}{n}$. Thus,

$$W = \lim_{n\to\infty} \sum_{k=1}^{n} f(x_k)\,\Delta x = \lim_{n\to\infty} \sum_{k=1}^{n} \left[1500 + 10\left(\frac{40k}{n}\right) - \frac{1}{2}\left(\frac{40k}{n}\right)^2 \right] \cdot \frac{40}{n}$$

$$= \lim_{n\to\infty} \sum_{k=1}^{n} \left[\frac{60{,}000}{n} + \frac{16{,}000k}{n^2} - \frac{32{,}000k^2}{n^3} \right] = \lim_{n\to\infty} \left[\frac{60{,}000}{n} \sum_{k=1}^{n} 1 + \frac{16{,}000}{n^2} \sum_{k=1}^{n} k - \frac{32{,}000}{n^3} \sum_{k=1}^{n} k^2 \right]$$

$$= \lim_{n\to\infty} \left(\frac{60{,}000}{n} \cdot n + \frac{16{,}000}{n^2} \cdot \frac{n(n+1)}{2} - \frac{32{,}000}{n^3} \cdot \frac{n(n+1)(2n+1)}{6} \right)$$

$$= \lim_{n\to\infty} \left(60{,}000 + 8{,}000 \cdot \frac{n+1}{n} - \frac{16{,}000}{3} \cdot \frac{(n+1)(2n+1)}{n^2} \right)$$

$$= \lim_{n\to\infty} \left[60{,}000 + 8{,}000 \cdot \left(1 + \frac{1}{n}\right) - \frac{16{,}000}{3} \cdot \left(1 + \frac{1}{n}\right)\left(2 + \frac{1}{n}\right) \right]$$

$$= 60{,}000 + 8000 - \frac{32{,}000}{3} = 57{,}333.33 \text{ ft-lb}$$

2. Work $=$ force $\times$ distance so the work done in moving the tree the kth interval is $w_k = f(x_k)\,\Delta x$, where $f(x) = 20x$,

$a = 0$, $b = 2$, $\Delta x = \dfrac{2-0}{n} = \dfrac{2}{n}$, and $x_k = \dfrac{2k}{n}$. Thus,

$$W = \lim_{n\to\infty} \sum_{k=1}^{n} f(x_k)\,\Delta x = \lim_{n\to\infty} \sum_{k=1}^{n} \left[20\left(\frac{2k}{n}\right) \right] \cdot \frac{2}{n} = \lim_{n\to\infty} \sum_{k=1}^{n} \left[\frac{80k}{n^2} \right] = \lim_{n\to\infty} \left[\frac{80}{n^2} \sum_{k=1}^{n} k \right]$$

$$= \lim_{n\to\infty} \left(\frac{80}{n^2} \cdot \frac{n(n+1)}{2} \right) = \lim_{n\to\infty} \left[40\left(\frac{n+1}{n}\right) \right] = \lim_{n\to\infty} \left[40\left(1 + \frac{1}{n}\right) \right] = 40 \text{ ft-lb}$$

3. (a) The force on the kth strip is $375x_k\,\Delta x$, so to find the force exerted on the window panel we must add the forces on each
of the strips, giving $\displaystyle \lim_{n\to\infty} \sum_{k=1}^{n} 375x_k\,\Delta x$.

(b) This is the area under the graph of $p(x) = 375x$ between $x = 0$ and $x = 4$.

(c) Using $\Delta x = \dfrac{4}{n}$, and $x_k = \dfrac{4k}{n}$,

$$P = \lim_{n\to\infty} \sum_{k=1}^{n} 375x_k\,\Delta x = \lim_{n\to\infty} \sum_{k=1}^{n} 375\left(\frac{4k}{n}\right) \cdot \frac{4}{n} = \lim_{n\to\infty} \sum_{k=1}^{n} \left[\frac{6000k}{n^2} \right] = \lim_{n\to\infty} \left[\frac{6000}{n^2} \sum_{k=1}^{n} k \right]$$

$$= \lim_{n\to\infty} \left(\frac{6000}{n^2} \cdot \frac{n(n+1)}{2} \right) = \lim_{n\to\infty} \left[3000\left(\frac{n+1}{n}\right) \right] = \lim_{n\to\infty} \left[3000\left(1 + \frac{1}{n}\right) \right] = 3000 \text{ lb}$$

(d) The area of the kth strip is $3\Delta x$, so the pressure on the kth strip is $187.5x_k\,\Delta x$. Now using $\Delta x = \dfrac{4}{n}$, and $x_k = \dfrac{4k}{n}$,
we have

$$P = \lim_{n\to\infty} \sum_{k=1}^{n} 187.5x_k\,\Delta x = \lim_{n\to\infty} \sum_{k=1}^{n} 187.5\left(\frac{4k}{n}\right) \cdot \frac{4}{n} = \lim_{n\to\infty} \sum_{k=1}^{n} \left[\frac{3000k}{n^2} \right] = \lim_{n\to\infty} \left[\frac{3000}{n^2} \sum_{k=1}^{n} k \right]$$

$$= \lim_{n\to\infty} \left(\frac{3000}{n^2} \cdot \frac{n(n+1)}{2} \right) = \lim_{n\to\infty} \left[1500\left(\frac{n+1}{n}\right) \right] = \lim_{n\to\infty} \left[1500\left(1 + \frac{1}{n}\right) \right] = 1500 \text{ lb}$$

4. (a) We divide the time into n small units of time, Δt. During the kth time period, the distance traveled is approximately $v(t_k) \cdot \Delta t$. Thus the total distance traveled is $\lim\limits_{n \to \infty} \sum\limits_{k=1}^{n} v(t_k)\,\Delta t$, where $\Delta t = \dfrac{b-a}{n}$ and $t_k = a + \dfrac{(b-a)\,k}{n}$.

(b) Using $v(t) = 6t + 0.1t^3$, $\Delta t = \dfrac{5-0}{n} = \dfrac{5}{n}$, and $t_k = \dfrac{5k}{n}$,

$$P = \lim_{n \to \infty} \sum_{k=1}^{n} v(t_k)\,\Delta t = \lim_{n \to \infty} \sum_{k=1}^{n} \left[6\left(\frac{5k}{n}\right) + 0.1\left(\frac{5k}{n}\right)^3 \right] \cdot \frac{5}{n} = \lim_{n \to \infty} \sum_{k=1}^{n} \left[\frac{150k}{n^2} + \frac{125k^3}{2n^4} \right]$$

$$= \lim_{n \to \infty} \left[\frac{150}{n^2} \sum_{k=1}^{n} k + \frac{125}{2n^4} \sum_{k=1}^{n} k^3 \right] = \lim_{n \to \infty} \left[\frac{150}{n^2} \cdot \frac{n(n+1)}{2} + \frac{125}{2n^4} \cdot \frac{n^2(n+1)^2}{4} \right]$$

$$= \lim_{n \to \infty} \left[75\left(\frac{n+1}{n}\right) + \tfrac{125}{8} \cdot \frac{(n+1)^2}{n^2} \right] = \lim_{n \to \infty} \left[75\left(1 + \frac{1}{n}\right) + \frac{125}{8}\left(1 + \frac{1}{n}\right)^2 \right] = \tfrac{725}{8} = 90.625 \text{ ft}$$

5. (a) $D(t) = 61 + \frac{6}{5}t - \frac{1}{25}t^2$, $a = 0$, $b = 24$, $\Delta x = \dfrac{24-0}{n} = \dfrac{24}{n}$, and $x_k = \dfrac{24k}{n}$, so the heating capacity generated is

$$\lim_{n \to \infty} \sum_{k=1}^{n} D(t_k)\,\Delta t = \lim_{n \to \infty} \sum_{k=1}^{n} \left[61 + \tfrac{6}{5}\left(\frac{24k}{n}\right) - \tfrac{1}{25}\left(\frac{24k}{n}\right)^2 \right] \cdot \frac{24}{n} = \lim_{n \to \infty} \sum_{k=1}^{n} \left[\frac{1464}{n} + \frac{3456k}{5n^2} - \frac{13824k^2}{25n^3} \right]$$

$$= \lim_{n \to \infty} \left[\frac{1464}{n} \sum_{k=1}^{n} 1 + \frac{3456}{5n^2} \sum_{k=1}^{n} k - \frac{13824}{25n^3} \sum_{k=1}^{n} k^2 \right]$$

$$= \lim_{n \to \infty} \left(\frac{1464}{n} \cdot n + \frac{3456}{5n^2} \cdot \frac{n(n+1)}{2} - \frac{13824}{25n^3} \cdot \frac{n(n+1)(2n+1)}{6} \right)$$

$$= \lim_{n \to \infty} \left(1464 + \tfrac{1728}{5} \cdot \frac{n+1}{n} - \tfrac{2304}{25} \cdot \frac{(n+1)(2n+1)}{n^2} \right)$$

$$= \lim_{n \to \infty} \left[1464 + \tfrac{1728}{5} \cdot \left(1 + \frac{1}{n}\right) - \tfrac{2304}{25} \cdot \left(1 + \frac{1}{n}\right)\left(2 + \frac{1}{n}\right) \right]$$

$$= 1464 + \tfrac{1728}{5} - \tfrac{4608}{25} = 1625.28 \text{ heating degree-hours}$$

(b) $D(t) = 61 + \frac{6}{5}t - \frac{1}{25}t^2 = -\frac{1}{25}\left(t^2 - 30t\right) + 61 = -\frac{1}{25}\left(t^2 - 30t + 225\right) + 61 + 9 = -\frac{1}{25}\left(t - 15\right)^2 + 70$. Thus the maximum temperature during the day was $70°$.

(c) In this case, $D(t) = 50 + 5t - \frac{1}{4}t^2$, $a = 0$, $b = 24$, $\Delta x = \dfrac{24-0}{n} = \dfrac{24}{n}$, and $x_k = \dfrac{24k}{n}$, so the heating capacity generated is

$$\lim_{n \to \infty} \sum_{k=1}^{n} D(t_k)\,\Delta t = \lim_{n \to \infty} \sum_{k=1}^{n} \left[50 + 5\left(\frac{24k}{n}\right) - \tfrac{1}{4}\left(\frac{24k}{n}\right)^2 \right] \cdot \frac{24}{n} = \lim_{n \to \infty} \sum_{k=1}^{n} \left[\frac{1200}{n} + \frac{2880k}{n^2} - \frac{3456k^2}{n^3} \right]$$

$$= \lim_{n \to \infty} \left[\frac{1200}{n} \sum_{k=1}^{n} 1 + \frac{2880}{n^2} \sum_{k=1}^{n} k - \frac{3456}{n^3} \sum_{k=1}^{n} k^2 \right]$$

$$= \lim_{n \to \infty} \left(\frac{1200}{n} \cdot n + \frac{2880}{n^2} \cdot \frac{n(n+1)}{2} - \frac{3456}{n^3} \cdot \frac{n(n+1)(2n+1)}{6} \right)$$

$$= \lim_{n \to \infty} \left(1200 + 1440 \cdot \frac{n+1}{n} - 576 \cdot \frac{(n+1)(2n+1)}{n^2} \right)$$

$$= \lim_{n \to \infty} \left[1200 + 1440 \cdot \left(1 + \frac{1}{n}\right) - 576 \cdot \left(1 + \frac{1}{n}\right)\left(2 + \frac{1}{n}\right) \right]$$

$$= 1200 + 1440 - 1152 = 1488 \text{ heating degree-hours}$$

(d) $D(t) = 50 + 5t - \frac{1}{4}t^2 = -\frac{1}{4}\left(t^2 - 20t\right) + 50 = -\frac{1}{4}\left(t^2 - 20t + 100\right) + 50 + 25 = -\frac{1}{4}\left(t - 10\right)^2 + 75$. Thus the maximum temperature during the day was $75°$.

(e) The day described in part (c) was hotter because the number of heating degree-hours was greater, meaning the average temperature of that day was higher.